WIN a fabulous Golf Break for two

with AA Lifestyle Guides ~~~~~~~~~~~~ -
winners of the AA Hotel Gro~~~~~~~~~~~~ he 2002

See overleaf fo~~~~~

C000092972

We have 5 golf b~~~~~~~~~~~~ ay.

Enjoy a break with a difference at any Marriott Hotel ~ ~~~~~~ he UK*.
Relax with a two night stay, including breakfast and dinner for two,
plus a free round of golf. All you need for a perfect weekend

For more information on Marriott Golf Breaks, call 0800 731 9068.

HOW TO ENTER
Just complete (in capitals please) and send off this card or alternatively, send your name and address on a stamped postcard to the address overleaf (no purchase required). Entries are limited to one per household. This card will require a stamp if posted in the Republic of Ireland or elsewhere overseas.
Closing date 4 September 2003.

MR/MRS/MISS/MS/OTHER, PLEASE STATE: _____

NAME: _____

ADDRESS: _____

_____

_____ POSTCODE: _____

TEL. NOS: _____ E-MAIL: _____

Are you an AA Member?   Yes/No
Have you bought this or any other AA Lifestyle Guide before?   Yes/No
If yes, please indicate the year of the last edition you bought:

AA Hotel Guide	____	AA Caravan & Camping (Europe)	____
AA Bed and Breakfast Guide	____	AA Britain Guide	____
AA Restaurant Guide	____	AA Days Out Guide	____
AA Pub Guide	____	AA B&B France	____
AA Caravan & Camping (Britain & Ireland)	____	Other, please state	_____

If you do not wish to receive further information or special offers from AA Publishing please tick the box ☐

G03

Terms and Conditions

One winner will be drawn from each of the five prize draws to take place on 03 January, 07 March, 02 May, 04 July and 05 September 2003.

Closing date for receipt of entries is midday on the relevant draw date. Final closing date for receipt of entries is 04 September 2003.
Entries received after any draw date other than the final one will go forward into the next available draw. Each entry will only be entered in one draw. Only one entry per household accepted.

Winners will be notified by post within 14 days of the relevant draw date.

Prizes must be booked within date specified on reverse of vouchers issued. Prizes are not transferable and there is no cash alternative.
This prize cannot be used in conjunction with any other discount, promotion or special offer.

Each prize consists of a Marriott Incentive Voucher Pack containing two B&B vouchers (one per night), two dinner vouchers (for two people), plus two golf vouchers. This pack can be used at any Marriott Hotel & Country Club in the UK, *with the exception of Hanbury Manor.
Marriott provides all hotel accommodation, services and facilities and AA Publishing is not party to your agreement with Marriott in this regard.

No purchase required.
The prize draw is open to UK residents over the age of 18, other than employees and agents of the Automobile Association or Marriott, members of their households or anyone else connected with the promotion.
For a list of winners, please send a stamped, self-addressed envelope to AA Lifestyle Guide Winners 2003, AA Publishing, Fanum House (14), Basingstoke, Hants, RG21 4EA.
This card must have an appropriate stamp.
Winners may be asked to participate in draw-related publicity.

Please
Affix
Stamp

AA Lifestyle Guide 2003 Prize Draw

AA PUBLISHING

FANUM HOUSE (14)

BASING VIEW

BASINGSTOKE

HANTS RG21 4EA

Fold along this line

Seal along this edge with sticky tape

AA

2003
guide to
GOLF
courses

Welcome to the 2003 edition of the AA Guide to Golf Courses, fully updated with lots of new places to play and stay across Britain and Ireland. Whether you are new to golf, an occasional golfer or play as often as you can with friends or a society, you will find all the information you need on over 2,500 courses and recommended hotels. Why not plan a golfing break, try out some new courses or book ahead to play some old favourites? New conference and meeting room information means it's easy to organise a corporate golf day, business meeting or even a wedding reception using the guide.

Produced by AA Publishing
Directory generated by the AA Establishment Database, Information Research, AA Hotel Services.
Advertisement Sales: advertisingsales@theAA.com
Editorial: lifestyleguides@theaa.com
Maps prepared by the Cartography Department of Automobile Association Developments Limited
Maps © The Automobile Association 2002.

Ordnance Survey This product includes mapping data licensed from Ordnance Survey® with the permission of the Controller of Her Majesty's Stationery Office.
© Crown copyright 2002.
All rights reserved. Licence number 399221.

Northern Ireland mapping reproduced by permission of the Director and Chief Executive, Ordnance Survey of Northern Ireland, acting on behalf of the Controller of Her Majesty's Stationery Office
© Crown copyright 2002. Permit number 1674.

Republic of Ireland mapping based on Ordnance Survey Ireland. Permit number MP003702 © Ordnance Survey Ireland and Government of Ireland.

A CIP catalogue record for this book is available from the British Library Published by AA Publishing, which is a trading name of Automobile Association Developments Limited, whose registered office is Millstream, Maidenhead Road, Windsor, Berkshire. SL4 5GD

Registered number 1878835

ISBN 0 7495 3432 X
A01262

Published in the USA by AAA

Designed by Richardson Carpenter Advertising Ltd, Cliddesden, Basingstoke.
Typeset/Repro by Avonset, 11 Kelso Place, Bath
Printed and bound by Graficas estelle, S.A., Navarra, Spain

The Automobile Association would like to thank the following photographers and libraries for the assistance in the preparation of this publication.
Front Cover: Action Images/Richard Heathcote
The remaining pictures are held in the Association's own library (AA PHOTO LIBRARY) and were taken by the following:
Kirk Lee Alder: 4, 9(b), Adrian Baker 11, 13(t); Steve Day 8(t); Caroline Jones 6(r); Rob Moore 5(c) 8(b); Ken Paterson 10(t); Clive Sawyer 13(b); Rick Strange 5(r), 6(l), 7(r); Lee Karen Stow 7(l); Michael Taylor 5(l), 10(b); Roy Victor 3, 9(t)

Abbreviations used for above (t) top; (b) bottom; (l) left; (r) right; (c) centre

Contents

How to use the Guide

The AA Guide to Golf Courses aims to provide useful information about a large selection of courses across Britain and Ireland. Golf courses are selected by the AA and their entry in the guide is free of charge. The guide is updated every year as many courses change, close, open, upgrade and add new features. Entries include the contact details for each course, a brief description of the type of course, and details of green fees, leisure, club, catering or conference facilities. AA recommended accommodation follows each entry. To avoid disappointment when visiting a golf course we recommend that you telephone in advance, please do mention the AA Guide to Golf Courses when you make an enquiry.

① Town name and map reference.
The directory is organised by county then alphabetically by town or village name. Use the atlas or index of course names if you are unsure of the location of a particular course. The map reference includes the map page number and National Grid reference. The grid references for the Republic of Ireland are unique to this atlas.

② Club name.
Where the club name appears in bold italics we have been unable to verify current course details with the club. You are strongly advised to check any details with club in advance of your visit.

③ Contact details.
Address, postcode, telephone, fax and e-mail information is provided where this is available.

④ Description.
A brief description of the course or courses is provided, significant features are highlighted.

⑤ Course statistics.
The number of holes, yardage, par, Standard Scratch Score, Course Record and number of club members appear here in italics.

⑥ Visitor information.
Details of booking requirements or restrictions. A small number of courses included in this guide are not open to visitors, however we have included limited details where possible for information.

⑦ Society information.
Details of booking requirements or restrictions for societies.

⑧ Green Fees.
Only the most up-to-date green fees are given, including any variations or restrictions. Where green fees are not confirmed we recommend that you contact the club direct for current details. An asterisk * denotes 2002 fees

⑨ Credit Cards.
Symbols appear for credit cards accepted by the club.

⑩ Professional.
The name of the club professional(s).

⑪ Facilities.
Please see the key to symbols on the left.

---

① — **OXFORD** Map 04 SP50

② — **North Oxford** Banbury Rd OX2 8EZ
③ — ☎ 01865 554924 Fax 01865 515921
④ — **Gently undulating parkland course.**
⑤ — *18 holes, 5736yds, Par 67, SSS 67, Course record 62. Club membership 700.*
⑥ — **Visitors** at weekends & bank holidays may only play after 4pm. **Societies** must contact in advance. **Green Fees** £35 ——**⑧**
⑦ per round. **Cards** 🟰 🟰 💳 **Prof** Robert Harris **Facilities** ——**⑩**
⑨ ⊗ 🍴 🍺 ☕ 🍵 👥 👜 🎣 ✈ **Conf** Thtr **Location** 3m N of ——**⑪**
⑫ city centre on A423 ——**⑬**

....

Hotel ★★★ 66% The Oxford Hotel, Godstow Rd, Wolvercote Roundabout, OXFORD ——**⑭**
☎ 01865 489988 173 en suite

☎ Telephone number	🛍 Well-stocked shop
€ (Republic of Ireland only. Consult your bank for the current rate)	🏌 Clubs for hire
	🛒 Motorised cart/trolley for hire
⊗ Lunch	🛺 Buggies for hire
🍴 Dinner	🎣 Trolley for hire
🍺 Bar snacks	⚐ Driving range
☕ Tea/coffee	★ AA star classification for hotels
⚲ Bar open midday and evenings	◉ AA Rosette Award (in championship course entries)
🛏 Accommodation at club	◆ AA Guest house classification
⛏ Changing rooms	TH Town House hotel

Finding a golf course in the directory

The directory is arranged by country and county, golf courses appear alphabetically by town within each county. Country divisions are listed on the contents page and golf courses are listed by name in the index.

⑫ Conference and function room capacities.

Thtr = theatre
Class = classroom style
Board = boardroom style.
Del = day delegate rate, minimum and maximum rates are given as a guide where these have been provided.

⑬ Location.
The location of the club is given in relation to the nearest town or motorway junction. Many golf courses are in rural locations and we are unable to provide detailed directions in this guide, we recommend that you contact the club direct.

⑭ Accommodation.
AA recommended hotel or guest accommodation is recommended for each entry. The star or diamond rating, % score and AA rosette award appear as applicable. Contact details and the number of rooms are given.

⑮ Photographs and advertisements.
Only golf courses and hotels selected for the guide are able to enhance their entry with a photograph or to take a display advertisement.

Selected highlighted courses
Green boxes in the guide highlight selected courses considered to be of particular merit or interest. These may include historic clubs, particularly testing or enjoyable courses or those in holiday areas popular with visiting golfers. The selection cannot be either exhaustive or totally objective, however it is independent, courses cannot pay to have an entry in the guide, nor can they pay to have a highlighted entry. Highlighted courses do not represent any formal category on quality or other grounds.

Championship Courses
Major championship courses have a full page entry in the guide with more extensive details. A selection of AA recommended restaurants and hotels are given for these courses.

Hotels
Golf course entries in the guide are followed by details of a nearby AA recognised hotel. In some cases the golf course will be in the grounds of the hotel. Most of the recommended hotels fall within the two, three and four star classifications. Where there is no nearby AA recognised hotel, AA guest accommodation will be recommended, with a classification from one to five diamonds.

Hotels with special arrangements for golf
In addition to recommended hotels next to each entry, there is an index of AA hotels with special arrangements for golf. These may include hotels with their own golf course, reduced green fees, preferential tee times or golfing packages.

Club accommodation at golf courses
Where courses offer club accommodation the bed symbol appears under Facilities. This is listed as an option for readers wishing to stay at the course, however, unless the club accommodation has an AA star or diamond classification, the only AA recommended accommodation is the hotel or guest house which follows the entry.

Recommendations
If you would like to recommend a new course which does not feature in the guide, please write to: The Editor, AA Guide to Golf Courses. Fanum House. Basing View. Basingstoke RG21 4EA

For a faster and easier way to book tee times, at many of the courses featured in this guide, contact Golf ENGLAND - England's new official programme for amateur golf. Just call 0870 243 2343 or visit our website at **www.golfengland.com** to view and book available tee times using our tee time booking service. Membership is free for club members, and non club members can join for the equivalent of just £4 per month.

Golfing Getaways

There are plenty of ways to plan a golfing break using this guide. Are there courses you've always wanted to play at? Why not enjoy a short break at one of the AA rated and inspected hotels or B&Bs nearby?

There are recommendations after each golf course in the guide to help you make arrangements direct, or choose a hotel or B&B from the AA website, www.TheAA.com.

Many places can be booked online, and the website will give you information about the latest special offers on accommodation.

A large number of AA rated hotels have special arrangements for golfers - there is a list at the back of the guide, with contact telephone numbers. The hotels may have their own courses, or special arrangements with local courses. Give them a call, and tell them you found them in the AA Guide to Golf Courses. From corporate golf days, golf society trips, or weekend escapes with some golf tuition, there is a great choice of destinations in this guide. Many AA hotels offer special packages - listed below are just a small selection. Don't forget all of this information is subject to change without notice – so make sure you check prices and what your break will include.

England

Cornwall
St Austell
The Carlyon Bay Hotel
Tel 01726 812304
E mail info@carlyonbay.co.uk

Various leisure breaks are available, and guests may play one round of golf a day free, subject to hotel conditions. Further rounds are available at a concession. Golf tuition holidays are available, three or five nights and various itineraries. Prices depend on the time of year.

Devon
Okehampton
Manor House Hotel
Tel 01837 53053

Various bargain breaks are offered with free golf on all breaks of two nights or more. For each night of stay, you can pre-book 27 holes free, or pay a supplement for 36 holes.

Plymton
Elfordleigh
Tel 01752 336428
E mail info@elfordleigh.co.uk

Golf and leisure breaks from around £110 per person (depending on time of year). Two nights bed and breakfast, one night's dinner, unlimited golf (or £20 voucher for beauty treatments). They also have a golf simulator, so you can play courses around the world!

Gloucestershire
Tewkesbury
Tewkesbury Park Hotel
Tel 01684 295405
E mail
tewkesburypark@corushotels.com

Golf breaks based on two people sharing, including dinner, bed and breakfast and 18 holes. Two nights minimum, not including Sundays. Prices from £62 depending on time of year. Sunday nights from £44, additional rounds of golf from £12.50 (Winter, week days) to £25 (Summer, weekends).

Hampshire
Shedfield
Marriott Meon Valley
Tel 01329 833455

Golf breaks - dinner, bed and breakfast plus 18 holes, from £80. Sunday Night golf special, dinner bed and breakfast and unlimited golf, from £65.

Kent
Hythe
Hythe Imperial
Tel 01303 267441
E mail
hytheimperial@marstonhotels.com

Leisure breaks from £82.50 per person, per night for a minimum of two nights. For £18 you can have up to 7 days play on the 9 hole, 18 tee course.

Maidstone
Marriott Tudor Park Hotel &
Country Club
Tel 01622 734334
E mail
tudorpark@marriotthotels.co.uk

Golf Winter Warmer, available
November – February. Monday-
Friday, full English breakfast,
unlimited golf and two course
dinner, £30.

Northumberland
Hexham
Slaley Hall
Tel 01434 673350
E mail slaley.hall@devere-hotels.com

Golf breaks, inclusive of full
Northumbrian breakfast, daily menu
in the restaurant and one round of
golf. Monday – Thursday from
around £77.50 per person per night,
Friday and Saturday £87.50 per
person per night, Sunday £65 per
person per night.

Shropshire
Telford
Telford Golf and Country Club
Tel 01952 429977

Two nights dinner, bed and breakfast,
18 holes, complimentary use of
leisure facilities from around £72 per
person per night, minimum two
nights. Sunday £50.

Suffolk
Woodbridge
Ufford Park
Tel 01394 383555
E mail uffordparkltd@btinternet.com

Golf lessons available. Break includes
overnight accommodation, three
course table d'hôte dinner, full
English breakfast, full use of extensive
leisure facilities, and up to three
rounds of golf (one round per day).
From £124 for two nights, extra
night from £62.

Wiltshire
Castle Combe
The Manor House
Tel 01249 782206
E mail enquiries@manor-house.co.uk

Minimum of any two nights,
unlimited golf on day of arrival
to noon on day of departure,
complimentary use of all outdoor
leisure facilities, four course dinner,
full English breakfast, early morning
tea and newspaper, from £200 per
room based on double occupancy.

Scotland

Scottish Borders
Kelso
The Roxburghe Hotel & Golf Course
Tel 01573 450331
E mail hotel@roxburghe.net

Midweek golf breaks from £105
per person per night, (April – Oct)
includes early morning tea, full
Scottish breakfast, table d'hôte
dinner, and one round of golf.
Extra round £25.

Dumfries & Galloway
Gatehouse of Fleet
Cally Palace Hotel
Tel 01557 814 341
E mail info@callypalace.co.uk

Spring and autumn/winter weekend
breaks from £80 per person per
night, includes dinner, bed and
breakfast and golf on the Cally
Course. Rates based on two people
sharing for a minimum of two nights.

Fife
St Andrews
St Andrews Golf Hotel
Tel 01334 474371
E mail
reservations@oldcoursehotel.co.uk

Guaranteed Old Course times.
Four night package, includes dinner,
bed and breakfast for a group of
eight (four couples sharing). Plus one
round on the Old Course and one on
the Jubilee course. Total cost for eight
£4200. Contact for further details.

Wales

Newport
Newport
Celtic Manor Resort Hotel
Tel 01633 413000
E mail postbox@celtic-manor.com

Available midweek and at weekends,
the golf break prices depend on
which course you want to play and
what time of year. Prices include golf,
dinner, bed and breakfast, from £99
per night.

Ireland

Co Kerry
Killarney
Aghadoe Heights
Tel 064 31766
E mail info@aghadoeheights.com

Can arrange tee times, caddies, club
hire and transport, and provide early
breakfast and drying facilities. Within
easy driving distance of Kerry's major
courses, various special break
packages are offered.

Co Wexford
Rosslare
Kelly's Resort Hotel
Tel 053 32114
E mail info@kellys.ie

Five day midweek breaks and two day
weekend breaks from €260. Special
rates at several courses. May Golf
Getaways include free golf clinic,
competitions etc.

AA Hotel Inspection

The AA inspects and classifies hotels and guest accommodation under quality standards agreed between the AA, English Tourism Council and RAC. Hotels receive a star classification from one to five stars and guest accommodation establishments receive between one and five diamonds.

AA recognised establishments pay an annual fee, this varies according to the classification level and the number of bedrooms.

The establishments receive an unannounced inspection visit from a qualified AA inspector who recommends the appropriate classification. Return visits are made to check that standards are maintained and the classification is not transferable if an establishment changes hands.

The AA Hotel Guide and AA Bed & Breakfast Guide, published annually, give further details of AA recognised establishments and the classification schemes.

Details of AA recommended hotels, guest accommodation, restaurants and pubs can be found on the AA website **www.theAA.com**

The quality % score appears after the star rating for hotels in this guide. This is an additional assessment made by AA hotel inspectors, covering everything the hotel has to offer, including hospitality.

The % allows a quick comparison between hotels with the same number of stars, the higher the % the better the hotel within the same star rating.

Red Stars are the highest accolade awarded by the AA to a small number of hotels which are considered to be outstanding. No % score is shown for hotels with red stars.

AA Star Classification

Quality standards you can expect from an AA recognised hotel

All hotels recognised by the AA should have the highest standards of cleanliness, proper records of booking, give prompt and professional service to guests, assist with luggage on request, accept and deliver messages, provide a designated area for breakfast and dinner with drinks available in a bar or lounge, provide an early morning call on request, good quality furniture and fittings, adequate heating and lighting and proper maintenance. A guide to some of the general expectations for each star classification is as follows:

What you can expect from a one star hotel ★

Polite, courteous staff providing a relatively informal yet competent style of service, available during the day and evening to receive guests. At least one designated eating area open to residents for breakfast (and for at least five days a week) dinner. A reasonable choice of hot and cold dishes and a short range of wines available. Television in lounge or bedroom. Majority of rooms en suite, bath or shower room available at all times.

What you can expect from a two star hotel ★★

Smartly and professionally presented management and staff providing competent, often informal service, available throughout the day and evening to greet guests. At least one restaurant or dining room open to residents for breakfast (and for at least five days a week) for dinner. Last orders for dinner (when available) no earlier than 7pm, a choice of substantial hot and cold dishes and a short range of wines available. Television in bedroom. En suite or private bath or shower and WC.

What you can expect from a three star hotel ★★★

Management and staff smartly and professionally presented and usually uniformed. Technical and social skills of a good standard in responding to requests. A dedicated receptionist on duty at peak times, clear direction to rooms and some explanation of hotel facilities. At least one restaurant or dining room open to residents and non-residents for breakfast and dinner whenever the hotel is open. A wide selection of drinks served in a bar or lounge, available to residents and their guest throughout the day and evening. Last orders for dinner no earlier than 8pm, full dinner service provided. Remote-control television, direct-dial telephone. En suite bath or shower and WC.

What you can expect from a four star hotel ★★★★

A formal, professional staffing structure with smartly presented, uniformed staff, anticipating and responding to your needs or requests. Usually spacious, well-appointed public areas. Bedrooms offering superior quality and comfort than at three star. A strong emphasis on food and beverages and a serious approach to cuisine. Reception staffed 24 hours per day by well-trained staff. Express checkout facilities where appropriate. Porterage available on request and readily provided by uniformed staff. Night porter available. Newspapers can be ordered and delivered to your room, additional services and concierge as appropriate to the style and location of the hotel. At least one restaurant open to residents and non-residents for breakfast and dinner seven days per week, and lunch to be available in a designated eating area. Drinks available to residents and their guests throughout the day and evening, table service available. Last orders for dinner no earlier than 9pm, an extensive choice of hot and

cold dishes and a comprehensive list of wines. Remote-control television, direct-dial telephone, a range of high-quality toiletries. En suite bath with fixed overhead shower, WC.

What you can expect from a five star hotel ★★★★★

Flawless guest services, professional, attentive staff, technical and social skills of the highest order. Spacious and luxurious accommodation and public areas with a range of extra facilities. As a minimum, first-time guests shown to their bedroom. Multilingual service consistent with the needs of the hotel's normal clientele. Guest accounts well explained and presented. Porterage offered and provided by uniformed staff. Luggage handling on arrival and departure. Doorman or means of greeting guests at the hotel entrance, full concierge service provided. At least one restaurant open to residents and non-residents for all meals seven days per week. Staff showing excellent knowledge of food and wine. A wide selection of drinks, including cocktails, available in a bar or lounge, table service provided. Last orders for dinner no earlier than 10pm. High-quality menu and wine list properly reflecting and complementing the style of cooking and providing exceptional quality. Evening turn-down service. Remote-control television, direct-dial telephone at bedside and desk, a range of luxury toiletries, bath sheets and robes. En suite bath with fixed overhead shower, WC.

How can I get away without the hassle of finding a place to stay?

Booking a place to stay can be a time-consuming process. You choose a place you like, only to find it's fully booked. That means going back to the drawing board again. Why not ask us to find the place that best suits your needs? No fuss, no worries and no booking fee.

Whatever your preference, we have the place for you. From a rustic farm cottage to a smart city centre hotel - we have them all. Choose from around 8,000 quality rated hotels and B&Bs in Great Britain and Ireland.

Hotel Booking Service

0870 50 50 505

accommodation@aabookings.com

www.theAA.com

You may contact us by using a Textphone on 0870 243 2456.
Information is available in large print, audio and Braille on request. Please call for details.

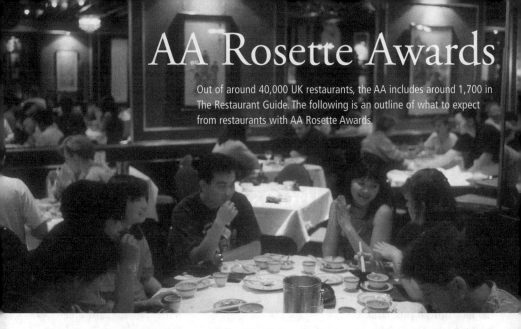

AA Rosette Awards

Out of around 40,000 UK restaurants, the AA includes around 1,700 in The Restaurant Guide. The following is an outline of what to expect from restaurants with AA Rosette Awards.

Excellent local restaurants serving food prepared with care, understanding and skill, using good quality ingredients. These restaurants all stand out in their local area. The same expectations apply to hotel restaurants where guests should be able to eat in with confidence and a sense of anticipation. Around 50% of restaurants with rosettes.

The best local restaurants, which aim for and achieve higher standards, better consistency and where a greater precision is apparent in the cooking. There will be obvious attention to the selection of quality ingredients. Around 40% of restaurants with rosettes.

Outstanding restaurants that demand recognition well beyond their local area. The cooking will be underpinned by the selection and sympathetic treatment of the highest quality ingredients. Timing, seasoning and the judgement of flavour combinations will be consistently excellent, supported by other elements such as intelligent service and a well-chosen wine list. Around 150 restaurants (less than 10% of those with rosettes).

Amongst the very best restaurants in the British Isles where the cooking demands national recognition. These restaurants will exhibit intense ambition, a passion for excellence, superb technical skills and remarkable consistency. They will combine appreciation of culinary traditions with a passionate desire for further exploration and improvement. Around a dozen restaurants with four rosettes.

The finest restaurants in the British Isles, where the cooking stands comparison with the best in the world. These restaurants will have highly individual voices, exhibit breathtaking culinary skills and set the standards to which others aspire. Around half a dozen restaurants with five rosettes.

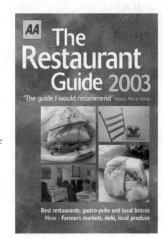

Golf ENGLAND –
Chipping Millions into the Game

The AA has joined forces with the English Golf Union (EGU) to launch the new official programme for amateur golf – Golf ENGLAND.

The programme has been set up to provide clubs and golfers with the broadest range of benefits and services.

Golf ENGLAND is committed to providing vital investment for the amateur game of golf, and 30% of all dividends made through this organisation will be channelled back into the game. £3m has already been deposited with the EGU to invest in the amateur game, and this figure is set to rise to £7m in 2003.

Golfers at every level can benefit from the new programme;

Golf club members are automatically entitled to free membership and receive a new smart card that stores their handicap using an in-built microchip.

Non club members can join for just the equivalent of £4 per month, and through a new scheme with the EGU can work towards gaining an Associate Member handicap stored on their membership card.

All members have exclusive access to savings on a range of golf-related products and services, including reduced green fees, a free quarterly magazine and comprehensive golf insurance. Members can

also apply to take a Golf ENGLAND credit card, which earns points redeemable against green fees and a variety of other products and services.

To join Golf ENGLAND, please call 0870 243 2343 or visit www.golfengland.com

England

g golf
ENGLAND

A power of good for golf.

ENGLAND

BEDFORDSHIRE

ASPLEY GUISE
Map 04 SP93

Aspley Guise & Woburn Sands West Hill MK17
8DX ☎ 01908 583596 📠 01908 583596 (Secretary)
A fine undulating course in expansive heathland
interspersed with many attractive clumps of gorse,
broom and bracken. Some well-established silver birch
are a feature. The 7th, 8th and 9th are really tough
holes to complete the first half.
18 holes, 6079yds, Par 71, SSS 70, Course record 67.
Club membership 560.
Visitors with member only at weekends. **Societies** Wed &
Fri normally booked 6 mths ahead. **Green Fees** not
confirmed. **Prof** Joe Awuku **Course Designer** Sandy
Herd **Facilities** ⊗ by prior arrangement ⅷ by prior
arrangement ⅊ 🖤 ♀ 🛆 🕈 🏌 **Location** 2m W of M1
junc 13

Hotel ★★★ 68% Moore Place Hotel, The Square,
ASPLEY GUISE ☎ 01908 282000 39 en suite 15 annexe
en suite

BEDFORD
Map 04 TL04

Bedford Great Denham Golf Village, Carnoustie Dr,
Biddenham MK40 4FF ☎ 01234 320022 📠 01234 320023
e-mail: thebedford1@ukonline.co.uk
American styled course with 89 bunkers, 8 large water
features and large contoured greens. Built on sand and
gravel the course is open all year round.
18 holes, 6471yds, Par 72, SSS 72, Course record 67.
Club membership 600.
Visitors contact in advance, limited weekends. **Societies**
telephone for details. **Green Fees** not confirmed. **Cards** 🖭
🖭 🖭 🖭 🖭 🖭 **Prof** Zac Thompson **Course Designer**
David Pottage **Facilities** ⊗ ⅷ ⅊ 🖤 ♀ 🛆 🖺 🕈 🏌 🛒 🏌 🏌
Location 2.5m W of Bedford off A428

Hotel ★★★ 74% Woodlands Manor Hotel, Green Ln,
Clapham, BEDFORD ☎ 01234 363281 30 en suite 3 annexe
en suite

Bedford & County Green Ln, Clapham MK41 6ET
☎ 01234 352617 📠 01234 357195
A mature parkland course established in 1912 with views
over Bedford and surrounding countryside. Beware of
the brook that discreetly meanders through the 7th, 10th,
11th and 15th holes. The testing par 4 15th is one of the
most challenging holes in the area.
18 holes, 6347yds, Par 70, SSS 70.
Club membership 600.
Visitors handicap certificate required, weekends with
member only. **Societies** welcome Mon,Tue,Thu & Fri,
telephone in advance. **Green Fees** £24 per round. **Prof** R
Tattersall **Facilities** ⊗ ⅷ by prior arrangement ⅊ 🖤 ♀ 🛆
🖺 🏌 **Location** 2m N off A6

Hotel ★★★ 74% Woodlands Manor Hotel, Green Ln,
Clapham, BEDFORD ☎ 01234 363281 30 en suite 3 annexe
en suite

Bedfordshire Bromham Rd, Biddenham MK40 4AF
☎ 01234 261669 📠 01234 261669
18 holes, 6305yds, Par 70, SSS 70, Course record 63.
Location 1m W on A428
continued

Telephone for further details

Hotel ★★★ 74% Woodlands Manor Hotel, Green Ln,
Clapham, BEDFORD ☎ 01234 363281 30 en suite 3 annexe
en suite

Mowsbury Cleat Hill, Kimbolton Rd, Ravensden MK41
8DQ ☎ 01234 771041 & 216374 (pro) 📠 01234 771041
e-mail: mgc@freenet.co.uk
Parkland municipal course in rural surroundings. Long
and testing 14-bay driving range and squash facilities.
18 holes, 6451yds, Par 72, SSS 71, Course record 66.
Club membership 550.
Visitors no restrictions. **Societies** apply in writing. **Green
Fees** not confirmed. **Prof** Malcolm Summers **Course
Designer** Hawtree **Facilities** ⊗ ⅷ by prior arrangement ⅊
🖤 ♀ 🛆 🖺 🕈 🏌 🏌 **Leisure** squash. **Location** 2m N of town
centre on B660

Hotel ★★★ 74% Woodlands Manor Hotel, Green Ln,
Clapham, BEDFORD ☎ 01234 363281 30 en suite 3 annexe
en suite

CHALGRAVE
Map 04 TL02

Chalgrave Manor Dunstable Rd LU5 6JN
☎ 01525 876556 📠 01525 876556
Undulating course constructed in 1994, offering a good
test of golf for all standards of golfer. Feature holes
include the short 10th (150 yards) that requires an
accurate shot across water to a splendid sloping green,
and the par 4 11th which incorporates an elevated tee, a
ditch, several bunkers, a pond and perilously close out of
bounds.
18 holes, 6382yds, Par 72, SSS 70, Course record 69.
Club membership 550.
Visitors welcome, dress code smart casual, after 11am at
weekends. **Societies** apply in writing or telephone, in
advance. **Green Fees** £25 per day; £15 per round (£20
weekends & bank holidays). **Cards** 🖭 🖭 🖭 🖭 **Prof**
Terry Bunyan **Course Designer** M Palmer **Facilities** ⊗ ⅷ
by prior arrangement ⅊ 🖤 ♀ 🛆 🛒 🏌 **Conf** Max 50
Class 50 Banquet 50 **Location** M1 junct 12 take A5120
through Toddington, entrance about 1m out, well signposted

Hotel ★★★ 66% Hanover International Hotel, Church St,
DUNSTABLE ☎ 01582 662201 68 en suite

COLMWORTH
Map 04 TL15

Colmworth & North Bedfordshire New Rd
MK44 2NU ☎ 01234 378181 📠 01234 376235

An easy walking course with well-bunkered greens,
opened in 1991. The course is often windy and plays
longer than the yardage suggests. Water comes into play
on 3 holes.
18 holes, 6435yds, Par 72, SSS 71, Course record 71.
continued

Club membership 200.
Visitors advisable to contact in advance, may only play at weekends after 9.30am. **Societies** telephone in advance. **Green Fees** terms on application. **Cards** ▨ ▨ ▨ ▨ ▨ **Prof** M Fields/S Bonham **Course Designer** John Glasgow **Facilities** ⊗ 🖫 🍴 ♀ 🏌 🏠 🛒 🖊 Ⅎ **Leisure** fishing, par 3 course. **Location** 7m NE of Bedford, off B660

Hotel ★★★ 69% The Barns Hotel, Cardington Rd, BEDFORD ☎ 01234 270044 48 en suite

DUNSTABLE Map 04 TL02

Dunstable Downs Whipsnade Rd LU6 2NB
☎ 01582 604472 ▤ 01582 478700
e-mail: dunstabledownsgc@aol.com
A fine downland course set on two levels with far-reaching views and frequent sightings of graceful gliders. The 9th hole is one of the best short holes in the country. There is a modernised clubhouse.
18 holes, 6251yds, Par 70, SSS 70, Course record 64.
Club membership 600.
Visitors welcome Mon, Tue, Thur and Fri, weekends with member only. Handicap certificate required. **Societies** apply in advance. **Green Fees** not confirmed. **Prof** Michael Weldon **Course Designer** James Braid **Facilities** ⊗ 🗙 by prior arrangement 🖫 🍴 ♀ 🏠 🛒 🖊 **Location** 2m S off B4541

Hotel ★★★ 66% Hanover International Hotel, Church St, DUNSTABLE ☎ 01582 662201 68 en suite

Griffin Chaul End Rd, Caddington LU1 4AX
☎ 01582 415573 ▤ 01582 415314
A challenging 18-hole course with ponds and lakes.
18 holes, 6240yds, Par 71, SSS 70.
Club membership 510.
Visitors welcome Mon-Fri & after 2pm weekends no need to book. **Societies** welcome midweek and Sat/Sun pm summer. Book by telephone. **Green Fees** not confirmed. **Facilities** ⊗ 🗙 🖫 🍴 ♀ 🏠 🏌 **Location** Off A505 Luton/Dunstable

Hotel ★★★ 66% Hanover International Hotel, Church St, DUNSTABLE ☎ 01582 662201 68 en suite

LEIGHTON BUZZARD Map 04 SP92

Leighton Buzzard Plantation Rd LU7 7JF
☎ 01525 244800 (Office) ▤ 01525 244801
e-mail: thesecretary@lbgc.net
Parkland course with easy walking. The 17th and 18th holes are challenging tree-lined finishing holes with tight fairways. The 11th par 3 is signature hole.
18 holes, 6101yds, Par 71, SSS 70, Course record 66.
Club membership 700.
Visitors may play yellow tees, may not play Tue (Ladies Day). May only play with member weekends and bank holidays. Handicap certificate required unless playing with member. **Societies** prior booking required. **Green Fees** £30 per day; £26 per round. **Prof** Maurice Campbell **Facilities** ⊗ 🗙 🖫 🍴 ♀ 🏠 🍴 🦯 🛒 🖊 **Conf** Max 60 Banquet 60 Del £75 to £125 * **Location** 1.5m N of town centre off A4146

Hotel ★★★ 66% Hanover International Hotel, Church St, DUNSTABLE ☎ 01582 662201 68 en suite

LOWER STONDON Map 04 TL13

Mount Pleasant Station Rd SG16 6JL
☎ 01462 850999
e-mail: davidsimsmpgolf@aol.com
A 9 hole course, which when played over 18 totals some
continued

6003yds. The course is undulating meadowland with mature hedges and trees and also 10,000 new trees. Two small ponds are crossed and there is a significant ditch in play on several holes. The 5th,11th and 14th holes are all 400yds and play long into the prevailing west wind. Visitors consider the greens some of the best conditioned in the area and with good drainage the course rarely has to close.
9 holes, 6003yds, Par 70, SSS 69, Course record 68.
Club membership 300.
Visitors no restrictions, book 2 days in advance, booking advisable weekends & evenings May-Sep. **Societies** telephone or apply in writing. **Green Fees** 18 holes £13; 9 holes £7.50 (£17/£10 weekends & bank holidays). **Cards** ▨ ▨ ▨ ▨ **Prof** Mike Roberts **Course Designer** Derek Young **Facilities** ⊗ 🗙 🖫 🍴 ♀ 🏠 🛒 🖊 **Location** 0.75m W of A600, 4m N of Hitchin

Hotel ★★★ 81% Menzies Flitwick Manor, Church Rd, FLITWICK ☎ 0870 6003013 17 en suite

LUTON Map 04 TL02

South Beds Warden Hill Rd LU2 7AE
☎ 01582 591500 ▤ 01582 495381
18 and 9 hole downland courses, slightly undulating.
Galley Hill Course: 18 holes, 6397yds, Par 71, SSS 71, Course record 64.
Warden Hill Course: 9 holes, 2424yds, Par 32, SSS 32.
Club membership 1000.
Visitors must contact in advance and have a handicap certificate. **Societies** telephone for details. **Green Fees** telephone for details. **Cards** ▨ ▨ ▨ ▨ **Prof** Eddie Cogle **Facilities** ⊗ 🗙 🖫 🍴 ♀ 🏠 🛒 🖊 **Location** 2m N of Luton on A6

Hotel ★★★ 59% The Chiltern, Waller Av, LUTON ☎ 01582 575911 91 en suite

Stockwood Park London Rd LU1 4LX
☎ 01582 413704 (pro shop)
Well laid out municipal parkland course with established trees and several challenging holes.
18 holes, 6049yds, Par 69, SSS 69, Course record 67.
Club membership 800.
Visitors no restrictions. **Societies** Mon, Tue & Thu only, telephone for application. **Green Fees** £9.50 per round (£12.70 weekends). **Cards** ▨ ▨ **Prof** Glyn McCarthy **Facilities** ⊗ 🗙 🖫 🍴 ♀ 🏠 🍴 🦯 🛒 🖊 Ⅎ **Location** 1m S

Hotel ★★★ 59% The Chiltern, Waller Av, LUTON ☎ 01582 575911 91 en suite

MILLBROOK Map 04 TL03

Lyshott Heath Millbrook Village MK45 2JB
☎ 01525 840252 ▤ 01525 406249
e-mail: enquiries@lyshott-heath.com
Long parkland course, on rolling countryside high above the Bedfordshire plains. Laid out on well-drained sandy soil with many fairways lined with silver birch, pine and larch.
18 holes, 7100yds, Par 74, SSS 73, Course record 69.
Club membership 366.
Visitors must contact in advance, may not play after 11am on Thu or after 11.30am at weekends. **Societies** telephone for details. **Green Fees** not confirmed. **Prof** Geraint Dixon **Course Designer** William Sutherland **Facilities** ⊗ 🗙 🖫 ♀. ♀ 🏠 🍴 🛒 🖊 **Location** M1 junct 12 & 13, then take A507 Woburn to Ampthill road
continued

Hotel ★★★ 81% Menzies Flitwick Manor, Church Rd, FLITWICK ☎ 0870 6003013 17 en suite

PAVENHAM   Map 04 SP95

Pavenham Park MK43 7PE
☎ 01234 822202 🖹 01234 826602
e-mail: kolvengolf@ukonline.co.uk
Mature, undulating parkland course with fast contoured greens.
18 holes, 6400yds, Par 72, SSS 71, Course record 63.
Club membership 790.
Visitors welcome weekdays, weekends as members guests only. Societies telephone in advance. Green Fees not confirmed. Cards ⬛⬛⬛ ☯ Prof Zac Thompson Course Designer Zac Thompson Facilities ⊗ ⫪ 🏌 🍺 ♀ ⚲ 🏠 ⛳ 🛒 🚃 ♿ Location 1.5m from A6, N of Bedford

Hotel ★★★ 74% Woodlands Manor Hotel, Green Ln, Clapham, BEDFORD ☎ 01234 363281 30 en suite 3 annexe en suite

SANDY   Map 04 TL14

John O'Gaunt Sutton Park SG19 2LY
☎ 01767 260360 🖹 01767 262834
Two magnificent parkland courses - John O'Gaunt and Carthagena - covering a gently undulating and tree-lined terrain. The John O'Gaunt course makes the most of numerous natural features, notably a river which crosses the fairways of four holes. The Carthagena course has larger greens, longer tees and from the back tees is a challenging course. Fine clubhouse.
John O'Gaunt Course: 18 holes, 6513yds, Par 71, SSS 71, Course record 64.
Carthagena Course: 18 holes, 5869yds, Par 69, SSS 69.
Club membership 1500.
Visitors must contact in advance. Societies must pre-book. Green Fees £45 per day/round (£50 weekends & bank holidays). Prof Lee Scarbrow Course Designer John O'Gaunt/Others Facilities ⊗ ⫪ 🏌 🍺 ♀ ⚲ 🏠 🛒 🚃 ♿ Location 3m NE of Biggleswade on B1040

Hotel ★★ 69% Abbotsley Golf Hotel & Country Club, Potton Rd, Eynesbury Hardwicke, ST NEOTS ☎ 01480 474000 42 annexe en suite

SHEFFORD   Map 04 TL13

Beadlow Manor Hotel & Golf & Country Club SG17 5PH ☎ 01525 860800 🖹 01525 861345
e-mail: beadlowmanor@talk21 co.uk
A 36-hole golf and leisure complex. The Baroness Manhattan and the Baron Manhattan golf courses are undulating with water hazards on numerous holes. These are good challenging courses for both the beginner and low handicap player.
Baroness Course: 18 holes, 6072yds, Par 71, SSS 69, Course record 67.
Baron Course: 18 holes, 6619yds, Par 73, SSS 72, Course record 67. Club membership 850.
Visitors book in advance & must adhere to dress code. Societies apply in writing or telephone in advance. Green Fees Baroness: £12 per round (£20 weekends); Baron: £10 per round (£17 weekends). Cards ⬛⬛⬛⬛⬛ ☯ Prof Geoff Swain Facilities ⊗ ⫪ 🏌 🍺 ♀ ⚲ 🏠 ⛳ 🏇 🚃 ♿ Conf Max 200 Thtr 200 Class 100 Board 100 Banquet 150 Del £5 to £28 * Location On A507

Hotel ★★ 67% Stratton House Hotel, London Rd, BIGGLESWADE ☎ 01767 312442 31 en suite

TILSWORTH   Map 04 SP92

Tilsworth Dunstable Rd LU7 9PU
☎ 01525 210721/2 🖹 01525 210465
e-mail: nick@tilsworthgolf.co.uk
An undulating 18 hole parkland course with a 30-bay floodlit driving range.
18 holes, 5306yds, Par 69, SSS 66, Course record 66.
Club membership 400.
Visitors may book up to 7 days in advance. May not play before 10am Sundays. Societies welcome weekdays, apply in advance to W Payne Green Fees terms on application. Cards ⬛⬛⬛ ⬛⬛ ☯ Prof Nick Webb Facilities ⊗ ⫪ 🏌 🍺 ♀ ⚲ 🏠 ⛳ 🚃 ♿ Location 0.5m NE off A5, N of Dunstable

Hotel ★★★ 66% Hanover International Hotel, Church St, DUNSTABLE ☎ 01582 662201 68 en suite

WHIPSNADE   Map 04 TL01

Whipsnade Park Studham Ln, Dagnall HP4 1RH
☎ 01442 842330 🖹 01442 842090
e-mail: whipsnadeparkgc@talk21.com
Parkland course situated on downs overlooking the Chilterns adjoining Whipsnade Zoo. Easy walking, good views.
18 holes, 6800yds, Par 73, SSS 72, Course record 66.
Club membership 600.
Visitors welcome weekdays, with member only at weekends. Must contact in advance. Societies by prior arrangement. Green Fees £37 per day; £27 per round. Cards ⬛⬛⬛ ⬛⬛ ☯ Prof Roland Perry Facilities ⊗ ⫪ 🏌 🍺 ♀ ⚲ 🏠 🚃 ♿ Location 1m E off B4506 between villages of Dagnall & Studham

Hotel ★★★ 66% Hanover International Hotel, Church St, DUNSTABLE ☎ 01582 662201 68 en suite

WYBOSTON   Map 04 TL15

Wyboston Lakes MK44 3AL
☎ 01480 223004 🖹 01480 407330
e-mail: venue@wybostonlakes.co.uk
Parkland course, with narrow fairways, small greens, set around four lakes and a river which provide the biggest challenge on this very scenic course.

18 holes, 5955yds, Par 70, SSS 69, Course record 65.
Club membership 300.
Visitors a booking system is in operation at weekends, book no more than 8 days in advance. Societies telephone in advance. Green Fees not confirmed. Cards ⬛⬛⬛ ⬛⬛ Prof Paul Ashwell Course Designer N Oakden Facilities ⊗ ⫪ 🏌 🍺 ♀ ⚲ 🏠 ⛳ 🏇 🚃 ♿ Leisure heated indoor swimming pool, fishing, sauna, solarium, gymnasium, watersports. Location 1m S of St Neots off A1/A428

continued

Hotel ★★★ 74% Woodlands Manor Hotel, Green Ln, Clapham, BEDFORD ☎ 01234 363281 30 en suite 3 annexe en suite

BERKSHIRE

ASCOT — Map 04 SU96

Berkshire Swinley Rd SL5 8AY ☎ 01344 621495
Two heathland courses with splendid tree-lined fairways. The Red Course, on slightly higher ground, is a little longer than the Blue. It has an unusual assortment of holes, six par 3s, six par 4s and six par 5s, the short holes, particularly the 10th and 16th, being the most intimidating. The Blue Course starts with a par 3 and shares with the 16th the reputation of being the finest holes of the 18.
Red Course: 18 holes, 6379yds, Par 72, SSS 71.
Blue Course: 18 holes, 6260yds, Par 71, SSS 71.
Visitors by prior arrangement Societies applications in writing only and must be registered. Green Fees £90 per day; £70 per round. Cards ▦ ▦ 🔢 Prof P Anderson Course Designer H Fowler Facilities ⊗ ▮ 🍺 ♀ ☒ 🏠 ⚐ 🏌 🛒 ♿ ✆ Location 2.5m NW of M3 jct 3 on A332

Hotel ★★★★ 64% The Berystede, Bagshot Rd, Sunninghill, ASCOT ☎ 0870 400 8111 90 en suite

Lavender Park Swinley Rd SL5 8BD ☎ 01344 893344
Public parkland course, ideal for the short game featuring challenging narrow fairways. Driving range with 9 hole par 3 course, floodlit until 10pm.
9 holes, 1102yds, Par 27, SSS 28.
Visitors no restrictions. Societies welcome, notice preferred. Green Fees not confirmed. Prof David Johnson/Andy Piper Facilities 🍺 ♀ 🏠 ⚐ ✆ Leisure snooker. Location 3.5m SW of Ascot, on A332

Hotel ★★★★ 64% The Berystede, Bagshot Rd, Sunninghill, ASCOT ☎ 0870 400 8111 90 en suite

Mill Ride Mill Ride SL5 8LT
☎ 01344 886777 📄 01344 886820
e-mail: archie@millride.com
Opened for play in 1991, this 18-hole course combines links and parkland styles. The holes require as much thinking as playing.

18 holes, 6807yds, Par 72, SSS 72, Course record 64.
Club membership 400.
Visitors must contact in advance, limited access at weekends. Societies apply in advance. Green Fees not confirmed. Cards ▦ ▦ 🔢 🔢 🔢 Prof Terry Wild Course Designer Donald Steel Facilities ⊗ ⅲ ▮ 🍺 ♀ ☒ 🏠 ⚐ 🚩 ✆ Leisure sauna. Location 2m W of Ascot
continued

Hotel ★★★★ 64% The Berystede, Bagshot Rd, Sunninghill, ASCOT ☎ 0870 400 8111 90 en suite

Royal Ascot Winkfield Rd SL5 7LJ
☎ 01344 625175 📄 01344 872330
Heathland course inside Ascot racecourse and exposed to weather.
18 holes, 5716yds, Par 68, SSS 68, Course record 65.
Club membership 620.
Visitors must be guest of member or contact secretary in advance. Not weekends. Societies telephone for provisional booking. Green Fees not confirmed. Prof Alistair White Course Designer J H Taylor Facilities ☒ 🏠 ✆ Location 0.5m N on A330

Hotel ★★★★ 64% The Berystede, Bagshot Rd, Sunninghill, ASCOT ☎ 0870 400 8111 90 en suite

Swinley Forest Coronation Rd SL5 9LE
☎ 01344 874979 (Secretary) 📄 01344 874733
e-mail: swinleyfgc@aol.com
An attractive and immaculate course of heather and pine situated in the heart of Swinley Forest. The 17th is as good a short hole as will be found, with a bunkered plateau green and the 12th hole is one of the most challenging par 4s.
18 holes, 6100yds, Par 69, SSS 70, Course record 62.
Club membership 350.
Visitors on introduction of a member or by invitation only. Societies must contact in writing. Green Fees terms on application. Cards ▦ 🔢 🔢 Prof Stuart Hill Course Designer Harry Colt Facilities ⊗ ▮ 🍺 ♀ ☒ 🏠 ⚐ 🏌 🛒 ✆ Location 1.5m S, off A330

Hotel ★★★★ 64% The Berystede, Bagshot Rd, Sunninghill, ASCOT ☎ 0870 400 8111 90 en suite

BINFIELD — Map 04 SU87

Blue Mountain Golf Centre Wood Ln RG42 4EX
☎ 01344 300200 📄 01344 360960
e-mail: bluemountain@americangolf.uk.com
An 18-hole Pay and Play course with many testing holes with water hazards. Greens are large, undulating and strategically placed bunkers provide a fair challenge.
18 holes, 6097yds, Par 70, SSS 70, Course record 63.
Club membership 400.
Visitors tee times bookable in advance by phoning 01344 300220, Societies must contact in advance. Green Fees £18 per 18 holes Mon-Thu, £20 Fri, £25 weekends and bank holidays. Cards ▦ ▦ 🔢 🔢 Prof Iain Looms Facilities ⊗ ⅲ ▮ 🍺 ♀ ☒ 🏠 ⚐ 🏌 🛒 ♿ ✆ Conf Max 500 Thtr 170 Class 72 Board 350 Location from M4 junct 10, follow A329(M) signposted to Bracknell. Take 1st exit signposted B3408 for Binfield. Go straight over roundabout and through traffic lights to the next roundabout. Take 2nd exit, first left into Wood Lane

Hotel ★★★★ 76% Coppid Beech, John Nike Way, BRACKNELL ☎ 01344 303333 205 en suite

CHADDLEWORTH — Map 04 SU47

West Berkshire RG20 7DU
☎ 01488 638574 & 638851 📄 01488 638781
Challenging and interesting downland course with views of the Berkshire Downs. The course is bordered by ancient woodland and golfers will find manicured fairways with well constructed greens and strategically placed hazards.
continued

The testing 627yds 5th hole is one of the longest par 5s in southern England. Bunkers are well placed from tees and around the greens to catch any wayward shots.
18 holes, 7001yds, Par 73, SSS 74.
Club membership 650.
Visitors must contact in advance, may play weekends pm only. **Societies** telephone in advance. **Green Fees** terms on application. **Cards** ▭ ▭ ▭ 🔲 **Prof** Paul Simpson **Course Designer** Robin Stagg **Facilities** ⊗ ⅃ ▪ ♀ ⌐ 🏠 🏌 𝄢 ｢
Location 1m S of village off A338

Hotel ★★★ 65% The Chequers, 6-8 Oxford St, NEWBURY ☎ 01635 38000 46 en suite 10 annexe en suite

COOKHAM
Map 04 SU88

Winter Hill Grange Ln SL6 9RP
☎ 01628 527613 (Secretary) 🖹 01628 527479
Parkland course set in a curve of the Thames with wonderful views across the river to Cliveden.
18 holes, 6408yds, Par 72, SSS 71, Course record 63.
Club membership 850.
Visitors phone in advance, not permitted weekends.
Societies welcome Wed & Fri, telephone initially. **Green Fees** terms on application. **Prof** Roger Frost **Course Designer** Charles Lawrie **Facilities** ⊗ ⅃ ▪ ♀ 🏠 🏌
Location 1m NW off B4447

Hotel ★★★★ 72% The Compleat Angler, Marlow Bridge, MARLOW ☎ 0870 400 8100 64 en suite

CROWTHORNE
Map 04 SU86

East Berkshire Ravenswood Ave RG45 6BD
☎ 01344 772041 🖹 01344 777378
e-mail: thesecretary@eastberksgc.golfagent.co.uk
An attractive heathland course with an abundance of heather and pine trees. Walking is easy and the greens are exceptionally good. Some fairways become tight where the heather encroaches on the line of play. The course is testing and demands great accuracy.
18 holes, 6344yds, Par 69, SSS 70.
Club membership 766.
Visitors must contact in advance and have a handicap certificate; must play with member at weekends & bank holidays. **Societies** telephone for availability. **Green Fees** £40 per day. **Prof** Arthur Roe **Course Designer** P Paxton **Facilities** ⊗ ⅃ ▪ ♀ 🏠 🏌 𝄢 **Location** W side of town centre off B3348

Hotel ★★★★★ 73% Pennyhill Park Hotel & Country Club, London Rd, BAGSHOT ☎ 01276 471774 26 en suite 97 annexe en suite

DATCHET
Map 04 SU97

Datchet Buccleuch Rd SL3 9BP
☎ 01753 543887 & 541872 🖹 01753 541872
9 holes, 5978yds, Par 70, SSS 69, Course record 63.
Location NW side of Datchet off B470
Telephone for further details

Hotel ★★★ 71% The Castle Hotel, 18 High St, WINDSOR ☎ 0870 400 8300 41 en suite 70 annexe en suite

MAIDENHEAD
Map 04 SU88

Bird Hills Drift Rd, Hawthorn Hill SL6 3ST
☎ 01628 771030 🖹 01628 631023
e-mail: info@birdhills.com
A gently undulating course with easy walking and many water hazards. Some challenging holes are the par 5 6th

continued

dog-leg, par 3 9th surrounded by water and bunkers, and the 16th which is a long uphill par 4 and a two-tier green.
18 holes, 6176yds, Par 72, SSS 69, Course record 65.
Club membership 400.

Bird Hills Golf Course

Visitors to book ring 7 days in advance, no 2 balls before noon weekends or bank holidays. **Societies** write or telephone in advance **Green Fees** £15 per 18 holes; £10 per 9 holes (£20/£14 weekends and bank holidays). **Cards** ▭ ▭ ▭ ▭ 🔲 **Prof** Nick Slimming **Facilities** ⊗ ⅃ ▪ ♀ ⌐ 🏠 🏌 𝄢 ｢ **Leisure** pool tables. **Conf** Thtr 80 Class 80 Board 30 Banquet 100 **Location** 4m S of M4 junct 8/9 on A330

Hotel ★★★ 70% Stirrups Country House, Maidens Green, BRACKNELL ☎ 01344 882284 29 en suite

Maidenhead Shoppenhangers Rd SL6 2PZ
☎ 01628 624693 🖹 01628 624693
A pleasant parkland course with excellent greens and some challenging holes. The long par 4, 4th and short par 3, 13th are only two of the many outstanding aspects of this course.
18 holes, 6364yds, Par 70, SSS 70.
Club membership 650.
Visitors may not play after noon on Fri or at weekends. Must contact in advance and have a handicap certificate. **Societies** must contact in writing. **Green Fees** £35 per day; £30 per round (£35 per round weekends). **Cards** ▭ **Prof** Steve Geary **Course Designer** Alex Simpson **Facilities** ⊗ ⅃ ▪ ♀ 🏠 🏌 𝄢 **Conf** Max 100 **Location** S side of town centre off A308

Hotel ★★★★ Fredrick's Hotel, Shoppenhangers Rd, MAIDENHEAD ☎ 01628 581000 37 en suite

Temple Henley Rd, Hurley SL6 5LH
☎ 01628 824795 🖹 01628 828119
An open parkland course offering extensive views over the Thames Valley. Firm, relatively fast greens, natural slopes and subtle contours provide a challenging test to golfers of all abilities. Excellent drainage assures play during inclement weather.
18 holes, 6248yds, Par 70, SSS 70, Course record 63.
Club membership 480.
Visitors must contact in advance, limited weekend access. May play yellow tees only. **Societies** contact Secretary for details. **Green Fees** £50 per day; £36 per round (£44 per round weekends). **Prof** James Whiteley **Course Designer** Willie Park (Jnr) **Facilities** ⊗ ⅃ ▪ ♀ 🏠 🏌 ＼ 𝄢 **Location** Exit M4 jct 8/9 take A404M then A4130,or M40 exit jct 4 take A404 then A4130,signposted Henley

Hotel ★★★★ 72% The Compleat Angler, Marlow Bridge, MARLOW ☎ 0870 400 8100 64 en suite

MORTIMER   Map 04 SU66

Wokefield Park Wokefield Park RG7 3AE
☎ 0118 9334018 ▯ 0118 9334162

Set in a prime location amid the peaceful and picturesque Berkshire countryside. The course architect has retained the numerous mature trees, and these, together with the winding streams, nine lakes and large bunkers, contribute to the beauty and challenge of this championship course.

18 holes, 6577yds, Par 72, SSS 72, Course record 65. Club membership 280.

Visitors no restrictions. **Societies** apply in writing/telephone in advance **Green Fees** £50 per day; £30 per round; £18 per 9 holes (£65/£45/£25 weekends). **Cards** 🖃 🖃 🖃 🖃 🖃 **Prof** Gary Smith **Course Designer** Jonathan Gaunt **Facilities** ⊗ ⅋ ⅃ ⅃ ⅃ ⅃ ⅃ ⅃ ⅃ ⅃ ⅃ **Leisure** hard tennis courts, heated indoor swimming pool, fishing, sauna, gymnasium, jacuzzi.**Conf** Thtr 400 Class 140 Board 64 Banquet 260 Del from £45 * **Location** M4 junct 11, A33 towards Basingstoke. 1st rdbt, 3rd exit towards Grazeley and Mortimer. After 2.5m and sharp right bend club on right

Hotel ★★★ 74% Romans Country House Hotel, Little London Rd, SILCHESTER ☎ 0118 970 0421 11 en suite 14 annexe en suite

NEWBURY   Map 04 SU46

Donnington Valley Snelsmore House, Snelsmore Common RG14 3BG ☎ 01635 568140 ▯ 01635 568141
e-mail: golf@donningtonvalley.co.uk

Undulating, testing course with mature trees and elevated greens, some protected by water.

18 holes, 6353yds, Par 71, SSS 71, Course record 71. Club membership 520.

Visitors booking system up to 7 days in advance, members have priority weekends. **Societies** write or telephone in advance. **Green Fees** terms on application. **Cards** 🖃 🖃 🖃 **Prof** Edward Lainchbury **Course Designer** Mike Smith **Facilities** ⊗ ⅋ ⅃ ⅃ ⅃ ⅃ ⅃ ⅃ ⅃ ⅃ ⅃ **Conf** Thtr 50 Board 14 Banquet 50 Del from £35 * **Location** 2m N of Newbury

Hotel ★★★★ 76% Donnington Valley Hotel & Golf Course, Old Oxford Rd, Donnington, NEWBURY ☎ 01635 551199 58 en suite

Newbury & Crookham Bury's Bank Rd, Greenham RG19 8BZ ☎ 01635 40035 ▯ 01635 40045
e-mail: june.hearsey@newburygolf.co.uk

A well-laid out, attractive course running mostly through woodland, and giving more of a challenge than its length suggests.

18 holes, 5940yds, Par 69, SSS 68. Club membership 800.

Visitors must play with member on weekends & bank holidays. Handicap certificate required. **Societies** must contact in advance. **Green Fees** £35 per day; £30 per round. **Cards** 🖃 🖃 🖃 **Prof** David Harris **Course Designer** J H Turner **Facilities** ⊗ ⅋ ⅃ ⅃ ⅃ ⅃ ⅃ ⅃ **Location** 2m SE off A34

Hotel ★★★ 65% The Chequers, 6-8 Oxford St, NEWBURY ☎ 01635 38000 46 en suite 10 annexe en suite

READING   Map 04 SU77

Calcot Park Bath Rd, Calcot RG31 7RN
☎ 0118 942 7124 ▯ 0118 945 3373
e-mail: info@calcotpark.com

A delightfully sporting, slightly undulating parkland course just outside the town. Hazards include streams, a lake and many trees. The 6th is a 503 yard par 5, with the tee-shot hit downhill over cross-bunkers to a well-guarded green, the 7th (156 yards) is played over the lake to an elevated green and the 13th (also 156 yards) requires a carry across a valley to a plateau green.

18 holes, 6216yds, Par 70, SSS 70, Course record 63. Club membership 730.

Visitors must have handicap certificate or letter of introduction from club. May play weekdays only, excluding bank holidays. **Societies** must apply in writing. **Green Fees** £40 per day/round; £25 after 2pm. **Prof** Ian Campbell **Course Designer** H S Colt **Facilities** ⊗ ⅋ ⅃ ⅃ ⅃ ⅃ ⅃ ⅃ **Leisure** fishing. **Conf** Max 25 Thtr 25 Class 25 Board 12 **Location** 1.5m from M4 junct 12 on A4 towards Reading

Hotel ★★★ 75% The Copper Inn Hotel & Restaurant, PANGBOURNE ☎ 0118 984 2244 14 en suite 8 annexe en suite

Hennerton Crazies Hill Rd, Wargrave RG10 8LT
☎ 0118 940 1000 ▯ 0118 940 1042

Overlooking the Thames Valley, this par 68 course has many existing natural features and a good number of hazards such as bunkers, mature trees and two small lakes. The most memorable hole is probably the 7th which is a par 3, 183 yards crossing a sharp valley to the green from which there are spectacular views of the course.

9 holes, 5460yds, Par 68, SSS 67, Course record 66. Club membership 450.

Visitors book 48 hours in advance, play weekends after 10am. **Societies** telephone or write for information. **Green Fees** £17 per 18 holes; £12 per 9 holes (£20/£15 Sundays and bank holidays). **Cards** 🖃 🖃 🖃 🖃 **Prof** William Farrow **Course Designer** Col D Beard **Facilities** ⊗ ⅃ ⅃ ⅃ ⅃ ⅃ ⅃ **Location** Follow signs from A321 Wargrave High Street

Hotel ★★★ 70% Red Lion Hotel, Hart St, HENLEY-ON-THAMES ☎ 01491 572161 26 en suite

Mapledurham Chazey Heath, Mapledurham RG4 7UD
☎ 0118 946 3353 ▯ 0118 946 3363

18-hole course designed by Bob Sandow. Flanked by hedgerows and mature woods, it is testing for players of all levels.

18 holes, 5635yds, Par 69, SSS 67, Course record 66. Club membership 2500.

continued   *continued*

Visitors advanced booking required. No play before 2pm at weekends. **Societies** must contact in advance. **Green Fees** £17.50 (£22.50 weekends). **Cards** ⊞ ▥ ▦ 🗂 📇 🈸 **Prof** Danny Peck **Course Designer** Robert Sandow **Facilities** ⊗ ⊪ ⅏ ☕ 𝍖 ⅄ 𓃺 ♨ ⚑ **Leisure** sauna, solarium, gymnasium. **Location** On A4074 to Oxford

Hotel ★★★ 77% The French Horn, SONNING ON THAMES ☎ 0118 969 2204
12 en suite 8 annexe en suite

Reading 17 Kidmore End Rd, Emmer Green RG4 8SG
☎ 0118 947 2909 (Secretary) 🗎 0118 946 4468
e-mail: secretary@readinggolfclub.com

Pleasant tree-lined parkland course, part hilly and part flat with interesting views and several challenging par 3s. After the opening holes the course moves across the valley. The par 4 5th is played from an elevated tee and although relatively short, the well-placed bunkers and trees come into play. The 470yd par 4 12th is a great hole. It has a slight dog-leg and requires an accurate second shot to hit a well-guarded green. The finishing hole requires two great shots to have any chance of reaching par.
18 holes, 6212yds, Par 70, SSS 70, Course record 65.
Club membership 585.
Visitors contact the professional. Welcome weekdays, with member only Fri & weekends. **Societies** apply by telephone, Tues-Thu only. **Green Fees** £38 per day; £25 per round. **Cards** ⊞ ▥ ▦ 📇 🈸 🗂 ⅏ **Prof** Scott Fotheringham **Course Designer** James Braid **Facilities** ⊗ ⊪ ⅏ ☕ 𝍖 ⅄ 📇 ⚑ **Leisure** indoor nets. **Location** 2m N off B481

Hotel ★★★ 64% Royal County Hotel, 4-8 Duke St, READING ☎ 0118 958 3455 52 en suite

Bearwood Mole Rd RG41 5DB ☎ 0118 976 0060
Flat parkland course with one water hazard, the 40 acre lake which features on the challenging 6th and 7th holes. Also driving range.
9 holes, 5610yds, Par 70, SSS 68, Course record 66.
Club membership 500.
Visitors welcome weekdays and weekend afternoons (contact in advance for pm weekend bookings) **Societies** apply in writing. **Green Fees** terms on application. **Cards** ⊞ ▥ ▦ 🈸 ⅏ **Prof** Bayley Tustin **Course Designer** Barry Tustin **Facilities** ⊗ ⊪ ⅏ ☕ 𝍖 ⅄ 𓃺 ♨ ⚑ ⚑ **Location** 1m SW on B3030

Hotel ★★★ 66% Edward Court Hotel, Wellington Rd, WOKINGHAM ☎ 0118 977 5886 27 en suite

Sonning Duffield Rd RG4 6GJ
☎ 0118 969 3332 🗎 0118 944 8409
e-mail: secretary@sonning-golf-club.co.uk

A quality parkland course and the scene of many county championships. Wide fairways, not overbunkered, and very good greens. Holes of changing character through wooded belts.
18 holes, 6366yds, Par 70, SSS 70, Course record 65.
Club membership 750.
Visitors weekdays only. Handicap certificate or proof of membership of another club required. **Societies** must apply in writing. Wed only, min 16. **Green Fees** £40.50 per day (£30.50 after 10.30am). **Prof** R McDougall **Course Designer** Hawtree **Facilities** ⊗ ⊪ by prior

continued

arrangement ⊪ ⅏ ☕ 𝍖 ⅄ 📇 ⚑ **Conf** Max 120 **Location** 1m S off A4

Hotel ★★★ 77% The French Horn, SONNING ON THAMES ☎ 0118 969 2204 12 en suite 8 annexe en suite

Goring & Streatley RG8 9QA
☎ 01491 873229 🗎 01491 875224
e-mail: secretary@gormggc.org

A parkland/moorland course that requires 'negotiating'. Four well-known first holes lead up to the heights of the 5th tee, to which there is a 300ft climb. Wide fairways, not overbunkered, with nice rewards on the way home down the last few holes. A delightful course that commands magnificent views of the Ridgeway and the River Thames.
18 holes, 6356yds, Par 71, SSS 70, Course record 65.
Club membership 740.
Visitors must contact in advance, with member only at weekends. Handicap certificate required. **Societies** telephone in advance. **Green Fees** £35 per day; £25 per round. **Cards** ⊞ ▥ ▦ 🈸 ⅏ **Prof** Jason Hadland **Course Designer** Tom Morris **Facilities** ⊗ ⊪ ⅏ ☕ 𝍖 ⅄ 📇 ⚑ **Conf** Max 100 Thtr 100 Class 90 Board 35 Banquet 60 Del £8 to £25 * **Location** N of village off A417

Hotel ★★★★ 67% The Swan at Streatley, High St, Streatley on Thames, STREATLEY ☎ 01491 878800 46 en suite

Sunningdale Ladies Cross Rd SL5 9RX
☎ 01344 620507
e-mail: ladiesgolf@lineone.net

A short 18-hole course with a typical Surrey heathland layout. A very tight course, making for a challenging game.
18 holes, 3616yds, Par 60, SSS 60, Course record 51.
Club membership 400.
Visitors telephone in advance. **Societies** apply in writing or by telephone. **Green Fees** £22 per day; £25 weekends. **Facilities** ⊗ ⊪ ⅏ ☕ 𝍖 ⅄ ⚑ **Leisure** Practice net. **Location** 1m S off A30

Hotel ★★★★ 64% The Berystede, Bagshot Rd, Sunninghill, ASCOT ☎ 0870 400 8111 90 en suite

Downshire Wayne Owers RG40 3DH
☎ 01344 302030 🗎 01344 301020
18 holes, 6416yds, Par 73, SSS 71.
Location 3m SW of Bracknell
Telephone for further details

Hotel ★★★★ 76% Coppid Beech, John Nike Way, BRACKNELL ☎ 01344 303333 205 en suite

Sand Martins Finchampstead Rd RG40 3RQ
☎ 0118 9792711 🗎 0118 977 0282
e-mail: lizroginski@sandmartins.com
Two different 9-hole loops: the front nine is mostly tree-

continued

lined with ponds and the back nine is similar to a links course.
18 holes, 6212yds, Par 70, SSS 70, Course record 65.
Club membership 800.

Sand Martins Golf Club

Visitors must telephone in advance. Restricted Fri, with member only at weekends. **Societies** prior arrangement by telephone. **Green Fees** £17.50 per 9 holes;£30.50 per 18 holes;£50.50 per day weekdays only. **Cards** **Prof** Andrew Hall **Course Designer** Edward Fox **Facilities** **Location** 1m S of Wokingham

Hotel ★★★ 66% Edward Court Hotel, Wellington Rd, WOKINGHAM ☎ 0118 977 5886 27 en suite

BRISTOL

BRISTOL Map 03 ST57

Bristol and Clifton Beggar Bush Ln, Failand BS8 3TH ☎ 01275 393474 01275 394611
e-mail: mansec@bristolgolf.co.uk
A downland course with splendid turf and fine tree-lined fairways. The 222-yard (par 3) 13th with the green well below, and the par 4 16th, with its second shot across an old quarry, are outstanding. There are splendid views over the Bristol Channel towards Wales.
18 holes, 6316yds, Par 70, SSS 70, Course record 64.
Club membership 650.
Visitors must have a handicap certificate. Weekends restricted. **Societies** telephone to enquire. **Green Fees** not confirmed. **Cards** **Prof** Peter Mawson **Facilities** **Leisure** chipping green, practical bunkers.**Conf** Max 50 Board 12 Banquet 50 **Location** M5 junct19, follow A369 for 4m, then take B3129. Club 1m on right

Hotel ★★★ 67% Redwood Lodge Hotel, Beggar Bush Ln, Failand, BRISTOL ☎ 01275 393901 112 en suite

Filton Golf Course Ln, Filton BS34 7QS
☎ 0117 969 4169 0117 931 4359
e-mail: thesecretary@filtongolfclub.co.uk
Challenging parkland course situated on high ground in a pleasant suburb to the north of the city. Extensive views can be enjoyed from the course, especially from the second tee and the clubhouse, where on a clear day the Cotswold Hills and the Brecon Beacons can be seen.
18 holes, 6208yds, Par 70, SSS 70, Course record 63.
Club membership 750.
Visitors advisable to contact in advance for availability, may not play at weekends unless with member. Must have a

continued

handicap certificate. **Societies** apply in writing/phone for details. **Green Fees** £27 per day; £22 per round. **Prof** D Robinson **Facilities** **Location** 5m NW off A38

Hotel ★★★ 69% Holiday Inn Bristol Filton, Filton Rd, Hambrook, BRISTOL ☎ 0870 400 9014 198 en suite

Henbury Henbury Hill, Westbury-on-Trym BS10 7QB
☎ 0117 950 0044 & 950 2121 (Prof) 0117 959 1928
e-mail: thesecretary@henburygolfclub.co.uk
A parkland course tree-lined and on two levels. The River Trym comes into play on the 7th drop-hole with its green set just over the stream. The last nine holes have the beautiful Blaise Castle woods for company.
18 holes, 6007yds, Par 69, SSS 70, Course record 65.
Club membership 825.
Visitors handicap certificate required, with member only at weekends. Advisable to contact in advance for availability. **Societies** apply in writing or telephone well in advance. Tue & Fri only. **Green Fees** not confirmed. **Cards** **Prof** Nick Riley **Facilities** by prior arrangement **Location** 3m NW of city centre on B4055 off A4018

Hotel ★★★ 65% Henbury Lodge Hotel, Station Rd, Henbury, BRISTOL ☎ 0117 950 2615 12 en suite 9 annexe en suite

Knowle West Town Ln, Brislington BS4 5DF
☎ 0117 977 0660 0117 972 0615
A parkland course with nice turf. The first five holes climb up and down hill but the remainder are on a more even plane.
18 holes, 6006yds, Par 69, SSS 69, Course record 61.
Club membership 700.
Visitors must have handicap certificate, must telephone professional 0117 977 9193 for weekends. **Societies** Thu only, apply in writing. **Green Fees** £27 per day; £22 per round (£32/27 weekends). **Prof** Robert Hayward **Course Designer** Hawtree/J H Taylor **Facilities** **Location** 3m SE of city centre off A37

Hotel ★★★ 77% Hunstrete House Hotel, HUNSTRETE ☎ 01761 490490 25 en suite

Mangotsfield Carsons Rd, Mangotsfield BS17 3LW
☎ 0117 956 5501
18 holes, 5337yds, Par 68, SSS 66, Course record 61.
Course Designer John Day **Location** 6m NE of city centre off B4465
Telephone for further details

Hotel ★★★ 69% Holiday Inn Bristol Filton, Filton Rd, Hambrook, BRISTOL ☎ 0870 400 9014 198 en suite

Shirehampton Park Park Hill, Shirehampton BS11 0UL ☎ 0117 982 2082 & 982 3059 0117 982 5280
e-mail: info@shirehamptonparkgolfclub.co.uk
A lovely parkland course with views across the Avon Gorge.
18 holes, 5430yds, Par 67, SSS 66, Course record 63.
Club membership 600.
Visitors with member only at weekends. Must have a handicap certificate. **Societies** weekdays (book through Secretary) **Green Fees** not confirmed. **Cards** **Prof** Brent Ellis **Facilities** **Location** 2m E of junct 18 M5 on B4054

continued on page 26

Sunningdale

Sunningdale, *Berkshire*   ☎ 01344 621681   Fax 01344 624154   Map 04 SU96

The Old Course, founded in 1900, was designed by Willie Park. It is a classic course at just 6308 yards long, with gorse and pine trees, silver birch, heather and immaculate turf. The new course is no less a challenge; created by HS Holt in 1922, it is 6443 yards. There is a long wait for anyone wishing to become a member of this prestigious club, its location within easy reach of London is an attraction in itself. Visitors playing two rounds will be asked to alternate onto the other course in the afternoon. Short rounds may be played by finishing at the 10th or 13th green on the Old Course, and the 10th or 11th green on the New Course. On Monday one course is designated the two ball course until 3.00pm, check when booking a tee time.

Visitors may not play Fri, Sat, Sun or public holidays. Must contact in advance, and have a handicap certificate and letter of introduction

Societies Tue, Wed, Thu by arrangement

Green Fees Old Course £120 per round; New Course £85 (Day ticket for both courses £145) ▬ ▬ ▬ ▬ 📷

Facilities ⊗ 🍴 🍺 ♀ ⛳ 🏠 🏌 ✓
Professional (Keith Maxwell)

Location Ridgemount Rd, Sunningdale, Ascot SL5 9RR (1m S of Sunningdale, off A30)

Holes/Par/Course record 36 holes.
Old Course: 18 holes, 6308 yds, Par 70, SSS 70
New Course: 18 holes, 6443 yds, Par 71, SSS 72

Championship Course

WHERE TO STAY AND EAT NEARBY

Hotels
ASCOT

★★★★67% The Royal Berkshire, London Rd, Sunninghill.
☎ 01344 623322. 63 en suite

★★★★64% The Berystede, Bagshot Rd, Sunninghill. ☎ 0870 400 8111.
90 en suite

★★74% Highclere, 19 Kings Rd, Sunninghill. ☎ 01344 625220. 11 en suite

★★65% Brockenhurst, Brockenhurst Rd.
☎ 01344 621912.
12 en suite 6 annexe en suite

BAGSHOT

★★★★★☺☺☺ 73% Pennyhill Park, London Rd. ☎ 01276 471774.
26 en suite 97 annexe en suite

Restaurant
BRAY

☺☺☺☺☺ Fat Duck, High Street.
☎01628 580333

☺☺☺☺ Waterside Inn, Ferry Rd.
☎ 01628 620691.

Hotel ★★★ 67% Redwood Lodge Hotel, Beggar Bush Ln, Failand, BRISTOL ☎ 01275 393901 112 en suite

Woodlands Trench Ln, Almondsbury BS32 4JZ
☎ 01454 619319 📄 01454 619397
e-mail: woodlands@tracypark.com
Situated on the edge of the Severn Valley, bordered by Hortham Brook and Shepherds Wood this interesting parkland course, features five testing par 3s set around the course's five lakes, notably the 206 yd 5th hole which extends over water.
18 holes, 6068yds, Par 70, SSS 69.
Club membership 45.
Visitors no restrictions. **Societies** Phone or write in advance. **Green Fees** £12 per round (£14 weekends & bank holidays). **Cards** ⬜ ⬜ 🔘 **Prof** N Warburton & L Riddiford **Facilities** ⊗ 🍴 🎴 🍺 ♀ ⚑ 🏌 **Leisure** fishing. **Location** N of Bristol off A38

Hotel ★★★ 69% Holiday Inn Bristol Filton, Filton Rd, Hambrook, BRISTOL ☎ 0870 400 9014 198 en suite

BUCKINGHAMSHIRE

AYLESBURY
Map 04 SP81

Aylesbury Golf Centre Hulcott Ln, Bierton HP22 5GA ☎ 01296 393644
A parkland course with magnificent views to the Chiltern Hills. A good test of golf with out of bounds coming into play on nine of the holes, also a number of water hazards and bunkers.
18 holes, 5965yds, Par 71, SSS 69.
Club membership 200.
Visitors no restrictions, but booking advisable. **Societies** telephone for details. **Green Fees** £10 per round (£15 weekends & bank holidays). **Cards** ⬜ ⬜ **Prof** Alex Saary **Course Designer** T S Benwell **Facilities** ⊗ 🍴 🎴 🍺 ♀ 🏌 ⚑ 🍺 ♀ ⚑ **Location** 1m N of Aylesbury on A418

Hotel ★★★ 69% Holiday Inn Aylesbury, Aston Clinton Rd, AYLESBURY ☎ 0870 400 9002 140 en suite

Aylesbury Park Andrews Way, Off Coldharbour Way, Oxford Rd HP17 8QQ ☎ 01296 399196 📄 01296 336830
Parkland course with mature trees, located just south-west of Aylesbury.
18 holes, 6148yds, Par 70, SSS 69, Course record 69.
Club membership 340.
Visitors may book up to 1 week in advance. **Societies** telephone for Society Pack **Green Fees** terms on application. **Cards** ⬜ ⬜ ⬜ 🔘 ⬜ 🔘 **Course Designer** M Hawtree **Facilities** ⊗ 🎴 🍺 ♀ ⚑ 🏌 🍺 ⚑ **Location** 0.5m SW of Aylesbury, on the A418

Hotel ★★★ 69% Holiday Inn Aylesbury, Aston Clinton Rd, AYLESBURY ☎ 0870 400 9002 140 en suite

Chiltern Forest Aston Hill, Halton HP22 5NQ
☎ 01296 631267 📄 01296 632709
e-mail: secretary@chilternforest.co.uk
This very hilly wooded parkland course is on two levels. It is a true test of skill to the low handicap golfer, as well as being a fair challenge to higher handicap golfers. The surrounding woodland makes the course very scenic.
18 holes, 5765yds, Par 70, SSS 70, Course record 65.
Club membership 650.
Visitors welcome weekdays, must play with member at

continued

weekends. **Societies** telephone in advance. **Green Fees** £25 per round. **Cards** ⬜ ⬜ ⬜ 🔘 **Prof** A Lavers **Facilities** ⊗ 🍴 🎴 🍺 ♀ ⚑ 🍺 🏌 ⚑ **Location** 1m NE off A4011

Hotel ★★★ 69% Holiday Inn Aylesbury, Aston Clinton Rd, AYLESBURY ☎ 0870 400 9002 140 en suite

Ellesborough Butlers Cross HP17 0TZ
☎ 01296 622114 📄 01296 622114
Once part of the property of Chequers, and under the shadow of the famous monument at the Wendover end of the Chilterns. A downland course, it is rather hilly with most holes enhanced by far-ranging views over the Aylesbury countryside.
18 holes, 6360yds, Par 71, SSS 71, Course record 64.
Club membership 700.
Visitors welcome on weekdays, handicap certificate required. **Societies** Wed & Thu only, by prior arrangement with General Manager. **Green Fees** not confirmed. **Prof** Mark Squire **Course Designer** James Braid **Facilities** ⊗ 🎴 🍺 ♀ ⚑ 🍺 ⚑ **Location** 1m E of Ellesborough on B4010

Hotel ★★★ 69% Holiday Inn Aylesbury, Aston Clinton Rd, AYLESBURY ☎ 0870 400 9002 140 en suite

BEACONSFIELD
Map 04 SU99

Beaconsfield Seer Green HP9 2UR
☎ 01494 676545 📄 01494 681148
e-mail: secretary@beaconsfieldgolfclub.co.uk
An interesting and, at times, testing tree-lined and parkland course which frequently plays longer than appears on the card! Each hole differs to a considerable degree and here lies the charm. Walking is easy, except perhaps to the 6th and 8th. Well bunkered.
18 holes, 6493yds, Par 72, SSS 71, Course record 63.
Club membership 850.
Visitors must contact in advance and have a handicap certificate. May not play weekends. **Societies** phone for details **Green Fees** £50 per day; £35 per round. **Prof** Michael Brothers **Course Designer** H S Colt **Facilities** ⊗ 🎴 🍺 ♀ ⚑ 🍺 🏌 ⚑ **Location** Exit M40 junct 2, adjacent to Seer Green railway station

Hotel ★★★★ 67% The Bellhouse, Oxford Rd, BEACONSFIELD ☎ 01753 887211 136 en suite

BLETCHLEY
Map 04 SP83

Windmill Hill Tattenhoe Ln MK3 7RB
☎ 01908 631113 & 366457 (Sec) 📄 01908 630034
Long, open-parkland course, the first championship course designed by Henry Cotton, opened in 1972. Proprietary Pay & Play. No winter greens.
Windmill Hill Golf Course: 18 holes, 6720yds, Par 73, SSS 72, Course record 68.
Club membership 400.
Visitors booking system in operation up to 7 days in advance. **Societies** packages available, contact for details. **Green Fees** £11 (£15 weekends). **Cards** ⬜ ⬜ ⬜ 🔘 **Prof** Colin Clingan **Course Designer** Henry Cotton **Facilities** ⊗ 🍴 🎴 🍺 ♀ ⚑ 🍺 🏌 ⚑ 🍺 **Leisure** pool. **Conf** Max 120 **Location** W side of town centre on A421

continued

Windmill Hill Golf Centre

Hotel ★★★ 63% Holiday Inn Milton Keynes, 500 Saxon Gate West, MILTON KEYNES ☎ 0870 400 9057 150 en suite

BUCKINGHAM   Map 04 SP63

Buckingham Tingewick Rd MK18 4AE
☎ 01280 815566 🖺 01280 821812
Undulating parkland course with a stream and river affecting 8 holes.
18 holes, 6082yds, Par 70, SSS 69, Course record 67.
Club membership 690.
Visitors welcome Mon-Fri, with member only at weekends. **Societies** by prior arrangement. **Green Fees** £28 per day. **Prof** Greg Hannah **Facilities** ⊗ ❍ ⮕ ☕ ♀ ⛳ 🏠 ⬧ **Leisure** snooker room. **Location** 1.5m W on A421

Hotel ★★★ 66% Buckingham Beales Hotel, Buckingham Ring Rd, BUCKINGHAM ☎ 01280 822622 70 en suite

BURNHAM   Map 04 SU98

Burnham Beeches Green Ln SL1 8EG
☎ 01628 661448 🖺 01628 668968
A wooded parkland course on the edge of the historic Burnham Beeches Forest with a good variety of holes.
18 holes, 6449yds, Par 70, SSS 71, Course record 66.
Club membership 670.
Visitors must contact in advance. May play on weekdays only. Handicap certificate required. **Societies** welcome Apr-Oct, write or telephone for information. **Green Fees** £56 per day; £38 per 18 holes. **Prof** Ronnie Bolton **Facilities** ⊗ ❍ ⮕ ☕ ♀ ⛳ 🏠 ⬧ **Location** 0.5m NE of Burnham

Hotel ★★★ 67% Burnham Beeches, Grove Rd, BURNHAM ☎ 01628 429955 82 en suite

Lambourne Dropmore Rd SL1 8NF
☎ 01628 666755 🖺 01628 663301
A championship standard 18 hole parkland course. Undulating terrain with many trees and several lakes, notably on the tricky 7th hole which has a tightly guarded green reached via a shot over a lake. Seven par 4s over 400yds with six picturesque lakes, excellent drainage and full irrigation.
18 holes, 6771yds, Par 72, SSS 73, Course record 67.
Club membership 650.
Visitors must contact in advance & have a handicap certificate. May not play at weekends. **Green Fees** £50 (weekdays). **Cards** 💳 💳 💳 💳 **Prof** David Hart **Course Designer** Donald Steel **Facilities** ⊗ ❍ ⮕ ☕ ♀ ⛳ 🏠 ⬧ **Leisure** sauna. **Location** Access via M4 junct 7 towards Burnham or M40 junct 2 towards Slough/Burnham   *continued*

Hotel ★★★ 67% Burnham Beeches, Grove Rd, BURNHAM ☎ 01628 429955 82 en suite

CHALFONT ST GILES   Map 04 SU99

Harewood Downs Cokes Ln HP8 4TA
☎ 01494 762184 🖺 01494 766869
e-mail: secretary@hdgc.co.uk
A testing undulating parkland course with sloping greens and plenty of trees.
18 holes, 5958yds, Par 69, SSS 69, Course record 64.
Visitors must contact in advance. **Societies** apply in writing or telephone. **Green Fees** £35 per day; £30 per round (£40/£35 weekends). **Cards** 💳 💳 💳 💳 💳 **Prof** G C Morris **Facilities** ⊗ ❍ ⮕ ☕ ♀ ⛳ 🏠 ⬧ 🚗 ⬧ **Location** 2m E of Amersham on A413

Hotel ★★★★ 67% The Bellhouse, Oxford Rd, BEACONSFIELD ☎ 01753 887211 136 en suite

Oakland Park Threehouseholds HP8 4LW
☎ 01494 871277 🖺 01494 874692
Parkland with mature trees, hedgerows and water features, designed to respect the natural features of the land and lakes whilst providing a good challenge for players at all levels.
18 holes, 5246yds, Par 67, SSS 66.
Club membership 750.
Visitors weekdays only. **Societies** Mon, Wed & Fri. Must apply in writing. **Green Fees** terms on application. **Cards** 💳 💳 💳 💳 **Prof** Allistair Thatcher **Course Designer** Johnathan Gaunt **Facilities** ⊗ ❍ ⮕ ☕ ♀ ⛳ 🏠 ⬧ 🚗 ⬧ ⛳ **Location** 3m N of M40 junct 3

Hotel ★★★★ 67% The Bellhouse, Oxford Rd, BEACONSFIELD ☎ 01753 887211 136 en suite

CHARTRIDGE   Map 04 SP90

Chartridge Park HP5 2TF ☎ 01494 791772
e-mail: petergibbins@tinyworld.co.uk
A family run, easy walking parkland course set high in the beautiful Chiltern Hills, affording breathtaking views.
18 holes, 5516yds, Par 69, SSS 67, Course record 65.
Club membership 700.
Visitors may not play before 10.30am weekends. **Societies** must telephone in advance. **Green Fees** £40. **Cards** 💳 💳 💳 💳 💳 **Prof** Peter Gibbins **Course Designer** John Jacobs **Facilities** ⊗ ❍ ⮕ ☕ ♀ ⛳ 🏠 ⬧ 🚗 ⬧ **Conf** Max 150 **Location** 3m NW of Chesham

Hotel ★★★ 69% The Crown, High St, AMERSHAM ☎ 0870 400 8103 19 en suite 18 annexe en suite

CHESHAM   Map 04 SP90

Chesham & Ley Hill Ley Hill Common HP5 1UZ
☎ 01494 784541 🖺 01494 785506
e-mail: the.secretary@clhgolfclub.co.uk
Wooded parkland course on hilltop with easy walking.
9 holes, 5296yds, Par 66, SSS 65, Course record 62.
Club membership 400.
Visitors may play Mon & Thu all day, Wed after noon, Fri up to 4pm. **Societies** subject to approval, Thu & Fri only. **Green Fees** £20 per day; £16 per 18 holes. **Facilities** ⊗ ❍ ⮕ ☕ ♀ ⛳ **Leisure** practice net. **Conf** Max 25 **Location** 2m E of Chesham, off A41on B4504 to Ley Hill.

Hotel ★★★ 69% The Crown, High St, AMERSHAM ☎ 0870 400 8103 19 en suite 18 annexe en suite

DENHAM   Map 04 TQ08

Buckinghamshire Denham Court Dr UB9 5BG
☎ 01895 835777 ▤ 01895 835210
e-mail: enquiries@bucks.dircon.co.uk
A John Jacobs designed championship-standard course. Visitors only welcome as guests of members to this beautiful course in 269 acres of lovely grounds including mature trees, five lakes and two rivers. The testing 7th hole requires a 185yd carry over a stream, followed by a second shot over a river to a green guarded by a lake.
18 holes, 6880yds, Par 72, SSS 73, Course record 70. Club membership 600.
Visitors contact 48 hours in advance, subject to availability. **Societies** must contact in advance. **Green Fees** £70 per 18 holes (£80 weekends). **Cards** ▭ ▬ ▬ ▬ ▬ ▨ **Prof** John O'Leary **Course Designer** John Jacobs **Facilities** ⊗ ▥ ▣ ▾ ♀ ♨ ☎ ✆ **Conf** Thtr 100 Class 36 Board 36 Banquet 80 Del £35 to £45 * **Location** M25 junct 16 signposted Uxbridge

Hotel ★★★★ 67% The Bellhouse, Oxford Rd, BEACONSFIELD ☎ 01753 887211 136 en suite

Denham Tilehouse Ln UB9 5DE
☎ 01895 832022 ▤ 01895 835340
e-mail: club.secretary@denhamgolfclub.co.uk
A beautifully maintained parkland/heathland course, home of many county champions. Slightly hilly and calling for good judgement of distance in the wooded areas.
18 holes, 6462yds, Par 70, SSS 71, Course record 66. Club membership 790.
Visitors must contact in advance & have handicap certificate. Must play with member Fri-Sun. **Societies** Tue-Thu. Must book in advance. **Green Fees** £65 per day; £48 per round. **Prof** Stuart Campbell **Course Designer** H S Colt **Facilities** ⊗ ▥ ▣ ▾ ♀ ♨ ☎ ✆ **Location** 0.5m N of North Orbital Road, 2m from Uxbridge

Hotel ★★★★ 67% The Bellhouse, Oxford Rd, BEACONSFIELD ☎ 01753 887211 136 en suite

FLACKWELL HEATH   Map 04 SU89

Flackwell Heath Treadaway Rd, High Wycombe
HP10 9PE ☎ 01628 520929 ▤ 01628 530040
e-mail: secretary@flackwellheathgolfclub.co.uk
Open sloping heath and tree-lined course on hills overlooking the Chilterns. Some good challenging par 3s and several testing small greens.
18 holes, 6211yds, Par 71, SSS 70, Course record 63. Club membership 700.
Visitors with member only at weekends. Must contact in advance and hold a handicap certificate. **Societies** Wed & Thu only, by prior booking. **Green Fees** £36 per day; £24 per round. **Prof** Paul Watson **Facilities** ⊗ ▥ ▣ ▾ ♀ ♨ ☎ ✆ **Conf** Board 24 Banquet 110 Del £15 to £25 * **Location** E side of High Wycombe,NE side of town centre

Hotel ★★★★ 67% The Bellhouse, Oxford Rd, BEACONSFIELD ☎ 01753 887211 136 en suite

GERRARDS CROSS   Map 04 TQ08

Gerrards Cross Chalfont Park SL9 0QA
☎ 01753 278500 ▤ 01753 883593
A wooded parkland course which has been modernised in recent years and is now a very pleasant circuit with
continued

infinite variety. The best part lies on the plateau above the clubhouse where there are some testing holes.
18 holes, 6295yds, Par 69, SSS 70, Course record 64. Club membership 787.
Visitors must contact professional in advance, a handicap certificate is required, may not play Tues, weekends or public holidays. **Societies** booking well in advance necessary, handicap certicates required, packages to suit. **Green Fees** £52 per day; £38 per round. **Cards** ▭ ▬ ▨ **Prof** Matthew Barr **Course Designer** Bill Pedlar **Facilities** ⊗ ▥ ▣ ▾ ♀ ♨ ☎ ✆ **Location** NE side of town centre off A413

Hotel ★★★★ 67% The Bellhouse, Oxford Rd, BEACONSFIELD ☎ 01753 887211 136 en suite

HIGH WYCOMBE   Map 04 SU89

Hazlemere Penn Rd, Hazlemere HP15 7LR
☎ 01494 719300 ▤ 01494 713914
e-mail: enquiries@hazlemeregolfclub.co.uk
Undulating parkland course in beautiful countryside with water hazards in play on some holes. Two long par 5s and a fine par 4 closing hole.
18 holes, 5810yds, Par 70, SSS 69, Course record 62. Club membership 700.
Visitors weekdays all day. Weekends by prior arrangement through Pro. shop telephone 01494 719306 **Societies** by prior telephone arrangement. **Green Fees** £45 per day; £30 per round (£42 per round weekends). **Cards** ▭ ▬ ▨ **Prof** Gavin Cousins/Paul Harrison **Course Designer** Terry Murray **Facilities** ⊗ ▥ ▣ ▾ ♀ ♨ ☎ ✆ **Location** On B474 between Beaconsfield and Hazlemere.,2m NE, A404 towards Amersham

Hotel ★★★ 69% The Crown, High St, AMERSHAM ☎ 0870 400 8103 19 en suite 18 annexe en suite

IVER   Map 04 TQ08

Iver Hollow Hill Ln, Langley Park Rd SL0 0JJ
☎ 01753 655615 ▤ 01753 654225
Fairly flat, pay and play parkland course with challenging par 5s, plenty of hazards - water and ditches - and strong crosswinds to contend with.
9 holes, 6288yds, Par 72, SSS 72, Course record 66. Club membership 275.
Visitors competitions at weekends, telephone to pre book tee times. **Societies** telephone in advance. **Green Fees** terms on application. **Cards** ▭ ▬ ▨ **Prof** Karl Teschner **Facilities** ⊗ ▣ ▾ ♀ ♨ ☎ ✆ ✆ **Leisure** bunker & chipping area. **Location** M4 junct 5, 1.5m SW off B470

Hotel ★★★★ 71% Slough/Windsor Marriott Hotel, Ditton Rd, Langley, SLOUGH ☎ 01753 544244 382 en suite

Richings Park Golf & Country Club
North Park SL0 9DL
☎ 01753 655370 & 655352(pro shop) ▤ 01753 655409
e-mail: info@richingspark.co.uk
Set amongst mature trees and attractive lakes, this testing par 70 parkland course provides a suitable challenge to golfers of all abilities. Well irrigated greens and abundant wildlife. There is an academy course with five short holes and teaching facilities on the driving range.
18 holes, 6144yds, Par 70, SSS 69. Club membership 525.
Visitors welcome but may not play until after 12 noon at weekends. **Societies** apply in writing or telephone. **Green**
continued

Fees terms on application. **Cards** 🖃 🖃 💳 🖾 🖾 🖾
Course Designer Alan Higgins **Facilities** ⊗ ⅷ 🖩 ⬛ ⬛ ♀ ♨
🏠 ⛳ ♦ 🏌 🏌 🏌 **Location** Junct 5 on M4, A4 towards
Colnbrook, left at lights, Sutton Lane, right at next lights
North Park

Hotel ★★★ 69% Courtyard by Marriott Slough/Windsor,
Church St, SLOUGH ☎ 01753 551551 150 en suite

Thorney Park Thorney Mill Rd SL0 9AL
☎ 01895 422095 📄 01895 431307
**Thorney Park is a 9 hole parkland course, which will test
both the beginner and established golfer. Fairway
irrigation ensures lush green fairways and smooth
putting surfaces. Many interesting holes including the
testing par 4 9th which needs a long drive to the water's
edge and a well-hit iron onto the bunker-guarded green.**
9 holes, 2834yds, Par 34, SSS 33, Course record 65.
Club membership 180.
Visitors must telephone in advance. **Societies** must
telephone in advance. **Green Fees** £13 per 18 holes; £8 per 9
holes (£16/£9.50 weekends). **Cards** 🖃 🖃 🖾 🖾 🖾 **Prof**
Andrew Killing **Facilities** ⊗ ⅷ 🖩 ⬛ ⬛ ♀ ♨ 🏠 ⛳ 🏌 **Conf**
Max 35 **Location** From M4 junct 5 left onto A4. Left into
Sutton Lane and right for Thorney Mill Road

Hotel ★★★★ 71% Slough/Windsor Marriott Hotel, Ditton
Rd, Langley, SLOUGH ☎ 01753 544244 382 en suite

LITTLE BRICKHILL See page 31

LITTLE CHALFONT Map 04 SU99

Little Chalfont Lodge Ln HP8 4AJ
☎ 01494 764877 📄 01494 762860
**Gently undulating parkland course surrounded by
mature trees.**
9 holes, 5852yds, Par 70, SSS 68, Course record 66.
Club membership 300.
Visitors no restrictions, please phone to ensure there are no
competitions in progress. **Societies** please telephone in advance. **Green Fees** £11.50
per 18 holes (£13.50 weekends and bank holidays). **Cards**
🖃 🖃 🖾 🖾 🖾 **Prof** M Dunne **Facilities** ⊗ ⅷ by prior
arrangement 🖩 ⬛ ⬛ ♀ ♨ 🏠 ⛳ 🏌 **Leisure** one motorised cart
for hire by arrangement. **Location** Between Little Chalfont &
Chorleywood 3m on A404 from M25 junct 18

Hotel ★★★ 69% The Crown, High St, AMERSHAM
☎ 0870 400 8103 19 en suite 18 annexe en suite

LOUDWATER Map 04 SU89

Wycombe Heights Golf Centre Rayners Ave
HP10 9SZ ☎ 01494 816686 📄 01494 816728
**An impressive tree-lined parkland course with panoramic
views of the Chilterns. The final four holes are**

**particularly challenging. A delightful 18 hole par 3
course and floodlit driving range complement the High
Course.**
*High Course: 18 holes, 6265yds, Par 70, SSS 71,
Course record 64. Club membership 600.*
Visitors booking advisable 7 days in advance. **Societies**
telephone to request information pack. **Green Fees** £20 per
day; £13 per round (£29/£18.50 weekends & bank holidays).
Cards 🖃 🖃 🖾 🖾 🖾 **Course Designer** John Jacobs
Facilities ⊗ ⅷ 🖩 ⬛ ⬛ ♀ ♨ 🏠 ⛳ ♦ 🏌 🏌 **Leisure** par 3
course.**Conf** Max 150 Thtr 150 Class 50 Board 30 **Location**
M40 junct 3, A40 towards High Wycombe. After 0.5m right
into Rayners Avenue at traffic lights

Hotel ★★★ 66% Holiday Inn High Wycombe, Handy
Cross, HIGH WYCOMBE ☎ 0870 400 9042 109 en suite

MARLOW Map 04 SU88

Harleyford Harleyford Estate, Henley Rd SL7 2SP
☎ 01628 402110 & 402149 📄 01628 478434
e-mail: info@harleyfordgolf.org
**Set in 160 acres, this Donald Steel designed course,
founded in 1996, makes the most of the natural rolling
contours of the beautiful parkland of the historic
Harleyford Estate. A challenging course to golfers of all
handicaps. Stunning views across the Thames Valley.**

*18 holes, 6653yds, Par 72, SSS 72, Course record 72.
Club membership 750.*
Visitors Soft spikes only. Must contact in advance. Can play
after 10am weekdays and 11.30am weekends. **Societies**
Telephone groups co-ordinator. **Green Fees** £40 per round
(£60 weekends). **Cards** 🖃 🖃 🖾 **Prof** Lee Jackson **Course
Designer** Donald Steel **Facilities** ⊗ ⅷ 🖩 ⬛ ⬛ ♀ ♨ 🏠 ⛳ ♦
♨ 🏌 **Conf** Thtr 50 Board 30 Del from £37.50 * **Location**
S side A4156 Marlow/Henley road, close to A404 Marlow
bypass linking junct 4 M40/junct 8/9 M4

Hotel ★★★★ 73% Danesfield House Hotel & Spa, Henley
Rd, MARLOW-ON-THAMES ☎ 01628 891010 87 en suite

MENTMORE Map 04 SP91

Mentmore Golf & Country Club LU7 0UA
☎ 01296 662020 📄 01296 662592
**Two 18-hole courses - Rosebery and Rothschild - set
within the wooded estate grounds of Mentmore Towers.
Gently rolling parkland course with mature trees and
lakes and two interesting feature holes; the long par 5
(606 yds) 9th on the Rosebery course with fine views of
the Chilterns and the par 4 (340yd) 14th on the
Rothschild course, in front of the Towers.**
*Rosebery Course: 18 holes, 6777yds, Par 72, SSS 72, Course
record 68.*
*Rothschild Course: 18 holes, 6700yds, Par 72, SSS 72.
Club membership 1100.*

continued

continued

Visitors must contact in advance, may not play weekends before 11am. **Societies** by prior arrangement. **Green Fees** not confirmed. **Cards** 🖃 🈺 📠 📠 🖩 **Prof** Pip Elson **Course Designer** Bob Sandow **Facilities** ⊗ ⅢⅡ 🖳 ♥ ♀ ⚘ 🏠 ⚐ ⚓ ⚑ ⚑ ⚐ ♛ **Leisure** hard tennis courts, heated indoor swimming pool, fishing, sauna, gymnasium. **Location** 4m S of Leighton Buzzard

Hotel ★★★ 69% Holiday Inn Aylesbury, Aston Clinton Rd, AYLESBURY ☎ 0870 400 9002 140 en suite

MILTON KEYNES   Map 04 SP83

Abbey Hill Monks Way, Two Mile Ash MK8 8AA
☎ 01908 562408
e-mail: steve.tompkins@ukonline.co.uk
Undulating municipal course within the new city. Tight fairways and well-placed bunkers. Stream comes into play on five holes. Also par 3 course.

18 holes, 6122yds, Par 71, SSS 69, Course record 71.
Club membership 300.
Visitors no restrictions. **Societies** must telephone (01908) 562408 in advance. **Green Fees** terms on application. **Cards** 🖃 🈺 📠 📠 🖩 **Prof** Keith Bond **Facilities** ⊗ ⅢⅡ 🖳 ♥ ♀ ⚘ 🏠 ⚐ ⚓ ⚑ ⚐ ♛ **Location** 2m W of new town centre off A5

Hotel ★★★ 63% Quality Hotel & Suites Milton Keynes, Monks Way, Two Mile Ash, MILTON KEYNES ☎ 01908 561666 88 en suite

Three Locks Great Brickhill MK17 9BH
☎ 01525 270470 & 270050 📠 01525 270470
Parkland course offering a challenge to beginners and experienced golfers, with water coming into play on ten holes. Magnificent views.
18 holes, 6036yds, Par 70, SSS 68, Course record 60.
Club membership 300.
Visitors telephone 01525 270050 to book tee times.
Societies write or telephone for details. **Green Fees** £28 per day; £16.50 per round (£34/£20 weekends& bank holidays).
Cards 🖃 🈺 📠 📠 🖩 **Prof** G Harding **Course Designer** MRM Sandow **Facilities** ⊗ 🖳 ♥ ♀ ⚘ 🏠 ⚐ ⚑ ⚑ ⚓ ♛ ⚐ **Leisure** fishing. **Conf** Max 30 **Location** A4146 between Leighton Buzzard/Bletchley

Hotel ★★★ 63% Holiday Inn Milton Keynes, 500 Saxon Gate West, MILTON KEYNES ☎ 0870 400 9057 150 en suite

PRINCES RISBOROUGH   Map 04 SP80

Whiteleaf Upper Icknield Way, Whiteleaf HP27 0LY
☎ 01844 274058 📠 01844 275551
e-mail: whiteleafgc@tiscali.co.uk
A picturesque 9 hole course on the edge of The Chilterns. Good views over The Vale of Aylesbury. A short
continued

challenging course requiring great accuracy.
9 holes, 5391yds, Par 66, SSS 66, Course record 64.
Club membership 300.
Visitors advisable to contact in advance, with member only at weekends. **Societies** on Thu only, must contact the secretary in advance. **Green Fees** £25 per day; £18 per round. **Prof** Ken Ward **Facilities** ⊗ ⅢⅡ 🖳 ♥ ♀ ⚘ 🏠 ⚐ **Location** 1m NE off A4010

Hotel ★★ 64% Rose & Crown Hotel, Wycombe Rd, SAUNDERTON ☎ 01844 345299 15 en suite

STOKE POGES   Map 04 SU98

Farnham Park Park Rd SL2 4PJ
☎ 01753 643332 & 647065 📠 01753 643332 & 647065
e-mail: farnhamparkgolfclub@btinternet.co.uk
Fine, public parkland course in a pleasing setting.
18 holes, 6172yds, Par 71, SSS 69, Course record 68.
Club membership 400.
Visitors telephone in advance for tee times. **Societies** apply in writing. **Green Fees** £11 per round(£15 weekends). **Cards** 🖃 🈺 📠 📠 🖩 **Prof** Paul Warner **Course Designer** Hawtree **Facilities** ⊗ 🖳 ♥ ♀ ⚘ 🏠 ⚐ ⚐ **Location** W side of village off B416

Hotel ★★★★ 71% Slough/Windsor Marriott Hotel, Ditton Rd, Langley, SLOUGH ☎ 01753 544244 382 en suite

Stoke Poges Stoke Park, Park Rd SL2 4PG
☎ 01753 717171 📠 01753 717181
e-mail: info@stokeparkclub.com
Judgement of the distance from the tee is all important on this first-class parkland course. Fairways are wide and the challenge seemingly innocuous. The 7th hole is the model for the well known 12th hole at Augusta. Stoke Poges is a 27 hole course and is considered the best traditional course in the British Isles.
Course 1: 18 holes, 6721yds, Par 71, SSS 72.
Course 2: 18 holes, 6551yds, Par 72, SSS 73.
Course 3: 18 holes, 6318yds, Par 71, SSS 70.
Club membership 1250.
Visitors must contact in advance. **Societies** telephone in advance. **Green Fees** terms on application. **Cards** 🖃 🈺 📠 📠 🖩 **Prof** Stuart Collier **Course Designer** Harry Shapland Colt **Facilities** ⊗ ⅢⅡ 🖳 ♥ ♀ ⚘ 🏠 ⚐ ⚑ ♛ ⚐ **Leisure** hard and grass tennis courts, heated indoor swimming pool, squash, fishing, solarium, gymnasium.**Conf** Max 150 Del £95 * **Location** Turn off A4 at Slough into Stoke Poges Lane B416, club is 1.5m on left

Hotel ★★★★ 71% Slough/Windsor Marriott Hotel, Ditton Rd, Langley, SLOUGH ☎ 01753 544244 382 en suite

STOWE   Map 04 SP63

Silverstone Silverstone Rd MK18 5LH
☎ 01280 850005 📠 01280 850156
e-mail: sgc@zonal.co.uk
Set in the rolling North Buckinghamshire countryside, the course offers an interesting challenge for both experienced players and those with a higher handicap. Three new holes are due to be opened in 2002, extending the course to 6500 yards and making a major contribution to providing championship standards for play.
18 holes, 6213yards, Par 71, SSS 71.
Club membership 418. *continued on page 32*

Woburn

Little Brickhill, *Buckinghamshire* ☎ 01908 370756 | Fax 01908 378436 | Map 04 SP93

e-mail: enquiries@woburngolf.com

Conveniently accessed from the M1, Woburn is famed not only for its golf courses, but also for the magnificent stately home and wildlife park. If you are unable to play the courses yourself these are well worth a visit. Charles Lawrie of Cotton Pennink designed two great golf courses here amongst the trees and beautiful countryside. From the back tees, they are rather long for the weekend amateur golfer. The Duke's is a tough challenge for golfers at all levels, while the Duchess Course although relatively easier, still demands a high level of skill to negotiate the fairways guarded by towering pines. The Dukes course has become the home of the increasingly popular Weetabix Women's British Open, held here since 1990.

The town of Woburn and the Abbey are both within Bedfordshire, while the golf and country club are over the border in Buckinghamshire.

Visitors Midweek by arrangement.

Societies must contact in advance.

Green Fees Not confirmed

Facilities ⊗ 🍴 ♀ ♣ 🏠 ⛳ ↖ 🛒 ♂ Conf 30 (Boardroom only) Professional (Luther Blacklock)

Location Little Brickhill, Milton Keynes MK17 9LJ 4m W of J13 M1, off A5130.

Holes/Par/Course record 54 holes: Dukes Course: 18 holes 6973 yds, Par 72, SSS 74. Course record 62. Duchess Course: 18 holes, 6651 yds, Par 72, SSS 72, Marquess Course 18 holes, 7214yds, par 72, SSS74

Championship Course

WHERE TO STAY AND EAT NEARBY

Hotels and Restaurants
FLITWICK

★★★81% ⊚⊚ Menzies Flitwick Manor, Church Road MK45 JAE
☎0870 6003013. 17 en suite

NEWPORT PAGNELL

♦♦♦♦♦ The Limes, North Square MK16 8EP ☎ 01908 617041 4 en suite

WOBURN

⊚⊚ Paris House Restaurant, Woburn Park MK17 9QP ☎ 01525 290692

GREAT BRICKHILL

The Old Red Lion, Ivy Lane MK17 9AH
☎ 01525 261715

Visitors no restrictions. **Societies** may play weekdays/weekends after noon. Telephone to book. **Green Fees** £14 per 18 holes (£18 weekends). **Cards** 🏧 💳 📇 📇 🅿 **Prof** Rodney Holt **Course Designer** David Snell **Facilities** ⊗ ⏍ ⮜ ⮝ ♀ ⌓ ☂ 🐾 ⚲ 🏌 ∢ **Conf** Max 100 Thtr 100 Class 60 Board 20 Banquet 80 Del £5 to £19 * **Location** from Silverstone village follow signs to the Grand Prix track. Golf club 1m past the entrance on right

Hotel ★★★ 72% Villiers Hotel, 3 Castle St, BUCKINGHAM ☎ 01280 822444 46 en suite

WAVENDON   Map 04 SP93

Wavendon Golf Centre Lower End Rd MK17 8DA
☎ 01908 281811 📠 01908 281257
e-mail: wavendon@jack-barker.co.uk
Pleasant parkland course set within mature oak and lime trees and incorporating several small lakes as water hazards. Easy walking.

18 holes, 5570yds, Par 69, SSS 68.
Club membership 300.
Visitors booking advised. **Societies** must contact in advance by telephone. **Green Fees** terms on application. **Cards** 🏧 💳 📇 📇 🅿 **Prof** Greg Iron **Course Designer** J Drake/N Elmer **Facilities** ⊗ ⏍ ⮜ ⮝ ♀ ⌓ ☂ 🐾 ⚲ **Conf** Max 48 Del from £25 * **Location** Just off A421, 8 mins from M1 junct 13

Hotel ★★★ 68% Moore Place Hotel, The Square, ASPLEY GUISE ☎ 01908 282000 39 en suite 15 annexe en suite

WESTON TURVILLE   Map 04 SP81

Weston Turville Golf & Squash Club New Rd HP22 5QT ☎ 01296 424084 📠 01296 395376
Parkland course situated at the foot of the Chiltern Hills and providing an excellent challenge for the accomplished golfer, yet not too daunting for the higher handicap player. Flat easy walking with water hazards and many interesting holes, notably the testing dog-leg 5th (418yds).
18 holes, 6008yds, Par 69, SSS 69, Course record 68.
Club membership 600.
Visitors no restrictions. **Societies** must contact in advance. **Green Fees** not confirmed. **Cards** 🏧 💳 📇 🅿 **Prof** Gary George **Facilities** ⊗ ⏍ ⮜ ⮝ ♀ ⌓ ☂ 🐾 ⚲ **Leisure** squash. **Location** 2m SE of Aylesbury, off A41

Hotel ★★★ 69% Holiday Inn Aylesbury, Aston Clinton Rd, AYLESBURY ☎ 0870 400 9002 140 en suite

WEXHAM STREET   Map 04 SU98

Wexham Park SL3 6ND
☎ 01753 663271 📠 01753 663318
e-mail: wexhamgolf@freenetname.co.uk
Gently undulating parkland course. Three courses. One 18 hole, one challenging 9 hole and another 9 hole suitable for beginners.

Blue: 18 holes, 5346yds, Par 68, SSS 66.
Red: 9 holes, 2822yds, Par 34.
Green: 9 holes, 2233yds, Par 32.
Club membership 850.
Visitors no restrictions **Societies** must contact in advance. **Green Fees** £7.50 per 9 holes;£12.50 per 18 holes(£9.50/£16.50 weekends). **Cards** 🏧 💳 📇 📇 🅿 **Prof** John Kennedy **Course Designer** E Lawrence/D Morgan **Facilities** ⊗ ⮜ ⮝ ♀ ⌓ ☂ 🐾 ⚲ 🏌 **Location** 0.5m S

Hotel ★★★★ 71% Slough/Windsor Marriott Hotel, Ditton Rd, Langley, SLOUGH ☎ 01753 544244 382 en suite

WING   Map 04 SP82

Aylesbury Vale Stewkley Rd LU7 0UJ
☎ 01525 240196 📠 01525 240848
e-mail: info@avgc.co.uk
This gently undulating course is set amid tranquil countryside. There are five ponds to pose the golfer problems, notably on the par 4 420 yd 13th - unlucky for some - where the second shot is all downhill with an inviting pond spanning the approach to the green. In addition there is a 10-bay driving range and practice putting green.
18 holes, 6612yds, Par 72, SSS 72, Course record 67.
Club membership 515.
Visitors must adhere to dress regulations. Must contact in advance. **Societies** telephone to book in advance. **Green Fees** £15 per 18 holes;£8 per 9 holes(£25 per 18 holes weekends). **Cards** 🏧 💳 📇 📇 🅿 **Prof** Guy Goble **Course Designer** D Wright **Facilities** ⊗ ⏍ ⮜ ⮝ ♀ ⌓ ☂ 🐾 ⚲ 🏌 **Conf** Max 120 Banquet 120 **Location** 2m NW of Leighton Buzzard on unclassified Stewkley road, between Wing/Stewkley

Hotel ★★★ 69% Holiday Inn Aylesbury, Aston Clinton Rd, AYLESBURY ☎ 0870 400 9002 140 en suite

CAMBRIDGESHIRE

BAR HILL   Map 05 TL36

Cambridgeshire Moat House Moat House Hotel, Bar Hill CB3 8EU ☎ 01954 780008 & 249971 📠 01954 780010
Mature undulating parkland course with tree-lined fairways, easy walking. Challenging opening and

continued

closing holes with water on the right and out of bounds on the left of both.
18 holes, 6734yds, Par 72, SSS 73, Course record 68.
Club membership 600.
Visitors must book in advance. Weekdays subject to availability, weekends after noon. **Societies** must telephone in advance. **Green Fees** £21 per round (£30 weekends & bank holidays). **Cards** 🖃🟦🟥🔵 **Prof** Paul Simpson **Facilities** ⊗ ⫶Ⅲ ᕒ 🏌 ♀ ☕ 🏠 ⛳ ⛳ 🏐 *Leisure* hard tennis courts, heated indoor swimming pool, sauna, solarium, gymnasium. **Conf** Thtr 180 Class 90 Board 80 Banquet 180 **Location** M11/A14, then B1050 (Bar Hill)

Hotel ★★★ 67% Holiday Inn Cambridge, Lakeview, Bridge Rd, Impington, CAMBRIDGE ☎ 0870 400 9015 165 en suite

---

been designated a Site of Special Scientific Interest (SSSI).
Old Course: 18 holes, 6400yds, Par 70, SSS 70, Course record 60.
Wandlebury: 18 holes, 6700yds, Par 72, SSS 72.
Club membership 1320.
Visitors Must contact in advance. Mon-Fri only. Weekends and bank holidays by special arrangement with secretary. **Societies** Tue & Thu by reservation. **Green Fees** £42 per day; £35 per round (£50 per round weekends & bank holidays). **Prof** Ian Bamborough **Course Designer** Hawtree Ltd **Facilities** ⊗ ⫶Ⅲ ᕒ 🏌 ♀ ☕ 🏠 ⛳ 🏐 ⛳ ⛳ **Location** 3m SE on A1307

Hotel ★★★ 70% Gonville Hotel, Gonville Place, CAMBRIDGE ☎ 01223 366611 & 221111 📄 01223 315470 78 en suite

---

BOURN Map 05 TL35

Bourn Toft Rd CB3 7TT
☎ 01954 718958 📄 01954 718908
Meadow/parkland golf course with many water features and some very challenging holes.
18 holes, 6417yards, SSS 71.
Visitors welcome. **Societies** apply for booking form. **Green Fees** terms on application. **Prof** Craig Watson **Course Designer** J Hull **Facilities** ⊗ ⫶Ⅲ ᕒ 🏌 ♀ 🏠 ⛳ 🏐 🏐 ⛳ *Leisure* sauna, solarium, gymnasium.

Hotel ⌂ Travelodge, Huntingdon Rd, LOLWORTH ☎ 01954 781335 20 en suite

BRAMPTON Map 04 TL27

Brampton Park Buckden Rd PE28 4NF
☎ 01480 434700 📄 01480 411145
e-mail: admin@bramptonparkgc.co.uk
Set in truly attractive countryside, bounded by the River Great Ouse and bisected by the River Lane. Great variety with mature trees, lakes and water hazards. One of the most difficult holes is the 4th, a par 3 island green, 175 yards in length.
18 holes, 6300yds, Par 71, SSS 72, Course record 62.
Club membership 650.
Visitors must contact in advance. **Societies** apply in advance. **Green Fees** terms on application. **Cards** 🖃🟥🟦 🟥🔵 **Prof** Alisdair Currie **Course Designer** Simon Gidman **Facilities** ⊗ ⫶Ⅲ ᕒ 🏌 ♀ 🏠 🏐 ⛳ ⛳ ⛳ **Location** Follow signs from A1 or A14 to RAF Brampton

Hotel ★★★ 77% The Old Bridge Hotel, 1 High St, HUNTINGDON ☎ 01480 424300 24 en suite

CAMBRIDGE Map 05 TL45

Gog Magog Shelford Bottom CB2 4AB
☎ 01223 247626 📄 01223 414990
e-mail: secretary@gogmagog.co.uk
Situated just outside the centre of the university town, Gog Magog, established in 1901, is known as the nursery of Cambridge undergraduate golf. The courses are on high ground, and it is said that if you stand on the highest point and could see far enough to the east the next highest ground would be the Ural Mountains! The courses are open but there are enough trees and other hazards to provide plenty of problems. Views from the high parts are superb. The nature of the ground ensures good winter golf. The area has
continued

ELY Map 05 TL58

Ely City 107 Cambridge Rd CB7 4HX
☎ 01353 662751 (Office) 📄 01353 668636
e-mail: elygolf@lineone.net
Parkland course slightly undulating with water hazards formed by lakes and natural dykes. Demanding par 4 5th hole (467yds), often into a headwind, and a testing par 3 2nd hole (160yds) played over two ponds. Magnificent views of cathedral.
18 holes, 6627yds, Par 72, SSS 72, Course record 65.
Club membership 825.
Visitors advisable to contact the club in advance,handicap certificate required. **Societies** Tue to Fri, advisable to contact club well in advance. **Green Fees** £30 per day (£36 weekends). **Prof** Andrew George **Course Designer** Sir Henry Cotton **Facilities** ⊗ ⫶Ⅲ ᕒ 🏌 ♀ 🏠 ⛳ 🏐 ⛳ *Leisure* snooker. **Location** S of city on A10

Hotel ★★★ 67% Lamb Hotel, 2 Lynn Rd, ELY ☎ 01353 663574 32 en suite

GIRTON Map 05 TL46

Girton Dodford Ln CB3 0QE
☎ 01223 276169 📄 01223 277150
e-mail: secretary@girtongolfclub.sagehost.co.uk
Flat, open parkland course with many trees and ditches. Easy walking.
18 holes, 6012yds, Par 69, SSS 69, Course record 66.
Club membership 800.
Visitors with member only at weekends. Contact professional in advance (01223 276991). **Societies** apply in writing. **Green Fees** £20 per round. **Prof** Scott Thomson **Course Designer** Allan Gow **Facilities** ⊗ ⫶Ⅲ ᕒ 🏌 ♀ 🏠 🏐 ⛳ ⛳ **Location** 3 miles from Cambridge. Just off junct 31 of A14

Hotel ★★★ 67% Holiday Inn Cambridge, Lakeview, Bridge Rd, Impington, CAMBRIDGE ☎ 0870 400 9015 165 en suite

HEMINGFORD ABBOTS Map 04 TL27

Hemingford Abbots Cambridge Rd PE28 9HQ
☎ 01480 495000 & 493900 📄 01480 4960000
Interesting 9-hole course featuring a par 5 dog-leg 4th with a testing tapering fairway, two ponds at the entrance to the 8th green and an island green on the 9th.
9 holes, 5468yds, Par 68, SSS 68, Course record 69.
Club membership 170.
continued

Visitors advisable to phone in advance, particularly for weekends. **Societies** advise in writing or telephone. **Green Fees** £15 per 18 holes; £10 per 9 holes (£17/£12 weekends and bank holidays). **Course Designer** Ray Paton **Facilities** ⊗ ㅏ ☕ ♀ ♤ 🏠 ✤ ⚿ ₵ **Conf** Max 50 **Location** A14 Hemingford Abbots turning, midway between St Ives and Huntingdon

Hotel ★★★ 77% The Old Bridge Hotel, 1 High St, HUNTINGDON ☎ 01480 424300 24 en suite

LONGSTANTON　　　　　　　Map 05 TL36

Cambridge Station Rd CB4 5DR ☎ 01954 789388
An undulating parkland course with bunkers and ponds.
18 holes, 6736yds, Par 72, SSS 73.
Club membership 300.
Visitors must telephone in advance to book. **Societies** must telephone in advance. **Green Fees** £10 per round (£13 weekends). **Cards** 🔳 🔳 🔳 **Prof** Geoff Huggett/A Engelman **Facilities** ⊗ ㅏ ㅏ ☕ ♀ ♤ 🏠 ✤ **Leisure** fishing, hot air ballons.**Conf** Max 50

Hotel ★★★ 67% Holiday Inn Cambridge, Lakeview, Bridge Rd, Impington, CAMBRIDGE
☎ 0870 400 9015 165 en suite

MARCH　　　　　　　　　　　Map 05 TL49

March Frogs Abbey, Grange Rd PE15 0YH
☎ 01354 652364 📠 01354 652364
Nine hole parkland course with a particularly challenging par 3 9th hole, with out of bounds on the right and high hedges to the left.
9 holes, 6204yds, Par 70, SSS 70, Course record 65.
Club membership 400.
Visitors contact in advance, with member only at weekends. **Societies** must contact in advance. **Green Fees** not confirmed. **Cards** 🔳 🔳 🔳 **Prof** Stewart Brown **Facilities** ☕ ♀ ♤ ✤ **Location** 0.5m off A141, March bypass

Hotel ★★ 64% Olde Griffin Hotel, High St, MARCH
☎ 01354 652517 20 rms (19 en suite)

MELDRETH　　　　　　　　　Map 05 TL34

Malton Malton Rd, Malton SG8 6PE
☎ 01763 262200 📠 01763 262209
e-mail: desk@maltongolf.co.uk
Set amongst 230 acres of beautiful undulating countryside. The River Cam bisects part of the course which is surrounded by woodlands and wetlands.
18 holes, 6708yards, Par 72, SSS 72, Course record 67.
Visitors must telephone in advance. **Societies** booking form available on request. **Green Fees** £17 per day; £10 per 18 holes (£26/£16 weekends and bank holidays), £13 Sat after noon). **Cards** 🔳 🔳 🔳 🔳 🔳 **Prof** Graham Harvey **Facilities** ⊗ ㅏ ㅏ ☕ ♀ ♤ 🏠 ✤ 🏠 ✤ ⚿ ₵ **Location** on unclassified road between Orwell and Meldreth

Hotel ★★★ 73% Duxford Lodge Hotel, Ickleton Rd, DUXFORD ☎ 01223 836444 11 en suite 4 annexe en suite

PETERBOROUGH　　　　　　Map 04 TL19

Elton Furze Bullock Rd, Haddon PE7 3TT
☎ 01832 280189 & 280614 (Pro shop) 📠 01832 280299
e-mail: secretary@eltonfurzegolfclub.co.uk
Wooded parkland 18-hole course in lovely surroundings.
18 holes, 6279yds, Par 70, SSS 71, Course record 67.
Club membership 620.
Visitors welcome, preferably Mon-Fri, weekends only with prior permission (phone in advance). **Societies** by prior

continued

arrangement telephone for details. **Green Fees** £38 per day; £28 per round (£32 per round weekends). **Cards** 🔳 🔳 **Prof** Frank Kiddie **Course Designer** Roger Fitton **Facilities** ⊗ ㅏ ㅏ ☕ ♀ ♤ 🏠 ⚿ ₵ **Location** 4m SW of Peterborough, off A605/A1

Hotel ★★★★ 68% Peterborough Marriott Hotel, Peterborough Business Park, Lynchwood, PETERBOROUGH ☎ 01733 371111 157 en suite

Orton Meadows Ham Ln, Orton Waterville PE2 5UU
☎ 01733 237478 📠 01733 332774
Pretty public parkland course set within the Nene Valley Country Park with large lakes and water hazards. Challenging 3rd hole (480yards from white tee) incorporating lots of water and 'out of bounds' areas. Also 12-hole pitch and putt course.
18 holes, 5269yds, Par 67, SSS 68, Course record 64.
Club membership 650.
Visitors phone for reservations 7 days in advance. **Societies** apply in advance. **Green Fees** terms on application. **Cards** 🔳 🔳 🔳 🔳 **Prof** Jason Mitchell **Course Designer** D & R Fitton **Facilities** ⊗ ㅏ ㅏ ☕ ♀ ♤ 🏠 ✤ **Leisure** 12 hole pitch & putt. **Location** 3m W of town on A605

Hotel ★★★ 67% Orton Hall Hotel, Orton Longueville, PETERBOROUGH ☎ 01733 391111 65 en suite

Peterborough Milton Milton Ferry PE6 7AG
☎ 01733 380489 📠 01733 380489
e-mail: miltongolfclub@aol.com
Designed by James Braid, this well-bunkered parkland course is set in the grounds of the Milton Estate, many of the holes being played in full view of Milton Hall. Challenging holes are the difficult dog-leg 10th and 15th. Easy walking.
18 holes, 6479yds, Par 71, SSS 72, Course record 62.
Club membership 800.
Visitors contact in advance. Handicap certificate required. **Societies** bookings by fax or telephone to secretary. **Green Fees** £40 per day; £30 per round. **Cards** 🔳 🔳 🔳 **Prof** Mike Gallagher **Course Designer** James Braid **Facilities** ⊗ ㅏ ㅏ ☕ ♀ ♤ 🏠 ✤ **Conf** Max 80 Class 20 Board 15 **Location** 2m W of Peterborough on A47,near the villages of Castor & Ailsworth

Hotel ★★★ 66% Butterfly Hotel, Thorpe Meadows, Longthorpe Parkway, PETERBOROUGH
☎ 01733 564240 70 en suite

Thorpe Wood Thorpe Wood, Nene Parkway PE3 6SE
☎ 01733 267701 📠 01733 332774
e-mail: enquiries@thorpewoodgolfcourse.co.uk
Gently undulating, parkland course designed by Peter Alliss and Dave Thomas. Challenging holes include the 5th, the longest hole, usually played with prevailing wind, and the 14th, which has a difficult approach shot over water to a two-tier green.
18 holes, 7086yds, Par 73, SSS 74, Course record 68.
Club membership 750.
Visitors phone for reservations 7 days in advance. **Societies** must telephone in advance, society bookings taken up to year ahead. **Green Fees** £11.50 per round (£15.20 weekends & bank holidays). **Cards** 🔳 🔳 🔳 🔳 **Prof** Roger Fitton **Course Designer** Peter Allis/Dave Thomas **Facilities** ⊗ ㅏ ㅏ ☕ ♀ ♤ 🏠 ✤ ⚿ **Location** 3m W of city centre on A47

Hotel ★★★ 66% Butterfly Hotel, Thorpe Meadows, Longthorpe Parkway, PETERBOROUGH
☎ 01733 564240 70 en suite

PIDLEY
Map 05 TL37

Lakeside Lodge Fen Rd PE28 3DF
☎ 01487 740540 🖷 01487 740852
e-mail: info@golf-lakeside-lodge.co.uk
A well designed, spacious course incorporating eight
lakes, 12,000 trees and a modern clubhouse. The 9th and
18th holes both finish dramatically alongside a lake in
front of the clubhouse. Also 9 hole par 3, and 25-bay
driving range. The Manor provides an interesting
contrast with its undulating fairways and angular greens.
*Lodge Course: 18 holes, 6821yds, Par 72, SSS 73, Course
record 72.*
The Manor: 9 holes, 3202yds, Par 68.
The Church: 12 holes, 3290yds, Par 44.
Club membership 850.
Visitors no restrictions. Societies must telephone in advance.
Green Fees £12 per 18 holes (£20 weekends). Cards ▨
▨▨ ▨ Prof Scott Waterman Course Designer A W
Headley Facilities ⊗ ⊅⊪ ⊾ ⊑ ♀ ⊿ ⊟ ⊓ ⊮ ⊘ ⊏
Leisure fishing, ten pin bowling, smart golf simulator.Conf
Max 220 Thtr 220 Class 80 Board 80 Banquet 100 Location
10m from A14/A1 at Huntingdon

Hotel ★★★ 69% Slepe Hall Hotel, Ramsey Rd, ST IVES
☎ 01480 463122 16 en suite

RAMSEY
Map 04 TL28

Old Nene Golf & Country Club Muchwood Ln,
Bodsey PE26 2XQ ☎ 01487 813519 & 815622
An easy walking well-drained course with water hazards
and tree-lined fairways There are excellent greens and
many challenging holes across water in either a head
wind or cross wind.
9 holes, 5605yds, Par 68, SSS 68, Course record 64.
Club membership 170.
Visitors book in advance especially evenings & weekends.
Dress code must be adhered to. Societies arrange in advance
with Secretary. Green Fees terms on application. Prof Ian
Galloway Course Designer R Edrich Facilities ⊗ ⊅⊪ ⊾ ⊑
♀ ⊿ ⊓ ⊮ ⊾ ⊘ ⊏ Leisure fishing, practice area. Location
0.75m N of Ramsey towards Ramsey Mereside

Hotel ★★★ 77% The Old Bridge Hotel, 1 High St,
HUNTINGDON ☎ 01480 424300 24 en suite

Ramsey 4 Abbey Ter PE26 1DD
☎ 01487 812600 🖷 01487 815746
Flat, parkland course with water hazards and well
irrigated greens, mature tees and fairways, assuring a
good surface whatever the conditions. It gives the
impression of wide open spaces, but the wayward shot is
soon punished.
18 holes, 5830yds, Par 71, SSS 68, Course record 64.
Club membership 750.
Visitors contact professional in advance 01487 813022, may
only play with member at weekends & bank holidays.
Societies apply in writing. Green Fees £25 per round. Prof
Stuart Scott Course Designer J Hamilton Stutt Facilities ⊗
by arrangement ⊪ by prior arrangement ⊾ ⊑ ⊿ ⊟
⊓ ⊘ Leisure snooker tables, bowls rinks. Location 12m SE
of Peterborough on B1040

Hotel ★★★ 77% The Old Bridge Hotel, 1 High St,
HUNTINGDON ☎ 01480 424300 24 en suite

AA website: www.theAA.com

ST IVES
Map 04 TL37

St Ives (Cambs) Westwood Rd PE27 6DH
☎ 01480 468392 🖷 01480 468392
e-mail: stivesgolfclub@zoom.co.uk
Picturesque parkland course.
9 holes, 6180yds, Par 70, SSS 70, Course record 68.
Club membership 500.
Visitors may not play weekends. Societies welcome Wed &
Fri. Green Fees terms on application. Prof Darren Glasby
Facilities ⊗ ⊅⊪ ⊾ ⊑ ♀ ⊿ ⊟ ⊓ ⊘ Location W side of
town centre off A1123

Hotel ★★★ 69% Slepe Hall Hotel, Ramsey Rd, ST IVES
☎ 01480 463122 16 en suite

ST NEOTS
Map 04 TL16

Abbotsley Golf & Squash Club Eynesbury
Hardwicke PE19 6XN
☎ 01480 474000 & 215153 🖷 01480 403280
e-mail: abbotsley@americangolf.uk.com
Set in 250 acres of idyllic countryside, with two 18 hole
courses and a 9 hole par 3. The Cromwell course is the
less challenging of the two, offering a contrast to the
renowned Abbotsley course with its holes meandering
through woods and streams. One of the most memorable
holes is the Abbotsley second hole known as the
Mousehole, which requires an accurate tee shot to a green
that is protected by a stream and shaded by the many
trees that surround and protect it.
*Abbotsley Course: 18 holes, 6311yds, Par 73, SSS 72,
Course record 69.*
*Cromwell Course: 18 holes, 6087yds, Par 70, SSS 69,
Course record 66.*
Club membership 550.
Visitors welcome at all times. Necessary to book weekends.
Societies prior booking essential. Green Fees Abbotsley:£20
per 18 holes;£13 per 9 holes(£30/£19 weekends and bank
holidays) Cromwell:£12 per 18 holes;£7 per 9 holes(£18/£9
weekends and bank holidays). Cards ▨ ▨ ▨ ▨
▨ Prof Denise Hastings/Steve Connolly Course Designer D
Young/V Saunders Facilities ⊗ ⊅⊪ ⊾ ⊑ ♀ ⊿ ⊟ ⊓ ⊮ ⊾
⊿ ⊘ ⊏ Leisure squash, solarium, gymnasium, holistic
health & beauty salon. Location 10 mins from A1 & A428

Hotel ★★ 69% Abbotsley Golf Hotel & Country Club,
Potton Rd, Eynesbury Hardwicke, ST NEOTS
☎ 01480 474000 42 annexe en suite

St Neots Crosshall Rd PE19 7GE
☎ 01480 472363 🖷 01480 472363
e-mail: office@stneots-golfclub.co.uk
Undulating and very picturesque parkland course with
lake and water hazards and exceptional greens, close to
the Kym and Great Ouse rivers. Easy, level walking.
18 holes, 6074yds, Par 69, SSS 69, Course record 64.
Club membership 630.
Visitors must book in advance. with member only at
weekends. Societies must contact in advance. Green Fees
£35 per day; £25 per round. Cards ▨ ▨ ▨ ▨ ▨ Prof
Jason Boast Course Designer H Vardon Facilities ⊗ ⊅⊪ ⊾
⊑ ♀ ⊿ ⊟ ⊓ ⊮ ⊾ ⊘ Location Just off the A1 with the
jct B1048 heading into St Neots

Hotel ★★ 69% Abbotsley Golf Hotel & Country Club,
Potton Rd, Eynesbury Hardwicke, ST NEOTS
☎ 01480 474000 42 annexe en suite

THORNEY   Map 04 TF20

Thorney English Drove, Thorney PE6 0TJ
☎ 01733 270570 📠 01733 270842
The 18-hole Fen course is ideal for the beginner, while the Lakes course has a challenging links-style layout with eight holes around water.
Fen Course: 18 holes, 6104yds, Par 70, SSS 69, Course record 66.
Lakes Course: 18 holes, 6402yds, Par 71, SSS 70, Course record 65. Club membership 400.
Visitors book in advance for Fen course, limited weekend play Lakes course. **Societies** contact in advance. **Green Fees** terms on application. **Cards** 🖃 🖃 🖃 🖃 🖃 **Prof** Mark Templeman **Course Designer** A Dow **Facilities** ⊗ ⊪ ᴸ ♥ ♀ ᴸ 🖨 ⚲ ♥ ♠ ✎ (**Leisure** gymnasium, par 3 course. **Location** Off A47, 7m NE of Peterborough

Hotel ★★★ 66% Butterfly Hotel, Thorpe Meadows, Longthorpe Parkway, PETERBOROUGH
☎ 01733 564240 70 en suite

TOFT   Map 05 TL35

Cambridge Meridian Comberton Rd CB3 7RY
☎ 01223 264700 📠 01223 264701
e-mail: meridian@golfsocieties.com
Set in 207 acres to a Peter Allis/Clive Clark design with sweeping fairways, lakes and well bunkered greens. The 4th hole has bunker complexes, a sharp dog-leg and a river with the green heavily guarded by bunkers. The 9th and 10th holes challenge the golfer with river crossings.
18 holes, 6651yds, Par 73, SSS 72, Course record 72.
Club membership 400.
Visitors must contact in advance. **Societies** telephone for provisional booking **Green Fees** terms on application. **Cards** 🖃 🖃 **Prof** Michael Clemons **Course Designer** Peter Alliss/Clive Clark **Facilities** ⊗ ⊪ ᴸ ♥ ♀ ᴸ 🖨 ⚲ ♥ ♠ ✎ **Location** 3m W of Cambridge, on B1046

Hotel ★★ 69% Abbotsley Golf Hotel & Country Club, Potton Rd, Eynesbury Hardwicke, ST NEOTS
☎ 01480 474000 42 annexe en suite

CHESHIRE

ALDERLEY EDGE   Map 07 SJ87

Alderley Edge Brook Ln SK9 7RU ☎ 01625 585583
Well-wooded, undulating pastureland course. A stream crosses 7 of the 9 holes.
9 holes, 5823yds, Par 68, SSS 68, Course record 62.
Club membership 400.
Visitors by arrangement on Thu. **Societies** Thu only, apply in writing or telephone. **Green Fees** not confirmed. **Prof** Peter Bowring **Facilities** ⊗ ⊪ ᴸ ♥ ♀ ᴸ 🖨 ✎ **Location** 1m NW on B5085

Hotel ★★★ 74% Alderley Edge Hotel, Macclesfield Rd, ALDERLEY EDGE ☎ 01625 583033 52 en suite

ALDERSEY GREEN   Map 07 SJ45

Aldersey Green CH3 9EH ☎ 01829 782453
Exciting, tricky, beautiful parkland course.
18 holes, 6145, Par 70, SSS 69, Course record 72.
Visitors advisable to book **Societies** by prior arrangement **Green Fees** £25 per day; £15 per 18 holes (£30/£20 weekends). **Facilities** ⊗ ⊪ ᴸ ♥ ♀ ✎ **Location** On A41 Whitchurch Rd

continued

Hotel ★★★★ 71% De Vere Carden Park Hotel, Carden Park, BROXTON ☎ 01829 731000
115 en suite 77 annexe en suite

ALSAGER   Map 07 SJ75

Alsager Golf & Country Club Audley Rd ST7 2UR
☎ 01270 875700 📠 01270 882207
e-mail: business@alsagergolfclub.com
An 18-hole parkland course situated in rolling Cheshire countryside and offering a challenge to all golfers whatever their standard. Clubhouse is well appointed with good facilities and a friendly atmosphere.
18 holes, 6225yds, Par 70, SSS 70, Course record 68.
Club membership 640.
Visitors must contact in advance, may not play Fri afternoon, can only play with member at weekends. **Societies** must contact in advance. **Green Fees** not confirmed. **Prof** Richard Brown **Facilities** ᴸ ♥ ♀ ᴸ 🖨 ✎ **Location** 2m NE of M6 junct 16

Hotel ★★★ 71% Manor House Hotel, Audley Rd, ALSAGER ☎ 01270 884000 57 en suite

ANTROBUS   Map 07 SJ68

Antrobus Foggs Ln CW9 6JQ
☎ 01925 730890 📠 01925 730100
e-mail: info@antrobusgolfclub.co.uk
Challenging parkland course where water is the main feature with streams and ponds in play on most holes. Large undulating greens.
18 holes, 6220yards, Par 71, SSS 71, Course record 65.
Club membership 500.
Visitors must contact in advance, may not play Sat. **Societies** telephone in advance/apply in writing. May play weekdays/Sun after 11am, not Sat. **Green Fees** £22 per day (£25 Sun). **Cards** 🖃 🖃 🖃 🖃 🖃 **Prof** Paul Farrance **Course Designer** Mike Slater **Facilities** ⊗ ⊪ ᴸ ♥ ♀ ᴸ 🖨 ⚲ ✎ (**Leisure** fishing. **Location** M56 Junct 10, take A559 towards Northwich, 2nd left after Birch & Bottle pub onto Knutsford Rd, 1st left into Foggs Lane

Hotel ★★ 66% Wincham Hall, Hall Ln, Wincham, NORTHWICH ☎ 01606 43453 10 rms (9 en suite)

CHESTER   Map 07 SJ46

Chester Curzon Park CH4 8AR
☎ 01244 677760 📠 01244 676667
Meadowland course on two levels contained within a loop of the River Dee. The car park overlooks the racecourse across the river.
18 holes, 6508yds, Par 72, SSS 71, Course record 66.
Club membership 820.
Visitors must contact in advance. **Societies** must telephone or write in advance. **Green Fees** £30 (£35 weekends). **Prof** George Parton **Facilities** ⊗ ⊪ ᴸ ♥ ♀ ᴸ 🖨 ⚲ ✎ **Location** 1m W of city centre

Hotel ★★★ 66% Grosvenor Pulford Hotel, Wrexham Rd, Pulford, CHESTER ☎ 01244 570560 75 en suite

De Vere Carden Park Hotel Carden Park
CH3 9DQ ☎ 01829 731000 📠 01829 731032
e-mail: reservations.carden@devere-hotels.com
A superb golf resort set in 750 acres of beautiful Cheshire countryside. Facilities include the mature parkland Cheshire Course, the Nicklaus Course, the 9 hole par 3 Azalea Course, Europe's first Jack Nicklaus Residential Golf School and a luxurious clubhouse.

continued

Cheshire: 18 holes, 6891yds, Par 72, SSS 71,
Course record 69.
Nicklaus: 18 holes, 6302yds, Par 72, SSS 72.
Club membership 250.

Carden Park Hotel Golf Resort & Spa

Visitors must contact in advance, handicap certificate required for the Nicklaus Course. Metal spikes cannot be worn. **Societies** contact for details, tel: 01829 731594. **Green Fees** Cheshire: £45; Nicklaus: £65. **Cards** ▭▬▬▬ ▭ **Prof** Peter Curtis **Course Designer** Jack Nicklaus **Facilities** ⊗ ⊪ ⅃ ▮ ♀ ♨ 🏠 ⚑ 🏐 ⇥ ♨ ♣ **Leisure** hard tennis courts, heated indoor swimming pool, sauna, solarium, gymnasium, residential golf school, snooker room, dance studio. **Conf** Max 520 Thtr 500 Class 315 Board 40 Banquet 460 Del £160 to £170 * **Location** S of City on A41, right at Broxton rdbt onto A534 signed Wrexham. Situated 1.5m on left

· ·

Hotel ★★★★ 71% De Vere Carden Park Hotel, Carden Park, BROXTON ☎ 01829 731000 115 en suite 77 annexe en suite

Eaton Guy Ln, Waverton CH3 7PH
☎ 01244 335885 & 335826 ▤ 01244 335782
e-mail: office@eatongolfclub.co.uk
A parkland course with a liberal covering of both mature trees and new planting enhanced by natural water hazards.
18 holes, 6562yds, Par 72, SSS 71, Course record 69.
Club membership 550.
Visitors must contact in advance particularly for weekends. **Societies** must contact in advance. May not play weekends (am) or Wednesdays. **Green Fees** £30 per round (£35 weekends). £5 reduction in winter. **Prof** William Tye **Course Designer** Donald Steel **Facilities** ⊗ ⊪ ⅃ ▮ ♀ ♨ 🏠 ⚑ 🏐 ♨ ♣ **Location** 3m SE of Chester off A41

· ·

Hotel ★★★★★ 79% The Chester Grosvenor, Eastgate, CHESTER ☎ 01244 324024 83 en suite

Upton-by-Chester Upton Ln, Upton-by-Chester
CH2 1EE ☎ 01244 381183 ▤ 01244 376955
Pleasant, tree-lined, parkland course. Not easy for low-handicap players to score well. Testing holes are 2nd (par 4), 14th (par 4) and 15th (par 3).
18 holes, 5808yds, Par 69, SSS 68, Course record 63.
Club membership 750.
Visitors must contact in advance. **Societies** apply in writing. **Green Fees** £30 per day; £20 per round; (£15 per round winter). **Cards** ▭▬▬ ▭ **Course Designer** Bill Davies **Facilities** ⊗ ⊪ ⅃ ▮ ♀ ♨ 🏠 🏐 ♨ ♣ **Location** N side off A5116

· ·

Hotel ★★★★ 66% Mollington Banastre Hotel, Parkgate Rd, CHESTER ☎ 01244 851471 63 en suite

Vicars Cross Tarvin Rd, Great Barrow CH3 7HN
☎ 01244 335595 ▤ 01244 335686
Tree-lined parkland course, with undulating terrain.
18 holes, 6428yds, Par 72, SSS 71, Course record 64.
Club membership 750.
Visitors advisable to contact in advance, visitors may not play competition days or Wed. **Societies** Tue & Thu only. Must book in advance. **Green Fees** £25 per day (£15 after 3pm). **Prof** J A Forsythe **Course Designer** J Richardson **Facilities** ⊗ ⊪ ⅃ ▮ ♀ ♨ 🏠 ⚑ 🏐 ♣ **Location** 4m E on A51

· ·

Hotel ★★★ 69% Rowton Hall Country House Hotel, Whitchurch Rd, Rowton, CHESTER ☎ 01244 335262 38 en suite

Astbury Peel Ln, Astbury CW12 4RE
☎ 01260 279139 ▤ 01260 291300
e-mail: admin@astburygolfclub.com
Parkland course in open countryside, bisected by a canal. The testing 12th hole involves a long carry over a tree-filled ravine. Large practice area.
18 holes, 6296yds, Par 71, SSS 70, Course record 61.
Club membership 720.
Visitors must be a member of a recognised golf club and possess official handicap. May only play weekdays Apr-Nov. **Societies** contact for details. **Green Fees** not confirmed. **Prof** Ashley Salt **Facilities** ⊗ ▮ ♀ ♨ 🏠 ♣ **Location** 1.5m S between A34 and A527

· ·

Inn ♦♦♦ Egerton Arms Hotel, Astbury Village, CONGLETON ☎ 01260 273946 6 rms (2 en suite)

Congleton Biddulph Rd CW12 3LZ ☎ 01260 273540
9 holes, 5103yds, Par 68, SSS 65.
Location 1.5m SE on A527
Telephone for further details

· ·

Inn ♦♦♦ Egerton Arms Hotel, Astbury Village, CONGLETON ☎ 01260 273946 6 rms (2 en suite)

Crewe Fields Rd, Haslington CW1 5TB
☎ 01270 584099 ▤ 01270 584099
e-mail: secretary@crewsgolfclub.co.uk
Undulating parkland course.
18 holes, 6424yds, Par 71, SSS 71, Course record 66.
Club membership 674.
Visitors may not play at weekends, contact professional for details. **Societies** Tue only, prior arrangement with the secretary. **Green Fees** not confirmed. **Prof** Mike Booker **Facilities** ⊗ ⊪ by prior arrangement ⅃ ▮ ♀ ♨ 🏠 ♣ **Location** 2.25m NE off A534

· ·

Hotel ★★★ 70% Hunters Lodge Hotel, Sydney Rd, Sydney, CREWE ☎ 01270 583440 47 en suite

Queen's Park Queen's Park Dr CW2 7SB
☎ 01270 666724 ▤ 01270 569902
9 holes, 4920yds, Par 68, SSS 64, Course record 67.
Location Located behind Queen's Park. Well signposted
Telephone for further details

· ·

Hotel ★★★ 70% Hunters Lodge Hotel, Sydney Rd, Sydney, CREWE ☎ 01270 583440 47 en suite

Where to stay, where to eat?
Visit www.theAA.com

DELAMERE   Map 07 SJ56

Delamere Forest Station Rd CW8 2JE
☎ 01606 883264 (Office) 883307 (Pro)
📠 01606 883800 (Sec)
18 holes, 6328yds, Par 72, SSS 70, Course record 63.

Course Designer H Fowler **Location** 1.5m NE,
off B5152
Telephone for further details

Hotel ★★★ Nunsmere Hall Country House Hotel,
Tarporley Rd, SANDIWAY ☎ 01606 889100 36 en suite

DISLEY   Map 07 SJ98

Disley Stanley Hall Ln SK12 2JX
☎ 01663 762071 & 764001 (Sec) 📠 01663 762678
Straddling a hilltop site above Lyme Park, this
undulating parkland/moorland course affords good views
and requires accuracy of approach to almost all the
greens which lie on either a ledge or plateau. Testing
holes are the 3rd and 4th.

18 holes, 6015yds, Par 71, SSS 69, Course record 63.
Club membership 658.
Visitors contact in advance, may not normally play at
weekends. **Societies** by prior arrangement. **Green Fees** not
confirmed. **Prof** Andrew Esplin **Facilities** ⊗ ⤖ ᴸ 💻 ♀ ᴧ
🏠 🏌 ♂ **Location** NW side of village off A6

Hotel ★★★ 60% County Hotel Bramhall, Bramhall Ln
South, BRAMHALL ☎ 0161 455 9988 65 en suite

ELLESMERE PORT   Map 07 SJ47

Ellesmere Port Chester Rd, Childer Thornton
CH66 1QF ☎ 0151 339 7689 📠 0151 339 7502
Municipal parkland course that is easy walking, with
natural hazards of woods, brook and ponds.
18 holes, 6432yds, Par 71, SSS 70.
Club membership 120.
Visitors must book with professional & send a deposit.

continued

Societies by arrangement with professional. **Green Fees**
£7.50 (£8.10 weekends). **Cards** ⤖ 💳 💳 💳 💳 **Prof**
Tony Roberts **Course Designer** Cotton, Pennick & Lawrie
Facilities ⊗ ⤖ ᴸ 💻 ♀ ᴧ 🏠 🏌 ♂ **Leisure** squash.
Location NW side of town centre. M53 junct 5, take A41 for
Chester, club 2m on left

Hotel ★★★ 66% Quality Hotel Chester,
Welsh Road/Berwick Rd, Little Sutton
☎ 0151 339 5121 53 en suite

FRODSHAM   Map 07 SJ57

Frodsham Simons Ln WA6 6HE
☎ 01928 732159 📠 01928 734070
e-mail: office@frodshamgc.golfagent.co.uk
Undulating parkland course with pleasant views from all
parts. Emphasis on accuracy over the whole course, the
long and difficult par 5 18th necessitating a drive across
water to the green. Crossed by two footpaths so extreme
care needed.
18 holes, 6298yds, Par 70, SSS 70, Course record 63.
Club membership 600.
Visitors must contact in advance. May not play at weekends.
Societies telephone for bookings. **Green Fees** terms on
application. **Cards** ⤖ 💳 💳 💳 💳 **Prof** Graham Tonge
Course Designer John Day **Facilities** ⊗ ⤖ ᴸ 💻 ♀ ᴧ 🏠
🏌 ♂ **Leisure** snooker. **Location** 1.5m SW,M56 junct
12,follow signs for Forest Hills Hotel,Golf Club 1st left on
Simons Lane

continued

Hotel ★★★ 68% Forest Hills Hotel & Leisure Complex, Overton Hill, FRODSHAM ☎ 01928 735255 58 en suite

HELSBY   Map 07 SJ47

Helsby Towers Ln WA6 0JB
☎ 01928 722021 📠 01928 725384
e-mail: len@hgc@aol.com
Parkland course with several tree plantations and natural pits as water hazards. Total of 41 bunkers.
18 holes, 6221yds, Par 70, SSS 70, Course record 69.
Club membership 590.
Visitors must contact in advance. Weekends and bank holidays with member only. **Societies** Tue & Thu. Booking through Hon Secretary. **Green Fees** £34 per day; £25 per round (£34 per round weekends). **Prof** Matthew Jones **Course Designer** James Braid (part) **Facilities** ⊗ ⅏ ⅃ ♥ ♀ ♨ 🏠 ⟙ ⌀ **Location** 6 miles from Chester,1 mile from M56 junct 14

Hotel ★★★★★ 79% The Chester Grosvenor, Eastgate, CHESTER ☎ 01244 324024 83 en suite

KNUTSFORD   Map 07 SJ77

Heyrose Budworth Rd, Tabley WA16 0HZ
☎ 01565 733664 📠 01565 734578
e-mail: secretary@heyrosegolfclub.com
An 18-hole course in wooded and gently undulating terrain. The par 3 16th (237yds), bounded by a small river in a wooded valley, is an interesting and testing hole - one of the toughest par 3s in Cheshire. Several water hazards. Both the course and the comfortable clubhouse have attractive views.
18 holes, 6513yds, Par 73, SSS 71, Course record 66.
Club membership 600.
Visitors not before 3.30pm Sat, ladies priority Wed and seniors priority Thu am. **Societies** must contact in advance. **Green Fees** £21 per round (£26 weekends & bank holidays). **Cards** 🃏 🃏 **Course Designer** C N Bridge **Facilities** ⊗ ⅏ by prior arrangement ⅃ ♥ ♀ ♨ 🏠 ⟙ ⌀ **Conf** Thtr 150 Class 35 **Location** 1m from M6 junct 19 follow tourist signs

Hotel ★★★★ 68% Cottons Hotel, Manchester Rd, KNUTSFORD ☎ 01565 650333 99 en suite

Knutsford Mereheath Ln WA16 6HS ☎ 01565 633355
Parkland course set in a beautiful old deer park. It demands some precise iron play.
9 holes, 6288yds, Par 70, SSS 70.
Club membership 230.
Visitors restricted Wed and weekends. Must contact in advance. **Societies** Thursday only by prior arrangement. **Green Fees** terms on application. **Prof** G Ogden **Facilities** ⊗ ⅃ ♥ ♀ ♨ ⌀ **Location** N side of town centre off A50

continued

Hotel ★★★★ 68% Cottons Hotel, Manchester Rd, KNUTSFORD ☎ 01565 650333 99 en suite

---

Mere Golf & Country Club Chester Rd,
Mere CW12 3DE ☎ 01565 830155 📠 01565 830713
e-mail: enquiries@meregolf.co.uk
A gracious parkland championship course designed by James Braid in the Cheshire sand belt, with several holes close to a lake. The round has a tight finish with four testing holes.

18 holes, 6817yds, Par 71, SSS 73, Course record 64.
Club membership 550.
Visitors by prior arrangement only, not able to play Wed, Fri, Sat & Sun. **Societies** apply by telephone to Karen Gallagher. **Green Fees** terms on application. **Cards** 🃏 🃏 🃏 🃏 🃏 🃏 🃏 **Prof** Peter Eyre **Course Designer** James Braid/George Duncan **Facilities** ⊗ ⅏ ⅃ ♥ ♀ ♨ 🏠 ⟙ ➴ ⌀ ♆ **Leisure** hard tennis courts, heated indoor swimming pool, squash, sauna, solarium, gymnasium. **Location** 1m E of M6 junct 19, 1m W of M56 junct 7

Hotel ★★★★ 68% Cottons Hotel, Manchester Rd, KNUTSFORD ☎ 01565 650333 99 en suite

---

Peover Plumley Moor Rd, Lower Peover WA16 9SE
☎ 01565 723337 📠 01565 723311
e-mail: mail@peovergolfclub.co.uk
Tees and greens have been positioned to maximise the benefits of the natural contours of the land. An excellent mix of holes varying in design and character with many doglegs and water hazards including a river which three of the fairways cross, including the first.
18 holes, 6702yds, Par 72, SSS 72, Course record 69.
Club membership 400.
Visitors full golfing attire required. Please book for tee times. **Societies** apply in writing/telephone in advance **Green Fees** terms on application. **Cards** 🃏 🃏 🃏 🃏 🃏 🃏 🃏 **Prof** Bobby Young **Course Designer** P A Naylor **Facilities** ⊗ ⅏ ⅃ ♥ ♀ ♨ 🏠 ➴ ➴ ⌀ **Conf** Max 50 Del £18 to £25 * **Location** M6 junct19/A556 onto Plumley Moor Rd

Hotel ★★ 75% The Longview Hotel & Restaurant, 55 Manchester Rd, KNUTSFORD ☎ 01565 632119 13 en suite 13 annexe en suite

LYMM   Map 07 SJ68

Lymm Whitbarrow Rd WA13 9AN
☎ 01925 755020 📠 01925 755020
e-mail: mail@lymmgolfclub.fsnet.co.uk
First ten holes are gently undulating with the Manchester Ship Canal running alongside the 6th hole. The remaining holes are comparatively flat.

continued

18 holes, 6304yds, Par 71, SSS 70.
Club membership 800.
Visitors may not play at weekends except with member.
Societies Wed only, must contact in advance. **Green Fees**
terms on application. **Prof** Steve McCarthy **Facilities** ⊗ ⵏⵎ
🏌 💺 ♀ ⛳ 🏠 ♂ **Location** 0.5m N off A6144

Hotel ★★★ 66% Lymm Hotel, Whitbarrow Rd, LYMM
☎ 01925 752233 15 en suite 48 annexe en suite

MACCLESFIELD   Map 07 SJ97

Macclesfield The Hollins SK11 7EA
☎ 01625 616952 (Pro) 🖷 01625 260061
e-mail: secretary@maccgolfclub.co.uk
Hillside heathland course situated on the edge of the
Pennines with excellent views across the Cheshire Plain.
A pleasant course providing a good test for players of all
abilities.
18 holes, 5700yds, Par 70, SSS 68, Course record 66.
Club membership 620.
Visitors apply in advance and have a handicap certificate.
Societies telephone initially. **Green Fees** £20 per day (£25
weekends). **Prof** Tony Taylor **Course Designer** Hawtree &
Son **Facilities** ⊗ ⵏⵎ 🏌 💺 ♀ ⛳ 🏠 ♂ **Location** SE side
of town centre off A523

Hotel ★★★ 69% Best Western Hollin Hall Hotel, Jackson
Ln, Kerridge, Bollington, MACCLESFIELD
☎ 01625 573246 54 en suite

Shrigley Hall Hotel Shrigley Park, Pott Shrigley
SK10 5SB ☎ 01625 575757 🖷 01625 575437
e-mail: shrigleyhall@paramount-hotels.co.uk
Parkland course set in 262-acre estate with breathtaking
views over the Peak District and Cheshire Plain. Designed
by Donald Steel, this championship standard course
provides a real sporting challenge while the magnificent
hotel provides a wealth of sporting facilities as well as
accommodation and food.
18 holes, 6281yds, Par 71, SSS 71, Course record 68.
Club membership 500.
Visitors must contact in advance by telephone. **Societies**
contact in advance. **Green Fees** £36 per round (£41
weekends & bank holidays). **Cards** 🖦 🖦 💳 **Prof** Tony
Stevens **Course Designer** Donald Steel **Facilities** ⊗ ⵏⵎ 🏌
💺 ♀ ⛳ 🏠 ♂ ⋈ 🍴 🛒 ♂ **Leisure** hard tennis courts,
heated indoor swimming pool, fishing, sauna, solarium,
gymnasium. **Conf** Max 250 Thtr 250 Class 200 Board 40
Banquet 220 Del from £53 * **Location** Off A523
Macclesfield to Stockport road

Hotel ★★★★ 67% Shrigley Hall Hotel Golf & Country
Club, Shrigley Park, Pott Shrigley, MACCLESFIELD
☎ 01625 575757 150 en suite

Tytherington Dorchester Way, Tytherington SK10 2JP
☎ 01625 506000 🖷 01625 506040
e-mail: tytherington.events@clubhaus.com
Modern championship course in beautiful, mature
parkland setting with eight water features and over 100
bunkers. Testing holes, notably the signature 12th hole
(par 5), played from an elevated tee with adjacent
snaking ditch and a lake guarding the green.
18 holes, 6765yds, Par 72, SSS 74.
Club membership 4800.
Visitors subject to availability and may not play weekends
am. **Societies** telephone and apply in writing. **Green Fees**
terms on application. **Cards** 🖦 🖦 💳 🖦 🖦 💳 **Prof** Neil
Coulson **Course Designer** Dave Thomas/Patrick Dawson
Facilities ⊗ ⵏⵎ 🏌 💺 ♀ ⛳ 🏠 ♂ ⛳ ♂ **Leisure** hard tennis
courts, heated indoor swimming pool, squash, sauna,
solarium, gymnasium. **Conf** Max 200 Thtr 200 Class 100
Board 16 Banquet 250 Del from £33 * **Location** 1m N of
Macclesfield off A523

Hotel ★★★★ 67% Shrigley Hall Hotel Golf & Country
Club, Shrigley Park, Pott Shrigley, MACCLESFIELD
☎ 01625 575757 150 en suite

NANTWICH   Map 07 SJ65

Reaseheath Reaseheath College CW5 6DF
☎ 01270 625131
The course here is attached to Reaseheath College, which
is one of the major centres of greenkeeper training in the
UK. It is a short 9-hole which can only be played with a
member.
9 holes, 1882yds, Par 62, SSS 58.
Club membership 600.
Visitors with member only. **Societies** by prior arrangement,
apply in writing. **Green Fees** terms on application. **Course
Designer** D Mortram **Facilities** ⛳ **Location** 1.5m NE of
Nantwich, off A51

Hotel ★★★🏅 77% Rookery Hall, Main Rd,
Worleston, NANTWICH ☎ 01270 610016
30 en suite 15 annexe en suite

OSCROFT   Map 07 SJ56

Pryors Hayes Willington Rd CH3 8NL
☎ 01829 741250 & 740140 🖷 01829 749077
e-mail: info@pryors-hayes.co.uk
Picturesque 18-hole parkland course set in the heart of
Cheshire. Gently undulating fairways demand accurate
drives, and numerous trees and water hazards make the
course a challenging test of golf.
18 holes, 6054yds, Par 69, SSS 69.
Club membership 530.
Visitors no restrictions. **Societies** apply for application form.
Green Fees £20 (£25 weekends). **Cards** 🖦 🖦 💳 🖦 🖦 💳
Prof Martin Redrup **Course Designer** John Day **Facilities**
⊗ ⵏⵎ 🏌 💺 ♀ ⛳ 🏠 🛒 🛒 ♂ **Location** Between A54 &
A51 roads, approx 6m E of Chester, village of Oscroft near
Tarvin

Hotel ★★★ 66% Blossoms Hotel, St John St, CHESTER
☎ 0870 400 8108 64 en suite

POYNTON   Map 07 SJ98

Davenport Worth Hall, Middlewood Rd SK12 1TS
☎ 01625 876951 🖷 01625 877489
Undulating parkland course. Extensive view over
Cheshire Plain from elevated 5th tee. Testing 17th hole,
par 4.

continued

18 holes, 6027yds, Par 69, SSS 69, Course record 64.
Club membership 700.
Visitors contact professional in advance, 01625 858387.
May not play Wed or Sat. **Societies** Tue and Thu only. Must
apply in advance. **Green Fees** £30 per day (£40 weekends).
Prof Gary Norcott **Facilities** ⊗ ⅷ ⅊ ⚑ ♀ ⚘ ⌂ ♂ **Leisure**
snooker. **Location** 1m E off A523

Hotel ★★★ 60% County Hotel Bramhall, Bramhall Ln
South, BRAMHALL ☎ 0161 455 9988 65 en suite

PRESTBURY   Map 07 SJ97

Prestbury Macclesfield Rd SK10 4BJ
☎ 01625 828241 ▤ 01625 828241
e-mail: office@prestburygolfclub.com
**Undulating parkland course, with many plateau
greens. The 9th hole has a challenging uphill 3-tier
green and the 17th is over a valley. Host to county and
inter-county championships.**

18 holes, 6359yds, Par 71, SSS 71, Course record 64.
Club membership 702.
Visitors must contact in advance and have an introduction
from own club, with member only at weekends. **Societies**
apply in writing, Thu only. **Green Fees** £45. **Cards** ⊟
▰▰ ▰▰ **Prof** Nick Summerfield **Course Designer** Harry S
Colt **Facilities** ⊗ ⅷ ⅊ ⚑ ♀ ⚘ ⌂ ♂ ⚐ **Location** S side
of village off A538

Hotel ★★★★ 69% Mottram Hall Hotel, Wilmslow Rd,
Mottram St Andrew, Prestbury,
☎ 01625 828135 132 en suite

RUNCORN   Map 07 SJ58

Runcorn Clifton Rd WA7 4SU
☎ 01928 574214 ▤ 01928 574214
**Parkland course with tree-lined fairways and easy
walking. Fine views over Mersey and Weaver valleys.
Testing holes: 7th par 5; 14th par 5; 17th par 4.**
18 holes, 6048yds, Par 69, SSS 69, Course record 63.
Club membership 570.
Visitors weekends restricted to playing with member only,
Tuesday Ladies Day. **Societies** telephone in advance. **Green
Fees** terms on application. **Prof** David Ingman **Facilities** ⊗
ⅷ by prior arrangement ⅊ ♀ ⚘ ⌂ ♂ **Location** 1.25m S
of Runcorn Station

Hotel ★★★ 66% Holiday Inn Runcorn, Wood Ln,
Beechwood, RUNCORN ☎ 0870 400 9070 150 en suite

SANDBACH   Map 07 SJ76

Malkins Bank Betchton Rd, Malkins Bank CW11 4XN
☎ 01270 765931
**Parkland course. Tight 13th hole with stream running
through.**   *continued*

18 holes, 6071yds, Par 70, SSS 69, Course record 65.
Club membership 500.
Visitors no restrictions. Advisable to book in advance.
Societies apply for booking form to course professional
Green Fees terms on application. **Cards** ⊟ ▰▰ ▰▰ ▰▰ ▥
Course Designer Hawtree **Facilities** ⊗ ⅷ ⅊ ⚑ ♀ ⚘ ⌂ ♂
♂ **Location** 1.5m SE off A533

Hotel ★★★ 66% Chimney House Hotel, Congleton Rd,
SANDBACH ☎ 01270 764141 48 en suite

SANDIWAY   Map 07 SJ67

Sandiway Chester Rd CW8 2DJ
☎ 01606 883247 (Secretary) ▤ 01606 888548
e-mail: info@sandiwaygolf.fsnet.co.uk
**Delightful undulating wood and heathland course with
long hills up to the 8th, 16th and 17th holes. Many dog-
legged and tree-lined holes give opportunities for the
deliberate fade or draw. True championship test and
one of the finest inland courses in North West
England.**
18 holes, 6404yds, Par 70, SSS 71, Course record 65.
Club membership 750.
Visitors book through secretary, members have reserved
tees 8.30-9.30 and 12.30-1.30 (11.30-12.30 winter).
Handicap certificate required **Societies** book in advance
through Secretary/Manager. **Green Fees** £45 per day; £40
per round (£55/£50 weekends). **Prof** William Laird
Course Designer Ted Ray **Facilities** ⊗ ⅷ ⅊ ⚑ ♀ ⚘ ⌂
♂ ♂ **Location** 2m W of Northwich on A556

Hotel ★★ 66% Wincham Hall, Hall Ln, Wincham,
NORTHWICH ☎ 01606 43453 10 rms (9 en suite)

SUTTON WEAVER   Map 07 SJ57

Sutton Hall Aston Ln WA7 3ED
☎ 01928 790747 ▤ 01928 759174
**Undulating parkland course with tricky greens, set in 140
acres on south facing slopes of the Weaver Valley.**
18 holes, 6608yards, Par 72, SSS 72, Course record 69.
Club membership 750.
Visitors contact in advance to book tee-time. **Societies**
write/telephone in advance. **Green Fees** £20 per round (£24
weekends). **Cards** ⊟ ▰▰ ▰▰ ▰▰ ▥ **Prof** Ian Smith
Facilities ⊗ ⅷ ⅊ ⚑ ♀ ⚘ ⌂ ⚐ ♂ **Location** M56 junct
12, follow signs for A56 to Warrington, on entering Sutton
Weaver take 1st turn right

Hotel ★★★ 66% Holiday Inn Runcorn, Wood Ln,
Beechwood, RUNCORN ☎ 0870 400 9070 150 en suite

TARPORLEY   Map 07 SJ56

Portal Golf & Country Club Cobbler's Cross Ln
CW6 0DJ ☎ 01829 733933 ▤ 01829 733928
e-mail: portalgolf@aol.com
**Opened in 1991, there are two 18-hole courses here -
Championship and Premier - one 9-hole course - Arderne
and the largest indoor golf academy in Britain. They are
set in mature, wooded parkland. There are fine views
over the Cheshire Plain and numerous water hazards.
The Championship 14th is just a short iron through trees,
but its green is virtually an island surrounded by water.**
*Championship Course: 18 holes, 7037yds, Par 73, SSS 74,
Course record 64.*
*Premier Course: 18 holes, 6508yds, Par 71, SSS 72, Course
record 64.*
Arderne Course: 9 holes, 1724yds, Par 30.
Club membership 300.   *continued*

Portal Golf & Country Club

Visitors must contact in advance. **Societies** must pre-book. **Green Fees** not confirmed. **Cards** 💳 💳 💳 **Prof** Mike Slater/Adrian Hill **Course Designer** Donald Steel **Facilities** ⊗ 🗝 🍴 🍺 🎱 🛋 🏌 📷 🎯 🎿 🍴 **Leisure** hard tennis courts, indoor golf academy. **Location** Off A49

Hotel ★★★ 67% The Wild Boar, Whitchurch Rd, Beeston, TARPORLEY ☎ 01829 260309 37 en suite

WARRINGTON   Map 07 SJ68

Birchwood Kelvin Close, Science Park North, Birchwood WA3 7PB ☎ 01925 818819 (Club) & 816574 (Pro) 📄 01925 822403

Very testing parkland course with many natural water hazards and the prevailing wind creating a problem on each hole. The 11th hole is particularly challenging.
Pilgrims: 18 holes, 6727yds, Par 71, SSS 73, Course record 66.
Progress: 18 holes, 6359yds, Par 71, SSS 72.
Mayflower (ladies course): 18 holes, 5849yds, Par 74, SSS 74. Club membership 745.
Visitors advisable to check with the professional to determine if course is fully booked. **Societies** Mon, Wed & Thu. Apply in writing, or telephone. **Green Fees** not confirmed. **Cards** 💳 💳 💳 **Prof** Paul McEwan **Course Designer** T J A Macauley **Facilities** ⊗ 🗝 🍴 🍺 🎱 🛋 🏌 📷 🎯 **Leisure** sauna. **Location** Junct 11 on M62, follow signs for Science Park North, 2m from the junct

Hotel ★★★ 66% Holiday Inn Haydock, Lodge Ln, HAYDOCK ☎ 0870 400 9039 138 en suite

Leigh Kenyon Hall, Broseley Ln, Culcheth WA3 4BG ☎ 01925 762943 (Secretary) 📄 01925 765097
A pleasant, well-wooded parkland course. Any discrepancy in length is compensated by the wide variety of golf offered here. The course is well maintained and there is a comfortable clubhouse.
18 holes, 5853yds, Par 69, SSS 68, Course record 64. Club membership 550.
Visitors contact professional for details. **Societies** Mon (ex bank holidays) & Tue, apply by telephone. **Green Fees** terms on application. **Prof** Andrew Baguley **Course Designer** James Braid **Facilities** ⊗ 🗝 🍴 🍺 🎱 🛋 🏌 📷 🎯 **Location** 5m NE off A579

Hotel ★★★ 72% Fir Grove Hotel, Knutsford Old Rd, WARRINGTON ☎ 01925 267471 40 en suite

Poulton Park Dig Ln, Cinnamon Brow, Padgate WA2 0SH ☎ 01925 822802 📄 01925 822802
Tight, flat parkland course with good greens and many trees. A straight drive off each tee is important. The
continued

4/13th has a fairway curving to the left with water and out-of-bounds on left and trees on right.
9 holes, 4978mtrs, Par 68, SSS 66, Course record 66. Club membership 350.
Visitors midweek only. Contact professional for details 01925 825220. **Societies** apply in advance. **Green Fees** terms on application. **Prof** Andrew Matthews **Facilities** ⊗ 🗝 🍴 🍺 🎱 🛋 🏌 **Location** 3m from Warrington on A574

Hotel ★★★ 72% Fir Grove Hotel, Knutsford Old Rd, WARRINGTON ☎ 01925 267471 40 en suite

Walton Hall Warrington Rd, Higher Walton WA4 5LU ☎ 01925 263061 (bookings)
A quiet, wooded, municipal parkland course on Walton Hall estate.
18 holes, 6647yds, Par 72, SSS 73, Course record 70. Club membership 250.
Visitors must book 6 days in advance. **Societies** must contact in writing. **Green Fees** not confirmed. **Prof** John Jackson **Facilities** ⊗ 🍴 🍺 🎱 🛋 🏌 📷 🎯 **Location** 2m from junct 11 of M56

Hotel ★★★ 72% Fir Grove Hotel, Knutsford Old Rd, WARRINGTON ☎ 01925 267471 40 en suite

Warrington Hill Warren, London Rd, Appleton WA4 5HR ☎ 01925 261775 (Secretary) 📄 01925 265933 e-mail: secretary@warrington-golf-club.co.uk
Meadowland, with varied terrain and natural hazards. Major work has recently been carried out on both the clubhouse and the course to ensure high standards. The course is a constant challenge with with ponds, trees and bunkers threatening the errant shot!

18 holes, 6305yds, Par 72, SSS 70, Course record 61. Club membership 840.
Visitors contact in advance. **Societies** by prior arrangement with Secretary. **Green Fees** £27 per day (£32 weekends & bank holidays). **Prof** Reay Mackay **Course Designer** James Braid **Facilities** ⊗ 🗝 🍴 🍺 🎱 🛋 🏌 📷 🎯 **Location** 1.5m N of junct 10 of M56 on A49

Hotel ★★★★ 71% Hanover International Hotel & Club, Stretton Rd, Stretton, WARRINGTON ☎ 01925 730706 140 en suite

WIDNES   Map 07 SJ58

Mersey Valley Warrington Rd, Bold Heath WA8 3XL ☎ 0151 4246060 📄 0151 2579097
Parkland course, very easy walking.
18 holes, 6374yards, Par 72, SSS 70, Course record 69. Club membership 500.
Visitors 6 day booking system available. **Societies** telephone in advance. Deposit required. **Green Fees** Mon/Tues £22 per day; £17 per 18 holes. Wed/Fri £28/£18. Weekends/BHs
continued

£35/£20. **Cards** 🖾 🖾 🖾 🖾 **Prof** Andy Stevenson **Course Designer** R Bush **Facilities** ⊗ ⫌ by prior arrangement 🍴 💷 🏌 ♨ 🏠 ⛳ 🚡 🚜 ⛳ **Location** M62 junct , follow A57 towards Warrington. Club 2m on left

....

Hotel ★★★ 65% Hillcrest Hotel, 75 Cronton Ln, WIDNES ☎ 0151 424 1616 50 en suite

St Michael Jubilee Dundalk Rd WA8 8BS
☎ 0151 424 6230 📠 0151 495 2124
e-mail: dchapmam@aol.com
Municipal parkland course dominated by the 'Stewards Brook'. It is divided into two sections which are split by the main road and joined by an underpass.
18 holes, 5925yds, Par 69, SSS 67.
Visitors welcome. **Societies** must contact in writing/telephone. **Green Fees** £7 per round (£8.30 weekends). **Prof** Darren Chapman **Facilities** ⊗ 🍴 💷 🏌 ♨ 🏠 ⛳ **Location** W side of town centre off A562

....

Hotel ⏢ Travelodge, Fiddlers Ferry Rd, WIDNES ☎ 08700 850950 32 en suite

Widnes Highfield Rd WA8 7DT
☎ 0151 424 2440 & 424 2995 📠 0151 495 2849
e-mail: arudder.wgc@uku.co.uk
Parkland course, easy walking.
18 holes, 5719yds, Par 69, SSS 68, Course record 64.
Club membership 700.

Visitors may play after 9am & after 4pm on competition days. Must contact in advance. **Societies** must contact the secretary in writing. **Green Fees** £18 per round (£24 weekends and bank holidays). **Prof** J O'Brien **Facilities** ⊗ ⫌ 🍴 💷 🏌 ♨ 🏠 **Location** M62 junct 7, A57 to Warrington, right at lights into Wilmere Lane, right at T junct. 1st left at rdbt into Birchfield Road, immediately right after 3rd pelican crossing to Highfield Road, right before traffic lights.

....

Hotel ⏢ Travelodge, Fiddlers Ferry Rd, WIDNES ☎ 08700 850950 32 en suite

────── WILMSLOW   Map 07 SJ88 ──────

Mottram Hall Wilmslow Rd, Mottram St Andrew
SK10 4QT ☎ 01625 828135 📠 01625 828950
e-mail: dmh.sales@devere-hotels.com
Championship standard course with flat meadowland on the front nine and undulating woodland on the back with well guarded greens. The course is unusual as each half opens and closes with par 5s. The hotel offers many leisure facilities.
18 holes, 7006yds, Par 72, SSS 74, Course record 65.
Club membership 500.
Visitors must contact in advance. Cannot play before midday Sat/Sun. Handicap certificate required. **Societies** must contact in advance. **Green Fees** £45 per round (£50

weekends). **Cards** 🖾 🖾 🖾 🖾 🖾 🖾 **Prof** Tim Rastall **Course Designer** Dave Thomas **Facilities** ⊗ ⫌ 🍴 💷 🏌 ♨ 🏠 ⛳ 🚡 🚜 ⛳ 🍴 **Leisure** hard tennis courts, heated indoor swimming pool, squash, sauna, solarium, gymnasium.**Conf** Max 180 Thtr 180 **Location** On A538 between Wilmslow and Prestbury

....

Hotel ★★★★ 69% Mottram Hall Hotel, Wilmslow Rd, Mottram St Andrew, Prestbury, ☎ 01625 828135 132 en suite

Styal Station Rd, Styal SK9 4JN
☎ 01625 531359 📠 01625 530063
Well designed flat parkland course with testing bunkers and water hazards. Boasts the longest hole in Cheshire!
18 holes, 6301yds, Par 70, SSS 70.
Club membership 800.
Visitors contact to reserve tee time. **Societies** telephone in advance. **Green Fees** £18 per round(£22 weekends)Par 3 course;£8 per 9 holes;£12 per 18 holes. **Cards** 🖾 🖾 🖾 🖾 **Prof** Simon Forrest **Course Designer** Tony Holmes **Facilities** ⊗ ⫌ 🍴 💷 🏌 ♨ 🏠 ⛳ 🚡 🚜 ⛳ 🍴 **Leisure** par 3 9 hole course.**Conf** Max 25 Board 25 **Location** off M56 junct 5.

....

Hotel ★★★★ 66% Belfry House Hotel, Stanley Rd, HANDFORTH ☎ 0161 437 0511 81 en suite

╔══════════════════════════════════════╗
║ **Wilmslow** Great Warford, Mobberley WA16 7AY
║ ☎ 01565 872148 📠 01565 872172
║ e-mail: wilmslowgolfclub@ukf.net
║ **A fine parkland championship course, of middle length, fair to all classes of player and almost in perfect condition.**
║ *18 holes, 6607yds, Par 72, SSS 72, Course record 62.*
║ *Club membership 800.*
║ **Visitors** must contact in advance. **Societies** Tue & Thu only application in writing. **Green Fees** £50 per day; £40 per round (£60/£50 weekends & bank holidays). **Prof** John Nowicki **Facilities** ⊗ ⫌ 🍴 💷 🏌 ♨ 🏠 ⛳ 🚡 🚜 ⛳
║ **Location** 2m SW off B5058
║ ....
║ **Hotel** ★★★ 74% Alderley Edge Hotel, Macclesfield Rd, ALDERLEY EDGE ☎ 01625 583033 52 en suite
╚══════════════════════════════════════╝

────── WINSFORD   Map 07 SJ66 ──────

Knights Grange Grange Ln CW7 2PT
☎ 01606 552780
An 18 hole golf course set in the beautiful Cheshire countryside on the town outskirts. The front 9 are mainly flat but players have to negotiate water, ditches and other hazards along the way. The back 9 take the player deep into the countryside with many of the tees offering panoramic views. A lake known as the Ocean is a feature of many holes - a particular hazard for slicers of the ball. There are also many mature woodlands areas to catch the wayward drive.
18 holes, 6010yds, Par 71, SSS 70.
Visitors 24 hr booking system for weekly play, after 10am Wed for weekend bookings. **Societies** apply in writing. **Green Fees** not confirmed. **Prof** Graham Moore **Facilities** 💷 ♨ 🍴 ⛳ **Leisure** hard and grass tennis courts. **Location** N side of town off A54

....

Hotel ★★ 66% Wincham Hall, Hall Ln, Wincham, NORTHWICH ☎ 01606 43453 10 rms (9 en suite)

continued

WINWICK   Map 07 SJ69

Alder Root Alder Root Ln WA2 8R2
☎ 01925 291919 📄 01925 291919
**A woodland course, flat in nature but with many
undulations. Several holes have water hazards. One of the
most testing nine hole courses in the north west.**
*9 holes, 5837yds, Par 69, SSS 68, Course record 67.
Club membership 400.*
Visitors telephone for details of dress code. **Societies** must
telephone in advance. **Green Fees** terms on application. **Prof**
C McKevitt **Course Designer** Mr Lander/Mr Millington
Facilities ⊗ ⌱ 🖤 ♀ ♨ 🏠 ⤸ 🛒 🏌 **Location** From M62
junct 9 take A49 N for 800mtrs then left at lights and 1st
right into Alder Root Lane

Hotel ★★ 65% Paddington House Hotel, 514 Old
Manchester Rd, WARRINGTON
☎ 01925 816767 37 en suite

> An asterisk * in the Green Fees or
> Conference facilities indicates that
> prices given are for 2002

> Where to stay, where to eat?
> Visit www.theAA.com

CORNWALL & ISLES OF SCILLY

BODMIN   Map 02 SX06

Lanhydrock Lostwithiel Rd, Lanhydrock PL30 5AQ
☎ 01208 73600 📄 01208 77325
e-mail: postmaster@lanhydrock-golf.co.uk
**An acclaimed parkland/moorland course adjacent to the
National Trust property Lanhydrock house. Nestling in a
picturesque wooded valley of oak and birch, this
undulating course provides an exciting and enjoyable
challenge to all abilities with discreet use of water and
bunkers.**

*18 holes, 6100yds, Par 70, SSS 70, Course record 66.
Club membership 300.*
Visitors tee time reservation in advance advised. **Societies**
please telephone in advance. **Green Fees** £29 per day; £24
per round (£34/£29 weekends). **Cards** ⚌ ▦ 💳 ▦ 🂫 🄯
Prof Jason Broadway **Course Designer** Hamilton Stutt
Facilities ⊗ ⁝ ⌱ 🖤 ♀ ♨ 🏠 ⤸ 🏇 ⤸ 🛒 🏌 ♜ **Conf** Max
150 Thtr 150 Class 80 Board 40 Banquet 120 **Location** 1m S
of Bodmin from B3268 via A30/A38

continued

Hotel ★★★ 65% Restormel Lodge Hotel, Hillside Gardens,
LOSTWITHIEL ☎ 01208 872223
21 en suite 12 annexe en suite

BUDE   Map 02 SS20

Bude & North Cornwall Burn View EX23 8DA
☎ 01288 352006 📄 01288 356855
**Seaside links course with natural sand bunkers, superb
greens and breathtaking views. Club established in 1893.**
*18 holes, 6057yds, Par 71, SSS 70.
Club membership 1000.*
Visitors book by telephone 6 days in advance for starting
time - or before 6 days with a deposit. Limited tee times at
weekends. **Societies** apply in writing or by telephone/fax.
Green Fees £25 per day (£30 weekends & bank holidays).
Cards ⚌ ▦ 💳 ▦ 🄯 **Prof** John Yeo **Facilities** ⊗ ⁝ ⌱ 🖤 ♀
♨ 🏠 ⤸ 🏌 **Leisure** snooker room. **Location** N side of town

Hotel ★★ 71% Camelot Hotel, Downs View, BUDE
☎ 01288 352361 24 en suite

BUDOCK VEAN   Map 02 SW73

Budock Vean Hotel on the River Mawnan Smith
TR11 5LG ☎ 01326 250288 (hotel) & 252102 (shop)
📄 01326 250892
e-mail: relax@budockvean.co.uk
**Set in 65 acres of mature grounds with a private
foreshore to the Helford River, this 18 tee undulating
parkland course has a tough par 4 5th hole (456yds)
which dog-legs at halfway around an oak tree. The 16th
hole measures 572 yds, par 5.**
*9 holes, 5255yds, Par 68, SSS 65, Course record 61.
Club membership 140.*
Visitors must contact in advance. **Societies** apply in writing
or telephone in advance. **Green Fees** £19 per day (£23
weekends and bank holidays). **Cards** ⚌ ▦ 💳 ▦ 🂫 🄯 **Prof**
Tony Ramsden **Course Designer** James Braid **Facilities** ⊗
⁝ ⌱ 🖤 ♀ ♨ 🏠 ⤸ 🏇 ⤸ 🛒 🏌 **Leisure** hard tennis courts,
heated indoor swimming pool, fishing, boating facilitiesu.
Conf Max 50 Del £15 to £25 * **Location** 1.5m SW of
Mawnan Smith

Hotel ★★★★⚐ 72% Budock Vean-The Hotel on the
River, MAWNAN SMITH ☎ 01326 252100 &
Freephone 0800 833927 📄 01326 250892 58 en suite

CAMBORNE   Map 02 SW64

Tehidy Park TR14 0HH
☎ 01209 842208 📄 01209 843680
**A well-maintained parkland course providing good
holiday golf.**
*18 holes, 6241yds, Par 71, SSS 71, Course record 62.
Club membership 850.*

continued

Visitors must contact in advance and have a handicap certificate. Societies telephone followed by letter. Green Fees £25.50 per day (£30.50 weekends & bank holidays). Prof James Dumbreck Facilities ⊗ ⍟ ⓛ 🖩 ♀ 🛆 🏠 ⛳ ⸓ Location On Portreath/Pool road, 2m S of Camborne

Hotel ★★★ 65% Penventon Hotel, REDRUTH
☎ 01209 203000 50 en suite

CAMELFORD   Map 02 SX18

Bowood Park Lanteglos PL32 9RF
☎ 01840 213017 📠 01840 212622
e-mail: golf@bowoodpark.com
A testing parkland course situated in Bowood Park, formerly the largest deer park in Cornwall. The first nine holes are designed around rolling hills; the back nine being played through the River Allen Valley. Plenty of wildlife, water and trees.

18 holes, 6692yds, Par 72, SSS 72.
Club membership 250.
Visitors booking system in operation Societies contact for details. Green Fees terms on application. Cards 💳 ⬛ 🔳 🔲 Ⓓ Prof John Phillips Course Designer Sandow Facilities ⊗ ⍟ ⓛ 🖩 ♀ 🛆 🏠 ⛳ 🏨 ⛴ 🛆 ⸓ ⓕ Leisure fishing. Location Through Camelford, 0.5m turn right Tintagel/Boscastle B3266, 1st left at garage

Hotel ★★ 65% The Wellington Hotel, Old Rd, BOSCASTLE ☎ 01840 250202 16 en suite

CARLYON BAY   Map 02 SX05

Carlyon Bay Hotel Sea Rd PL25 3RD
☎ 01726 814250 📠 01726 814250
Championship-length, cliff-top course moving into parkland. Magnificent views surpassed only by the quality of the course. The 230-yard (par 3) 18th with railway and road out-of-bounds holds the player's interest to the end.
18 holes, 6597yds, Par 72, SSS 71, Course record 66.
Club membership 500.
Visitors must contact in advance. Societies must contact in advance. Green Fees from £25-£37 per round depending on season. Cards 💳 ⬛ 🔳 Ⓓ Prof Mark Rowe Facilities ⓛ 🖩 ♀ 🛆 🏠 ⛳ 🏨 ⛴ 🛆 ⸓ ⓕ Leisure hard tennis courts, outdoor and indoor heated swimming pools, sauna, solarium.

Hotel ★★★★ 74% Carlyon Bay Hotel, Sea Rd, Carlyon Bay, ST AUSTELL ☎ 01726 812304 73 en suite

CONSTANTINE BAY   Map 02 SW87

Trevose PL28 8JB
☎ 01841 520208 📠 01841 521057
e-mail: info@trevose-gc.co.uk
Well known links course with early holes close to the sea on excellent springy turf. A championship course affording varying degrees of difficulty appealing to both the professional and higher handicap player. It is a good test with well-positioned bunkers, and a meandering stream, and the wind playing a decisive role in preventing low scoring. Self-catering accommodation is available at the club.
Championship Course: 18 holes, 6461yds, Par 71, SSS 71, Course record 66.
New Course: 9 holes, 3031yds, Par 35.
Short Course: 9 holes, 1360yds, Par 29.
Club membership 1500.
Visitors subject to reservations, handicap certificate required for championship course. Advisable to contact in advance. Societies telephone or write to the secretary. Green Fees Championship course: £25-£38. Short course: £10. New course: £18-£25. Cards 💳 ⬛ 🔳 🔲 Ⓓ Prof Gary Alliss Course Designer H S Colt Facilities ⊗ ⍟ ⓛ 🖩 ♀ 🛆 🏠 ⛳ 🏨 ⛴ 🛆 ⸓ ⓕ Leisure hard tennis courts, heated outdoor swimming pool, snooker & games room. Conf Max 120 Banquet 120 Location 4m W of Padstow on B3276, to St Merryn, proceed 500yds past crossroads and take right turn, signposted

Hotel ★★★ 77% Treglos Hotel, CONSTANTINE BAY ☎ 01841 520727 44 en suite

FALMOUTH   Map 02 SW83

Falmouth Swanpool Rd TR11 5BQ
☎ 01326 314296 📠 01326 317783
e-mail: falmouthgolfclub@freezone.co.uk
Seaside/parkland course with outstanding coastal views. Sufficiently bunkered to punish any inaccurate shots. Five acres of practice grounds.

continued

18 holes, 5937yds, Par 71, SSS 70.
Club membership 500.
Visitors please book for tee time. **Societies** must contact in advance. **Green Fees** £35 per day; £25 per round. **Cards** 💳 📇 🔲 ▣ **Prof** Bryan Patterson **Facilities** ⊗ ⊞ ⅃ 🍴 ♨ ☕ 🏌 ♿ ⛳ **Location** SW side of town centre

Hotel ★★★★ 69% Royal Duchy Hotel, Cliff Rd, FALMOUTH ☎ 01326 313042 43 en suite

HOLYWELL BAY   Map 02 SW75

Holywell Bay TR8 5PW
☎ 01637 830095 📠 01637 831000
e-mail: golf@trevornick.co.uk
Situated beside a family fun park with many amenities. The course is an 18 hole par 3 with excellent sea views. Fresh Atlantic winds make the course hard to play and there are several tricky holes, particularly the 18th over the trout pond. The site also has an excellent 18 hole Pitch & Putt course for the whole family.

18 holes, 2784yds, Par 61, Course record 58.
Club membership 100.
Visitors no restrictions. **Societies** telephone in advance. **Green Fees** not confirmed. **Course Designer** Hartley **Facilities** ⊗ ⊞ ⅃ ▣ ♨ ☕ 🏌 ♿ **Leisure** heated outdoor swimming pool, fishing. **Location** Off A3075 Newquay/ Perranporth road

Hotel ★★★ 70% Barrowfield Hotel, Hilgrove Rd, NEWQUAY ☎ 01637 878878
81 en suite 2 annexe en suite

LAUNCESTON   Map 02 SX38

Launceston St Stephens PL15 8HF
☎ 01566 773442 📠 01566 777506
e-mail: charleshicks@tesco.net
Highly rated golf course with magnificent views over the historic lawn and moors. Dominated by the 'The Hill' up which the 8th and 11th fairways rise, and on which the 8th, 9th, 11th and 12th greens sit.
18 holes, 6407yds, Par 70, SSS 71, Course record 65.
Club membership 800.
Visitors must contact in advance, may not play weekends Apr-Oct. **Societies** telephone in first instance. **Green Fees** £25 per day (£28 weekends & bank holidays). **Prof** John Tozer **Facilities** ⊗ ⊞ ⅃ ▣ ♨ ☕ 🏌 ♿ **Location** NW side of town centre on B3254

Hotel ★★ 65% Eagle House, Castle St, LAUNCESTON ☎ 01566 772036 14 en suite

Where to stay, where to eat?
Visit www.theAA.com

Trethorne Kennards House PL15 8QE
☎ 01566 86903 📠 01566 86981
e-mail: mark@trethornegolfclub.com
Rolling parkland course with well maintained fairways and computer irrigated greens. Plenty of trees and natural water hazards make this well respected course a good challenge.
18 holes, 6432yds, Par 71, SSS 71, Course record 69.
Club membership 500.
Visitors must contact in advance on 01566 86903. **Societies** write or telephone Mark Boundy. **Green Fees** £28 per round. **Cards** 💳 📇 🔲 ▣ **Prof** Mark Boundy **Course Designer** Frank Frayne **Facilities** ⊗ ⊞ ⅃ ▣ ♨ ☕ 🏌 ♿ ⛳ **Leisure** leisure farm and tenpin bowling. **Location** Off A30, 3m W of Launceston, on junct with A395, Camelford

LELANT   Map 02 SW53

West Cornwall TR26 3DZ
☎ 01736 753401 & 753177 📠 01736 753401
e-mail: malcolm@westcornwallgolfclub.fsnet.uk.co
A seaside links with sandhills and lovely turf adjacent to the Hayle estuary and St Ives Bay. A real test of the player's skill, especially 'Calamity Corner' starting at the 5th on the lower land by the River Hayle. A small (3 hole) course is available for practice.
18 holes, 5884yds, Par 69, SSS 69, Course record 63.
Club membership 748.

Visitors must prove handicap certificate, be a member of a club affiliated to the EGU, advisable to contact in advance. **Societies** must apply in writing. **Green Fees** not confirmed. **Prof** Paul Atherton **Course Designer** Reverend Tyack **Facilities** ⊗ ⊞ ⅃ ▣ ♨ ☕ 🏌 ♿ ⛳ **Leisure** snooker. **Location** N side of village off A3074

Hotel ★★ 74% Pedn-Olva Hotel, West Porthminster Beach, ST IVES ☎ 01736 796222 26 en suite 4 annexe en suite

LOOE   Map 02 SX25

Looe Widegates PL13 1PX
☎ 01503 240239 📠 01503 240864
Designed by Harry Vardon in 1935, this downland/parkland course commands panoramic views over south-east Cornwall and the coast. Easy walking.
18 holes, 5940yds, Par 70, SSS 69, Course record 64.
Club membership 600.
Visitors handicap certificate preferred, booking in advance recommended, no limitations subject to availability.
Societies telephone in advance, booking to be confirmed in

continued

writing. **Green Fees** terms on application. **Cards** ▦ ▦ ▦
▦ ▢ **Prof** Alistair Macdonald **Course Designer** Harry
Vardon **Facilities** ⊗ ⌂ ♨ ♀ ⚓ ☂ ⛱ ♨ ✎ **Location**
3.5m NE off B3253

Hotel ★★★ 64% Hannafore Point Hotel, Marine Dr, West
Looe, LOOE ☎ 01503 263273 37 en suite

LOSTWITHIEL   Map 02 SX15
Lostwithiel Hotel, Golf & Country Club
Lower Polscoe PL22 0HQ
☎ 01208 873550 📠 01208 87479
e-mail: reception@golf-hotel.co.uk
An undulating, parkland course with water hazards.
Overlooked by Restormel Castle and the River Fowey
flows alongside the course. Driving range.
*18 holes, 5984yds, Par 72, SSS 71, Course record 67.
Club membership 500.*
Visitors must contact in advance. **Societies** contact in
advance. **Green Fees** £25 (£29 weekends). **Cards** ▦ ▦
continued

▦ ▢ ▦ ▦ ▢ **Prof** Tony Nash **Course Designer** S Wood
Facilities ⊗ ⍟ ⌂ ♨ ♀ ⚓ ☂ ⛱ ♨ ✎ ♩ **Leisure** hard
tennis courts, heated indoor swimming pool, fishing,
gymnasium.**Conf** Max 120 Thtr 120 Class 80 Board 40
Banquet 120 Del £8 to £25 * **Location** 1m outside
Lostwithiel off A390

Hotel ★★★ 61% Lostwithiel Hotel Golf & Country Club,
Lower Polscoe, LOSTWITHIEL ☎ 01208 873550 19 en
suite

MAWGAN PORTH   Map 02 SW86
Merlin TR8 4DN ☎ 01841 540222 📠 01841 541031
A heathland course with fine views of the coast and
countryside. Fairly easy walking. The most challenging
hole is the par 4 18th with out of bounds on the left and
ponds on either side of the green.
*18 holes, 6210yds, Par 71, SSS 71.
Club membership 350.*
Visitors no restrictions, except during club competitions,
continued

must contact in advance. **Societies** telephone in advance.
Green Fees £15 per day/round. **Cards** 〰 ▨ ▦ ◨ **Course
Designer** Ross Oliver **Facilities** ⊗ ⅲ ♭ ♥ ♀ ♨ ☎ ▸ ♦
♨ ♂ ♬ **Conf** Max 150 **Location** On the coast rd Newquay/
Padstow. After Mawgan Porth follow signs for St Eval, golf
course on right

Hotel ★★ 65% Tredragon Hotel, MAWGAN PORTH
☎ 01637 860213 26 en suite

MAWNAN SMITH
See **Budock Vean**

MULLION   Map 02 SW61

Mullion Cury TR12 7BP
☎ 01326 240685 & 241176(pro) 🖹 01326 240685
**Founded in 1895, a clifftop and links course with
panoramic views over Mounts Bay. A steep downhill
slope on 6th and the 10th descends to the beach with a
deep ravine alongside the green. Most southerly course
in the British Isles.**
18 holes, 6037yds, Par 70, SSS 70.
Club membership 750.
Visitors preferable to contact in advance, restricted during
club competitions. **Societies** must contact in advance.
Green Fees £25 per day/round (£30 weekends). **Cards**
▨ **Course Designer** W Sich **Facilities** ⊗ ⅲ ♭ ♥ ♀ ♨
☎ ▸ ♨ ♂ **Leisure** golf academy. **Location** 1.5m NW
of Mullion, off A3083

Hotel ★★★ 70% Polurrian Hotel, MULLION
☎ 01326 240421 39 en suite

NEWQUAY   Map 02 SW86

Newquay Tower Rd TR7 1LT
☎ 01637 874354 🖹 01637 874066
e-mail: newquaygolfclub@smartone.co.uk
**One of Cornwall's finest seaside links with magnificent
views over the Atlantic ocean. Open to the unpredictable
nature of the elements and possessing some very
demanding greenside bunkers, the prerequisite for good
scoring at Newquay is accuracy.**
18 holes, 6150yds, Par 69, SSS 69, Course record 63.
Club membership 600.
Visitors please telephone in advance. **Societies** apply in
writing or telephone. **Green Fees** £30 per day; £25 per
round. **Cards** 〰 ▨ ▦ ▨ ◨ **Prof** Mark Bevan **Course
Designer** H Colt **Facilities** ⊗ ⅲ ♭ ♥ ♀ ♨ ☎ ▸ **Leisure**
hard tennis courts, Snooker. **Location** W side of town

Hotel ★★★ 69% Hotel Bristol, Narrowcliff, NEWQUAY
☎ 01637 875181 74 en suite

Treloy TR8 4JN ☎ 01637 878554 🖹 01637 871710
e-mail: paull@treloy.freeserve.co.uk
**An executive course constructed in 1991 to American
specifications with large contoured and mounded greens.
Offers an interesting round for all categories of player.**
9 holes, 2143yds, Par 32, SSS 31, Course record 63.
Visitors no restrictions. **Societies** telephone in advance.
Green Fees not confirmed. **Cards** 〰 ▨ ▦ **Course
Designer** M R M Sandow **Facilities** ♭ ♥ ♀ ♨ ☎ ▸ ♨ ♂
Location On A3059 Newquay to St Columb Major Road

Hotel ★★ 71% Whipsiderry Hotel, Trevelgue Rd, Porth,
NEWQUAY ☎ 01637 874777 24 rms (19 en suite)

PADSTOW
See **Constantine Bay**

PERRANPORTH   Map 02 SW75

Perranporth Budnic Hill TR6 0AB
☎ 01872 573701 🖹 01872 573701
e-mail: perranporth@golfclub92.fsnet.co.uk
**There are three testing par 5 holes on the links course
(2nd, 5th, 11th). This seaside links course has magnificent
views of the North Cornwall coastline, and excellent
greens. The drainage of the course, being sand-based, is
also exceptional.**

18 holes, 6288yds, Par 72, SSS 72, Course record 62.
Club membership 600.
Visitors must contact in advance, no reserved tee times.
Societies by prior arrangement. **Green Fees** £25 per day
(£30 weekends and bank holidays). **Cards** 〰 ▨ ▦ ▨
Prof D Michell **Course Designer** James Braid **Facilities** ⊗
ⅲ ♭ ♥ ♀ ♨ ☎ ▸ ▭ ♂ **Location** 0.75m NE on B3285

Hotel ★★★♨ 69% Rose in Vale Country House Hotel,
Rose in Vale, Mithian, ST AGNES ☎ 01872 552202
18 en suite

PRAA SANDS   Map 02 SW52

Praa Sands Germoe Cross Roads TR20 9TQ
☎ 01736 763445 🖹 01736 763399
e-mail: praasandsgolf@aol.com
**A beautiful parkland course, overlooking Mount's Bay
with outstanding sea views from every tee and green.**

9 holes, 4122yds, Par 62, SSS 60, Course record 59.
Club membership 220.
Visitors restricted Sun 8-12.30pm, no need to phone.
Societies telephone in advance for details. **Green Fees** from
£10. **Course Designer** R Hamilton **Facilities** ⊗ ⅲ ♭ ♥ ♀
♨ ☎ ▸ ♂ **Leisure** pool, darts. **Location** A394 midway
between Penzance/Helston

Hotel ★★ 79% Nansloe Manor Hotel, Meneage Rd,
HELSTON ☎ 01326 574691 7 rms (6 en suite)

ROCK   Map 02 SW97

St Enodoc PL27 6LD
☎ 01208 863216 ▤ 01208 862976
Classic links course with huge sand hills and rolling fairways. James Braid laid out the original 18 holes in 1907 and changes were made in 1922 and 1935. On the Church, the 10th is the toughest par 4 on the course and on the 6th is a truly enormous sand hill known as the Himalayas. The Holywell is not as exacting as the Church; it is less demanding on stamina but still a real test of skill for golfers of any handicap.
Church Course: 18 holes, 6243yds, Par 69, SSS 70, Course record 64.
Holywell Course: 18 holes, 4142yds, Par 63, SSS 61.
Club membership 1300.
Visitors may not play on bank holidays. Must have a handicap certificate of 24 or below for Church Course. Must contact in advance. **Societies** must contact in writing/telephone. **Green Fees** Church: £55 per day; £38 per round (£45 per round weekends). Holywell: £25 per day; £15 per round (£15 per round weekends). **Cards** ▦ ▦▦ ▦▦ ▣ ▦▦ ▦▦ ▨ **Prof** Nick Williams **Course Designer** James Braid **Facilities** ⊗ Ⅲ ᖿ ⬤ ♀ ⌖ 🖬 ⚑ ➴ ⚭ ♟ ⚐ **Location** W side of village
....
Hotel ★★ 65% The Molesworth Arms Hotel, Molesworth St, WADEBRIDGE ☎ 01208 812055 16 rms (14 en suite)

ST AUSTELL   Map 02 SX05

Porthpean Porthpean PL26 6AY
☎ 01726 64613 ▤ 01726 71643
A picturesque 18 hole course, the outward holes are in a pleasant parkland setting whilst the return holes command spectacular views over St Austell Bay.
18 holes, 5210yds, Par 67, SSS 66.
Club membership 300.
Visitors no restrictions **Societies** telephone in advance. **Green Fees** £14 per day/round; £9 per 9 holes. **Cards** ▦ ▦▦ ▦▦ ▦▦ ▨ **Facilities** ⊗ ᖿ ⬤ ♀ ⌖ 🖬 ⚑ ⚭ **Location** 1.5m from St Austell by-pass
....
Hotel ★★ 71% The Pier House, Harbour Front, Charlestown, ST AUSTELL ☎ 01726 67955 26 en suite

St Austell Tregongeeves Ln PL26 7DS
☎ 01726 74756 ▤ 01726 71978
Very interesting inland parkland course designed by James Braid and offering glorious views of the surrounding countryside. Undulating, well-covered with tree plantations and well-bunkered. Notable holes are 8th (par 4) and 16th (par 3).
18 holes, 6089yds, Par 69, SSS 69, Course record 64.
Club membership 700.
Visitors advisable to contact in advance, weekend play is limited. Must be a member of a recognised golf club and hold a handicap certificate. **Societies** must apply in writing. **Green Fees** not confirmed. **Prof** Tony Pitts **Facilities** ⊗ ᖿ ⬤ ♀ ⌖ 🖬 ⚭ ♟ **Location** 1m W of St Austell on A390
....
Hotel ★★★ 67% Porth Avallen Hotel, Sea Rd, Carlyon Bay, ST AUSTELL ☎ 01726 812802 24 en suite

> **Looking for a driving range?**
> **See the index at the back of the guide**

ST IVES   Map 02 SW54

Tregenna Castle Hotel, Golf & Country Club
TR26 2DE ☎ 01736 797381 ▤ 01736 796066
Parkland course surrounding a castellated hotel and overlooking St Ives Bay and harbour.
18 holes, 3260yds, Par 60, SSS 58.
Club membership 140.
Visitors no booking needed. Dress code in operation. **Societies** telephone for details. **Green Fees** not confirmed. **Cards** ▦ ▦▦ ▦▦ ▣ ▦▦ ▦▦ ▨ **Course Designer** Abercrombie **Facilities** ⊗ Ⅲ ᖿ ⬤ ♀ ⌖ 🖬 ⚑ ♟ **Leisure** hard tennis courts, outdoor and indoor heated swimming pools, squash, sauna, solarium, gymnasium. **Location** From A30 Penzance road turn off just past Hayle onto A3074
....
Hotel ★★★ 66% Tregenna Castle Hotel, ST IVES ☎ 01736 795254 84 en suite

ST JUST (NEAR LAND'S END)   Map 02 SW33

Cape Cornwall Golf & Country Club Cape
Cornwall TR19 7NL ☎ 01736 788611 ▤ 01736 788611
Coastal parkland, walled course. The walls are an integral part of its design. Britain's first and last 18 hole golf course overlooking the only cape in England, with views of the North Cornish coast and old fishing coves. Features a flat front nine followed by a challenging back nine. Extremely scenic views.
18 holes, 5650yds, Par 69, SSS 68, Course record 64.
Club membership 630.
Visitors may not play before 11.30am at weekends. **Societies** must contact in advance. **Green Fees** £20 per round. **Cards** ▦ ▦▦ ▦▦ ▣ ▦▦ ▦▦ ▨ **Prof** Paul Atherton **Course Designer** Bob Hamilton **Facilities** ⊗ Ⅲ ᖿ ⬤ ♀ ⌖ 🖬 ⚑ ➴ ⚭ **Leisure** heated indoor swimming pool, sauna, solarium, gymnasium. **Location** 1m W of St Just
....
Hotel ★★★ 63% Higher Faugan Country House Hotel, Newlyn, PENZANCE ☎ 01736 362076 11 en suite

ST MELLION See page 51

ST MINVER   Map 02 SW97

Roserrow Golf & Country Club Roserrow
PL27 6QT ☎ 01208 863000 ▤ 01208 863002
e-mail: roserrow.co.uk
Challenging par 72 course in an undulating wooded valley. Stunning views over the Cornish countryside and out to Hayle Bay. Accommodation and numerous facilities on site.

18 holes, 6551yds, Par 72, SSS 72.
Club membership 400.
Visitors by arrangement weekdays or weekends, must pre book tee times. **Societies** apply in writing or telephone in
continued

advance. **Green Fees** terms on application. **Cards** ▦ ▦
▦ ▦ ▣ **Prof** Andrew Cullen **Facilities** ⊗ ⊤ ▤ ▦ ♀ ⅄
▥ ⫪ ⊨ ▨ ▨ ✇ (**Leisure** hard tennis courts, heated
indoor swimming pool, sauna, solarium, gymnasium.
Location Between Wadebridge and Polzeath off the B3314

....

Hotel ★★ 65% The Molesworth Arms Hotel, Molesworth
St, WADEBRIDGE ☎ 01208 812055 16 rms (14 en suite)

China Fleet Country Club PL12 6LJ
☎ 01752 848668 ▤ 01752 848456
e-mail: sales@china-fleet.co.uk
A parkland course with river views. The 14th tee shot has
to carry a lake of approximately 150yards.
18 holes, 6551yds, Par 72, SSS 72, Course record 69.
Club membership 550.
Visitors may play anytime and can book up to 7 days in
advance. **Societies** telephone 01752 854657 for provisional
booking. **Green Fees** terms on application. **Cards** ▦ ▦
▦ ▣ **Prof** Robert Moore **Course Designer** Hawtree
Facilities ⅄ ▥ ⫪ ⊨ ▨ ✇ (**Leisure** hard tennis courts,
heated indoor swimming pool, squash, sauna, solarium,
gymnasium.**Conf** Max 60 Thtr 60 Class 30 Board 30
Banquet 50 **Location** 1m from the Tamar Bridge

....

Hotel ⇧ Travelodge, Callington Rd, Carkeel, SALTASH
☎ 08700 850950 31 en suite

Whitsand Bay Hotel Golf & Country Club
Portwrinkle PL11 3BU ☎ 01503 230276 ▤ 01503 230329
e-mail: earlehotels@btconnect.com
Testing seaside course laid-out on cliffs overlooking
Whitsand Bay. Easy walking after 1st hole. The par 3
(3rd) hole is acknowledged as one of the most attractive
holes in Cornwall.
18 holes, 6030yds, Par 69, SSS 68, Course record 62.
Club membership 400.
Visitors visitors welcome. **Societies** must contact in advance.
Green Fees £20 per round(£25 weekends). **Cards** ▦ ▦
▣ ▦ ▦ ▣ **Prof** Stephen Poole **Course Designer** Fernie
Facilities ⊗ ⊤ ▤ ▦ ♀ ⅄ ▥ ⫪ ⊨ ▨ ▨ ✇ **Leisure**
heated indoor swimming pool, sauna, solarium, gymnasium.
Conf Max 150 Thtr 150 Class 80 Board 40 Banquet 80 Del
£20 to £50 * **Location** 5m from Torpoint off A374

....

Hotel ★★ 70% Whitsand Bay Hotel, Golf & Country Club,
Portwrinkle, TORPOINT ☎ 01503 230276
39 rms (37 en suite)

Killiow Park Kea TR3 6AG
☎ 01872 270246 & 240915 ▤ 01872 240915
e-mail: office@killiow.fsnet.co.uk
Picturesque parkland course with mature oaks and
woodland and five holes played across or around water
hazards. Floodlit, all-weather driving range and practice
facilities.
18 holes, 5274yds, Par 69, SSS 68, Course record 70.
Club membership 500.
Visitors must telephone in advance to check on course
availability. **Societies** apply in writing/telephone, limited
catering facilities at present. **Green Fees** £18.50 per round;
£25 per day. **Cards** ▦ ▦ ▦ ▦ ▣ **Course Designer**
Ross Oliver **Facilities** ▦ ♀ ⅄ ✇ (**Location** 3m SW of
Truro, off A39

....

Hotel ★★★ 69% Alverton Manor, Tregolls Rd, TRURO
☎ 01872 276633 34 en suite

Truro Treliske TR1 3LG ☎ 01872 278684 (manager) &
272640 (club) ▤ 01872 278684
Picturesque and gently undulating parkland course with
lovely views over the cathedral city of Truro and the
surrounding countryside. The 5300 yard course offers a
great challenge to golfers of all standards and ages. The
many trees and shrubs offer open invitations to
wayward balls, and with many fairways boasting out of
bound markers, play needs to be safe and sensible.
Fairways are tight and the greens small and full of
character making it difficult to play to one's handicap.
18 holes, 5306yds, Par 66, SSS 66, Course record 59.
Club membership 900.
Visitors must have handicap certificate, advisable to ring for
availability although casual fees welcome. **Societies**
telephone for details. **Green Fees** £20 per day (£25
weekends & bank holidays). **Prof** Nigel Bicknell **Course
Designer** Colt, Alison & Morrison **Facilities** ⊗ ⊤ ▤ ▦ ♀
⅄ ▥ ▨ ✇ **Location** 1.5m W on A390 towards Redruth,
adjacent to Treliske Hospital

....

Hotel ★★★ 69% Alverton Manor, Tregolls Rd, TRURO
☎ 01872 276633 34 en suite

St Kew St Kew Highway PL30 3EF
☎ 01208 841500 ▤ 01208 841500
e-mail: st-kew-golf-club@ic24.net
An interesting, well-laid out 9-hole parkland course with
6 holes with water and 15 bunkers. In a picturesque
setting there are 10 par 4s and 8 par 3s. No handicap
certificate required but some experience of the game is
essential. Nine extra tees have now been provided
allowing a different teeing area for the back nine.

continued on page 52

St Mellion Hotel

St Mellion, *Cornwall*   ☎ 01579 351351   Fax 01579 350537   Map 02 SX36

e-mail: stay@st-mellion.co.uk

Set amongst 450 acres of glorious undulating Cornish countryside, St Mellion International is heralded as the premier Golf and Country Club in the SouthWest.

St Mellion boasts two outstanding golf courses, the first being the interesting and demanding Old Course, which is perfect for golfers of all abilities. Complete with ideally sited bunkers, stategically tiered greens and difficult water features, the Old Course is definitely one not to be overlooked.

However, if you really want to test your game, look no further than the renowned Nicklaus Course, designed by the great man himself. On its opening in 1998 Jack said "St Mellion is potentially the finest golf course in Europe". An inspiration to all golfers, the Nicklaus Course offers spectacularly sculptured fairways and carpet-like greens to all who take up its challenge.

Visitors telephone in advance 01579 352002

Societies apply in writing or telephone in advance

Green Fees Nicklaus Course: £50 per round. Old Course: £35 per round. Reduced winter rates.

Facilities ⊗ ⅷ ⅃ ⬛ ♟ ⋈ ⬣ ⛁ ⚐ ⚑ ⚒
♐ Ⅰ Professional (David Moon)

Leisure tennis, swimming, sauna, solarium, gymnasium

Location Saltash PL12 6SD (0.5m NW off A388)

Holes/Par/Course record 36 holes.

Nicklaus Course: 18 holes, 6651 yds, Par 72, SSS 72, Course record 63
The Old Course: 18 holes, 5782 yds, Par 68, SSS 68

Championship Course

WHERE TO STAY NEARBY

Hotels
ST MELLION
★★★68% St Mellion International
☎ 01579 351351. 39 annexe en suite

LISKEARD
★★⊛⊛⊛ ♨ Well House, St Keyne
☎ 01579 342001. 9 en suite

★★63% Lord Eliot, Castle St.
☎ 01579 342717. 15 (14 en suite)

9 holes, 4550yds, Par 64, SSS 62, Course record 63.
Club membership 270.
Visitors no restrictions. Start time system in operation allowing prebooking. **Societies** apply in writing, telephone or fax **Green Fees** £10 per 9 holes; £15 per 18 holes. **Cards** ▦ ▦ ▦ **Prof** Nick Rogers **Course Designer** David Derry **Facilities** ⊗ ⫢ ⓛ ♨ ♀ ⛊ 🏠 ♍ ⅆ ℓ **Leisure** fishing. **Location** 2m N,of Wadebridge main A39

Hotel ★★ 65% The Molesworth Arms Hotel, Molesworth St, WADEBRIDGE ☎ 01208 812055 16 rms (14 en suite)

CUMBRIA

ALSTON   Map 12 NY74

Alston Moor The Hermitage, Middleton in Teesdale Rd CA9 3DB
☎ 01434 381675 & 381354 (Sec) ▤ 01434 381675
Parkland and Fell, in process of upgrading to full 18 holes, stunning views of the North Pennines.
10 holes, 5518yds, Par 68, SSS 66, Course record 67.
Club membership 170.
Visitors usually turn up and play but for weekends telephone secretary for information and availability. **Societies** telephone or write in advance. **Green Fees** terms on application. **Facilities** ⫢ ♀ ⛊ **Location** 1 S of Alston on B6277

Hotel ★★ 68% Lowbyer Manor Country House Hotel, ALSTON ☎ 01434 381230 11 en suite

APPLEBY-IN-WESTMORLAND   Map 12 NY62

Appleby Brackenber Moor CA16 6LP
☎ 017683 51432 ▤ 017683 52773
This remotely situated heather and moorland course offers interesting golf with the rewarding bonus of several long par 4 holes that will be remembered. There are superb views of the Pennines and the Lakeland hills.
18 holes, 5901yds, Par 68, SSS 68, Course record 63.
Club membership 800.
Visitors phone for details. May not play before 3pm weekends/competition days. **Societies** must contain in advance by letter. **Green Fees** not confirmed. **Prof** Gary Key **Course Designer** Willie Fernie **Facilities** ⊗ ⫢ ⓛ ♨ ♀ ⛊ 🏠 ♍ ⅆ ℓ **Location** 2m E of Appleby 0.5m off A66

Hotel ★★★ 77% Appleby Manor Country House Hotel, Roman Rd, APPLEBY-IN-WESTMORLAND ☎ 017683 51571 23 en suite 7 annexe en suite

Swim, Bubble & Golf!

Enjoy your par 68 round on Appleby's eighteen beautiful moorland holes (5901 yds), then it's five-minutes by car to return to your favourite Country House Hotel for a refreshing swim and a relaxing jacuzzi in the indoor leisure club, followed by a superb meal in the award-winning restaurant.

Phone 017 683 51571 now for a free interactive CD-ROM and a full-colour brochure.

Best Western   ★★★ 77%

APPLEBY·MANOR
COUNTRY HOUSE HOTEL
Appleby-in-Westmorland
Cumbria CA16 6JB
www.applebymanor.co.uk

ASKAM-IN-FURNESS   Map 07 SD27

Dunnerholme Duddon Rd LA16 7AW
☎ 01229 462675 & 465095 ▤ 01229 462675
e-mail: meg@dunnerholme.co.uk
Unique 10-hole (18 tee) links course with view of the Cumbrian mountains and Morecambe Bay. Two streams run through and around the course, providing water hazards on the 1st, 2nd, 3rd and 9th holes. The par 3, 6th is the feature hole on the course playing to an elevated green on Dunnerholme Rock, an imposing limestone outcrop jutting out into the estuary.
10 holes, 6154yds, Par 72, SSS 70.
Club membership 400.
Visitors restricted times on Sun. **Societies** apply in writing to the secretary. **Green Fees** not confirmed. **Facilities** ♨ ♀ ⛊ **Location** 1m N on A595

Hotel ★★ 62% Lisdoonie Hotel, 307/309 Abbey Rd, BARROW-IN-FURNESS ☎ 01229 827312 12 en suite

BARROW-IN-FURNESS   Map 07 SD26

Barrow Rakesmoor Ln, Hawcoat LA14 4QB
☎ 01229 825444 & 832121 (Pro) ▤ 01229 832121
Pleasant course laid out on two levels on meadowland with extensive views of the nearby Lakeland fells. Upper level is affected by easterly winds.
18 holes, 6184yds, Par 71, SSS 70, Course record 66.
Club membership 700.
Visitors must be a member of a recognised golf club or hold a handicap certificate, advisable to contact the professional regarding tee time. Small groups ring professional for details, groups over 12 apply to the secretary in advance. **Green Fees** not confirmed. **Prof** Andy Whitehall **Facilities** ⊗ ⫢ ⓛ ♨ ♀ ⛊ 🏠 ♍ ⅆ **Location** 2m from Barrow off A590

continued

Hotel ★★ 62% Lisdoonie Hotel, 307/309 Abbey Rd,
BARROW-IN-FURNESS ☎ 01229 827312 12 en suite

Furness Central Dr LA14 3LN ☎ 01229 471232
Links golf with a fairly flat first half but a much sterner
second nine played across subtle sloping ground. Good
views of the Lakes, North Wales and the Isle of Man.
18 holes, 6363yds, Par 71, SSS 71, Course record 65.
Club membership 630.
Visitors must contact the secretary in advance. **Societies**
apply in writing, must be member of recognised club with
handicap certificate. **Green Fees** £17 per day (£25 weekends
and bank holidays). **Facilities** ⊗ ⅷ ⅙ ⬛ ♀ ⬥ ⩊ ♂
Location 1.75 W of town centre off A590 to Walney Island

Hotel ★★ 62% Lisdoonie Hotel, 307/309 Abbey Rd,
BARROW-IN-FURNESS ☎ 01229 827312 12 en suite

Windermere Clearbarrow LA23 3NB
☎ 015394 43123 ▤ 015394 43123
Enjoyable holiday golf on a short, slightly hilly but
sporting course in this delightful area of the Lake
District National Park, with superb views of the
mountains as the backcloth to the lake and the course.
18 holes, 5122yds, Par 67, SSS 65, Course record 58.
Club membership 1043.
Visitors contact pro shop 7 days before day of play, 10-12
& 2-4.30 or before 9am by arrangement. **Societies** by
arrangement contact the secretary. **Green Fees** not
confirmed. **Cards** ▤ ▤ ▤ ▤ ▣ **Prof** W S M Rooke
Course Designer G Lowe **Facilities** ⊗ ⅷ ⅙ ⬛ ♀ ⩊ ⬥
⁀ ⬥ ♂ **Leisure** snooker. **Location** B5284 1.5m from
Bowness

Hotel ★★★ 64% Wild Boar Hotel, Crook,
WINDERMERE ☎ 015394 45225 36 en suite
See advert on page 56

Brampton Talkin Tarn CA8 1HN
☎ 016977 2255 & 2000 ▤ 016977 41487
Challenging golf across glorious rolling fell country
demanding solid driving and many long second shots.
A number of particularly fine holes, the pick of which
may arguably be, the 3rd and 11th. The course offers
unrivalled panoramic views from its hilly position.
18 holes, 6407yds, Par 72, SSS 71, Course record 68.
Club membership 800.
Visitors visitors intending to play at weekends are
recommended to telephone in advance. **Societies** apply in
writing to M Ogilvie (Hon Commercial Sec), 3 Warwick
St, Carlisle, Cumbria CA3 8QW or telephone 01228
continued

TARN END HOUSE HOTEL

AA
★★

Comfortable traditional family-run hotel set in own secluded
grounds with rooms having delightful views over the lake.
We have a fine reputation for the quality and value of our
food and wine. Adjacent to local course.
Concessionary green fees. All rooms en suite.
B&B £27.50-£35.00, D.B.B. £40.00-£50.00.
All per person per night.
All inclusive Golf Packages can be arranged.
E.T.B. ★★   Johansens Recommended.

**Talkin Tarn, Brampton,
Cumbria CA8 1LS
Tel: 016977 2340**

401996. **Green Fees** £22 per day/round (£30 weekends &
bank holidays). **Cards** ▤ ▤ ▤ ▣ **Prof** Stewart
Wilkinson **Course Designer** James Braid **Facilities** ⊗ ⅷ
⅙ ⬛ ♀ ⩊ ⬥ ⁀ ♂ **Leisure** games room. **Location** 1.5m
SE of Brampton on B6413

Hotel ★★ 67% The Tarn End House Hotel, Talkin Tarn,
BRAMPTON ☎ 016977 2340 7 en suite

Carlisle Aglionby CA4 8AG ☎ 01228 513029
(secretary) & 510164 (bookings) ▤ 01228 513303
e-mail: carlislegolfclub@aol.com
Majestic looking parkland course with great appeal. A
complete but not too severe test of golf, with fine turf,
natural hazards, a stream and many beautiful trees. A
qualifying course for the Open Championship.
18 holes, 6278yds, Par 71, SSS 70, Course record 63.
Club membership 800.
continued

Visitors may not play before 9am and between 12-1.30 and when tee is reserved. Very limited play Sunday and with member only Saturday and Tuesday. **Societies** Mon, Wed & Fri, contact professional in advance for details,01228 513241. **Green Fees** £45 per day; £30 per round (Sun £40 per round). **Prof** Martin Heggie **Course Designer** Mackenzie Ross **Facilities** ⊗ ⼶ ⋿ ⚑ ♀ ⚒ 🖻 ⊤ ⚙ ♿ **Location** On A69 0.5m E of M6 junc 43

Hotel ★★★ 69% Crown Hotel, Wetheral, CARLISLE ☎ 01228 561888 49 en suite 2 annexe en suite

Stony Holme Municipal St Aidans Rd CA1 1LS
☎ 01228 625511
18 holes, 5783yds, Par 69, SSS 68, Course record 68.

Location 2m W of M6 (junct 43) and A69
Telephone for further details

Hotel ★★★ 67% Holiday Inn Carlisle, Parkhouse Rd, CARLISLE ☎ 0870 400 9018 127 en suite

Cockermouth Embleton CA13 9SG
☎ 017687 76223 & 76941 ▤ 017687 76941
Fell-land course, fenced, with exceptional views and a hard climb on the 3rd and 11th holes. Testing holes: 10th and 16th (rearranged by James Braid).

18 holes, 5496yds, Par 69, SSS 67, Course record 62.
Club membership 500.
Visitors restricted Wed, Sat & Sun. **Societies** apply in writing to the secretary. **Green Fees** not confirmed. **Course Designer** J Braid **Facilities** ⋿ ⚑ ♀ ⚒ ⚙ **Location** 3m E off A66

Hotel ★★★ 71% The Trout Hotel, Crown St, COCKERMOUTH ☎ 01900 823591 29 en suite

Eden CA6 4RA
☎ 01228 573003 & 573013 ▤ 01228 818435
e-mail: alistair.wannop@virgin.net
Open, championship-length parkland course following the River Eden. A large number of water hazards, including the river on certain holes, demands accuracy, as do the well designed raised greens. Flood-lit driving range and excellent clubhouse facilities.

18 holes, 6410yds, Par 72, SSS 72, Course record 64.
Club membership 500.
Visitors must contact in advance. **Societies** telephone to check availability. **Green Fees** not confirmed. **Cards** ▤ ▤ 🞶 **Prof** Steve Harrison **Facilities** ⊗ ⼶ ⋿ ⚑ ♀ ⚒ 🖻 ⊤ ⚙ ⚒ **Leisure** hard tennis courts. **Location** 5m from M6 junc 44,on A689 towards Brampton & Newcastle-Upon-Tyne

Hotel ★★★⚘ 78% Crosby Lodge Country House Hotel, High Crosby, Crosby-on-Eden, CARLISLE ☎ 01228 573618 9 en suite 2 annexe en suite

AA website: www.theAA.com

GRANGE-OVER-SANDS — Map 07 SD47

Grange Fell Fell Rd LA11 6HB ☎ 015395 32536
Hillside course with magnificent views over
Morecambe Bay and the surrounding Lakeland
mountains.
9 holes, 5278yds, Par 70, SSS 66, Course record 65.
Club membership 400.
Visitors may normally play Mon-Sat. **Green Fees** £15 per
day Mon-Sat (£20 Sun & bank holidays). **Facilities** ☕ ♀
⛳ **Location** 1m W on Grange-Over-Sands/Cartmel

Hotel ★★★ 71% Netherwood Hotel, Lindale Rd,
GRANGE-OVER-SANDS ☎ 015395 32552 28 en suite

Grange-over-Sands Meathop Rd LA11 6QX
☎ 015395 33180 or 33754 ▤ 015395 33754
e-mail: grangegolfclub@aol.com
Interesting parkland course with well sited tree
plantations, ditches and water features. The four par 3s
are considered to be some of the best in the area.
18 holes, 5958yds, Par 70, SSS 69, Course record 68.
Club membership 650.
Visitors must be a member of Golf Club or recognised Golf
Society, advisable to contact in advance for play at
weekends. **Societies** apply in writing. **Green Fees** £25 per
day; £20 per round (£30/£25 weekends & bank holidays).
Cards ▦ ▦ ▦ ▨ 🗑 **Prof** Andrew Pickering **Course
Designer** Mackenzie (part) **Facilities** ⊗ ⦙ ⛳ ♣ ♥ ♀ ⛳ 🏠⛳
⛳ **Location** NE of town centre off B5277

Hotel ★★★ 65% Graythwaite Manor Hotel, Fernhill Rd,
GRANGE-OVER-SANDS ☎ 015395 32001 & 33755
▤ 015395 35549 21 en suite

KENDAL — Map 07 SD59

Carus Green Burneside Rd LA9 6EB
☎ 01539 721097 ▤ 01539 721097
e-mail: fred_eileen@hotmail.com
Flat 18 hole course surrounded by the rivers Kent and
Mint with an open view of the Kentmere and Howgill
fells. The course is a mixture of relatively easy and
difficult holes. These rivers come into play on five holes
and there are also a number of ponds and bunkers.
18 holes, 5691yds, Par 70, SSS 68.
Club membership 500.
Visitors no restrictions except during club competitions at
weekend, check by phone. **Societies** telephone for details.
Green Fees £13 per round (£15 weekends & bank holidays).
Prof D Turner **Course Designer** W Adamson **Facilities** ⛳
♥ ♀ ⛳ 🏠 ⛳ ⛳ ⛳

Hotel ★★ 66% Garden House Hotel, Fowl-Ing Ln,
KENDAL ☎ 01539 731131 11 en suite

Kendal The Heights LA9 4PQ
☎ 01539 723499 (pro) & 733708 (office) ▤ 01539 733708
Elevated parkland/fell course affording breathtaking
views of Lakeland fells and surrounding district.
18 holes, 5765yds, Par 70, SSS 67, Course record 65.
Club membership 737.
Visitors must have a handicap certificate, weekends subject
to availability. Telephone to reserve tee-off time. **Societies**
must contact in advance. **Green Fees** £22 per day (£27.50
weekends). **Cards** ▦ ▦ ▦ ▦ ▨ 🗑 **Prof** Peter Scott
Facilities ⊗ ⦙ ⛳ ♣ ♥ ♀ ⛳ 🏠 ⛳ ⛳ ⛳ **Leisure** Golf clinic
with computer analysis. **Location** 1m W of town centre

Hotel ★★ 66% Garden House Hotel, Fowl Ing Ln,
KENDAL ☎ 01539 731131 11 en suite

KESWICK — Map 11 NY22

Keswick Threlkeld Hall, Threlkeld CA12 4SX
☎ 017687 79324 ▤ 017687 79861
e-mail: keswickgolfclub@netscapeonline.co.uk
Varied fell and tree-lined course with commanding views
of Lakeland scenery.
18 holes, 6225yds, Par 71, SSS 72, Course record 67.
Club membership 866.
Visitors booking up to 7 days in advance 017687 79010.
Restricted on competition days. **Societies** apply in writing to
secretary. **Green Fees** not confirmed. **Prof** Paul Rawlinson
Course Designer Eric Brown **Facilities** ⊗ ⦙ ⛳ ♣ ♥ ♀ ⛳ 🏠
⛳ ⛳ **Leisure** fishing. **Location** 4m E of Keswick, off A66

Hotel ★★★ 65% Keswick Country House Hotel, Station
Rd, KESWICK ☎ 017687 72020 74 en suite

KIRKBY LONSDALE — Map 07 SD67

Kirkby Lonsdale Scaleber Ln, Barbon LA6 2LJ
☎ 015242 76365 ▤ 015242 76503
e-mail: KLGolf@Dial.Pipex.com/
Parkland course on the east bank of the River Lune and
crossed by Barbon Beck. Mainly following the lie of the
land, the gently undulating course uses the beck to
provide water hazards.
18 holes, 6481yds, Par 72, SSS 71, Course record 68.
Club membership 600.
Visitors restricted on Sunday, must telephone in advance or
call in at pro shop. **Societies** apply in writing for society
package. **Green Fees** £25 per day (£30 weekends & bank
holidays). **Prof** Chris Barrett **Course Designer** Bill Squires
Facilities ⊗ ⦙ ⛳ ♣ ♥ ♀ ⛳ 🏠 ⛳ ⛳ **Location** 3m NE of
Kirkby Lonsdale on A683

Hotel ★★ 70% Pheasant Inn, CASTERTON
☎ 015242 71230 11 en suite

MARYPORT — Map 11 NY03

Maryport Bankend CA15 6PA
☎ 01900 812605 ▤ 815626
A tight seaside links course exposed to Solway breezes.
Fine views across Solway Firth. Course comprises 9 holes
links and 9 holes parkland and small streams can be
hazardous on several holes. The first three holes have the
seashore on their left and an errant tee shot can land in
the water. Holes 6-14 are parkland in quality, gently
undulating and quite open. Holes 15-18 revert to links.
18 holes, 6088yds, Par 70, SSS 69, Course record 65.
Club membership 450.
Visitors booking advisable for weekends. **Societies** must
apply in writing. **Green Fees** £17 per day (£22 weekends &
bank holidays). **Facilities** ⊗ ⦙ ⛳ ♣ ♥ ♀ ⛳ **Location** 1m N
on B5300

Hotel ★★★ 79% Washington Central Hotel, Washington
St, WORKINGTON ☎ 01900 65772 46 en suite

PENRITH — Map 12 NY53

Penrith Salkeld Rd CA11 8SG
☎ 01768 891919 ▤ 01768 891919
A beautiful and well-balanced course, always changing
direction, and demanding good length from the tee. It
is set on rolling moorland with occasional pine trees
and some fine views.
18 holes, 6047yds, Par 69, SSS 69, Course record 63.
Club membership 850.

continued

Visitors contact in advance. Handicap certificate required.
Societies telephone in advance. **Green Fees** £25 per day;
£20 per round (£30/£25 weekends and bank holidays).
Prof Garry Key **Facilities** ⊗ ⅲ ⅃ ⚐ ♀ ⚒ 📶 ✂ ⚑
Location M6 junct 41, follow A6 to Penrith, left after
30mph sign and follow signs for golf club

Hotel ★★ 67% Brantwood Country Hotel, Stainton,
PENRITH ☎ 01768 862748 6 en suite 5 annexe en suite

ST BEES   Map 11 NX91

St Bees CA27 0EJ ☎ 01946 824300
Links course, down hill and dale, with sea views.
9 holes, 5082yds, Par 65, SSS 65, Course record 61.
Club membership 400.
Visitors not allowed after 4pm Wednesday and before 3pm
weekends. **Societies** apply in writing in advance to club
secretary. **Green Fees** £12 per day. **Facilities** ⚐ ♀
Location 0.5m W of village off B5345

Hotel ★★★ 76% Ennerdale Country House Hotel,
CLEATOR ☎ 01946 813907 30 en suite

SEASCALE   Map 06 NY00

Seascale The Banks CA20 1QL
☎ 019467 28202 📠 019467 28202
e-mail: secretary@seascalegolfclub.org
**A tough links requiring length and control. The
natural terrain is used to give a variety of holes and
considerable character. Undulating greens add to the
challenge. Fine views over the Western Fells, the Irish
Sea and Isle of Man.**
18 holes, 6416yds, Par 71, SSS 71, Course record 64.
Club membership 650.
Visitors no restrictions, but advisable to contact for tee
reservation times. **Societies** telephone to make provisional
booking. **Green Fees** £29 per day; £24 per round
(£32/£27 weekends & bank holidays). **Prof** Sean Rudd
Course Designer Willie Campbell **Facilities** ⊗ ⅲ ⅃ ⚐
♀ ⚒ 📶 ✂ ⚑ **Conf** Max 20 Del from £20 * **Location**
NW side of village off B5344

Hotel ★★ 71% Westlakes Hotel, GOSFORTH
☎ 019467 25221 9 en suite

SEDBERGH   Map 07 SD69

Sedbergh Dent Rd LA10 5SS
☎ 015396 21551 (Club) & 20993 (Sec)
**A tree-lined grassland course with superb scenery in the
Yorkshire Dales National Park. Feature hole is the par 3
2nd (110yds) where the River Dee separates the tee from
the green.**
9 holes, 5624yds, Par 70, SSS 68, Course record 66.
Club membership 250.
Visitors must book to play on weekends & bank holidays.
Societies must contact in advance. **Green Fees** £22 per day;
£16 per round (£25/£18 weekends). **Course Designer** W G
Squires **Facilities** ⊗ ⅲ ⅃ ⚐ ♀ ⚒ 📶 ✂ **Conf** Max 100
Location 1m S off A683, 5m junct 37 M6

Hotel ★★ 66% Garden House Hotel, Fowl-Ing Ln,
KENDAL ☎ 01539 731131 11 en suite

Birdie, Eagle, Albatross ...
... or even if you're looking for the elusive 'hole-in-one', Windermere is the place.

Situated only a mile from this challenging 18
hole golf course, The Wild Boar Hotel set in
the tranquil Gilpin Valley, with its unique
traditional character offers you a friendly
and welcoming atmosphere.
Reflect, whilst sampling our excellent
cuisine of our award winning AA ❀
restaurant on your 67 par round. Residents
enjoy free use of extensive leisure facilities
and discounted green fees.

Wild Boar Hotel ★★★ 67%
Crook, Nr. Windermere, Cumbria LA23 3NF
Tel: (015 394) 45225 Fax: (015 394) 42498
E-mail: wildboar@elhmail.co.uk
www.elh.co.uk

SILECROFT   Map 06 SD18

Silecroft 30 Lowther Rd LA18 4PQ
☎ 01229 774342 (sec) & 774250 (clubhouse)
**Seaside links course parallel to the coast of the Irish Sea.
Often windy. Easy walking. Spectacular views inland of
Lakeland hills.**
9 holes, 5877yds, Par 68, SSS 68, Course record 66.
Club membership 300.
Visitors May be restricted competition days & bank holidays
contact secretary in advance. **Societies** must contact in
writing. **Green Fees** £15 per day/round (£20 weekends).
Facilities ⚐ by prior arrangement ♀ on request △
Location 3m W of Millom

Guesthouse ◆◆◆◆ The Duddon Pilot Hotel, Devonshire Rd,
MILLOM ☎ 01229 774116 6 en suite

SILLOTH   Map 11 NY15

Silloth on Solway The Clubhouse CA7 4BL
☎ 016973 31304 & 32404 📠 016973 31782
**Billowing dunes, narrow fairways, heather and gorse
and the constant subtle problems of tactics and
judgement make these superb links on the Solway an
exhilarating and searching test. The 13th is a good
long hole. Superb views.**
18 holes, 6614yds, Par 72, SSS 73, Course record 65.
Club membership 700.
Visitors must contact in advance. **Societies** telephone for
times available. **Green Fees** terms on application. **Cards**
▭▭ ▭▭ ▭ 🖳 **Prof** J Graham **Course Designer** David
Grant/Willie Park Jnr **Facilities** ⊗ ⅲ ⅃ ⚐ ♀ △ ⚒ ✂
Location S side of village off B5300

Hotel ★★ 64% Golf Hotel, Criffel St, SILLOTH
☎ 016973 31438 22 en suite

ULVERSTON — Map 07 SD27

Ulverston Bardsea Park LA12 9QJ
☎ 01229 582824 ▤ 01229 588910
Inland golf with many medium length holes on undulating parkland. The 17th is a testing par 4. Overlooking Morecambe Bay the course offers extensive views to the Lakeland Fells.
18 holes, 6201yds, Par 71, SSS 70, Course record 64.
Club membership 750.
Visitors must contact in advance, be a member of an accredited golf club with a handicap certificate. May not play on Sat, competition days & restricted on Tue (Ladies Day). **Societies** by arrangement in writing. **Green Fees** terms on application. **Prof** M R Smith **Course Designer** A Herd/H S Colt (1923) **Facilities** ⊗ ⌬ ⌷ ☕ ♀ ⚲ 🏠 ⛿
⚐ **Location** 2m S off A5087

Hotel ★★★ 66% Whitewater Hotel, The Lakeland Village, NEWBY BRIDGE ☎ 015395 31133 35 en suite

WINDERMERE

See **Bowness-on-Windermere**

WORKINGTON — Map 11 NY02

Workington Branthwaite Rd CA14 4SS
☎ 01900 67828 ▤ 01900 607123
e-mail: golf@workingtongolfclub.freeserve.co.uk
Meadowland course, undulating, with natural hazards created by stream and trees. Good views of Solway Firth and Lakeland Hills. 10th, 13th and 15th holes are particularly testing.

18 holes, 6217yds, Par 72, SSS 70, Course record 65.
Club membership 735.
Visitors advisable to contact pro for weekday, weekends are generally very busy & Tue is Ladies Day. No visitors before 9.30am. **Societies** booking required for over 8 people. **Green Fees** not confirmed. **Prof** Aidrian Drabble **Course Designer** James Braid **Facilities** ⊗ ⌬ ⌷ ☕ ♀ ⚲ 🏠 ⚒ ⚐ **Leisure** snooker table. **Location** 1.75m E off A596

Hotel ★★★ 79% Washington Central Hotel, Washington St, WORKINGTON ☎ 01900 65772 46 en suite

DERBYSHIRE

ALFRETON — Map 08 SK45

Alfreton Wingfield Rd, Oakerthorpe DE55 7LH
☎ 01773 832070
A small well established parkland course with tight fairways and many natural hazards.

continued

11 holes, 5393yds, Par 67, SSS 66, Course record 67.
Club membership 350.
Visitors advisable to contact first. Weekends by arrangement only. **Societies** apply in writing or telephone in advance.
Green Fees £22 per day ; £16 per round. **Prof** Peter Buttifant **Facilities** ⊗ by prior arrangement ⌬ by prior arrangement ☕ ♀ ⚲ 🏠 **Location** 1m W on A615

Hotel ★★★★ 70% Renaissance Derby/Nottingham Hotel, Carter Ln East, SOUTH NORMANTON
☎ 01773 812000 158 en suite

ASHBOURNE — Map 07 SK14

Ashbourne Wyaston Rd DE6 1NB
☎ 01335 342078 & 347960(pro shop) ▤ 01335 347937
With fine views over surrounding countryside, the course uses natural contours and water features.
18 holes, 6402yds, Par 72, SSS 72.
Club membership 650.
Visitors must contact professional in advance, may not play on competition days. **Societies** telephone in advance. **Green Fees** not confirmed. **Prof** Andrew Smith **Course Designer** D Hemstock **Facilities** ⊗ ⌬ ⌷ ☕ ♀ ⚲ 🏠 ⚐ **Leisure** snooker table. **Location** Off Wyaston Road

Hotel ★★★♨ 73% Callow Hall, Mappleton Rd, ASHBOURNE ☎ 01335 300900 16 en suite

BAKEWELL — Map 08 SK26

Bakewell Station Rd DE45 1GB
☎ 01629 812307
Parkland course, hilly, with plenty of natural hazards to test the golfer. Magnificent views across the Wye Valley.
9 holes, 5240yds, Par 68, SSS 66.
Club membership 325.
Visitors limited at weekends due to competitions. **Societies** apply in writing. **Green Fees** £15 (£20 weekends & bank holidays). **Facilities** ⊗ ⌬ ⌷ ☕ ♀ ⚲ **Location** E side of town off A6

Hotel ★★ 73% Croft Country House Hotel, Great Longstone, BAKEWELL ☎ 01629 640278 9 en suite

BAMFORD — Map 08 SK28

Sickleholme Saltergate Ln S33 0BN
☎ 01433 651306 ▤ 01433 659498
e-mail: sickleholme.gc@btconnect.com.
Undulating downland course in the lovely Peak District, with rivers and ravines and spectacular scenery.
18 holes, 6064yds, Par 69, SSS 69, Course record 62.
Club membership 700.
Visitors must contact in advance, restricted weekends. **Societies** telephone in advance. **Green Fees** £29 per round/day (£34 weekends). **Prof** P H Taylor **Facilities** ⊗ ⌬ ⌷ ☕ ♀ ⚲ 🏠 ⚐ **Location** 0.75m S on A6013

Hotel ★★ 70% Yorkshire Bridge Inn, Ashopton Rd, Hope Valley, BAMFORD ☎ 01433 651361 14 en suite

BREADSALL — Map 08 SK33

Marriot Breadsall Priory Hotel & Country Club Moor Rd, Morley DE7 6DL
☎ 01332 832235 ▤ 01332 833509
Set in 200 acres of mature parkland, the Priory Course is built on the site of a 13th-century priory. Full use has been made of natural features and fine old trees. In contrast the Moorland Course, designed by Donald Steel and built by Brian Piersen, features Derbyshire stone

continued

walls and open moors heavily affected by winds. Open when most other clubs are closed in winter.
Priory Course: 18 holes, 6100yds, Par 72, SSS 69, Course record 63.
Moorland Course: 18 holes, 6028yds, Par 70, SSS 69.
Club membership 900.
Visitors must contact in advance, 10 day booking service. **Societies** telephone in advance. **Green Fees** green fees seasonal from £25 to £45. **Cards** 🖃 ▬ ▭ 💳 🔄 💷 **Prof** Darren Steels **Course Designer** D Steel **Facilities** ⊗ ⊞ ⓑ 💷 ♀ 🛆 🖾 🍴 🎿 🏌 🚜 ⚐ ℂ **Leisure** hard tennis courts, heated indoor swimming pool, sauna, solarium, gymnasium. **Location** 0.75m W

Hotel ★★★★ 65% Marriott Breadsall Priory Hotel& Country Club, Moor Rd, MORLEY ☎ 01332 832235 12 en suite 100 annexe en suite

Buxton & High Peak Waterswallows Rd SK17 7EN
☎ 01298 26263 & 23453 📠 26333
e-mail: sec@bhpgc.fsnet.co.uk
Bracing, well-drained meadowland course; the highest in Derbyshire. Challenging course where wind direction is a major factor on some holes; others require blind shots to sloping greens.
18 holes, 5966yds, Par 69, SSS 69.
Club membership 650.
Visitors By prior arrangment only. **Societies** Prior arrangement only. Phone or write to Jane Dobson. **Green Fees** £29 per day, £23 per round (£34/£29 weekends & bank holidays). **Cards** 🖃 ▬ ▭ 🔄 💷 **Prof** Gary Brown **Course Designer** J Morris **Facilities** ⊗ ⓑ 💷 ♀ 🛆 🖾 🍴 🚜 ⚐ **Conf** Max 30 **Location** 1m NE off A6

Hotel ★★★★ 64% Palace Hotel, Palace Rd, BUXTON ☎ 01298 22001 122 en suite

Cavendish Gadley Ln SK17 6XD
☎ 01298 79708 📠 01298 79708
This parkland/moorland course with its comfortable clubhouse nestles below the rising hills. Generally open to the prevailing west wind, it is noted for its excellent surfaced greens which contain many deceptive subtleties. Designed by Dr Alastair McKenzie, good holes include the 8th, 9th and 18th.
18 holes, 5721yds, Par 68, SSS 68, Course record 61.
Club membership 650.
Visitors must contact in advance, weekends are restricted by competitions. Ladies day Thursday **Societies** telephone professional on 01298 25052. **Green Fees** not confirmed. **Prof** Paul Hunstone **Course Designer** Dr Mackenzie **Facilities** ⊗ ⓑ 💷 ♀ 🛆 🖾 🍴 ℂ **Location** 0.75m W of town centre off A53

Hotel ★★★ 76% Best Western Lee Wood Hotel, The Park, BUXTON ☎ 01298 23002 35 en suite 5 annexe en suite

Chapel-en-le-Frith The Cockyard, Manchester Rd SK23 9UH
☎ 01298 812118 & 813943 (sec) 📠 01298 814990
e-mail: info@chapelgolf.co.uk
Scenic parkland course, with testing holes at the 14th (par 4) and 18th (517 yds), par 5. Good views.
18 holes, 6434yds, Par 70, SSS 69, Course record 67.
Club membership 676.

continued

Visitors must contact professional or secretary in advance. **Societies** apply in advance to Secretary. **Green Fees** terms on application. **Cards** 🖃 ▬ 🔄 **Prof** David J Cullen **Course Designer** David Williams **Facilities** ⊗ ⊞ ⓑ 💷 ♀ 🛆 🖾 🍴 ⚐ **Location** On B5470

Hotel ★★★ 76% Best Western Lee Wood Hotel, The Park, BUXTON ☎ 01298 23002 35 en suite 5 annexe en suite

Chesterfield Walton S42 7LA
☎ 01246 279256 📠 01246 276622
A varied and interesting, undulating parkland course with trees picturesquely adding to the holes and the outlook alike. Stream hazard on back nine.
18 holes, 6261yds, Par 71, SSS 70, Course record 65.
Club membership 600.
Visitors must contact in advance, must play with member on Sat & bank holidays,may play on Sun after 1.30. A handicap certificate is generally required. **Societies** apply in writing. **Green Fees** £35 per day (Mon-Fri); £26 per round, Mon-Fri (£30 per round Sun). **Prof** Mike McLean **Facilities** ⊗ ⊞ ⓑ 💷 ♀ 🛆 🖾 ⚐ **Location** 2m SW off A632

Hotel ★★ 70% Abbeydale Hotel, Cross St, CHESTERFIELD ☎ 01246 277849 11 en suite

Grassmoor Golf Centre North Wingfield Rd, Grassmoor S42 5EA ☎ 01246 856044 📠 01246 853486
e-mail: helen.chester@ruffordpark.co.uk
An 18-hole heathland course with interesting and challenging water features. 26-bay floodlit driving range, practice bunkers and putting area.
18 holes, 5723yds, Par 69, SSS 69, Course record 67.
Club membership 450.
Visitors contact Manager in advance. Smart dress code. **Societies** telephone Manager in advance. **Green Fees** £15 per day; £10 per round (£12 per round weekends & bank holidays). **Cards** 🖃 ▬ 💷 **Prof** Gary Hagues **Course Designer** Hawtree **Facilities** ⊗ ⊞ ⓑ 💷 ♀ 🛆 🖾 🍴 🚜 ⚐ ℂ **Location** 4m from M1 junct 29, between Chesterfield & Grassmoor, off B6038

Hotel ★★ 70% Abbeydale Hotel, Cross St, CHESTERFIELD ☎ 01246 277849 11 en suite

Stanedge Walton Hay Farm, Stonedge, Ashover S45 0LW ☎ 01246 566156
Moorland course in hilly situation open to strong winds. Some tricky short holes with narrow fairways, so accuracy is paramount. Magnificent views over four counties. Extended course now open.
9 holes, 5786yds, Par 69, SSS 68, Course record 68.
Club membership 310.
Visitors with member only Sat & Sun, and may not play after 2pm weekdays. **Societies** apply in writing. **Green Fees** terms on application. **Facilities** ⓑ 💷 ♀ 🛆 **Location** 5m SW off B5057 nr Red Lion public house

Hotel ★★ 70% Abbeydale Hotel, Cross St, CHESTERFIELD ☎ 01246 277849 11 en suite

Tapton Park Municipal Tapton Park, Tapton S41 0EQ ☎ 01246 239500 & 273887 📠 01246 558024
Municipal parkland course with some fairly hard walking. The 620 yd (par 5) 5th is a testing hole.
Tapton Main: 18 holes, 6013yds, Par 71, SSS 69.
Dobbin Clough: 9 holes, 2613yds, Par 34, SSS 34.
Club membership 750.

continued

Visitors must contact in advance. No caddies allowed. **Societies** apply in writing. **Green Fees** not confirmed. **Prof** Andrew Carnall **Facilities** ⊗ ⫙ ⤙ 🖫 ♀ ⚲ 🖻 ⌁ ✓ **Location** 0.5m E of Chesterfield Station

··············

Hotel ★★ 70% Abbeydale Hotel, Cross St, CHESTERFIELD ☎ 01246 277849 11 en suite

CODNOR   Map 08 SK44

Ormonde Fields Golf & Country Club
Nottingham Rd DE5 9RG
☎ 01773 570043 (Secretary) 🖥 01773 742987
Parkland course with undulating fairways and natural hazards. There is a practice area.
18 holes, 6502yds, Par 71, SSS 72, Course record 68.
Club membership 500.
Visitors must contact in advance. **Societies** telephone in advance. **Green Fees** terms on application. **Cards** 🔤 **Prof** Matthew Myford **Course Designer** John Fearn **Facilities** ⊗ ⫙ ⤙ 🖫 ♀ ⚲ 🖻 ✓ **Location** 1m SE on A610

··············

Hotel ★★★ 71% Makeney Hall Country House Hotel, Makeney, Milford, BELPER ☎ 01332 842999 27 en suite 18 annexe en suite

DERBY   Map 08 SK33

Allestree Park Allestree Hall, Duffield Rd, Allestree
DE22 2EU ☎ 01332 550616 🖥 01332 541195
Public course, picturesque and undulating set in 300 acre park with views across Derbyshire.
18 holes, 5806yds, Par 68, SSS 68.
Visitors start times may be booked in advance by telephone, visitors welcome any day. **Societies** apply in writing or by telephone in advance. **Green Fees** terms on application. **Prof** Leigh Woodward **Facilities** ⊗ ⫙ ⤙ 🖫 ♀ ⚲ 🖻 ⌁ ✓ **Leisure** fishing. **Location** N of Derby, from A38 take A6 towards N, Course in 1.5m on left

··············

Hotel ★★★★ 65% Marriott Breadsall Priory Hotel& Country Club, Moor Rd, MORLEY ☎ 01332 832235 12 en suite 100 annexe en suite

Derby Wilmore Rd, Sinfin DE24 9HD
☎ 01332 766462 🖥 01332 769004
Municipal parkland course with tree lined fairways an excellent test of golf. Generally a flat course it is suitable for golfers of all ages.
Sinfin Golf Course: 18 holes, 6163yds, Par 70, SSS 69.
Visitors starting time must be booked in advance by telephone, visitors welcome any day. **Societies** apply in writing or by telephone in advance. **Green Fees** terms on application. **Cards** 🔤 🔤 🔤 🔤 **Prof** Steve Astle **Facilities** ⊗ ⫙ ⤙ 🖫 ♀ ⚲ 🖻 ⌁ ✓ **Location** 3.5m S of city centre

··············

Hotel ★★★ 63% International Hotel, 288 Burton Rd, DERBY ☎ 01332 369321 41 en suite 21 annexe en suite

Mickleover Uttoxeter Rd, Mickleover DE3 9AD
☎ 01332 518662 🖥 01332 512092
Undulating parkland course of two loops of nine holes, in a pleasant setting and affording splendid country views. There is a premium in hitting tee shots in the right place for approaches to greens, some of which are on elevated plateaux. Some attractive par 3s which are considered to be very exacting.
18 holes, 5702yds, Par 68, SSS 68, Course record 64.
Club membership 800.

continued

Visitors must contact Professional in advance. **Societies** apply in writing/telephone. **Green Fees** terms on application. **Cards** 🔤 **Prof** Tim Coxon **Course Designer** J Pennink **Facilities** ⊗ ⫙ ⤙ 🖫 ♀ ⚲ 🖻 ⌁ ✓ **Location** 3m W of Derby on A516/B5020

··············

Hotel ★★★★ 75% Menzies Mickleover Court, Etwall Rd, Mickleover, DERBY ☎ 0870 6003013 99 en suite

DRONFIELD   Map 08 SK37

Hallowes Hallowes Ln S18 1UR
☎ 01246 411196 🖥 01246 411196
Attractive moorland/parkland course set in the Derbyshire hills. Several testing par 4s and splendid views.
18 holes, 6342yds, Par 71, SSS 71, Course record 64.
Club membership 630.
Visitors may only play with member at weekends. Must contact in advance. **Societies** contact in advance, various packages. **Green Fees** £35 per day; £30 per round. **Prof** Philip Dunn **Facilities** ⊗ ⫙ ⤙ 🖫 ♀ ⚲ 🖻 🥢 ✓ **Leisure** snooker. **Location** S side of town. From Sheffield follow old A61(not bypass

··············

Hotel ★★ 69% Chantry Hotel, Church St, DRONFIELD ☎ 01246 413014 7 en suite

DUFFIELD   Map 08 SK34

Chevin Golf Ln DE56 4EE
☎ 01332 841864 🖥 01332 841864
e-mail: secretary@chevingolf.fsnet.co.uk
A mixture of parkland and moorland, this course is rather hilly which makes for some hard walking, but with most rewarding views of the surrounding countryside. The 8th hole, aptly named "Tribulation", requires an accurate tee shot, and is one of the most difficult holes in the country.
18 holes, 6057yds, Par 69, SSS 69, Course record 64.
Club membership 750.
Visitors not before 9.30am or off first tee between 12.30 and 2pm. Proof of handicap required. **Societies** contact in advance. **Green Fees** £30 per day; £25 per round. **Prof** Willie Bird **Course Designer** J Braid **Facilities** ⊗ ⫙ ⤙ 🖫 ♀ ⚲ 🖻 ⌁ ✓ **Location** N side of town off A6

··············

Hotel ★★★ 71% Makeney Hall Country House Hotel, Makeney, Milford, BELPER ☎ 01332 842999 27 en suite 18 annexe en suite

GLOSSOP   Map 07 SK09

Glossop and District Hurst Ln, off Sheffield
Rd SK13 7PU ☎ 01457 865247(club house) & 853117(pro shop)
Moorland course in good position, excellent natural hazards. Difficult closing hole (9th & 18th).
11 holes, 5800yds, Par 68, SSS 68, Course record 64.
Club membership 350.
Visitors may not play Saturdays, Sundays by appointment/reservation. **Societies** must apply in writing to professional, steward or secretary. **Green Fees** £20 (£25 weekends). **Prof** Daniel Marsh **Facilities** ⊗ ⫙ ⤙ 🖫 ♀ ⚲ 🖻 ⌁ ✓ **Location** 1m E off A57 from town centre

··············

Hotel ★★ 71% York House Hotel, York Place, Richmond St, ASHTON-UNDER-LYNE ☎ 0161 330 9000 24 en suite 10 annexe en suite

HORSLEY   Map 08 SK34

Horsley Lodge Smalley Mill Rd DE21 5BL
☎ 01332 780838 📠 01332 781118
e-mail: @horsleylodge.co.uk.
This lush meadowland course set in 180 acres of
Derbyshire countryside, has some challenging holes. Also
par 3 course and floodlit driving range. USGA world
class greens designed by former World Champion Peter
McEvoy.
18 holes, 6400yds, Par 72, SSS 71, Course record 72.
Club membership 650.
Visitors must contact professional in advance and have
handicap. May not play weekends before noon. **Societies**
must telephone in advance. **Green Fees** terms on application.
Cards 💳 💳 💳 💳 💳 **Prof** G Lyall **Course Designer**
Bill White **Facilities** ⊗ ⫫ ⓑ 💪 ♀ ⌂ ⌂ 🍴 ⛳ 🐎 🚜 🏌 ⬅
Leisure fishing, sauna, solarium.**Conf** Max 120 Thtr 120
Class 40 Board 40 Banquet 100 Del £60 to £120 * **Location**
4m NE of Derby, off A38 at Belper then follow tourist signs

· · · · · · · · · · · · · · · · · ·

Hotel ★★★★ 65% Marriott Breadsall Priory Hotel&
Country Club, Moor Rd, MORLEY ☎ 01332 832235
12 en suite 100 annexe en suite

KEDLESTON   Map 08 SK34

Kedleston Park DE22 5JD
☎ 01332 840035 📠 01332 840035
e-mail: secretary@kedlestonpark.sagehost.co.uk
The course is laid out in flat mature parkland with fine
trees and background views of historic Kedleston Hall
(National Trust). Many testing holes are included in
each nine and there is an excellent modern clubhouse.
18 holes, 6675yds, Par 72, SSS 72, Course record 66.
Club membership 847.
Visitors must contact in advance. **Societies** weekdays
only, apply in writing. **Green Fees** £45 per day; £35 per
round. **Cards** 💳 💳 💳 💳 💳 💳 💳 **Prof** Paul
Wesselingh **Course Designer** James Braid **Facilities** ⊗
⫫ ⓑ 💪 ♀ ⌂ 🍴 🐎 🚜 🏌 **Leisure** sauna.
Conf Max 80 Del £10 to £20 * **Location** Signposted
Kedleston Hall from A38

· · · · · · · · · · · · · · · · · ·

Hotel ★★★ 63% International Hotel, 288 Burton Rd,
DERBY ☎ 01332 369321 41 en suite 21 annexe en suite

LONG EATON   Map 08 SK43

Trent Lock Golf Centre Lock Ln, Sawley NG10 2FY
☎ 0115 946 4398 📠 0115 946 1183
Main course has two par 5, five par 3 and eleven par 4
holes, plus water features and three holes adjacent to the
river. A challenging test of golf. A 24 bay floodlit golf
range is available.
*Main Course: 18 holes, 5717yds, Par 69, SSS 68, Course
record 73.*
9 hole: 9 holes, 2911yds, Par 36.
Club membership 500.
Visitors no restriction Mon-Fri am but booking system 12pm
Fri-closing Sun. May play 9 hole course at any time.
Societies apply in writing or telephone in advance. **Green
Fees** not confirmed. **Prof** M Taylor **Course Designer** E
McCausland **Facilities** 🐎 ⌂ 🐎 🚜 🏌 ⬅

· · · · · · · · · · · · · · · · · ·

Hotel ★★★ 66% Novotel Nottingham, Bostock Ln, LONG
EATON ☎ 0115 946 5111 108 en suite

MATLOCK   Map 08 SK36

Matlock Chesterfield Rd, Matlock Moor DE4 5LZ
☎ 01629 582191 📠 01629 582135
Moorland course with fine views of the beautiful Peak
District.
18 holes, 5996yds, Par 70, SSS 69, Course record 63.
Club membership 700.
Visitors with member only weekends & bank holidays.
Members only weekdays 12.30-1.30pm. **Societies** prior
arrangement with Secretary. **Green Fees** £30 per day; £25
per round. **Prof** M A Whithorn **Course Designer** Tom
Williamson **Facilities** ⊗ ⫫ ⓑ 💪 ♀ ⌂ 🍴 ⬅ **Location**
1.5m NE of Matlock on A632

· · · · · · · · · · · · · · · · · ·

Hotel ★★★ 70% New Bath Hotel, New Bath Rd,
MATLOCK BATH ☎ 0870 400 8119 55 en suite

MICKLEOVER   Map 08 SK33

Pastures Social Centre, Hospital Ln DE3 5DQ
☎ 01332 521074
Challenging course laid out on undulating meadowland
with good views across the Trent valley. Numerous
testing par 3s.
9 holes, 5095yds, Par 64, SSS 65, Course record 67.
Club membership 320.
Visitors must be accompanied by a member, may not play on
Sun & between noon-4pm Sat. Handicap certificate required.
Societies Mon & Tue, must contact in advance. **Green Fees**
not confirmed. **Course Designer** J F Pennik **Facilities** ⓑ 💪
♀ evenings ⬅ ⌂ **Location** 1m SW off A516

· · · · · · · · · · · · · · · · · ·

Hotel ★★★ 63% International Hotel, 288 Burton Rd,
DERBY ☎ 01332 369321 41 en suite 21 annexe en suite

MORLEY   Map 08 SK34

Morley Hayes Main Rd DE7 6DG
☎ 01332 780480 📠 01332 781094
e-mail: golf@morleyhayes.com
Peaceful pay and play course set in a splendid valley and
incorporating charming water features and woodland.
Floodlit driving range. Challenging 9 hole short course
(Tower Course).

Manor Course: 18 holes, 6726yds, Par 72, SSS 72.
Tower Course: 9 holes, 1614yds, Par 30.
Visitors welcome. **Societies** booking essential telephone for
details. **Green Fees** terms on application. **Cards** 💳 💳 💳
💳 💳 💳 **Prof** Mark Marriott **Facilities** ⊗ ⫫ ⓑ 💪 ♀ ⬅
⌂ 🍴 🐎 🚜 🏌 **Conf** Max 100 Thtr 100 Class 40 Board 30
Banquet 70 Del £26.50 to £28.50 * **Location** 4m N of Derby
between Derby and Heanor on A608

· · · · · · · · · · · · · · · · · ·

Hotel ★★★★ 65% Marriott Breadsall Priory Hotel &
Country Club, Moor Rd, MORLEY ☎ 01332 832235
12 en suite 100 annexe en suite

NEW MILLS   Map 07 SK08

New Mills Shaw Marsh SK22 4QE ☎ 01663 743485
Moorland course with panoramic views and first-class greens.
9 holes, 5633yds, Par 68, SSS 67.
Club membership 389.
Visitors contact secretary/professional in advance, cannot play during competitions. **Societies** must contact secretary or professional in advance. **Green Fees** not confirmed. **Prof** Carl Cross **Course Designer** Williams **Facilities** ⊗ ⑴⑴ ⓑ ☒ ♀ ♧ 🏡 ⚑ ⦚ ♣ ✐ ⦗ **Location** 0.5m N off B6101

Inn ♦♦♦♦ Matteo's Bar & Country Hotel, Rock Tavern, Glossop Rd, Marple Bridge, MARPLE ☎ 01457 852418 5 en suite

RENISHAW   Map 08 SK47

Renishaw Park Club House, Mill Ln S21 3UZ
☎ 01246 432044 & 435484 🖷 01246 432116
Part parkland and part meadowland with easy walking.
18 holes, 6107yds, Par 71, SSS 70, Course record 65.
Club membership 750.
Visitors Visitors not allowed on competition days. Contact professional on 01246 435484 for other days. **Societies** Telephone Secretary's office to arrange. **Green Fees** £35 per day; £26 per round (£40 weekends and bank holidays). **Prof** John Oates **Course Designer** Sir George Sitwell **Facilities** ⊗ ⑴⑴ ⓑ ☒ ♀ ♧ 🏡 ✐ **Location** 1.5m W of junct 30 M1

Hotel ★★★ 64% Sitwell Arms Hotel, Station Rd, RENISHAW ☎ 01246 435226 30 en suite

RISLEY   Map 08 SK43

Maywood Rushy Ln DE72 3ST ☎ 0115 939 2306
18 holes, 6424yds, Par 72, SSS 71, Course record 70.
Course Designer P Moon **Location** Near junct 25 on M1
Telephone for further details

Hotel ★★★ 73% Risley Hall Hotel, Derby Rd, RISLEY ☎ 0115 939 9000 16 en suite 18 annexe en suite

SHIRLAND   Map 08 SK45

Shirland Lower Delves DE55 6AU ☎ 01773 834935
Rolling parkland and tree-lined course with extensive views of Derbyshire countryside.

18 holes, 6072yds, Par 71, SSS 70, Course record 67.
Club membership 450.
Visitors contact professional in advance. **Societies** contact Professional. **Green Fees** terms on application. **Prof** Neville Hallam **Facilities** ⊗ ⑴⑴ ⓑ ☒ ♀ ♧ 🏡 ⚑ ♣ ✐ **Location** S side of village off A61

Hotel ★★★★ 70% Renaissance Derby/Nottingham Hotel, Carter Ln East, SOUTH NORMANTON ☎ 01773 812000 158 en suite

STANTON-BY-DALE   Map 08 SK43

Erewash Valley DE7 4QR
☎ 0115 932 3258 🖷 0115 932 2984
Parkland/meadowland course overlooking valley and M1. Unique 4th and 5th in Victorian quarry bottom: 5th-testing par 3.
18 holes, 6557yds, Par 72, SSS 71, Course record 67.
Club membership 750.
Visitors no restrictions except when club events in progress. **Societies** contact in advance. **Green Fees** terms on application. **Prof** M J Ronan **Course Designer** Hawtree **Facilities** ⊗ ⑴⑴ ⓑ ☒ ♀ ♧ 🏡 ⚑ ♣ ✐ ⦗ **Location** 1m W, 2m from junct 25 on M1

Hotel ★★★ 73% Risley Hall Hotel, Derby Rd, RISLEY ☎ 0115 939 9000 16 en suite 18 annexe en suite

UNSTONE   Map 08 SK37

Birch Hall Sheffield Rd S18 4DB
☎ 01246 291979 🖷 01246 412912
18 holes, 6379yds, Par 73, SSS 71, Course record 72.
Course Designer D Tucker **Location** Turn off A61 between Sheffield and Chesterfield, outskirts of Unstone village
Telephone for further details

Hotel ★★ 69% Chantry Hotel, Church St, DRONFIELD ☎ 01246 413014 7 en suite

DEVON

AXMOUTH   Map 03 SY29

Axe Cliff Squires Ln EX12 4AB
☎ 01297 21754 & 24371
Undulating links course with coastal views.
18 holes, 6000yds, Par 70, SSS 70, Course record 64.
Club membership 400.
Visitors must contact in advance. **Societies** must contact in advance. **Green Fees** terms on application. **Prof** Mark Dack **Facilities** ⊗ ⑴⑴ ⓑ ☒ ♀ ♧ 🏡 ✐ **Location** 0.75m S on B3172

Hotel ★★ 76% Swallows Eaves, COLYFORD ☎ 01297 553184 8 en suite

BIGBURY-ON-SEA   Map 03 SX64

Bigbury TQ7 4BB ☎ 01548 810557 (Secretary) 810412 (Pro Shop) 🖷 01548 810207
Clifftop, heathland course with easy walking. Exposed to winds, but with fine views over the sea and River Avon. 7th hole particularly tricky.
18 holes, 6061yds, Par 70, SSS 69, Course record 65.
Club membership 850.
Visitors must have handicap certificate. Must contact in advance. **Societies** must apply in writing. **Green Fees** £27 per day (£30 weekends). **Prof** Simon Lloyd **Course Designer** J H Taylor **Facilities** ⊗ ⑴⑴ ⓑ ☒ ♀ ♧ 🏡 ⚑ ♣ ✐ **Location** 1m S on B3392 between Bigbury and Bigbury-on-Sea

Hotel ★★★★ 72% Thurlestone Hotel, THURLESTONE ☎ 01548 560382 64 en suite

BLACKAWTON   Map 03 SX85

Dartmouth Golf & Country Club TQ9 7DE
☎ 01803 712686 & 712650 🖷 01803 712628
e-mail: info@dgcc.co.uk
The 9-hole Club course and the 18-hole Championship

continued

course are both worth a visit and not just for the beautiful views. The Championship is one of the most challenging courses in the West Country with 12 water hazards on the course and a daunting par 5 4th hole that visitors will always remember. The spectacular final hole looking downhill and over a water hazard to the green, can be difficult to judge and has been described as one of the most picturesque finishing holes in the country.
Championship Course: 18 holes, 6663yds, Par 72, SSS 72, Course record 68.
Dartmouth Course: 9 holes, 4791yds, Par 66, SSS 64.
Club membership 700.
Visitors must contact in advance, visitors welcome subject to availability. Normal dress standards apply on both courses.Tee times must be pre booked for both courses. **Societies** telephone in advance. **Green Fees** terms on application. **Cards** 🟦 🟥 🟥 🟦 🟥 🟩 **Prof** Steve Dougan **Course Designer** Jeremy Pern **Facilities** ⊗ 🍴 🛗 🍺 ⌣ ⛳ 🏌 🛒 ⚑ 🛺 ✎ ⛴ **Leisure** heated indoor swimming pool, sauna, solarium, gymnasium.**Conf** Thtr 300 Class 100 Board 100 Banquet 250 Del from £26.95 * **Location** On A3122 Totnes/Dartmouth road, 4m from Dartmouth

Hotel ★★★ 68% Stoke Lodge Hotel, Stoke Fleming, DARTMOUTH ☎ 01803 770523 25 en suite

---

East Devon Links Rd EX9 6DG
☎ 01395 443370 📠 01395 445547
e-mail: secretary@edge.co.uk
An interesting course with downland turf, much heather and gorse, and superb views over the bay. The early holes climb to the cliff edge. The downhill 17th has a heather section in the fairway, leaving a good second to the green.
18 holes, 6231yds, Par 70, SSS 70, Course record 61.
Club membership 850.
Visitors advisable to contact in advance, no visitors before 9am. Visitors must be member of a recognised club and must produce proof of handicap. **Societies** Thu only, must contact in advance. **Green Fees** £40 per 27/36 holes; £30 per 18 holes. **Cards** 🟦 🟥 🟥 🟦 🟥 🟩 **Prof** Trevor Underwood **Facilities** ⊗ 🍴 🛗 🍺 ⌣ ⛳ 🏌 🛒 ✎ **Location** W side of town centre

Hotel ★★ 70% Barn Hotel, Foxholes Hill, Marine Dr, EXMOUTH ☎ 01395 224411 11 en suite

---

Highbullen Hotel EX37 9HD
☎ 01769 540561 📠 01769 540492
e-mail: info@highbutton.co.uk
Mature parkland course with water hazards and outstanding scenic views to Exmoor and Dartmoor. Excellent facilities offered by the hotel.
18 holes, 5755yds, Par 68, SSS 67.
Club membership 100.
Visitors to book tee time telephone 01769 540530 daytime, 01769 540561 evenings. **Societies** must contact in advance. **Green Fees** not confirmed. **Prof** Paul Weston **Course Designer** M Neil/ J Hamilton **Facilities** ⌣ 🛗 🛒 ⚑ 🛺 ✎ 🛺 ⛴ **Leisure** hard tennis courts, outdoor and indoor heated swimming pools, squash, fishing, sauna, solarium, gymnasium. **Location** 0.5m S of village

Hotel ★★★🛏 69% Highbullen Hotel, CHITTLEHAMHOLT ☎ 01769 540561 12 en suite 25 annexe en suite

---

Teign Valley EX6 7PA
☎ 01647 253026 📠 01647 253026
18 holes, 5913yds, Par 70, SSS 68.

Course Designer P Nicholson **Location** Take Teign Valley exit off A38, Exeter/Plymouth Expressway and follow GC signs up valley on B3193
Telephone for further details

Hotel ★★★★ 67% Le Meridien Manor House, MORETONHAMPSTEAD ☎ 01647 440355 90 en suite

Chulmleigh Leigh Rd EX18 7BL
☎ 01769 580519 📠 01769 580519
e-mail: howard@chulmleighgolf.freeserve.co.uk
Situated in a scenic area with views to distant Dartmoor, this undulating meadowland course offers a good test for the most experienced golfer and is enjoyable for newcomers to the game. Short 18 hole summer course with a tricky 1st hole; in winter the course is changed to 9 holes and made longer for players to extend their game.
Summer Short Course: 18 holes, 1450yds, Par 54, SSS 54, Course record 49.
Winter Course: 9 holes, 2310yds, Par 54, SSS 54, Course record 57.
Club membership 85.
Visitors welcome anytime. **Societies** telephone in advance. **Green Fees** £11.50 per day; £9.50 per 36 holes; £6.50 per 18 holes; (9 holes £4.50, 18 holes £6.50, winter). **Course Designer** John Goodban **Facilities** 🛗 🍺 ⌣ ⛳ 🛒 ⚑ ✎ **Location** SW side of village just off A377

Hotel ★★★ Northcote Manor, BURRINGTON ☎ 01769 560501 11 en suite

---

Churston Dartmouth Rd TQ5 0LA
☎ 01803 842751 & 842218 📠 01803 845738
e-mail: manager@churstongc.fsnet.co.uk
A cliff-top downland course with splendid views over Brixham harbour and Tor Bay. There is some gorse with a wooded area inland. A variety of shot is called for, with particularly testing holes at the 3rd, 9th and 15th, all par 4. Conference facilities and a well equipped shop are also available.
18 holes, 6219yds, Par 70, SSS 70, Course record 64.
Club membership 700.
Visitors must telephone in advance and be a member of recognised golf club with a handicap certificate. **Societies** apply in writing or telephone. **Green Fees** £30(£35 weekends). **Cards** 🟥 **Prof** Neil Holman **Facilities** ⊗ 🍴

continued

🛍 ♨ ♀ ⚲ 🏠 ⛳ ♂ **Conf** Max 40 Del £15 to £30 *
Location NW side of village on A379

Hotel ★★ 65% Dainton Hotel, 95 Dartmouth Rd,
Three Beaches, Goodrington, PAIGNTON
☎ 01803 550067 & 525901 🗎 01803 666339 11 en suite

CREDITON   Map 03 SS80

Downes Crediton Hookway EX17 3PT
☎ 01363 773025 & 774464 🗎 01363 775060
e-mail: downescreditongolfclub@compuserve.com
Parkland course with water features. Flat front nine.
Hilly and wooded back nine.
18 holes, 5951yds, Par 70, SSS 69.
Club membership 700.
Visitors handicap certificate required, must contact in
advance, restricted at weekends. **Green Fees** £24 per day (£27 weekends). **Prof**
Howard Finch **Facilities** ⊗ ⅶ 🛍 ♨ ♀ ♨ 🏠 ⛳ ♂
Location 1.5m SE off A377

Hotel ★★★ 73% Barton Cross Hotel & Restaurant,
Huxham, Stoke Canon, EXETER
☎ 01392 841245 9 en suite

CULLOMPTON   Map 03 ST00

Padbrook Park EX15 1RU
☎ 01884 38286 🗎 01884 34359
e-mail: richard2406@btinternet.com
A 9-hole, 18 tee parkland course with many water and
woodland hazards and spectacular views. The dog-leg
2nd and pulpit 7th are of particular challenge to golfers
of all standards.
9 holes, 6108yds, Par 70, SSS 70, Course record 67.
Club membership 250.
Visitors welcome at all times but preferable to book in
advance. **Societies** apply in writing or telephone. **Green Fees**
£20 per day; £13 per 18 holes; £10 per 9 holes (£27/£17/£12
weekends). **Cards** 〰 ▦ 🟥 **Prof** Stewart Adwick **Course
Designer** Bob Sandow **Facilities** ⊗ 🛍 ♨ ♀ ♨ 🏠 ⛳ 🖐 🏌
♂ **Leisure** fishing, solarium, gymnasium, indoor bowling
centre, health suite. **Conf** Max 100 Thtr 40 Class 40 Board
70 Del from £10.95 * **Location** M5 junct 28, 1m on S edge
of town

Hotel ★★★ 67% The Tiverton Hotel, Blundells Rd,
TIVERTON ☎ 01884 256120 74 en suite

DAWLISH WARREN   Map 03 SX97

Warren EX7 0NF
☎ 01626 862255 & 864002 🗎 01626 888005

Typical flat, genuine links course lying on spit between
sea and Exe estuary. Picturesque scenery, a few trees but
continued

much gorse. Testing in windy conditions. The 7th hole
provides the opportunity to go for the green across a bay
on the estuary.
18 holes, 5965yds, Par 69, SSS 69, Course record 65.
Club membership 600.
Visitors must contact in advance & have handicap
certificate. **Societies** prior arrangement essential. **Green Fees**
not confirmed. **Prof** Darren Prowse **Facilities** ⊗ ⅶ 🛍 ♨ ♀
♨ 🏠 ♂ **Location** E side of village

Hotel ★★★ 68% Langstone Cliff Hotel, Dawlish Warren,
DAWLISH ☎ 01626 868000 61 en suite 4 annexe en suite

DOWN ST MARY   Map 03 SS70

Waterbridge EX17 5LG ☎ 01363 85111
A testing course of 9-holes set in a gently sloping valley.
The Par of 32 will not be easily gained with 1 par 5, 3 par
4s and 5 par 3s, although the course record holder has
par 29! The 3rd hole which is a raised green is
surrounded by water and the 4th (439 yards) is
demanding for beginners.
9 holes, 3910yds, Par 64, SSS 64.
Club membership 50.
Visitors no restrictions. **Societies** no restrictions. **Green Fees**
£10 per 18 holes; £6 per 9 holes (£12/£7 weekends & bank
holidays). **Prof** David Ridyard **Course Designer** D Taylor
Facilities ♨ 🖐 ♂ **Location** From Exeter on A377 towards
Barnstaple. 1 mile past Copplestone L

Hotel ★★★ Northcote Manor, BURRINGTON
☎ 01769 560501 11 en suite

EXETER   Map 03 SX99

Exeter Golf & Country Club Topsham Rd,
Countess Wear EX2 7AE
☎ 01392 874139 🗎 01392 874914
e-mail: info@exetergcc.fsnet.co.uk
A sheltered parkland course with some very old trees and
known as the flattest course in Devon. 15th & 17th are
testing par 4 holes. Small, well guarded greens.
18 holes, 6008yds, Par 69, SSS 69, Course record 62.
Club membership 800.
Visitors welcome but may not play during match or
competitions, very busy pre booking needed up to 1 week in
advance. Must have handicap certificate. Ring starter in
advance on 01392 876303 **Societies** welcome Thu only,
booking available by telephone to manager tel 01392
874639. **Green Fees** £38 per day; £28 per round (£42/£35
weekends). **Cards** 〰 ▦ 🟥 🎴 **Prof** Mike Rowett **Course
Designer** J Braid **Facilities** ⊗ ⅶ 🛍 ♨ ♀ 🏠 🏠 ♂ **Leisure**
hard tennis courts, heated indoor plus outdoor swimming
pool, squash, sauna, solarium, gymnasium, jacuzzi. **Location**
SE side of city centre off A379

Hotel ★★★ 67% The Buckerell Lodge Hotel, Topsham Rd,
EXETER ☎ 01392 221111 53 en suite

Woodbury Park Hotel, Golf & Country
Club Woodbury Castle, Woodbury EX5 1JJ
☎ 01395 233500 🗎 01395 233384
e-mail: golfbookings@woodburypark.co.uk
Irrigated 18 hole Oaks Championship course and
excellent 9 hole Acorns course set in 500 acres of wooded
parkland with stunning views.
Oaks: 18 holes, 6870yds, Par 72, SSS 72, Course record 66.
Acorn: 9 holes, 2297yds, Par 32, SSS 32.
Club membership 750.
Visitors welcome, please reserve tee times in advance.
Societies contact in advance on 01395 237384. **Green Fees**
continued

terms on application. **Cards** ▭ ▬ ▬ ▣ ▦ ▧ ☑ **Prof**
Alan Richards **Course Designer** J Hamilton-Stutt **Facilities**
⊗ ⧱ ⓛ ♨ ⚲ ⚙ 🏌 ⌂ ╲ ⛳ ⟋ ✆ **Leisure** hard tennis
courts, heated indoor swimming pool, squash, fishing, sauna,
gymnasium.**Conf** Max 250 Banquet 250 Del from £32 *

Hotel ★★ 65% Ebford House Hotel, Exmouth Rd,
EBFORD ☎ 01392 877658 16 en suite

HIGH BICKINGTON   Map 02 SS52

Libbaton EX37 9BS
☎ 01769 560269 & 560167 🖅 01769 560342
e-mail: jackbrough@intol.co.uk
**Parkland course on undulating land with no steep slopes.
Floodlit driving range.**
18 holes, 6494yds, Par 73, SSS 72, Course record 72.
Club membership 500.
Visitors book in advance. No jeans, trainers or collarless
shirts. **Societies** telephone to book in advance. **Green Fees**
terms on application. **Cards** ▭ ▬ **Prof** Sarah Burnell
Course Designer Col Badham **Facilities** ⊗ ⧱ ⓛ ♨ ⚲ ⚙
⌂ ⛳ ╲ ⟋ ✆ **Location** B3217,1m of High Bickington,
off A377

Hotel ★★★⚑ 69% Highbullen Hotel,
CHITTLEHAMHOLT ☎ 01769 540561
12 en suite 25 annexe en suite

HOLSWORTHY   Map 02 SS30

Holsworthy Killatree EX22 6LP
☎ 01409 253177 🖅 01409 253177
e-mail: hgcsecretary@aol.com
**Pleasant parkland course with gentle slopes, numerous
trees and a few strategic sand bunkers.**
18 holes, 6100yds, Par 70, SSS 69, Course record 64.
Club membership 500.
Visitors book with professional on 01409 254177. **Societies**
by arrangement with secretary or professional. **Green Fees**
£20 per day/round (£10 twilight after 6pm). **Prof** Graham
Webb **Facilities** ⊗ ⧱ ⓛ ♨ ⚲ ⚙ ⌂ ⛳ ╲ ⟋ ✆ **Conf**
Max 40 **Location** 1.5m W on A3072 towards Bude

Hotel ★★★ 71% Falcon Hotel, Breakwater Rd, BUDE
☎ 01288 352005 27 en suite

HONITON   Map 03 ST10

Honiton Middlehills EX14 9TR
☎ 01404 44422 & 42943 🖅 01404 46383
**Founded in 1896, this level parkland course is situated on
a plateau 850ft above sea level. Easy walking and good
views. The 4th hole is a testing par 3. The 17th and 18th
provide a challenging finish.**
18 holes, 5902yds, Par 69, SSS 68.
Club membership 800.
Visitors must contact in advance. **Societies** society bookings
on Thursdays. **Green Fees** £24 per day (£30 weekends &
bank holidays). **Prof** Adrian Cave **Facilities** ⊗ ⧱ ⓛ ♨ ⚲
⚙ ⌂ ⛳ ⟋ **Location** 1.25m SE of Honiton,turn towards
Farway at Tower Cross on A35

Hotel ★★ 69% Home Farm Hotel & Restaurant,
Wilmington, HONITON ☎ 01404 831278
9 en suite 5 annexe en suite

ILFRACOMBE   Map 02 SS54

Ilfracombe Hele Bay EX34 9RT
☎ 01271 862176 & 863328 🖅 01271 867731
e-mail: ilfracombe.golfclub@virgin.net
A sporting, clifftop, heathland course with views over the

continued

Bristol Channel and moors from every tee and green.
18 holes, 5893yds, Par 69, SSS 69, Course record 66.
Club membership 520.

Visitors recommended to make tee reservation prior to visit,
member only before 10am on weekends. **Societies** telephone
in advance. **Green Fees** £25 per day; £20 per round (£30/£25
weekends and bank holidays). **Cards** ▭ ▬ ▦ ▧ ☑ **Prof**
Mark Davies **Course Designer** T K Weir **Facilities** ⊗ ⓛ ♨
⚲ ⚙ ⌂ ⛳ ⟋ **Location** 1.5m E off A399

Hotel ★★ 71% Elmfield Hotel, Torrs Park, ILFRACOMBE
☎ 01271 863377 11 en suite 2 annexe en suite

IPPLEPEN   Map 03 SX86

Dainton Park Totnes Rd, Ipplepen TQ12 5TN
☎ 01803 815000 🖅 01803 815009
e-mail: dpgolf@globalnet.co.uk
**A challenging parkland type course in typical Devon
countryside, with gentle contours, tree-lined fairways and
raised tees. Water hazards make the two opening holes
particularly testing. The 8th, a dramatic 180yard drop
hole totally surrounded by sand, is one of four tough par
3s on the course. It is advisable to book start times.**
18 holes, 6207yds, Par 71, SSS 70, Course record 70.
Club membership 650.
Visitors prior booking by phone advisable to guarantee start
time. **Societies** must contact in advance. **Green Fees** £18 per
round (£20 weekends). **Cards** ▭ ▬ ☑ **Prof** Martin Tyson
Course Designer Adrian Stiff **Facilities** ⊗ ⧱ ⓛ ♨ ⚲ ⌂
⛳ ╲ ⟋ ✆ **Leisure** solarium, gymnasium. **Location** 2m S of
Newton Abbot on A381

Hotel ★★ 68% Queens Hotel, Queen St, NEWTON
ABBOT ☎ 01626 363133 20 en suite

IVYBRIDGE   Map 02 SX65

Dinnaton Fitness & Golf Blachford Rd PL21 9HU
☎ 01752 690020 & 892512 🖅 01752 698334
e-mail: golf@dinnaton.co.uk
**Challenging 9-hole moorland course overlooking the
South Hams. With 5 par 4 and 4 par 3 holes, three lakes
and tight fairways; excellent for improving the short
game. Floodlit practice area.**
9 holes, 4089yds, Par 64, SSS 60.
Club membership 275.
Visitors no restrictions. **Societies** telephone in advance.
Green Fees £15 per day; £8 per 9 holes. **Cards** ▭ ▬ ▦
▧ ☑ **Prof** Douglas Gray **Course Designer** Cotton & Pink
Facilities ⓛ ♨ ⚲ ⌂ ⛳ ⟋ ✆ **Leisure** hard tennis courts,
heated indoor swimming pool, squash, sauna, solarium,
gymnasium. **Location** Leave A38 at Ivybridge junct and
continue towards town centre. At first rdbt follow signs for
club approx 1m

continued

Hotel ★★ 74% Glazebrook House Hotel & Restaurant, SOUTH BRENT ☎ 01364 73322 11 en suite

MORETONHAMPSTEAD — Map 03 SX78

Le Meridien Manor House Hotel TQ13 8RE
☎ 01647 440998 🖹 01647 440961
e-mail: manortee@aol.com
This enjoyable parkland course has enough hazards to make any golfer think. Most hazards are natural such as the Rivers Bowden and Bovey which meander through the first eight holes.
18 holes, 6016yds, Par 69, SSS 69, Course record 63.
Club membership 130.
Visitors must contact in advance and pre-arrange starting times. Societies must telephone for reservation in advance. Green Fees £40 per day; £30 per round (£45/£37 weekends). Cards ⬛ 🔳 🔳 🔳 📶 Prof Richard Lewis Course Designer J Abercrombie Facilities ⊗ ⽧ ⽧ ⽧ ⽧ ⽧ ⽧ ⽧ ⽧ ⽧ ⽧ ⽧ Leisure hard tennis courts, fishing. Conf Thtr 120 Class 60 Board 40 Banquet 70 Del from £30 * Location 2m W of Moretonhampstead, off B3212

Hotel ★★★★ 67% Le Meridien Manor House, MORETONHAMPSTEAD ☎ 01647 440355 90 en suite

MORTEHOE — Map 02 SS44

Mortehoe & Woolacombe EX34 7EH
☎ 01271 870225 & 870566
Attached to a camping and caravan site, this 9-hole course has 2 par 3s and 7 par 4s. The gently sloping clifftop course has spectacular views across Morte Bay.
9 holes, 4690yds, Par 66, SSS 63, Course record 66.
Club membership 245.
Visitors no restrictions. Societies must telephone or write in advance. Green Fees £12 per 18 holes; £7 per 9 holes.
Course Designer D Hoare Facilities ⊗ ⽧ ⽧ ⽧ ⽧ ⽧ ⽧ ⽧ Leisure heated indoor swimming pool, indoor bowls.
Location 0.25m before Mortehoe on station road

Hotel ★★★ 75% Watersmeet Hotel, Mortehoe, WOOLACOMBE ☎ 01271 870333 22 en suite

NEWTON ABBOT — Map 03 SX87

Newton Abbot (Stover) Bovey Rd TQ12 6QQ
☎ 01626 352460 (Secretary) 🖹 01626 330210
Mature wooded parkland course with water coming into play on eight holes.
18 holes, 5764yds, Par 69, SSS 68, Course record 63.
Club membership 800.
Visitors must have proof of membership of recognised club or current handicap certificate. Advised to contact in advance. Societies by arrangement on Thu only. Green Fees £30 per day; £25 per round (£32/£28 weekends). Cards ⬛ 🔳 Prof Malcolm Craig Course Designer James Braid Facilities ⊗ ⽧ ⽧ ⽧ ⽧ ⽧ ⽧ Location 3m N on A382

Hotel ★★ 68% Queens Hotel, Queen St, NEWTON ABBOT ☎ 01626 363133 20 en suite

OKEHAMPTON — Map 02 SX59

Ashbury Higher Maddaford EX20 4NL
☎ 01837 55453 🖹 01837 55468
Parkland style courses with natural undulations and hazards. Set in 235 acres of Devon countryside with 137 bunkers and 18 lakes, the courses comprise a loop of 27

continued

holes, the 18 hole Oakwood course and an 18 hole par 3 course. Each hole has a purpose built alternative green so that greens can be changed in adverse weather.
Ashbury Beeches, Pines Willows: 27 holes, 8100yds.
Ashbury Oakwood: 18 holes, 5343yds, Par 68, SSS 66.
Ashbury Acorns: 18 holes, 2018yds, Par 54.
Club membership 170.
Visitors must contact in advance. Green Fees £20 per day (£25 weekends). Cards ⬛ 🔳 🔳 🔳 📶 Prof Reg Cade Course Designer David Fensom Facilities ⊗ ⽧ ⽧ ⽧ ⽧ ⽧ ⽧ ⽧ ⽧ Leisure hard tennis courts, heated indoor swimming pool, fishing, sauna, solarium, Indoor bowls, Snooker. Location Off A3079 Okehampton-Holsworthy

Hotel ★★ 66% Ashbury Hotel, Higher Maddaford, Southcott, OKEHAMPTON ☎ 01837 55453 26 en suite 29 annexe en suite

Okehampton Tors Rd EX20 1EF
☎ 01837 52113 🖹 01837 52734
e-mail: okehamptongc@btconnect.com
A good combination of moorland, woodland and river make this one of the prettiest, yet testing courses in Devon.
18 holes, 5268yds, Par 68, SSS 65, Course record 66.
Club membership 600.
Visitors advance booking recommended, limited times available at weekends. Saturdays by prior arrangement only Societies by prior arrangement. Green Fees £20 per day; £17 per round (£25/£20 Saturday). Cards ⬛ 🔳 🔳 🔳 📶 Prof Simon Jefferies Course Designer J F Taylor Facilities ⊗ ⽧ ⽧ ⽧ ⽧ ⽧ ⽧ ⽧ ⽧ Conf Banquet 80 Location 1m S off A30, signposted from town centre

Hotel ★★ 66% Oxenham Arms, SOUTH ZEAL ☎ 01837 840244 & 840577
🖹 01837 840791 8 rms (7 en suite)

PLYMOUTH — Map 02 SX45

Elfordleigh Colebrook, Plympton PL7 5EB
☎ 01752 336428 (hotel) & 348425 (golf shop)
🖹 01752 344581
e-mail: elfordleigh@btinternet.com
Undulating, scenic parkland course offering a true challenge to all levels of player. The 11th hole, par 3 is one of the best in the South West area.
18 holes, 5664yds, Par 69, SSS 67, Course record 66.
Club membership 600.
Visitors prior arrangement required. Societies by arrangement. Green Fees £25 per round (£30 weekends & bank holidays). Cards ⬛ 🔳 🔳 🔳 📶 Prof John Nolan Course Designer J H Taylor Facilities ⊗ ⽧ ⽧ ⽧ ⽧ ⽧ ⽧ ⽧ ⽧ ⽧ Leisure hard tennis courts, outdoor and indoor heated swimming pools, squash, sauna, solarium, gymnasium, golf tuition breaks.Conf Max 150 Thtr 150 Class 100 Board 50 Banquet 100 Del from £25 * Location 2m NE off A374, follow signs from Plympton town centre

Hotel ★★★ 68% Boringdon Hall, Colebrook, Plympton, PLYMOUTH ☎ 01752 344455 41 en suite

Staddon Heights Plymstock PL9 9SP
☎ 01752 402475 🖹 01752 401998
Seaside course affording spectacular views across Plymouth Sound, Dartmoor and Bodmin Moor. Testing holes include the par 3 17th with its green cut into a hillside and the par 4 14th across a road. Easy walking.
18 holes, 5804yds, Par 68, SSS 68, Course record 66.
Club membership 750.

continued on page 67

SAUNTON GOLF CLUB

Situated on the North Devon coast, 2 miles out of Braunton on the B3231 to Croyde. Saunton offers two magnificent 18 hole Championship standard traditional links courses both of which are included in list of the top 100 courses in the UK. Golf has been played at Saunton for more than 100 years (the Club was founded in 1897) and the East Course (6729 yds Par 71), redesigned in 1919 by the famous W. H. Fowler has remained essentially unchanged, whilst the newer West Course (6403 yds Par 71), having been lost as a battle training ground during World War II, was rebuilt in the early 1970's by Frank Pennick and is in many ways, although shorter, a more exacting test of golf than the more famous East Course. A recent addition is the provision of a covered practice facility which is in addition to a number of other practice areas, including 2 putting greens and a well stocked Professional's Shop with well trained staff able to offer tuition and advice on equipment. The Clubhouse has a large lounge and excellent restaurant overlooking the courses.

The Club has hosted most of the major amateur Championship over the years and one of the more notable recent winners being Sergio Garcia who won the R & A's British Boys Championship at the age of 16 in 1997. The Faldo Junior Series Finals was played at Saunton in September 2001, which was won by the young Russian Grigory Bondarenko. The PGA hold the Qualifying School for the EuroPro Tour (formerly the MasterCard Tour) over both courses early in the season each year and the Club will host the PGA Club Professionals Championship in 2002.

Saunton, Nr. Braunton, North Devon EX33 1LG
Tel: 01271 8712436 Fax: 01271 814241
www.sauntongolf.co.uk   E-mail: info@sauntongolf.co.uk

Visitors must have handicap certificate and contact the pro or secretary in advance. **Societies** apply by telephone in advance. **Green Fees** £20 (£24 weekends). **Prof** Ian Marshall **Course Designer** Hamilton Stutt **Facilities** ⊗)Ⅲ ⓛ ▤ ▆ ♀ ⚘ 🖳 🎯 ✧ **Location** 5m SW of city centre

Hotel ★★★ 65% Posthouse Plymouth, Cliff Rd, The Hoe, PLYMOUTH ☎ 0870 400 9064 113 en suite

SAUNTON
Map 02 SS43

Saunton EX33 1LG
☎ 01271 812436 📱 01271 814241
e-mail: info@sauntongolf.co.uk
Two traditional championship links courses. Windy, with natural hazards.

East Course: 18 holes, 6373yds, Par 71, SSS 71, Course record 65.
West Course: 18 holes, 6138yds, Par 71, SSS 70, Course record 67. Club membership 1450.
Visitors prior booking recommended and must have handicap certificate. **Societies** must apply in advance, handicap certificates required. **Green Fees** terms on application. **Cards** ⬛ ▬ 🟦 **Prof** A T MacKenzie **Course Designer** F Pennick/W H Fowler **Facilities** ⊗)Ⅲ ⓛ ▆ ♀ ⚘ 🖳 🎯 ✧ ✦ **Location** S side of village off B3231

Hotel ★★★★ 70% Saunton Sands Hotel, SAUNTON ☎ 01271 890212 92 en suite
Additional hotel ★★ 67% Kittiwell House Hotel & Restaurant, St Mary's Rd, CROYDE ☎ 01271 890247 📱 01271 890469 4 en suite 8 annexe en suite

SIDMOUTH
Map 03 SY18

Sidmouth Cotmaton Rd, Peak Hill EX10 8SX
☎ 01395 513451 & 516407 📱 01395 514661
Situated on the side of Peak Hill, offering beautiful coastal views. Club founded in 1889.
18 holes, 5100yds, Par 66, SSS 65, Course record 59.
Club membership 700.
Visitors by prior arrangement. **Societies** by prior arrangement with the secretary. **Green Fees** £24 per day; £20 per round. **Prof** Gaele Tapper **Course Designer** J H Taylor **Facilities** ⚘ 🖳 🎯 ✧ **Location** W side of town centre

Hotel ★★★★ 72% Victoria Hotel, The Esplanade, SIDMOUTH ☎ 01395 512651 61 en suite

SOUTH BRENT
Map 03 SX66

Wrangaton (S Devon) Golf Links Rd, Wrangaton
TQ10 9HJ ☎ 01364 73229 📱 01364 73229
Unique 18 hole course with 9 holes on moorland and 9 holes on parkland. The course lies within Dartmoor National Park. Spectacular views towards sea and rugged
continued

terrain. Natural fairways and hazards include bracken, sheep and ponies.
18 holes, 6083yds, Par 70, SSS 69, Course record 66.
Club membership 660.
Visitors contact in advance. **Societies** write or telephone.
Green Fees £20 per 18 holes. **Cards** ⬛ ▬ **Prof** Glenn Richards **Course Designer** D M A Steel **Facilities** ⊗)Ⅲ ⓛ ▆ ♀ ⚘ 🖳 🎯 🛒 ✧ **Location** 2.25 m SW off A38, between South Brent & Ivybridge

Hotel ★★ 74% Glazebrook House Hotel & Restaurant, SOUTH BRENT ☎ 01364 73322 11 en suite

SPARKWELL
Map 02 SX55

Welbeck Manor & Sparkwell Golf Course
Blacklands PL7 5DF ☎ 01752 837219 📱 01752 837219
A mature parkland course with several challenging holes, it features fairway and greenside bunkers, mature trees and streams. The house on the site, now the hotel, was built by Isambard Kingdom Brunel. Several holes commemorate his famous works - the 6th being The Great Western. This very challenging par 5 tee is out of bounds all the way up the left.
9 holes, 2886yds, Par 68, SSS 68, Course record 68.
Club membership 200.
Visitors no restrictions **Societies** telephone in advance.
Green Fees £6 per 9 holes; £10 per 18 holes (£7/£12 weekends and bank holidays). **Cards** ⬛ ▬ 🟥 ▤ **Course Designer** John Gabb **Facilities** ⊗)Ⅲ ⓛ ▆ ♀ ⚘ 🖳 🎯 ✧ **Leisure** 9 hole par 3. **Conf** Thtr 40 Board 18 Banquet 40 Del £1.50-£68.50. **Location** 1m N of A38 Plymouth/ Ivybridge road

Hotel ★★★ 68% Boringdon Hall, Colebrook, Plympton, PLYMOUTH ☎ 01752 344455 41 en suite

TAVISTOCK
Map 02 SX47

Hurdwick Tavistock Hamlets PL19 0LL
☎ 01822 612746
An executive parkland course with many bunkers and fine views. Executive golf originated in America and the concept is that a round should take no longer than 3 hours whilst offering solid challenge.
18 holes, 5302yds, Par 68, SSS 67.
Club membership 180.
Visitors no restrictions. **Societies** must contact in advance. **Green Fees** £15 per day. **Course Designer** Hawtree **Facilities** ⊗ ⓛ ▆ ♀ ⚘ 🎯 🛒 ✧ **Location** 1m N of Tavistock

Hotel ★★★ 69% Bedford Hotel, 1 Plymouth Rd, TAVISTOCK ☎ 01822 613221 30 en suite

Tavistock Down Rd PL19 9AQ
☎ 01822 612344 📱 01822 612344
e-mail: tavygolf@freeserve.net
Set on Whitchurch Down in south-west Dartmoor with easy walking and magnificent views over rolling countryside into Cornwall. Downland turf with some heather, and interesting holes on undulating ground.
18 holes, 6250yds, Par 70, SSS 70, Course record 64.
Club membership 700.
Visitors advisable to contact in advance. **Societies** by arrangement with secretary. **Green Fees** not confirmed.
Prof D Rehaag **Course Designer** H Fowler **Facilities** ⊗)Ⅲ ⓛ ▆ ♀ ⚘ 🖳 🎯 ✧ **Location** 1m SE of town centre, on Whitchurch Down

Hotel ★★★ 69% Bedford Hotel, 1 Plymouth Rd, TAVISTOCK ☎ 01822 613221 30 en suite

TEDBURN ST MARY
Map 03 SX89

Fingle Glen
EX6 6AF ☎ 01647 61817 📠 01647 61135
9-hole course containing six par 4s and three par 3s set in 52 acres of rolling countryside. Testing 4th, 5th and 9th holes. 12-bay floodlit driving range.
9 holes, 4818yds, Par 66, SSS 63, Course record 63.
Club membership 500.
Visitors must contact in advance. **Societies** write or telephone in advance. **Green Fees** not confirmed. **Cards** 🖃 🖩 🖩 💳 **Prof** Stephen Gould **Course Designer** Bill Pile **Facilities** ⊗ 〗ⅲ ⓛ ⚑ ⚑ ⚑ ⚑ ⚑ ⚑ ⚑ **Location** 5m W of Exeter, off A30

Hotel ★★★ 70% Lord Haldon Country House Hotel, Dunchideock, EXETER ☎ 01392 832483 19 en suite

TEIGNMOUTH
Map 03 SX97

Teignmouth
Haldon Moor TQ14 9NY
☎ 01626 777070 📠 01626 777070
e-mail: teignmouth.g.c@btclick.com
This fairly flat heathland course is high up with a fine panoramic views of sea, moors and river valley. Good springy turf with some heather and an interesting layout makes for very enjoyable holiday golf. Designed by Dr Alister MacKenzie, the world famous architect who also designed Augusta GC USA.
18 holes, 6200yds, Par 71, SSS 70, Course record 65.
Club membership 900.
Visitors handicap certificate required. **Societies** Tue & Thu only, telephone in advance and confirm in writing. **Green Fees** £25 (£27.50 weekends). **Prof** Peter Ward **Course Designer** Dr Alister Mackenzie **Facilities** ⊗ 〗ⅲ ⓛ ⚑ ⚑ ⚑ ⚑ ⚑ ⚑ **Location** 2m NW off B3192

Hotel ★★ 71% Ness House Hotel, Marine Dr, Shaldon, TEIGNMOUTH ☎ 01626 873480
7 en suite 5 annexe en suite

THURLESTONE
Map 03 SX64

Thurlestone
TQ7 3NZ
☎ 01548 560405 📠 01548 562149
Situated on the edge of the cliffs with typical downland turf and good greens. The course, after an interesting opening hole, rises to higher land with fine seaviews, and finishes with an excellent 502-yard downhill hole to the clubhouse.
18 holes, 6340yds, Par 71, SSS 70, Course record 65.
Club membership 770.
Visitors must contact in advance & have handicap certificate from a recognised club. **Green Fees** £32 per round. **Cards** 🖃 🖩 🖩 💳 **Prof** Peter Laugher **Course Designer** Harry S Colt **Facilities** ⊗ 〗ⅲ by prior arrangement ⓛ ⚑ ⚑ ⚑ ⚑ ⚑ **Leisure** hard and grass tennis courts. **Location** S side of village

Hotel ★★★★ 72% Thurlestone Hotel, THURLESTONE ☎ 01548 560382 64 en suite

---

TIVERTON
Map 03 SS91

Tiverton
Post Hill EX16 4NE ☎ 01884 252187
A parkland course where the many different species of tree are a feature and where the lush pastures ensure some of the finest fairways in the south-west. There are a number of interesting holes which visitors will find a real challenge.
18 holes, 6236yds, Par 71, SSS 71, Course record 65.
Club membership 725.
Visitors must have a current handicap certificate. **Societies** apply in writing or telephone. **Green Fees** not confirmed. **Prof** David Sheppard **Course Designer** Braid **Facilities** ⊗ 〗ⅲ by prior arrangement ⓛ ⚑ ⚑ ⚑ ⚑

Hotel ★★★ 75% Midland Hotel, Midland Rd, DERBY ☎ 01332 345894 100 en suite

TORQUAY
Map 03 SX96

Torquay
30 Petitor Rd, St Marychurch TQ1 4QF
☎ 01803 314591 📠 01803 316116
e-mail: torquaygolfclub@skynow.net
Unusual combination of cliff and parkland golf, with wonderful views over the sea and Dartmoor.
18 holes, 6175yds, Par 69, SSS 69, Course record 63.
Club membership 700.
Visitors must contact in advance. **Societies** must apply in writing. **Green Fees** Summer; £25-£30 day/round: Winter £20-£25. **Prof** Martin Ruth **Facilities** ⊗ 〗ⅲ ⓛ ⚑ ⚑ ⚑ ⚑ ⚑ ⚑ ⚑ **Location** 1.25m N

Hotel ★★ 68% Meadfoot Bay Hotel, Meadfoot Sea Road, Torquay ☎ 01803 294722 22 en suite

TORRINGTON (GREAT)
Map 02 SS41

Torrington
Weare Trees, Great Torrington EX38 7EZ
☎ 01805 622229 & 623878 📠 01805 623878
e-mail: theoffice@torringtongolf.fsnet.co.uk
Attractive and challenging 9 hole course. Free draining to allow play all year round. Excellent greens and outstanding views.
9 holes, 4423yds, Par 64, SSS 62, Course record 58.
Club membership 420.
Visitors contact in advance. May not play Tues, Wed, Sat, Sun or bank holidays before noon. **Societies** by arrangement. **Green Fees** £14 per round. **Facilities** ⊗ 〗ⅲ ⓛ ⚑ ⚑ ⚑ ⚑ ⚑ **Location** 1m W of Torringdon

Hotel ★★★ 67% Royal Hotel, Barnstaple St, BIDEFORD ☎ 01237 472005 31 en suite

WESTWARD HO!
Map 02 SS42

Royal North Devon
Golf Links Rd EX39 1HD
☎ 01237 473817 📠 01237 423456
e-mail: info@royalnorthdevongolfclub.co.uk
Oldest links course in England with traditional links features and a museum in the clubhouse.
18 holes, 6716yds, Par 72, SSS 72, Course record 68.
Club membership 1150.
Visitors advisable to telephone and book tee time, handicap certificate preferred or letter of introduction from club. **Societies** apply in writing or telephone. **Green Fees** £38 per day; £32 per round (£42/£38 weekends & bank holidays). **Cards** 🖃 🖩 💳 **Prof** Richard Herring **Course Designer** Old Tom Morris **Facilities** ⊗ ⓛ ⚑ ⚑ ⚑ ⚑ ⚑ ⚑ **Leisure** Museum of Golf Memorabilia, snooker. **Location** N side of village off B3236

continued

Entries with a green background identify courses considered to be particularly interesting

Guesthouse ♦♦♦♦ Culloden House Hotel, Fosketh Hill, WESTWARD HO! ☎ 01237 479421 9 rms (7 en suite)

WOOLSERY — Map 02 SS32

Hartland Forest Woolsery EX39 5RA
☎ 01237 431442 📠 01237 431734
e-mail: alanc@hartland-forest.demon.co.uk
Exceptionally varied course with many water hazards.
18 holes, 6015yds, Par 71, SSS 69.
Club membership 60.
Visitors no restrictions. **Societies** telephone in advance or apply in writing. **Green Fees** terms on application. **Cards** ▨ ▤▧ ▨ ▨ **Course Designer** A Cartwright **Facilities** ⊗ ⫙ ▙ 🖫 ♀ ⚲ ⚐ 🏴 🛢 ✐ **Leisure** hard tennis courts, heated indoor swimming pool, fishing, sauna, solarium. **Location** 1.7m E of A39, 4 miles south of Clovelly Cross on A39

Hotel ★★★ 72% Penhaven Country House, Rectory Ln, PARKHAM ☎ 01237 451388 & 451711 📠 01237 451878 12 en suite

YELVERTON — Map 02 SX56

Yelverton Golf Links Rd PL20 6BN
☎ 01822 852824 📠 01822 854869
e-mail: secretary@yelvertongc.co.uk
An excellent course on Dartmoor with plenty of gorse and heather. Tight lies in the fairways, fast greens and challenging hazards. Boasts 3 of the best holes in Devon (12th, 13th & 16th). Outstanding views.

18 holes, 6351yds, Par 71, SSS 71, Course record 67.
Club membership 650.
Visitors must have handicap certificate and subject to availability, contact in advance. **Societies** must be booked in advance, by telephone initially. **Green Fees** £30 per day (£40 Sat). **Prof** Tim McSherry **Course Designer** Herbert Fowler **Facilities** ⊗ ⫙ ▙ 🖫 ♀ ⚲ ⚐ ✐ **Leisure** indoor golf academy. **Conf** Max 80 Class 80 Board 10 Banquet 80 **Location** 1m S of Yelverton, off A386

continued

Hotel ★★★ 72% Moorland Links Hotel, YELVERTON ☎ 01822 852245 45 en suite

DORSET

ASHLEY HEATH — Map 04 SU10

Moors Valley Horton Rd BH24 2ET
☎ 01425 479776 📠 01425 471656
e-mail: golfcentre@moorsvalley.fsnet.co.uk
This municipal course is set in the beautiful surroundings of a country park. It offers a test for all standards. It is gently undulating, with water hazards on six holes.
Moors Valley Golf Centre: 18 holes, 6337yds,
Par 72, SSS 70.
Club membership 340.
Visitors must contact in advance. **Societies** telephone for availability. **Green Fees** £12.50 weekdays (£15 weekends & bank holidays). **Cards** ▨ ▤▧ ▨ ▨ **Prof** Roger Tuddenham **Course Designer** Hawtree & Son **Facilities** ⊗ ⫙ ▙ 🖫 ♀ ⚲ ⚐ ✐ **Location** Signposted from A31 Ashley Heath roundabout

Hotel ★★ 72% Moortown Lodge Hotel, 244 Christchurch Rd, RINGWOOD ☎ 01425 471404 6 rms (5 en suite)

BEAMINSTER — Map 03 ST40

Chedington Court South Perrott DT8 3HU
☎ 01935 891413 📠 01935 891217
This beautiful 18 hole parkland course is set on the Dorset-Somerset borders with mature trees and interesting water hazards.
18 holes, 5924yds, Par 70, SSS 70, Course record 71.
Club membership 400.
Visitors must book tee time in advance at weekends. **Societies** apply in writing or telephone. **Green Fees** not confirmed. **Course Designer** David Hemstock **Facilities** ⊗ ⫙ ▙ 🖫 ♀ ⚲ ⚐ ✐ **Location** 5m NE of Beaminster on A356 Dorchester-Crewkerne

Hotel ★★★ 71% Bridge House Hotel, 3 Prout Bridge, BEAMINSTER ☎ 01308 862200 9 en suite 5 annexe en suite

BELCHALWELL — Map 03 ST70

Dorset Heights DT11 0EG
☎ 01258 861386 📠 01258 860900
18 holes, 6138yds, Par 70, SSS 70, Course record 74.
Course Designer David Astill
Telephone for further details

Hotel ★★★ 67% Crown Hotel, West St, BLANDFORD FORUM ☎ 01258 456626 32 en suite

BERE REGIS — Map 03 SY89

East Dorset BH20 7NT
☎ 01929 472244 📠 01929 471294
e-mail: edgc@golf.co.uk
Lakeland is a long 18-hole parkland course with natural water features. The Woodland is a second 9-hole, 18-tee course set amongst trees and rhododendrons. Floodlit 22-bay driving range, golf shop.
Lakeland Course: 18 holes, 6580yds, Par 72, SSS 73, Course record 69.
Woodland Course: 9 holes, 5032yards, Par 66, SSS 64.
Club membership 550.

continued

Visitors must book in advance and handicap certificate required for Lakeland course. **Societies** apply in advance. **Green Fees** not confirmed. **Prof** Derwynne Honan **Course Designer** Martin Hawtree **Facilities** ⊗ ⁂ 🍴 ⬛ 🍺 ♀ 🏌 🏠 🏐 🏕 🐟 🚣 🏌 ⛳ **Location** 5m from Bere Regis on Wool Road

Hotel ★★ 70% Kemps Country House Hotel, East Stoke, WAREHAM ☎ 01929 462563
5 rms (4 en suite) 10 annexe en suite

BLANDFORD FORUM Map 03 ST80

Ashley Wood Wimborne Rd DT11 9HN
☎ 01258 452253 📠 01258 450590
e-mail: ashleywoodgolfclub@hotmail.com
Undulating and well drained downland course with superb views over the Tarrant and Stour Valleys.
18 holes, 6276yds, Par 70, SSS 70, Course record 65.
Club membership 700.
Visitors phone in advance. Handicap certificate required weekends unless with member. **Societies** apply to Secretary. **Green Fees** terms on application. **Prof** Jon Shimmons **Course Designer** P Tallack **Facilities** ⊗ ⁂ 🍴 ⬛ 🍺 ♀ 🏌 🏠 🐟 🚣 ⛳ **Location** 2m E on B3082

Hotel ★★★ 67% Crown Hotel, West St, BLANDFORD FORUM ☎ 01258 456626 32 en suite

BOURNEMOUTH Map 04 SZ09

The Club at Meyrick Park Central Dr, Meyrick Park BH2 6LH ☎ 01202 786000 📠 01202 786020
e-mail: meyrickpark.lodge@clubhaus.com
Picturesque municipal parkland course founded in 1890.
The Club At Meyrick Park: 18 holes, 5600yds,
Par 69, SSS 69.
Visitors book up to 7 days in advance. **Societies** telephone in advance. **Green Fees** £17 per round (£20 weekends and bank holidays). **Cards** 🖃 💳 💳 💳 💳 **Prof** David Miles
Facilities ⊗ ⁂ 🍴 ⬛ 🍺 ♀ 🏌 🏠 🏕 🏐 ⛳ **Leisure** heated indoor swimming pool, sauna, solarium, gymnasium, spa and steam room. **Conf** Max 50 Thtr 50 Class 30 Board 20

Hotel ★★★ 65% Burley Court Hotel, Bath Rd, BOURNEMOUTH ☎ 01202 552824 & 556704
📠 01202 298514 38 en suite

Knighton Heath Francis Av, West Howe BH11 8NX
☎ 01202 572633 📠 01202 590774
e-mail: khgc@btclick.com
Undulating heathland course on high ground inland from Poole.
18 holes, 6084yds, Par 70, SSS 69.
Club membership 700.
Visitors may not play weekend. Phone for availability. **Societies** must book in advance. **Green Fees** £25 per round £30 per day. **Facilities** ⊗ 🍴 ⬛ 🍺 ♀ 🏌 🏠 ⛳ **Location** N side of Poole, junct of A348/A3409 signposted at rdbt

Hotel ★★ 77% Beechleas Hotel & Restaurant, 17 Poole Rd, WIMBORNE MINSTER ☎ 01202 841684 5 en suite 4 annexe en suite

Open Golf Centres Riverside Av, off Castle Ln East
BH7 7ES ☎ 01202 436436 📠 01202 436400
e-mail: info@opengolfcentres.co.uk
A well drained meadowland course beside the River Stour with many mature trees and lakes on five holes.

continued

Enjoyable for intermediates and beginners off yellow or white tees and a test for any golfer off the back blue tees. Greens are superb and need careful reading.
Lakes Course: 18 holes, 6277yards, Par 72, SSS 69.
Club membership 300.
Visitors may play any time. Advisable to book in advance for weekends. **Societies** telephone in advance **Green Fees** £27 per 36 holes; £14.50 per 18 holes (£17.50 per 18 holes weekends). Par 3 course £8 per 18 holes; £4.50 per 9 holes (£10/£5.50 weekends). **Cards** 🖃 💳 💳 💳 💳 **Prof** Lawrence Moxon/Andie Anderson **Course Designer** John Jacobs Golf Associates **Facilities** ⊗ ⁂ 🍴 ⬛ 🍺 ♀ 🏌 🏠 🏐 🐟 🚣 ⛳ **Leisure** 9 hole par 3 course. **Location** off A338 Bournemouth to Southampton road, approx 2m from town centre. At Cooper Dean roundabout take A3060 towards Christchurch, over mini roundabout then turn left into Riverside Avenue. Entrance 500 yds on right

Guesthouse ◆◆◆◆ Amitie Guest House, 1247 Christchurch Rd, BOURNEMOUTH ☎ 01202 427255 7 en suite

Queen's Park Queens Park Dr West BH8 9BY
☎ 01202 302611 📠 01202 302611
e-mail: dgibb@qpbgc.fsnet.co.uk
Undulating parkland course of pine and heather, with narrow, tree-lined fairways. Public course played over by Boscombe Golf Club and Bournemouth Artisans Golf Club.
18 holes, 6305yds, Par 72, SSS 70, Course record 69.
Club membership 370.
Visitors Not open for play Sun pm. **Societies** Must book in advance. **Green Fees** not confirmed. **Cards** 🖃 💳 💳 💳 💳 **Prof** Richard Hill **Facilities** ⊗ ⁂ 🍴 ⬛ 🍺 ♀ 🏌 🏠 ⛳ **Location** 2m NE of Bournemouth town centre off A338

Hotel ★★★ 68% Queens Hotel, Meyrick Rd, East Cliff, BOURNEMOUTH ☎ 01202 554415 109 en suite

BRIDPORT Map 03 SY49

Bridport & West Dorset Burton Rd DT6 4PS
☎ 01308 421491 & 421095 📠 01308 421095
Seaside links course on the top of the east cliff, with fine views over Lyme Bay and surrounding countryside. A popular feature is the pretty and deceptive 14th hole, its sunken green lying 90 feet below the tee and guarded by natural hazards and bunkers.
18 holes, 6488yds, Par 73, SSS 71.
Club membership 600.
Visitors must contact in advance. **Societies** must contact in writing in advance. **Green Fees** £22 per day; £16 after noon, £10 after 5pm. **Prof** David Parsons **Course Designer** Hawtree **Facilities** ⊗ 🍴 ⬛ 🍺 ♀ 🏠 ⛳ 🏌 **Leisure** pitch & putt (holiday season). **Location** 2m SE of Bridport on B3157

continued

Hotel ★★★ 64% Haddon House Hotel, West Bay,
BRIDPORT ☎ 01308 423626 & 425323 ▤ 01308 427348
12 en suite

BROADSTONE · Map 03 SZ09

Broadstone (Dorset) Wentworth Dr BH18 8DQ
☎ 01202 692595 ▤ 01202 692595
e-mail: admin@broadstonegolfclub.com
**Undulating and demanding heathland course with the
2nd, 7th, 13th and 16th being particularly challenging
holes.**
*18 holes, 6315yds, Par 70, SSS 70, Course record 66.
Club membership 700.*
Visitors restricted at weekends & bank holidays. Must
contact in advance. Handicap certificate required.
Societies contact in advance. **Green Fees** £35 per round
(£45 per round weekends). **Prof** Nigel Tokely **Course
Designer** Colt/Dunn **Facilities** ⊗ ⽶ ⽧ ⽨ ♀ ⛤ 🏠 ⛳ ⚘
⚑ **Location** N side of village off B3074

Hotel ★★ 77% Beechleas Hotel & Restaurant, 17 Poole
Rd, WIMBORNE MINSTER ☎ 01202 841684
5 en suite 4 annexe en suite

CHRISTCHURCH · Map 04 SZ19

Dudmoor Farm Dudmoor Farm Rd, Off Fairmile Rd
BH23 6AQ ☎ 01202 473826 ▤ 01202 480207
**A testing par 3 & 4 woodland course in an area of
outstanding natural beauty.**
9 holes, 1428mtrs, Par 31.
Visitors no restrictions. **Societies** telephone in advance.
Green Fees £6.50 per 9/18 holes. **Facilities** ⽧ ♀ ⛤ ⛳ ⚑ ⚘
Leisure squash, fishing. **Location** Located on a private road
off B3073 Christchurch to Hurn road

Hotel ★★★ 74% Waterford Lodge Hotel, 87 Bure Ln,
Friars Cliff, Mudeford, CHRISTCHURCH
☎ 01425 272948 & 278801 ▤ 01425 279130 18 en suite

Iford Bridge Barrack Rd BH23 2BA ☎ 01202 473817
9 holes, 2165yds, Par 34, SSS 32.
Location W side of town centre on A35
Telephone for further details

Hotel ★★★ 74% Waterford Lodge Hotel, 87 Bure Ln,
Friars Cliff, Mudeford, CHRISTCHURCH
☎ 01425 272948 & 278801 ▤ 01425 279130 18 en suite

DORCHESTER · Map 03 SY69

Came Down Came Down DT2 8NR
☎ 01305 813494 (manager) & 812670 (pro)
▤ 01305 813494
**Scene of the West of England Championships on
several occasions, this fine course lies on a high plateau
commanding glorious views over Portland. Three par
5 holes add interest to a round. The turf is of the
springy, downland type.**
*18 holes, 6244yds, Par 70, SSS 71.
Club membership 750.*
Visitors advisable to phone in advance, must have
handicap certificate. May play after 9am weekdays &
after noon Sun. **Societies** by arrangement on Wed only.
Green Fees not confirmed. **Prof** David Holmes **Course
Designer** J H Taylor **Facilities** ⊗ ⽶ ⽧ ⽨ ♀ ⛤ 🏠 ⛳
⚘ ⚑ **Location** 2m S off A354

continued

Guesthouse ◆◆◆◆◆ Yalbury Cottage Hotel & Restaurant,
Lower Bockhampton, DORCHESTER
☎ 01305 262382 8 en suite

FERNDOWN · Map 04 SU00

Dudsbury 64 Christchurch Rd BH22 8ST
☎ 01202 593499 ▤ 01202 594555
e-mail: glegg@dudsbury.demon.co.uk
**Set in 160 acres of beautiful Dorset countryside rolling
down to the River Stour. Wide variety of interesting and
challenging hazards, notably water which comes into play
on 14 holes. The well-drained greens are protected by
large bunkers and water hazards. A feature hole is the
16th where the green is over two lakes; the more
aggressive the drive the greater the reward.**
*Championship Course: 18 holes, 6904yds, Par 71, SSS 73,
Course record 64.
Club membership 700.*
Visitors welcome by arrangement with secretary or golf
professional. **Societies** telephone in advance. **Green Fees**
£42 per 36 holes; £32 per 18 holes (£47/£37 weekend and
bank holidays). **Cards** ⊟ 💳 💳 💳 🌐 **Prof** Kevin
Spurgeon **Course Designer** Donald Steel **Facilities** ⊗ ⽶ ⽧
♀ ⛤ 🏠 ⛳ ⚘ 🛒 ⚑ ⚑ **Leisure** fishing, 6 Hole Par 3
Academy Course.**Conf** Thtr 230 Class 125 Board 115
Banquet 250 Del from £200 * **Location** 3m N of
Bournemouth on B3073, between Parley and Longham

Hotel ★★★★ 70% The Dormy, New Rd, FERNDOWN
☎ 01202 872121 115 en suite

Ferndown 119 Golf Links Rd BH22 8BU
☎ 01202 874602 ▤ 01202 873926
e-mail: ferndowngc@lineone.net
**Fairways are gently undulating amongst heather,
gorse and pine trees giving the course a most attractive
appearance. There are a number of dog-leg holes.**
*Championship Course: 18 holes, 6452yds, Par 71, SSS
71, Course record 65.
Presidents Course: 9 holes, 5604yds, Par 70, SSS 68.
Club membership 600.*
Visitors must contact in advance & have handicap
certificate, no visitors on Thursdays except on Presidents
course, numbers restricted at weekends. **Societies**
welcome Tue & Fri only, telephone in advance. **Green
Fees** Championship: £55 per day; £45 per round (£60/£50
weekends). President : £20 per day (£25 weekends).
Cards ⊟ 💳 💳 🌐 **Prof** Iain Parker **Course Designer**
Harold Hilton **Facilities** ⊗ ⽶ ⽧ ♀ ⛤ 🏠 ⛳ 🛒 ⚘
Location S side of town centre off A347

Hotel ★★★★ 70% The Dormy, New Rd, FERNDOWN
☎ 01202 872121 115 en suite

Ferndown Forest Forest Links Rd BH22 9QE
☎ 01202 876096 ▨ 01202 894095
e-mail: golfingpleasure@supanet.com
Flat parkland course dotted with mature oak trees, several interesting water features, and some tight fairways.
18 holes, 5068yds, Par 68, SSS 65.
Club membership 400.
Visitors advisable to contact in advance. **Societies** apply in writing. **Green Fees** £17 per day; £12 weekdays (£20/£14weekends) per day. **Cards** ▨▨▨▨ **Prof** Mike Dodd **Course Designer** Guy Hunt/Richard Graham **Facilities** ⊗ ⊪ ⊾ ⊒ ⊻ ⊿ ⋔ ⊘ ⋐ **Location** From London M3 then A31, end of dual carriageway Dolmans Crossing rdbt right exit Forest Links Rd. Signposted towards Dorset police station

Hotel ★★★★ 70% The Dormy, New Rd, FERNDOWN
☎ 01202 872121 115 en suite

HALSTOCK   Map 03 ST50

Halstock Common Ln BA22 9SF
☎ 01935 891689 ▨ 01935 891839
e-mail: halstock.golf@feeuk.com
Halstock is a short tight course, but presents an interesting challenge to players of all abilities. The terrain is gently undulating in places and there are plenty of trees and water hazards.
18 holes, 4481yds, Par 66, SSS 63, Course record 63.
Club membership 200.
Visitors must telephone in advance. Restricted until 10.30am on Sundays. **Societies** telephone in advance. **Green Fees** £16 per day; £11 per 18 holes; £6.50 per 9 holes (£18/£13/£8 weekends). **Cards** ▨▨▨▨ **Prof** Robert Harris **Facilities** ⊒ ⊻ ⊿ ⋔ ⊘ ⋐ **Location** 6m S of Yeovil

Hotel ★★★♨♨ Summer Lodge, EVERSHOT
☎ 01935 83424 11 en suite 7 annexe en suite

HIGHCLIFFE   Map 04 SZ29

Highcliffe Castle 107 Lymington Rd BH23 4LA
☎ 01425 272210 ▨ 01425 272210
Picturesque parkland course with easy walking.
18 holes, 4776yds, Par 64, SSS 63, Course record 58.
Club membership 500.
Visitors must have handicap certificate and be a member of recognised club. Telephone in advance. **Societies** write or telephone in advance. **Green Fees** terms on application. **Facilities** ⊗ ⊾ ⊒ ⊻ ⊿ **Location** SW side of town on A337

Hotel ★★★ 74% Waterford Lodge Hotel, 87 Bure Ln, Friars Cliff, Mudeford, CHRISTCHURCH
☎ 01425 272948 & 278801 ▨ 01425 279130 18 en suite

HURN   Map 04 SZ19

Parley Parley Green Ln BH23 6BB
☎ 01202 591600 & 593131
Flat parkland course with few hazards and only one par 5.
9 holes, 4938yds, Par 66, SSS 64, Course record 69.
Club membership 226.
Visitors good standard of dress expected. **Societies** write or telephone. **Green Fees** terms on application. **Cards** ▨▨ ⊠ **Prof** Jane Miles/Chris Brook **Course Designer** P Goodfellow **Facilities** ⊗ ⊪ ⊾ ⊒ ⊻ ⊿ ⊘ ⋐ **Location** Opposite Bournemouth airport

Hotel ★★★★ 70% The Dormy, New Rd, FERNDOWN
☎ 01202 872121 115 en suite

☆☆☆
SALTERNS
·HOTEL·

AA 3 star & 80% rating –
2 AA Rosettes

Superb Waterside hotel with outstanding food. 20 beautifully furnished bedrooms overlooking Poole Harbour and Brownsea Island. Many top national awards presented for exceptionally high levels of customer care and outstanding service. Only a pitch and a put away (¼ mile) from Parkstone Golf Club!

38 Salterns Way, Lilliput, Poole, Dorset, BH14 8JR
Tel: 01202 707321

Best Western

LYME REGIS   Map 03 SY39

Lyme Regis Timber Hill DT7 3HQ ☎ 01297 442963
Undulating cliff-top course with magnificent views of Golden Cap and Lyme Bay.
18 holes, 6283yds, Par 71, SSS 70, Course record 67.
Club membership 575.
Visitors must contact in advance & have handicap certificate or be a member of recognised golf club. No play on Thu & Sun mornings. **Societies** Tue, Wed & Fri; must contact in writing. **Green Fees** £25 per round; £20 after 2pm. **Cards** ▨▨▨ **Prof** Andrew Black **Course Designer** Donald Steel **Facilities** ⊗ ⊪ by prior arrangement ⊾ ⊒ ⊻ ⊿ ⊘ **Location** W end of Charmouth bypass (A5), take A3052 to Lyme Regis. 1.5m from A3052/A35 rdbt

Hotel ★★★ 70% Alexandra Hotel, Pound St, LYME REGIS ☎ 01297 442010 25 en suite 1 annexe en suite

POOLE   Map 04 SZ09

Parkstone Links Rd, Parkstone BH14 9QS
☎ 01202 707138 ▨ 01202 796027
Very scenic heathland course with views of Poole Bay. Designed in 1909 by Willie Park Jnr and enlarged in 1932 by James Braid. The result of this highly imaginative reconstruction was an intriguing and varied test of golf set among pines and heather fringed fairways where every hole presents a different challenge.
18 holes, 6250yds, Par 72, SSS 70, Course record 63.
Club membership 700.
Visitors must contact in advance and have handicap certificate. **Societies** apply in writing/telephone in advance. **Green Fees** £50 per day; £35 per round
continued

(£60/£45 weekends & bank holidays). **Cards** ▭ ▭ 🗎
Prof Martyn Thompson **Course Designer** Willie Park Jnr
Facilities ⊗ ℍ ㋿ ㋿ ㋿ ㋿ 🗎 ㋿ ㋿ ㋿ **Location** E side
of town centre off A35

Hotel ★★★ 80% Salterns Hotel, 38 Salterns Way,
Lilliput, POOLE ☎ 01202 707321 20 en suite

Sherborne Higher Clatcombe DT9 4RN
☎ 01935 814431 🗎 01935 814218
e-mail: enquiries@sherbornegolfclub.fsnet.co.uk
A sporting course of first-class fairways with far-
reaching views over the lovely Blackmore Vale and the
Vale of Sparkford. Parkland in character, the course
has many well-placed bunkers. The dog-leg 2nd calls
for an accurately placed tee shot, and another testing
hole is the 7th, a 194 yard, par 3. There is a practice
area.
18 holes, 5882yds, Par 70, SSS 68, Course record 63.
Club membership 600.
Visitors must contact in advance & have handicap
certificate. **Societies** prior booking (Tue & Wed only).
Green Fees not confirmed. **Prof** Stewart Wright **Course**
Designer James Braid (part) **Facilities** ⊗ ℍ ㋿ ㋿ ㋿ ㋿
🗎 ㋿ **Location** 2m N off B3145

Hotel ★★★ 71% Eastbury Hotel, Long St,
SHERBORNE ☎ 01935 813131 15 en suite

Bulbury Woods Bulbury Ln BH16 6HR
☎ 01929 459574 🗎 01929 459000
e-mail: general@bulbury-woods.co.uk
Parkland course amidst ancient woodland, with a
mixture of American and traditional style greens and
extensive views over the Purbecks and Poole Harbour.
18 holes, 6002yds, Par 71, SSS 69.
Club membership 600.
Visitors visitors may book 7 days in advance and subject to
availability. **Societies** must contact in advance. **Green Fees**
£15 per 18 holes (£20 weekends). **Cards** ▭ ▭ ▭ ▭ 🗎
Prof David Adams **Facilities** ⊗ ℍ ㋿ ㋿ ㋿ ㋿ 🗎 ㋿ ㋿ ㋿
Conf Max 35 Thtr 35 Del from £13 * **Location** A35 Poole
to Dorchester, 3m from Poole centre

Hotel ★★★🏨 73% Priory Hotel, Church Green,
WAREHAM ☎ 01929 551666 15 en suite 4 annexe en suite

> Looking for a driving range?
> See the index at the back of the guide

Sturminster Marshall Moor Ln BH21 4AH
☎ 01258 858444 🗎 01258 858262
Privately owned club with pay & play facilities set in
beautiful Dorset countryside. Played off 18 different tees
the course is ideal for golfers of all standards.
9 holes, 4882yds, Par 68, SSS 64.
Club membership 350.
Visitors no restrictions. **Societies** must contact in advance.
Green Fees not confirmed. **Cards** ▭ ▭ ▭ **Prof** Graham
Howell **Course Designer** John Sharkey/David Holdsworth
Facilities ⊗ ℍ ㋿ ㋿ ㋿ ㋿ 🗎 ㋿ ㋿ ㋿ **Location** On A350.
Signposted from village

Hotel ★★★ 67% Crown Hotel, West St, BLANDFORD
FORUM ☎ 01258 456626 32 en suite

Isle of Purbeck BH19 3AB
☎ 01929 450361 & 450354 🗎 01929 450501
Purbeck Course: 18 holes, 6295yds, Par 70, SSS 71,
Course record 66.
Dene Course: 9 holes, 4014yds, Par 60.

Course Designer H Colt **Location** 2.5m N on B3351
Telephone for further details

Hotel ★★★ 67% The Pines Hotel, Burlington Rd,
SWANAGE ☎ 01929 425211 49 en suite

Crane Valley The Club House BH31 7LE
☎ 01202 814088 🗎 01202 813407
Two secluded parkland courses set amid rolling Dorset
countryside and mature woodland - a 9-hole Pay and Play
and an 18-hole Valley course for golfers holding a
handicap certificate.The 6th nestles in the bend of the
River Crane and there are four long par 5s ranging from
499 to 545 yards.
Valley: 18 holes, 6445yds, Par 72, SSS 71, Course record 66.
Woodland: 9 holes, 2060yds, Par 33, SSS 30.
Club membership 700.
Visitors must have handicap certificate for Valley course.
Woodland course is pay and play. **Societies** telephone in
advance. **Green Fees** Valley: £25 per round; £35 per day
(£35/£45 weekends and bank holidays) Woodland: £5.50 per
9 hole (£6.50 weekends). **Cards** ▭ ▭ ▭ ▭ 🗎 **Prof**
Darrel Ranson **Course Designer** Donald Steel **Facilities** ⊗
ℍ ㋿ ㋿ ㋿ ㋿ 🗎 ㋿ ㋿ ㋿ ㋿ **Location** 6m W of
Ringwood on B3081

Hotel ★★★★ 70% The Dormy, New Rd, FERNDOWN
☎ 01202 872121 115 en suite

WAREHAM — Map 03 SY98

Wareham Sandford Rd BH20 4DH
☎ 01929 554147 🖹 01929 554147
e-mail: admin@warehamgolfclub.com
At the entrance to the Purbecks with splendid views over Poole Harbour and Wareham Forest. A mixture of undulating parkland and heathland fairways. A challenge for golfers of all abilities.
18 holes, 5753yds, Par 69, SSS 68, Course record 66.
Club membership 500.
Visitors Handicap preferred.Course available after 09.30 weekdays and after 1pm weekends **Societies** weekdays only.
Green Fees £28 per day; £22 per round(£25 per round weekends). **Prof** Gary Prince **Facilities** ⊗ 🎤 🖫 🖳 ♀ 🏖 🏠 🎽 🗻 🛴 🛠 **Location** 0.5 mile N of Wareham on A351

Hotel ★★★ 68% Springfield Country Hotel & Leisure Club, Grange Rd, WAREHAM ☎ 01929 552177 48 en suite

WEYMOUTH — Map 03 SY67

Weymouth Links Rd DT4 0PF ☎ 01305 773981 (Secretary) & 773997 (Prof) 🖹 01305 788029
e-mail: weymouthgolfclub@aol.com
Seaside parkland course. The 5th is played off an elevated tee over copse.
18 holes, 5981yds, Par 70, SSS 69, Course record 63.
Club membership 750.
Visitors advisable to contact in advance. **Societies** apply in writing/telephone/e-mail/fax **Green Fees** £24 per round/day(£30 weekends and bank holidays). **Prof** Des Lochrie **Course Designer** James Braid **Facilities** ⊗ 🎤 🖫 🖳 ♀ 🏖 🏠 🎽 🛠 **Location** N side of town centre off B3157

Hotel ★★★ 61% Hotel Rex, 29 The Esplanade, WEYMOUTH ☎ 01305 760400 31 en suite

WIMBORNE — Map 03 SZ09

Canford Magna Knighton Ln BH21 2AS
☎ 01202 592552 🖹 01202 592550
Lying in 350 acres of Dorset countryside, the Canford Magna Golf Club provides 45 holes of challenging golf for the discerning player. The 18 hole Parkland and Riverside courses are quite different and, for the short game, the new 9 hole Knighton course demands the same level of playing skill. For those wishing to improve their handicap, the Golf Academy offers a covered driving range, pitching greens, a chipping green and bunkers, together with a 6 hole par 3 academy course.
Parkland: 18 holes, 6495yds, Par 71, SSS 71,
Course record 66.
Riverside: 18 holes, 6214yds, Par 70, SSS 70,
Course record 68.
Knighton: 9 holes, 1377yds, Par 27, Course record 26.
Club membership 1000. continued

Visitors are advised to contact in advance. **Societies** must telephone in advance. **Green Fees** from £17 per 18 holes.
Cards 💳 💳 💳 💳 💳 **Prof** Martin Cummins **Course Designer** Howard Swan **Facilities** ⊗ 🎤 🖫 🖳 ♀ 🏖 🏠 🎽 🛴 🛠 **Leisure** Golf lessons. **Conf** thr 100 Class 150 Board 60 Banquet 90 **Location** On A341

Hotel ★★ 77% Beechleas Hotel & Restaurant, 17 Poole Rd, WIMBORNE MINSTER ☎ 01202 841684 5 en suite 4 annexe en suite

CO DURHAM

BARNARD CASTLE — Map 12 NZ01

Barnard Castle Harmire Rd DL12 8QN
☎ 01833 638355 🖹 01833 695551
e-mail: christine.sec@talk21.com
Perched high on the steep bank of the River Tees, the extensive remains of Barnard Castle with its splendid round tower dates back to the 12th and 13th centuries. The parkland course is flat and lies in open countryside.

18 holes, 6406yds, Par 73, SSS 71, Course record 65.
Club membership 650.
Visitors must contact in advance, restricted at weekends. Handicap certificate required. **Societies** apply in writing. **Green Fees** not confirmed. **Prof** Darren Pearce **Course Designer** A Watson **Facilities** ⊗ 🎤 🖫 🖳 ♀ 🏖 🏠 🎽 🛠 **Location** 1m N of town centre on B6278

Hotel ★★ 79% Rose & Crown Hotel, ROMALDKIRK ☎ 01833 650213 7 en suite 5 annexe en suite

BEAMISH — Map 12 NZ25

Beamish Park DH9 0RH
☎ 0191 370 1382 🖹 0191 370 2937
Parkland course. Designed by Henry Cotton and W Woodend.
18 holes, 6204yds, Par 71, SSS 70, Course record 64.
Club membership 630.
Visitors must contact in advance and may only play weekdays. **Societies** telephone in advance. **Green Fees** terms on application. **Prof** Chris Cole **Course Designer** H Cotton **Facilities** ⊗ 🎤 🖫 🖳 ♀ 🏖 🏠 🛠 **Location** 1m NW off A693

Hotel ★★★ 69% Beamish Park Hotel, Beamish Burn Rd, MARLEY HILL ☎ 01207 230666 47 en suite

BILLINGHAM — Map 08 NZ42

Billingham Sandy Ln TS22 5NA
☎ 01642 533816 & 554494 🖹 01642 533816
e-mail: eddiedouglas@billgolfclub.fsnet.co.uk
Parkland course on edge of urban-rural district, with hard walking and water hazards. continued

18 holes, 6391yds, Par 73, SSS 70, Course record 61.
Club membership 1050.
Visitors contact professional in advance on 01642 557060 a handicap certificate may be requested. **Societies** apply in writing to Secretary/Manager. **Green Fees** £25 per day (£40 weekends). **Prof** Michael Ure **Course Designer** F Pennick **Facilities** ⊗ ⅷ ⅼ ⬛ ♀ ⚲ 📠 ⌁ ∅ **Location** 1m W of town centre E of A19

Hotel ★★★ 71% Parkmore Hotel, 636 Yarm Rd, Eaglescliffe, STOCKTON-ON-TEES ☎ 01642 786815 55 en suite

BISHOP AUCKLAND   Map 08 NZ22

Bishop Auckland High Plains, Durham Rd DL14 8DL ☎ 01388 663648 & 661618 (pro) 🖷 01388 607005
e-mail: enquiries@bagc.co.uk
A rather hilly parkland course with many well-established trees offering a challenging round. A small ravine adds interest to several holes including the short 7th, from a raised tee to a green surrounded by a stream, gorse and bushes. Pleasant views down the Wear Valley and over the residence of the Bishop of Durham. Has the distinction of having three consecutive par 5 holes and two consecutive par 3s.
18 holes, 6420yds, Par 72, SSS 71, Course record 64.
Club membership 950.
Visitors parties must contact in advance. Handicap certificate advisable. Dress rules apply. **Societies** weekdays only; must contact in advance. **Green Fees** £26 per day; £22 per round (£28 per round weekends). **Cards** 🖃 🖃 🖃 🖃 💳 **Prof** David Skiffington **Course Designer** James Kay **Facilities** ⊗ ⅷ ⅼ ⬛ ♀ ⚲ 📠 ∅ **Leisure** snooker. **Conf** Max 30 Class 30 **Location** 1m NE on A689

Hotel ★★★ 68% Swallow Eden Arms Hotel, RUSHYFORD ☎ 01388 720541 45 en suite

BURNOPFIELD   Map 12 NZ15

Hobson Municipal Hobson NE16 6BZ
☎ 01207 271605 🖷 01207 271069
e-mail: s_fox@derwentside.org.uk
Meadowland course with very easy walking.
18 holes, 6403yds, Par 69, SSS 68, Course record 65.
Club membership 700.
Visitors must book in advance at weekends. **Societies** must contact in advance. **Green Fees** not confirmed. **Cards** 🖃 🖃 🖃 💳 **Prof** Jack Ord **Facilities** ⊗ ⅷ ⅼ ♀ ⚲ 📠 ⌁ ∅ **Location** 0.75m S on A692

Hotel ★★★ 65% Swallow Hotel, High West St, GATESHEAD ☎ 0191 477 1105 103 en suite

CHESTER-LE-STREET Map 12 NZ25

Chester-le-Street Lumley Park DH3 4NS
☎ 0191 388 3218 (Secretary) 🖷 0191 388 1220
Parkland course in castle grounds, good views, easy walking.
18 holes, 6437yds, Par 71, SSS 71, Course record 71.
Club membership 650.
Visitors must contact in advance and have an introduction from own club or handicap certificate. **Societies** must apply in writing. **Green Fees** not confirmed. **Prof** David Fletcher **Course Designer** J H Taylor **Facilities** ⊗ ⅷ ⅼ ⬛ ♀ ⚲ 📠 ⌁ ∅ **Location** 0.5m E off B1284

continued

Hotel ★★★ 70% Ramside Hall Hotel, Carrville, DURHAM ☎ 0191 386 5282 80 en suite

Roseberry Grange Grange Villa DH2 3NF
☎ 0191 370 0670 🖷 0191 370 0660
Testing holes on this parkland course include the uphill par 3 12th (147yds) and the par 4 8th (438yds) with a ditch crossing the fairway.
18 holes, 5628yds, Par 70, SSS 69.
Club membership 550.
Visitors after 11.30am Sun & 10.30am Sat in summer, pay and play Mon-Fri. **Societies** booking form available on request. **Green Fees** not confirmed. **Cards** 🖃 🖃 🖃 🖃 💳 **Prof** Alan Hartley **Course Designer** Durham County Council **Facilities** ⊗ ⅷ ⅼ ⬛ ♀ ⚲ 📠 ⌁ ∅ ⌇

Hotel ★★★ 65% George Washington Golf & Country Club, Stone Cellar Rd, District 12, High Usworth, WASHINGTON ☎ 0191 402 9988 103 en suite

CONSETT   Map 12 NZ15

Consett & District Elmfield Rd DH8 5NN
☎ 01207 502186 🖷 01207 505060
e-mail: secretary@consettgolfclub.safe.co.uk
Undulating parkland/moorland course with views across the Derwent Valley to the Cheviot Hills.
18 holes, 6080yds, Par 71, SSS 69, Course record 63.
Club membership 650.
Visitors advised to contact Professional in advance on 01207 580210. **Societies** apply in writing. **Green Fees** £18 per day (£26 weekends). **Prof** Stuart Ord **Course Designer** Harry Vardon **Facilities** ⊗ ⅷ ⅼ ⬛ ♀ ⚲ 📠 🚜 **Leisure** snooker room. **Location** N side of town on A691

Hotel ★★ 69% Lord Crewe Arms Hotel, BLANCHLAND ☎ 01434 675251 9 en suite 10 annexe en suite

CROOK   Map 12 NZ13

Crook Low Jobs Hill DL15 9AA
☎ 01388 762429 & 767926
Meadowland/parkland course in elevated position with natural hazards, varied holes and terrain. Panoramic views over Durham and Cleveland Hills.
18 holes, 6102yds, Par 70, SSS 69, Course record 64.
Club membership 550.
Visitors weekends by arrangement. **Societies** apply in writing to Secretary. **Green Fees** £16 per day (mon-fri);(£25 sun & bank holidays). **Prof** Craig Dilley **Facilities** ⊗ ⅷ ⅼ ⬛ ♀ ⚲ 📠 **Location** 0.5m E off A690

Hotel ★★ 66% Kensington Hall Hotel, Kensington Ter, WILLINGTON ☎ 01388 745071 10 en suite

DARLINGTON   Map 08 NZ21

Blackwell Grange Briar Close, Blackwell DL3 8QX
☎ 01325 464458 🖷 01325 464458
e-mail: Secretary@blackwell-grange.demon.co.uk
Pleasant parkland course with good views, easy walking.
18 holes, 5621yds, Par 68, SSS 67, Course record 63.
Club membership 1000.
Visitors restricted Wed & weekends. **Societies** welcome weekdays except Wed (Ladies Day). **Green Fees** £25 per day; £20 per round (£30 per round weekends and bank holidays). **Prof** Joanne Furby **Course Designer** F Pennink **Facilities** ⊗ ⅷ ⅼ ⬛ ♀ ⚲ 📠 ⌁ ∅ **Location** 1m SW off A66, turn into Blackwell, signposted

continued

Hotel ★★★ 68% Blackwell Grange, Blackwell Grange, DARLINGTON ☎ 01325 509955 99 en suite 11 annexe en suite

Darlington Haughton Grange DL1 3JD
☎ 01325 355324 🖳 01325 488126
e-mail: darlingtongolf.club1@virgin.net
Fairly flat parkland course with tree-lined fairways, and large first-class greens.
18 holes, 6271yds, Par 71, SSS 70, Course record 65.
Club membership 850.
Visitors may not play weekends unless accompanied by member. **Societies** by prior arrangement with the Secretary but not at weekends. **Green Fees** not confirmed. **Prof** Mark Rogers **Course Designer** Dr Alistair McKenzie **Facilities** ⊗ ℿ ⅃ ⅃ ♀ ⅃ 🏠 ⅀ ℐ **Location** N side of town centre off A1150

Hotel ★★★♨♨ 71% Headlam Hall Hotel, Headlam, Gainford, DARLINGTON ☎ 01325 730238 19 en suite 17 annexe en suite

Hall Garth Golf & Country Club Hotel Coatham
Mundeville DL1 3LU ☎ 01325 320246 🖳 01325 310083
A 6621 yard course with mature trees and Victorian deer folly. The challenging 165 yard par 3 3rd requires teeing over water, whilst the 500 yard par 5 6th hole features the picturesque River Swale running alongside the fairway and the green.

9 holes, 6621yds, Par 72, SSS 72.
Visitors tee times bookable 7 days in advance. **Societies** prior booking by telephone. **Green Fees** not confirmed.
Cards ▬▬ ▬▬ 🖳 ▬▬ 🔤 🔤 **Course Designer** Brian Moore **Facilities** ⊗ ℿ ⅃ ⅃ ♀ ⅃ 🏠 ⅀ 🏊 ℐ Leisure heated indoor swimming pool, sauna, solarium, gymnasium.
Location 0.5m from A1(M), junct 59 off A167

Hotel ★★★ 73% Hall Garth Golf and Country Club Hotel, Coatham Mundeville, DARLINGTON ☎ 01325 300400 30 en suite 11 annexe en suite

Stressholme Snipe Ln DL2 2SA
☎ 01325 461002 🖳 01325 461002
Picturesque municipal parkland course, long but wide, with 98 bunkers and a par 3 hole played over a river.
18 holes, 6431yds, Par 71, SSS 70, Course record 68.
Club membership 350.
Visitors must book 7 days in advance. **Societies Green Fees** £12 per round (£15 weekends). **Cards** ▬▬ ▬▬ 🔤 🔤 🖳 **Prof** Ralph Givens **Facilities** ⊗ ℿ ⅃ ⅃ ♀ ⅃ 🏠 ⅀ ℐ ⅃ **Location** SW side of town centre on A67

Hotel ★★★ 68% Blackwell Grange, Blackwell Grange, DARLINGTON ☎ 01325 509955 99 en suite 11 annexe en suite

DURHAM   Map 12 NZ24

Brancepeth Castle Brancepeth Village DH7 8EA
☎ 0191 378 0075 🖳 0191 378 3835
e-mail: brancepethcastle@btclick.com
Parkland course overlooked at the 9th hole by beautiful Brancepeth Castle.
18 holes, 6234yds, Par 70, SSS 70, Course record 64.
Club membership 780.
Visitors must contact in advance, restricted weekends.
Societies must contact in advance. **Green Fees** £30 per day; £25 per round (£35 per round weekends). **Cards** ▬▬ ▬▬ 🔤 🖳 **Prof** David Howdon **Course Designer** H S Holt **Facilities** ⊗ ℿ ⅃ ⅃ ♀ ⅃ 🏠 ⅀ ℐ **Location** 4m from Durham A690 towards Crook, left at crossroads in Brancepath, left turn at Castle Gates, 400yds

Hotel ★★★★ 72% Durham Marriott Hotel, Royal County, Old Elvet, DURHAM ☎ 0191 386 6821 142 en suite 8 annexe en suite

Durham City Littleburn, Langley Moor DH7 8HL
☎ 0191 378 0806 & 378 0069 🖳 0191 378 4265
e-mail: durhamcitygolf@lineone.net
Undulating parkland course bordered on several holes by the River Browney.
18 holes, 6326yds, Par 71, SSS 70, Course record 67.
Club membership 750.
Visitors restricted on competition days, preferential to contact in advance. Club competitors have priority. **Societies** apply in writing or telephone the club professional on 0191 378 0029 **Green Fees** £24 (£30 weekends & bank holidays). **Prof** Steve Corbally **Course Designer** C Stanton **Facilities** ⊗ ℿ ⅃ ⅃ ♀ ⅃ 🏠 ⅀ 🏊 ℐ **Location** 2m W of Durham City, turn left off A690 into Littleburn Ind Est

Hotel ★★★ 69% Swallow Three Tuns Hotel, New Elvet, DURHAM ☎ 0191 386 4326 50 en suite

Mount Oswald South Rd DH1 3TQ
☎ 0191 386 7527 🖳 0191 386 0975
e-mail: information@mountoswald.co.uk
Gently rolling course providing a test for all golfers.
18 holes, 6101yds, Par 71, SSS 69.
Club membership 125.
Visitors must contact in advance for weekends but may not play before 10am on Sun, please ring for available tee times.
Societies must telephone in advance. **Green Fees** £12.50 Mon-Thu (£15 Fri-Sun & bank holidays). **Cards** ▬▬ ▬▬ 🔤 🖳 **Facilities** ⊗ ℿ ⅃ ⅃ ♀ ⅃ 🏠 ⅀ 🏊 ℐ **Conf** Max 80 Thtr 80 Class 80 Board 60 Banquet 70 Del £4.25 to £15.95 * **Location** On A177, 1m SW of city centre

Hotel ★★★ 70% Ramside Hall Hotel, Carrville, DURHAM ☎ 0191 386 5282 80 en suite

Ramside Hall Carrville DH1 1TD
☎ 0191 386 9514 🖳 0191 386 9519
e-mail: ramsidehall@ukonline.co.uk
Three recently constructed 9-hole parkland courses - Princes, Bishops, Cathedral - with 14 lakes and panoramic views surrounding an impressive hotel. Excellent golf academy and driving range.
Princes: 9 holes, 3235yds, Par 36, SSS 36.
Bishops: 9 holes, 3285yds, Par 36.
Cathedral: 9 holes, 2874yds, Par 34.
Club membership 450.

continued

Ramside Hall Golf Club

Visitors open at all times subject to tee availability. **Societies** telephone in advance. **Green Fees** £30 per 18 holes; £17 per 9 holes (£37/£20 weekends). **Cards** 🖾 💳 💳 💳 💳 🖾 **Prof** Robert Lister **Course Designer** Johnathan Gaunt **Facilities** ⊗ 🎿 ▮ 🏌 ♀ 👤 🏠 🚩 🍴 🦌 ♂ 🍵 Leisure sauna, steam room. **Location** 500mtrs from A1/A690 interchange

Hotel ★★★ 70% Ramside Hall Hotel, Carrville, DURHAM ☎ 0191 386 5282 80 en suite

---

Eaglescliffe and District Yarm Rd TS16 0DQ
☎ 01642 780098 & 780238 📠 01642 780238
e-mail: egcsec@lineone.net
This hilly course offers both pleasant and interesting golf to all classes of player. It lies in a delightful setting on a rolling plateau, shelving to the River Tees. There are fine views to the Cleveland Hills.
18 holes, 6275yds, Par 72, SSS 70, Course record 64.
Club membership 970.
Visitors restricted Tue, Thu, Fri & weekends. **Societies** must contact in advance, apply to secretary on 01642 780238 **Green Fees** £35 per day; £26 per round (£50/£36 weekends). **Prof** Graeme Bell **Course Designer** J Braid/H Cotton **Facilities** ⊗ 🎿 ▮ 🏌 ♀ 👤 🏠 ♂ **Conf** Max 20 **Location** On eastern side of A135 between Yarm and Stockton-on-Tees

Hotel ★★★★ 63% Swallow Hotel, John Walker Square, STOCKTON-ON-TEES ☎ 01642 679721 0800 7317549 📠 01642 601714 125 en suite

---

Castle Eden & Peterlee Castle Eden TS27 4SS
☎ 01429 836510 📠 01429 836510
e-mail: derek.livingston@btinternet.com
Beautiful parkland course alongside a nature reserve. Hard walking but trees provide wind shelter.
18 holes, 6262yds, Par 70, SSS 70, Course record 64.
Club membership 750.
Visitors with member only at certain times, must contact pro in advance 01429 836689. Visitors play off yellow tees. **Societies** must contact in advance tel: 01429 836510. **Green Fees** £25 per day (£35 weekends). **Prof** Peter Jackson **Course Designer** Henry Cotton **Facilities** ⊗ 🎿 ▮ 🏌 ♀ 👤 🏠 🚩 🦌 ♂ Leisure snooker. **Location** 2m S of Peterlee on B1281 off A19

continued

Hotel ★★ 69% Hardwicke Hall Manor Hotel, Hesleden, PETERLEE ☎ 01429 836326 15 en suite

Hartlepool Hart Warren TS24 9QF
☎ 01429 274398 📠 01429 274129
A seaside course, half links, overlooking the North Sea. A good test and equally enjoyable to all handicap players. The 10th, par 4, demands a precise second shot over a ridge and between sand dunes to a green down near the edge of the beach, alongside which several holes are played.
18 holes, 5981yds, Par 70, SSS 70, Course record 62.
Club membership 700.
Visitors with member only on Sun. **Societies** must apply in writing in advance. **Green Fees** not confirmed. **Prof** Malcolm E Cole **Course Designer** Partly Braid **Facilities** ⊗ 🎿 ▮ 🏌 ♀ 👤 🏠 🚩 ♂ **Location** N of Hartlepool, off A1086

Hotel ★★ 60% The Grand Hotel, Swainson St, HARTLEPOOL ☎ 01429 266345 47 en suite

---

Dinsdale Spa Neasham Rd DL2 1DW
☎ 01325 332297 📠 01325 332297
A mainly flat, parkland course on high land above the River Tees with views of the Cleveland Hills. Water hazards in front 10th tee and green, the prevailing west wind affects the later holes. There is a practice area by the clubhouse.
18 holes, 6099yds, Par 71, SSS 69, Course record 65.
Club membership 870.
Visitors welcome Mon & Wed-Fri, contact for further details. **Societies** bookings through office, no weekends or Tue. Apply in writing or telephone. **Green Fees** terms on application. **Prof** Neil Metcalfe **Facilities** ⊗ 🎿 ▮ 🏌 ♀ 👤 🏠 ♂ **Location** 1.5m SW

Hotel ★★★ 64% The St George, Middleton St George, Darlington, TEES-SIDE AIRPORT ☎ 01325 332631 59 en suite

---

Oakleaf Golf Complex School Aycliffe Ln DL5 6QZ
☎ 01325 310820 📠 01325 310820
e-mail: andy@oakleafgolfshop.fsnet.co.uk
A parkland course in a country setting.
18 holes, 6100yds, Par 70, SSS 70, Course record 67.
Club membership 450.
Visitors dress code enforced and must contact in advance for weekends. **Societies** apply in writing or telephone. **Green Fees** £10.50 per round (£12 weekends). **Cards** 💳 🟥 💳

continued

🏠 📺 💿 **Prof** Andrew Waites **Facilities** ⊗ ⅷ ╠ ♣ ♀ ㅿ
📠 ⚲ ♂ ℓ **Leisure** squash, fishing.**Conf** Max 75 **Location**
6m N of Darlington, off A6072

Hotel ★★★★ 71% Redworth Hall Hotel, REDWORTH
🕿 01388 770600 100 en suite

Woodham Golf & Country Club Burnhill Way

DL5 4PN 🕿 01325 320574 (Office) 315257 (Pro Shop)
💿 01325 315254
The golf course was originally opened in 1981 and the
excellent design was by James Hamilton Scott. It is laid
out in 229 acres of parkland with the two loops of nine
holes starting and finishing at the clubhouse. Mature
woodland with large trees and numerous lakes.
18 holes, 6688yds, Par 73, SSS 72, Course record 66.
Club membership 694.
Visitors must book 1 week in advance for weekends.
Societies telephone or write in advance. **Green Fees** £22 per
day; £16.50 per round (£33/£26.50 weekends and bank
holidays). **Cards** 🖃 🌫 🖼 📺 💿 **Prof** Ernie Wilson
Course Designer James Hamilton Stutt **Facilities** ⊗ ⅷ ╠
♣ ♀ ㅿ 📠 ⚲ ♣ ♂ **Location** From A1 take A689 towards
Bishop Auckland 0.5m from Rushford village

Hotel ★★★ 68% Swallow Eden Arms Hotel,
RUSHYFORD 🕿 01388 720541 45 en suite

Seaham Dawdon SR7 7RD

🕿 0191 581 2354 & 581 1268 (Sec)
Heathland links course with several holes affected by
strong prevailing winds.
18 holes, 6017yds, Par 70, SSS 69, Course record 64.
Club membership 600.
Visitors contact professional at all times, with member only
weekends until 3.30pm. **Societies** must apply in advance.
Green Fees terms on application. **Prof** Glyn Jones **Facilities**
⊗ ⅷ by prior arrangement ╠ ♣ ♀ ㅿ 📠 ⚲ ♂ **Location**
3m E of A19, exit for Seaham

Hotel ★★★★ 70% Sunderland Marriott Hotel, Queen's
Pde, Seaburn, SUNDERLAND 🕿 0191 529 2041
82 en suite

Seaton Carew Tees Rd TS25 1DE

🕿 01429 261040 & 266249
A championship links course taking full advantage of
its dunes, bents, whins and gorse. Renowned for its par
4 17th; just enough fairway for an accurate drive
followed by another precise shot to a pear-shaped,
sloping green that is severely trapped.
The Old Course: 18 holes, 6604yds, Par 72, SSS 72.
Brabazon Course: 18 holes, 6900yds, Par 73, SSS 73.
Club membership 650.
Visitors restricted until after 10am at weekends & bank
holidays, and after 09.30am midweek. **Societies** must
apply in writing. **Green Fees** £34 (£44 weekends & bank
holidays). **Prof** Mark Rogers **Course Designer** McKenzie
Facilities ⊗ ⅷ ╠ ♣ ♀ ㅿ 📠 ⚲ ♀ ♣ ♂ **Location** SE
side of village off A178

Hotel ★★ 60% The Grand Hotel, Swainson St,
HARTLEPOOL 🕿 01429 266345 47 en suite

Knotty Hill Golf Centre TS21 2BB

🕿 01740 620320 💿 01740 622227
e-mail: khgc21@btopenworld.com
The 18-hole Princes course is set in rolling parkland with
many holes routed through shallow valleys. Several holes
are set wholly or partially within woodland and water
hazards abound. Bishops Course is a developing 18-hole
course with varied water features on attractive terrain.
Several holes are routed through mature woodland.
Princes Course (A+B): 18 holes, 6577yds, Par 72, SSS 71.
Bishops Course (C+D): 18 holes, 5859yds, Par 70.
Visitors telephone for tee reservations. **Societies** package
available on request. **Green Fees** £13 per round (£14 Fri &
weekends) £8 per 9 holes. **Course Designer** C Stanton
Facilities ⊗ ⅷ ╠ ♣ ♀ ㅿ 📠 ⚲ ♀ ♣ ♂ ℓ **Leisure**
gymnasium, tuition range.**Conf** Max 50 **Location** 1m N of
Sedgefield on A177, 2m from junct 60 on A1(M)

Hotel ★★★ 68% Hardwick Hall Hotel, SEDGEFIELD
🕿 01740 620253 51 en suite

South Moor The Middles, Craghead DH9 6AG

🕿 01207 232848 & 283525(pro) 💿 01207 284616
Moorland course with natural hazards designed by Dr
Alistair McKenzie in 1926 and remains one the most
challenging of its type in north east England. Out of
bounds features on 11 holes from the tee and the testing
par 5 12th hole is uphill and usually against a strong
headwind.
18 holes, 6271yds, Par 72, SSS 70, Course record 66.
Club membership 650.
Visitors welcome except Sun, must contact in advance.
Handicap certificate required. **Societies** apply in writing to
Secretary. **Green Fees** £22 per day; £15 per round (£26 per
day/round weekends & bank holidays). **Prof** Shaun Cowell
Course Designer Dr Alistair Mackenzie **Facilities** ⊗ ⅷ ╠
♣ ♀ ㅿ 📠 ⚲ ♀ ♣ ♂ **Location** 1.5m SE on B6313

Hotel ★★★ 69% Beamish Park Hotel, Beamish Burn Rd,
MARLEY HILL 🕿 01207 230666 47 en suite

Norton Norton TS20 1SU

🕿 01642 676385 💿 01642 608467
An interesting parkland course with long drives from the
7th and 17th tees. Several water hazards.
18 holes, 5855yds, Par 70.
Visitors no visiting party tee times booked on weekends.
Societies apply in advance. **Green Fees** £10 per 18 holes
(£12 weekends and bank holidays). **Cards** 🖃 🌫 🖼 📺 💿
Course Designer T Harper **Facilities** ⊗ ⅷ ╠ ♣ ♀ ♂
Leisure bowling green. **Location** At Norton 2m N off A19

Hotel ★★★ 71% Parkmore Hotel, 636 Yarm Rd,
Eaglescliffe, STOCKTON-ON-TEES 🕿 01642 786815
55 en suite

Teesside Acklam Rd, Thornaby TS17 7JS

🕿 01642 616516 & 673822 (pro) 💿 01642 676252
e-mail: teesidegolfclub@btconnect.com
Flat parkland course, easy walking.
18 holes, 6535yds, Par 72, SSS 71, Course record 64.
Club membership 700.
Visitors with member only weekdays after 4.30pm,
weekends after 11am. **Societies** must contact in writing.

continued

Green Fees terms on application. **Prof** Ken Hall **Course Designer** Makepiece & Dr Somerville **Facilities** ⊗ ⏶ ᐟᐟ ⚑ **Location** 1.5m SE on A1130, off A19 at Mandale interchange

Hotel ★★★ 69% Holiday Inn Middlesbrough/Teesside, Low Ln, Stainton Village, Thornaby, STOCKTON-ON-TEES ☎ 0870 400 9081 136 en suite

ESSEX

ABRIDGE   Map 05 TQ49

Abridge Golf and Country Club Epping Ln, Stapleford Tawney RM4 1ST
☎ 01708 688396 ᐟ 01708 688550
e-mail: lynn@abridgegolf.freeserve.co.uk
A parkland course with easy walking. The quick drying course is by no means easy to play. This has been the venue of several professional tournaments. Abridge is a Golf and Country Club and has all the attendant facilities.
18 holes, 6692yds, Par 72, SSS 72, Course record 67. Club membership 650.
Visitors must have current handicap certificate, contact in advance. May play weekends after 2pm. **Societies** telephone in advance. **Green Fees** not confirmed. **Cards** ⚏ ⚏ ⚏ ⚏ **Prof** Stuart Layton **Course Designer** Henry Cotton **Facilities** ⊗ ᐟᐟ ⚑ ⚑ **Leisure** heated outdoor swimming pool, sauna.
Location 1.75m NE

Hotel ★★★ 63% Posthouse Epping, High Rd, Bell Common, EPPING ☎ 0870 400 9027 79 annexe en suite

BASILDON   Map 05 TQ78

Basildon Clay Hill Ln, Kingswood SS16 5JP
☎ 01268 533297 ᐟ 01268 533849
Undulating municipal parkland course. Testing 13th hole (par 4).
18 holes, 6236yds, Par 72, SSS 70. Club membership 350.
Visitors contact professional in advance 01268 533532. **Societies** may contact for details. **Green Fees** not confirmed. **Cards** ⚏ ⚏ **Prof** M Oliver **Course Designer** A Cotton **Facilities** ⊗ ᐟᐟ ⚑ ⚑ **Location** 1m S off A176

Hotel ★★★ 65% Holiday Inn Basildon, Cranes Farm Rd, BASILDON ☎ 0870 400 9003 149 en suite

BENFLEET   Map 05 TQ78

Boyce Hill Vicarage Hill, South Benfleet SS7 1PD
☎ 01268 793625 & 752565 ᐟ 01268 750497
e-mail: boycehill@hotmail.com
Hilly parkland course with good views.
18 holes, 6003yds, Par 68, SSS 69, Course record 61. Club membership 700.
Visitors must have a handicap certificate, must contact 24hrs in advance, may not play at weekends. **Societies** Thu only, book well in advance by telephone. **Green Fees** £25 up to 36 holes. **Prof** Graham Burroughs **Course Designer** James Braid **Facilities** ⊗ ᐟᐟ ⚑ ⚑ **Location** 0.75m NE of Benfleet Station

Hotel ★★★ 65% Holiday Inn Basildon, Cranes Farm Rd, BASILDON ☎ 0870 400 9003 149 en suite

BILLERICAY   Map 05 TQ69

The Burstead Tye Common Rd, Little Burstead CM12 9SS ☎ 01277 631171 ᐟ 01277 632766
The Burstead is an attractive parkland course set amidst some of the most attractive countryside in south Essex. It is an excellent test of golf to players of all standards with the greens showing maturity beyond their years. Challenging holes include the par 4 16th hole which at 348yds requires an accurate tee shot to leave a second shot played over a lake protecting an attractive contoured green. The 18th is the longest hole on the course.
18 holes, 6275yds, Par 71, SSS 70, Course record 69. Club membership 850.
Visitors Must book in advance and may not play weekends am. **Societies** Apply in writing or telephone for reservation. **Green Fees** terms on application. **Cards** ⚏ ⚏ ⚏ ⚏ **Prof** Keith Bridges **Course Designer** Patrick Tallack **Facilities** ⊗ ᐟᐟ ⚑ ⚑ **Location** M25 onto A127, located off A176.

Hotel ★★★ 69% Chichester Hotel, Old London Rd, Wickford, BASILDON ☎ 01268 560555 2 en suite 32 annexe en suite

Stock Brook Golf & Country Club Queens Park Av, Stock CM12 0SP ☎ 01277 653616 & 650400 ᐟ 01277 633063
e-mail: events@stockbrook.com
Set in 250 acres of picturesque countryside the 27 holes comprise three undulating 9s, offering the challenge of water on a large number of holes. Any combination can be played, but the Stock and Brook courses make the 18-hole, 6750 yard championship course. There are extensive clubhouse facilities.
Stock & Brook Courses: 18 holes, 6728yds, Par 72, SSS 72, Course record 66.
Manor Course: 9 holes, 2997yds, Par 35.
Visitors handicap certificate required, must contact 24hrs in advance. **Societies** apply in writing or telephone. **Green Fees** £25 per day; £15 per 9 holes (£30 per 18 holes; £15 per 9 holes). **Cards** ⚏ ⚏ ⚏ ⚏ **Prof** Kevin Merry **Course Designer** Martin Gillet **Facilities** ⊗ ᐟᐟ ⚑ ⚑ **Leisure** hard tennis courts, outdoor and indoor heated swimming pools, sauna, gymnasium, bowls.**Conf** Max 400 Thtr 400 Class 400 Board 35 Banquet 260 Del £20 to £30 *

Hotel ★★★ 68% The Heybridge Hotel, Roman Rd, INGATESTONE ☎ 01277 355355 22 en suite

BRAINTREE   Map 05 TL72

Braintree Kings Ln, Stisted CM7 8DA
☎ 01376 346079 ᐟ 01376 348677
e-mail: manager@braintreegolfclub.freeserve.co.uk
Parkland course with many unique mature trees. Good par 3s with the 14th - 'Devils Lair' - regarded as one of the best in the county.
18 holes, 6228yds, Par 70, SSS 70, Course record 65. Club membership 750.
Visitors contact the pro shop in advance 01376 343465. No visitors Sun before noon. **Societies** society days Wed & Thu early booking advised. **Green Fees** £25 (£45 weekends after noon). **Prof** Tony Parcell **Course Designer** Hawtree **Facilities** ⊗ ᐟᐟ ⚑ ⚑ **Location** 1m E, off A120

Hotel ★★★ 63% White Hart Hotel, Bocking End, BRAINTREE ☎ 01376 321401 31 en suite

Towerlands Panfield Rd CM7 5BJ
☎ 01376 326802 ▤ 01376 552487
Undulating, grassland course. Driving range and sports hall.
9 holes, 2749yds, Par 34, SSS 66.
Club membership 300.
Visitors must not play before 12.30pm weekends or before 5pm Wed. Correct dress at all times. Must contact in advance. **Societies** must contact in advance by telephone.
Green Fees not confirmed. **Cards** ▭ ▭ ▭ ▭ ▭ **Course Designer** G Shiels **Facilities** ⊗ ⨤ ⅃ 🛌 🖤 🍴 ⅄ 🏠 ⛷ ✓ ⅃
Leisure squash, gymnasium. **Location** On B1053

Hotel ★★★ 63% White Hart Hotel, Bocking End, BRAINTREE ☎ 01376 321401 31 en suite

---

BRENTWOOD   Map 05 TQ59

Bentley Ongar Rd CM15 9SS
☎ 01277 373179 ▤ 01277 375097
Parkland course with water hazards.
18 holes, 6709yds, Par 72, SSS 72.
Club membership 600.
Visitors should contact in advance, may not play at weekends. **Societies** must write or telephone in advance.
Green Fees not confirmed. **Cards** ▭ ▭ ▭ ▭ ▭ **Prof** Nick Garrett **Course Designer** Alec Swann **Facilities** 🛌 🖤 ⅃ ⅄ 🏠 🚃 ✓ **Location** 3m NW on A128

Hotel ★★★ 69% Holiday Inn Brentwood, Brook St, BRENTWOOD ☎ 0870 400 9012 150 en suite

---

Hartswood King George's Playing Fields, Ingrave Rd CM14 5AE ☎ 01277 218850 ▤ 01277 218850
Municipal parkland course, easy walking.
18 holes, 6192yds, Par 70, SSS 69, Course record 64.
Club membership 500.
Visitors pre-book by telephone up to five days ahead on 01277 214830 **Societies** weekdays only, must contact in advance. **Green Fees** not confirmed. **Cards** ▭ ▭ ▭ ▭ ⅃ **Prof** Stephen Cole **Facilities** ⊗ 🛌 🖤 ⅃ ⅄ 🏠 ⛷ ✓ **Location** 0.75m SE on A128

Hotel ★★★ 69% Holiday Inn Brentwood, Brook St, BRENTWOOD ☎ 0870 400 9012 150 en suite

---

Warley Park Magpie Ln, Little Warley CM13 3DX
☎ 01277 224891 ▤ 01277 200679
e-mail: enquiries@warleyparkgc.com
Parkland course with reasonable walking. Numerous water hazards. There is also a golf-practice ground.
1st & 2nd: 18 holes, 5967yds, Par 69, SSS 67, Course record 66.
1st & 3rd: 18 holes, 5925yds, Par 71, SSS 69, Course record 65.
2nd & 3rd: 18 holes, 5917yds, Par 70, SSS 69, Course record 70.
Club membership 800.
Visitors must have handicap certificate and contact in advance. May not play at weekends. **Societies** telephone in advance for provisional booking. **Green Fees** £30 per round.
Cards ▭ ▭ ⅃ **Prof** Jason Groat **Course Designer** Reg Plumbridge **Facilities** ⊗ ⨤ by prior arrangement 🛌 🖤 ⅃ ⅄ 🏠 🚃 ✓ ⅃ **Conf** Max 50 Del £50 to £200 * **Location** 0.5m N off junct 29 of M25/A127

Hotel ★★★ 69% Holiday Inn Brentwood, Brook St, BRENTWOOD ☎ 0870 400 9012 150 en suite

---

Weald Park Coxtie Green Rd, South Weald CM14 5RJ
☎ 01277 375101 ▤ 01277 374888
e-mail: wealdpark@americangolf.uk.com
Tranquil parkland course with many mature oak trees, lakes, ponds and plentiful wildlife. The undulating terrain and the numerous hedges and ponds make this par 71 course a fair test of golf for all abilities.
18 holes, 6285yds, Par 71, SSS 70, Course record 65.
Club membership 570.
Visitors telephone booking preferable, no weekday restrictions, weekend afternoons only. **Societies** apply in writing or telephone for package. **Green Fees** not confirmed.
Cards ▭ ▭ ▭ ▭ ⅃ **Prof** Ian Parker **Course Designer** Reg Plumbridge **Facilities** ⊗ 🛌 🖤 ⅃ ⅄ 🏠 🚃 ✓
Location 3m from M25

Hotel ★★★★ 72% Marygreen Manor Hotel, London Rd, BRENTWOOD ☎ 01277 225252 3 en suite 40 annexe en suite

---

BULPHAN   Map 05 TQ68

Langdon Hills Golf Centre Lower Dunton Rd RM14 3TY ☎ 01268 548444 ▤ 01268 490084
Well situated with the Langdon Hills on one side and dramatic views across London on the other, the Centre offers an interchangeable 27 hole course, a floodlit 22-bay driving range and three academy holes.
Langdon & Bulphan Course: 18 holes, 6500yds, Par 72, SSS 71, Course record 67.
Bulphan & Horndon Course: 18 holes, 6422yds, Par 73, SSS 71.
Horndon & Langdon Course: 18 holes, 6186yds, Par 71, SSS 70.
Club membership 800.
Visitors preference given to members on weekend mornings and visitors may not play Langdon course before 10.30am. Cannot book more than 5 days in advance. **Societies** apply in writing or telephone. **Green Fees** terms on application.
Cards ▭ ▭ ▭ ▭ ⅃ **Prof** Terry Moncur **Course Designer** Howard Swan **Facilities** ⊗ ⨤ 🛌 🖤 ⅃ ⅄ 🏠 ⛷ 🚃 ✓ ⅃ **Conf** Max 90 Thtr 90 Class 90 Board 30 Banquet 80 Del £5 to £75 * **Location** Between A13 & A127 N of A128 S of Basildon

Hotel ★★★★ 72% Marygreen Manor Hotel, London Rd, BRENTWOOD ☎ 01277 225252 3 en suite 40 annexe en suite

---

BURNHAM-ON-CROUCH   Map 05 TQ99

Burnham-on-Crouch Ferry Rd, Creeksea CM0 8PQ
☎ 01621 782282 ▤ 01621 784489
e-mail: burnhamgolf@hotmail.com
Undulating meadowland riverside course, easy walking.
18 holes, 6056yds, Par 70, SSS 69, Course record 66.
Club membership 586.
Visitors welcome weekdays. Must play with member at weekends. **Societies** apply in writing or telephone. **Green Fees** £26 per day/round. **Prof** Steven Cardy **Course Designer** Swan **Facilities** ⊗ ⨤ 🛌 🖤 ⅃ ⅄ 🏠 🚃 ✓ **Location** 1.25m W off B1010

CANEWDON   Map 05 TQ99

Ballards Gore Gore Rd SS4 2DA
☎ 01702 258917 ▤ 01702 258571
A parkland course with several lakes.
18 holes, 6874yds, Par 73, SSS 73, Course record 69.
Club membership 500.
Visitors must contact in advance. May play weekdays and

continued

Sun after 2pm. **Societies** apply in advance. **Green Fees** terms on application. **Cards** 🏧 ▬ ▬ 💳 ▬ 💳 ▢ **Prof** Richard Emery **Course Designer** D & J J Caton **Facilities** ⊗ ⬧ 💺 🍽 ♀ 🏌 🏠 🚜 🏌 **Location** 2m NE of Rochford

Hotel ★★★ 66% Hotel Renouf, Bradley Way, ROCHFORD ☎ 01702 541334 24 en suite

CANVEY ISLAND   Map 05 TQ78

Castle Point Somnes Av SS8 9FG
☎ 01268 696298 (Secretary) & 510830 (Pro)
e-mail: sec@castlepointgolfclub.freeserve.co.uk
A flat seaside links and part parkland course with water hazards on 13 holes and views of the estuary and Hadleigh Castle. Always a test for any golfer when the wind starts to blow.
18 holes, 6176yds, Par 71, SSS 69, Course record 69.
Club membership 275.
Visitors must book for weekends. **Societies** phone or write for details. **Green Fees** not confirmed. **Prof** Michael Utteridge **Facilities** ⊗ ⬧ 💺 🍽 ♀ 🏌 🏠 🏌 🚜 🏌 🏌 **Location** SE of Basildon, A130 to Canvey Island

Hotel ★★★ 69% Chichester Hotel, Old London Rd, Wickford, BASILDON ☎ 01268 560555 2 en suite 32 annexe en suite

CHELMSFORD   Map 05 TL70

Channels Belstead Farm Ln, Little Waltham CM3 3PT
☎ 01245 440005 ▤ 01245 442032
e-mail: info@channelsgolf.co.uk
The Channels course is built on land from reclaimed gravel pits, 18 very exciting holes with plenty of lakes providing an excellent test of golf. Belsteads, a nine hole course, is mainly flat but has 3 holes where water has to be negotiated.
Channels Course: 18 holes, 6402yds, Par 71, SSS 71, Course record 67.
Belsteads: 9 holes, 2467yds, Par 34, SSS 32.
Club membership 650.
Visitors Channels Course: must contact in advance and may only play with member at weekends. Belsteads Course: available anytime. **Societies** telephone starter on 01245 443311. **Green Fees** Channels: £40 per day; £28 per round. Belsteads: £12 per 9 holes, £18 per 18 holes (£14/£20 weekends). **Prof** Ian Sinclair **Course Designer** Cotton & Swan **Facilities** ⊗ 🍽 ⬧ 💺 🍽 ♀ 🏠 🏌 🚜 🏌 🏌 **Leisure** fishing, 9 hole pitch & putt course. **Conf** Thtr 160 Board 50 Banquet 120 Del from £25 * **Location** 2m NE on A130

Hotel ★★★ 71% County Hotel, Rainsford Rd, CHELMSFORD ☎ 01245 455700 54 en suite 8 annexe en suite

Chelmsford Widford Rd CM2 9AP
☎ 01245 256483 ▤ 01245 256483
e-mail: office@chelmsfordgc.sagehost.co.uk
An undulating parkland course, hilly in parts, with 3 holes in woods and four difficult par 4s. From the reconstructed clubhouse there are fine views over the course and the wooded hills beyond.
18 holes, 5981yds, Par 68, SSS 69, Course record 63.
Club membership 650.
Visitors must contact in advance. Society days Wed/Thu, Ladies Day Tue. With member only at weekends. **Societies** must contact in advance. **Green Fees** please contact professional. **Prof** Mark Welch **Course Designer** Tom Dunn **Facilities** ⊗ ⬧ 💺 🍽 ♀ 🏠 🏌 🚜 🏌 **Location** 1.5m S of town centre off A12   *continued*

Hotel ★★★ 71% Pontlands Park Country Hotel, West Hanningfield Rd, Great Baddow, CHELMSFORD ☎ 01245 476444 36 en suite

CHIGWELL   Map 05 TQ49

Chigwell High Rd IG7 5BH
☎ 020 8500 2059 ▤ 020 8501 3410
e-mail: info@chigwellgolfclub.co.uk
A course of high quality, mixing meadowland with parkland. For those who believe 'all Essex is flat' the undulating nature of Chigwell will be a refreshing surprise. The greens are excellent and the fairways tight with mature trees.
18 holes, 6279yds, Par 71, SSS 70, Course record 66.
Club membership 774.
Visitors must contact in advance & have handicap certificate, but must be accompanied by member at weekends. **Societies** recognised societies welcome by prior arrangement. **Green Fees** telephone Secretary's office. **Prof** Ray Beard **Course Designer** Hawtree/Taylor **Facilities** ⊗ ⬧ 💺 🍽 ♀ 🏠 🏌 🚜 🏌 **Location** 0.5m S on A113

Hotel ★★★ 60% Roebuck Hotel, North End, BUCKHURST HILL ☎ 020 8505 4636 28 en suite

CHIGWELL ROW   Map 05 TQ49

Hainault Forest Romford Rd, Chigwell Row IG7 4QW
☎ 020 8500 2131 ▤ 020 8501 5196
e-mail: info@essexgolfcentres.com
Club playing over Borough of Redbridge public courses; hilly parkland subject to wind. Two courses, driving range.
No 1 Course: 18 holes, 5687yds, Par 70, SSS 67, Course record 65.
No 2 Course: 18 holes, 6238yds, Par 71, SSS 71.
Club membership 250.
Visitors booking recommended. No restrictions except dress code, no jeans, football shorts/shirts or track suit bottoms. **Societies** please telephone,write or email. **Green Fees** £16 per 18 holes (£20 weekends). Day tickets available. **Cards** 🏧 ▬ ▬ ▢ **Prof** C Hope, S Jackson, B Preston **Course Designer** Taylor & Hawtree **Facilities** ⊗ ⬧ 💺 🍽 ♀ 🏠 🏌 🏌 🚜 🏌 🏌 **Conf** Max 70 **Location** 0.5m S on A1112

Hotel ★★★ 62% County Hotel Epping Forest, 30 Oak Hill, WOODFORD GREEN ☎ 020 8787 9988 99 en suite

CLACTON-ON-SEA   Map 05 TM11

Clacton West Rd CO15 1AJ
☎ 01255 421919 ▤ 01255 424602
Windy, seaside course.
18 holes, 6494yds, Par 71, SSS 69.
Club membership 650.
Visitors must contact in advance. **Societies** apply in writing/telephone. **Green Fees** not confirmed. **Prof** S J Levermore **Facilities** ⊗ 🍽 ⬧ 💺 🍽 ♀ 🏠 🚜 🏌 **Location** 1.25m SW of town centre

Hotel ★★ 72% Maplin Hotel, Esplanade, FRINTON-ON-SEA ☎ 01255 673832 11 rms (10 en suite)

AA website: www.theAA.com

COLCHESTER   Map 05 TL92

Birch Grove Layer Rd, Kingsford CO2 0HS
☎ 01206 734276 📠 01206 734276
A pretty, undulating course surrounded by woodland -
small but challenging with excellent greens. Challenging
6th hole cut through woodland with water hazards and
out of bounds.
9 holes, 4532yds, Par 66, SSS 63.
Club membership 250.
Visitors restricted Sun mornings. Societies apply in writing
or telephone. Green Fees terms on application. Course
Designer L A Marston Facilities ⊗ 🍴 🛍 💺 ♀ 🎿 🏧 ✧
Location 2.5m S on B1026
....
Hotel ★★★ 73% George Hotel, 116 High St,
COLCHESTER ☎ 01206 578494 47 en suite

Colchester Braiswick CO4 5AU
☎ 01206 853396 📠 01206 852698
e-mail: colchester.golf@btinternet.com
A fairly flat, yet scenic, parkland course with tree-lined
fairways and small copses. Mainly level walking.
18 holes, 6307yds, Par 70, SSS 70, Course record 64.
Club membership 700.
Visitors by prior arrangement, must contact in advance and
may not play weekends. Societies apply in writing or by
telephone, Mon, Thu & Fri only. Green Fees £40 all day;
£30 per round. Prof Mark Angel Course Designer James
Braid Facilities ⊗ 💺 ♀ 🎿 🏧 ✧ ↾ Location 1.5m NW of
town centre on B1508
....
Hotel ★★★ 73% George Hotel, 116 High St,
COLCHESTER ☎ 01206 578494 47 en suite

Colchester & Lexden Golf Centre Bakers Ln
CO3 4AU ☎ 01206 843333 📠 01206 854775
18 holes, 5500yds, Par 67.
Course Designer J Johnson Location Adjacent to A12. Take
Colchester Central from A12 and then follow tourist signs
Telephone for further details
....
Hotel ★★★ 65% Holiday Inn Colchester, Abbotts Ln, Eight
Ash Green, COLCHESTER ☎ 0870 400 9020 110 en suite

Stoke-by-Nayland Keepers Ln, Leavenheath CO6 4PZ
☎ 01206 262836 📠 01206 263356
e-mail: info@golfclub.co.uk
Two undulating courses (Gainsborough and Constable)
situated in Dedham Vale. Some water hazards and
hedges. On Gainsborough the 10th (par 4) takes 2 shots
over a lake; very testing par 3 at 11th.
Gainsborough Course: 18 holes, 6581yds, Par 72, SSS 71,
Course record 68.
Constable Course: 18 holes, 6544yds, Par 72, SSS 71,
Course record 67.
Club membership 1360.
Visitors write or telephone for details. Societies write or
telephone for brochures and booking forms. Green Fees £25
per round; £40 per day. Cards ▭ ▭ ▭ 💳 ▭ 🖬
Prof Kevin Lovelock Course Designer R Swan Facilities ⊗
🍴 🛍 💺 ♀ 🎿 🏧 🎯 🏕 ↢ 🛥 ✧ ↾ Leisure heated indoor
swimming pool, squash, fishing, sauna, solarium,
gymnasium.Conf Max 400 Banquet 400 Del £28 to £32 *
Location 1.5m NW of Stoke-by-Nayland on B1068
....
Hotel ★★★🏩 Maison Talbooth, Stratford Rd, DEDHAM
☎ 01206 322367 10 en suite

EARLS COLNE   Map 05 TL82

Colne Valley Station Rd CO6 2LT
☎ 01787 224233 📠 01787 224126
An 18-hole course along the valley of the River Colne.
18 holes, 6301yds, Par 70, SSS 70, Course record 68.
Club membership 450.
Visitors only after 11.00am at weekends, must dress
correctly, no sharing of clubs. Must contact in advance.
Societies apply in writing, minimum of 12 persons. Green
Fees not confirmed. Cards ▭ ▭ ▭ ▭ 🖬 Prof James
Taylor Course Designer Howard Swan Facilities ⊗ 🛍 💺 ♀
🎿 🏧 🛥 ✧ Leisure sauna. Location Off A604
....
Hotel ★★★ 65% White Hart Hotel, Market End,
COGGESHALL ☎ 01376 561654 18 en suite

Essex Golf & Country Club CO6 2NS
☎ 01787 224466 📠 01787 224410
Created on the site of a World War II airfield, this
challenging course contains 10 lakes and strategically
placed bunkering. Also a nine hole course and a variety of
leisure facilities.
County Course: 18 holes, 6916yds, Par 73, SSS 73, Course
record 67.
Garden Course: 9 holes, 2190yds, Par 34, SSS 34.
Club membership 700.
Visitors contact golf reception for bookings up to 3 days in
advance. Societies apply in writing to the Functions Manager
or telephone for details. Green Fees Country Course: £25
per round (£30 weekends & bank holidays). Garden Course:
£17 per 18 holes, £12 per 9 holes. Cards ▭ ▭ ▭ ▭ 🖬
Prof Lee Cocker Course Designer Reg Plumbridge
Facilities ⊗ 🍴 🛍 💺 ♀ 🎿 🏧 🎯 🏕 ↢ 🛥 ✧ ↾ Leisure
hard tennis courts, heated indoor swimming pool, fishing,
sauna, solarium, gymnasium, video golf tuition studio.Conf
Max 200 Thtr 200 Class 120 Board 76 Banquet 200 Del
£28.50 to £45 * Location Off the A120 onto the B1024
....
Hotel ★★★ 65% White Hart Hotel, Market End,
COGGESHALL ☎ 01376 561654 18 en suite

EPPING   Map 05 TL40

Epping Fluxs Ln CM16 7PE
☎ 01992 572282 📠 01992 575512
e-mail: neilsjoberg@hotmail.com
Rolling tree-lined parkland course with ponds and
panoramic country views. Designed to use every club in
the bag, the picturesque 4th is driveable but rarely
birdied. The spectacular 18th "Happy Valley" is rarely
parred.
18 holes, 5405yds, Par 68, SSS 66, Course record 67.
Club membership 350.
Visitors welcome. Societies telephone in advance. Green
Fees £9 per round (£5 after 1pm); £12 weekends (£8
twilight). Course Designer Sjoberg Facilities ⊗ 🛍 💺 🎿
🏧 🎯 ↢ 🛥 ✧ ↾ Location 0.5m downhill from Epping tube
station on Central Line.
....
Hotel ★★★ 63% Posthouse Epping, High Rd, Bell
Common, EPPING ☎ 0870 400 9027 79 annexe en suite

Nazeing Middle St, Nazeing EN9 2LW
☎ 01992 893798 📠 01992 893882
Parkland course built with American sand based greens
and tees and five strategically placed lakes. One of the
most notable holes is the difficult par 3 13th with out of
bounds and a large lake coming into play.

continued

18 holes, 6617yds, Par 72, SSS 72, Course record 68.
Club membership 400.
Visitors contact for weekend and bank holidays, may only
play pm. **Societies** prior arrangement required in writing.
Green Fees Mon £16 per round; £20 Tue-Fri; £28 weekends
pm. **Cards** 🔲 ▨ 🔲 🔲 **Prof** Robert Green **Course
Designer** M Gillete **Facilities** ⊗ ⅷ ㅂ 🖢 🎗 ㅅ 🖻 🎺 🕳 ⚡
Conf Max 100 **Location** Just outside Waltham Abbey

....

Hotel ★★★★ 70% Waltham Abbey Marriott Hotel, Old
Shire Ln, WALTHAM ABBEY ☎ 01992 717170
162 en suite

FRINTON-ON-SEA
Map 05 TM22

Frinton 1 The Esplanade CO13 9EP
☎ 01255 674618 📄 01255 674618
e-mail: frintongolf@lineone.net
**Deceptive, flat seaside links course providing fast, firm
and undulating greens that will test the best putters and
tidal ditches that cross many of the fairways, requiring
careful placement of shots. Its open character means that
every shot has to be evaluated with both wind strength
and direction in mind. Easy walking.**

*Long Course: 18 holes, 6265yds, Par 71, SSS 70, Course
record 64.*
Short Course: 9 holes, 2734yds, Par 58.
Club membership 850.
Visitors must contact in advance, weekends available by
arrangment. **Societies** by arrangement, apply in writing to the
secretary, Wed, Thu and some Fri. **Green Fees** not
confirmed. **Cards** 🔲 ▨ 🔲 🔲 🔲 **Prof** Peter Taggart
Course Designer Willy Park Jnr **Facilities** ⊗ ⅷ by prior
arrangement ㅂ 🖢 🎗 ㅅ 🖻 🎺 🕳 ⚡ **Conf** Max 70
Location SW side of town centre,17m East of Colchester

....

Hotel ★★ 72% Maplin Hotel, Esplanade, FRINTON-ON-
SEA ☎ 01255 673832 11 rms (10 en suite)

GOSFIELD
Map 05 TL72

Gosfield Lake The Manor House, Hall Dr CO9 1RZ
☎ 01787 474747 📄 01787 476044
e-mail: gosfieldlakegc@btconnect.com
**Parkland course with bunkers, lakes and water hazards.
Designed by Sir Henry Cotton/Howard Swan. Also 9-hole
course; ideal for beginners and improvers.**
*Lakes Course: 18 holes, 6615yds, Par 72, SSS 72,
Course record 68.*
Meadows Course: 9 holes, 4180yds, Par 64, SSS 61.
Club membership 650.
Visitors Lakes Course: must contact in advance. Sat & Sun
from 3.30 only. Meadows Course: Booking advisable.
Societies By prior arrangement. **Green Fees** not confirmed.
Prof Richard Wheeler **Course Designer** Henry

continued

Cotton/Howard Swan **Facilities** ⊗ ⅷ ㅂ 🖢 🎗 ㅅ 🖻 🎺 🕳
⚡ **Leisure** sauna. **Location** 1m W of Gosfield off B1017

....

Hotel ★★★ 63% White Hart Hotel, Bocking End,
BRAINTREE ☎ 01376 321401 31 en suite

HARLOW
Map 05 TL40

Canons Brook Elizabeth Way CM19 5BE
☎ 01279 421482 📄 01279 626393
**Challenging parkland course designed by Henry Cotton.
Accuracy is the key requiring straight driving from the
tees, especially on the par 5 11th to fly a gap with out of
bounds left and right before setting up the shot to the
green.**
18 holes, 6800yds, Par 73, SSS 72, Course record 65.
Club membership 850.
Visitors may not play at weekends. **Societies** welcome Mon,
Wed and Fri, must book in advance by telephone. **Green
Fees** terms on application. **Cards** 🔲 ▨ 🔲 🔲 🔲 **Prof**
Alan McGinn **Course Designer** Henry Cotton **Facilities** ㅅ
🖻 🎺 🕳 ⚡ **Conf** Max 120 **Location** 3m NW of junct 7 on
M11

....

Hotel ★★★ 71% Swallow Churchgate Hotel, Churchgate St
Village, Old Harlow, HARLOW ☎ 01279 420246 85 en
suite

North Weald Rayley Ln, North Weald CM16 6AR
☎ 01992 522118 📄 01992 522881
**Although only opened in November 1995, the blend of
lakes and meadowland give this testing course an air of
maturity.**
18 holes, 6311yds, Par 71, SSS 70, Course record 66.
Club membership 500.
Visitors must contact in advance weekday, limited at
weekends after 11am. **Societies** contact in advance. **Green
Fees** £20 per round (£27.50 weekends). **Cards** 🔲 🔲 **Prof**
David Rawlings **Course Designer** David Williams **Facilities**
⊗ ⅷ ㅂ 🖢 🎗 ㅅ 🖻 🎺 🕳 ⚡ **Leisure** gymnasium.
Location M11 exit 7,off A414 towards Chipping Ongar &
Chelmsford

....

Hotel ★★★ 63% Posthouse Epping, High Rd, Bell
Common, EPPING ☎ 0870 400 9027 79 annexe en suite

HARWICH
Map 05 TM23

Harwich & Dovercourt Station Rd, Parkeston
CO12 4NZ ☎ 01255 503616 📄 01255 503323
Flat parkland course with easy walking.
9 holes, 5900yds, Par 70, SSS 69, Course record 58.
Club membership 420.
Visitors visitors with handicap certificate may play by prior
arrangement, with member only at weekends. **Societies** prior
arrangement essential. **Green Fees** not confirmed. **Facilities**
⊗ ⅷ ㅂ 🖢 🎗 ㅅ 🖻 ⚡ **Location** Off A120 near Ferry
Terminal

....

Hotel ★★★ 73% The Pier at Harwich, The Quay,
HARWICH ☎ 01255 241212 7 en suite 7 annexe en suite

INGRAVE
Map 05 TQ69

Thorndon Park CM13 3RH
☎ 01277 811666 & 810335 📄 01277 810645
e-mail: tpgc@btclick.com
**Course built on clay substructure and playable even at
the wettest time of the year. Holes stand on their own
surrounded by mature oaks, some of which are 700 to
800 years old. The lake in the centre of the course**

continued

provides both a challenge and a sense of peace and tranquillity. The Palladian magnificence of Thorndon Hall, site of the old clubhouse, sets the backdrop to the closing hole.
18 holes, 6492yds, Par 71, SSS 71.
Club membership 620.
Visitors must contact in advance, at weekends with member only except after 1pm Suns. **Societies** welcome Mon, Tue and Fri but must apply in writing. **Green Fees** £55 per day; £40 per round (£50 per round Sun after 1p.m. **Prof** Brian White **Course Designer** Colt/Alison **Facilities** ⊗ ⅷ by prior arrangement ⅃ ⅃ ♀ ⚐ ⚐ ⚑ ♂ **Location** W side of village off A128

Hotel ★★★ 69% Holiday Inn Brentwood, Brook St, BRENTWOOD ☎ 0870 400 9012 150 en suite

LOUGHTON　　　　　Map 05 TQ49

High Beech Wellington Hill IG10 4AH
☎ 020 8508 7323
Short 9-hole course set in Epping Forest.
9 holes, 1477, Par 27, Course record 25.
Visitors welcome. **Green Fees** terms on application. **Prof** Clark Baker **Facilities** ⅊ ⚐ ⚑ ♂ **Location** Close to M25 Waltham Abbey junct

Loughton Clays Ln, Debden Green IG10 2RZ
☎ 020 8502 2923
9-hole parkland course on the edge of Epping Forest. A good test of golf.
9 holes, 4652yds, Par 66, SSS 63, Course record 71.
Club membership 150.
Visitors must contact in advance for weekend play. **Societies** telephone in advance. **Green Fees** £12 per 18 holes; £7 per 9 holes (£14/£8 weekends). **Prof** Richard Layton **Facilities** ⅃ ⅊ ♀ ⚐ ⚐ ⚑ ♂ **Location** 1.5m SE of Theydon Bois

Hotel ★★★ 63% Posthouse Epping, High Rd, Bell Common, EPPING ☎ 0870 400 9027 79 annexe en suite

MALDON　　　　　Map 05 TL80

Forrester Park Beckingham Rd, Great Totham CM9 8EA ☎ 01621 891406 ▤ 01621 891406
Set in undulating parkland in the Essex countryside and commanding some beautiful views across the River Blackwater. Accuracy is more important than distance and judgement more important than strength on this traditional 'club' course. There is a separate 10-acre practice ground.
18 holes, 6073yds, Par 71, SSS 69, Course record 69.
Club membership 1000.
Visitors must contact in advance and may not play before noon weekends & bank holidays. **Societies** must apply in advance. **Green Fees** £18 per round before 10.30am; £15 after 2.30pm. **Cards** ⚏ ⚏ ⚏ ⚏ **Prof** Gary Pike **Course Designer** T R Forrester-Muir **Facilities** ⊗ ⅃ ⅊ ♀ ⚐ ⚐ ♂ ⚑ **Leisure** hard tennis courts. **Conf** Max 150 Thtr 150 Board 40 Banquet 120 Del £5 to £9.50 * **Location** 3m NE of Maldon off B1022

Hotel ★★★ 71% Pontlands Park Country Hotel, West Hanningfield Rd, Great Baddow, CHELMSFORD ☎ 01245 476444 36 en suite

Maldon Beeleigh, Langford CM9 6LL
☎ 01621 853212 ▤ 01621 855232
e-mail: maldon.golf@virgin.net
Flat, parkland course in a triangle of land bounded by the River Chelmer and the Blackwater Canal. Alternate tees on second nine holes. Testing par 3 14th (166yds) demanding particular accuracy to narrow green guarded by bunkers and large trees.
9 holes, 6253yds, Par 71, SSS 70, Course record 66.
Club membership 360.
Visitors telephone to check availability, may only play with member at weekends. Handicap certificate required. **Societies** intially telephone then confirm in writing. **Green Fees** £20 per day; £15 per round (£17/£12 weekends). **Course Designer** Thompson of Felixstowe **Facilities** ⊗ ⅷ by prior arrangement ⅃ ⅊ ♀ ⚐ **Location** 1m NW off B1019

Hotel ★★★ 71% Pontlands Park Country Hotel, West Hanningfield Rd, Great Baddow, CHELMSFORD ☎ 01245 476444 36 en suite

ORSETT　　　　　Map 05 TQ68

Orsett Brentwood Rd RM16 3DS
☎ 01375 891352 ▤ 01375 892471
e-mail: orsettgc@aol.com
A very good test of golf - this heathland course with its sandy soil is quick drying and provides easy walking. Close to the Thames estuary it is seldom calm and the main hazards are the prevailing wind and thick gorse. Any slight deviation can be exaggerated by the wind and result in a ball lost in the gorse. The clubhouse has been modernised to very high standards.
18 holes, 6614yds, Par 72, SSS 72, Course record 68.
Club membership 750.
Visitors weekdays only. Must contact in advance and have a handicap certificate. **Societies** must contact in advance. **Green Fees** terms on application. **Prof** Paul Joiner **Course Designer** James Braid **Facilities** ⊗ ⅷ ⅃ ⅊ ♀ ⚐ ⚐ ⚑ ♂ **Leisure** coaching. **Location** At junct of A13 off A128, towards Chadwell St Mary

Hotel ★★★ 65% Holiday Inn Basildon, Cranes Farm Rd, BASILDON ☎ 0870 400 9003 149 en suite

PURLEIGH　　　　　Map 05 TL80

Three Rivers Stow Rd, Cold Norton CM3 6RR
☎ 01621 828631 ▤ 01621 828060
e-mail: devers@clubhaus.com
Set in landscaped wooded parkland, Kings Course is fully matured with 18-holes, affording good valley views over the Crouch, Blackwater and Roach rivers that give the club its name. With ponds and dog-legs among the challenges it is ideal for seasoned golfers. The Jubilee Course offers an alternative in both style and challenge with all weather tees and greens built to USGA specification.
Kings Course: 18 holes, 6449yds, Par 72, SSS 71.
Jubilee Course: 18 holes, 4501yds, Par 64, SSS 62.
Club membership 900.
Visitors telephone before visit, must book in advance for Kings Course. **Societies** apply in writing or telephone. **Green Fees** not confirmed. **Cards** ⚏ ⚏ ⚏ ⚏ ⚏ **Prof** Scott Clark **Course Designer** Hawtree **Facilities** ⊗ ⅷ ⅃ ⅊ ♀ ⚐ ⚐ ⚑ ♂ **Leisure** hard tennis courts, video swing analysis centre. **Location** 2.5m from South Woodham Ferrers

continued

Where to stay, where to eat?
Visit www.theAA.com

Hotel ★★★ 71% Pontlands Park Country Hotel, West Hanningfield Rd, Great Baddow, CHELMSFORD ☎ 01245 476444 36 en suite

ROCHFORD   Map 05 TQ89

Rochford Hundred Hall Rd SS4 1NW
☎ 01702 544302 ▤ 01702 541343
e-mail: rochfordhundred@rhgc.sagehost.co.uk
Parkland course with ponds and ditches as natural hazards.
18 holes, 6292yds, Par 72, SSS 70, Course record 64.
Club membership 800.
Visitors must have handicap certificate. Visitors may not play Tue morning (Ladies) or Sun without a member. **Societies** must contact in writing. **Green Fees** terms on application. **Prof** Graham Hill **Course Designer** James Braid **Facilities** ⚒ 🏠 🍴 ℓ **Location** W on B1013

Hotel ★★★ 66% Hotel Renouf, Bradley Way, ROCHFORD ☎ 01702 541334 24 en suite

SAFFRON WALDEN   Map 05 TL53

Saffron Walden Windmill Hill CB10 1BX
☎ 01799 522786 ▤ 01799 522786
e-mail: office@swgc.com
Undulating parkland course, beautiful views.
18 holes, 6606yds, Par 72, SSS 72, Course record 63.
Club membership 950.
Visitors must contact in advance and have a handicap certificate. With member only at weekends. **Societies** must contact in advance. **Green Fees** £35 per day/round. **Prof** Philip Davis **Facilities** ⊗ 🌐 🏌 🏐 ♀ ⚒ 🏠 🍴 ℓ ℓ **Location** N side of town centre off B184

Hotel ★★ 68% The Crown House, GREAT CHESTERFORD ☎ 01799 530515 8 en suite 10 annexe en suite

SOUTHEND-ON-SEA   Map 05 TQ88

Belfairs Eastwood Rd North, Leigh on Sea SS9 4LR
☎ 01702 525345 & 520202
Municipal parkland course run by the Borough Council. Tight second half through thick woods, easy walking.
18 holes, 5840yds, Par 70, SSS 68, Course record 68.
Club membership 350.
Visitors contact for booking, correct dress code must be adhered to. **Societies** contact 01702 520202 **Green Fees** terms on application. **Prof** Nick Webber **Course Designer** H S Colt **Facilities** ⊗ 🌐 🏌 🏐 ♀ 🍴 ℓ **Leisure** hard tennis courts. **Location** Off A127

Hotel ★★ 70% Balmoral Hotel, 34 Valkyrie Rd, Westcliffe-on-Sea, SOUTHEND-ON-SEA ☎ 01702 342947 29 en suite

Thorpe Hall Thorpe Hall Av, Thorpe Bay SS1 3AT
☎ 01702 582205 ▤ 01702 584498
e-mail: thgc@hotmail.com
Parkland course with narrow fairways where placement rather than length is essential.
18 holes, 6319yds, Par 71, SSS 71, Course record 68.
Club membership 995.
Visitors must contact in advance, with member only weekends & bank holidays. **Societies** apply in writing, only a certain number a year. **Green Fees** not confirmed. **Prof** Bill McColl **Course Designer** Various **Facilities** ⊗ 🌐 🏌 🏐 ♀ ⚒ 🏠 🍴 ℓ **Leisure** squash, sauna, snooker room. **Location** 2m E off A13

Hotel ★★ 70% Balmoral Hotel, 34 Valkyrie Rd, Westcliffe-on-Sea, SOUTHEND-ON-SEA ☎ 01702 342947 29 en suite

SOUTH OCKENDON   Map 05 TQ58

Belhus Park Belhus Park RM15 4QR
☎ 01708 854260 ▤ 01708 851952
A well established 18 hole course set in beautiful parkland.
18 holes, 5589yds, Par 69, SSS 68, Course record 67.
Club membership 200.
Visitors no restrictions. Must have proper golf shoes and shirts be worn at all times. Booking advisable at weekends. **Societies** contact in writing or telephone **Green Fees** not confirmed. **Prof** Gary Lunn **Course Designer** Capability Brown **Facilities** ⚒ 🏠 🍴 ℓ ℓ **Leisure** heated indoor swimming pool, solarium, gymnasium. **Location** Off the B1335, follow brown tourist signs to course

Hotel ⬦ Hotel Ibis Thurrock, Weston Av, WEST THURROCK ☎ 01708 686000 102 en suite

Top Meadow Fen Ln, North Ockendon RM14 3PR
☎ 01708 852239
e-mail: info@topmeadow.co.uk
Set in the Essex countryside with a panoramic view of the area. Excellent test of golf for all standards.
18 holes, 6348yds, Par 72, SSS 71, Course record 68.
Club membership 600.
Visitors welcome Mon-Fri. **Societies** telephone in advance. **Green Fees** £12 per round inc breakfast. **Cards** 💳 💳 💳 **Prof** Roy Porter **Course Designer** Burns/Stock **Facilities** ⊗ 🌐 🏌 🏐 ♀ ⚒ 🏠 🍴 ℓ 🎣 ⚒ ℓ ℓ **Leisure** fishing. **Conf** Max 100 **Location** Junct 29 off M25, A127 towards Southend, B186 towards Ockendon, Fen Lane

Hotel ⬦ Travelodge Brentwood, EAST HORNDON ☎ 01277 810819 22 en suite

STANFORD-LE-HOPE   Map 05 TQ68

St Clere's Hall London Rd SS17 0LX
☎ 01375 361565 ▤ 01375 361565
All year round golf with views of the Thames, with several challenging par 3s, notably the 223 yard 13th.
18 holes, 6474yds, Par 72, SSS 71, Course record 71.
Club membership 460.
Visitors welcome after 9.30am Mon-Fri, and 10am Sat & Sun. Telephone for times. **Societies** welcome Mon, Tue and Thu, telephone for details. **Green Fees** terms on application. **Cards** 💳 💳 💳 💳 💳 💳 **Prof** David Wood **Course Designer** A Stiff **Facilities** ⊗ 🌐 🏌 🏐 ♀ ⚒ 🏠 🍴 🎣 ⚒ ℓ **Conf** Class 40 Board 25 Banquet 40 **Location** 5m from M25 E of London on A13, take Stanford turn off in direction Linford, St Clere on the left

Hotel ★★★ 65% Holiday Inn Basildon, Cranes Farm Rd, BASILDON ☎ 0870 400 9003 149 en suite

STAPLEFORD ABBOTTS   Map 05 TQ59

Stapleford Abbotts Horsemanside, Tysea Hill RM4 1JU ☎ 01708 381108 ▤ 01708 386345
Abbotts course, provides a challenging test for players of all abilities as mature trees, large greenside bunkers and many lakes are all brought into play. The Priors course with its links-type layout gives a fresh challenge on each hole.
Abbotts Course: 18 holes, 6501yds, Par 72, SSS 71.
Priors Course: 18 holes, 5735yds, Par 70, SSS 69.
Friars Course: 9 holes, 1140yds, Par 27, SSS 27.
Club membership 800.

continued

continued

Visitors Abbotts Course booking required, only after 12 at weekends. Priors and Friars, 7 days per week. Advisable to telephone starter on 01277 373344 for Priors and 01277 381108 for Abbotts and Friars. **Societies** must be pre booked. **Green Fees** Abbotts:£13(£30 weekends), Priors: £24 (£18 weekends). **Cards** 〰 ▦ ▦ ▦ 🄰 **Course Designer** Henry Cotton/Howard Swan **Facilities** ⊗ ⌇Ⅲ ⅃ ♨ ♀ ⚲ ⚑ ⚒ ⚓ ⚔ 𝒷 **Leisure** sauna. **Conf** Max 100 Thtr 100 Class 50 Board 30 Banquet 100 **Location** 1m E of Stapleford Abbotts, off B175

Hotel ★★★★ 72% Marygreen Manor Hotel, London Rd, BRENTWOOD ☎ 01277 225252
3 en suite 40 annexe en suite

STOCK   Map 05 TQ69

Crondon Park Stock Rd CM4 9DP

☎ 01277 841115 📄 01277 841356
e-mail: paul@crondon.com
Undulating parkland course with many water hazards.
18 holes, 6585yards, Par 72, SSS 71, Course record 66.
Club membership 700.
Visitors may play at weekends after mid-day. **Societies** telephone in advance. **Green Fees** £20 per 18 holes (£30 weekends). **Cards** 〰 ▦ 🄰 **Prof** Paul Barham/Freddie Sunderland **Course Designer** Mr M Gillet **Facilities** ⊗ Ⅲ ⅃ ⚑ ♀ ⚲ ⚓ ⚒ 𝒷 ❨ **Conf** Max 250 Banquet 140 **Location** On B1007,between Stock village and A12

Hotel ★★★ 68% The Heybridge Hotel, Roman Rd, INGATESTONE ☎ 01277 355355 22 en suite

THEYDON BOIS   Map 05 TQ49

Theydon Bois Theydon Rd CM16 4EH

☎ 01992 812460 & 813054 📄 01992 813054
e-mail: theydongolf@hotmail.com
The course was originally nine holes built into Epping Forest. It was later extended to 18 holes which were well-planned and well-bunkered but in keeping with the 'forest' tradition. The old nine in the Forest are short and have two bunkers between them, but even so a wayward shot can be among the trees. The autumn colours here are truly magnificent.

18 holes, 5480yds, Par 68, SSS 68, Course record 64.
Club membership 600.
Visitors may not play Wed, Thu, Sat & Sun mornings, ring 01992 812460 in advance to be sure a tee is available. **Societies** book through the secretary. **Green Fees** not confirmed. **Prof** R Hall **Course Designer** James Braid **Facilities** ⊗ Ⅲ ⅃ ⚑ ♀ ⚲ ⚓ ⚒ 𝒷 **Location** 2m from junct 26 on M25

Hotel ★★★ 63% Posthouse Epping, High Rd, Bell Common, EPPING ☎ 0870 400 9027 79 annexe en suite

FIVE LAKES
Hotel, Golf, Country Club & Spa

Two 18 hole courses
* The Lakes – championship course
* The Links – par 71
* Covered floodlit driving range
* Putting & chipping greens
* Exclusive Club House
* Hotel with 114 bedrooms
* Fully equipped Country Club & Spa

Colchester Road, Tolleshunt Knights, Maldon, Essex. CM9 8HX
Tel: 01621 862326
Fax: 01621 869696
E-mail enquiries@fivelakes.co.uk
Web http://www.fivelakes.co.uk

TOLLESHUNT KNIGHTS   Map 05 TL91

Five Lakes Hotel Golf & Country Club

Colchester Rd CM9 8HX ☎ 01621 868888 📄 869696
e-mail: enquiries@fivelakes.co.uk
Set in 320 acres, the two 18 hole courses both offer their own particular challenges. The Lakes, a PGA championship course, offers generous fairways with water features. The Links has narrow fairways and strategically placed bunkers.

Links Course: 18 holes, 6181yds, Par 71, SSS 70,
Course record 67.
Lakes Course: 18 holes, 6768yds, Par 72, SSS 72,
Course record 63.
Club membership 534.
Visitors must book in advance. **Societies** must contact in advance. **Green Fees** Links Course: £20(£28 weekends and bank holidays). Lakes Course: £27 (£35 weekends and bank holidays). **Cards** 〰 ▦ ▦ ▦ ▦ 🄰 **Prof** Gary Carter **Course Designer** Neil Cole **Facilities** ⊗ Ⅲ ⅃ ⚑ ♀ ⚲ ⚓

continued

Leisure hard tennis courts, heated indoor swimming pool, squash, sauna, solarium, gymnasium, snooker, badminton, health & beauty spa. **Conf** Max 2000 Thtr 2000 Class 700 Board 50 Banquet 300 Del from £49 * **Location** 1.75m NE on B1026. Signposted by brown tourist sign.

Hotel ★★★★ 72% Five Lakes Hotel, Golf, Country Club & Spa, Colchester Rd, TOLLESHUNT KNIGHTS ☎ 01621 868888 114 en suite

TOOT HILL — Map 05 TL50

Toot Hill School Rd CM5 9PU
☎ 01277 365523 01277 364509
Pleasant course with several water hazards and sand greens.
18 holes, 6053yds, Par 70, SSS 69, Course record 65.
Club membership 400.
Visitors welcome by prior arrangement, handicap certificate may be required. **Societies** Tue & Thu contact in advance. **Green Fees** £25 per round(£30 weekends). **Prof** Mark Bishop **Course Designer** Martin Gillett **Facilities** **Location** 7m SE of Harlow, off A414

Hotel ★★★ 63% Posthouse Epping, High Rd, Bell Common, EPPING ☎ 0870 400 9027 79 annexe en suite

WITHAM — Map 05 TL81

Benton Hall Wickham Hill CM8 3LH
☎ 01376 502454 01376 521050
e-mail: d.reeves@clubhaus.com
Set in rolling countryside surrounded by dense woodland, this challenging course provides a severe test even to the best golfers. The River Blackwater dominates the front nine and natural lakes come into play on five other holes.
18 holes, 6574yds, Par 72, SSS 72, Course record 64.
The Bishops: 1074yds, Par 27, SSS 27, Course record 24.
Club membership 470.
Visitors visitors can book 7 days in advance **Societies** telephone in advance. **Green Fees** £20 per round (£25 weekends after 2pm). **Cards** **Prof** Colin Fairweather **Course Designer** Alan Walker/Charles Cox **Facilities** **Conf** Max 300 Thtr 300 Class 250 Board 120 Banquet 120 Del £20 to £120 * **Location** Witham turn off on A12, signposted

Hotel ★★★ 63% White Hart Hotel, Bocking End, BRAINTREE ☎ 01376 321401 31 en suite

Braxted Park Braxted Park Estate CM8 3EN
☎ 01376 572372 01621 892840
e-mail: estate-office@braxted-park.demon.co.uk
9 holes, 2940yds, Par 35, SSS 34.
Course Designer Sir Allen Clark **Location** 2m from A12 near Kelvedon/Witham, at Gt Braxted
Telephone for further details

Hotel ★★★ 63% White Hart Hotel, Bocking End, BRAINTREE ☎ 01376 321401 31 en suite

WOODHAM WALTER — Map 05 TL80

Bunsay Downs Little Baddow Rd CM9 6RU
☎ 01245 222648 01245 223989
Attractive 9-hole public course, challenging for all abilities. Also par 3 course.
9 holes, 2932yds, Par 70, SSS 68.
Badgers: 9 holes, 1319yds, Par 54.
Club membership 400.

continued

Visitors no restrictions. **Societies** Mon-Fri only. Must contact in advance. **Green Fees** not confirmed. **Cards** **Prof** Mickey Walker/Henry Roblin **Course Designer** John Durham **Facilities** **Location** 2m signposted from Danbury on A414

Hotel ★★★ 71% County Hotel, Rainsford Rd, CHELMSFORD ☎ 01245 455700 54 en suite 8 annexe en suite

Warren CM9 6RW ☎ 01245 223258 01245 223989
Attractive parkland course with natural hazards and good views.
18 holes, 6229yds, Par 70, SSS 70, Course record 65.
Club membership 765.
Visitors contact in advance, weekend pm only, Wed pm only. **Societies** arrange by telephone, confirm in writing, weekdays ex Wed. **Green Fees** not confirmed. **Prof** Mickey Walker **Facilities** **Location** 0.5m SW

Hotel ★★★ 71% County Hotel, Rainsford Rd, CHELMSFORD ☎ 01245 455700 54 en suite 8 annexe en suite

GLOUCESTERSHIRE

ALMONDSBURY — Map 03 ST68

Bristol St Swithins Park, Blackhorse Hill BS10 7TP
☎ 01454 620000 01454 202700
e-mail: enquiries@bristolgolfclub.co.uk
An undulating parkland course with USGA specified constructed greens, mature trees and numerous water features. Magnificent views over the Severn estuary and surrounding countryside.
18 holes, 6133yds, Par 71, SSS 69, Course record 65.
Club membership 600.
Visitors must book in advance. **Societies** must contact in advance by telephone/writing **Green Fees** terms on application. **Cards** **Prof** Richard Berry **Course Designer** Pierson **Facilities** **Leisure** par 3 academy course. **Conf** Max 150 Thtr 150 Class 80 Board 40 Banquet 120 Del £35 * **Location** 100yds off M5 junct17

Hotel ★★★ 65% Henbury Lodge Hotel, Station Rd, Henbury, BRISTOL ☎ 0117 950 2615 12 en suite 9 annexe en suite

CHELTENHAM — Map 03 SO92

Cotswold Hills Ullenwood GL53 9QT
☎ 01242 515264 01242 515317
e-mail: golf@chgc.freeserve.co.uk
A gently undulating course with open aspects and views of the Cotswolds.
18 holes, 6565yds, Par 72, SSS 71, Course record 67.
Club membership 750.
Visitors telephone in advance, handicap certificate preferred. May play at weekend if no competitions. **Societies** must apply in writing or telephone. **Green Fees** £30 per day (£35 weekends & bank holidays). **Cards** **Prof** Norman Allen **Course Designer** M D Little **Facilities** **Location** 3m SE on A435 and A436

Hotel ★★★ 68% Holiday Inn Gloucester, Crest Way, Barnwood, GLOUCESTER ☎ 0870 400 9034 122 en suite

Lilley Brook
Cirencester Rd, Charlton Kings GL53 8EG
☎ 01242 526785 📠 01242 256880
e-mail: secretary@lilleybrookgc.fsnet.co.uk
Undulating parkland course. Magnificent views over Cheltenham and surrounding coutryside.
18 holes, 6212yds, Par 69, SSS 70, Course record 61.
Club membership 900.
Visitors advisable to enquire of availability. Handicap certificate required. May not play Sat or Sun morning **Societies** apply in writing. **Green Fees** £25 (£30 weekends & bank holidays). **Cards** ⚏ ▦ **Prof** Forbes Hadden **Course Designer** Mackenzie **Facilities** ⊗ ⅷ ㋿ 🛢 ♀ ♬ 🏠 ⚑ ❀ ♨ ♂ **Location** 2m S of Cheltenham on A435

Hotel ★★★★ 66% Cheltenham Park Hotel, Cirencester Rd, Charlton Kings, CHELTENHAM ☎ 01242 222021 33 en suite 110 annexe en suite

Shipton
Shipton Oliffe, Andoverford GL54 4HT
☎ 01242 890237 📠 01242 820336
Deceptive, easy walking course situated in the heart of the Cotswolds giving a fair challenge and panoramic views.
9 holes, 2516yds, Par 34, Course record 33.
Visitors pay & play course no bookings taken. **Societies** welcome. **Green Fees** not confirmed. **Facilities** ♀ 🏠 ⚑ ♂ **Location** On A436, south of junct with A40

Hotel ★★★ 68% Charlton Kings Hotel, London Rd, Charlton Kings, CHELTENHAM ☎ 01242 231061 14 en suite

CHIPPING SODBURY   Map 03 ST78

Chipping Sodbury
BS37 6PU
☎ 01454 319042 📠 01454 320052
e-mail: info@chippingsodburygolfclub.co.uk
Parkland courses of championship proportions on the edge of the Cotswolds. The old course may be seen from the large opening tee by the clubhouse at the top of the hill. Two huge drainage dykes cut through the course and form a distinctive hazard on eleven holes. The 527 yard par 5 18th provides a fitting finale.
New Course: 18 holes, 6912yds, Par 73, SSS 73, Course record 65.
Club membership 800.
Visitors must have a handicap certificate and may only play until after noon at weekends. **Societies** must contact in writing. **Green Fees** terms on application. **Prof** Mike Watts **Course Designer** Hawtree **Facilities** ⊗ ⅷ ㋿ 🛢 ♀ 🏠 ⚑ ❀ ♨ ♂ **Location** 0.5m N

Hotel ★★ 70% Compass Inn, TORMARTON
☎ 01454 218242 & 218577 📠 01454 218741 26 en suite

CIRENCESTER   Map 04 SP00

Cirencester
Cheltenham Rd, Bagendon GL7 7BH
☎ 01285 653939 & 652465 📠 01285 650665
e-mail: cirencestergolf@compuserve.com
Undulating open Cotswold course with excellent views.
18 holes, 6055yds, Par 70, SSS 69, Course record 65.
Club membership 800.
Visitors restricted availability at weekends, contact professional shop in advance on 01285 656124. **Societies** telephone Secretary/Manager. **Green Fees** £25 per round/day (£30 weekends). **Cards** ⚏ ▦ ▦ 🞖 **Prof** Peter Garratt **Course Designer** J Braid **Facilities** ⊗ ⅷ ㋿ 🛢 ♀ 🏠 ♨ ♂ **Leisure** 6 hole par 3 Academy course. **Conf** Max 20 **Location** 2m N of Cirencester on A435

continued

Hotel ★★★ 69% Stratton House Hotel, Gloucester Rd, CIRENCESTER ☎ 01285 651761 41 en suite

CLEEVE HILL   Map 03 SO92

Cleeve Hill
GL52 3PW
☎ 01242 672025 📠 01242 67444
Undulating and open heathland course affected by crosswinds.
18 holes, 6411yds, Par 72, SSS 71, Course record 69.
Club membership 600.
Visitors bookings taken 7 days in advance. Limited play weekends. **Societies** telephone pro shop in advance (01242 672592) **Green Fees** £12 per round (£15 weekends). **Cards** ⚏ ▦ ▦ 🞖 **Prof** Dave Finch **Facilities** ⊗ ⅷ ㋿ 🛢 ♀ **Location** 1m NE on B4632

Hotel ★★★ 64% The Prestbury House Hotel & Restaurant, The Burgage, Prestbury, CHELTENHAM ☎ 01242 529533 8 en suite 9 annexe en suite

COALPIT HEATH   Map 03 ST68

The Kendleshire
Henfield Rd BS36 2TG
☎ 0117 956 7007 📠 0117 957 3433
e-mail: info@kendleshire.co.uk
A course opened in 1997 to much acclaim, which is high on the priority list of many players. With water coming into play on 10 of the holes, the course is never short of interest and the greens have been built to USGA specification. The most difficult holes are probably the 11th, a short hole with an island green set in a 3 acre lake and the 16th, with the second shot played over water.
18 holes, 6550, Par 71, SSS 71, Course record 63.
Club membership 900.
Visitors must contact in advance and wear soft spikes. **Societies** telephone in advance **Green Fees** £25 per round (£40 weekends). **Cards** ⚏ ▦ 🞖 🞖 **Prof** Mike Bessell **Course Designer** A Stiff **Facilities** ⊗ ⅷ ㋿ 🛢 ♀ 🏠 ⚑ ❀ ♨ ♂ ♂ **Location** off M32 junct 1 on Avon Ring Road.

Hotel ★★★★ 64% Jurys Bristol Hotel, Prince St, BRISTOL ☎ 0117 923 0333 191 en suite

COLEFORD   Map 03 SO51

Forest Hills
Mile End Rd GL16 7BY
☎ 01594 810620 📠 01594 810823
e-mail: rchrdbllrd@aol.com
A parkland course on a plateau with panoramic views of Coleford and Forest of Dean. Some testing holes with the par 5 13th hole sitting tight on a water hazard, and the challenging 18th with second shot over large pond to a green protected by another pond and bunker - all in front of the clubhouse.
18 holes, 6740yds, Par 72, SSS 68, Course record 64.
Club membership 550.
Visitors no restrictions. **Societies** contact in advance. **Green Fees** £17 per day (£25 weekends). **Cards** ⚏ ▦ 🞖 **Prof** Richard Ballard **Course Designer** A Stiff **Facilities** ⊗ ⅷ ㋿ 🛢 ♀ 🏠 ⚑ ❀ ♨ ♂ ♂ **Leisure** fishing, solarium. **Conf** Max 300 Thtr 300 Class 200 Board 150 Banquet 200 Del from £15 *

Hotel ★★★ 67% The Speech House, COLEFORD ☎ 01594 822607 16 en suite 17 annexe en suite

Forest of Dean Golf Club & Bells Hotel

Lords Hill GL16 8BE ☎ 01594 832583 ▤ 01594 832584
e-mail: enquiries@bells-hotel.co.uk
Established in 1973 and now matured into an extremely pleasant parkland course. Well bunkered with light rough, a few blind tee shots and water in play on several holes.
18 holes, 6033yds, Par 70, SSS 69, Course record 63.
Club membership 450.
Visitors are required to book tee-off times. Societies must telephone in advance. Green Fees from £9.95. Cards 💳 ▆ ▆▆ 🗟 Prof Andy Gray Course Designer John Day Facilities ⊗ 》⊪ ᗋ ♨ ♡ 占 ⇑ 🏄 ㄟ 畚 ℓ Leisure hard tennis courts, bowling green. Conf Max 305 Thtr 190 Class 60 Board 80 Banquet 180 Location 0.25m from Coleford town centre on B4431 Coleford to Parkend road

Hotel ★★★ 67% The Speech House, COLEFORD ☎ 01594 822607 16 en suite 17 annexe en suite

---

DURSLEY — Map 03 ST79

Stinchcombe Hill Stinchcombe Hill GL11 6AQ
☎ 01453 542015 ▤ 01453 549545
e-mail: stinchcombehill@golfers.net
High on the hill with splendid views of the Cotswolds, the River Severn and the Welsh hills. A downland course with good turf, some trees and an interesting variety of greens. Protected greens make this a challenging course in windy conditions.

18 holes, 5734yds, Par 68, SSS 68, Course record 63.
Club membership 550.
Visitors restricted at weekends. Must contact professional in advance 01453 543878. Societies must apply in advance. Green Fees £22 per 18 holes (£27 weekends). Cards 💳 ▆ ▆▆ 🗟 Prof Paul Bushell Course Designer Arthur Hoare Facilities ⊗ 》⊪ ᗋ ♨ 占 ⇑ ℓ Location 1m W off A4135

Hotel ★★★ 66% Prince of Wales Hotel, Berkeley Rd, BERKELEY ☎ 01453 810474 43 en suite

---

GLOUCESTER — Map 03 SO81

Brickhampton Court Cheltenham Rd, Churchdown GL2 9QF ☎ 01452 859444 ▤ 01452 859333
e-mail: info@brickhampton.co.uk
27 holes, including the county's first intermediate course (9-hole par 31) for the new and developing golfer, set in undulating parkland. The Spa course offers a good golfing challenge, featuring lakes, streams and well placed bunkers.
Spa: 18 holes, 6449yds, Par 71, SSS 71, Course record 66.
Glevum: 9 holes, 1859yds, Par 31.
Club membership 700.

continued

Visitors advance booking recommended, recognised golfing attire to be worn and evidence of golfing ability preferred. Societies contact for information and booking form. Green Fees not confirmed. Cards 💳 ▆ ▆▆ 🗟 Prof Bruce Wilson Course Designer Simon Gidman Facilities ⊗ 》⊪ ᗋ ♨ ♡ 占 ⇑ 🏄 ㄟ 畚 ℓ Location Junct 11 M5, A40 towards Gloucester, at Elmbridge Court rdbt B4063 signed Churchdown, approx 2m

Hotel ★★★ 62% Hatherley Manor Hotel, Down Hatherley Ln, GLOUCESTER ☎ 01452 730217 56 en suite

---

Jarvis Gloucester Hotel & Country Club

Matson Ln, Robinswood Hill GL4 6EA
☎ 01452 411331 ▤ 01452 307212
Undulating, wooded course, built around a hill with superb views over Gloucester and the Cotswolds. The 12th is a drive straight up a hill, nicknamed 'Coronary Hill'.
18 holes, 6170yds, Par 70, SSS 69, Course record 65.
Club membership 600.
Visitors can book up to 7 days in advance. Societies telephone in advance. Green Fees not confirmed. Cards 💳 ▆ ▆▆ 🗟 Prof Chris Gillick/John Whiddon Facilities ⊗ 》⊪ ᗋ ♨ ♡ 占 ⇑ 🏄 ㄟ 畚 ℓ 𝕃 Leisure hard tennis courts, heated indoor swimming pool, squash, sauna, solarium, gymnasium. Location 2.5m SE of Gloucester, off B4073

Hotel ★★★ 72% Hatton Court, Upton Hill, Upton St Leonards, GLOUCESTER ☎ 01452 617412 17 en suite 28 annexe en suite

---

Rodway Hill Newent Rd, Highnam GL2 8DN

☎ 01452 384222 ▤ 01452 313814
e-mail: jrawl98589@aol.com
A challenging 18-hole course with superb panoramic views. Testing front 5 holes and the par 3 13th and par 5 16th being affected by strong crosswinds off the River Severn.
18 holes, 6070yds, Par 70, SSS 69, Course record 71.
Club membership 400.
Visitors no restrictions. Societies telephone in advance. Green Fees terms on application. Cards 💳 ▆ ▆▆ 🗟 Prof Tony Grubb Course Designer John Gabb Facilities ⊗ 》⊪ ᗋ ♨ ♡ 占 ⇑ 🏄 ㄟ ℓ Location 2m outside Gloucester on B4215

Hotel ★★★ 62% Hatherley Manor Hotel, Down Hatherley Ln, GLOUCESTER ☎ 01452 730217 56 en suite

---

LYDNEY — Map 03 SO60

Lydney Lakeside Av GL15 5QA
☎ 01594 843940 (secretary) & 842614 (clubhouse)
e-mail: dennis@barnardd.fsnet.co.uk
Flat parkland/meadowland course with prevailing wind along fairways.
9 holes, 5298yds, Par 66, SSS 66, Course record 63.
Club membership 350.
Visitors with member only at weekends & bank holidays. Societies apply to Secretary. Green Fees £10 per day. Facilities 𝕃 by prior arrangement ᗋ 占 Location SE side of town centre

Hotel ★★★ 67% The Speech House, COLEFORD ☎ 01594 822607 16 en suite 17 annexe en suite

MINCHINHAMPTON — Map 03 SO80

Minchinhampton (New Course) New Course

GL6 9BE ☎ 01453 833866 ▤ 01453 837360
e-mail: sec@mgcnew.co.uk
The Cherington course is set in undulating upland. Large contoured greens, pot bunkers, and, at times, a stiff breeze present a very fair test of skill. The Avening course has a variety of holes including water on the 10th and 13th.
Avening: 18 holes, 6263yds, Par 70, SSS 70,
Course record 61.
Cherington: 18 holes, 6430yds, Par 71, SSS 71.
Club membership 1200.
Visitors must contact in advance. Societies must contact by telephone. Green Fees £28 per day (£32 weekends & bank holidays). Cards ▦ ▣ Prof Chris Steele Course Designer Hawtree & Son Facilities ⊗ ⅋ ▙ ♥ ♀ ♣ ⌂ ⛳ ✆ ⚑ Location From Nailsworth take B4014 to Avening/Tetbury. In Avening village left at Cross pub, towards Minchinhampton. Club 0.25m on right
....

Hotel ★★ 70% Egypt Mill Hotel, NAILSWORTH
☎ 01453 833449 8 en suite 10 annexe en suite

Minchinhampton (Old Course) Old Course

GL6 9AQ ☎ 01453 832642 & 836382 ▤ 01453 832642
e-mail: mgc.old@btinternet.com
An open grassland course 600 feet above sea level. The numerous humps and hollows around the greens tests the golfer's ability to play a variety of shots - often in difficult windy conditions. Panoramic Cotswold views. Two of the par 3s, the 8th and the 16th often require an accurate long iron or wood depending on the strength and direction of the wind.
18 holes, 6019yds, Par 71, SSS 69.
Club membership 650.
Visitors must contact in advance. Green Fees £12 per day/round (£15 weekend and bank holidays). Cards ▦ ▣ Facilities ⊗ ▙ ♥ ♀ ♣ ⌂ ⛳ ✆ Location 1m NW
....

Hotel ★★ 70% Egypt Mill Hotel, NAILSWORTH
☎ 01453 833449 8 en suite 10 annexe en suite

NAUNTON — Map 04 SP12

Naunton Downs GL54 3AE

☎ 01451 850090 ▤ 01451 850091
Naunton Downs course plays over beautiful Cotswold countryside. A valley running through the course is one of the main features, creating 1 par 3 hole that crosses over it. The prevailing wind adds extra challenge to the par 5s (which play into the wind), combined with small undulating greens.
18 holes, 6135yds, Par 71, SSS 69, Course record 67.
Club membership 750.
Visitors must contact in advance. Societies telephone for details. Green Fees £19 (£27.50 weekends). Cards ▦ ▣ ▤ ▣ Prof Nick Ellis Course Designer J Pott Facilities ⊗ ⅋ ▙ ♥ ♀ ♣ ⌂ ⛳ ➘ ⚒ ✆ Leisure hard tennis courts. Location B4068 Stow/Cheltenham
....

Hotel ★★★ Lords of the Manor, UPPER SLAUGHTER
☎ 01451 820243 27 en suite

PAINSWICK — Map 03 SO80

Painswick GL6 6TL ☎ 01452 812180

Downland course set on Cotswold Hills at Painswick Beacon, with fine views. Short course more than *continued*

compensated by natural hazards and tight fairways.
18 holes, 4895yds, Par 67, SSS 63, Course record 61.
Club membership 480.
Visitors member only on Sat pm & Sun. Societies must apply in advance. Green Fees terms on application. Cards ▦ ▣ ▣ Facilities ⊗ ⅋ ▙ ♥ ♀ ♣ ⌂ ⛳ ✆ Location 1m N on A46
....

Hotel ★★★ 75% Painswick Hotel, Kemps Ln, PAINSWICK ☎ 01452 812160 19 en suite

TEWKESBURY — Map 03 SO83

Hilton Puckrup Hall Puckrup GL20 6EL

☎ 01684 296200 & 271591 (golf shop) ▤ 01684 850788
e-mail: puckruphall@hotmail.com
Set in 140 acres of undulating parkland with lakes, existing trees and marvellous views of the Malvern hills. There are water hazards at the 5th and a cluster of bunkers on the long 14th before the challenging tee shot across the water to the par 3 18th.

18 holes, 6189yds, Par 70, SSS 70, Course record 63.
Club membership 500.
Visitors must be a regular golfer familiar with rules and etiquette, must book a tee time, may book up to 5 days in advance. Societies telephone in advance. Green Fees £25 per round (£30 weekends). Cards ▦ ▣ ▣ ▣ ▣ ▣ Prof Kevin Pickett Course Designer Simon Gidman Facilities ⊗ ⅋ ▙ ♥ ♀ ♣ ⌂ ⛤ ➘ ⚒ ✆ Leisure heated indoor swimming pool, sauna, solarium, gymnasium. Conf Thtr 200 Class 200 Banquet 225 Location 4m N, of Tewkesbury on A38 or junct 1 M50
....

Hotel ★★ 61% Bell Hotel, 57 Church St, TEWKESBURY
☎ 01684 293293 25 en suite

Tewkesbury Park Hotel Golf & Country Club Lincoln Green Ln GL20 7DN

☎ 01684 295405 ▤ 01684 292386
e-mail: tewkesburypark@corushotels.com
A parkland course overlooking the Abbey and rivers Avon and Severn. The par 3, 5th is an exciting hole calling for accurate distance judgment. The hotel and country club offer many sports and club facilities including a well equipped gym with cardio theatre.
18 holes, 6533yds, Par 73, SSS 71, Course record 66.
Club membership 550.
Visitors must book in advance via pro shop/hotel reservations. Societies telephone initially. Green Fees £25 per round(£30 weekends). Cards ▦ ▣ ▣ ▣ ▣ ▣ Prof Charlie Boast Course Designer Frank Pennick Facilities ⊗ ⅋ ▙ ♥ ♀ ♣ ⌂ ⛳ ➙ ➘ ⚒ ✆ ⛳ Leisure hard tennis courts, heated indoor swimming pool, squash, sauna, solarium, gymnasium. Conf Thtr 150 Class 100 Board 50 Banquet 130 Del from £42 * Location 1m SW off A38
continued

Hotel ★★★ 69% Tewkesbury Park Hotel Golf & Country Club, Lincoln Green Ln, TEWKESBURY ☎ 01684 295405 78 en suite

Westonbirt Golf Club

Visitors no restrictions. **Societies** no reserved tees. **Green Fees** £9.50. **Facilities** ☟ ᕟ **Conf** Max 400 Thtr 400 Class 250 Board 50 Banquet 125 **Location** E side of village off A433

Hotel ★★★ 69% Hare & Hounds Hotel, Westonbirt, TETBURY ☎ 01666 880233 24 en suite 7 annexe en suite

> An asterisk * in the Green Fees or Conference facilities indicates that prices given are for 2002

THORNBURY
Map 03 ST69

Thornbury Golf Centre Bristol Rd BS35 3XL
☎ 01454 281144 ▤ 01454 281177
Two 18 hole pay & play courses designed by Hawtree and set in undulating terrain with exstensive views towards the Severn estuary. The Low 18 is a par 3 with holes ranging from 80 to 207 yards and is ideal for beginners. The High course puts to test the more experienced golfer. Excellent 25 bay floodlit driving range.

High Course: 18 holes, 6154yds, Par 71, SSS 69, Course record 70.
Low Course: 18 holes, 2195yds, Par 54.
Club membership 540.
Visitors welcome at all times, telephone to reserve. **Societies** apply in writing. **Green Fees** not confirmed. **Cards** ▤ ▤ ▤ ▤ **Prof** Simon Hubbard **Course Designer** Hawtree **Facilities** ⊗ ⅷ ᕟ ☟ ♀ ᕟ 🏠 ⚑ 🖙 🏌 🛒 ∕ ₵ **Location** Off A38

Hotel ★★ 67% Thornbury Golf Lodge, Bristol Rd, THORNBURY ☎ 01454 281144 11 en suite

WESTONBIRT
Map 03 ST88

Westonbirt Westonbirt School GL8 8QG
☎ 01666 880242 ▤ 01666 880385
A parkland course with good views.
9 holes, 4504yds, Par 64, SSS 64.
Club membership 225.

WICK
Map 03 ST77

The Gloucestershire Tracy Park Estate, Bath Rd BS30 5RN ☎ 0117 937 2251 ▤ 0117 937 4288
e-mail: golf@thegloucestershire.com
Two 18 hole championship courses on the south-western escarpment of the Cotswolds, affording fine views. Both courses present a challenge to all levels of player, with water playing a part on a number of occasions. The clubhouse dates back to 1600 and is a building of great beauty and elegance, set in the 221 acre estate of this golf and country club.
Crown Course: 18 holes, 6252yds, Par 69, SSS 70.
Cromwell Course: 18 holes, 6246yds, Par 71, SSS 70.
Club membership 700.
Visitors no restrictions, must book tee time(0117 3039123) **Societies** must telephone/write to Robert Ford **Green Fees** £30 per round (£38 weekends and bank holidays). **Cards** ▤ ▤ ▤ ▤ ♀ **Facilities** ⊗ ⅷ ᕟ ☟ ♀ ᕟ 🏠 ⚑ 🖙 🏌 ∕ ₵ **Conf** Thtr 150 Class 60 Board 50 Banquet 110 Del from £25 * **Location** S side of village off A420

Hotel ★★★ The Queensberry Hotel, Russel St, BATH ☎ 01225 447928 29 en suite

WOTTON-UNDER-EDGE
Map 03 ST79

Cotswold Edge Upper Rushmire GL12 7PT
☎ 01453 844167 ▤ 01453 845120
e-mail: nnewman@cotswoldedgegolfclub.org.uk
Meadowland course situated in a quiet Cotswold valley with magnificent views. First half flat and open, second half more varied.
18 holes, 6170yds, Par 71, SSS 71.
Club membership 800.
Visitors preferable to contact in advance, at weekends may only play with member. **Societies** must contact in writing or telephone in advance. **Green Fees** £15(£20 weekends). **Prof** David Gosling **Facilities** ⊗ ᕟ ☟ ♀ ᕟ 🏠 ⚑ 🖙 🏌 ∕ **Location** N of town on B4058 Wotton-Tetbury road

Hotel ★★ 70% Egypt Mill Hotel, NAILSWORTH ☎ 01453 833449 8 en suite 10 annexe en suite

continued

GREATER LONDON

Those courses which fall within the confines of the London Postal District area (i.e. have London postcodes - W1, SW1 etc.) are listed under the county heading of **London** in the gazetteer (see page 165).

GREATER LONDON

ADDINGTON   Map 05 TQ36

The Addington 205 Shirley Church Rd CR0 5AB
☎ 020 8777 1055 📠 020 7777 1701
e-mail: theaddgc@dialstart.net
Designed by Abercromby, the famous golf course architect, and not altered since. Thought and skill are required at every hole including the world famous 13th.
18 holes, 6338yds, Par 68, SSS 71, Course record 66.
Visitors handicap certificate required. **Societies** weekdays only, telephone for prior arrangement. **Green Fees** £50.
Cards 🔲 🔲 🔲 ⬛ **Course Designer** Abercromby **Facilities** ⊗ ⊞ ⅃ 🍺 ⅂ ♨ ✐

Hotel ★★★★ 70% Le Meridien Selsdon Park, Addington Rd, Sanderstead, CROYDON ☎ 020 8657 8811 204 en suite

Addington Court Featherbed Ln CR0 9AA
☎ 020 8657 0281 (booking) & 8651 5270 (admin)
📠 020 8651 0282
Challenging, well-drained courses designed by F. Hawtree. Two 18 hole courses, 9 hole course and an 18 hole par 3 course designed to suit all standards.

Championship Course: 18 holes, 5577yds, Par 68, SSS 67, Course record 60.
Falconwood: 18 holes, 5472yds, Par 68, SSS 67.
9 Hole: 9 holes, 1804yds, Par 31.
Club membership 350.
Visitors no restrictions. Advisable to phone in advance to play on Championship Course. **Societies** must telephone in advance. **Green Fees** not confirmed. **Cards** 🔲 ⬛ 🔲 ⬛ **Prof** Tony Healy **Course Designer** Hawtree Snr **Facilities** ⊗ ⊞ ⅃ 🍺 ⅂ ♨ 🏠 ⅂ ➤ ♨ ✐ (**Location** 1m S off A2022

Hotel ★★★★ 70% Le Meridien Selsdon Park, Addington Rd, Sanderstead, CROYDON ☎ 020 8657 8811 204 en suite

Addington Palace Addington Park, Gravel Hill CR0 5BB ☎ 020 8654 3061 📠 020 8655 3632
Hard-walking parkland course, with many testing holes especially the par 4 2nd and 10th.

continued

18 holes, 6286yds, Par 71, SSS 71, Course record 63.
Club membership 700.
Visitors telephone in advance. May play weekdays only.
Societies weekdays only, telephone in advance. **Green Fees** not confirmed. **Prof** Roger Williams **Course Designer** J H Taylor **Facilities** ⊗ ⊞ ⅃ 🍺 ⅂ ♨ 🏠 ✐ **Location** 2miles SE of Croydon station on A212

Hotel ★★★★ 70% Le Meridien Selsdon Park, Addington Rd, Sanderstead, CROYDON ☎ 020 8657 8811 204 en suite

BARNEHURST   Map 05 TQ57

Barnehurst Mayplace Rd East DA7 6JU
☎ 01322 552952 📠 01322 552952
Public parkland course with well matured greens. Easy walking.
9 holes, 4796yds, Par 70, SSS 67.
Visitors Reasonable standard of dress required. No jeans.
Societies telephone in advance. **Green Fees** not confirmed.
Cards 🔲 🔲 **Course Designer** James Braid **Facilities** ⊗ ⊞ ⅃ 🍺 ⅂ ♨ 🏠 ⅂ ✐ **Location** 0.75m NW of Crayford off A2000

Hotel ★★★ 66% Holiday Inn Bexley, Black Prince Interchange, Southwold Rd, BEXLEY ☎ 0870 400 9006 108 en suite

BARNET   Map 04 TQ29

Arkley Rowley Green Rd EN5 3HL
☎ 020 8449 0394 📠 020 8440 5214
e-mail: secretary@arkleygolfclub.co.uk
Wooded parkland course situated on highest spot in Hertfordshire with fine views.
9 holes, 6117yds, Par 69, SSS 67.
Club membership 450.
Visitors may play weekdays only. **Societies** must contact in advance. **Green Fees** £22 per day. **Prof** Martin Porter **Course Designer** Braid **Facilities** ⊗ ⊞ ⅃ 🍺 ⅂ ♨ 🏠 ✐ **Location** Off A1 at Arkley sign

Hotel ★★★ 72% Edgwarebury Hotel, Barnet Ln, ELSTREE ☎ 020 8953 8227 47 en suite

Dyrham Park Country Club Galley Ln EN5 4RA
☎ 020 8440 3361 📠 020 8441 9836
18 holes, 6369yds, Par 71, SSS 70, Course record 65.
Location 3m NW off A1081
Telephone for further details

Hotel ★★★ 66% Holiday Inn South Mimms, SOUTH MIMMS ☎ 0870 400 9072 143 en suite

Old Fold Manor Old Fold Ln, Hadley Green EN5 4QN
☎ 020 8440 9185 📠 020 8441 4863
e-mail: manager@oldfoldmanor.co.uk
Heathland course, good test of golf.
18 holes, 6447yds, Par 71, SSS 70, Course record 66.
Club membership 520.
Visitors with member only weekends & bank holidays.
Societies must apply in writing. **Green Fees** £35 per day; £25 per round (£20/£15 Mon-Wed); £30 per round weekends & bank holidays. **Cards** 🔲 🔲 🔲 🔲 ⬛ **Prof** Peter McEvoy **Facilities** ⊗ ⅃ 🍺 ⅂ ♨ 🏠 ⅂ ➤ ♨ ✐ **Location** Off A1000 between Barnet/Potters Bar

Hotel ★★★★★ 70% West Lodge Park Hotel, Cockfosters Rd, HADLEY WOOD ☎ 020 8216 3900 46 en suite 13 annexe en suite

BECKENHAM Map 05 TQ36

Beckenham Place Park The Mansion, Beckenham Place Park BR3 2BP ☎ 020 8650 2292 📠 020 8663 1201
18 holes, 5722yds, Par 68, SSS 68.
Location Main Catford/Beckenham road, just off A21
Telephone for further details

....

Hotel ★★★ 73% Bromley Court Hotel, Bromley Hill, BROMLEY ☎ 020 8461 8600 116 en suite

Langley Park Barnfield Wood Rd BR3 6SZ
☎ 020 8658 6849 📠 020 8658 6310
This is a pleasant, but difficult, well-wooded, parkland course with natural hazards including a lake at the 18th hole.
18 holes, 6488yds, Par 69, SSS 71, Course record 65.
Club membership 700.
Visitors must contact in advance and may not play weekends. **Societies** Wed & Thu only, telephone to book.
Green Fees not confirmed. **Prof** Colin Staff **Course Designer** J H Taylor **Facilities** ⊗ ⑪ ⓵ 🏌 ☂ ♀ ⚘ 🏠 ⚐ ✆
Location 0.5 N on B2015

....

Hotel ★★★ 73% Bromley Court Hotel, Bromley Hill, BROMLEY ☎ 020 8461 8600 116 en suite

BEXLEYHEATH Map 05 TQ47

Bexleyheath Mount Rd DA6 8JS ☎ 020 8303 6951
Undulating course.
9 holes, 5162yds, Par 66, SSS 66, Course record 65.
Club membership 330.
Visitors must contact Secretary in advance, may not play weekends. **Societies** telephone in advance. **Green Fees** terms on application. **Facilities** ⊗ ⑪ ⓵ 🏌 ☂ ♀ ⚘ **Location** 1m SW

....

Hotel ★★★ 66% Holiday Inn Bexley, Black Prince Interchange, Southwold Rd, BEXLEY
☎ 0870 400 9006 108 en suite

BIGGIN HILL Map 05 TQ45

Cherry Lodge Jail Ln TN16 3AX
☎ 01959 572250 & 572989 📠 01959 540672
Undulating parkland course set 600 feet above sea level with panoramic views of the surrounding Kent countryside. An enjoyable test of golf for all standards. The 14th is 434 yards across a valley and uphill, requiring two good shots to reach the green.

18 holes, 6652yds, Par 72, SSS 73, Course record 66.
Club membership 700.
Visitors must contact pro shop for weekday reservation. May only play with member at weekends. **Societies** must telephone in advance. **Green Fees** £35 per 18 holes *continued*

At 6,652 yards the undulating par 72 course enjoys spectacular views over the surrounding Kent countryside while providing a challenging test for golfers of all standards. Delicious cuisine, created by our award-winning chefs and complimented by the finest personal service, ensures the perfect day.

Memberships for all categories
Society & Corporate golf day
Weddings & Functions

Cherry Lodge Golf Club
Tel: 01959 572 250
Fax: 01959 540 672
Email: info@cherrylodgegc.co.uk
Website: www.cherrylodgegc.co.uk

weekdays only. **Prof** Nigel Child **Course Designer** John Day **Facilities** ⊗ ⓵ 🏌 ☂ ♀ ⚘ 🏠 ⚘ ✆ ⚐ **Location** 1m E

....

Hotel ★★★ 69% Donnington Manor, London Rd, Dunton Green, SEVENOAKS ☎ 01732 462681 60 en suite

BROMLEY Map 05 TQ46

Bromley Magpie Hall Ln BR2 8JF
☎ 020 8462 7014 📠 020 8462 6916
Flat course, ideal for beginners.
9 holes, 2745yds, Par 70, SSS 67.
Club membership 100.
Visitors no restrictions. **Societies** apply in writing. **Green Fees** terms on application. **Cards** 🔲 🔳 🔲 🔳 **Prof** Alan Hodgson **Facilities** 🏌 🏠 ⚐ ⚘ **Location** 2m SE off A21

....

Hotel ★★★ 73% Bromley Court Hotel, Bromley Hill, BROMLEY ☎ 020 8461 8600 116 en suite

Shortlands Meadow Rd, Shortlands BR2 0DX
☎ 020 8460 8828 📠 020 8460 8828
Easy walking parkland course with a brook as a natural hazard.
9 holes, 5261yds, Par 65, SSS 66, Course record 59.
Club membership 500.
Visitors must be guest of member. **Societies** must contact in advance. **Green Fees** terms on application. **Prof** Mick Taylor **Facilities** ⊗ ⑪ ⓵ 🏌 ☂ ♀ ⚘ 🏠 ⚘ **Location** 0.75m W off A222

....

Hotel ★★★ 73% Bromley Court Hotel, Bromley Hill, BROMLEY ☎ 020 8461 8600 116 en suite

Sundridge Park Garden Rd BR1 3NE
☎ 020 8460 0278 🖳 020 8289 3050
The East course is longer than the West but many think the shorter of the two courses is the more difficult. The East is surrounded by trees while the West is more hilly, with good views. Both are certainly a good test of golf.
East Course: 18 holes, 6516yds, Par 71, SSS 71, Course record 63.
West Course: 18 holes, 6019yds, Par 69, SSS 69, Course record 65.
Club membership 1200.
Visitors may only play on weekdays. Must contact in advance and must have a handicap certificate. No advance booking necessary. Societies must contact well in advance. Green Fees not confirmed. Prof Bob Cameron Course Designer Willie Park Facilities ⊗ ⫿ 占 💺 ♀ ▲ 🏠 ✂ Location N side of town centre off A2212

Hotel ★★★ 73% Bromley Court Hotel, Bromley Hill, BROMLEY ☎ 020 8461 8600 116 en suite

CARSHALTON   Map 04 TQ26

Oaks Sports Centre Woodmansterne Rd SM5 4AN
☎ 020 8643 8363 🖳 020 8770 7303
e-mail: golf@oaks.sagehost.co.uk
Public parkland course with floodlit, covered driving range.

18 Holes: 18 holes, 6025yds, Par 70, SSS 69, Course record 65.
The Oaks: 9 holes, 1443yds, Par 28, SSS 28.
Club membership 565.
Visitors no restrictions weekdays. May not play mornings at weekends. Societies must apply in writing. Green Fees 18 Hole: £15.25 (£18 weekends). The Oaks: £7.50 (£9 weekends). Prof Horley/Russell/Pilkington Facilities ⊗ ⫿ by prior arrangement 占 💺 ▲ 🏠 ♀ 🏌 ✂ ✂ Leisure squash.Conf Max 92 Thtr 92 Class 40 Board 60 Banquet 70 Location 0.5m S on B278

Hotel ★★★ 65% Posthouse Croydon, Purley Way, CROYDON ☎ 0870 400 9022 83 en suite

CHESSINGTON   Map 04 TQ16

Chessington Garrison Ln KT9 2LW
☎ 020 8391 0948 🖳 020 8397 2068
e-mail: info@chessingtongolf.co.uk
Tree-lined parkland course designed by Patrick Tallack, with panoramic views over the Surrey countryside.
9 holes, 1679yds, Par 30, SSS 28.
Club membership 90.
continued

Visitors may not play before 10am on Sun. Societies Telephone in advance. Green Fees £7.50 per round (£9 weekends). Cards 🔳 🔳 🔳 🔳 🔳 Prof Mark Janes Course Designer Patrick Tallack Facilities ⊗ 占 💺 ♀ 🏠 🏌 🍴 🍴 ✂ ✂ Location M25 junct 9, 3m N on A243

Hotel ⇧ Travel Inn, Leatherhead Rd, CHESSINGTON ☎ 01372 744060 42 en suite

CHISLEHURST   Map 05 TQ47

Chislehurst Camden Park Rd BR7 5HJ
☎ 020 8467 2782 🖳 020 8295 0874
Pleasantly wooded undulating parkland/heathland course. Magnificent clubhouse with historical associations.
18 holes, 5106yds, Par 66, SSS 65, Course record 61.
Club membership 750.
Visitors with member only weekends, handicap certificate required during the week. Societies weekdays only, telephone in advance. Green Fees £25 per round (£15 winter). Prof Jonathan Bird Course Designer Park Facilities ⊗ ⫿ 占 💺 ♀ ▲ 🏠 🏌 ✂ Conf Max 120 Del £3.50 to £25*

Hotel ★★★ 73% Bromley Court Hotel, Bromley Hill, BROMLEY ☎ 020 8461 8600 116 en suite

COULSDON   Map 04 TQ25

Coulsdon Manor Hotel Coulsdon Court Rd CR5 2LL
☎ 020 8668 0414 🖳 020 8668 3118
e-mail: coulsdonmanor@marstonhotels.com
Set in its own 140 acres of landscaped parkland.
18 holes, 6037yds, Par 70, SSS 68.
Visitors must telephone up to 5 days in advance. Societies
continued

by arrangement. **Green Fees** not confirmed. **Cards** 🔳 🔳 🔳 📷 **Prof** David Copsey **Course Designer** Harry Colt **Facilities** ⊗ ⏛ ⮣ 💺 ♀ 👜 ⛳ 🏸 🛴 ⛳ **Leisure** hard tennis courts, squash, sauna, solarium, gymnasium. **Location** 0.75m E off A23 on B2030

Hotel ★★★★ 77% Coulsdon Manor, Coulsdon Court Rd, Coulsdon, CROYDON ☎ 020 8668 0414 35 en suite

Woodcote Park Meadow Hill, Bridle Way CR5 2QQ ☎ 020 8668 2788 📋 020 8668 2788 **Slightly undulating parkland course.** *18 holes, 6669yds, Par 71, SSS 72, Course record 66. Club membership 650.* **Visitors** handicap certificate required, contact professional for details. Visitors may not play weekends. **Societies** must contact Secretary in advance. **Green Fees** not confirmed. **Prof** I Golding **Facilities** ⮣ 👜 ⛳ **Location** 1m N of town centre off A237

Hotel ★★★ 65% Posthouse Croydon, Purley Way, CROYDON ☎ 0870 400 9022 83 en suite

CROYDON   Map 04 TQ36

Croham Hurst Croham Rd CR2 7HJ
☎ 020 8657 5581 📋 020 8657 3229 e-mail: secretary@chgc.co.uk **Parkland course with tree-lined fairways and bounded by wooded hills. Easy walking.** *18 holes, 6290yds, Par 70, SSS 70. Club membership 800.* **Visitors** must contact in advance & have handicap certificate. With member only weekends & bank holidays. **Societies** Apply in writing/telephone in advance **Green Fees** £37 (£46 weekends & bank holidays). **Prof** Eric Stillwell **Course Designer** Hawtree **Facilities** ⊗ ⏛ ⮣ 💺 ♀ 👜 ⛳ 👜 ⛳ **Location** 1.5m SE,of Croydon between South Croydon & Selsdon on B269

Hotel ★★★★ 70% Le Meridien Selsdon Park, Addington Rd, Sanderstead, CROYDON ☎ 020 8657 8811 204 en suite

Le Meridien Selsdon Park Addington Rd,
Sanderstead CR2 8YA ☎ 020 8657 8811 📋 020 8651 6171 **Parkland course. Full use of hotel's sporting facilities by residents.** *18 holes, 6473yds, Par 73, SSS 71, Course record 63.* **Visitors** welcome, booking advisable, booking 1 week in advance for weekends. **Societies** telephone in advance. **Green Fees** from £20 per round (from £25 weekends). **Cards** 🔳 🔳 🔳 📷 🔳 🔳 💳 **Prof** Malcolm Churchill **Course Designer** J H Taylor **Facilities** ⊗ ⏛ ⮣ 💺 ♀ ⮣ 👜 ⛳ 🏸 🛴 ⛳ ⛳ **Leisure** hard and grass tennis courts, outdoor and indoor heated swimming pools, squash, sauna, *continued*

*Le*MERIDIEN
Selsdon Park and Golf Course
Sanderstead, South Croydon
Tel: 020-8657-8811/Fax: 020-8657-3401
www.lemeridien.com

A challenging and stunningly picturesque pay and play parkland course, 6473yds, Par 73. Designed in 1929 by 5 times British Open Champion J. H. Taylor *Society & Corporate days our speciality*
- Overnight accommodation and full English breakfast from £49.00 pppn
- 18 hole championship golf course
- Visitors welcome 7 days a week
- Putting green, practice area, driving range
- Green fees from £20.00 per person
- 204 de-luxe en-suite bedrooms

solarium, gymnasium. **Conf** Max 350 Thtr 350 Class 100 Board 60 Banquet 180 Del £39 to £79 * **Location** 3m S on A2022

Hotel ★★★★ 70% Le Meridien Selsdon Park, Addington Rd, Sanderstead, CROYDON ☎ 020 8657 8811 204 en suite

Shirley Park 194 Addiscombe Rd CR0 7LB ☎ 020 8654 1143 📋 020 8654 6733 e-mail: secretary@shirleyparkgolfclub.co.uk **This parkland course lies amid fine woodland with good views of Shirley Hills. The more testing holes come in the middle section of the course. The remarkable 7th hole calls for a 187-yard iron or wood shot diagonally across a narrow valley to a shelved green set right-handed into a ridge. The 13th hole, 160yds, is considered to be one of the finest short holes in the county.** *18 holes, 6210yds, Par 71, SSS 70, Course record 66. Club membership 600.* *continued*

Shirley Park Golf Club

Visitors should contact in advance. With member only at weekends. **Societies** by arrangement. **Green Fees** £35 (£40 Sun). **Cards** 🖃 🖃 💷 🖃 🖃 💷 **Prof** Wraith Grant **Course Designer** Tom Simpson/Herbert Fowler **Facilities** ⊗ ⅢⅢ ⅃ 🖤 ♀ ♨ 🖰 🏌 ♂ **Conf** Max 100 Thtr 100 Class 100 Board 100 **Location** E side of town centre on A232

Hotel ★★★★ 70% Le Meridien Selsdon Park, Addington Rd, Sanderstead, CROYDON ☎ 020 8657 8811 204 en suite

---

DOWNE   Map 05 TQ46

High Elms High Elms Rd BR6 7JL
☎ 01689 853232 & 858175 bookings 📠 01689 856326
Municipal parkland course. Very tight 13th, 221 yds (par 3).
18 holes, 6210yds, Par 71, SSS 70, Course record 68.
Club membership 450.
Visitors should phone to book/enquire about availability **Societies** telephone to book. Tel 01689 861813. **Green Fees** not confirmed. **Prof** Peter Remy **Course Designer** Hawthorn **Facilities** ⊗ ⅢⅢ ⅃ 🖤 ♀ ♨ 🖰 🏌 🐾 ♂ **Location** 2m E of A21

Hotel ★★★ 73% Bromley Court Hotel, Bromley Hill, BROMLEY ☎ 020 8461 8600 116 en suite

West Kent West Hill BR6 7JJ
☎ 01689 851323 📠 01689 858693
e-mail: golf@wkgc.co.uk
Partly hilly downland course.
18 holes, 6399yds, Par 70, SSS 70, Course record 62.
Club membership 700.
Visitors with member only at weekends. Must contact in advance. **Societies** must apply in writing. **Green Fees** £50 per day; £35 per round. **Prof** Roger Fidler **Course Designer** W Fowler & J Abercrombie **Facilities** ⊗ ⅃ 🖤 ♀ ♨ 🖰 🐾 ♂ **Location** M25 junct 4, take A21 towards Bromley, turn left at sign for Downe, proceed through village on Luxted road 0.5m, West Hill located on right

Hotel ★★★ 73% Bromley Court Hotel, Bromley Hill, BROMLEY ☎ 020 8461 8600 116 en suite

---

ENFIELD   Map 04 TQ39

Crews Hill Cattlegate Rd, Crews Hill EN2 8AZ
☎ 020 8363 6674 📠 020 8364 5641
Parkland course in country surroundings.
18 holes, 6250yds, Par 70, SSS 70, Course record 65.
Club membership 600.
Visitors all day Mon, 7-9.30am Tue-Fri and after 2pm Wed & Fri. Handicap certificate required.Not permitted to use club house facilities. **Societies** Wed-Fri; must apply in writing. **Green Fees** £35 per day; £25 per round. **Cards** 🖃

🖃 🖃 💷 🖃 🖃 💷 **Prof** Neil Wichelow **Course Designer** Harry Colt **Facilities** ⊗ ⅢⅢ ⅃ 🖤 ♀ ♨ 🖰 🐾 🐾 ♂ **Location** M25 junct 24, take A1005 for Enfield and follow signs

Hotel ★★ 71% Oak Lodge Hotel, 80 Village Rd, Bush Hill Park, ENFIELD ☎ 020 8360 7082 7 en suite

Enfield Old Park Rd South EN2 7DA
☎ 020 8363 3970 📠 020 8342 0381
e-mail: enfieldgolfclub@dial.pipex.com
Parkland course. Salmons Brook crosses 7 holes.
18 holes, 6154yds, Par 72, SSS 70, Course record 61.
Club membership 700.
Visitors must contact the Professional in advance,weekends and bank holidays by arrangement only. **Societies** must contact the secretary in advance. **Green Fees** not confirmed. **Prof** Lee Fickling **Course Designer** James Braid **Facilities** ⊗ ⅢⅢ ⅃ 🖤 ♀ ♨ 🖰 ♂ **Location** M25 jnct 24, A1005 to Enfield to rdbt with church on left, right down Slades Hill, 1st left to end

Hotel ★★ 71% Oak Lodge Hotel, 80 Village Rd, Bush Hill Park, ENFIELD ☎ 020 8360 7082 7 en suite

Whitewebbs Park Whitewebbs Ln EN2 9HH
☎ 020 8363 4454 📠 020 8366 2257
Gently undulating wooded parkland course with an attractive brook running through four holes.
18 holes, 5782yds, Par 68, SSS 68, Course record 67.
Club membership 190.
Visitors can play all times, can book in advance **Societies** must apply in writing or by phone to Course Manager. **Green Fees** £13 (£16.50 weekends, £6 twilight). **Cards** 🖃 🖃 🖃 💷 **Prof** Gary Sherriff **Facilities** ⊗ ⅢⅢ ⅃ 🖤 ♀ ♨ 🖰 🐾 ♂ **Location** N side of town centre

Hotel ★★ 71% Oak Lodge Hotel, 80 Village Rd, Bush Hill Park, ENFIELD ☎ 020 8360 7082 7 en suite

---

GREENFORD   Map 04 TQ18

C & L Golf & Country Club Westend Rd, Northolt UB5 6RD ☎ 020 8845 5662 📠 020 8841 5515
Demanding parkland course with long par 3s and ideal for all golfers.
18 holes, 4458yds, Par 67, SSS 62, Course record 58.
Club membership 150.
Visitors welcome, but may not play Sun mornings. **Societies** contact for details. **Green Fees** £4.50 (£7 weekends). **Cards** 🖃 🖃 🖃 💷 **Prof** Richard Kelly **Course Designer** Patrick Tallack **Facilities** ⊗ ⅢⅢ ⅃ 🖤 ♀ **Leisure** hard tennis courts, gymnasium. **Conf** Max 450 Thtr 400 Class 300 Board 300 Banquet 450 **Location** Junct Westend Road/A40

Hotel ★★★ 69% The Bridge Hotel, Western Av, GREENFORD ☎ 020 8566 6246 68 en suite

Ealing Perivale Ln UB6 8SS
☎ 020 8997 0937 📠 020 8998 0756
The home of English and European champions. Inland parkland course with River Brent providing natural hazards across several holes.
18 holes, 6216yds, Par 70, SSS 70, Course record 64.
Club membership 650.
Visitors Mon-Fri only on application to pro shop. **Societies** Mon, Wed & Thu only by arrangement. **Green Fees** £30 per round. **Cards** 🖃 🖃 💷 **Course Designer** H S Colt **Facilities** ⊗ ⅢⅢ by prior arrangement ⅃ 🖤 ♀ ♨ 🐾 🐾 ♂ **Location** Off A40 travelling W from London

continued   *continued*

Hotel ★★★ 69% The Bridge Hotel, Western Av, GREENFORD ☎ 020 8566 6246 68 en suite

Horsenden Hill Whitton Av, Woodland Rise UB6 0RD
☎ 020 8902 4555
A well-kept, tree-lined short course.
9 holes, 1632yds, Par 28, SSS 28.
Club membership 135.
Visitors no restrictions. **Societies** telephone for details.
Green Fees not confirmed. **Prof** Simon Hoffman **Facilities**
⊗ ⊪ ⅃ ♞ ♀ ⅄ 🖻 ⚑ ∂ **Location** 3m NE on A4090

Hotel ★★★ 69% The Bridge Hotel, Western Av, GREENFORD ☎ 020 8566 6246 68 en suite

Lime Trees Park Ruislip Rd, Northolt UB5 6QZ
☎ 020 8842 0442 📄 0208 8420542
Parkland course.
9 holes, 5836yds, Par 71, SSS 69.
Club membership 300.
Visitors no restrictions, but advisable to book for weekends.
Societies contact for details. **Green Fees** not confirmed. **Prof**
Ian Godleman **Facilities** ⊗ ⊪ ♞ ♀ ⅄ 🖻 ⚑ 🛒 ∂ ⚑
Location 300yds off A40 at Polish War Memorial/A4180
towards Hayes

Hotel ★★★ 69% The Bridge Hotel, Western Av, GREENFORD ☎ 020 8566 6246 68 en suite

Perivale Park Stockdove Way UB6 8TJ
☎ 020 8575 7116
Parkland course.
9 holes, 2667yds, Par 68, SSS 67.
Club membership 250.
Visitors no restrictions. **Societies** one weeks notice required.
Green Fees not confirmed. **Cards** 〓 〓 〓 🔲 📄 **Prof**
Peter Bryant **Facilities** ⅄ 🖻 ⚑ ∂ **Location** E side of town
centre, off A40

Hotel ★★★ 67% Cumberland Hotel, 1 St Johns Rd,
HARROW ☎ 020 8863 4111 31 en suite 53 annexe en suite

HADLEY WOOD   Map 04 TQ29

Hadley Wood Beech Hill EN4 0JJ
☎ 020 8449 4328 & 4486 📄 020 8364 8633
e-mail: gen.mgr@hadleywoodgc.com
**A parkland course on the northwest edge of London.
The gently undulating fairways have a friendly width
inviting the player to open his shoulders, though the
thick rough can be very punishing to the unwary. The
course is pleasantly wooded and there are some
admirable views.**

18 holes, 6514yds, Par 72, SSS 71, Course record 67.
Club membership 600.   continued

Visitors handicap certificate required, may not play Tue
mornings & weekends.Must contact in advance. **Societies**
must contact in advance. **Green Fees** terms on
application. **Prof** Peter Jones **Course Designer** Alistair
Mackenzie **Facilities** ⊗ ⊪ ⅃ ♞ ♀ ⅄ 🖻 ⚑ ∂ ⚑ **Conf**
Thtr 100 Class 80 Board 10 Banquet 160 **Location** E side
of village

Hotel ★★★★♨ 70% West Lodge Park Hotel,
Cockfosters Rd, HADLEY WOOD
☎ 020 8216 3900 46 en suite 13 annexe en suite

HAMPTON   Map 04 TQ17

Fulwell Wellington Rd, Hampton Hill TW12 1JY
☎ 020 8977 3844 & 020 8977 2733 📄 020 8977 7732
**Championship-length parkland course with easy walking.
The 575-yd 17th is notable.**
18 holes, 6544yds, Par 71, SSS 71.
Club membership 750.
Visitors may not play Tue & weekends. Must contact in
advance and have a handicap certificate. **Societies** must
apply in writing. **Green Fees** not confirmed. **Prof** Nigel
Turner **Facilities** ⅄ 🖻 ⚑ 🛒 ∂ **Location** 1.5m N on A311

Hotel ★★★ 68% The Richmond Hill Hotel, Richmond Hill,
RICHMOND UPON THAMES
☎ 020 8940 2247 138 en suite

HAMPTON WICK   Map 04 TQ16

Home Park KT1 4AD
☎ 020 8977 2423 📄 020 8977 4414
Flat, parkland course with easy walking.
18 holes, 6584yds, Par 71, SSS 70.
Club membership 550.
Visitors welcome all week subject to club competitions.
Societies apply in writing. **Green Fees** not confirmed. **Prof**
Len Roberts **Facilities** ⊗ ⊪ ♞ ♀ ⅄ 🖻 ∂ **Location** Off
A308 on W side of Kingston Bridge

Hotel ★★★ 68% The Richmond Hill Hotel, Richmond Hill,
RICHMOND UPON THAMES
☎ 020 8940 2247 138 en suite

HILLINGDON   Map 04 TQ08

Hillingdon 18 Dorset Way UB10 0JR
☎ 01895 233956 & 239810 📄 01895 233956
Parkland course west of London, with gentle undulations.
9 holes, 5490yds, Par 68, SSS 67.
Club membership 370.
Visitors must contact in advance. May not play Thu,
weekends, or bank holidays. Handicap certificate required.
Societies must apply in writing. **Green Fees** not confirmed.
Prof Phil Smith **Facilities** ⊗ ⊪ ⅃ ♞ ♀ ⅄ 🖻 ∂ **Location**
W side of town off A4020

Hotel ★★★ 70% Novotel Heathrow, Junction 4 M4, Cherry
Ln, WEST DRAYTON ☎ 01895 431431 178 en suite

HOUNSLOW   Map 04 TQ17

Airlinks Southall Ln TW5 9PE
☎ 020 8561 1418 📄 88136284
Meadowland/parkland course. Four water holes.
18 holes, 6000yds, Par 71, SSS 69, Course record 63.
Club membership 550.
Visitors welcome all times.Must contact in advance   continued

Societies telephone in advance. **Green Fees** £12 per 18 holes (£18 weekends). **Cards** 🎫 💳 💳 💳 💳 💳 **Prof** Tony Martin **Course Designer** P Alliss/D Thomas **Facilities** ⊗ ⍤ 🍴 🍺 🏌 🛄 🏌 🍴 **Leisure** hard tennis courts, outdoor and indoor heated swimming pools, squash, sauna, solarium, gymnasium. **Location** W of Hounslow off M4 J3

....

Hotel ★★★ 65% Master Robert Hotel, 366 Great West Rd, HOUNSLOW ☎ 020 8570 6261 96 annexe en suite

Hounslow Heath Municipal Staines Rd TW4 5DS

☎ 020 8570 5271 📠 020 8570 5205

Heathland course in a conservation area, planted with an attractive variety of trees. The 15th hole lies between the fork of two rivers.

18 holes, 5901yds, Par 69, SSS 68, Course record 62.
Club membership 300.

Visitors pay & play, bookings taken for weekends & bank holidays seven days in advance. **Societies** must telephone and confirm at least 14 days in advance. **Green Fees** £9 (£13 weekends & bank holidays). **Prof** Joe Smith **Course Designer** Fraser M Middleton **Facilities** ⊗ ⍤ 🍴 🍺 🛄 🍴 🍴 **Location** On A315 towards Bedfont

....

Hotel ★★★★ 67% Holiday Inn London Heathrow, Sipson Rd, WEST DRAYTON ☎ 020 8759 2323 610 en suite

Ilford Wanstead Park Rd IG1 3TR

☎ 020 8554 2930 📠 020 8554 0822

Fairly flat parkland course with the River Roding running through it. The river borders four holes, and is crossed by three holes. While not a particularly long course, the small greens, and many holes requiring brains rather than brawn, provide a challenging test to all.

18 holes, 5299yds, Par 67, SSS 66, Course record 61.
Club membership 500.

Visitors must contact in advance, book with pro on 020 8554 0094. **Societies** telephone for provisional date and booking form. **Green Fees** £20 per day; £15 per round (£19 per round weekends & bank holidays). **Cards** 🎫 💳 💳 💳 💳 **Prof** S Dowsett **Course Designer** Whitehead **Facilities** ⊗ ⍤ 🍺 🍴 🛄 🍴 🍴 **Location** NW side of town centre off A12

....

Hotel ★★★ 62% County Hotel Epping Forest, 30 Oak Hill, WOODFORD GREEN ☎ 020 8787 9988 99 en suite

Wyke Green Syon Ln TW7 5PT

☎ 020 8847 0685 (Prof) & 8560 8777 (Sec)
📠 020 8569 8392
e-mail: office@wykegreen.golfagent.co.uk
Fairly flat parkland course. 7 par 4 holes over 420 yards.
18 holes, 6211yds, Par 69, SSS 70, Course record 64.
Club membership 650.

Visitors may not play before 4pm weekends and bank holidays **Societies** must apply in writing or telephone in advance. **Green Fees** £28 per round; (£30 weekends). **Prof** Neil Smith **Course Designer** Hawtree **Facilities** ⊗ ⍤ 🍺 🍺 🍴 🛄 🍴 🍴 **Location** 0.5m N on B454 off A4 at Gillette Corner

....

Hotel ★★★ 65% Master Robert Hotel, 366 Great West Rd, HOUNSLOW ☎ 020 8570 6261 96 annexe en suite

Coombe Hill Golf Club Dr, Coombe Ln West

KT2 7DF ☎ 020 8336 7600 📠 020 8336 7601
A splendid course in wooded terrain. The undulations and trees make it an especially interesting course of great charm. And there is a lovely display of rhododendrons in May and June.

18 holes, 6293yds, Par 71, SSS 71, Course record 67.
Club membership 550.

Visitors must contact in advance. With member only at weekends. **Societies** must book in advance. **Green Fees** not confirmed. **Cards** 🎫 💳 **Prof** Craig Defoy **Course Designer** J F Abercromby **Facilities** ⊗ 🍺 🍴 🍺 🍴 🛄 🍴 🍴 **Leisure** sauna.
Location 1.75m E on A238

....

Hotel ★★★ 70% Kingston Lodge Hotel, Kingston Hill, KINGSTON UPON THAMES
☎ 0870 400 8115 63 en suite

Coombe Wood George Rd, Kingston Hill KT2 7NS

☎ 020 8942 0388 📠 020 8942 5665
Mature parkland course with seven varied and challenging par 3's.

18 holes, 5299yds, Par 66, SSS 66, Course record 61.
Club membership 660.

Visitors must play with member at weekends. **Societies** Wed, Thu & Fri; must contact in advance. **Green Fees** not confirmed. **Cards** 🎫 💳 **Prof** David Butler **Course Designer** Tom Williamson **Facilities** ⊗ ⍤ by prior arrangement 🍺 🍺 🍴 🛄 🍴 🍴 **Location** 1.25m NE on A308

....

Hotel ★★★ 70% Kingston Lodge Hotel, Kingston Hill, KINGSTON UPON THAMES ☎ 0870 400 8115 63 en suite

Mitcham Carshalton Rd CR4 4HN

☎ 020 8648 4280 📠 020 8647 4197
A wooded heathland course on a gravel base.
18 holes, 5935yds, Par 69, SSS 68, Course record 65.
Club membership 500.

Visitors must telephone & book in advance, restricted play at weekends. **Societies** must phone in advance. **Green Fees** £16 (£18 weekends). **Cards** 🎫 💳 💳 💳 💳 **Prof** Jeff Godfrey **Course Designer** T Scott/T Morris **Facilities** ⊗ 🍺 🍺 🍴 🛄 🍴 🍴 **Location** 1m S

....

Hotel ★★★ 65% Posthouse Croydon, Purley Way, CROYDON ☎ 0870 400 9022 83 en suite

New Malden
Map 04 TQ26

Malden Traps Ln KT3 4RS
☎ 020 8942 0654 🖹 020 8336 2219
e-mail: maldengc@lwcdial.net
Parkland course with the hazard of the Beverley Brook which affects 4 holes (3rd, 7th, 8th and 12th).
18 holes, 6295yds, Par 71, SSS 70.
Club membership 800.
Visitors restricted weekends and bank holidays. Advisable to telephone. **Societies** must apply in writing. **Green Fees** £27.50 per round (£50 weekends). **Prof** Robert Hunter **Facilities** ⊗ ᛒ ♥ ♀ ♔ 🕾 ↯ ✓ **Location** N side of town centre off B283

Hotel ★★★ 70% Kingston Lodge Hotel, Kingston Hill, KINGSTON UPON THAMES ☎ 0870 400 8115 63 en suite

Northwood
Map 04 TQ09

Haste Hill The Drive HA6 1HN
☎ 01923 825224 🖹 01923 824683
Parkland course with stream running through. Excellent views.

18 holes, 5787yds, Par 68, SSS 68, Course record 67.
Club membership 250.
Visitors advised to book in advance 01923 825224 **Societies** must apply in advance. **Green Fees** terms on application. **Cards** 🖃 💳 💳 🖃 💳 **Prof** Cameron Smilie **Facilities** ⊗ Ⅶ by prior arrangement ᛒ ♥ ♀ ♔ 🕾 ↯ ✓ **Location** 0.5m S off A404

Hotel ★★★ 67% Quality Harrow Hotel, 12-22 Pinner Rd, HARROW ☎ 020 8427 3435 79 en suite 23 annexe en suite

Northwood Rickmansworth Rd HA6 2QW
☎ 01923 821384 🖹 01923 840150
e-mail: secretary@northwoodgc.com.uk
A high quality parkland course in the heart of Middlesex. The course provides a good test of golf to the experienced golfer and can hold many surprises for the unsuspecting. The par 4, 10th hole 'Death or Glory' has wrecked many good cards in the past, whilst the 5th hole requires two very good approach shots to make par.
18 holes, 6535yds, Par 71, SSS 71, Course record 65.
Club membership 650.
Visitors must contact in advance. May not play weekends. **Societies** must apply in writing. **Green Fees** £40 per day; £30 per round. **Prof** C J Holdsworth **Course Designer** James Braid **Facilities** ⊗ Ⅶ ᛒ ♥ ♀ ♔ 🕾 ↯ ✓ **Location** On main A404

Hotel ★★★ 67% Quality Harrow Hotel, 12-22 Pinner Rd, HARROW ☎ 020 8427 3435 79 en suite 23 annexe en suite

Sandy Lodge Sandy Lodge Ln HA6 2JD
☎ 01923 825429 🖹 01923 824319
e-mail: sandy-lodge@lineone.net
A links-type, very sandy, heathland course.
18 holes, 6347yds, Par 71, SSS 71, Course record 64.
Club membership 780.
Visitors must contact in advance, may not play at weekends. Handicap certificate required. **Societies** must telephone in advance. **Green Fees** terms on application. **Prof** Jeff Pinsent **Course Designer** H Vardon **Facilities** ⊗ Ⅶ ᛒ ♥ ♀ ♔ 🕾 ↯ ✓ **Location** N side of town centre off A4125

Hotel ★★★ 64% The White House, Upton Rd, WATFORD ☎ 01923 237316 60 en suite

Orpington
Map 05 TQ46

Chelsfield Lakes Golf Centre Court Rd BR6 9BX
☎ 01689 896266 🖹 01689 824577
18 holes, 6077yds, Par 71, SSS 69, Course record 64.
Warren: 9 holes, 1188yds, Par 27.
Course Designer M Sandow **Location** Exit M25 junct 4, on A224 Court Rd
Telephone for further details

Hotel ★★★ 73% Bromley Court Hotel, Bromley Hill, BROMLEY ☎ 020 8461 8600 116 en suite

Cray Valley Sandy Ln, St Paul's Cray BR5 3HY
☎ 01689 837909 & 871490 🖹 01689 891428
An easy walking open parkland course comprising an 18 hole par 70 and a 9 hole par 32. Challenging for all standards of golfers.
18 hole: 18 holes, 5669yds, Par 70, SSS 67.
9 holes: 9 holes, 2140yds, Par 32.
Club membership 700.
Visitors no restrictions, may book up to 7 days in advance. **Societies** by arrangement. **Green Fees** not confirmed. **Cards** 🖃 💳 💳 🖃 💳 **Prof** Gary Stewart **Facilities** ⊗ ᛒ ♥ ♀ ♔ 🕾 ↯ ✓ **Location** 1m off A20, Critley's Corner junction

Hotel ★★★ 73% Bromley Court Hotel, Bromley Hill, BROMLEY ☎ 020 8461 8600 116 en suite

Lullingstone Park Parkgate Rd, Chelsfield BR6 7PX
☎ 01959 533793 & 533794 🖹 01959 533795
Main Course: 18 holes, 6778yds, Par 72, SSS 72, Course record 71.
9 hole course: 9 holes, 2432yds, Par 33, SSS 31.
Location Leave M25 junct 4 and take Well Hill turn
Telephone for further details

Hotel ★★★ 73% Bromley Court Hotel, Bromley Hill, BROMLEY ☎ 020 8461 8600 116 en suite

Ruxley Park Golf Centre Sandy Ln, St Paul's Cray BR5 3HY ☎ 01689 871490 🖹 01689 891428
Undulating parkland course with public, floodlit driving range. Difficult 6th hole, par 4. Easy walking and good views.
18 holes, 5703yds, Par 70, SSS 68, Course record 63.
Club membership 1000.
Visitors may book 7 days in advance and regular dress code expected. **Societies** telephone for details 01689 839677.
Green Fees not confirmed. **Cards** 🖃 💳 💳 🖃 💳

continued

Prof Andy Langdon **Facilities** ⊗ ⬛ ♨ ♀ ♨ ➲ ⛳ ➤ ☕ ♂
⦗ Location 2m NE on A223

Hotel ★★★ 73% Bromley Court Hotel, Bromley Hill,
BROMLEY ☎ 020 8461 8600 116 en suite

PINNER   Map 04 TQ18

Grims Dyke Oxhey Ln, Hatch End HA5 4AL
☎ 020 8428 4539 ▤ 020 8421 5494
Pleasant, undulating parkland course.
18 holes, 5596yds, Par 69, SSS 67, Course record 61.
Club membership 500.

Visitors May not play weekends except as guest of a
member. **Societies** Apply in writing or by phone. Deposit
required. **Green Fees** terms on application. **Cards** ▭ ▬
▭ ▦ ▭ ▤ ⊠ **Prof** Nathan Stephens **Course Designer**
James Baird **Facilities** ⊗ ⬛ ♨ ♀ ♨ ➲ ☕ ♂ **Conf** Max
40 Thtr 40 Class 30 Board 40 Banquet 40 Del from £2 *
Location 3m N of Harrow on A4008

Hotel ★★★ 67% Cumberland Hotel, 1 St Johns Rd,
HARROW ☎ 020 8863 4111 31 en suite 53 annexe en suite

Pinner Hill Southview Rd, Pinner Hill HA5 3YA
☎ 020 8866 0963 ▤ 020 8868 4817
e-mail: pinnerhillgc@uk2.net
**On the top of Pinner Hill surrounded by rolling parkland
and mature woods, this peaceful atmosphere will make
you feel a million miles from North West London's
suburbia. Two nine hole loops of mature fairways and
undulating greens will lift and challenge your game.**
18 holes, 6630yds, Par 71, SSS 69.
Club membership 710.
Visitors are required to have handicap certificate on Mon,
Tue & Fri. Public days Wed & Thu. Contact in advance.
Societies Mon, Tue & Fri only, by arrangement. **Green Fees**
£30 per day, Mon, Tue & Fri; £15 Wed & Thur. **Prof** Mark
Grieve **Course Designer** J H Taylor **Facilities** ⊗ ⫟ ⬛ ♨ ♀
♨ ➲ ⛳ ➤ ☕ ♂ **Location** 2m NW off A404

Hotel ★★★ 67% Quality Harrow Hotel, 12-22 Pinner Rd,
HARROW ☎ 020 8427 3435 79 en suite 23 annexe en suite

PURLEY   Map 05 TQ36

Purley Downs 106 Purley Downs Rd CR2 0RB
☎ 020 8657 8347 ▤ 020 8651 5044
e-mail: info@purleydowns.co.uk
Hilly downland course which is a good test for golfers.
18 holes, 6262yds, Par 70, SSS 70, Course record 64.
Club membership 650.
Visitors must contact in advance & play on weekends only
with member. **Societies** must contact in advance. **Green Fees**
not confirmed. **Prof** Graham Wilson **Course Designer** J
Taylor/H S Colt **Facilities** ⊗ ⬛ ♨ ♀ ♨ ➲ ♂ ♂
Location E side of town centre off A235   *continued*

Hotel ★★★ 65% Posthouse Croydon, Purley Way,
CROYDON ☎ 0870 400 9022 83 en suite

RICHMOND UPON THAMES   Map 04 TQ17

Richmond Sudbrook Park, Petersham TW10 7AS
☎ 020 8940 4351 (office) & 8940 7792 (shop)
▤ 8940 8332/7914
e-mail: hilkka_rgc@lineone.net
**A beautiful and historic wooded, parkland course on
the edge of Richmond Park, with six par 3 holes. The
4th is often described as the best short hole in the
south of England. Low scores are uncommon because
cunningly sited trees call for great accuracy. The
clubhouse is one of the most distinguished small
Georgian mansions in England.**
18 holes, 6007yds, Par 70, SSS 69.
Club membership 700.
Visitors may not play weekends before 3.30pm. **Societies**
must apply in writing. **Green Fees** £58 per day; £37 per
round (£32 per round weekends after 3.30pm). **Cards** ▭
▭ ▬ ▭ ▦ ▭ ⊠ **Prof** Nick Job **Facilities** ⊗ ⫟ by prior
arrangement ⬛ ♨ ♀ ♨ ➲ ⛳ ♂ ⦗ **Location** 1.5m S off
A307

Hotel ★★★ 68% The Richmond Hill Hotel, Richmond
Hill, RICHMOND UPON THAMES ☎ 020 8940 2247
138 en suite

Royal Mid-Surrey Old Deer Park TW9 2SB
☎ 020 8940 1894 ▤ 020 8332 2957
**A long playing parkland course. The flat fairways are
cleverly bunkered. The 18th provides an exceptionally**
continued

good par 4 finish with a huge bunker before the green to catch the not quite perfect long second.
Outer Course: 18 holes, 6343yds, Par 69, SSS 70, Course record 62.
Inner Course: 18 holes, 5544yds, Par 68, SSS 67.
Club membership 1400.
Visitors may not play at weekends. Must contact in advance and bring a handicap certificate. **Societies** must apply in writing. **Green Fees** terms on application. **Cards** ▭ ▭ ▭ 🄳 **Prof** Philip Talbot **Course Designer** J H Taylor **Facilities** ⊗ 🖢 ♥ ♀ ⚲ 🏠 ⛳ 🥄 ⛳ ⚘ **Location** 0.5m N of Richmond upon Thames off A316

Hotel ★★★ 68% The Richmond Hill Hotel, Richmond Hill, RICHMOND UPON THAMES
☎ 020 8940 2247 138 en suite

Maylands Golf Club & Country Park
Colchester Rd, Harold Park RM3 0AZ
☎ 01708 346466 🗎 01708 373080
Picturesque undulating parkland course.
18 holes, 6361yds, Par 71, SSS 70, Course record 65.
Club membership 500.
Visitors handicap certificate required. **Societies** Mon, Wed & Fri only, by arrangement. **Green Fees** terms on application.
Cards ▭ ▭ **Course Designer** H S Colt **Facilities** ⊗ 🎢 🖢 ♥ ♀ ⚲ 🏠 🥄 ⛳ **Location** Junct 28 off M25, 0.5m down A12 towards London, club on right hand side

Hotel ★★★ 69% Holiday Inn Brentwood, Brook St, BRENTWOOD ☎ 0870 400 9012 150 en suite

Risebridge Golf Centre Risebridge Chase, Lower
Bedfords Rd RM1 4DG ☎ 01708 741429 🗎 01708 741429
e-mail: pa.jennings@virgin.net
A well matured parkland golf course, with many challenging holes especially the long 12th, the par 4 13th and par 5 14th with water and a two tiered green.
18 holes, 6000yds, Par 71, SSS 70, Course record 66.
Club membership 300.
Visitors no restrictions. **Societies** must telephone in advance. **Green Fees** terms on application. **Prof** Paul Jennings **Course Designer** Hawtree **Facilities** ⊗ 🎢 🖢 ♥ ♀ ⚲ 🏠 ⛳ ⚘ **Location** Between Colier Row and Harold Hill

Hotel ★★★ 69% Holiday Inn Brentwood, Brook St, BRENTWOOD ☎ 0870 400 9012 150 en suite

Romford Heath Dr, Gidea Park RM2 5QB
☎ 01708 740986 🗎 01708 752157
A many-bunkered parkland course with easy walking. It is said there are as many bunkers as there are days in the year. The ground is quick drying making a good course for winter play when other courses might be too wet.
18 holes, 6410yds, Par 72, SSS 70, Course record 64.
Club membership 693.
Visitors with member only weekends & bank holidays. Must contact professional in advance & have handicap certificate. **Societies** must telephone in advance. **Green Fees** not confirmed. **Prof** Chris Goddard **Course Designer** H Colt **Facilities** ⊗ 🎢 🖢 ♥ ♀ ⚲ 🏠 ⚘ **Location** 1m NE on A118

Hotel ★★★ 69% Holiday Inn Brentwood, Brook St, BRENTWOOD ☎ 0870 400 9012 150 en suite

Ruislip Ickenham Rd HA4 7DQ
☎ 01895 638081 & 638835 🗎 01895 635780
Municipal parkland course. Many trees.

18 holes, 5700yds, Par 69, SSS 68, Course record 65.
Club membership 300.
Societies must contact in advance. **Green Fees** £12.50 per round (£18.50 weekends). **Cards** ▭ ▭ ▭ ▭ 🄳 **Prof** Paul Glozier **Course Designer** Sand Herd **Facilities** ⊗ 🎢 🖢 ♥ ♀ ⚲ 🏠 🥄 ⛳ ⚘ ⛳ **Location** 0.5m SW on B466

Hotel ★★★ 67% Quality Harrow Hotel, 12-22 Pinner Rd, HARROW ☎ 020 8427 3435 79 en suite 23 annexe en suite

Sidcup 7 Hurst Rd DA15 9AE
☎ 020 8300 2150 🗎 0208 3002150
Easy walking parkland course with natural water hazards.
9 holes, 5722yds, Par 68, SSS 68.
Club membership 370.
Visitors contact in advance and may not play weekends or bank holidays. **Societies** must contact in advance. **Green Fees** £18 per round. **Prof** Nigel Willis **Course Designer** James Braid **Facilities** ⊗ 🎢 🖢 ♥ ♀ ⚲ 🏠 **Location** N side of town centre off A222

Hotel ★★★★ 69% Bexleyheath Marriott Hotel, 1 Broadway, BEXLEYHEATH ☎ 020 8298 1000 138 en suite

West Middlesex Greenford Rd UB1 3EE
☎ 020 8574 3450 🗎 020 8574 2383
e-mail: westmid.gc@virgin.net
Gently undulating parkland course founded in 1891, the oldest private course in Middlesex designed by James Braid.
18 holes, 6242yds, Par 69, SSS 69, Course record 64.
Club membership 700.
Visitors must contact in advance and may only play at weekends after 3pm **Societies** must apply in advance. **Green Fees** £12 Mon; £24 Tue,Thu & Fri; £14 Wed; £30 weekends after 3pm. **Prof** I P Harris **Course Designer** James Braid **Facilities** ⊗ 🎢 🖢 ♥ ♀ ⚲ 🏠 ⚘ **Leisure** squash. **Location** W side of town centre on A4127 off A4020

Hotel ★★★ 65% Master Robert Hotel, 366 Great West Rd, HOUNSLOW ☎ 020 8570 6261 96 annexe en suite

Stanmore 29 Gordon Av HA7 2RL
☎ 020 8954 2599 🗎 0208 9546418
North London parkland course.
18 holes, 5860yds, Par 68, SSS 68, Course record 61.
Club membership 560.

continued

Visitors may not play weekends. Contact professional 0208 954 2646. **Societies** phone in advance for booking sheet. **Green Fees** not confirmed. **Prof** V Law **Facilities** ⊗ 〗▥ by prior arrangement ▥ ▰ ♀ ♨ ☎ ✆ **Location** S side of town centre, between Stanmore & Belmont

Hotel ★★★ 67% Quality Harrow Hotel, 12-22 Pinner Rd, HARROW ☎ 020 8427 3435 79 en suite 23 annexe en suite

Surbiton Woodstock Ln KT9 1UG ☎ 020 8398 3101 (Sec) & 8398 6619 (Pro) 🖥 020 8339 0992
e-mail: surbitongolfclub@hotmail.com
Parkland course with easy walking.
18 holes, 6055yds, Par 70, SSS 69, Course record 63.
Club membership 700.
Visitors must call in advance, handicap certificate required. With member only at weekends & bank holidays. No visitors Tue am (Ladies Day). **Societies** Mon & Fri only. **Green Fees** £30 per round; £45 per day. **Prof** Paul Milton **Course Designer** Tom Dunn **Facilities** ⊗ ▥ ▰ ♀ ♨ ☎ ✆ **Location** 2m S off A3, take A309 from Hook junct of A3,turn left into Woodstock Lane

Hotel ⛺ Travel Inn, Leatherhead Rd, CHESSINGTON ☎ 01372 744060 42 en suite

Strawberry Hill Wellesley Rd, Strawberry Hill TW2 5SD ☎ 020 8894 0165
e-mail: secretary@strawberry-hill.fsnet.co.uk
Parkland course with easy walking.
9 holes, 4762yds, Par 64, SSS 63, Course record 59.
Club membership 300.
Visitors must contact in advance, with member only at weekends. **Societies** must apply in writing. **Green Fees** terms on application. **Cards** 💳 **Prof** Peter Buchan **Course Designer** J H Taylor **Facilities** ⊗ 〗▥ ▰ ♀ ♨ ☎ ✆ **Location** S side of town centre off A316

Hotel ★★★ 68% The Richmond Hill Hotel, Richmond Hill, RICHMOND UPON THAMES ☎ 020 8940 2247 138 en suite

Twickenham Staines Rd TW2 5JD
☎ 020 8783 1748 & 1698 🖥 020 8941 9134
Interesting tree lined parkland course with water feature.
9 holes, 3180yds, Par 36, SSS 69.
Visitors must book in advance for weekends & bank holidays. **Societies** apply in advance **Green Fees** not confirmed. **Cards** 💳 **Prof** Suzy Watt **Facilities** ▥ ▰ ♀ ☎ ✆ ✆ **Location** 2m W on A305

Hotel ★★★ 68% The Richmond Hill Hotel, Richmond Hill, RICHMOND UPON THAMES ☎ 020 8940 2247 138 en suite

Upminster 114 Hall Ln RM14 1AU
☎ 01708 222788 (Secretary) 220000 (Pro) 🖥 01708 222788
The meandering River Ingrebourne features on several holes of this partly undulating parkland course situated on one side of the river valley. It provides a challenge for golfers of all abilities. The clubhouse is a beautiful Grade II listed building.
18 holes, 6076yds, Par 69, SSS 69, Course record 65.
Club membership 1000.
Visitors contact in advance, may not play at weekends. **Societies** telephone initially. **Green Fees** £25 per round; £30
continued

per day. **Prof** Steve Cipa **Course Designer** W G Key **Facilities** ⊗ 〗▥ ▰ ♀ ♨ ☎ ✆ **Location** 2m W from A127 junct with M25

Hotel ★★★ 69% Holiday Inn Brentwood, Brook St, BRENTWOOD ☎ 0870 400 9012 150 en suite

Stockley Park Stockley Park UB11 1AQ
☎ 020 8813 5700 8561 6339 tee times 🖥 020 8813 5655
e-mail: l.newell@pgaetc.co.uk
Hilly and challenging parkland championship course designed by Trent Jones in 1993 and situated within two miles of Heathrow Airport.
18 holes, 6548yds, Par 72, SSS 71.
Visitors 6 day in advance reservation facility. **Societies** please telephone for details. **Green Fees** £25 per round (£35 weekends). **Cards** 💳 **Prof** Alex Knox, Martin Hulse **Course Designer** Robert Trent Jones Snr **Facilities** ⊗ ▥ ▰ ♀ ♨ ☎ ✆ **Conf** Max 50 **Location** 1m N of junct4 M4, off A408

Hotel ★★★★ 75% Crowne Plaza London - Heathrow, Stockley Rd, WEST DRAYTON ☎ 01895 445555 458 en suite

Uxbridge The Drive, Harefield Place UB10 8AQ
☎ 01895 237287 🖥 01895 813539
e-mail: higolf@btinternet.com
Municipal parkland course, undulating and tricky.

18 holes, 5750yds, Par 68, SSS 68, Course record 66.
Club membership 270.
Visitors no restrictions. **Societies** by arrangment. **Green Fees** not confirmed. **Cards** 💳 **Prof** Robert Mullane **Facilities** ⊗ 〗▥ ▰ ♀ ♨ ☎ ✆ ✆ **Location** 2m N off B467

Hotel ★★★★ 75% Crowne Plaza London - Heathrow, Stockley Rd, WEST DRAYTON ☎ 01895 445555 458 en suite

> AA website: www.theAA.com

Sudbury Bridgewater Rd HA0 1AL
☎ 020 8902 3713 🖥 020 8903 2966
Undulating parkland course very near centre of London.
18 holes, 6282yds, Par 69, SSS 70.
Club membership 650.
Visitors must have handicap certificate. With member only at weekends. **Societies** must apply in writing. **Green Fees** not confirmed. **Prof** Neil Jordan **Course Designer** Colt
continued

Sudbury Golf Club

Facilities ⊗)Ⅲ 🝙 💺 ♀ ⅏ 🏠 ❀ 🝙 ♂ **Location** SW side of town centre on A4090

Hotel ★★★ 69% The Bridge Hotel, Western Av, GREENFORD ☎ 020 8566 6246 68 en suite

WEST DRAYTON   Map 04 TQ07

Heathpark Stockley Rd UB7 9NA
☎ 01895 444232 📋 01895 444232
Fairly large, testing, hilly par 4 course suitable both for beginners and scratch players. New clubhouse opened in 2001.
9 holes, 2032yds, Par 64, SSS 60, Course record 64.
Club membership 80.
Visitors may not play before 11.15am weekends. Restricted play on club compitition days. Telephone for details.
Societies by arrangement. **Green Fees** not confirmed. **Cards** 🝙 🝙 🝙 🝙 **Course Designer** Neil Coles **Facilities** ⊗)Ⅲ 🝙 💺 ♀ ⅏ 🏠 ❀ ♂ **Leisure** heated indoor swimming pool, sauna, solarium, gymnasium. **Location** 1m SE off A408 via junct 4 on M4

Hotel ★★★★ 75% Crowne Plaza London - Heathrow, Stockley Rd, WEST DRAYTON ☎ 01895 445555 458 en suite

WOODFORD GREEN   Map 05 TQ49

Woodford Sunset Av IG8 0ST
☎ 020 8504 3330 & 8504 0553 📋 020 8559 0504
e-mail: office@woodfordgolfclub.fsnet.co.uk
Forest land course on the edge of Epping Forest. Views over the Lea Valley to the London skyline.
9 holes, 5806yds, Par 70, SSS 68, Course record 66.
Club membership 420.
Visitors advisable to contact in advance. May not play Sat or Sun morning, must wear major item of red. **Societies** telephone for details. **Green Fees** £15 per round; £18 per day. **Prof** Richard Layton **Course Designer** Tom Dunn **Facilities** ⊗ 💺 ♀ ⅏ 🏠 **Location** NW side of town centre off A104

Hotel ★★★ 62% County Hotel Epping Forest, 30 Oak Hill, WOODFORD GREEN ☎ 020 8787 9988 99 en suite

GREATER MANCHESTER

ALTRINCHAM   Map 07 SJ78

Altrincham Stockport Rd WA15 7LP
☎ 0161 928 0761
18 holes, 6162yds, Par 71, SSS 69.
Location 0.75 E of Altrincham on A560
Telephone for further details

Hotel ★★★ 67% Cresta Court Hotel, Church St, ALTRINCHAM ☎ 0161 927 7272 137 en suite

Dunham Forest Oldfield Ln WA14 4TY
☎ 0161 928 2605 📋 0161 929 8975
e-mail: email@dunhamforestgolfclub.com
Attractive parkland course cut through magnificent beech woods.
18 holes, 6636yds, Par 72, SSS 72.
Club membership 680.
Visitors by prior arrangement. May not play weekends & bank holidays. **Societies** apply in writing or telephone in advance. **Green Fees** £40 per round; £45 per 27 holes (£45 per round weekends). **Cards** 🝙 🝙 🝙 🝙 **Prof** Ian Wrigley **Course Designer** Dave Thomas **Facilities** ⊗)Ⅲ by prior arrangement 🝙 💺 ♀ ⅏ 🏠 ❀ 🝙 ♂ **Leisure** hard tennis courts. **Location** 1.5m W off A56

Hotel ★★★ 66% Quality Hotel Altrincham, Langham Rd, Bowdon, ALTRINCHAM ☎ 0161 928 7121 91 en suite

Ringway Hale Mount, Hale Barns WA15 8SW
☎ 0161 980 8432 (pro) & 0161 980 2630 📋 0160 980 4414
e-mail: enquiries@ringwaygolfclub.co.uk
Parkland course, with interesting natural hazards. Easy walking, good views.
18 holes, 6494yds, Par 71, SSS 71, Course record 67.
Club membership 700.
Visitors must have handicap certificate, may not play before 9.30am or between 1-2pm, play restricted Tue, Fri & Sat. **Societies** Thu only May-Sep. **Green Fees** not confirmed. **Cards** 🝙 🝙 🝙 🝙 **Prof** Nick Ryan **Course Designer** Colt **Facilities** ⊗)Ⅲ 🝙 💺 ♀ ⅏ 🏠 ♂ **Location** M56 junct 6, take A538 signposted Hale & Altrincham

Hotel ★★★ 67% Cresta Court Hotel, Church St, ALTRINCHAM ☎ 0161 927 7272 137 en suite

ASHTON-IN-MAKERFIELD   Map 07 SJ59

Ashton-in-Makerfield Garswood Park, Liverpool Rd WN4 0YT ☎ 01942 719330 📋 01942 719330
Well-wooded parkland course. Easy walking.
18 holes, 6250yds, Par 70, SSS 70, Course record 63.
Club membership 800.
Visitors with member only weekends & bank holidays. No visitors Wed. **Societies** apply in writing. **Green Fees** not confirmed. **Prof** Peter Allan **Facilities** ⊗)Ⅲ 🝙 💺 ♀ ⅏ 🏠 ❀ ♂ **Conf** Max 100 **Location** 0.5m W of M6 (junc 24) on A58

Hotel ★★★ 66% Holiday Inn Haydock, Lodge Ln, HAYDOCK ☎ 0870 400 9039 138 en suite

ASHTON-UNDER-LYNE   Map 07 SJ99

Ashton-under-Lyne Gorsey Way, Higher Hurst OL6 9HT ☎ 0161 330 1537 📋 0161 330 6673
A testing, varied moorland course, with large greens. Easy walking.
18 holes, 5754yds, Par 69, SSS 68, Course record 64.
Club membership 730.
Visitors must contact in advance. **Societies** apply in advance. **Green Fees** £25 per day. **Cards** 🝙 🝙 🝙 **Prof** Colin Boyle **Facilities** ⊗)Ⅲ 🝙 💺 ♀ ⅏ 🏠 ♂ **Conf** Max 120 **Location** N off B6194

Hotel ★★ 71% York House Hotel, York Place, Richmond St, ASHTON-UNDER-LYNE ☎ 0161 330 9000 24 en suite 10 annexe en suite

Looking for a driving range?
See the index at the back of the guide

Dukinfield Lyne Edge, Yew Tree Ln SK16 5DF
☎ 0161 338 2340
18 holes, 5303yds, Par 67, SSS 66.
Location S off B6175
Telephone for further details

Hotel ★★ 71% York House Hotel, York Place, Richmond
St, ASHTON-UNDER-LYNE ☎ 0161 330 9000
24 en suite 10 annexe en suite

BOLTON   Map 07 SD70

Bolton Lostock Park, Chorley New Rd BL6 4AJ
☎ 01204 843067 & 843278 📋 01204 843067
e-mail: hms@boltongolf.golfagent.co.uk
**This well maintained heathland course is always a
pleasure to visit. The 12th hole should be treated with
respect and so too should the final four holes which
have ruined many a card.**
18 holes, 6237yds, Par 70, SSS 70, Course record 64.
Club membership 612.
Visitors not able to play Tue before 2.30pm or on
competition days or before 10am and between 12-2pm.
Societies write or telephone in advance, not accepted Tue,
Sat or Sun. **Green Fees** £36 per day; £30 per round
(£40/£33 weekends & bank holidays). **Prof** R Longworth
Facilities ⊗ ⅷ ⅃ ⅃ ♀ ⅃ 🏠 ♂ **Location** 3m W of
Bolton, on A673

Hotel ★★★ 64% Holiday Inn Bolton, Beaumont Rd,
BOLTON ☎ 0870 400 9011 96 en suite

Breightmet Red Bridge, Ainsworth BL2 5PA
☎ 01204 527381
Long parkland course.
9 holes, 6416yds, Par 72, SSS 71, Course record 68.
Club membership 350.
Visitors may not play Wed or weekends. **Societies** welcome
Mon, Tue, Thu & Fri only, apply in advance in writing.
Green Fees terms on application. **Facilities** ⊗ ⅷ ⅃ ⅃ ♀
⅃ **Location** E side of town centre off A58

Hotel ★★★ 64% Holiday Inn Bolton, Beaumont Rd,
BOLTON ☎ 0870 400 9011 96 en suite

Deane Broadford Rd, Deane BL3 4NS
☎ 01204 61944 (professional) 651808(secretary)
**Undulating parkland course with small ravines on
approaches to some holes.**
18 holes, 5652yds, Par 68, SSS 67, Course record 64.
Club membership 470.
Visitors must be a member of a golf club or member's guest.
Restricted weekends. Must contact in advance. **Societies**
must telephone in advance and confirm in writing. **Green
Fees** not confirmed. **Prof** David Martindale **Facilities** ⊗ ⅷ
⅃ ⅃ ♀ ⅃ 🏠 ♂ **Location** 1m from exit 5 on M61
towards Bolton

Hotel ★★★ 64% Holiday Inn Bolton, Beaumont Rd,
BOLTON ☎ 0870 400 9011 96 en suite

Dunscar Longworth Ln, Bromley Cross BL7 9QY
☎ 01204 303321 📋 01204 303321
e-mail: secretary@dunscargolfclub.fsnet.co.uk
**A scenic moorland course with panoramic views. A warm
friendly club.**
18 holes, 6085yds, Par 71, SSS 69, Course record 63.
Club membership 600.
Visitors must telephone 01204 592992 in advance and have
a handicap certificate. **Societies** must apply in writing.
continued

Green Fees £20 per round (£30 weekends & bank holidays).
Prof Gary Treadgold **Facilities** ⊗ ⅷ ⅃ ⅃ ♀ ⅃ 🏠 ♂
Location 2m N off A666

Hotel ★★★ 64% Holiday Inn Bolton, Beaumont Rd,
BOLTON ☎ 0870 400 9011 96 en suite

Great Lever & Farnworth Plodder Ln, Farnworth
BL4 0LQ ☎ 01204 656137 📋 01204 656137
Downland course with easy walking.
18 holes, 6064yds, Par 70, SSS 69, Course record 67.
Club membership 600.
Visitors must contact in advance, weekend by prior
arrangement. handicap certificate required. **Societies** must
contact in advance. **Green Fees** £20 (£27 weekends & bank
holidays). **Prof** Tony Howarth **Facilities** ⊗ ⅷ ⅃ ⅃ ♀ ⅃
🏠 ♂ **Location** 1m junct 4 M61

Hotel ★★★ 64% Holiday Inn Bolton, Beaumont Rd,
BOLTON ☎ 0870 400 9011 96 en suite

Harwood Springfield, Roading Brook Rd, Harwood BL2
4JD ☎ 01204 522878 & 524233 (Sec) 📋 01204 524233
Mainly flat parkland course.
18 holes, 5778yds, Par 70, SSS 69.
Club membership 584.
Visitors must be members of a golf club and hold a current
handicap certificate. May not play at weekends. **Societies**
contact the Secretary by telephone or in writing. **Green Fees**
not confirmed. **Prof** A Rogers **Course Designer** G
Shuttleworth **Facilities** ⊗ ⅷ ⅃ ⅃ ♀ ⅃ **Location** 2.5m
NE off B6196

Hotel ★★★ 64% Holiday Inn Bolton, Beaumont Rd,
BOLTON ☎ 0870 400 9011 96 en suite

Old Links Chorley Old Rd, Montserrat BL1 5SU
☎ 01204 842307 📋 01204 842307 ext 25
e-mail: mail@boltonoldlinks.co.uk
Championship moorland course.
18 holes, 6406yds, Par 72, SSS 72.
Club membership 600.
Visitors must contact in advance and may only play
weekends with member. **Societies** apply by letter or
telephone. **Green Fees** £30 per day (£40 weekends & bank
holidays). **Prof** Paul Horridge **Course Designer** Dr Alistair
MacKenzie **Facilities** ⊗ ⅷ ⅃ ⅃ ♀ ⅃ 🏠 ♂ ♂ **Location**
NW of town centre on B6226

Hotel ★★★ 64% Holiday Inn Bolton, Beaumont Rd,
BOLTON ☎ 0870 400 9011 96 en suite

Regent Park Links Rd, Chorley New Rd BL2 9XX
☎ 01204 844170
Parkland course.
18 holes, 6130yds, Par 70, SSS 69, Course record 67.
Club membership 200.
Visitors must book 6 days in advance. **Societies** must
telephone 01204 495421 in advance. **Green Fees** not
confirmed. **Cards** 💳 **Prof** P A Wells **Facilities** ⊗ ⅷ ⅃ ⅃ ♀
⅃ 🏠 ♒ ♂ **Location** 3.5m W off A673

Hotel ★★★ 64% Holiday Inn Bolton, Beaumont Rd,
BOLTON ☎ 0870 400 9011 96 en suite

BRAMHALL   Map 07 SJ88

Bramall Park 20 Manor Rd SK7 3LY
☎ 0161 485 3119 & 7101 (secretary) 📋 0161 485 7101
**Well-wooded parkland course with splendid views of the
Pennines.**   *continued*

18 holes, 6043yds, Par 70, SSS 69.
Club membership 829.
Visitors must contact resident professional or club secretary.
Societies apply in writing. **Green Fees** terms on application.
Prof M Proffitt **Facilities** ⊗ ⅢⅡ Ꮠ ♥ ♀ ♏ 🄑 ⌀
Location NW side of town centre off B5149

....

Hotel ★★★ 60% County Hotel Bramhall, Bramhall Ln
South, BRAMHALL ☎ 0161 455 9988 65 en suite

Bramhall Ladythorn Rd SK7 2EY
☎ 0161 439 6092 ▤ 0161 439 0264
Undulating parkland course, easy walking.
18 holes, 6340yds, Par 70, SSS 70.
Club membership 700.
Visitors must contact in advance. **Societies** apply in writing.
Green Fees terms on application. **Prof** Richard Green
Facilities ⊗ Ꮠ ♥ ♀ ♏ 🄑 ⌀ **Location** E side of town
centre off A5102

....

Hotel ★★★ 60% County Hotel Bramhall, Bramhall Ln
South, BRAMHALL ☎ 0161 455 9988 65 en suite

Turton Wood End Farm, Chapeltown Rd BL7 9QH
☎ 01204 852235
**Moorland course with panoramic views. A wide variety of
holes which challenge any golfer's technique.**
18 holes, 6124yds, Par 70, SSS 69, Course record 68.
Club membership 450.
Visitors avoid 10.30-12.30; 2.00-3.00pm on Wed (Ladies
day). Sat tee available after last competition. Restricted Sun.
Societies must contact in writing. **Green Fees** £20 per day
(£25 weekends & bank holidays). **Course Designer** Alex
Herd **Facilities** ⊗ Ꮠ ♥ ♀ ♏ **Location** 3m N off A666,
follow signs for 'Last Drop Village'

....

Hotel ★★★ 64% Holiday Inn Bolton, Beaumont Rd,
BOLTON ☎ 0870 400 9011 96 en suite

Bury Unsworth Hall, Blackford Bridge, Manchester Rd
BL9 9TJ ☎ 0161 766 4897 ▤ 0161 796 3480
**Moorland course, difficult in part. Tight and good test of
golf.**
18 holes, 5961yds, Par 69, SSS 69, Course record 64.
Club membership 650.
Visitors may not normally play at weekends. Must contact in
advance. **Societies** telephone 0161 766 4897. **Green Fees** not
confirmed. **Course Designer** Mackenzie **Facilities** ♏ 🄑 ⌀
Location 2m S on A56

....

Hotel ★★★ 66% Bolholt Country Park Hotel, Walshaw Rd,
BURY ☎ 0161 762 4000 65 en suite

Lowes Park Hilltop, Lowes Rd BL9 6SU
☎ 0161 764 1231 ▤ 0161 763 9503
**Moorland course, with easy walking. Exposed outlook
with good views.**
9 holes, 6009yds, Par 70, SSS 69, Course record 65.
Club membership 350.
Visitors may not play Wed & Sat, by appointment Sun. Must
contact in advance. **Societies** apply in writing. **Green Fees**
£15 (£20 weekends). **Facilities** ⊗ ⅢⅡ Ꮠ ♥ ♀ ♏ **Location**
N side of town centre off A56

....

Hotel ★★★ 66% Bolholt Country Park Hotel, Walshaw Rd,
BURY ☎ 0161 762 4000 65 en suite

Walmersley Garretts Close, Walmersley BL9 6TE
☎ 0161 764 1429 & 0161 764 7770 ▤ 0161 764 7770
**Moorland hillside course, with wide fairways, large
greens and extensive views. Testing holes: 2nd (484 yds)
par 5; 5th par 4 with severe dogleg and various hazards.**
18 holes, 5341yds, Par 69, SSS 66.
Club membership 475.
Visitors welcome by arrangement with Secretary. May only
play with member at weekend, **Societies** must apply in
writing. **Green Fees** £20 per day. **Prof** P Thorpe **Course
Designer** S Marnoch **Facilities** ⊗ ⅢⅡ Ꮠ ♥ ♀ ♏ 🄑 ⌀
Location 2m N off A56

....

Hotel ★★★ 66% Bolholt Country Park Hotel, Walshaw Rd,
BURY ☎ 0161 762 4000 65 en suite

Cheadle Cheadle Rd SK8 1HW ☎ 0161 491 4452
9 holes, 5006yds, Par 64, SSS 65.
Course Designer T Renouf **Location** S side of village off
A5149
Telephone for further details

....

Hotel ★★ 68% The Wycliffe Hotel, 74 Edgeley Rd,
Edgeley, STOCKPORT ☎ 0161 477 5395 20 en suite

Denton Manchester Rd M34 2GG ☎ 0161 336 3218
**Easy, flat parkland course with brook running through.
Notable hole is one called 'Death and Glory'.**
18 holes, 6541yds, Par 72, SSS 71, Course record 66.
Club membership 585.
Visitors must contact in advance & may not play summer
weekends. **Societies** apply in advance. **Green Fees** £25. **Prof**
M Hollingworth **Course Designer** R McCauley **Facilities** ⊗
Ꮠ ♥ ♀ ♏ 🄑 ⌀ **Location** 1.5m W on A57, M60 junc 24

....

Hotel ★★ 71% York House Hotel, York Place, Richmond
St, ASHTON-UNDER-LYNE ☎ 0161 330 9000 24 en suite
10 annexe en suite

Brookdale Medlock Rd M35 9WQ
☎ 0161 681 4534 ▤ 0161 688 6872
e-mail: info@brookdalegolfclub.co.uk
**Undulating parkland course, with river crossed five times
in play. Hard walking and tricky approach shots.**
18 holes, 5841yds, Par 68, SSS 68, Course record 64.
Club membership 700.
Visitors advisable to contact in advance. May only play as
guest of member at weekends. **Societies** must contact in
advance. **Green Fees** terms on application. **Prof** Tony
Cuppello **Facilities** ⊗ ⅢⅡ Ꮠ ♥ ♀ ♏ 🄑 ⌀ ♏ ⌀
Location M60/A62, exit for Oldham. and proceed towards
Manchester. Turn left at Nat West bank, follow road to end,
turn left and immediately right. Turn right at mini
roundabout. Course 1 mile on left.

....

Hotel ★★ 71% York House Hotel, York Place, Richmond
St, ASHTON-UNDER-LYNE ☎ 0161 330 9000 24 en suite
10 annexe en suite

William Wroe Municipal Pennybridge Ln, Flixton
Rd M41 5DX ☎ 0161 928 9542
18 holes, 4395yds, Par 68, SSS 65.
Location E side of village off B5158
Telephone for further details   *continued*

Hotel ⬧ Travel Inn Manchester South, Carrington Ln, Ashton-Upon-Mersey, SALE ☎ 0161 962 8113 40 en suite

GATLEY
Map 07 SJ88

Gatley Waterfall Farm, Styal Rd, Heald Green SK8 3TW ☎ 0161 437 2091
Parkland course. Moderately testing.
9 holes, 5934yds, Par 68, SSS 68.
Club membership 400.
Visitors may not play Tue & Sat. With member only weekends. Handicap certificate required. **Societies** apply in writing. **Green Fees** not confirmed. **Prof** James Hopley **Facilities** ⊗ ⅷ ⓑ ▬ ♀ ⚘ 🏠 **Location** S side of village off B5166

Hotel ★★★★ 66% Belfry House Hotel, Stanley Rd, HANDFORTH ☎ 0161 437 0511 81 en suite

HALE
Map 07 SJ78

Hale Rappax Rd WA15 0NU ☎ 0161 980 4225
9 holes, 5780yds, Par 70, SSS 68, Course record 65.
Location Off Bankhall Lane close to Altrincham Priory Hospital
Telephone for further details

Hotel ★★★ 66% Quality Hotel Altrincham, Langham Rd, Bowdon, ALTRINCHAM ☎ 0161 928 7121 91 en suite

HAZEL GROVE
Map 07 SJ98

Hazel Grove Buxton Rd SK7 6LU ☎ 0161 483 3978
Testing parkland course with tricky greens and water hazards coming into play on several holes.
18 holes, 6310yds, Par 71, SSS 71, Course record 62.
Club membership 600.
Visitors must contact in advance tel: 0161 483 7272.
Societies must apply in writing, Thu & Fri only. **Green Fees** £30 per day; £25.50 per round (£35.50/£30.50 weekends & bank holidays). **Prof** J Hopley **Facilities** ⊗ ⅷ ⓑ ▬ ♀ ⚘ 🏠 ⏌ ♂ **Location** 1m E off A6

Hotel ★★★ 60% County Hotel Bramhall, Bramhall Ln South, BRAMHALL ☎ 0161 455 9988 65 en suite

HINDLEY
Map 07 SD60

Hindley Hall Hall Ln WN2 2SQ
☎ 01942 255131 🖥 01942 253871
Parkland course with mostly easy walking.
18 holes, 5913yds, Par 69, SSS 68, Course record 64.
Club membership 430.
Visitors must contact in advance, may not play on weekend competition days. **Societies** apply in advance to Secretary **Green Fees** £20 per day (£27 weekends). **Prof** David Clarke **Facilities** ⊗ ⅷ ⓑ ▬ ♀ ⚘ 🏠 ♂ **Location** 1m N off A58, 3 miles from M61 junct 6

Hotel ★★★ 66% Quality Hotel Wigan, Riverway, WIGAN ☎ 01942 826888 88 en suite

HYDE
Map 07 SJ99

Werneth Low Werneth Low Rd, Gee Cross SK14 3AF ☎ 0161 368 2503 336 9496(secretary) 🖥 0161 320 0053
e-mail: mel.gregg@btinternet.com
Hard walking but good views from this moorland course. Exposed to wind.
11 holes, 6113yds, Par 70, SSS 70, Course record 66.
Club membership 375.
Visitors may not play Tue mornings, Thu afternoons or Sun and by prior arrangement on Sat. **Societies** must contact in at

least 14 days in advance. **Green Fees** terms on application.
Cards 🎫 ▬ 🎴 🖥 **Prof** Tony Bacchus **Facilities** ⊗ ⅷ ⓑ ▬ ♀ ⚘ 🏠 ♂ **Location** 2m S of town centre

Hotel ★★ 77% Wind in the Willows Hotel, Derbyshire Level, Sheffield Rd, GLOSSOP ☎ 01457 868001 12 en suite

KEARSLEY
Map 07 SD70

Manor Moss Ln BL4 8SF
☎ 01204 701027 🖥 01204 796914
Parkland course with water features. Treelined fairways including evergreen and deciduous trees. Suitable for players of all levels.
18 holes, 5010yds, Par 66, SSS 64, Course record 65.
Club membership 500.
Visitors book in advance. Must observe dress code. **Societies** contact in advance for details. **Green Fees** not confirmed.
Cards 🎫 ▬ 🎫 🎴 **Course Designer** Jeff Yates **Facilities** ⊗ ⅷ ⓑ ▬ ♀ ⚘ 🏠 ⏌ ♂ **Leisure** fishing.
Location Off A666, Manchester Rd

Hotel ★★★ 66% Novotel Manchester West, Worsley Brow, WORSLEY ☎ 0161 799 3535 119 en suite

LITTLEBOROUGH
Map 07 SD91

Whittaker Whittaker Ln OL15 0LH ☎ 01706 378310
Moorland 9-hole course with outstanding views of Hollingworth Lake Countryside Park and the Pennine Hills.
9 holes, 5632yds, Par 68, SSS 67, Course record 61.
Club membership 240.
Visitors welcome except for Tue pm and Sun. **Societies** apply to Secretary. **Green Fees** £14 per day (£18 weekends and bank holidays). **Facilities** ♀ ⚘ **Location** 1.5m out of Littleborough off A58

Hotel ★★★★ 64% Norton Grange Hotel, Manchester Rd, Castleton, ROCHDALE ☎ 01706 630788 51 en suite

MANCHESTER
Map 07 SJ89

Blackley Victoria Ave East, Blackley M9 7HW
☎ 0161 643 2980 & 654 7770 🖥 0161 653 8300
Parkland course crossed by a footpath. The course has recently been redesigned giving greater challenge and interest including water features.
18 holes, 6237yds, Par 70, SSS 70.
Club membership 800.
Visitors with member only Thu, weekends and bank holidays. **Societies** apply in advance. **Green Fees** terms on application. **Prof** Craig Gould **Facilities** ⊗ ⅷ ⓑ ▬ ♀ ⚘ 🏠 🛺 🚜 ♂ ⏌ **Location** 4m N of city centre, on Rochdale Rd

Hotel ★★★ 74% Malmaison, Piccadilly, MANCHESTER ☎ 0161 278 1000 167 en suite

Chorlton-cum-Hardy Barlow Hall, Barlow Hall Rd, Chorlton-cum-Hardy M21 7JJ
☎ 0161 881 5830 🖥 0161 881 4532
e-mail: chorltongolf@hotmail.com
Meadowland course with trees, stream and several ditches.
18 holes, 5980yds, Par 70, SSS 69, Course record 64.
Club membership 802.
Visitors handicap certificate required. **Societies** on Thu & Fri only by prior booking. **Green Fees** £25 (£35 weekends and bank holidays). **Prof** David Valentine **Facilities** ⊗ ⅷ ⓑ ▬ ♀ ⚘ 🏠 ⏌ ♂ **Location** 4m S of Manchester A5103/A5145

continued

continued

Hotel ★★★ 65% Willow Bank Hotel, 340-342 Wilmslow Rd, Fallowfield, MANCHESTER ☎ 0161 224 0461 118 en suite

Davyhulme Park Gleneagles Rd, Davyhulme M41 8SA ☎ 0161 748 2260 ▤ 0161 747 4067
Parkland course.
18 holes, 6237yds, Par 72, SSS 70, Course record 67.
Club membership 700.
Visitors may play Mon, Tue & Thu. **Societies** telephone in advance. **Green Fees** £32 per day; £26 per round. **Prof** Dean Butler **Facilities** ⊗ ▙ ♥ ♀ ♨ ☎ ♂ **Leisure** snooker. **Location** 8m S adj to Trafford General Hospital

Hotel ⇧ Travel Inn Manchester South, Carrington Ln, Ashton-Upon-Mersey, SALE ☎ 0161 962 8113 40 en suite

Didsbury Ford Ln, Northenden M22 4NQ
☎ 0161 998 9278 ▤ 0161 998 9278
e-mail: golf@didsburygolfclub.com
Parkland course.
18 holes, 6273yds, Par 70, SSS 70, Course record 60.
Club membership 750.
Visitors advised to check dates/times with manager or professional. **Societies** Thu & Fri, must contact in advance. **Green Fees** £28 per day (£32 weekends). **Cards** ▦▦ ▦▦ **Prof** Peter Barber **Facilities** ⊗ ⊮ ▙ ♥ ♀ ♨ ☎ ♂ ♂ **Location** 6m S of city centre off A5145

Hotel ★★★ 64% Posthouse Manchester, Palatine Rd, Northenden, MANCHESTER ☎ 0870 400 9056 190 en suite

Fairfield "Boothdale", Booth Rd, Audenshaw M34 5GA ☎ 0161 370 1641 & 370 2292
Parkland course set around a reservoir. Course demands particularly accurate placing of shots.
18 holes, 4956yds, Par 68, SSS 66, Course record 65.
Club membership 450.
Visitors may not play mornings at weekends & may be restricted on Wed & Thu. **Societies** prior booking through Secretary. **Green Fees** not confirmed. **Prof** Stephen Pownell **Facilities** ⊗ ⊮ ▙ ♥ ♀ ♨ ☎ ♂ **Location** 5m E of Manchester, off A635

Hotel ★★ 71% York House Hotel, York Place, Richmond St, ASHTON-UNDER-LYNE ☎ 0161 330 9000 24 en suite 10 annexe en suite

Marriott Worsley Park Hotel & Country Club Worsley Park, Worsley M28 2QT
☎ 0161 975 2043 ▤ 0161 975 2058
Set in 200 acres of parkland with a range of tee positions, 8 lakes and 70 strategically placed bunkers and providing an exciting challenge to golfers of all abilities, very often requiring brains rather than brawn to make a successful score.
18 holes, 6611yds, Par 71, SSS 72.
Club membership 400.
Visitors must have a handicap certificate. Must contact in advance. **Societies** weekdays only. Telephone in advance. **Green Fees** terms on application. **Cards** ▦▦ ▦▦ ▦ ▦▦
▦ ▤ **Prof** David Screeton **Course Designer** Ross McMurray **Facilities** ⊗ ⊮ ▙ ♥ ♀ ♨ ☎ ☎ ♂ ♂ ♂ ♂
Leisure heated indoor swimming pool, sauna, solarium, gymnasium. **Conf** Max 250 Thtr 250 Class 150 Board 100 Banquet 200 Del from £50 * **Location** M60 junct 13, follow A585 for 0.5m, course on left

continued

Hotel ★★★★ 71% Marriott Worsley Park Hotel & Country Club, Worsley Park, Worsley, MANCHESTER
☎ 0161 975 2000 158 en suite

Northenden Palatine Rd, Northenden M22 4FR
☎ 0161 998 4738 ▤ 0161 998 5592
Parkland course surrounded by the River Mersey.
18 holes, 6503yds, Par 72, SSS 71, Course record 64.
Club membership 800.
Visitors must contact professional in advance on 0161 945 3386. **Societies** Tue & Fri only, apply in advance to Secretary. **Green Fees** £28 per day (£32 weekends & bank holidays). **Prof** J Curtis **Course Designer** Renouf **Facilities** ⊗ ⊮ ▙ ♥ ♀ ♨ ☎ ♂ **Leisure** indoor teaching facility. **Location** 6.5m S of city centre on B1567 off A5103

Hotel ★★★ 64% Posthouse Manchester, Palatine Rd, Northenden, MANCHESTER ☎ 0870 400 9056 190 en suite

Withington 243 Palatine Rd, West Didsbury M20 2UE ☎ 0161 445 9544 ▤ 0161 445 5210
Flat parkland course bordering the River Mersey. Easy walking with an extremely tough finish.
18 holes, 6410yds, Par 71, SSS 71.
Club membership 600.
Visitors welcome except Thu, must contact in advance, restricted at weekends. **Societies** telephone in advance, welcome except Thu, Sat & Sun. **Green Fees** terms on application. **Prof** R J Ling **Facilities** ⊗ ⊮ ▙ ♥ ♀ ♨ ☎ ♂ **Location** 4m SW of city centre off B5167

Hotel ★★★ 64% Posthouse Manchester, Palatine Rd, Northenden, MANCHESTER ☎ 0870 400 9056 190 en suite

Worsley Stableford Av, Worsley M30 8AP
☎ 0161 789 4202 ▤ 0161 789 3200
Well-wooded parkland course.
18 holes, 6252yds, Par 71, SSS 70, Course record 65.
Club membership 600.
Visitors must contact professional in advance restricted during club competitions. **Societies** apply in advance. **Green Fees** terms on application. **Prof** Ceri Cousins **Course Designer** James Braid **Facilities** ⊗ ⊮ ▙ ♥ ♀ ♨ ☎ ♂ ♂ ♂ **Location** 6.5m NW of city centre off A572

Hotel ★★★ 66% Novotel Manchester West, Worsley Brow, WORSLEY ☎ 0161 799 3535 119 en suite

MELLOR   Map 07 SJ98

Mellor & Townscliffe Gibb Ln, Tarden SK6 5NA ☎ 0161 427 2208 (secretary) & 427 9700 (club) ▤ 0161 4270103
Scenic parkland and moorland course, undulating with some hard walking. Good views. Testing 200 yd, 9th hole, par 3.

continued

18 holes, 5925yds, Par 70, SSS 69.
Club membership 650.
Visitors with member only weekends & bank holidays.
Societies apply by letter or telephone. **Green Fees** £22 per
day. **Prof** Gary R Broadley **Facilities** ⊗ ⅷ ┗ ⬛ ♀ ♨ ➌ ✓
Conf Max 120 Thtr 120 Class 120 Board 120 Banquet 100
Del from £75 * **Location** 7m SE of Stockport off A626

Inn ◆◆◆◆ Matteo's Bar & Country Hotel, Rock Tavern,
Glossop Rd, Marple Bridge, MARPLE ☎ 01457 852418
5 en suite

MIDDLETON   Map 07 SD80

Manchester Hopwood Cottage, Rochdale Rd
M24 6QP ☎ 0161 643 3202 ▤ 0161 643 9174
e-mail: mec@zen.co.uk
Moorland golf of unique character over a spaciously
laid out course with generous fairways sweeping along
to large greens. A wide variety of holes will challenge
the golfer's technique, particularly the testing last
three holes.
18 holes, 6519yds, Par 72, SSS 72, Course record 65.
Club membership 650.
Visitors must contact in advance, limited play weekends
and Wed. **Societies** telephone in advance. **Green Fees**
£30 per round (£45 weekends). **Cards** ▤ ▤ 🟦 **Prof**
Brian Connor **Course Designer** Shapland Colt **Facilities**
⊗ ⅷ ┗ ⬛ ♀ ♨ ➌ ➘ ➚ ✓ ⦅ **Leisure** snooker.
Location 2.5m N off A664. M62 junct 20

Hotel ★★★★ 64% Norton Grange Hotel, Manchester
Rd, Castleton, ROCHDALE ☎ 01706 630788 51 en suite

New North Manchester Rhodes House, Manchester
Old Rd M24 4PE ☎ 0161 643 9033 ▤ 0161 643 7775
e-mail: secretary@nmgc.co.uk
A delightful moorland/parkland course with several
water features. Challenging but fair for the accomplished
golfer.
18 holes, 6527yds, Par 72, SSS 72, Course record 66.
Club membership 700.
Visitors contact Pro Shop on 0161 643 7094 for availability.
May not play Saturdays. **Societies** telephone in advance.
Green Fees £28 per day; £25 per round (£30 Sundays). **Prof**
Jason Peel **Course Designer** J Braid **Facilities** ⊗ ⅷ ┗ ⬛ ♀
♨ ➌ ✓ **Location** W side of town centre off A576

Hotel ★★★★ 66% Menzies Avant Hotel, Windsor Rd,
Manchester St, OLDHAM ☎ 0870 6003013 103 en suite

MILNROW   Map 07 SD91

Tunshill Kiln Ln OL16 3TS ☎ 01706 342095
Testing moorland course with two demanding par 5s and
out of bounds features on 8 of the 9 holes.
9 holes, 5743yds, Par 70, SSS 68, Course record 64.
Club membership 300.
Visitors must contact in advance, restricted weekends &
evenings. **Societies** apply in writing. **Green Fees** terms on
application. **Facilities** ⊗ by prior arrangement ⅷ by prior
arrangement ┗ by prior arrangement ⬛ by prior
arrangement ♀ ♨ **Conf** Max 80 Thtr 80 **Location** 1m NE
M62 exit junct 21 off B6225

Hotel ★★★★ 64% Norton Grange Hotel, Manchester Rd,
Castleton, ROCHDALE ☎ 01706 630788 51 en suite

OLDHAM   Map 07 SD90

Crompton & Royton Highbarn OL2 6RW
☎ 0161 624 0986 ▤ 0161 652 4711
Undulating moorland course.
18 holes, 6214yds, Par 70, SSS 70, Course record 63.
Club membership 700.
Visitors must contact in advance and may not play Tue or
Sat, limited play Sun pm and Wed. **Societies** apply in
advance **Green Fees** not confirmed. **Prof** David Melling
Facilities ⊗ ⅷ ┗ ⬛ ♀ ♨ ➌ ✓ **Location** 0.5m NE of
Royton

Hotel ★★★★ 66% Menzies Avant Hotel, Windsor Rd,
Manchester St, OLDHAM ☎ 0870 6003013 103 en suite

Oldham Lees New Rd OL4 5PN ☎ 0161 624 4986
Moorland course, with hard walking.
18 holes, 5122yds, Par 66, SSS 65, Course record 62.
Club membership 370.
Visitors no restrictions. **Societies** must contact in advance.
Green Fees not confirmed. **Prof** C Atkinson **Facilities** ⊗ ⅷ
┗ ⬛ ♀ ♨ ➌ ✓ **Location** 2.5m E off A669

Hotel ★★ 71% York House Hotel, York Place, Richmond
St, ASHTON-UNDER-LYNE ☎ 0161 330 9000 24 en suite
10 annexe en suite

Werneth Green Ln, Garden Suburb OL8 3AZ
☎ 0161 624 1190
Semi-moorland course, with a deep gulley and stream
crossing eight fairways. Testing hole: 3rd (par 3).
18 holes, 5363yds, Par 68, SSS 66, Course record 63.
Club membership 460.
Visitors may not play on Tue or Thu and weekends. Must
contact in advance. **Societies** must contact in advance. **Green
Fees** not confirmed. **Prof** Roy Penney **Course Designer**
Sandy Herd **Facilities** ⊗ ⅷ ┗ ⬛ ♀ ♨ ➌ ✓ **Location** S
side of town centre off A627

Hotel ★★ 71% York House Hotel, York Place, Richmond
St, ASHTON-UNDER-LYNE ☎ 0161 330 9000 24 en suite
10 annexe en suite

PRESTWICH   Map 07 SD80

Heaton Park Municipal Heaton Park, Middleton Rd
M25 2SW ☎ 0161 654 9899 ▤ 0161 653 2003
A parkland style course in historic Heaton Park with
rolling hills and lakes, boasting some spectacular holes. A
good test of skill for golfers of all abilities.
Championship: 18 holes, 5755yds, Par 70, SSS 68.
Visitors restricted to club members only between 8-10am Sat
& Sun. **Societies** apply in writing or by telephone to the
centre manager. **Green Fees** £10 per round (£12.50
weekends). **Cards** ▤ ▤ ▤ **Course Designer** J H
Taylor **Facilities** ⊗ ⅷ ┗ ⬛ ♀ ♨ ➌ ⚐ ✓ ⦅ **Leisure**
fishing, 18 hole par 3 course. **Conf** Banquet 40 **Location** N
of Manchester near junct 18 of M62

Hotel ⌂ Premier Lodge (Manchester West), East Lancs Rd,
SWINTON ☎ 0870 700 1472 27 en suite

Prestwich Hilton Ln M25 9XB
☎ 0161 773 1404 ▤ 0161 772 0700
Well manicured tree-lined parkland course, near to
Manchester city centre. A testing course with small
greens.
18 holes, 4846yds, Par 65, SSS 65, Course record 60.
Club membership 565.

continued

Visitors weekdays by arrangement. Restricted at weekends, ladies day Tue. **Societies** apply in writing or telephone. **Green Fees** £20 per day (£20 per round weekends). **Prof** Simon Wakefield **Facilities** ⊗ ⅢⅢ ⓛ ⛳ ♀ ⚘ 🏠 ⛳ ⛳ **Leisure** squash, sauna, solarium, gymnasium. **Location** N side of town centre on A6044

. . . .

Hotel ★★★ 66% Novotel Manchester West, Worsley Brow, WORSLEY ☎ 0161 799 3535 119 en suite

ROCHDALE   Map 07 SD81

Castle Hawk Chadwick Ln, Castleton OL11 3BY
☎ 01706 640841 📧 01706 860587
e-mail: teeoff@castlehawk.co.uk
Two parkland courses that are an ideal place to start for beginners whilst still offering a stern test for the better golfer. The 18 hole course consists of 17 par 3s and one par 4. The 9 hole course is a more traditional test of golf with seven par 4s and two par 3s, each offering a test of skill be it length, accuracy or both.
New Course: 9 holes, 2699yds, Par 34, SSS 34,
Course record 30.
Old Course: 18 holes, 3189yds, Par 55, SSS 55.
Club membership 290.
Visitors 9 Holes member only from 9am-6.30 pm in summer. **Societies** must telephone in advance. **Green Fees** £9 per day (£11 Sundays). **Cards** 🗱 ▨ 🗱 🗱 🗱 🗱 **Prof** Andy Duncan/Frank Accleton **Course Designer** John Andrew Duncan/Frank Accleton **Course Designer** John **Facilities** ⊗ ⅢⅢ ⓛ ⛳ ♀ ⚘ 🏠 ⛳ ⛳ 𝄞 **Leisure** Golf lessons from professional. **Location** S of Rochdale, nr junc 20 (M62)

. . . .

Hotel ★★★★ 64% Norton Grange Hotel, Manchester Rd, Castleton, ROCHDALE ☎ 01706 630788 51 en suite

Rochdale Edenfield Rd OL11 5YR
☎ 01706 643818 📧 01706 861113
Parkland course with enjoyable golf and easy walking.
18 holes, 6050yds, Par 71, SSS 69, Course record 65.
Club membership 750.
Visitors must telephone in advance. **Societies** apply in writing or telephone **Green Fees** not confirmed. **Prof** Andrew Laverty **Course Designer** George Lowe **Facilities** ⊗ ⅢⅢ ⓛ ⛳ ♀ ⚘ 🏠 ⛳ 𝄞 **Location** 1.75m W on A680

. . . .

Hotel ★★★★ 64% Norton Grange Hotel, Manchester Rd, Castleton, ROCHDALE ☎ 01706 630788 51 en suite

Springfield Park Springfield Park, Bolton Rd OL11 4RE ☎ 01706 56401 (weekend only)
18 holes, 5237yds, Par 67, SSS 66, Course record 64.
Location 1.5m SW off A58
Telephone for further details

. . . .

Hotel ★★★★ 64% Norton Grange Hotel, Manchester Rd, Castleton, ROCHDALE ☎ 01706 630788 51 en suite

ROMILEY   Map 07 SJ99

Romiley Goose House Green SK6 4LJ ☎ 0161 430 2392 📧 0161 430 7258
Semi-parkland course on the edge of the Derbyshire Hills, providing a good test of golf with a number of outstanding holes, notably the 6th, 9th, 14th and 16th. The latter enjoys magnificent views from the tee.
18 holes, 6454yds, Par 70, SSS 71, Course record 66.
Club membership 700.
Visitors are advised to contact in advance, may not play Thu or Sat before 4pm. **Societies** Tue & Wed, must book in advance. **Green Fees** terms on application. **Prof** Robert N

continued

Giles **Facilities** ⊗ ⅢⅢ ⓛ ⛳ ♀ ⚘ 🏠 𝄞 **Location** E side of town centre off B6104

. . . .

Hotel ★★ 68% The Wycliffe Hotel, 74 Edgeley Rd, Edgeley, STOCKPORT ☎ 0161 477 5395 20 en suite

SALE   Map 07 SJ79

Ashton on Mersey Church Ln M33 5QQ
☎ 0161 976 4390 & 962 3727 📧 0161 976 4390
Parkland course with easy walking alongside the River Mersey.
9 holes, 6146yds, Par 71, SSS 69, Course record 66.
Club membership 485.
Visitors with member only Sun & bank holidays, not Sat or Tue. **Societies** Thu only. Apply in writing. **Green Fees** not confirmed. **Prof** Mike Williams **Facilities** ⊗ ⅢⅢ ⓛ ⛳ ♀ ⚘ 🏠 𝄞 **Leisure** sauna. **Location** 1m W of M60,junc 7, off Glebelands Road

. . . .

Hotel ★★★ 67% Cresta Court Hotel, Church St, ALTRINCHAM ☎ 0161 927 7272 137 en suite

Sale Golf Rd M33 2XU ☎ 0161 973 1638 (Gen Man)
📧 0161 962 4217
e-mail: billi@sandiway87.fsnet.co.uk
Tree-lined parkland course. Feature holes are the 13th - Watery Gap - and the par 3 (117yd) 17th.
18 holes, 6352yds, Par 71, SSS 70.
Club membership 700.
Visitors contact professional in advance. **Societies** apply by letter. **Green Fees** not confirmed. **Prof** Mike Stewart **Facilities** ⊗ ⅢⅢ ⓛ ⛳ ♀ ⚘ 🏠 𝄞 **Location** 0.5m from M60 J6, NW side of town centre off A6144

. . . .

Hotel ★★★ 67% Cresta Court Hotel, Church St, ALTRINCHAM ☎ 0161 927 7272 137 en suite

SHEVINGTON   Map 07 SD50

Gathurst 62 Miles Ln WN6 8EW
☎ 01257 255235 (Secretary) 📧 01257 255953
e-mail: gathurst.golfclub@genie.co.uk
Testing parkland course, slightly hilly.
18 holes, 6016yds, Par 70, SSS 69, Course record 64.
Club membership 630.
Visitors may play anytime except competition days,with members only at weekends. **Societies** welcome Mon, Tue, Thu & Fri. Apply in writing to Secretary. **Green Fees** £26 per round. **Prof** David Clarke **Course Designer** N Pearson **Facilities** ⊗ ⅢⅢ ⓛ ⛳ ♀ ⚘ 🏠 𝄞 **Location** W side of village B5375,1m S off junct 27 of M6

. . . .

Hotel ★★★★ 64% Kilhey Court Hotel, Chorley Rd, Standish, WIGAN ☎ 01257 472100 62 en suite

STALYBRIDGE   Map 07 SJ99

Stamford Oakfield House, Huddersfield Rd SK15 3PY
☎ 01457 832126 & 834829
e-mail: stamford.golfclub@bigfoot.com
Undulating moorland course.
18 holes, 5701yds, Par 70, SSS 68, Course record 62.
Club membership 600.
Visitors limited play at weekends. **Societies** apply in writing or telephone 0161 633 5721 **Green Fees** terms on application. **Cards** 🗱 ▨ 🗱 🗱 🗱 🗱 **Facilities** ⊗ ⅢⅢ ⓛ ⛳ ♀ ⚘ 🏠 𝄞 **Location** 2m NE off A635

. . . .

Hotel ★★ 71% York House Hotel, York Place, Richmond St, ASHTON-UNDER-LYNE ☎ 0161 330 9000 24 en suite 10 annexe en suite

STANDISH   Map 07 SD51

Standish Court Rectory Ln WN6 0XD
☎ 01257 425777 📠 01257 425888
e-mail: info@standishgolf.co.uk
Undulating 18 hole parkland course, not overly long but provides a good test for all level of players. Front nine more open with room for errors, back nine very scenic through woodland, a number of tight driving holes. Greens in excellent condition.
18 holes, 5625yds, Par 68, SSS 66.
Club membership 375.
Visitors can play anytime, phone in advance for tee time, standard golfing dress required. **Societies** telephone in advance. **Green Fees** not confirmed. **Cards** 🁢 🁢 🁢 🁢
🁢 **Prof** J Kershaw **Course Designer** P Dawson **Facilities** ⊗ 🏂 🖫 ⚑ 💺 🍴 ⛳ ↑ **Location** Off M61,junct 6, follow signs to Aspoll/Haigh

Hotel ★★★★ 64% Kilhey Court Hotel, Chorley Rd, Standish, WIGAN ☎ 01257 472100 62 en suite

STOCKPORT   Map 07 SJ89

Heaton Moor Heaton Mersey SK4 3NX
☎ 0161 432 2134 📠 0161 432 2134
e-mail: hmgc@ukgateway.net
Conveniently located for motorway access. Pleasantly situated in a gently undulating parkland course with two separate 9 holes starting from the clubhouse.
18 holes, 5968, Par 70, SSS 69, Course record 66.
Club membership 400.
Visitors restricted Tue, bank holidays & Sat (summer). **Societies** apply in writing. **Green Fees** £23 per day ;£31 weekends(£18/£26 winter). **Prof** Simon Marsh **Facilities** ⊗ 🏂 🖫 💺 🍴 🛒 ⛳ ⚑ **Location** N of town centre off B5169

Hotel ★★ 68% Saxon Holme Hotel, 230 Wellington Rd, STOCKPORT ☎ 0161 432 2335 33 en suite

Houldsworth Houldsworth Park, Reddish SK5 6BN
☎ 0161 442 1712 📠 0161 947 9678
Flat parkland course, tree-lined and with water hazards. Testing holes 9th (par 5) and 13th (par 5).
18 holes, 6209yds, Par 71, SSS 70, Course record 65.
Club membership 680.
Visitors may not play weekends & bank holidays unless by prior arrangement with professional. **Societies** by prior arrangement, telephone Secretary.wellcome on mon,thur & fri **Green Fees** terms on application. **Prof** David Naylor **Course Designer** Dave Thomas **Facilities** ⊗ 🏂 🖫 💺 🍴 ⛳ 🛒 ⚑ ⛳ **Location** 4m SE of city centre off A6

Hotel ★★★ 65% Willow Bank Hotel, 340-342 Wilmslow Rd, Fallowfield, MANCHESTER ☎ 0161 224 0461 118 en suite

Marple Barnsfold Rd, Hawk Green, Marple SK6 7EL
☎ 0161 427 2311 & 427 1125 📠 0161 427 1125
e-mail: marple.golf.club@ukgateway-net
Parkland course.
18 holes, 5552yds, Par 68, SSS 67, Course record 66.
Club membership 640.
Visitors restricted Thu afternoon & weekend competition days. **Societies** apply in writing to professional. **Green Fees** terms on application. **Prof** David Myers **Facilities** ⊗ 🏂 🖫 💺 🍴 🛒 ⚑ **Leisure** snooker. **Location** S side of town centre   *continued*

Hotel ★★★ 67% Bredbury Hall Hotel & Country Club, Goyt Valley, BREDBURY ☎ 0161 430 7421 150 en suite

Reddish Vale Southcliffe Rd, Reddish SK5 7EE
☎ 0161 480 2359 📠 0161 477 8242
e-mail: admin@reddishvalegolfclub.co.uk
Undulating heathland course designed by Dr. A Mackenzie and situated in the River Tame valley.
18 holes, 6100yds, Par 69, SSS 69, Course record 64.
Club membership 550.
Visitors must play with member at weekends. Book in advance through professional. **Societies** must contact in writing. **Green Fees** £25 per 18 holes. **Prof** Bob Freeman **Course Designer** Dr A Mackenzie **Facilities** ⊗ 🏂 🖫 💺 🍴 🛒 ⚑ ⛳ **Location** Off Reddish Road, M6 junct 1 southbound, junct 27 northbound

Hotel ★★ 68% The Wycliffe Hotel, 74 Edgeley Rd, Edgeley, STOCKPORT ☎ 0161 477 5395 20 en suite

Stockport Offerton Rd, Offerton SK2 5HL
☎ 0161 427 8369 (Secretary) & 427 2421 (Pro)
📠 0161 449 8293
e-mail: stockportgolf@genie.co.uk
A beautifully situated course in wide open countryside with views of the Cheshire and Derbyshire hills. It is not too long but requires that the player plays all the shots, to excellent greens. Demanding holes include the dog-leg 3rd, 12th, and 18th and the 460 yard opening hole is among the toughest in Cheshire.
18 holes, 6326yds, Par 71, SSS 71, Course record 66.
Club membership 500.
Visitors must contact professional in advance, limited play weekends. **Societies** Wed & Thu only, apply in writing to Secretary. **Green Fees** terms on application. **Prof** Mike Peel **Course Designer** P Barrie/A Herd **Facilities** ⊗ 🏂 🖫 💺 🍴 ⚑ 🛒 ⛳ **Location** 4m SE on A627

Hotel ★★★ 67% Bredbury Hall Hotel & Country Club, Goyt Valley, BREDBURY ☎ 0161 430 7421 150 en suite

SWINTON   Map 07 SD70

Swinton Park East Lancashire Rd M27 5LX
☎ 0161 794 0861 📠 0161 281 0698
One of Lancashire's longest inland courses.
18 holes, 6726yds, Par 73, SSS 72, Course record 66.
Club membership 600.
Visitors may not play weekends or Thu. Must contact in advance and have handicap certificate. **Societies** apply by letter. **Green Fees** not confirmed. **Prof** James Wilson **Course Designer** James Braid **Facilities** ⊗ 🏂 🖫 💺 🍴 ⚑ **Location** 1m W off A580

Hotel ★★★ 66% Novotel Manchester West, Worsley Brow, WORSLEY ☎ 0161 799 3535 119 en suite

UPPERMILL   Map 07 SD90

Saddleworth Mountain Ash OL3 6LT
☎ 01457 873653 📠 01457 820647
e-mail: secretary@saddleworthgolfclub.org.uk
Moorland course, with superb views of Pennines.
18 holes, 5976yds, Par 71, SSS 69, Course record 61.
Club membership 800.
Visitors must contact in advance, restricted at weekends. **Societies** contact in advance. **Green Fees** £23 per day; (£30 weekends). **Prof** Robert Johnson **Course Designer** George Lowe/Dr McKenzie **Facilities** ⊗ 🏂 🖫 💺 🍴 🛒 🛒 ⚑ 🛒 ⛳ **Location** E side of town centre off A670   *continued*

Hotel ★★★ 73% Hotel Smokies Park, Ashton Rd, Bardsley, OLDHAM ☎ 0161 785 5000 73 en suite

URMSTON
Map 07 SJ79

Flixton Church Rd, Flixton M41 6EP
☎ 0161 748 2116 📄 0161 748 2116
Meadowland course bounded by River Mersey.
9 holes, 6410yds, Par 71, SSS 71.
Club membership 430.
Visitors contact professional in advance, with member only weekends & bank holidays. **Societies** apply in writing.
Green Fees terms on application. **Cards** ▭ ▭ ▭ 🔲 **Prof** David Wade **Facilities** ⊗ ⅷ ⮐ ⚑ ♀ △ 🛒 ⚲ **Location** S side of town centre on B5213

Hotel ★★★★ 65% Copthorne Hotel Manchester, Clippers Quay, Salford Quays, MANCHESTER
☎ 0161 873 7321 166 en suite

WALKDEN
Map 07 SD70

Brackley Municipal M38 9TR ☎ 0161 790 6076
9 holes, 3003yds, Par 35, SSS 69.
Location 2m NW on A6
Telephone for further details

Hotel ★★★ 66% Novotel Manchester West, Worsley Brow, WORSLEY ☎ 0161 799 3535 119 en suite

WESTHOUGHTON
Map 07 SD60

Hart Common Wigan Rd BL5 2BX
☎ 01942 813195 📄 01942 840775
e-mail: hartcommon@ukgolfer.org
A parkland course on green belt land with many water features, including the signature hole, the 7th, which has water all down the left hand side.
18 holes, 5719yards, Par 71, SSS 68.
Club membership 400.
Visitors must book in advance. **Societies** apply in writing
Green Fees £10 (£15 weekends and bank holidays). **Cards** ▭ ▭ ▭ ▭ 🔲 **Prof** Gareth Benson **Course Designer** Mike Shattock **Facilities** ⊗ ⅷ ⮐ ⚑ ♀ △ ⚲ 🛒 ⚲ ⚲
Leisure par 3 Academy course. **Location** situated on A58 between Bolton (M61 junct 5) and Hindley/Wigan

Hotel ★★★ 64% Holiday Inn Bolton, Beaumont Rd, BOLTON ☎ 0870 400 9011 96 en suite

Westhoughton Long Island, School St BL5 2BR
☎ 01942 811085 & 608958 📄 01942 608958
Compact downland course.
9 holes, 2886yds, Par 70, SSS 68, Course record 64.
Club membership 280.
Visitors with member only at weekends. **Societies** telephone in advance or apply in writing. **Green Fees** terms on application. **Prof** Jason Seed **Facilities** ⊗ ⅷ ⮐ ⚑ ♀ △ 🛒
Location 0.5m NW off A58

Hotel ★★★ 64% Holiday Inn Bolton, Beaumont Rd, BOLTON ☎ 0870 400 9011 96 en suite

WHITEFIELD
Map 07 SD80

Stand The Dales, Ashbourne Grove M45 7NL
☎ 0161 766 3197 📄 0161 796 3234
A semi-parkland course with five moorland holes. A fine test of golf with a very demanding finish.
18 holes, 6411yds, Par 72, SSS 71, Course record 66.
Club membership 500.
Visitors must contact professional in advance. **Societies** Wed
continued

& Fri, apply by telephone. **Green Fees** terms on application.
Cards ▭ 🔲 **Prof** Mark Dance **Course Designer** G Lowe/A Herd **Facilities** ⊗ ⅷ ⮐ ⚑ ♀ △ 🛒 ⚲ ⚲ **Location** 1m W off A667

Hotel ★★★ 66% Bolholt Country Park Hotel, Walshaw Rd, BURY ☎ 0161 762 4000 65 en suite

Whitefield Higher Ln M45 7EZ
☎ 0161 351 2700 📄 0161 351 2712
e-mail: golfclub@whitefield.u-net.com
Fine sporting parkland course with well-watered greens.
18 holes, 6045yds, Par 69, SSS 69, Course record 64.
Club membership 540.
Visitors play restricted Tue & Sun. Booking essential weekends and bank holidays, contact the professional shop on 0161 7663096. **Societies** must contact in advance. **Green Fees** not confirmed. **Cards** ▭ ▭ ▭ ▭ 🔲 **Prof** Paul Reeves **Facilities** ⊗ ⅷ ⮐ ♀ △ 🛒 ⚲ **Leisure** hard tennis courts, snooker room. **Location** N side of town centre on A665

Hotel ★★★ 74% Malmaison, Piccadilly, MANCHESTER
☎ 0161 278 1000 167 en suite

WIGAN
Map 07 SD50

Haigh Hall Golf Complex Copperas Ln, Haigh WN2 1PE ☎ 01942 831107 📄 01942 831417
e-mail: hhgen@wiganmgc.gov.uk
This recently completed golf complex provides all the golfer requires for playing or practice/tuition facilities. The scenic setting provides an excellent location for the two courses, an 18 hole and a 9 hole.
Balcarres Course: 18 holes, 6300yards, Par 70, SSS 71.
Crawford Course: 9 holes, 1446yards, Par 28.
Club membership 150.
Visitors advisable to book in advance, especially for peak times. **Societies** apply in writing, enquiries by telephone.
Green Fees 18 hole course: £7.50 to £15. 9 hole course: £4 to £5. **Cards** ▭ ▭ ▭ ▭ 🔲 **Prof** Ian Lee **Course Designer** Steve Marnoch **Facilities** ⊗ ⅷ ⮐ ⚑ ♀ △ 🛒 ⚲ ⚲ ⚲ **Leisure** golf academy. **Location** M6 junct 27/M61 junct 5 or 6, follow Haigh Hall direction signs

Hotel ★★ 65% Bel-Air Hotel, 236 Wigan Ln, WIGAN
☎ 01942 241410 11 en suite

Wigan Arley Hall, Haigh WN1 2UH ☎ 01257 421360
Among the best of Lancashire's 18-hole courses. The fine old clubhouse is the original Arley Hall, and is surrounded by a 12th century moat.
18 holes, 6009yds, Par 69, SSS 69.
Club membership 200.
Visitors must contact in advance. May not play Tue or Sat.
Societies apply by telephone. **Green Fees** £25 per 18 holes(£30 weekends). **Course Designer** Gaunt & Marnoch
Facilities ⊗ ⅷ ⮐ ⚑ ♀ △ **Location** M6 junct 27, 3m NE off B5238

Hotel ★★★ 66% Quality Hotel Wigan, Riverway, WIGAN
☎ 01942 826888 88 en suite

WOODFORD
Map 07 SJ88

Avro Old Hall Ln SK7 1QR ☎ 0161 439 2709
An attractive, tight and challenging 9-hole course.
9 holes, 5735yds, Par 69, SSS 68.
Club membership 400. Not able to take societies.
Green Fees terms on application. **Facilities** ⮐ ♀ △
Location W side of village on A5102
continued

Hotel ★★★ 60% County Hotel Bramhall, Bramhall Ln South, BRAMHALL ☎ 0161 455 9988 65 en suite

WORSLEY Map 07 SD70

Ellesmere Old Clough Ln M28 7HZ
☎ 0161 799 0554 (office) & 790 8591 (pro)
e-mail: honsec@ellesmeregolf.fsnet.co.uk
Parkland course with natural hazards. Testing holes: 3rd (par 5), 9th (par 3), 15th (par 5). Hard walking.
18 holes, 6248yds, Par 70, SSS 70, Course record 67.
Club membership 700.
Visitors welcome except club competition days & bank holidays. **Societies** apply in advance. **Green Fees** £28 per day; £22 per round (£28 per round weekends). **Prof** Terry Morley **Facilities** ⊗ ⍥ ⊾ ⊻ ♀ ⚲ ⚘ ∅ **Location** N side of village off A580

Hotel ★★★ 66% Novotel Manchester West, Worsley Brow, WORSLEY ☎ 0161 799 3535 119 en suite

HAMPSHIRE

ALDERSHOT Map 04 SU85

Army Laffans Rd GU11 2HF
☎ 01252 337272 ☷ 01252 337562
e-mail: agc@ic24.net
The second oldest course in Hampshire. Picturesque heathland course with three par 3s, over 200 yds.
18 holes, 6550yds, Par 71, SSS 71, Course record 66.
Club membership 825.
Visitors may not play weekends. **Societies** apply in writing. **Green Fees** terms on application. **Cards** ▦ ▦ ▦ ▦ ⚹ **Prof** Graham Cowley **Facilities** ⊗ ⍥ ⊾ ⊻ ♀ ⚲ ⚘ ∅ **Location** 1.5m N of town centre off A323/A325

Hotel ★★★ 69% Potters International Hotel, 1 Fleet Rd, ALDERSHOT ☎ 01252 344000 97 en suite

ALRESFORD Map 04 SU53

Alresford Cheriton Rd, Tichborne Down SO24 0PN
☎ 01962 733746 ☷ 01962 736040
e-mail: secretary@alresford-golf.demon.co.uk
A testing downland course on well drained chalk. Expanded to 18 holes, incorporating the original twelve, but changing direction of play to give two starting points and two closing greens near clubhouse.
18 holes, 5905yds, Par 69, SSS 68, Course record 63.
Club membership 750.
Visitors must contact in advance. **Societies** must telephone in advance. **Green Fees** £25 (£40 weekends & bank holidays). **Cards** ▦ ▦ ▦ ⚹ **Prof** Malcolm Scott **Course Designer** Scott Webb Young **Facilities** ⊗ ⍥ ⊾ ⊻ ♀ ⚲ ⚘ ∅ **Location** 1m S on B3046

Hotel ★★ 61% Swan Hotel, 11 West St, ALRESFORD ☎ 01962 732302 & 734427 ☷ 01962 735274
11 rms (10 en suite) 12 annexe en suite

ALTON Map 04 SU73

Alton Old Odiham Rd GU34 4BU
☎ 01420 82042 & 86518
Undulating meadowland course.
9 holes, 5744yds, Par 68, SSS 68, Course record 62.
Club membership 350.
Visitors must contact in advance and must have a handicap certificate to play at weekends. Correct golf attire must be

continued

worn. **Societies** must contact in advance. **Green Fees** terms on application. **Prof** Paul Brown **Course Designer** James Braid **Facilities** ⊾ ⊻ ♀ ⚲ ⚘ ∅ **Location** 2m N of Alton off B3349 at Golden Pot

Hotel ★★★ 67% Alton House Hotel, Normandy St, ALTON ☎ 01420 80033 39 en suite

Worldham Park Cakers Ln, East Worldham GU34 3BF ☎ 01420 543151 ☷ 01420 84124
The course is in a picturesque woodland setting with an abundance of challenging holes (doglegs, water and sand).
18 holes, 6209yds, Par 71, SSS 70.
Club membership 500.
Visitors are advised to book in advance at weekends. **Societies** must contact in advance. **Green Fees** £11 per round (£14 weekends). **Cards** ▦ ▦ ▦ ⚹ **Prof** Jon Le Roux **Course Designer** F J Whidborne **Facilities** ⊗ ⍥ ⊾ ⊻ ♀ ⚲ ⚘ ⚞ ⚘ ∅ ∫ **Location** B3004, 2mins from Alton

Hotel ★★★ 68% Alton Grange Hotel, London Rd, ALTON ☎ 01420 86565 26 en suite 4 annexe en suite

AMPFIELD Map 04 SU42

Ampfield Par Three Winchester Rd SO51 9BQ
☎ 01794 368480
Pretty parkland course designed by Henry Cotton in 1963. Well-bunkered greens.
18 holes, 2478yds, Par 54, SSS 53, Course record 49.
Club membership 470.
Visitors must contact in advance & have a handicap certificate to play at weekends & bank holidays, recognised golfshoes must be worn. **Societies** must contact in advance. **Green Fees** terms on application. **Prof** Steve Hunter **Course Designer** Henry Cotton **Facilities** ⊗ ⍥ ⊾ ⊻ ♀ ⚲ ⚘ ⚞ ∅ **Conf** Max 80 Banquet 60 **Location** 4m NE of Romsey on A31

Hotel ★★★ 67% Potters Heron Hotel, Winchester Rd, Ampfield, ROMSEY ☎ 023 8026 6611 54 en suite

ANDOVER Map 04 SU34

Andover 51 Winchester Rd SP10 2EF
☎ 01264 358040 ☷ 01264 358040
e-mail: play@andovergolfclub.fsnet.co.uk
Undulating downland course combining a good test of golf for all abilities with breathtaking views across Hampshire countryside. Well guarded greens and a notable par 3, 9th (225yds) with the tee perched on top of a hill, 100ft above the green.
9 holes, 6096yds, Par 70, SSS 69, Course record 66.
Club membership 450.
Visitors must contact professional in advance tel: 01264 324151. **Societies** Mon-Wed only. Must contact in advance. **Green Fees** £20 per day; £18 per 18 holes (£20 per 18 holes weekends). **Prof** D Lawrence **Course Designer** J H Taylor **Facilities** ⊗ ⍥ ⊾ ⊻ ♀ ⚲ ⚘ **Location** 0.5m S on A3057

Hotel ★★★ 63% Quality Hotel Andover, Micheldever Rd, ANDOVER ☎ 01264 369111 13 en suite 36 annexe en suite

Hampshire Winchester Rd SP11 7TB ☎ 01264 357555 (pro shop) & 356462 (office) ☷ 01264 356606
e-mail: enquiries@thehampshiregolfclub.co.uk
A pleasant undulating parkland course, based on chalk which provides very good drainage, with a superb finishing hole
18 holes, 6359yds, Par 72, SSS 70, Course record 67.
Club membership 650.

continued

Hampshire Golf Club

Visitors advisable to book 3 days in advance. **Societies** apply by phone to Jan Miles (01264 356462) **Green Fees** £28 per day; £17 per round (£27 per round weekends & bank holidays). **Cards** 〰️ ▬ 🔲 🔲 **Prof** Stewart Cronin **Facilities** ⊗ 🛍 💺 ♀ ⚓ 🏠 🏌️ 🐟 🔨 🏌️ ⛴ **Leisure** 9 hole par 3 course.**Conf** Max 80 Thtr 80 Board 60 Banquet 80 **Location** located 1.5m S of Andover on A3057 Winchester road

....

Hotel ★★★ 63% Quality Hotel Andover, Micheldever Rd, ANDOVER ☎ 01264 369111 13 en suite 36 annexe en suite

---

BARTON-ON-SEA   Map 04 SZ29

Barton-on-Sea Milford Rd BH25 5PP
☎ 01425 615308 📠 01425 621457
Though not strictly a links course, it is situated on a coastal cliff with views over the Solent to the Isle of Wight. With 27 holes (three loops of nine), sea breezes often add to the test.
Becton-Needles: 18 holes, 6521yds, Par 72, SSS 71, Course record 65.
Stroller: 9 holes, Par 35.
Club membership 940.
Visitors must contact in advance and have a handicap certificate. **Societies** must telephone in advance. **Green Fees** not confirmed. **Prof** Peter Rodgers **Course Designer** Hamilton Stutt **Facilities** ⊗ 🏌️ by prior arrangement 🛍 💺 ♀ ⚓ 🏠 🏌️ 🐟 🔨 🏌️ **Leisure** snooker tables. **Location** B3058 SE side of town

....

Hotel ★★★★★🏊 Chewton Glen Hotel, Christchurch Rd, NEW MILTON ☎ 01425 275341 62 en suite

---

BASINGSTOKE   Map 04 SU65

Basingstoke Kempshott Park RG23 7LL
☎ 01256 465990 📠 01256 331793
A well-maintained parkland course with wide and inviting fairways. You are inclined to expect longer drives than are actually achieved - partly on account of the trees. There are many two-hundred-year-old beech trees, since the course was built on an old deer park.
18 holes, 6350yds, Par 70, SSS 70, Course record 66.
Club membership 700.
Visitors must contact in advance and play Mon-Fri only (ex bank holidays). **Societies** must contact in advance. **Green Fees** £40 per day; £30 per round (Mon-Fri only). **Cards** 〰️ ▬ 🔲 **Prof** Guy Shoesmith **Course Designer** James Braid **Facilities** ⊗ 🏌️ 🛍 💺 ♀ ⚓ 🏠 🏌️ 🐟 🔨 🏌️ **Conf** Max 80 Thtr 80 Class 40 Board 30 Banquet 40 **Location** 3.5m SW on A30 M3 exit 7

....

Hotel ★★★ 65% Holiday Inn Basingstoke, Grove Rd, BASINGSTOKE ☎ 0870 400 9004 86 en suite

---

Dummer Dummer RG25 2AR
☎ 01256 397888 📠 01256 397889
e-mail: golf@dummergc.co.uk
Designed by Peter Alliss/Clive Clark, this course is set in 180 acres of countryside with panoramic views. It provides a challenge for all playing categories and is open all year round. All facilities, including the clubhouse have recently been enhanced.

18 holes, 6385yds, Par 72, SSS 70, Course record 64.
Club membership 750.
Visitors must contact in advance, adhere to dress code, handicap required, limited at weekends. **Societies** contact in advance. **Green Fees** £28 (£35 weekends). **Cards** 〰️ ▬ ▬ 🔲 🔲 **Prof** A Fannon/S Watson/D Chivers **Course Designer** Peter Alliss/Clive Clark **Facilities** ⊗ 🏌️ 🛍 💺 ♀ ⚓ 🏠 🏌️ 🐟 🔨 🏌️ **Leisure** sauna. **Conf** Max 45 Del £15 to £21 * **Location** Off junc 7 of M3 towards Dummer village

....

Hotel ⭓ Premier Lodge (Basingstoke), NORTH WALTHAM ☎ 0870 700 1312 28 en suite

---

Weybrook Park Rooksdown Ln RG24 9NT
☎ 01256 320347 📠 01256 812973
e-mail: secretary@weybrookpark.fsnet.co.uk
A course designed to be enjoyable for all standards of player. Easy walking with fabulous views.
18 holes, 6468yds, Par 71, SSS 71.
Club membership 600.
Visitors telephone for availability. **Societies** telephone in advance for availability and confirm in writing. **Green Fees** not confirmed. **Cards** 〰️ ▬ 🔲 **Prof** Anthony Dillon **Facilities** ⊗ 🛍 💺 ♀ ⚓ 🏠 🏌️ 🐟 🔨 🏌️ **Location** 2m W of town centre, entrance via A339

....

Hotel ★★★★ 68% Apollo Hotel, Aldermaston Roundabout, BASINGSTOKE ☎ 01256 796700 125 en suite

---

BORDON   Map 04 SU73

Blackmoor Firgrove Rd, Whitehill GU35 9EH
☎ 01420 472775 📠 01420 487666
e-mail: ctupper@blackmoorgolf.co.uk
A first-class moorland course with a great variety of holes. Fine greens and wide pine tree-lined fairways are a distinguishing feature. The ground is mainly flat and walking easy.
18 holes, 6164yds, Par 69, SSS 69, Course record 63.
Club membership 750.
Visitors must contact in advance, must have handicap certificate and may not play at weekends. **Societies** telephone in advance. **Green Fees** £47 per 36 holes; £35 per 18 holes (weekdays only). **Prof** Stephen Clay **Course Designer** H S Colt **Facilities** ⊗ by prior arrangement 🏌️

continued

by prior arrangement ⓑ ⓦ ♀ ♤ ⓐ ♂ **Conf** Max 80
Location Travelling S on A325, 6m beyond Farnham,
pass through Whitehill and turn right at roundabout

Hotel ★★★ 67% Alton House Hotel, Normandy St,
ALTON ☎ 01420 80033 39 en suite

BOTLEY   Map 04 SU51

Botley Park Hotel, Golf & Country Club
Winchester Rd, Boorley Green SO32 2UA
☎ 01489 780888 ▤ 01489 789242
e-mail: info@botleypark.macdonald.hotels.co.uk
Pleasantly undulating course with water hazards. Driving range and country club facilities.
18 holes, 6341yds, Par 70, SSS 70, Course record 67.
Club membership 1500.
Visitors must play with member at weekends. Must contact in advance & have handicap certificate. **Societies** contact in advance. **Green Fees** not confirmed. **Cards** ▧■■ ▩
▨ ⓩ **Prof** Tim Barter **Course Designer** Ewan Murray
Facilities ⊗ ⅲ ⓑ ⓦ ♀ ♤ ⓐ ⓣ ⓗ ⓥ ♂ ⓡ **Leisure** hard tennis courts, heated indoor swimming pool, squash, sauna, solarium, gymnasium, health and beauty spa. **Location** 1m NW of Botley on B3354

Hotel ★★★★ 69% Botley Park Hotel Golf & Country Club, Winchester Rd, Boorley Green, BOTLEY
☎ 01489 780888 100 en suite

BROCKENHURST   Map 04 SU20

Brokenhurst Manor Sway Rd SO42 7SG
☎ 01590 623332 (Secretary) ▤ 01590 624140
e-mail: pclifford@bmgcltd.freeserve.co.uk
An attractive woodland/heathland course set at the edge of the New Forest, with the unusual feature of three loops of six holes each to complete the round. Fascinating holes include the short 5th and 12th, and the 4th and 17th, both dog-legged. A stream also features on seven of the holes.
18 holes, 6222yds, Par 70, SSS 70, Course record 63.
Club membership 700.
Visitors must contact in advance, numbers limited. Must have a handicap certificate. **Societies** Thu only, apply in writing. **Green Fees** not confirmed. **Cards** ▧■■
▨ ⓩ **Prof** Bruce Parker **Course Designer** H S Colt
Facilities ⊗ ⅲ ⓑ ⓦ ♀ ♤ ⓐ ♂ **Location** 1m S on B3055

Hotel ★★ 67% Watersplash Hotel, The Rise,
BROCKENHURST ☎ 01590 622344 23 en suite

★★
The Watersplash Hotel
Brockenhurst in the New Forest

The Watersplash Hotel is recommended for its excellent food, friendly service and accommodation. Brockenhurst Manor Golf Club, situated just half a mile away, is one of ten courses within easy reach of the hotel. Personally supervised by resident proprietor Robin Foster who specialise in catering for the individual and small golf parties. Well-stocked bar and extensive wine list. All 23 bedrooms have private bathroom, colour TV, tea and coffee making facilities, direct dial telephone and radio. Four-poster Room with double Jacuzzi Bath. Heated outdoor pool in season. For further details ask for our colour brochure.

The Watersplash Hotel, The Rise,
Brockenhurst, Hampshire SO42 7ZP.
Tel: (01590) 622344 Fax: (01590) 624047
Web: watersplash.co.uk
E-mail:bookings@watersplash.co.uk

BURLEY   Map 04 SU20

Burley Cott Ln BH24 4BB
☎ 01425 402431 & 403737 ▤ 01425 402431
Undulating heather and gorseland. The 7th requires an accurately placed tee shot to obtain par 4. Played off different tees on second nine.
9 holes, 6149yds, Par 71, SSS 69, Course record 68.
Club membership 520.
Visitors must contact in advance & preferably have a handicap certificate or be a member of a recognised golf club. May not play before 4pm Sat or 8am Sun. **Societies** telephone in advance, parties up to 14 only. **Green Fees** terms on application. **Facilities** ⓑ ⓦ ♀ ♤ ♂ **Location** E side of village

Hotel ★★★ 63% Moorhill House, BURLEY
☎ 01425 403285 24 en suite

CORHAMPTON   Map 04 SU62

Corhampton Sheep's Pond Ln SO32 3LP
☎ 01489 877279 ▤ 01489 877680
e-mail: corhamptongc@netscapeonline.co.uk
Free draining downland course situated in the heart of the picturesque Meon Valley.
18 holes, 6444yds, Par 71, SSS 71.
Club membership 800.
Visitors weekdays only and must contact in advance.
Societies Mon & Thu only, contact in writing or telephone.
Green Fees £24 per 18 holes; £34 per 36 holes. **Prof** Ian Roper **Facilities** ⊗ ⅲ ⓑ ⓦ ♀ ♤ ⓐ ⓥ ♂ **Location** 1m W of Corhampton, off B3035

Hotel ★★ 68% Old House Hotel, The Square, WICKHAM
☎ 01329 833049 9 en suite

CRONDALL
Map 04 SU74

Oak Park Heath Ln GU10 5PB
☎ 01252 850850 🖩 01252 850851
e-mail: oakpark@americangolf.uk.com
Village: Gently undulating parkland course overlooking pretty village. 16-bay floodlit driving range, practice green and practice bunker. Woodland: Undulating on holes 10 to 13. Panoramic views, mature trees, very challenging.

Woodland: 18 holes, 6352yds, Par 70, SSS 70.
Village: 9 holes, 3279yds, Par 36.
Club membership 550.
Visitors restricted to members 7.30-10.30 Sat & Sun. All tee times bookable in advance. **Societies** must telephone and book in advance, min 12 persons. **Green Fees** £22 per 18 holes (£25 Fri, £32 weekends). **Cards** 🃏🃏🃏 💳 **Prof** Gary Murton **Course Designer** Patrick Dawson **Facilities** ⊗ ⌬ 🍴 🛢 💆 ♀ 🎍 🏠 🛈 🧺 🏌 Leisure gymnasium.**Conf** Max 70 Thtr 70 Class 30 Board 20 Del £37.50 * **Location** 0.5m E of village off A287 Farnham-Odiham

Hotel ★★★🏅 61% Farnham House Hotel, Alton Rd, FARNHAM ☎ 01252 716908 25 en suite

DENMEAD
Map 04 SU61

Furzeley Furzeley Rd PO7 6TX
☎ 023 92231180 🖩 023 92230921
A well laid parkland course with many features including several strategically placed lakes which provide a good test set in beautiful scenery. Straight hitting and club selection on the short holes is the key to manufacturing a low score.
18 holes, 4363yds, Par 62, SSS 61, Course record 56.
Club membership 250.
Visitors may book 2 days in advance. **Societies** must telephone in advance and confirm in writing. **Green Fees** not confirmed. **Prof** Derek Brown **Course Designer** Mark Sale/Robert Brown **Facilities** ⊗ ⌬ by prior arrangement 🛢 💆 ♀ 🎍 🏠 🛈 🏌 **Location** From Waterlooville take Hambledon Road NW and follow golf course signs

Hotel ★★★★ 65% Portsmouth Marriott Hotel, North Harbour, PORTSMOUTH ☎ 023 9238 3151 170 en suite

DIBDEN
Map 04 SU40

Dibden Main Rd SO45 5TB ☎ 023 80207508
Municipal parkland course with views over Southampton Water. A pond guards the green at the par 5, 3rd hole. Twenty-bay driving range.
Course 1: 18 holes, 5931yds, Par 70, SSS 69, Course record 64.
Course 2: 9 holes, 1520yds, Par 29.
Club membership 600.

Visitors must book in advance for 18 hole course. 9 hole is pay & play. **Societies** must contact in advance. **Green Fees** not confirmed. **Prof** Paul Smith & John Slade **Course Designer** Hamilton Stutt **Facilities** ⊗ ⌬ 🛢 💆 ♀ 🎍 🏠 🏌 🛈 **Location** 2m NW of Dibden Purlieu, off A326 to Hythe

Hotel ★★★ 66% Forest Lodge Hotel, Pikes Hill, Romsey Rd, LYNDHURST ☎ 023 8028 3677 28 en suite

EASTLEIGH
Map 04 SU41

Fleming Park Passfield Av SO50 9NL
☎ 023 80612797 🖩 023 80651686
Parkland course with stream - 'Monks Brook' - running through.
18 holes, 4436yds, Par 65, SSS 62, Course record 62.
Club membership 300.
Visitors must contact in advance, no restrictions. **Societies** must contact in advance. **Green Fees** not confirmed. **Cards** 🃏🃏🃏🃏 💳 **Prof** Chris Strickett **Course Designer** David Miller **Facilities** ⊗ ⌬ 🛢 💆 ♀ 🎍 🏠 🛈 🏌 🧺 🏌 **Leisure** hard and grass tennis courts, heated indoor swimming pool, squash, sauna, solarium, gymnasium. **Location** E side of town centre

Hotel ★★★ 68% Holiday Inn Eastleigh, Leigh Rd, EASTLEIGH ☎ 0870 400 9075 120 en suite

EAST WELLOW
Map 04 SU32

Wellow Ryedown Ln SO51 6BD
☎ 01794 323833 & 322872 🖩 01794 323832
Three 9-hole courses set in 217 acres of parkland surrounding Embley Park, former home of Florence Nightingale.
Ryedown & Embley: 18 holes, 5966yds, Par 70, SSS 69, Course record 65.
Embley & Blackwater: 18 holes, 6295yds, Par 72, SSS 70.
Blackwater & Ryedown: 18 holes, 5819yds, Par 70, SSS 68.
Club membership 600.
Visitors advisable to contact in advance weekdays only. **Societies** telephone in advance, Mon-Fri not bank holidays. **Green Fees** £17 per 18 holes (£21 weekends and bank holidays). **Prof** Neil Bratley **Course Designer** W Wiltshire **Facilities** ⊗ ⌬ 🛢 💆 ♀ 🎍 🏠 🧺 🏌 **Leisure** gymnasium. **Conf** Max 100 Board 70 Banquet 100 **Location** Exit2 of M27, then A36 to Salisbury then 1m right

Hotel ★★★ 62% The White Horse, Market Place, ROMSEY ☎ 0870 400 8123 26 en suite 7 annexe en suite

FAREHAM
Map 04 SU50

Cams Hall Cams Hall Estate PO16 8UP
☎ 01329 827222 🖩 01329 827111
e-mail: camshall@americangolf.co.uk
Two Peter Alliss/Clive Clark designed golf courses. The Creek Course is coastal and has salt and fresh water lakes and the fairways are lined with undulating hills. The Park Course is designed in the grounds of Cams Hall.
Creek Course: 18 holes, 6244yds, Par 71, SSS 70, Course record 69.
Park Course: 9 holes, 3247yds, Par 36, SSS 36.
Club membership 950.
Visitors must contact in advance, tee times available any time. **Societies** telephone for details and society golf day pack. **Green Fees** terms on application. **Cards** 🃏🃏🃏 💳 **Prof** Jason Neve **Course Designer** Peter Alliss **Facilities** ⊗ ⌬ 🛢 💆 ♀ 🎍 🏠 🛈 🧺 🏌 🏌 **Leisure** sauna. **Location** M27 exit 11 to A27

continued

continued

Hotel ★★★ 65% Lysses House Hotel, 51 High St, FAREHAM ☎ 01329 822622 21 en suite

FARNBOROUGH — Map 04 SU85

Southwood Ively Rd, Cove GU14 0LJ
☎ 01252 548700 📠 01252 515855
Municipal parkland course with stream running through.
18 holes, 5738yds, Par 69, SSS 68, Course record 61.
Club membership 650.
Visitors must book in advance. **Societies** must contact in advance. **Green Fees** not confirmed. **Cards** 🖃 🖃 🖃 🖃
🎫 **Prof** Bob Hammond **Course Designer** Hawtree & Son
Facilities ⚒ 🍴 🛈 🍴 🦮 🏌 **Location** 0.5m W

Hotel ★★★ 69% Holiday Inn Farnborough, Lynchford Rd, FARNBOROUGH ☎ 0870 400 9029 143 en suite

FLEET — Map 04 SU85

North Hants Minley Rd GU51 1RF
☎ 01252 616443 📠 01252 811627
e-mail: secretary@north-hants-fleetgc.co.uk
Picturesque tree-lined course with much heather and gorse close to the fairways. A comparatively easy par 4 first hole may lull the golfer into a false sense of security, only to be rudely awakened at the testing holes which follow. The ground is rather undulating and, though not tiring, does offer some excellent 'blind' shots, and more than a few surprises in judging distance.

18 holes, 6519yds, Par 71, SSS 72.
Club membership 600.
Visitors must contact at least 48 hours in advance. Must play with member at weekends. **Societies** Tue & Wed only. Subject to pre-booking. **Green Fees** terms on application. **Prof** Steve Porter **Course Designer** James Braid **Facilities** ⊗ 🎿 🍴 🍺 🏌 🛈 🍴 🏌 **Location** 0.25m N of Fleet station on B3013

Hotel ★★★ 63% Lismoyne Hotel, Church Rd, FLEET ☎ 01252 628555 62 en suite

GOSPORT — Map 04 SZ69

Gosport & Stokes Bay Off Fort Rd, Haslar PO12 2AT ☎ 023 92527941 📠 023 92527941
A testing links course overlooking the Solent, with plenty of gorse and short rough. Changing winds.
9 holes, 5999yds, Par 70, SSS 69, Course record 65.
Club membership 499.
Visitors may not play Sun and Thu. **Societies** must contact in writing. **Green Fees** terms on application. **Facilities** 🎿 🍺 🍴 🍴 🍴 🏌 **Location** A32 S from Fareham, E on Fort rd to Haslar

Hotel ★★★ 62% Belle Vue Hotel, 39 Marine Pde East, Lee-on-Solent, GOSPORT ☎ 023 9255 0258 24 en suite 3 annexe en suite

HARTLEY WINTNEY — Map 04 SU75

Hartley Wintney London Rd RG27 8PT
☎ 01252 844211 (Sec) & 843779 (Prof) 📠 01252 844211
Easy walking, parkland course in pleasant countryside. Played off different tees on back nine, with testing par 4s at 4th and 13th.
18 holes, 6240yds, Par 71, SSS 71, Course record 63.
Club membership 750.
Visitors must contact in advance, restricted at weekends. **Societies** Tue & Thu only by prior arrangement. **Green Fees** terms on application. **Prof** Martin Smith **Facilities** ⊗ 🍺 🍱 🍴 🏌 **Location** NE side of village on A30

Hotel ★★★ 63% Lismoyne Hotel, Church Rd, FLEET ☎ 01252 628555 62 en suite

HAYLING ISLAND — Map 04 SU70

Hayling Links Ln PO11 0BX
☎ 023 92464446 📠 023 92464446
e-mail: hgcltd@aol.com
A delightful links course among the dunes offering fine sea-scapes and views across to the Isle of Wight. Varying sea breezes and sometimes strong winds ensure that the course seldom plays the same two days running. Testing holes at the 12th and 13th, both par 4. Club selection is important.
18 holes, 6531yds, Par 71, SSS 71, Course record 65.
Club membership 900.
Visitors must contact in advance by telephone or in writing and have a handicap certificate, no jeans, denims or collarless shirts allowed. **Societies** welcome Tue & Wed, or half days Mon & Thu, apply in writing or telephone. **Green Fees** £44 per day; £36 per round (£50 per round weekends). **Cards** 🖃 🖃 🖃 🎫 **Prof** Raymond Gadd **Course Designer** Taylor 1905, Simpson 1933 **Facilities** ⊗ 🎿 🍺 🍱 ⚒ 🍴 🍴 🏌 **Conf** Max 40 Board 20 **Location** SW side of island at West Town

Hotel ★★★ 68% Brookfield Hotel, Havant Rd, EMSWORTH ☎ 01243 373363 & 376383 📠 01243 376342 40 en suite

KINGSCLERE — Map 04 SU55

Sandford Springs Wolverton RG26 5RT
☎ 01635 296800 & 296808 (Pro Shop) 📠 01635 296801
The course has unique variety in beautiful surroundings and offers three distinctive loops of 9 holes. There are water hazards, woodlands and gradients to negotiate, providing a challenge for all playing categories.
The Park: 9 holes, 2963yds, Par 34.
The Lakes: 9 holes, 3042yds, Par 35.
The Wood: 9 holes, 3180yds, Par 36.
Club membership 650.
Visitors must contact in advance. Restricted at weekends. **Societies** must contact in advance. **Green Fees** not confirmed. **Cards** 🖃 🖃 🖃 🎫 **Prof** Gary Edmunds/Kim Brake **Course Designer** Hawtree & Son **Facilities** ⊗ 🎿 🍺 🍱 ⚒ 🍴 🍴 🏌 **Location** On A339 between Basingstoke and Newbury

Hotel ★★★ 65% The Chequers, 6-8 Oxford St, NEWBURY ☎ 01635 38000 46 en suite 10 annexe en suite

continued

KINGSLEY   Map 04 SU73

Dean Farm GU35 9NG ☎ 01420 489478 & 472313
Undulating downland course.
9 holes, 1500yds, Par 29.
Visitors no restrictions. **Societies** telephone to book. **Green
Fees** £5.50 per 9 holes. **Cards** ▣ **Facilities** ⊗ ⋈ ᛒ ♥ ♀ ⌨
ⴵ ♂ **Leisure** hard tennis courts. **Location** W side of village
off B3004

Hotel ★★★ 68% Alton Grange Hotel, London Rd, ALTON
☎ 01420 86565 26 en suite 4 annexe en suite

LECKFORD   Map 04 SU33

Leckford SO20 6JF ☎ 01264 810320 ▤ 01264 811122
e-mail: golf@leckfordestate.co.uk
A testing downland course with good views.
Old Course: 9 holes, 6444yds, Par 70, SSS 71.
New Course: 9 holes, 4562yds, Par 66, SSS 62.
Club membership 200.
Visitors Phone Secretary/Manager. **Societies** phone
Secretary/Manager **Green Fees** £10 per day (£14 weekends
& bank holidays). **Prof** Tony Ashton **Facilities** ♥ ᛒ ♂
Location 1m SW off A3057

Hotel ★★★ 70% Fifehead Manor, MIDDLE WALLOP
☎ 01264 781565 8 en suite 8 annexe en suite

LEE-ON-THE-SOLENT   Map 04 SU50

Lee-on-Solent Brune Ln PO13 9PB
☎ 023 92551170 ▤ 023 92554233
e-mail: leegolfclub@yahoo.com
A modest parkland/heathland course, yet a testing one.
The five short holes always demand a high standard of

continued

play and the 13th is rated one of the best in the country.
The last 6 holes are amongst the most difficult in
Hampshire.
18 holes, 5933yds, Par 69, SSS 69, Course record 64.
Club membership 750.
Visitors may not play before 9am or after 2.30pm on
weekends. Handicap certificate required. **Societies** must
contact in advance. **Green Fees** not confirmed. **Cards** ▦
▦ ▧ ▣ **Prof** John Richardson **Facilities** ⊗ ⋈ ᛒ ♥ ♀
⛳ 🏠 ♂ ☖ **Location** 1m N off B3385

Hotel ★★★ 62% Belle Vue Hotel, 39 Marine Pde East,
Lee-on-Solent, GOSPORT ☎ 023 9255 0258
24 en suite 3 annexe en suite

LIPHOOK   Map 04 SU83

Liphook Wheatsheaf Enclosure GU30 7EH
☎ 01428 723271 & 723785 ▤ 01428 724853
e-mail: liphookgolfclub@btconnect.com
Heathland course with easy walking and fine views.
18 holes, 6167yds, Par 70, SSS 69, Course record 67.
Club membership 800.
Visitors must contact in advance; may not play Tue,
competition days etc. **Societies** Wed-Fri only. Must
contact in advance. **Green Fees** £42 per day; £35 per
round (£53/£45 Sat) £53 Sun and bank holidays. **Prof**
Geoffrey Lee **Course Designer** A C Croome **Facilities** ⊗
ᛒ ♥ ♀ ☖ 🏠 ⛳ ⚑ ♂ **Location** 1m S on B2030 (old
A3)

Hotel ★★★★ 65% Lythe Hill Hotel, Petworth Rd,
HASLEMERE ☎ 01428 651251 41 en suite

The Perfect Setting

Different

Why? Because at Old Thorns, we
specialise in creating the most relaxing
experience possible. Whether it be for a
sales conference or a quiet weekend for
two, our facilities and atmosphere are
unique.

Set in 400 acres of rolling Hampshire
countryside, Old Thorns is one of Southern
England's most picturesque country house
hotels. Originally a 17th-century farmhouse, it
is now a cosy hotel that overlooks it's own 18-
hole championship golf course. Two superb
restaurants, including the award winning
Japanese Nippon Kan and a first-class Country
Club with swimming pool, sauna, solarium,
tennis courts and a fully equipped gymnasium
complete this charming hotel.

For more information please call us on
01428 724555 or visit our website.

OLD THORNS
HOTEL, GOLF & COUNTRY CLUB

Griggs Green, Liphook, Hampshire GU30 7PE
Tel: (01428) 724555   Fax: (01428) 725036
Website: www.oldthorns.com   Email: info@oldthorns.com

Old Thorns Hotel, Golf & Country Club
Griggs Green GU30 7PE
☎ 01428 724555 ▤ 01428 725036
e-mail: generalmanager@oldthorns.freeserve.co.uk
A challenging 18-hole championship-standard course
designed around magnificent oaks, beeches, Scots pine
and lakes.
18 holes, 6581yds, Par 72, SSS 71, Course record 69.
Club membership 250.
Visitors subject to availability. **Societies** must telephone
in advance. **Green Fees** terms on application. **Cards** 💳
■■ ▦ ⬜ ▨ ⬜ **Prof** Kieron Stevenson **Course**
Designer Peter Alliss/Dave Thomas **Facilities** ⊗ ⫿⫿⫿ ⬛
🍺 ⬜ 🧑 🏠 ⛽ 🚗 🛒 ✓ **Leisure** hard tennis courts,
heated indoor swimming pool, sauna, solarium,
gymnasium. **Location** Leave A3 at Griggs Green, S of
Liphook, signposted 'Old Thorns'
See advertisement on page 117

Hotel ★★★ 71% Old Thorns Hotel, Golf & Country
Club, Longmoor Rd, Griggs Green, LIPHOOK
☎ 01428 724555 29 en suite 4 annexe en suite

Bramshaw Brook SO43 7HE
☎ 023 80813433 ▤ 023 80813460
e-mail: golf@bramshaw.co.uk
Two 18-hole courses. The Manor Course is landscaped
parkland with excellent greens, and features mature
trees and streams. The Forest course is set amidst
beautiful open forest. Easy walking. The Bell Inn
Hotel, attached to the club, provides fine
accommodation just a wedge shot from the first tee,
and reserved tee times for its guests.
Manor Course: 18 holes, 6517yds, Par 71, SSS 71,
Course record 65.
Forest Course: 18 holes, 5774yds, Par 69, SSS 68,
Course record 65.
Club membership 950.
Visitors limited availability weekends and bank holidays
unless accompanied by member or resident of Bell Inn.
Phone in advance. **Societies** apply in writing or telephone
in advance. **Green Fees** Manor course £32; Forest course
£27 (£35/£30 weekends). Both courses £47 per day.
Reduced winter rates. **Prof** Clive Bonner **Facilities** ⊗ ⫿⫿⫿
⬛ 🍺 ⬜ 🧑 🏠 ⛽ 🚗 🛒 ✓
Location On B3079 1m W of M27 junc 1

Hotel ★★★ 67% Bell Inn, BROOK
☎ 023 8081 2214 25 en suite

New Forest Southampton Rd SO43 7BU
☎ 023 8028 2752 ▤ 023 8028 2484
e-mail: barbara@nfgc.sagehost.co.uk
This picturesque heathland course is laid out in a
typical stretch of the New Forest on high ground a
little above the village of Lyndhurst. Natural hazards
include the inevitable forest ponies. The first two holes
are somewhat teasing, as is the 485-yard (par 5) 9th.
Walking is easy.
18 holes, 5742yds, Par 69, SSS 68.
Club membership 600.
Visitors must contact in advance, dress code applies.
Societies must contact in advance. **Green Fees** terms on
application. **Prof** Danny Harris **Facilities** ⊗ ⫿⫿⫿ by prior
arrangement ⬛ 🍺 ⬜ 🧑 🏠 ✓ **Location** 0.5m NE off
A35)

Hotel ★★★ 68% Crown Hotel, High St, LYNDHURST
☎ 023 8028 2922 39 en suite

Chewton Glen Hotel Christchurch Rd BH25 6QS
☎ 01425 275341 ▤ 01425 272310
e-mail: reservations@chewtonglen.com
A 9-hole, par 3 course with the hotel grounds plus a
practice area. ONLY open to residents of the hotel or as a
guest of a member of the club.
9 holes, 854yds, Par 27.
Club membership 150.
Visitors non residents must play with member. **Societies**
must contact in advance. **Green Fees** terms on application.
Cards 💳 ■■ ▦ ⬜ ▨ ⬜ **Facilities** ⊗ by prior
arrangement ⫿⫿⫿ by prior arrangement 🍺 ⬜ 🧑 🏠 ✓ **Leisure**
hard tennis courts, outdoor and indoor heated swimming
pools, sauna, gymnasium, Health Club, Croquet Lawn,
Indoor Tennis Centre.**Conf** Max 80 Thtr 120 Class 60 Board
30 Banquet 120 **Location** M27 to A31. Through Emmery
Down to A35, right on A35 toward Christchurch. In Huton
left at staggered junct, through Walkford. Golf course on left

Hotel ★★★★★⬛ Chewton Glen Hotel, Christchurch Rd,
NEW MILTON ☎ 01425 275341 62 en suite

Test Valley Micheldever Rd RG25 3DS
☎ 01256 771737 ▤ 01256 770916
A downland course with excellent drainage, fine year-
round greens and prominent water and bunker features.
On undulating terrain with lovely views over the
Hampshire countryside. Has hosted the Hampshire Open
and the PGA Lombard Trophy.
18 holes, 6165yds, Par 72, SSS 69.
Club membership 500.
Visitors must phone in advance. Must play after 11am
weekends & bank holidays. **Societies** apply in writing or
telephone in advance. **Green Fees** not confirmed. **Cards** 💳
■■ ▨ ⬜ **Prof** Alastair Briggs **Course Designer** Don Wright
Facilities ⊗ ⫿⫿⫿ ⬛ 🍺 ⬜ 🧑 🏠 ⛽ 🚗 🛒 ✓ **Location** 1.5m
N of A303 on road to Overton

Hotel ★★★ 71% The Hampshire Centrecourt Hotel, Centre
Dr, Chineham, BASINGSTOKE
☎ 01256 816664 50 en suite

OWER
Map 04 SU31

Paultons Golf Centre Old Salisbury Rd SO51 6AN
☎ 023 80813992 🖥 023 8081 3993
e-mail: paultons@americangolf.uk.com
A Pay and Play parkland/woodland 18-hole course built within the original Paultons parkland which was laid out by 'Capability' Brown. The water features on four of the holes and the tree-lined fairways challenge the ability off all golfers. There is also a 9-hole academy course, ideal for beginners or players wishing to improve their short games as well as a 20-bay floodlit driving range.
27 holes, 6238yds, Par 71, SSS 70, Course record 67.
Club membership 500.
Visitors can book up to 7 days in advance. Societies telephone for details. Green Fees £16 per 18 holes (£20 weekends). Cards ⬛ 🟥 🔲 🟦 🔳 🟢 Prof Mark Williamson/Mark Patience Course Designer J R Smith Facilities ⊗ 🎖 ᖯ ⚐ ♀ ⚲ 🛍 ⚐ 🍴 🥂 ⚐ 🍴 Leisure 9 hole academy course.Conf Max 100 Thtr 100 Class 15 Board 24 Banquet 70 Location M27 junct 2, A36 towards Salisbury, at 1st rdbt 1st exit, then 1st right at Vine public house

Hotel ★★★ 71% Bartley Lodge, Lyndhurst Rd, CADNAM ☎ 023 8081 2248 31 en suite

PETERSFIELD
Map 04 SU72

Petersfield (New Course) Tankerdale Ln, Liss
GU33 7QY ☎ 01730 895165 (office) & 895216 (pro)
🖥 01730 894713
e-mail: richard@petersfieldgolfclub.co.uk
Gently undulating course with mature trees and hedgerows. All the advantages of a course recently built to USGA specifications.
18 holes, 6387yds, Par 72, SSS 71, Course record 68.
Club membership 725.
Visitors start times required at weekends, may play only after 12pm weekends Societies booking forms and deposit required. Green Fees terms on application. Prof Greg Hughes Course Designer M Hawtree Facilities ⊗ 🎖 ᖯ ⚲ 🛍 🚜 ⚐ Location Off the A3 (M), between the Liss/Petersfield exits southbound

Hotel ★★★♨ 68% Southdowns Country Hotel, Dumpford Ln, Trotton, MIDHURST ☎ 01730 821521 20 en suite

Petersfield (Old Course) Sussex Rd GU31 4EJ
☎ 01730 267732 🖥 01730 894713
9 hole parkland course on level ground in an area of outstanding natural beauty. Numerous trees and water features. Part of Petersfield Golf Club although 1.5m away from the 18 hole New Course.
9 holes, 3005yds, Par 72, SSS 69.
Visitors starting times required, pay & play at all times. Societies booking form must be completed & deposit paid. Green Fees terms on application. Prof Greg Hughes Facilities 🍴 🥂 ♀ ⚐ Location Off Sussex Road , B214

Hotel ★★★♨ 68% Southdowns Country Hotel, Dumpford Ln, Trotton, MIDHURST ☎ 01730 821521 20 en suite

PORTSMOUTH
Map 04 SU60

Great Salterns Public Course Burrfields Rd
PO3 5HH ☎ 023 92664549 🖥 023 92650525
Easy walking, seaside course with open fairways and testing shots onto well-guarded, small greens. Testing 13th hole, par 4, requiring 130yd shot across a lake.

continued

Great Salterns Golf Course: 18 holes, 5575yds, Par 70, SSS 67, Course record 64.
Club membership 700.
Visitors book up to 1 week in advance. Societies must contact in advance. Green Fees £10.50 per round (£13.50 weekends). Cards ⬛ 🟥 🔲 🟦 🔳 🟢 Prof Terry Healy Facilities ⊗ 🎖 ᖯ ♀ 🛍 ⚐ 🍴 🥂 🍴 Location NE of town centre on A2030

Hotel ★★★ 64% Innlodge Hotel, Burrfields Rd, PORTSMOUTH ☎ 023 9265 0510 74 en suite

Southsea The Clubhouse, Burrfields Rd PO3 5JJ
☎ 023 92664549 🖥 023 92668667
Municipal, meadowland course.
Great Salterns: 18 holes, 5800yds, Par 71, SSS 68, Course record 64.
Club membership 400.
Visitors no restrictions. Booking advisable via pro shop. Societies must contact in advance. Green Fees not confirmed. Cards ⬛ 🟥 🔲 🟦 🔳 🟢 Prof Terry Healy Facilities 🛍 ⚐ ⚐ 🍴 Location 0.5m off M27

Hotel ★★★ 64% Innlodge Hotel, Burrfields Rd, PORTSMOUTH ☎ 023 9265 0510 74 en suite

ROMSEY
Map 04 SU32

Dunwood Manor Danes Rd, Awbridge SO51 0GF
☎ 01794 340549 🖥 01794 341215
e-mail: admin@dunwood-golf.co.uk
Undulating parkland course with fine views. Fine holes running through mature woodland.
18 holes, 5767yds, Par 69, SSS 68, Course record 65.
Club membership 620.
Visitors always welcome advisable to contact in advance; essential for weekends after 11am. Societies must contact in advance. Green Fees £37 per day; £25 per round. Prof Heath Teschner Facilities ⊗ 🎖 ᖯ ♀ 🛍 🚜 🥂 🍴 ⚐ ⚐ Location 4m W off A27

Hotel ★★★ 67% Bell Inn, BROOK ☎ 023 8081 2214 25 en suite

Romsey Romsey Rd, Nursling SO16 0XW
☎ 023 80734637 🖥 023 80741036
e-mail: sally@romseygolf.co.uk
Parkland/woodland course with narrow tree-lined fairways. Six holes are undulating, rest are sloping. There are superb views over the Test valley.
18 holes, 5851yds, Par 69, SSS 68.
Club membership 800.
Visitors welcome Mon-Fri, must play with member weekends and bank holidays. Societies Mon, Tue & Thu, must contact in advance. Green Fees £26. Prof Mark Desmond Facilities ⊗ 🎖 ᖯ ♀ 🛍 ⚐ Conf Max 100 Thtr 100 Location 3m S on A3057 or 1m N off M27 junct 3

Hotel ★★★ 62% The White Horse, Market Place, ROMSEY ☎ 0870 400 8123 26 en suite 7 annexe en suite

ROTHERWICK
Map 04 SU75

Tylney Park RG27 9AY
☎ 01256 762079 🖥 01256 763079
A very scenic parkland course with many trees and a practice area.
18 holes, 6109yds, Par 70, SSS 69, Course record 66.
Club membership 730.

continued

Visitors must be with member at weekends or have a handicap certificate. Societies must apply by phone in advance. Green Fees £26 (£33 weekends). Cards 🌐 💳 📶 🖳 Prof Chris de Bruin Course Designer W Wiltshire Facilities ⊗ 🝆 by prior arrangement 🝆 ♨ ♟ ⛳ 🏌 Location 0.5m SW of Rotherwick, 2m NW of Hook, 2.5m from M3 junct 5 via Newnham

Hotel ★★★★💤 Tylney Hall Hotel, ROTHERWICK ☎ 01256 764881 35 en suite 75 annexe en suite

ROWLANDS CASTLE   Map 04 SU71

Rowlands Castle 31 Links Ln PO9 6AE
☎ 023 92412784 📋 023 92413649
e-mail: manager@rowlandscastlegolfclub.co.uk
Reasonably dry in winter, the flat parkland course is a testing one with a number of tricky dog-legs and bunkers much in evidence. The par 4 13th is a signature hole necessitating a drive to a narrow fairway and a second shot to a two-tiered green. The 7th, at 522yds, is the longest hole on the course and leads to a well-guarded armchair green.
18 holes, 6612yds, Par 72, SSS 72, Course record 68. Club membership 800.
Visitors may not play Sat; must contact in advance and hold a handicap certificate. Societies Tue & Thu only; must contact in writing. Green Fees £30 per day/round (£35 Sundays). Cards 💳 Prof Peter Klepacz Course Designer Colt Facilities ⊗ 🝆 🝆 ♨ ♟ ⛳ 🏌 🐾 Location W side of village off B2149

Hotel ★★★ 68% Brookfield Hotel, Havant Rd, EMSWORTH ☎ 01243 373363 & 376383 📋 01243 376342 40 en suite

SHEDFIELD   Map 04 SU51

Marriott Meon Valley Hotel & Country Club Sandy Ln SO32 2HQ
☎ 01329 833455 📋 01329 834411
It has been said that a golf course architect is as good as the ground on which he has to work. Here Hamilton Stutt had magnificent terrain at his disposal and a very good and lovely parkland course is the result. There are three holes over water. The hotel provides many sports facilities.
Meon Course: 18 holes, 6520yds, Par 71, SSS 71, Course record 66.
Valley Course: 9 holes, 2721yds, Par 35, SSS 33.
Club membership 700.
Visitors may book up to seven days in advance. Societies telephone in advance, written confirmation. Green Fees terms on application. Cards 🌐 📶 💳 📶 🖳 Prof Rod Cameron Course Designer Hamilton Stutt Facilities ⊗ 🝆 🝆 🝆 ♨ ♟ ⛳ 🏌 🐾 ⛳ 🏌 Leisure hard tennis courts, heated indoor swimming pool, sauna, solarium, gymnasium, health & beauty salon, spa bath, aerobics studio. Location Off A334 between Botley and Wickham. Access via junct 7 M27

Hotel ★★★★ 65% Marriott Meon Valley Hotel & Country Club, Sandy Ln, SHEDFIELD ☎ 01329 833455 113 en suite

Where to stay, where to eat?
Visit www.theAA.com

SOUTHAMPTON   Map 04 SU41

Chilworth Main Rd, Chilworth SO16 7JP
☎ 023 80740544
A course with two loops of nine holes, with a booking system to allow undisturbed play. The front nine are fairly long and undulating and include water hazards. The back nine are tighter and quite a challenge.
Manor Golf Course: 18 holes, 5837yds, Par 69, SSS 69, Course record 68. Club membership 600.
Visitors no restrictions. Societies telephone in advance and complete booking form, various packages available. Green Fees £12 per 18 holes; £6 per 9 holes (£15/£7.50 weekends). Cards 🌐 💳 📶 📶 📶 🖳 Course Designer J Garner Facilities ⊗ 🝆 🝆 🝆 ♨ ♟ ⛳ 🏌 Location A27 between Chilworth and Romsey

Hotel ★★★ 64% Highfield House, Highfield Ln, Portswood, SOUTHAMPTON ☎ 023 8035 9955 66 en suite

Southampton Golf Course Rd, Bassett SO16 7LE
☎ 023 80760478 & 80760546 (booking) 📋 023 80760472
e-mail: golf.course@southampton.gov.uk
This beautiful municipal parkland course always ensures a good game, fast in summer, slow in winter. Three par 4s over 450 yds.
18 holes, 6103yds, Par 69, SSS 70.
9 holes, 2395yds, Par 33.
Visitors 18 hole course: min 2 players (3 weekends and bank holidays) booking advisable but not always necessary. 9 hole course: 1-4 players per tee Societies welcome, book up to 1yr in advance. Green Fees terms on application by ringing 023 807 60546. Prof Richard Benfield Course Designer Halmree/A P Taylor Facilities ⊗ 🝆 🝆 🝆 ♨ ♟ ⛳ 🏌 🏌 Location 4m N of city centre off A33

Hotel ★★ 63% The Star Hotel & Restaurant, 26 High St, SOUTHAMPTON ☎ 023 8033 9939 43 rms (37 en suite)

Stoneham Monks Wood Close, Bassett SO16 3TT
☎ 023 80769272 📋 023 80766320
e-mail: stonehamgc@stoneham09.freeserve.co.uk
A hilly, heather course with sand or peat sub-soil; the fairways are separated by belts of woodland and heather to present a varied terrain. The interesting 4th is a difficult par 4 and the fine 11th has cross-bunkers about 150 yards from the tee.
18 holes, 6387yds, Par 72, SSS 70, Course record 63. Club membership 800.
Visitors advisable to contact in advance, handicap certificate required. Societies Mon, Thu & Fri only. Must telephone in advance or apply in writing. Green Fees £36 per day; £32 per 18 holes(£55/£44 weekends). Cards 🌐 📶 📶 📶 🖳 Prof Ian Young Course Designer Willie Park Facilities ⊗ 🝆 🝆 🝆 ♨ ♟ ⛳ 🏌 Location 4m N of city centre off A27

Hotel ★★★ 64% Highfield House, Highfield Ln, Portswood, SOUTHAMPTON ☎ 023 8035 9955 66 en suite

SOUTHWICK   Map 04 SU60

Southwick Park Naval Recreation Centre
Pinsley Dr PO17 6EL ☎ 023 92380131 📋 023 92210289
Set in 100 acres of parkland.
18 holes, 5884yds, Par 69, SSS 69, Course record 64. Club membership 700.

continued

Visitors contact in advance, welcome weekends after 2pm **Societies** Tue only, telephone in advance. **Green Fees** terms on application. **Prof** John Green **Course Designer** C Lawrie **Facilities** ⊗ ⅷ ⓛ ▆ ♀ ⚐ 🏠 ↑ ∅ **Location** 0.5m SE off B2177

Hotel ★★ 68% Old House Hotel, The Square, WICKHAM ☎ 01329 833049 9 en suite

TADLEY   Map 04 SU66

Bishopswood Bishopswood Ln RG26 4AT
☎ 0118 9812200 📠 0118 9408606
e-mail: bishopswood@hampshiregolf.u-net.com
Wooded course, fairly tight, with stream and natural water hazards.
9 holes, 6474yds, Par 72, SSS 71, Course record 66.
Club membership 400.
Visitors must contact in advance. No play weekends or bank holidays. **Societies** must contact by telephone. **Green Fees** £11 per 9 holes; £16.50 per 18 holes. **Cards** 🔲 💳 **Prof** Steve Ward **Course Designer** M W Phillips/G Blake **Facilities** ⊗ ⅷ ⓛ ▆ ♀ ⚐ 🏠 ∅ ↑ **Location** 6m N of Basingstoke off the A340

Hotel ★★★ 74% Romans Country House Hotel, Little London Rd, SILCHESTER ☎ 0118 970 0421
11 en suite 14 annexe en suite

WATERLOOVILLE   Map 04 SU60

Portsmouth Crookhorn Ln, Purbrook PO7 5QL
☎ 023 92372210 📠 023 92200766
Hilly, challenging course with good views of Portsmouth Harbour. Rarely free from the wind and the picturesque 6th, 17th and 18th holes can test the best.
18 holes, 6139yds, Par 69, SSS 70, Course record 64.
Club membership 600.
Visitors must book in advance. **Societies** must book in advance, in writing or by telephone. **Green Fees** £10.50 per 18 holes (£13.50 weekends); £7 per 9 holes(£8 weekends). **Cards** 🔲 💳 **Prof** Jason Banting **Course Designer** Hawtree **Facilities** ⊗ ⅷ ⓛ ▆ ♀ ⚐ 🏠 ↑ **Conf** Max 15 **Location** 2m S, off A3

Hotel ★★★★ 65% Portsmouth Marriott Hotel, North Harbour, PORTSMOUTH ☎ 023 9238 3151 170 en suite

Waterlooville Cherry Tree Av, Cowplain PO8 8AP
☎ 023 92263388 📠 023 92347513
e-mail: secretary@waterloovillegolfclub.co.uk
Parkland course, easy walking. Challenging course with 5 par 5s over 500 yards and featuring four ponds and a stream running through.
18 holes, 6602yds, Par 72, SSS 72, Course record 64.
Club membership 800.
Visitors must contact in advance & may only play on weekdays. Handicap certificate required. **Societies** Thu only; apply by letter or telephone. **Green Fees** £30 per round;£35 per day. **Prof** John Hay **Course Designer** Henry Cotton **Facilities** ⊗ ⅷ ⓛ ▆ ♀ ⚐ ∅ **Location** NE side of town centre off A3

Hotel ★★★ 68% Brookfield Hotel, Havant Rd, EMSWORTH ☎ 01243 373363 & 376383
📠 01243 376342 40 en suite

Looking for a driving range?
See the index at the back of the guide

WICKHAM   Map 04 SU51

Wickham Park Titchfield Ln PO17 5PJ
☎ 01329 833342 📠 01329 834798
e-mail: wpgc@crownsportsplc.com
An attractive 18 hole parkland course set in the Meon Valley. Ideal for beginners and established golfers alike. The course is not overly demanding but is challenging enough to provide an enjoyable round of golf.
18 holes, 5898yds, Par 70, SSS 68, Course record 69.
Club membership 600.
Visitors may book up to 7 days in advance. May play after 9.30am at weekends. **Societies** weekdays/weekends after noon. **Green Fees** £13 per round (£16 weekends). **Cards** 🔲 💳 **Prof** Scott Edwards **Facilities** ⓛ ▆ ♀ ⚐ 🏠 ↑ ∅ **Leisure** driving net, chipping area.

Hotel ★★ 68% Old House Hotel, The Square, WICKHAM ☎ 01329 833049 9 en suite

WINCHESTER   Map 04 SU42

Hockley Twyford SO21 1PL
☎ 01962 713165 📠 01962 713612
e-mail: hockleygolfclub@aol.com
Downland course with good views.
18 holes, 6336yds, Par 71, SSS 70, Course record 64.
Club membership 750.
Visitors are advised to phone in advance. Restricted times at weekends. Handicap certificate required. **Societies** must telephone in advance and confirm in writing with deposit. **Green Fees** £33 per round;£42 per day (£45 per round weekends). **Prof** Terry Lane **Course Designer** James Braid **Facilities** ⊗ ⅷ ⓛ ▆ ♀ ⚐ 🏠 ♨ ∅ **Location** Jct 11 M3, follow sign to Twyford

Hotel ★★★★ 65% The Wessex, Paternoster Row, WINCHESTER ☎ 0870 400 8126 94 en suite

Royal Winchester Sarum Rd SO22 5QE
☎ 01962 852462 📠 01962 865048
e-mail: royalwinchestergolfclub.com
The Royal Winchester course is a sporting downland course centred on a rolling valley, so the course is hilly in places. Royal Winchester must be included in any list of notable clubs, because of its age (it dates from 1888) and also because the club was involved in one of the very first professional matches.
18 holes, 6204yds, Par 71, SSS 70, Course record 65.
Club membership 800.
Visitors must play with member at weekends. Must contact in advance and have a handicap certificate. **Societies** must contact in writing or by telephone. **Green Fees** terms on application. **Prof** Steven Hunter **Course Designer** J H Taylor **Facilities** ⊗ ⅷ ⓛ ▆ ♀ ⚐ 🏠 ∅ **Location** 1.5m W off A3090

Hotel ★★★★🍴 77% Lainston House Hotel, Sparsholt, WINCHESTER ☎ 01962 863588 41 en suite

South Winchester Romsey Rd SO22 5QW
☎ 01962 877800 📠 01962 877900
e-mail: w.sheffield@crownsportsplc.com
This Dave Thomas designed course incorporates downland, meadows and seven lakes. Home of the Hampshire PGA and the venue for European Ladies Tour Pro-Ams.
18 holes, 7086yds, Par 72, SSS 74, Course record 68.
Club membership 750.

continued

South Winchester Golf Club

Visitors guests only by arrangement. **Societies** must contact in advance. **Green Fees** £25 (£40 weekends after 11pm). **Cards** **Prof** Richard Adams **Course Designer** Dave Thomas **Facilities** **Leisure** beauty rooms.**Conf** Max 60 Del £100 to £200 * **Location** M3 junct 11,on A3090 Romsey road

Hotel ★★★ 73% The Winchester Royal, Saint Peter St, WINCHESTER ☎ 01962 840840 75 en suite

HEREFORDSHIRE

CLIFFORD

Summerhill HR3 5EW ☎ 01497 820451

Undulating parkland course set deep in the Wye Valley on the Welsh Border overlooking the Black Mountains.

9 holes, 2929yds, Par 70, SSS 67, Course record 72.
Club membership 240.

Visitors welcome anytime except Sun mornings and Thu evenings. **Societies** contact for information on main phone number or 07970 076881. **Green Fees** £10 per 18 holes (£12 weekends and bank holidays). **Prof** Andy Gealy **Course Designer** Bob Sandow **Facilities** by prior arrangement **Conf** Max 120 Banquet 100 Del £2 to £20 * **Location** 0.5 mile from Hay-on-Wye into Herefordshire on right hand side of B4350

Inn ♦♦♦♦♦ The Talkhouse, Ty Siarad, Pontdolgoch, CAERSWS ☎ 01686 688919 3 en suite

HEREFORD Map 03 SO53

Belmont Lodge Belmont HR2 9SA
☎ 01432 352666 01432 358090
e-mail: info@belmont-hereford.co.uk

Parkland course designed in two loops of nine. The first nine take the higher ground, offering magnificent views over Herefordshire. The second nine run alongside the River Wye with five holes in play against the river.

continued

18 holes, 6511yds, Par 72, SSS 71, Course record 66.
Club membership 450.

Visitors advised to contact in advance at weekends. Tel: 01432 352666 or 352717. **Societies** must telephone in advance. **Green Fees** terms on application. **Cards** **Prof** Mike Welsh **Course Designer** Bob Sandow **Facilities** **Leisure** hard tennis courts, fishing. **Conf** Max 30 Thtr 40 Class 20 Board 15 Del from £15 * **Location** 2m S off A465

Hotel ★★★ 59% Belmont Lodge & Golf, Belmont, HEREFORD ☎ 01432 352666 30 en suite

Burghill Valley Tillington Rd, Burghill HR4 7RW
☎ 01432 760456 01432 761654
e-mail: golf@bvgc.co.uk

The course is situated in typically beautiful Herefordshire countryside. The walking is easy on gently rolling fairways with a background of hills and woods and in the distance, the Welsh mountains. Some holes are played through mature cider orchards and there are two lakes to negotiate. A fair but interesting test for players of all abilities.

18 holes, 6239yds, Par 71, SSS 70, Course record 66.
Club membership 700.

Visitors contact in advance. **Societies** apply in writing or telephone in advance. **Green Fees** £20 per round (£25 weekends & bank holidays). **Cards** **Prof** Nigel Clarke **Course Designer** M Barnett **Facilities** **Leisure** chipping practice area. **Location** 4m NW of Hereford

Hotel ★★★ 62% The Green Dragon, Broad St, HEREFORD ☎ 0870 400 8113 83 en suite

Hereford Municipal Hereford Leisure Centre, Holmer Rd HR4 9UD ☎ 01432 344376 01432 266281

This municipal parkland course is more challenging than first appearance. The well-drained greens are open all year round with good drainage for excellent winter golf.

9 holes, 3060yds, Par 35, SSS 69.
Club membership 195.

Visitors restrictions on race days. **Societies** telephone in advance. **Green Fees** £6.90 18 holes, £4.60 9 holes (£8.50/£5.60 weekends). **Cards** **Prof** Gary Morgan **Course Designer** J Leek **Facilities** **Leisure** squash, gymnasium, Leisure centre. **Location** Located with race course on Holmer Rd, on A49 Hereford to Leominster

Hotel ★★★ 62% The Green Dragon, Broad St, HEREFORD ☎ 0870 400 8113 83 en suite

KINGTON Map 03 SO25

Kington Bradnor Hill HR5 3RE
☎ 01544 230340 (club) & 231320 (pro shop)
01544 230340 /231320 (pro)

The highest 18-hole course in England, with magnificent views over seven counties. A natural heathland course with easy walking on mountain turf cropped by sheep. There is bracken to catch any really bad shots but no sand traps. The greens play true and fast.

18 holes, 5980yds, Par 70, SSS 68, Course record 63.
Club membership 510.

Visitors contact the professional, particularly at weekends by phoning 01544 231320. **Societies** must book in advance through the Professional. **Green Fees** not

continued

confirmed. **Prof** Dean Oliver **Course Designer** Major
Hutchison **Facilities** ⊗ 〵 ﻝ 🍺 ♀ ⚐ 🛆 🔔 ✂ 𝒹 ⚲
Location 0.5m N of Kington, off B4355

Hotel ★★★ 65% Talbot Hotel, West St, LEOMINSTER
☎ 01568 616347 20 en suite

LEOMINSTER   Map 03 SO45

Leominster Ford Bridge HR6 0LE ☎ 01568 611402
(Prof) & 610055 (Sec/Mngr) 🖹 01568 610055
e-mail: leominstergolf@freeuk.com
**On undulating parkland with the lower holes running
alongside the River Lugg and others on the higher part of
the course affording fine panoramic views over the
surrounding countryside.**
18 holes, 6026yds, Par 70, SSS 69.
Club membership 570.
Visitors must contact in advance. **Societies** must telephone
in advance. **Green Fees** Mon & Fri £8; Tue-Thu £15.50 per
round (£22 weekends & bank holidays). **Cards** 💳 **Prof**
Andrew Ferriday **Course Designer** Bob Sandow **Facilities**
⊗ 〵 ﻝ 🍺 ♀ 🛆 🔔 𝒹 **Leisure** fishing. **Conf** Max 100
Location 3m S of Leominster on A49. Clearly signposted
from Leominster by-pass

Hotel ★★★ 65% Talbot Hotel, West St, LEOMINSTER
☎ 01568 616347 20 en suite

ROSS-ON-WYE   Map 03 SO62

Ross-on-Wye Two Park, Gorsley HR9 7UT
☎ 01989 720267 🖹 01989 720212
e-mail: secretary@therossonwyegolfclub.co.uk
**The undulating, parkland course has been cut out of a
silver birch forest; the fairways being well-screened
from each other. The fairways are tight, the greens
good and the bunkers have been restructured.**
18 holes, 6451yds, Par 72, SSS 71, Course record 68.
Club membership 760.
Visitors must contact secretary or professional in
advance. **Societies** apply in writing/telephone in advance.
Green Fees £46 per 36 holes; £42 per 27 holes; £36 per
round. **Cards** 💳 💳 **Prof** Nick Catchpole **Course
Designer** Mr C K Cotton **Facilities** ⊗ 〵 ﻝ 🍺 ♀ 🛆 🔔
🎯 𝒹 ⚲ **Location** On B4221 N side of M50 junct 3

Hotel ★★★ 77% Pengethley Manor, Pengethley Park,
ROSS-ON-WYE ☎ 01989 730211
11 en suite 14 annexe en suite

★★★

West Street – Leominster – Herefordshire – HR6 8EP

South Herefordshire Twin Lakes HR9 7UA
☎ 01989 780535 🖹 01989 740611
e-mail: shgc.golf@clara.co.uk
**Impressive 6672 yard parkland course fast maturing into
one of Herefordshire's finest. Magnificent panoramic
views of the Welsh mountains and countryside. Drains
well and is playable in any weather. The landscape has
enabled the architect to design 18 individual and varied
holes.**

*Twin Lakes: 18 holes, 6672yds, Par 71, SSS 72, Course
record 71.*
Club membership 300.
Visitors must contact in advance. **Societies** phone in
advance. **Green Fees** £15 per round (£20 weekends). **Cards**
💳 💳 💳 **Prof** Edward Litchfield **Course Designer** John
Day **Facilities** ⊗ 〵 ﻝ 🍺 ♀ 🛆 🔔 🎯 ⛳ 🏌 𝒹 ⚲ **Location**
J4 M50 to Upton Bishop, right to B4224,1m left

Hotel ★★★♨ 69% Pencraig Court Hotel, Pencraig, ROSS-
ON-WYE ☎ 01989 770306 11 en suite

UPPER SAPEY   Map 03 SO66

Sapey WR6 6XT ☎ 01886 853288 & 853567
📠 01886 853485
e-mail: anybody@sapeygolf.co.uk
Parkland course with views of the Malvern Hills. Trees, lakes and water hazards. Not too strenuous a walk.
The Rowan: 18 holes, 5935yds, Par 69, SSS 68, Course record 63.
The Oaks: 9 holes, 1203, Par 27, SSS 27.
Club membership 500.
Visitors must contact in advance. **Societies** must contact in advance. **Green Fees** The Rowan: £18 per round (£23 weekends and bank holidays),The Oaks: £4 per round(£5 weekends and bank holidays). **Cards** 🌐 💳 📇 **Prof** Chris Knowles **Course Designer** R McMurray **Facilities** ⊗ ⅋ ፟⅃
🍺 ♀ ⚲ 🏌 🍴 ⚲ **Leisure** bowling green. **Location** B4203 Bromyard/Stourport Rd

Hotel ★★★ 65% Talbot Hotel, West St, LEOMINSTER
☎ 01568 616347 20 en suite

WORMSLEY   Map 03 SO44

Herefordshire Ravens Causeway HR4 8LY
☎ 01432 830219 & 830465 (pro) 📠 01432 830095
e-mail: herefordshire@golf.sagehost.co.uk
Undulating parkland course with expansive views of the Clee Hills to the east and the Black Mountains to the west.
18 holes, 6078yds, Par 70, SSS 69, Course record 61.
Club membership 750.
Visitors must contact in advance, possibility of weekend play if no competitions are taking place. **Societies** must apply in advance. **Green Fees** £25 per day; £20 per round (£32/£25 weekends & bank holidays). **Cards** 🌐 💳 📇 📇 **Prof** David Hemming **Course Designer** James Braid **Facilities** ⊗ ⅋ ፟⅃ 🍺 ♀ ⚲ 🏌 🍴 ⚲ **Location** 7m nw of Hereford on A 'B'road to Weobley

Hotel ★★★ 62% The Green Dragon, Broad St, HEREFORD ☎ 0870 400 8113 83 en suite

HERTFORDSHIRE

ALDBURY   Map 04 SP91

Stocks Hotel Golf & Country Club Stocks Rd HP23 5RX ☎ 01442 851341 📠 01442 851253
e-mail: jljegard@stockshotel-golf.co.uk
An 18-hole parkland course is one of the many facilities at this country club.
18 holes, 6804yds, Par 72, SSS 73, Course record 65.
Club membership 550.
Visitors must contact in advance and have a handicap certificate. May not play before 12pm at weekends. **Societies** must contact in advance. **Green Fees** £35 per round (£45 weekends). **Cards** 🌐 💳 📇 📇 📇 **Prof** Peter Lane **Course Designer** Mike Billcliffe **Facilities** ⊗ ፟⅃ 🍺 ♀ ⚲ 🏌 🍴 ⚲ **Leisure** sauna, solarium, chipping green, practice bunker. **Conf** Thtr 60 Class 30 Board 25 Banquet 85 Del from £45 * **Location** 2m from A41 at Tring, towards Tring station

Hotel ★★★★ 65% Pendley Manor, Cow Ln, TRING
☎ 01442 891891 74 en suite

ALDENHAM   Map 04 TQ19

Aldenham Golf and Country Club Church Ln
WD25 8NN ☎ 01923 853929 📠 01923 858472
e-mail: aldenhamgolf@ukonline.co.uk
Undulating parkland course with many specimen trees. Beautiful views across countryside.
Old Course: 18 holes, 6480yds, Par 70, SSS 71.
White Course: 9 holes, 2350yds, Par 33, SSS 32.
Club membership 550.
Visitors Old Course restricted weekends before noon. White Course no restrictions. **Societies** must contact in advance. **Green Fees** Old Course: £25 per round (£32 weekends). White Course £10 per round (£12 weekends). **Cards** 🌐 📇 📇 💳 **Prof** Tim Dunstan **Facilities** ⊗ ⅋ ፟⅃ 🍺 ♀ ⚲ 🏌 ⚲ **Conf** Max 25 Thtr 25 Class 20 Board 16 Banquet 16 **Location** W side of village, 0.5 miles from M1 junct 5

Hotel ★★★ 64% The White House, Upton Rd, WATFORD
☎ 01923 237316 60 en suite

BERKHAMSTED   Map 04 SP90

Berkhamsted The Common HP4 2QB
☎ 01442 865832 📠 01442 863730
e-mail: golf agent.com/clubsites/Berkhamsted
There are no sand bunkers on this Championship heathland course but this does not make it any easier to play. The natural hazards will test the skill of the most able players, with a particularly testing hole at the 11th, 568 yards, par 5. Fine Greens, long carries and heather and gorse. The clubhouse is very comfortable.
18 holes, 6605yds, Par 71, SSS 72, Course record 65.
Club membership 700.
Visitors must contact in advance and be competent golfer. **Societies** must contact in advance. **Green Fees** not confirmed. **Cards** 🌐 💳 📇 💳 **Prof** Basil Proudfoot **Course Designer** Colt/Braid **Facilities** ⊗ ⅋ ፟⅃ 🍺 ♀ ⚲ 🏌 ⚲ **Location** 1.5m E

Hotel ★★★★ 65% Pendley Manor, Cow Ln, TRING
☎ 01442 891891 74 en suite

BISHOP'S STORTFORD   Map 05 TL42

Bishop's Stortford Dunmow Rd CM23 5HP
☎ 01279 654715 📠 01279 655215
e-mail: bishopstortfordgc@hotmail.com
Well established parkland course, fairly flat, but undulating, with easy walking.

18 holes, 6404yds, Par 71, SSS 71, Course record 66.
Club membership 900.
Visitors must have a valid handicap certificate, must play with member at weekends. Ladies day Tue. **Societies** must

continued

AA website: www.theAA.com

contact in writing. **Green Fees** £35 per day; £32 per 27 holes; £28 per 18 holes. **Prof** Stephen M Bryan **Course Designer** James Braid **Facilities** ⊗ ⅢⅢ ㅛ 💺 ♀ ♨ 🏠 🚩 🐾 ♣ ∅ **Leisure** snooker tables. **Conf** Max 180 Thtr 180 Class 180 Board 14 Banquet 180 **Location** 0.5m W of M11 junc 8 on A1250

··········

Hotel ★★★★ 71% Down Hall Country House Hotel, Hatfield Heath, BISHOP'S STORTFORD ☎ 01279 731441 99 en suite

Great Hadham Golf & Country Club Great Hadham Rd, Much Hadham SG10 6JE

☎ 01279 843558 📄 01279 842122

An undulating open meadowland/links course offering excellent country views and a challenge with its ever present breeze.

18 holes, 6854yds, Par 72, SSS 73, Course record 67.
Club membership 800.

Visitors welcome all times except am Mon, Wed, Sat & Sun. **Societies** weekdays only, by advance booking in writing. **Green Fees** terms on application. **Cards** 🌐 ▦▦ ▦▦ **Prof** Kevin Lunt **Course Designer** Iain Roberts **Facilities** ⊗ ⅢⅢ ㅛ 💺 ♀ ♨ 🏠 🚩 ∅ ♣ **Conf** Max 100 Thtr 100 Class 80 Board 20 Banquet 80 **Location** On the B1004, 3m SW of Bishop's Stortford

··········

Hotel ★★★★ 71% Down Hall Country House Hotel, Hatfield Heath, BISHOP'S STORTFORD ☎ 01279 731441 99 en suite

Brickendon Grange Pembridge Ln SG13 8PD

☎ 01992 511258 📄 01992 511411

e-mail: genman@brickendongrangegc.co.uk

Undulating parkland course with some fine par 4s. 17th hole reputed to be best in the county.

18 holes, 6395yds, Par 71, SSS 70, Course record 66.
Club membership 680.

Visitors must have handicap certificate. With member only at weekends & bank holidays. **Societies** by arrangement. **Green Fees** £38 per day; £28 per round. **Prof** Graham Tippett **Course Designer** C K Cotton **Facilities** ⊗ ⅢⅢ ㅛ 💺 ♀ ♨ 🏠 🚩 🐾 ♣ ∅ **Location** W side of village

··········

Hotel ★★★ 64% The White Horse, Hertingfordbury, HERTFORD ☎ 0870 400 8114 42 en suite

Brookmans Park Golf Club Rd AL9 7AT

☎ 01707 652487 📄 01707 661851

e-mail: clubbp@aol.com

Brookman's Park is an undulating parkland course, with several cleverly constructed holes. But it is a fair course, although it can play long. The 11th, par 3, is a testing hole which plays across a lake.

18 holes, 6460yds, Par 71, SSS 71, Course record 66.
Club membership 750.

Visitors must contact professional in advance 01707 652468 and have a handicap certificate; must play with member at weekends & bank holidays. **Societies** must telephone or write in advance. **Green Fees** £42 per day; £32 per round. **Prof** Ian Jelley **Course Designer** Hawtree/Taylor **Facilities** ⊗ ⅢⅢ ㅛ 💺 ♀ ♨ 🏠 🚩 🐾 ♣ ∅ **Location** N side of village off A1000

··········

Hotel ★★★ 66% Holiday Inn South Mimms, SOUTH MIMMS ☎ 0870 400 9072 143 en suite

Hertfordshire Broxbournebury Mansion, White Stubbs Ln ☎ 01992 466666 & 441268 (pro shop)

📄 01992 470326

e-mail: hertfordshire@americangolf.uk.com

An 18 hole course of a 'Nicklaus' design set around a Grade II listed clubhouse to full USGA specifications. Considered to be one of the best 'pay and play' courses to appear in recent years.

18 holes, 6314yds, Par 70, SSS 70, Course record 62.
Club membership 600.

Visitors book 7 days in advance, soft spikes only **Societies** telephone in advance, deposit required. **Green Fees** not confirmed. **Cards** ▦▦ ▦▦ 💳 🌐 ▦▦ 💳 **Prof** Adrian Shearn **Facilities** ⊗ ⅢⅢ ㅛ 💺 ♀ ♨ 🏠 🚩 🐾 ∅ ♣ **Leisure** hard tennis courts, heated indoor swimming pool, fishing, sauna, solarium, gymnasium, jacuzzis.
Location on A10 take Broxbourne exit and follow signs for Paradise Wildlife Park. Turn left at Bell Lane and follow road over A10, course on right.

··········

Hotel ★★★ 64% The White Horse, Hertingfordbury, HERTFORD ☎ 0870 400 8114 42 en suite

East Herts Hamels Park SG9 9NA

☎ 01920 821922(Pro) 📄 01920 823700

e-mail: secretary@ehgc.fsnet.co.uk

An attractive undulating parkland course with magnificent specimen trees.

18 holes, 6456yds, Par 71, SSS 71.
Club membership 750.

Visitors must contact in advance & have handicap certificate, but may not play on Wed & weekends. **Societies** apply in writing. **Green Fees** £38 per day/round, weekdays only. **Prof** G Culmer **Facilities** ⊗ ㅛ 💺 ♀ ♨ 🏠 🚩 🐾 ♣ ∅ **Location** 1m N of Puckeridge off A10

··········

Hotel ★★★ 66% Novotel Stevenage, Knebworth Park, STEVENAGE ☎ 01438 346100 100 en suite

Bushey Golf & Country Club High St WD23 1TT

☎ 020 8950 2215(pro shop) 📄 020 8386 1181

Undulating parkland with challenging 2nd and 9th holes. The latter has a sweeping dog-leg left, playing to a green in front of the club house. For the rather too enthusiastic golfer, Bushey offers its own physiotherapist!

9 holes, 6120yds, Par 70, SSS 69, Course record 67.
Club membership 411.

Visitors must contact in advance and subject to club competition times. **Societies** apply in writing or by

continued

telephone. **Green Fees** not confirmed. **Cards** **Prof** Grahame Atkinson **Facilities** **Leisure** sauna, solarium, gymnasium, health & fitness club.

Hotel ★★★ 72% Edgwarebury Hotel, Barnet Ln, ELSTREE ☎ 020 8953 8227 47 en suite

Bushey Hall Bushey Hall Dr WD23 2EP
☎ 01923 222253 01923 229759
e-mail: info@golfclubuk.co.uk
Tree lined parkland course.
18 holes, 6099yds, Par 70, SSS 69.
Club membership 500.
Visitors may book 14 days in advance and may only play after 11am weekends. **Societies** must contact in writing. **Green Fees** £25 per round (£32 weekends & bank holidays). **Cards** **Prof** Ken Wickham **Course Designer** Clouston **Facilities** by prior arrangement **Conf** Max 60 Thtr 60 Class 30 Board 14 Banquet 40 **Location** 1.5m NW on A4008

Hotel ★★★ 72% Edgwarebury Hotel, Barnet Ln, ELSTREE ☎ 020 8953 8227 47 en suite

Hartsbourne Golf & Country Club Hartsbourne Ave WD2 1JW ☎ 020 8950 1133
18 holes, 6305yds, Par 71, SSS 70, Course record 62.
Location 5m SE of Watford
Telephone for further details

Hotel ★★★ 72% Edgwarebury Hotel, Barnet Ln, ELSTREE ☎ 020 8953 8227 47 en suite

CHESHUNT Map 05 TL30

Cheshunt Cheshunt Park, Park Ln EN7 6QD
☎ 01992 624009
Municipal parkland course, well-bunkered with ponds, easy walking.
18 holes, 6692yds, Par 72, SSS 71.
Club membership 350.
Visitors must book tee-times through Reception. Must contact in advance. **Societies** must apply in writing. **Green Fees** £14 per round (£18.50 weekends & bank holidays). **Cards** **Prof** David Banks **Course Designer** P Wawtry **Facilities** **Location** 1.5m NW off B156, 3m N of M25 junct 25

Hotel ★★★ 63% Posthouse Epping, High Rd, Bell Common, EPPING ☎ 0870 400 9027 79 annexe en suite

CHORLEYWOOD Map 04 TQ09

Chorleywood Common Rd WD3 5LN
☎ 01923 282009 01923 286739
e-mail: chorleywood.gc@btclick.com
Very attractive mix of woodland and heathland with natural hazards and good views.
9 holes, 5712yds, Par 68, SSS 67.
Club membership 300.
Visitors must contact in advance, restricted weekends & Tues. **Societies** initial contact by telephone. **Green Fees** terms on application. **Facilities** by prior arrangement **Location** M25 junct 18,E side of village off A404

Hotel ★★★ 71% The Bedford Arms Chenies, CHENIES ☎ 01923 283301 10 en suite

ELSTREE Map 04 TQ19

Elstree Watling St WD6 3AA
☎ 020 8953 6115 or 8238 6941 020 8207 6390
e-mail: admin@elstree-golf.co.uk
Parkland course.
18 holes, 6556yds, Par 73, SSS 72.
Club membership 400.
Visitors advisable to contact in advance, no restrictions weekdays, may not play until after 12pm, weekends unless tee time available day prior. **Societies** telephone in advance. **Green Fees** £33 per day; £27.50 per round (£33 per round weekends & bank holidays). **Cards** **Prof** Marc Warwick **Course Designer** Donald Steel **Facilities** by prior arrangement **Leisure** snooker.**Conf** Max 125 Board 30 **Location** A5183 between Radlett and Elstree

Hotel ★★★ 72% Edgwarebury Hotel, Barnet Ln, ELSTREE ☎ 020 8953 8227 47 en suite

ESSENDON Map 04 TL20

Hatfield London Country Club Bedwell Park AL9 6JA ☎ 01707 642624(old course) & 663131(new course) 01707 646187 & 278475
e-mail: hlccgolf@aol.com
Parkland course with many varied hazards, including ponds, a stream and a ditch. 19th-century manor clubhouse. 9-hole pitch and putt.
Old Course: 18 holes, 6808yds, Par 72, SSS 72.
New Course: 18 holes, 7091yds, Par 72, SSS 74.
Club membership 250.
Visitors must contact in advance. Societies only for New Course. **Societies** must contact in advance. **Green Fees** terms on application. **Cards** **Prof** Norman Greer **Course Designer** Fred Hawtry **Facilities** by prior arrangement **Leisure** hard tennis courts, 9 hole pitch and putt (Old Course) Japanese bath & jacuzzi (New Course). **Location** On B158 1m S

Hotel ★★★ 62% Quality Hotel Hatfield, Roehyde Way, HATFIELD ☎ 01707 275701 76 en suite

GRAVELEY Map 04 TL22

Chesfield Downs Jack's Hill SG4 7EQ
☎ 01462 482929 01462 482930
18 holes, 6648yds, Par 71, SSS 72.
Course Designer J Gaunt **Location** Jct 8 of A1, B197 to Graveley
Telephone for further details

Hotel Hotel Ibis, Danestrete, STEVENAGE
☎ 01438 779955 98 en suite

HARPENDEN Map 04 TL11

Aldwickbury Park Piggottshill Ln AL5 1AB
☎ 01582 760112 01582 760113
e-mail: enquiries@aldwickburyparkgolfclub.com
Attractive parkland course with large areas of mature woodland and good views across the Lee Valley.
18 holes, 6352yds, Par 71, SSS 70, Course record 66.
Club membership 700.
Visitors may book up to 3 days in advance by telephone. May only play after 1pm weekends. **Societies** telephone for brochure, various packages available. **Green Fees** not confirmed. **Cards** **Prof** Simon Plumb **Course Designer** Ken Brown/Martin Gillett **Facilities** **Leisure** 9 hole par 3 course.

continued

Location Located just off Wheathampstead Road, between Harpenden/Wheathampstead, 10mins from junct 9 of M1

Hotel ★★★ 68% Harpenden House, 18 Southdown Rd, HARPENDEN ☎ 01582 449955
17 en suite 59 annexe en suite

Harpenden Hammonds End, Redbourn Ln AL5 2AX
☎ 01582 712580 ▤ 01582 712725
e-mail: harpgolf@hammonds94.freeservce.co.uk
Gently undulating parkland course, easy walking.
18 holes, 6381yds, Par 70, SSS 70, Course record 67.
Club membership 800.
Visitors must contact in advance. May not play Thu & weekends. **Societies** must apply in writing. **Green Fees** £36 per day; £26 per round (£30 per round weekends and bank holidays). **Cards** 🖃 🖃 🖃 🖃 🖃 **Prof** Peter Cherry **Course Designer** Hawtree & Taylor **Facilities** ⊗ ⊪ 🖳 🖳 ♀ ⚐ ⬤ ⚐ ⚑ **Location** 1m S on B487

Hotel ★★★ 68% Harpenden House, 18 Southdown Rd, HARPENDEN ☎ 01582 449955
17 en suite 59 annexe en suite

Harpenden Common Cravells Rd, East Common
AL5 1BL ☎ 01582 715959 ▤ 01582 715959
Flat, easy walking, good greens, typical common course.
18 holes, 6214yds, Par 70, SSS 70, Course record 64.
Club membership 710.
Visitors must contact in advance. **Societies** Thu & Fri only. Must apply in writing. **Green Fees** £30 per day; £25 per round(£30 per round weekends). **Prof** Danny Fitzsimmons **Course Designer** K Brown **Facilities** ⊗ ⊪ 🖳 🖳 ♀ ⚐ ⬤ **Location** 1m S on A1081

Hotel ★★★ 70% Hanover International Hotel, 1 Luton Rd, HARPENDEN ☎ 01582 760271 60 en suite

Boxmoor 18 Box Ln, Boxmoor HP3 0DJ
☎ 01442 242434
e-mail: boxmoor90@freeserve.com
Challenging, very hilly, moorland course with sloping fairways divided by trees. Fine views. Testing holes: 3rd (par 3), 4th (par 4).
9 holes, 4812yds, Par 64, SSS 63, Course record 62.
Club membership 280.
Visitors may not play on Sun & bank holidays. Restricted some Sat. **Societies** must contact in advance. **Green Fees** not confirmed. **Facilities** 🖳 🖳 ♀ ⚐ **Location** 2m SW on B4505

Hotel ★★ 72% The Two Brewers, The Common, CHIPPERFIELD ☎ 01923 265266 20 en suite

Little Hay Box Ln, Bovingdon HP3 0DQ
☎ 01442 833798 ▤ 01442 831399
e-mail: chris.gordon@dacorum.gov.uk
Semi-parkland, inland links.
18 holes, 6300yds, Par 72, SSS 72.
Visitors advisable to contact in advance. **Societies** telephone for details. **Green Fees** terms on application. **Cards** 🖃 🖃 🖃 🖃 **Prof** N Allen/M Perry **Course Designer** Hawtree **Facilities** ⊗ ⊪ 🖳 🖳 ♀ ⚐ 🖳 ⚐ ⬤ ⚐ ⚑ **Location** 1.5m SW on B4505 off A41

Hotel ★★★ 68% Holiday Inn Hemel Hempstead, Breakspear Way, HEMEL HEMPSTEAD ☎ 0870 400 9041 145 en suite

Shendish Manor London Rd, Apsley HP3 0AA
☎ 01442 251806 ▤ 01442 230683
18 holes, 5660yds, Par 70, SSS 67.
Course Designer D Steel **Location** Just off A4251
Telephone for further details

Hotel ★★★★ 65% Pendley Manor, Cow Ln, TRING ☎ 01442 891891 74 en suite

Knebworth Deards End Ln SG3 6NL
☎ 01438 812752 ▤ 01438 815216
Parkland course, easy walking.
18 holes, 6492yds, Par 71, SSS 71, Course record 66.
Club membership 900.
Visitors must have handicap certificate, must play with member at weekends. **Societies** Mon, Tue & Thu. Must contact in advance. **Green Fees** £30 per day/round. **Cards** 🖃 🖃 🖃 🖃 **Prof** Garry Parker **Course Designer** W Park (Jun) **Facilities** ⊗ ⊪ 🖳 🖳 ♀ ⚐ 🖳 ⚐ **Location** N side of village off B197

Hotel ★★★ 61% Posthouse Stevenage, Old London Rd, Broadwater, STEVENAGE ☎ 0870 400 9076 54 en suite

Letchworth Letchworth Ln SG6 3NQ
☎ 01462 683203 ▤ 01462 484567
Planned more than 50 years ago by Harry Vardon, this adventurous, parkland course is set in a peaceful corner of 'Norman' England. To its variety of natural and artificial hazards is added an unpredictable wind.
18 holes, 6181yds, Par 70, SSS 69, Course record 65.
Club membership 750.
Visitors with member only at weekends. Must contact in advance and have a handicap certificate. **Societies** Wed, Thu & Fri only, must telephone in advance. **Green Fees** terms on application. **Prof** S Allen **Course Designer** Harry Vardon **Facilities** ⊗ ⊪ 🖳 🖳 ♀ ⚐ 🖳 ⚐ ⚑ **Leisure** 9 hole par 3 course. **Location** S side of town centre off A505

Hotel ★★★ 65% Cromwell Hotel, High St, Old Town, STEVENAGE ☎ 01438 779954 76 en suite

Ashridge HP4 1LY ☎ 01442 842244 ▤ 01442 843770
e-mail: info@ashridgegolfclub.ltd.uk
Good parkland course, challenging but fair. Good clubhouse facilities.
18 holes, 6547yds, Par 72, SSS 71, Course record 63.
Club membership 720.
Visitors must contact in advance, be a member of a recognised club & have handicap certificate, may not play weekends. **Societies** must apply in writing and complete booking form. **Green Fees** not confirmed. **Cards** 🖃 🖃 🖃 🖃 **Prof** Andrew Ainsworth **Course Designer** Sir G Campbell/C Hutchinson/N Hutchinson **Facilities** ⊗ ⊪ 🖳 🖳 ♀ ⚐ 🖳 ⚐ ⚑ **Location** 5m N of Berkhamsted on the B4506

Hotel ★★★ 68% Harpenden House, 18 Southdown Rd, HARPENDEN ☎ 01582 449955
17 en suite 59 annexe en suite

MUCH HADHAM
Map 05 TL41

Much Hadham Little Hadham Rd SG10 6HD
☎ 01279 843253 📧 01920 468686
18 holes, 6516yds, Par 71, Course record 71.
Course Designer Martin Gillett **Location** 1.5m S of A120
fom Little Hadham traffic lights
Telephone for further details

Hotel ★★★ 62% Roebuck Hotel, Baldock St, WARE
☎ 01920 409955 50 en suite

POTTERS BAR
Map 04 TL20

Potters Bar Darkes Ln EN6 1DE
☎ 01707 652020 📧 01707 655051
e-mail: info@pottersbargolfclub.com
Undulating parkland course.
18 holes, 6279yds, Par 71, SSS 70.
Club membership 650.
Visitors with member only at weekends, Ladies Day Wed
morning. **Societies** Mon-Fri & Wed (pm only) by
arrangement with Secretary. **Green Fees** £25 per round. **Prof**
Gary A'Ris/Julian Harding **Course Designer** James Braid
Facilities ⊗ ╚ ▆ ♀ ㊂ 🏠 ⚐ ⚲ ⛏ ✿ **Location** 1m N of
M25 junct 24

Hotel ★★★ 66% Holiday Inn South Mimms, SOUTH
MIMMS ☎ 0870 400 9072 143 en suite

RADLETT
Map 04 TL10

Porters Park Shenley Hill WD7 7AZ
☎ 01923 854127 📧 01923 855475
e-mail: info@porterspark.fsnet.co.uk
**A splendid, undulating parkland course with fine trees
and lush grass. The holes are all different and
interesting - on many, accuracy of shot to the green is
of paramount importance.**
18 holes, 6313yds, Par 70, SSS 70, Course record 64.
Club membership 1000.
Visitors must book 24hrs in advance. With member only
weekends. **Societies** Wed & Thu only, must apply in
writing. **Green Fees** terms on application. **Prof** David
Gleeson **Course Designer** Braid **Facilities** ⊗ ㊂ ╚ ▆ ♀
㊂ 🏠 ⚐ ✿ ⛏ **Location** NE side of village off A5183

Hotel ★★★ 66% Holiday Inn South Mimms, SOUTH
MIMMS ☎ 0870 400 9072 143 en suite

REDBOURN
Map 04 TL11

Redbourn Kinsbourne Green Ln AL3 7QA
☎ 01582 793493 📧 01582 794362
e-mail: enquiries@redbourngolfclub.com
**Testing parkland course (five par 4s over 400 yds). Also
9-hole par 3 course.**
*Ver Course: 18 holes, 6506yds, Par 70, SSS 71,
Course record 67.*
Kingsbourne Course: 9 holes, 1361yds, Par 27.
Club membership 750.
Visitors must contact up to 3 days in advance for Ver
Course. No restrictions for par 3. **Societies** must telephone in
advance. **Green Fees** terms on application. **Cards** ▒▒ ▒▒▒
▒▒▒ ▒▒ 🄯 **Prof** Stephen Hunter **Facilities** ⊗ ㊂ ╚ ▆ ♀ ㊂
🏠 ⚐ ⚲ ⛏ ✿ ⛏ **Location** 1m N off A5183

Hotel ★★★ 68% Harpenden House, 18 Southdown Rd,
HARPENDEN ☎ 01582 449955
17 en suite 59 annexe en suite

RICKMANSWORTH
Map 04 TQ09

Moor Park WD3 1QN
☎ 01923 773146 📧 01923 777109
e-mail: enquiries@moorparkgc.co.uk
**Two parkland courses - High Course is challenging
and will test the best golfer and West Course demands
a high degree of accuracy.**
*High Golf Course: 18 holes, 6713yds, Par 72, SSS 72,
Course record 63.*
*West Golf Course: 18 holes, 5815yds, Par 69, SSS 68,
Course record 62.*
Club membership 1700.
Visitors must contact in advance but may not play at
weekends, bank holidays or before 1pm on Tue & Thu.
Societies must contact in advance. **Green Fees** High: £65
per round. West: £40 per round. **Cards** ▒▒ ▒▒▒ ▒▒▒ ▒▒ 🄯
Prof Lawrence Farmer **Course Designer** H S Colt
Facilities ⊗ ╚ ▆ ♀ ㊂ 🏠 ⚐ ⚲ ⛏ ✿ ⛏ **Leisure** hard
and grass tennis courts.**Conf** Max 140 Thtr 140 Class 80
Board 30 Banquet 124 Del £47.50 to £90 * **Location** Off
A404 to Northwood,close to junct 17 & 18 on M25

Hotel ★★★ 71% The Bedford Arms Chenies, CHENIES
☎ 01923 283301 10 en suite

Rickmansworth Public Course Moor Ln
WD3 1QL ☎ 01923 775278
**Undulating, municipal parkland course, short but tests
skills to the full.**
18 holes, 4656yds, Par 65, SSS 63.
Club membership 240.
Visitors must contact the club in advance, 7 day booking.
Set of clubs per person. **Societies** must contact in advance.
Green Fees £11 per round (£15.50 weekends). **Cards** ▒▒
▒▒ ▒▒ 🄯 **Prof** Alan Dobbins **Course Designer** Colt
Facilities ⊗ ㊂ ╚ ▆ ♀ ㊂ 🏠 ⚐ ⚲ ⛏ ✿ **Conf** Max 60
Location 2m S of town off A4145

Hotel ★★★ 71% The Bedford Arms Chenies, CHENIES
☎ 01923 283301 10 en suite

ROYSTON
Map 05 TL34

Barkway Park Nuthampstead Rd, Barkway SG8 8EN
☎ 01763 849070 & 848215
**An undulating course criss-crossed by ditches which
come into play on several holes. The challenging par 3 7th
features a long, narrow green with out of bounds close to
the right edge of the green.**
18 holes, 6997yds, Par 74, SSS 74.
Club membership 310.
Visitors must contact in advance, telephone for tee times.
Societies apply for booking form. **Green Fees** not
confirmed. **Cards** ▒▒ ▒▒▒ ▒▒ ▒▒ **Prof** Jamie Bates **Course
Designer** Vivien Saunders **Facilities** ⊗ ╚ ▆ ♀ ㊂ 🏠 ⛏
✿ **Location** Off B1368 from A10

Hotel ★★★ 73% Duxford Lodge Hotel, Ickleton Rd,
DUXFORD ☎ 01223 836444 11 en suite 4 annexe en suite

Heydon Grange Golf & Country Club Heydon
SG8 7NS ☎ 01763 208988 📧 01763 208926
e-mail: enquiries@heydon-grange.co.uk
**Three 9-hole parkland courses - the Essex,
Cambridgeshire and Hertfordshire - situated in gently
rolling countryside. Courses are playable all year round.**
Essex: 9 holes, 3013yds, Par 36, SSS 35, Course record 66.
Cambridgeshire: 9 holes, 3323yds, Par 36, SSS 36.

continued

Hertfordshire: 9 holes, 3180yds, Par 36, SSS 36.
Club membership 250.
Visitors must contact to book tee times, welcome all times weekends included. **Societies** telephone in advance for booking form. **Green Fees** terms on application. **Cards** 🔲 🔲 🔲 🔲 🔲 **Prof** John Saxon-Mills **Course Designer** Cameron Sinclair **Facilities** ⊗ ℿ ℔ 💺 ♨ ⚖ 🏠 ⚑ ♙ 🚿 ⚘ ⚒ **Location** A505 between Royston/Duxford, off junct 10 on M11

Hotel ★★★ 73% Duxford Lodge Hotel, Ickleton Rd, DUXFORD ☎ 01223 836444 11 en suite 4 annexe en suite

Kingsway Cambridge Rd, Melbourn SG8 6EY
☎ 01763 262727 🖹 01763 263298
The Melbourn course is short and deceptively tricky. This 9-hole course provides a good test for both beginners and experienced golfers. Out of bounds and strategically placed bunkers come into play on several holes, in particular the tough par 3 7th.
Melbourn Course: 9 holes, 2455yds, Par 33, SSS 32.
Orchard Course: 9 holes, 727yds, Par 27, SSS 27.
Club membership 150.
Visitors welcome. **Societies** telephone for details. **Green Fees** £5.50 per 9 holes; £9 per 18 holes (£7.50/£12 weekends). **Cards** 🔲 🔲 🔲 🔲 🔲 **Prof** S Brown/D Hastings/M Sturgess **Facilities** ⊗ ℔ 💺 ♨ ⚖ 🏠 ⚑ ⚒ ⚘ **Location** Off the A10

Hotel ★★★ 73% Duxford Lodge Hotel, Ickleton Rd, DUXFORD ☎ 01223 836444 11 en suite 4 annexe en suite

Royston Baldock Rd SG8 5BG
☎ 01763 242696 🖹 01763 246910
e-mail: roystongolf@btconnect.com
Heathland course on undulating terrain and fine fairways. The 8th, 10th and 15th are the most notable holes on this all weather course.

18 holes, 6052yds, Par 70, SSS 70, Course record 65.
Club membership 850.
Visitors Mon-Fri only subject to availability. Must contact in advance. **Societies** by arrangement Mon-Fri. **Green Fees** £30 per day; £25 per round. **Cards** 🔲 🔲 🔲 🔲 🔲 **Prof** Sean Clark **Course Designer** Harry Vardon **Facilities** ⊗ ℔ 💺 ♨ ⚖ 🏠 ⚒ ⚘ **Location** 0.5m W of town centre

Hotel ★★★ 73% Duxford Lodge Hotel, Ickleton Rd, DUXFORD ☎ 01223 836444 11 en suite 4 annexe en suite

Abbey View Westminster Lodge Leisure Ctr, Hollywell Hill AL1 2DL ☎ 01727 868227 🖹 01727 848508
e-mail: westminsterlodge/leisureconnection@circanotesdomain
Abbey View is a picturesque public golf course in the centre of the city, designed for beginners, but sufficiently
continued

challenging for experienced golfers.
9 holes, 1383yds, Par 29.
Visitors welcome but no sharing clubs, suitable footwear & wide wheel trolleys. **Societies** telephone or write in advance. **Green Fees** terms on application. **Prof** Roddy Watkins **Facilities** ⊗ ℿ ℔ 💺 ♨ ⚖ 🏠 ⚑ ⚒ **Leisure** hard and grass tennis courts, heated indoor swimming pool, sauna, solarium, gymnasium. **Location** Centre of St Albans, off Holywell hill

Hotel ★★ 67% Apples Hotel, 133 London Rd, ST ALBANS ☎ 01727 844111 9 en suite

Batchwood Hall Batchwood Dr AL3 5XA
☎ 01727 844250 🖹 01727 858506
e-mail: batchwood@leisureconnection.co.uk
Municipal parkland course designed by J H Taylor and opened in 1935.
Batchwood Hall Golf Club:18 holes, 6487yds, Par 71, SSS 71.
Club membership 350.
Visitors can contact/book over the telephone up to 7 days in advance. **Societies** contact the events manager by phone or e-mail. **Green Fees** £10.80(£13.90 weekends). **Cards** 🔲 🔲 **Prof** Mark Flitton **Course Designer** J H Taylor **Facilities** ⊗ ℿ ℔ 💺 ♨ ⚖ 🏠 ⚑ ⚒ **Leisure** hard tennis courts, squash, solarium, gymnasium, Indoor tennis courts. **Location** 1m NW off A5183

Hotel ★★★ 77% St Michael's Manor, Fishpool St, ST ALBANS ☎ 01727 864444 23 en suite

Verulam London Rd AL1 1JG
☎ 01727 853327 🖹 01727 812201
e-mail: genman@verulamgolf.co.uk
Easy walking parkland course with fourteen holes having out-of-bounds. Water affects the 12th, 13th and 14th holes. Samuel Ryder was Captain here in 1927 when he began the now celebrated Ryder Cup Competition.
18 holes, 6448yds, Par 72, SSS 71, Course record 67.
Club membership 720.
Visitors must contact pro shop in advance. With member only at weekends. **Societies** must contact advance. **Green Fees** Mon: £17.50, £25 per round(£17.50 weekends). **Cards** 🔲 🔲 🔲 🔲 **Prof** Nick Burch **Course Designer** Braid **Facilities** ⊗ ℿ by prior arrangement ℔ 💺 ♨ ⚖ 🏠 ⚒ **Location** 0.5m from St Albans town centre on London Rd A1081, signposted by railway bridge

Hotel ★★★★ 74% Sopwell House Hotel, Country Club & Spa, Cottonmill Ln, Sopwell, ST ALBANS ☎ 01727 864477 112 en suite 16 annexe en suite

Manor of Groves Golf & Country Club High Wych CM21 0LA ☎ 01279 722333 🖹 01279 726972
The course is set out over 150 acres of established parkland and rolling countryside and is a true test of golf for the club golfer.
18 holes, 6280yds, Par 71, SSS 70, Course record 63.
Club membership 450.
Visitors telephone bookings preferred, restrictions on Tue, Thu and weekends. **Societies** Mon-Fri by prior arrangement, telephone in advance. **Green Fees** not confirmed. **Cards** 🔲 🔲 🔲 🔲 🔲 **Prof** Craig Laurence **Course Designer** S Sharer **Facilities** ⊗ ℿ ℔ 💺 ♨ ⚖ 🏠 ⚑ 🏇 ♙ 🚿 ⚒ **Location** 1.5m on west side of town

Hotel ★★★ 71% Swallow Churchgate Hotel, Churchgate St Village, Old Harlow, HARLOW ☎ 01279 420246 85 en suite

STANSTEAD ABBOTS   Map 05 TL31

Briggens House Hotel Briggens Park, Stanstead Rd
SG12 8LD ☎ 01279 793742 🖹 01279 793685
An attractive 9-hole course set in the grounds of a hotel
which was once a stately house in 80 acres of countryside.
9 holes, 2793yds, Par 36, SSS 69, Course record 31.
Club membership 230.
Visitors may not play Thu 5-6pm and Sun am. No jeans.
Must have own clubs and golf shoes (hire available).
Societies must contact in advance. Green Fees £15 per 18
holes;£11 per 9 holes(£18/£14 weekends). Cards 🖃 🔳
🔳 🔲 🔳 🔳 🔲 Prof Alan McGinn Facilities ⊗ ⅏ 🖳 ☕ ♀
🏃 🏠 🏋 🏄 🐾 🚣 🏌 Leisure hard tennis courts, heated
outdoor swimming pool, fishing. Conf Max 100 Thtr 100
Class 50 Board 45 Banquet 100 Del £45 to £55 * Location
Off Stanstead road A414

Hotel ★★★★ 62% Briggens House Hotel, Stanstead Rd,
STANSTEAD ABBOTTS ☎ 01279 829955 54 en suite

STEVENAGE   Map 04 TL22

Stevenage Golf Centre Aston Ln SG2 7EL
☎ 01438 880424 & 880223 🖹 01438 880040
18 holes, 6451yds, Par 72, SSS 71.
Course Designer John Jacobs Location 4m SE off B5169
Telephone for further details

Hotel ★★★ 61% Posthouse Stevenage, Old London Rd,
Broadwater, STEVENAGE ☎ 0870 400 9076 54 en suite

WARE See page 131

WARE   Map 05 TL31

Chadwell Springs Hertford Rd SG12 9LE
☎ 01920 461447 🖹 01920 466596
Quick drying moorland course on high plateau subject to
wind. The first two holes are par 5 and notable.
9 holes, 6418yds, Par 72, SSS 71, Course record 68.
Club membership 650.
Visitors with member only at weekends. Societies bookings
accepted, Mon, Wed & Fri only. Green Fees not confirmed.
Cards 🖃 🔳 🔳 🔲 🔳 🔳 🔲 Prof Mark Wall Facilities
⊗ ⅏ 🖳 ☕ ♀ 🏃 🏠 🏌 Location 0.75m W on A119

Hotel ★★★ 62% Roebuck Hotel, Baldock St, WARE
☎ 01920 409955 50 en suite

Whitehill Dane End SG12 0JS
☎ 01920 438495 🖹 01920 438891
e-mail: whitehillgolfcentre@btinternet.com
Undulating course providing a good test for both the
average golfer and the low handicapper. Several lakes in
challenging positions.

continued

18 holes, 6618yds, Par 72, SSS 72.
Club membership 600.
Visitors handicap certificate must be produced or
competence test taken (free), appropriate clothing must be
worn. Societies telephone or write for booking form. Green
Fees not confirmed. Cards 🖃 🔳 🔳 🔳 🔲 Prof David
Ling Facilities ⊗ ⅏ 🖳 ☕ ♀ 🏃 🏠 🏌 🏄 🐾 🚣 🏌

Hotel ★★★ 62% Roebuck Hotel, Baldock St, WARE
☎ 01920 409955 50 en suite

WATFORD   Map 04 TQ19

West Herts Cassiobury Park WD3 3GG
☎ 01923 236484 🖹 01923 222300
Another of the many clubs that were inaugurated in
the 1890s when the game of golf was being given a
tremendous boost by the the performances of the first
star professionals, Braid, Vardon and Taylor. The
West Herts course is close to Watford but its tree-lined
setting is beautiful and tranquil. Set out on a plateau
the course is exceedingly dry. It also has a very severe
finish with the 17th, a hole of 378 yards, the toughest
on the course. The last hole measures over 480 yards.
18 holes, 6400yds, Par 72, SSS 71, Course record 65.
Club membership 700.
Visitors must contact in advance. Societies must
telephone in advance and confirm in writing. Green Fees
terms on application. Cards 🖃 🔳 🔲 Prof Charles
Gough Course Designer Tom Morris Facilities ⊗ ⅏ 🖳
🖳 ♀ 🏃 🏠 🏌 🐾 🚣 🏌 Leisure indoor teaching facility.
Location W side of town centre off A412

Hotel ★★★ 64% The White House, Upton Rd,
WATFORD ☎ 01923 237316 60 en suite

WELWYN GARDEN CITY   Map 04 TL21

Mill Green Gypsy Ln AL6 4TY
☎ 01707 276900 & 270542 (Pro shop) 🖹 01707 276898
e-mail: millgreen@americangolf.uk.com
The course plays over the second 9 holes around the lakes
and sweeps back through the woods. The first 9 holes are
subject to the prevailing winds. The par 3 9-hole gives a
good test for improving the short game.
18 holes, 6615yds, Par 72, SSS 72, Course record 64.
Club membership 850.
Visitors must contact in advance by telephone. 3 day
booking arrangement. Societies apply in writing for details.
Green Fees terms on application. Cards 🖃 🔳 🔳 🔲
🔳 🔲 Prof Ian Parker Course Designer Alliss & Clark
Facilities ⊗ ⅏ 🖳 ☕ ♀ 🏃 🏠 🏌 🐾 🚣 🏌 Leisure 9 hole
par 3 course.Conf Max 80 Location Exit 4 of A1(M), A414
to Mill Green

Hotel ★★★ 63% Quality Hotel Welwyn, The Link,
WELWYN ☎ 01438 716911 96 en suite

Panshanger Golf & Squash Complex Old Herns
Ln AL7 2ED ☎ 01707 333350 & 333312 🖹 01707 390010
e-mail: r.preece@welhat.gov.uk
Picturesque, mature course overlooking Mimram Valley.
18 holes, 6347yds, Par 72, SSS 70, Course record 65.
Club membership 400.
Visitors advisable to book 1 week in advance by telephone.
Dress code in force. Societies telephone for details. Green
Fees £13.50 per 18 holes(£18.50 weekends). Cards 🖃 🔳
🔳 🔲 Prof Bryan Lewis/Mick Corlass Course Designer
Peter Kirkham Facilities ⊗ 🖳 ☕ ♀ 🏃 🏌 🐾 🚣 🏌

continued on page 132

Marriott Hanbury Manor

Ware, *Hertfordshire* ☎ 01920 487722 Fax 01920 487692 Map 05 TL31

This PGA European Tour venue has played host to many major championships, most recently it has been a regular venue for the English Open. Golf clinics, tuition, swing analysis and corporate events are available, complemented by the extensive leisure facilities.

The superb parkland course was first built around the family home in 1890, the original Harry Vardon course has since been sympathetically redesigned by Jack Nicklaus II to create something unforgettable. Its cleverly sited trees and several picturesque water features offer a true challenge to anyone who enjoys their golf. The Par 4 13th hole is an interesting dog-leg which requires a mid iron second shot over a lake to a well-guarded two tiered green, being stroke index two it could make or break your score.

Visitors with handicap certificate, members guests and hotel residents welcome. Must contact in advance

Societies must be booked in advance. Mon-Wed only

Green Fees £50-£85 per round as hotel guest according to time of year

Facilities ⊗ 🎿 ⓑ ⛳ ♀ ⋈ ⚲ ☎ ⚙ ⚒ ⚓ ✓ ⚖

Professional David Ingram

Leisure tennis, swimming, sauna, solarium, gymnasium

Location Ware SG12 0SD (adjacent to A10. From N just past sign for Thunderidge)

Holes/Par/Course record 18 holes, 7016 yds, Par 72, SSS 72, Course record 61

WHERE TO STAY AND EAT NEARBY

Hotel
WARE

★★★★★ ◎◎ 73% Marriott Hanbury Manor Hotel & Country Club
☎ 01920 487722.
134 en suite 27 annexe en suite

Championship Course

Leisure squash. **Conf** Max 50 Thtr 80 Class 50 Board 40 Banquet 120 **Location** N side of town centre signposted off B1000

Hotel ★★★ 63% Quality Hotel Welwyn, The Link, WELWYN ☎ 01438 716911 96 en suite

Welwyn Garden City Mannicotts, High Oaks Rd
AL8 7BP ☎ 01707 325243 📠 01707 393213
Undulating parkland course with a ravine. A former course record holder is Nick Faldo.
18 holes, 6074yds, Par 70, SSS 69, Course record 63.
Club membership 975.
Visitors must contact in advance but may not play Sun am. **Societies** must contact in advance. **Green Fees** terms on application. **Cards** 〰 🔳 📇 💳 **Prof** Richard May **Facilities** ⊗ ⅏ ⅃ 💄 🍸 🏖 🏡 🍴 💆 **Location** W side of city, exit 6 off A1

Hotel ★★★ 63% Quality Hotel Welwyn, The Link, WELWYN ☎ 01438 716911 96 en suite

Mid Herts Lamer Ln, Gustard Wood AL4 8RS
☎ 01582 832242 📠 01582 834834
e-mail: secretary@mid-hertsgolfclub.co.uk
Commonland, wooded with heather and gorse-lined fairways.
18 holes, 6060yds, Par 69, SSS 69.
Club membership 760.
Visitors may not play Tue, Wed afternoons & weekends. **Societies** must contact in writing/telephone **Green Fees** not confirmed. **Prof** Barney Puttick **Facilities** ⊗ 💄 🍸 ⅃ 💆 🏡 💆 **Location** 1m N on B651

Hotel ★★★ 68% Harpenden House, 18 Southdown Rd, HARPENDEN ☎ 01582 449955 17 en suite 59 annexe en suite

KENT

West Malling London Rd ME19 5AR
☎ 01732 844785 📠 01732 844795
Two 18-hole parkland courses.
Spitfire Course: 18 holes, 6142yds, Par 70, SSS 70, Course record 67.
Hurricane Course: 18 holes, 6281yds, Par 70, SSS 70, Course record 68.
Visitors must contact in advance, may not play weekends until 12 noon. **Societies** prior booking required. **Green Fees** £30 per day; £25 per round (£30 per round weekends & bank holidays after 12 noon). **Cards** 〰 🔳 📇 💳 **Prof** Duncan Lambert **Course Designer** Max Falkner **Facilities** ⊗ ⅏ 💄 🍸 ⅃ 💆 🏡 🍸 🏖 💆 🍴 **Leisure** gymnasium, jacuzzi & steam room. **Conf** Max 100 **Location** 1m S off A20

Hotel ★★★ 64% Larkfield Priory Hotel, London Rd, Larkfield, MAIDSTONE ☎ 01732 846858 52 en suite

The London South Ash Manor Estate TN15 7EN
☎ 01474 879899 📠 01474 879912
e-mail: golf@londongolf.co.uk
Visitors may only play the courses at LGC as guests of members or prospective members by invitation.The courses were designed by Jack Nicklaus: both include a

continued

number of lakes, generous fairways framed with native grasses and many challenging holes. A state-of-the-art drainage system ensures continuous play.
Heritage Course: 18 holes, 7208yds, Par 72, SSS 74, Course record 68.
International Course: 18 holes, 7005yds, Par 72, SSS 74.
Club membership 500.
Visitors guest of member & prospective members invited by the membership office only. **Societies** must write in advance **Green Fees** International Course : £75 per round (£80 weekends). **Cards** 〰 🔳 📇 💳 **Prof** Andrew Brooks **Course Designer** Jack Nicklaus **Facilities** ⊗ ⅏ 💄 🍸 ⅃ 💆 🏡 🍸 🏖 🏝 💆 🍴 **Leisure** sauna, spa bath.**Conf** Max 100 Thtr 90 Class 60 Board 30 Banquet 110 Del £42 to £55 * **Location** A20, 2m from Brands Hatch

Hotel ★★★ 64% Larkfield Priory Hotel, London Rd, Larkfield, MAIDSTONE ☎ 01732 846858 52 en suite

Ashford Sandyhurst Ln TN25 4NT
☎ 01233 622655 📠 01233 622655
Parkland course with good views and easy walking. Narrow fairways and tightly bunkered greens ensure a challenging game.
18 holes, 6263yds, Par 71, SSS 70, Course record 65.
Club membership 650.
Visitors must contact in advance & have handicap certificate. **Societies** Tue & Thu only, by arrangement. **Green Fees** terms on application. **Prof** Hugh Sherman **Course Designer** Cotton **Facilities** ⊗ ⅏ by prior arrangement 💄 🍸 ⅃ 💆 🏡 💆 **Location** 1.5m NW off A20

Hotel ★★★★ 64% Ashford International, Simone Weil Av, ASHFORD ☎ 01233 219988 200 en suite

Homelands Bettergolf Centre Ashford Rd,
Kingsnorth TN26 1NJ ☎ 01233 661620 📠 01233 720553
e-mail: isj@bettergolf.co.uk
Challenging 9-hole course designed by Donald Steel to provide a stern test for experienced golfers and for others to develop their game. With 4 par 3s and 5 par 4s it demands accuracy rather than length. Floodlit driving range.
9 holes, 2205yds, Par 32, SSS 31, Course record 32.
Club membership 400.
Visitors no restrictions, but booking essential for weekend and summer evenings. **Societies** prior arrangements are essential. **Green Fees** £11 per round (£14 weekends). **Cards** 〰 🔳 📇 **Prof** Tony Bowers **Course Designer** Donald Steel **Facilities** 💄 🍸 ⅃ 💆 🏡 🍸 🏖 💆 🍴 **Location** Take exit 10 off M20, follow A2070, course signposted from 2nd rdbt to Kingsnorth

Hotel ⇧ Travel Inn, Hall Av, Orbital Park, Sevington, ASHFORD ☎ 01233 500755 60 en suite

Broome Park The Broome Park Estate CT4 6QX
☎ 01227 830728 📠 01227 832591
e-mail: broomepark@u.genie.co.uk
Championship standard parkland course in a valley, with a 350-year-old mansion clubhouse.
18 holes, 6610yds, Par 72, SSS 72, Course record 66.
Club membership 700.
Visitors advisable to contact in advance, must have handicap certificate, but may not play Sat/Sun mornings. **Societies** Mon-Fri and Sat-Sun after 1pm, apply in writing or by

continued

telephone. **Green Fees** terms on application. **Cards**  **Prof** Tienne Britz **Course Designer** Donald Steel **Facilities** ⊗ ⫙ ᗏ ♨ ♀ ⚐ 🏌 🛺 ⛳ **Leisure** hard tennis courts. **Location** 1.5m SE on A260

Hotel ★★★ 66% The Chaucer, Ivy Ln, CANTERBURY ☎ 0870 400 8106 42 en suite

BEARSTED   Map 05 TQ85

Bearsted Ware St ME14 4PQ
☎ 01622 738198 🖹 01622 735608
Parkland course with fine views of the North Downs.
18 holes, 6437yds, Par 72, SSS 71.
Club membership 780.
Visitors must have handicap certificate and may not play weekends unless with member. Must contact in advance. **Societies** write for reservation forms. **Green Fees** £41per 36 holes; £31per 18 holes. **Prof** Tim Simpson **Facilities** ⊗ ⫙ ᗏ ♨ ♀ ⚐ ⛳ **Location** M20 junct 7, right at roundabout, left at mini-roundabout, left at 2nd mini-roundabout. Follow road passing Bell pub on right, under bridge and golf club on left.

Hotel ★★★★ 71% Marriott Tudor Park Hotel & Country Club, Ashford Rd, Bearsted, MAIDSTONE ☎ 01622 734334 120 en suite

BIDDENDEN   Map 05 TQ83

Chart Hills Weeks Ln TN27 8JX
☎ 01580 292222 🖹 01580 292233
e-mail: info@charthills.co.uk
Created by Nick Faldo, this huge course of grand design measures 7,000 yards from the back tees. Facilities include a David Leadbetter Golf Academy.

18 holes, 7119yds, Par 72, SSS 74, Course record 66.
Club membership 490.
Visitors may play Tue, Thu, Fri & Sun. **Societies** telephone for details. **Green Fees** not confirmed. **Cards**  **Prof** Danny French **Course Designer** Nick Faldo **Facilities** ⊗ ⫙ ᗏ ♨ ♀ ⚐ 🛺 ⛳ **Leisure** sauna, solarium, gymnasium, teaching academy. **Location** 1m N of Biddenden off A274

Hotel ★★🛏🛏 Kennel Holt Hotel, Goudhurst Rd, CRANBROOK ☎ 01580 712032 10 en suite

BOROUGH GREEN   Map 05 TQ65

Wrotham Heath Seven Mile Ln TN15 8QZ
☎ 01732 884800 🖹 01732 887370
Heathland woodland course with magnificent views of North Downs.
18 holes, 5954yds, Par 70, SSS 69, Course record 66.
Club membership 550.
Visitors weekends with member only. **Societies** Thu & Fri
continued

only, by arrangement. **Green Fees** £25 per round. **Cards**  **Prof** Harry Dearden **Course Designer** Donald Steel (part) **Facilities** ⊗ ⫙ ᗏ ♨ ♀ ⚐ ⛳ **Location** 2.25m E on B2016

Hotel ★★★ 68% Holiday Inn Maidstone, London Rd, Wrotham Heath, WROTHAM ☎ 0870 400 9054 106 en suite

BRENCHLEY   Map 05 TQ64

Moatlands Watermans Ln TN12 6ND
☎ 01892 724400 🖹 01892 723300
e-mail: moatlandsgolf@btinternet.com
A rolling parkland course with dramatic views over the Weald of Kent. The challenging holes are the par 4 8th with its tough dogleg, the 10th where there is a wooded copse with a Victorian bath-house to be avoided and the 14th where the approach to the green is guarded by oak trees.
18 holes, 6693yds, Par 72, SSS 72, Course record 63.
Club membership 620.
Visitors must book in advance. **Societies** apply in writing or telephone. **Green Fees** £29 per 18 holes (£39 weekends & bank holidays). **Cards**  **Prof** Simon Wood **Course Designer** T Saito **Facilities** ⊗ ⫙ ᗏ ♨ ♀ ⚐ 🏌 🛺 ⛳ **Leisure** hard tennis courts, heated indoor swimming pool, sauna, gymnasium.**Conf** Thtr 200 Class 60 Board 24 Banquet 150 Del £5 to £25 * **Location** 3m N of Brenchley off B2160

Hotel ★★ 65% Russell Hotel, 80 London Rd, TUNBRIDGE WELLS ☎ 01892 544833 19 en suite 5 annexe en suite

BROADSTAIRS   Map 05 TR36

North Foreland Convent Rd, Kingsgate CT10 3PU
☎ 01843 862140 🖹 01843 862663
e-mail: bpre342845@aol.com
A picturesque cliff top course situated where the Thames Estuary widens towards the sea. One of the few courses where the sea can be seen from every hole. Walking is easy and the wind is deceptive. The 8th and 17th, both par 4, are testing holes. There is also an 18 hole approach and putting course.
18 holes, 6430yds, Par 71, SSS 71, Course record 65.
Club membership 1100.
Visitors for Main course required to book in advance & have handicap certificate. May play afternoons only Mon and Tue, weekends restricted and no visitors Sun morning. Northcliffe course has no restrictions. **Societies** Wed & Fri only, by arrangement. **Green Fees** £40 per day; £30 per round (£60/40 per round weekends). **Cards**  **Prof** Darren Parris **Course Designer** Fowler & Simpson **Facilities** ⊗ ⫙ ᗏ ♨ ♀ ⚐ 🏌 🛺 ⛳ **Leisure** hard tennis courts, 18 hole par 3 course. **Location** 1.5m N off B2052

Hotel ★★★ 64% Royal Albion Hotel, Albion St, BROADSTAIRS ☎ 01843 868071 19 en suite

CANTERBURY   Map 05 TR15

Canterbury Scotland Hills, Littlebourne Rd CT1 1TW
☎ 01227 453532 🖹 01227 784277
e-mail: cgc@freeola.com
Undulating parkland course, densely wooded in places, with elevated tees and challenging drives on several holes.
continued

Canterbury Golf Club

18 holes, 6249yds, Par 70, SSS 70, Course record 64.
Club membership 650.
Visitors may play after 9.30am except when competitions being held. Restricted times weekends and bank holidays. Must have handicap certificate. **Societies** by arrangement. **Green Fees** £36 per day, £30 per round; (£36 weekends). **Cards** ▨ ▬ ▨ ▨ ▨ ◨ **Prof** Paul Everard **Course Designer** Harry Colt **Facilities** ⊗ ⅷ ⅃ ♨ ♀ ⚲ ☖ ✆ **Conf** Max 60 **Location** 1.5m E on A257

Hotel ★★★ 66% The Chaucer, Ivy Ln, CANTERBURY
☎ 0870 400 8106 42 en suite

The Ridge Chartway St, East Sutton ME17 3DL
☎ 01622 844382
This flat parkland course was designed by Patrick Dawson around mature orchards to challenge all levels of player. The par 5, 18th has two lakes to negotiate.
18 holes, 6254yds, Par 71, SSS 70, Course record 68.
Club membership 650.
Visitors weekdays only, must have handicap certificate. **Societies** Tue & Thu, by arrangement. **Green Fees** not confirmed. **Prof** Tim Milford **Course Designer** Tyton Design **Facilities** ⊗ ⅷ ⅃ ♨ ♀ ⚲ ☖ ✆ ⚒ ♒ ✆ **Leisure** solarium, gymnasium. **Location** 5m S of Bearsted, off A274

Hotel ★★★★ 71% Marriott Tudor Park Hotel & Country Club, Ashford Rd, Bearsted, MAIDSTONE
☎ 01622 734334 120 en suite

Hemsted Forest Golford Rd TN17 4AL
☎ 01580 712833 ▤ 01580 714274
e-mail: golf@hemsteadforest.co.uk
Scenic, parkland course with easy terrain, backed by Hemstead Forest and close to Sissinghurst Castle (1m) and Bodiam Castle (6m). The course has been transformed over recent years with the introduction of over 5,000 mature pine trees. Keeping the ball straight is paramount, a challenging test of golf for all levels.
18 holes, 6305yds, Par 70, SSS 71, Course record 64.
Club membership 1600.
Visitors welcome weekdays after 8am, weekends after 11am. Tee reservations may be booked up to one calendar month in advance. **Societies** telephone to book. **Green Fees** £25 per round (£35 weekends). **Cards** ▨ ▨ ▨ ◨ **Prof** Karl Steptoe **Course Designer** Commander J Harris **Facilities** ⊗ ⅷ ⅃ ♀ ⚲ ☖ ✆ ✆ **Conf** Max 50 **Location** 2m E

Hotel ★★♨ Kennel Holt Hotel, Goudhurst Rd, CRANBROOK ☎ 01580 712032 10 en suite

Birchwood Park Birchwood Rd, Wilmington DA2 7HJ
☎ 01322 662038 & 660554 ▤ 01322 667283
The main course offers highly challenging play and will test golfers of all abilities. Beginners and those requiring a quick game or golfers wishing to improve their short game will appreciate the Orchard course where holes range from 96 to 258yards.
18 holes, 6364yds, Par 71, SSS 70, Course record 64.
Orchard: 9 holes, 1349yds, Par 29.
Club membership 500.
Visitors must contact in advance for Main Course. **Societies** telephone for details. **Green Fees** not confirmed. **Cards** ▨ ▨ ▨ ▨ ◨ **Course Designer** Howard Swann **Facilities** ⊗ ⅷ ⅃ ♨ ♀ ⚲ ☖ ⚒ ♒ ⚒ ✆ ✆ **Leisure** sauna, solarium, gymnasium. **Location** B258 between Dartford & Swanley

Hotel ★★★★ 69% Bexleyheath Marriott Hotel, 1 Broadway, BEXLEYHEATH ☎ 020 8298 1000 138 en suite

Dartford Heath Ln (Upper), Dartford Heath DA1 2TN
☎ 01322 226455
e-mail: dartfordgolf@hotmail.com
Heathland course.
18 holes, 5914yds, Par 69, SSS 69, Course record 62.
Club membership 700.
Visitors may not play at weekends. Must have a handicap certificate. **Societies** Mon & Fri only by prior arrangement with Secretary. **Green Fees** not confirmed. **Prof** John Gregory **Course Designer** James Braid **Facilities** ⊗ ⅷ ⅃ ♀ ⚲ ☖ ✆

Hotel ★★★ 66% Holiday Inn Bexley, Black Prince Interchange, Southwold Rd, BEXLEY
☎ 0870 400 9006 108 en suite

Royal Cinque Ports Golf Rd CT14 6RF
☎ 01304 374007 ▤ 01304 379530
e-mail: rcpgcsec@aol.com
Famous championship seaside links, windy but with easy walking. Outward nine is generally considered the easier, inward nine is longer and includes the renowned 16th, perhaps the most difficult hole. On a fine day there are wonderful views across the Channel.
18 holes, 6761yds, Par 72, SSS 73.
Club membership 950.
Visitors restricted Wed mornings, weekends & bank holidays. Must contact in advance and have a handicap certificate. Men max 24 handicap; Ladies max 36 handicap. **Societies** must contact in advance. **Green Fees** £65 per day/round; £55 after 1pm. **Cards** ▨ ▨ ◨ **Prof** Andrew Reynolds **Course Designer** James Braid **Facilities** ⊗ ⅷ by prior arrangement ⅃ ♀ ⚲ ☖ ⚒ ♒ ✆ ✆ **Location** Along seafront at N end of Deal

Hotel ★★★ 70% Dunkerleys Hotel & Restaurant, 19 Beach St, DEAL ☎ 01304 375016 16 en suite

Edenbridge Golf & Country Club Crouch House Rd TN8 5LQ ☎ 01732 865097 & 867381 ▤ 01732 867029
Two parkland course with water on many holes, quiet with excellent views of rural Kent and Surrey.
Old Course: 18 holes, 6646yds, Par 73, SSS 72.
New Course: 18 holes, 5605yds, Par 67, SSS 68.
Club membership 750.   *continued*

Edenbridge Golf & Tennis Centre

Visitors must contact in advance for Old Course. All tee times bookable 7 days in advance. **Societies** contact in advance. **Green Fees** terms on application. **Cards** 🔲 🔲 🔲 🔲 **Facilities** ⊗ 🎿 🏌 🍽 ♟ 🏊 🏠 🏌 🚗 🏌 ⚑ **Leisure** hard tennis courts, sauna, gymnasium.**Conf** Max 200 **Location** 0.75m W of town centre, signposted 'Golf Course'

Hotel ★★★ 🏨 Gravetye Manor Hotel, EAST GRINSTEAD ☎ 01342 810567 18 en suite

Sweetwoods Park Cowden TN8 7JN ☎ 01342 850729 (Pro shop) & 850942 (Secretary) 📠 01342 850866
An undulating and mature parkland course with very high quality greens, testing water hazards and fine views across the Weald from four holes. A good challenge off the back tees. Signature holes include the 2nd, 4th and 14th.
18 holes, 6512yds, Par 71, SSS 71, Course record 67. Club membership 800.
Visitors no restrictions. **Societies** Mon-Fri after 9am & Sat pm. Contact for details. **Green Fees** not confirmed. **Cards** 🔲 🔲 🔲 🔲 🔲 **Prof** Ben Clover **Course Designer** P Strand **Facilities** ⊗ 🎿 🏌 🍽 ♟ 🏊 🏠 🏌 🚗 🏌 ⚑ **Location** 5m E of East Grinstead on the A264

Hotel ★★★ 64% Woodbury House Hotel, Lewes Rd, EAST GRINSTEAD ☎ 01342 313657 13 en suite

EYNSFORD   Map 05 TQ56

Austin Lodge Upper Austin Lodge Rd DA4 0HU
☎ 01322 863000 📠 01322 862406
A well drained course designed to lie naturally in three secluded valleys in rolling countryside. Over 7000 yds from the medal tees. Practice ground, nets and a putting green add to the features.
18 holes, 6600yds, Par 73, SSS 71, Course record 68. Club membership 600.
Visitors must contact in advance, may not play until after 1pm on weekends. **Societies** telephone for bookings. **Green Fees** £20 per round (£25 weekends). **Cards** 🔲 🔲 🔲 🔲 **Prof** Trevour Dongate **Course Designer** P Bevan **Facilities** ⊗ 🎿 🏌 🍽 ♟ 🏊 🏠 🏌 🚗 🏌 ⚑ **Location** 6m S of Dartford

Hotel ★★★ 67% Brandshatch Place, Brands Hatch Rd, Fawkham, BRANDS HATCH ☎ 01474 875000 29 en suite 12 annexe en suite

FAVERSHAM   Map 05 TR06

Boughton Brickfield Ln, Boughton ME13 9AJ
☎ 01227 752277 📠 01227 752361
Rolling parkland/downland course set in 160 acres of Kent countryside, providing a good test of golf, even for the more accomplished players.   *continued*

18 holes, 6469yds, Par 72, SSS 71, Course record 68. Club membership 350.
Visitors Must phone in advance. **Societies** telephone for details. **Green Fees** not confirmed. **Cards** 🔲 🔲 🔲 🔲 **Prof** Trevor Dungate **Course Designer** P Sparks **Facilities** ⊗ 🎿 🏌 🍽 ♟ 🏊 🏠 🏌 🚗 🏌 ⚑ **Location** Off junct 7 of M2 - Brenley Corner

Hotel ★★★★ 🏨 75% Eastwell Manor, Eastwell Park, Boughton Lees, ASHFORD ☎ 01233 213000 23 en suite 39 annexe en suite

Faversham Belmont Park ME13 0HB
☎ 01795 890561 📠 01795 890760
e-mail: manager@faversham golf.co.uk
A beautiful inland course laid out over part of a large estate with pheasants walking the fairways quite tamely. Play follows two heavily wooded valleys but the trees affect only the loose shots going out of bounds. Fine views.
18 holes, 5965yds, Par 70, SSS 69, Course record 63. Club membership 800.
Visitors must have handicap certificate. With member only at weekends. Contacting the club in advance is advisable. **Societies** must contact in advance. **Green Fees** £35 per day; £30 per round. **Cards** 🔲 **Prof** Stuart Rokes **Facilities** ⊗ 🎿 🏌 🍽 ♟ 🏊 🏠 🏌 🚗 **Location** 3.5m S on road to Belmont

Hotel ★★★★ 🏨 75% Eastwell Manor, Eastwell Park, Boughton Lees, ASHFORD ☎ 01233 213000 23 en suite 39 annexe en suite

FOLKESTONE   Map 05 TR23

Etchinghill Canterbury Rd, Etchinghill CT18 8FA
☎ 01303 863863 📠 01303 863210
A varied course incorporating parkland on the outward 9 holes and an interesting downland landscape with many challenging holes on the back 9.
18 holes, 6121yds, Par 69, SSS 69, Course record 67. Club membership 600.
Visitors advisable to reserve tee time in advance. **Societies** telephone or write, packages available. **Green Fees** £18 (£24 weekends and bank holidays). **Cards** 🔲 🔲 🔲 🔲 🔲 **Prof** Chris Hodgson **Course Designer** John Sturdy **Facilities** ⊗ 🎿 🏌 🍽 ♟ 🏊 🏠 🏌 🚗 🏌 ⚑ **Leisure** 9 hole par3.**Conf** Max 35 **Location** N of M20, access from junct 11 or 12

Hotel ★★★ 69% Clifton Hotel, The Leas, FOLKESTONE ☎ 01303 223949 80 en suite

GILLINGHAM   Map 05 TQ76

Gillingham Woodlands Rd ME7 2AP
☎ 01634 853017 (office) & 855862 (pro) 📠 01634 574749
Parkland course.
18 holes, 5557yds, Par 69, SSS 67, Course record 64. Club membership 800.
Visitors contact in advance, weekends only with member, must have handicap certificate. **Societies** must apply in writing. **Green Fees** not confirmed. **Prof** Mark Day **Course Designer** James Braid/Steel **Facilities** ⊗ 🏌 🍽 ♟ 🏊 🏠 🏌 🚗 ⚑ **Location** 1.5m SE on A2

Hotel ★★★ 69% Holiday Inn Rochester, Maidstone Rd, ROCHESTER ☎ 0870 400 9069 145 en suite

GRAVESEND   Map 05 TQ67

Mid Kent Singlewell Rd DA11 7RB
☎ 01474 568035 📠 01474 564218
A well-maintained downland course with some easy walking and some excellent greens. The first hole is short, but nonetheless a real challenge. The slightest hook and the ball is out of bounds or lost.
18 holes, 6199yds, Par 69, SSS 69, Course record 60.
Club membership 900.
Visitors must contact in advance & have handicap certificate. May not play weekends. **Societies** Tue only, apply in writing. **Green Fees** £35 per day; £25 per round. **Prof** Mark Foreman **Course Designer** Frank Pennick **Facilities** ⊗ ⫿⫿ by prior arrangement 🏌 ☕ ♀ 🏌 🍴 ⛳ **Location** S side of town centre off A227

Hotel ⬆ Travel Inn, Wrotham Rd, GRAVESEND ☎ 01474 533556 36 en suite

Southern Valley Thong Ln, Shorne DA12 4LF
☎ 01474 568568 📠 01474 360366
e-mail: info@southernvalley.co.uk
All year playing conditions on a course landscaped with gorse, bracken and thorn and designed to enhance the views across the Thames Estuary. The course features undulating greens, large trees and rolling fairways with both the 9th and 18th holes located close to the clubhouse.,
18 holes, 6100yds, Par 69, SSS 69.
Club membership 450.
Visitors no restrictions. **Societies** must telephone in advance. **Green Fees** £16 mon-thur, £16.50 fri, (£19 weekends). **Cards** 🔳 🔳 🔳 🔳 🔳 **Prof** Larry Batchelor **Course Designer** Richardson **Facilities** ⊗ ⫿⫿ 🏌 ☕ ♀ 🏌 🍴 ⛳ ⛳ **Location** From A2 junct 4 at top of slip-road turn left into Thong Lane and continue for 1m

Hotel ★★★ 72% Manor Hotel, Hever Court Rd, GRAVESEND ☎ 01474 353100 52 en suite

HALSTEAD   Map 05 TQ46

Broke Hill Sevenoaks Rd TN14 7HR
☎ 01959 533225 📠 01959 532680
Testing downland course featuring 80 bunkers, strategically placed water hazards and good views.

18 holes, 6454yds, Par 72, SSS 71, Course record 69.
Club membership 650.
Visitors weekdays only. Must book in advance. **Societies** telephone for details. **Green Fees** not confirmed. **Cards** 🔳 🔳 🔳 🔳 🔳 **Prof** Chris West **Course Designer** David Williams **Facilities** ⊗ ⫿⫿ 🏌 ☕ ♀ 🏌 🍴 ⛳ ⛳ ⛳ **Leisure** sauna. **Location** Off junct 4 of M25, opposite Knockholt railway station

continued

Hotel ★★★ 69% Donnington Manor, London Rd, Dunton Green, SEVENOAKS ☎ 01732 462681 60 en suite

HAWKHURST   Map 05 TQ73

Hawkhurst High St TN18 4JS
☎ 01580 754074 & 752396 📠 01580 754074
e-mail: hawkhead@tesco.net
Undulating parkland course.
9 holes, 5751yds, Par 70, SSS 68, Course record 69.
Club membership 500.
Visitors may play weekdays, weekends after 12 noon. **Societies** must apply in advance. **Green Fees** £18 per round (£20 weekends). **Prof** Tony Collins **Course Designer** W A Baldock **Facilities** ⊗ ⫿⫿ 🏌 ☕ ♀ 🏌 🍴 ⛳ **Leisure** squash. **Conf** Max 100 **Location** W side of village off A268

Hotel ★★ 65% Tudor Court Hotel, Rye Rd, HAWKHURST ☎ 01580 752312 18 en suite

HEADCORN   Map 05 TQ84

Weald of Kent Maidstone Rd TN27 9PT
☎ 01622 891671 📠 01622 891793
Enjoying delightful views over the Weald of Kent, this pay and play course features a range of natural hazards, including lakes, trees, ditches and undulating fairways. A good test to golfers of every standard.
18 holes, 6240yds, Par 70, SSS 70, Course record 64.
Club membership 450.
Visitors can book 3 days in advance, smart casual dress no jeans. **Societies** apply in writing or by telephone. **Green Fees** terms on application. **Cards** 🔳 🔳 🔳 🔳 **Prof** Paul Fosten **Course Designer** John Millen **Facilities** ⊗ ⫿⫿ 🏌 ☕ ♀ 🏌 🍴 ⛳ ⛳ ⛳ ⛳ **Leisure** training facilites available. **Conf** Max 250 Thtr 200 Class 200 Board 50 Banquet 180 **Location** From M20 Leeds castle junct, through Leeds village take A274 towards Headcorn, golf course on left

Hotel ★★★★ 71% Marriott Tudor Park Hotel & Country Club, Ashford Rd, Bearsted, MAIDSTONE ☎ 01622 734334 120 en suite

HERNE BAY   Map 05 TR16

Herne Bay Eddington CT6 7PG ☎ 01227 374727
Parkland course with bracing air.
18 holes, 5567yds, Par 68, SSS 68.
Club membership 500.
Visitors may not play mornings at weekends. **Societies** apply in advance. **Green Fees** terms on application. **Prof** A Sharpin **Course Designer** James Braid **Facilities** ⊗ by prior arrangement ⫿⫿ by prior arrangement 🏌 ☕ ♀ 🏌 🍴 ⛳ **Location** On A299 at Herne Bay/Canterbury junct

Hotel ★★★ 67% Falstaff Hotel, 8-10 St Dunstans St, Westgate, CANTERBURY ☎ 01227 462138 25 en suite 22 annexe en suite

HEVER   Map 05 TQ44

Hever Hever Rd, Edenbridge TN8 7NP
☎ 01732 700771 📠 01732 700775
e-mail: golf@hever.com
This 27-hole parkland course is set in 250 acres with water hazards and outstanding holes like the par 3 12th which is similar to the 12th at Augusta.
27 holes, 6761yds, Par 72, SSS 73, Course record 69.
Club membership 450.
Visitors May not play before 10.30am weekdays and 11.00am weekends. **Societies** Apply in writing or by phone.

continued

Hever Golf Club

Green Fees not confirmed. **Cards** 🔲 🔲 🔲 🔲 🔲 🔲
Prof Peter Parks **Course Designer** Dr Nicholas **Facilities** ✪
🌐 🏧 🔳 ♀ ⚒ 🏠 🚩 🚁 🏌 ♩ **Leisure** hard tennis courts,
heated indoor swimming pool, sauna, solarium, gymnasium.
Location 10mins from M25, 1 mile past Hever Castle on the
right.

Hotel ★★★ *77%* The Spa Hotel, Mount Ephraim,
TUNBRIDGE WELLS ☎ 01892 520331 71 en suite

HILDENBOROUGH   Map 05 TQ54

Nizels Nizels Ln TN11 9LU
☎ 01732 838926 (Bookings) 📖 01732 833764
18 holes, 6408yds, Par 72, SSS 71, Course record 66.
Course Designer Donaldson/Edwards Partnership
Location Off B245
Telephone for further details

Hotel ★★★ *66%* Rose & Crown Hotel, 125 High St,
TONBRIDGE ☎ 01732 357966 49 en suite

HOO   Map 05 TQ77

Deangate Ridge Dux Court Rd ME3 8RZ
☎ 01634 251180 📖 01634 250537
Parkland, municipal course designed by Fred Hawtree.
18-hole pitch and putt.
18 holes, 6300yds, Par 71, SSS 70, Course record 65.
Club membership 500.
Visitors no restrictions. **Societies** please telephone 01634
254481 **Green Fees** terms on application. **Cards** 🔲 🔲
🔳 📖 **Prof** Richard Fox **Course Designer** Hawtree **Facilities**
✪ 🌐 🏧 🔳 ♀ ⚒ 🏠 🚩 🚁 🏌 ♩ **Leisure** hard tennis courts,
gymnasium. **Location** 4m NE of Rochester off A228

Hotel ★★★ *69%* Holiday Inn Rochester, Maidstone Rd,
ROCHESTER ☎ 0870 400 9069 145 en suite

HYTHE   Map 05 TR13

Hythe Imperial Princes Pde CT21 6AE
☎ 01303 267441 📖 01303 264610
e-mail: hytheimperial@marstonhotels.com
A 9-hole 18 tee links course bounded by the Royal
Military Canal and the English Channel. Although the
course is relatively flat, its aspect offers an interesting
and challenging round to a wide range of golfers
9 holes, 5560yds, Par 68, SSS 66, Course record 62.
Club membership 300.
Visitors course closed some Sun until 11am for
competitions. **Societies** advisable to telephone. **Green Fees**
£18. **Cards** 🔲 🔲 🔲 📇 🔲 🔳 📖 **Prof** Gordon Ritchie
Facilities ✪ 🌐 🏧 🔳 ♀ ⚒ 🏠 🚩 🚁 🏌 ♩ **Leisure** hard and
grass tennis courts, heated indoor swimming pool, squash,
sauna, solarium, gymnasium, croquet, snooker, hair & beauty

continued

salon. **Conf** Max 250 Thtr 250 Class 100 Board 60 Banquet
220 Del £45 * **Location** SE side of town

Hotel ★★★★ *77%* The Hythe Imperial Hotel, Princes Pde,
HYTHE ☎ 01303 267441 100 en suite
Additional hotel ★★★ *73%* Stade Court, West Pde,
HYTHE ☎ 01303 268263 Fax 01303 261803 42 en suite

Sene Valley Sene CT18 8BL ☎ 01303 268513
(Manager) & 268514 (Pro) 📖 01303 237513
A two-level downland course which provides interesting
golf over an undulating landscape with sea views.
18 holes, 6196yds, Par 71, SSS 70, Course record 61.
Club membership 600.
Visitors must contact professional in advance. **Societies**
telephone in advance. **Green Fees** terms on application.
Cards 🔲 🔲 **Prof** Nick Watson **Course Designer** Henry
Cotton **Facilities** ✪ 🌐 🏧 🔳 ♀ ⚒ 🏠 🚁 🏌 **Location** 1m
NE off B2065

Hotel ★★★★ *77%* The Hythe Imperial Hotel, Princes Pde,
HYTHE ☎ 01303 267441 100 en suite

KINGSDOWN   Map 05 TR34

Walmer & Kingsdown The Leas CT14 8EP
☎ 01304 373256 & 363017 📖 01304 382336
e-mail: kingsdown.golf@gtwiz.co.uk
This beautiful downland site is situated near Deal and
offers breathtaking views of the channel from every
hole. The course is famous as being the one on which,
in 1964, Assistant Professional, Roger Game became
the first golfer in Britain to hole out in one at two
successive holes; the 7th and 8th. The course is
situated on top of the cliffs, with fine views.

18 holes, 6444yds, Par 72, SSS 71, Course record 66.
Club membership 680.
Visitors must contact in advance. Not before 9.30am
weekdays and noon weekends & bank holidays. **Societies**
apply in advance. **Green Fees** £35 per day; £30 per round
(£35 per round weekends). **Prof** Matthew Paget **Course**
Designer James Braid **Facilities** ✪ 🌐 🏧 🔳 ♀ ⚒ 🏠 🚩
🚁 🏌 **Location** 1.5m E of Ringwould off A258 Dover-
Deal road

Hotel ★★★ *70%* Dunkerleys Hotel & Restaurant, 19
Beach St, DEAL ☎ 01304 375016 16 en suite

LAMBERHURST   Map 05 TQ63

Lamberhurst Church Rd TN3 8DT
☎ 01892 890591 📖 01892 891140
e-mail: secretary@lamberhurstgolfclub.com
Parkland course crossing river twice. Fine views.
18 holes, 6345yds, Par 72, SSS 70, Course record 65.
Club membership 650. *continued*

Visitors may only play after noon weekends unless with member, handicap certificate required. **Societies** Tue, Wed & Thu only from Apr-Oct, by arrangement. **Green Fees** terms on application. **Cards** 🌐 💳 📇 💳 **Prof** Brian Impett **Facilities** ⊗ 🍽 ⬥ 🍺 ♀ ⛴ 🏠 🛥 ♣ ✓ **Location** N side of village on B2162

Hotel ★★★ 77% The Spa Hotel, Mount Ephraim, TUNBRIDGE WELLS ☎ 01892 520331 71 en suite

LITTLESTONE   Map 05 TR02

Littlestone St Andrew's Rd TN28 8RB
☎ 01797 363355 📠 01797 362740
e-mail: secretary@littlestonegolfclub.org.uk
Located in the Romney Marshes, this flattish seaside links course calls for every variety of shot. The 8th, 15th, 16th and 17th are regarded as classics by international golfers. Easy going for all ages.
18 holes, 6471yds, Par 71, SSS 72, Course record 67.
Club membership 550.
Visitors must contact in advance, no visitors before 3pm weekends and bank holidays. **Societies** must apply in advance. **Green Fees** £50 per day; £36 per round (£60/£45 weekends and bank holidays). **Cards** 🌐 💳 📇 💳 **Prof** Andrew Jones **Course Designer** Laidlaw Purves **Facilities** ⊗ 🍽 ⬥ 🍺 ♀ ⛴ 🏠 🛥 ✓ **Leisure** hard tennis courts. **Location** 1m from New Romney off Littlestone road B2070

Hotel ★★★★ 77% The Hythe Imperial Hotel, Princes Pde, HYTHE ☎ 01303 267441 100 en suite

Romney Warren St Andrews Rd TN28 8RB
☎ 01797 362231 📠 01797 363511
e-mail: info@romneywarrengolfclub.org.uk
A links style course, normally very dry. Flat providing easy walking and play challenged by sea breezes.
18 holes, 5126yds, Par 67, SSS 65, Course record 63.
Club membership 300.
Visitors contact professional in advance. **Societies** contact in advance. **Green Fees** £15 per round (£20 weekends and bank holidays). **Cards** 🌐 💳 📇 💳 **Prof** Andrew Jones **Facilities** ⊗ 🍽 ⬥ 🍺 ♀ ⛴ 🏠 🛥 ✓ **Location** N side of Littlestone

Hotel ★★★★ 77% The Hythe Imperial Hotel, Princes Pde, HYTHE ☎ 01303 267441 100 en suite

LYDD   Map 05 TR02

Lydd Romney Rd TN29 9LS
☎ 01797 320808 & 321201 📠 01797 321482
e-mail: info@luddgolfclub.co.uk
A links-type course offering some interesting challenges, including a number of eye-catching water hazards, wide fairways and plenty of semi-rough. A good test for experienced golfers and appealing to the complete novice.
18 holes, 6517yds, Par 71, SSS 71, Course record 65.
Club membership 490.
Visitors contact in advance, may play weekends subject to availability. **Societies** telephone in advance. **Green Fees** £30 per day; £17 per round (£40/£25 weekends). **Cards** 🌐 💳 📇 💳 **Prof** Stuart Smith **Course Designer** Mike Smith **Facilities** ⊗ 🍽 by prior arrangement ⬥ 🍺 ♀ ⛴ 🏠 🛥 ✓ **Conf** Class 50 Board 50 Banquet 50 **Location** Off A259 onto B2075 by Lydd Airport

Hotel ★★★ 63% The George, High St, RYE
☎ 01797 222114 22 en suite

MAIDSTONE   Map 05 TQ75

Cobtree Manor Park Chatham Rd, Sandling ME14 3AZ ☎ 01622 753276 📠 01634 262003
An undulating parkland course with some water hazards.
18 holes, 5611yds, Par 69, SSS 69, Course record 66.
Club membership 500.
Visitors no restrictions but advisable to telephone 4 days in advance. **Societies** Mon-Fri only, by arrangement tel: 01622 751881. **Green Fees** terms on application. **Cards** 🌐 💳 📇 💳 **Prof** Paul Foston **Facilities** ⊗ ⬥ 🍺 ♀ ⛴ 🏠 🛥 **Location** On A229 0.25m N of M20 junc 6

Hotel ★★★ 69% Russell Hotel, 136 Boxley Rd, MAIDSTONE ☎ 01622 692221 42 en suite

Leeds Castle Ashford Rd ME17 1PL
☎ 01622 767828 & 880467 📠 01622 735616
e-mail: golf@leeds-castle.co.uk
Situated around Leeds Castle, this is one of the most picturesque courses in Britain. Redesigned in the 1980s by Neil Coles, it is a challenging 9-hole course with the added hazard of the Castle moat.

9 holes, 2681yds, Par 33, SSS 33, Course record 30.
Visitors bookings taken from 6 days in advance. **Societies** must telephone in advance. **Green Fees** terms on application. **Cards** 🌐 💳 📇 💳 **Prof** Steve Purves **Course Designer** Neil Coles **Facilities** ⊗ 🍺 ♀ ⛴ 🏠 🛥 ✓ **Leisure** Green fees include admission to Leeds Castle's Gardens & Attractions. **Location** On A20 towards Lenham, 4m E of Maidstone via M20 junct 8

Hotel ★★★★ 71% Marriott Tudor Park Hotel & Country Club, Ashford Rd, Bearsted, MAIDSTONE ☎ 01622 734334 120 en suite

Marriott Tudor Park Hotel & Country Club
Ashford Rd, Bearsted ME14 4NQ
☎ 01622 734334 📠 01622 735360
e-mail: emma.andrews@marriotthotels.co.uk
The course is set in a 220 acre former deerpark with the pleasant undulating Kent countryside as a backdrop. The natural features of the land have been incorporated into this picturesque course to form a challenge for those of both high and intermediate standard. The par 5 14th is particularly interesting. It can alter your score dramatically should you gamble with a drive to a narrow fairway. This hole has to be carefully thought out from tee to green depending on the wind direction.
18 holes, 6041yds, Par 70, SSS 69, Course record 64.
Club membership 725.
Visitors may not play Sat & Sun before noon. Contact pro shop 01622 739412 for bookings. **Societies** please call the Golf Manager. **Green Fees** terms on application. **Cards** 🌐 💳 📇 🏦 💳 **Prof** Nick McNally **Course Designer**

continued

Donald Steel **Facilities** ⊗ ⫴ 🏧 ⚑ ♀ 🛆 🏠 🛒 🛏 🐾 🚜 ✐
Leisure hard tennis courts, heated indoor swimming pool, sauna, solarium, gymnasium, steam room & jacuzzi, golf academy, health & beauty salon. **Conf** Thtr 250 Class 100 Board 60 Banquet 200 **Location** On A20, 1.25m W of M20 junct 8

Hotel ★★★★ 71% Marriott Tudor Park Hotel & Country Club, Ashford Rd, Bearsted, MAIDSTONE
☎ 01622 734334 120 en suite

RAMSGATE — Map 05 TR36

St Augustine's Cottington Rd, Cliffsend CT12 5JN
☎ 01843 590333 ▤ 01843 590444
e-mail: sagc@ic24.net
A comfortably flat course in this famous bracing Championship area of Kent. Neither as long nor as difficult as its lordly neighbours, St Augustine's will nonetheless extend most golfers. Dykes run across the course.
18 holes, 5254yds, Par 69, SSS 66, Course record 61.
Club membership 670.
Visitors must contact in advance. **Societies** must contact in advance. **Green Fees** terms on application. **Prof** Derek Scott **Course Designer** Tom Vardon **Facilities** ⊗ ⫴ 🏧 ⚑ ♀ 🛆 🏠 🚜 ✐ **Location** Off A256 Ramsgate/Sandwich

Hotel ★★★ 67% San Clu Hotel, Victoria Pde, East Cliff, RAMSGATE ☎ 01843 592345 44 en suite

ROCHESTER — Map 05 TQ76

Rochester & Cobham Park Park Pale ME2 3UL
☎ 01474 823411 ▤ 01474 824446
e-mail: rcpgc@talk21.com
A first-rate course of challenging dimensions in undulating parkland. All holes differ and each requires accurate drive placing to derive the best advantage. The clubhouse and course are situated a quarter of a mile from the western end of the M2.
18 holes, 6596yds, Par 71, SSS 72, Course record 67.
Club membership 720.
Visitors must contact in advance & have handicap certificate. No visitors weekends. **Societies** apply in advance. **Green Fees** £40 per day; £30 per round. **Prof** Iain Higgins **Course Designer** Donald Steel **Facilities** ⊗ ⫴ 🏧 ⚑ ♀ 🛆 🏠 🛒 🚜 ✐ ✐ **Location** 2.5m W on A2

Hotel ★★★★ 75% Bridgewood Manor Hotel, Bridgewood Roundabout, Walderslade Woods, CHATHAM ☎ 01634 201333 100 en suite

Play a Piece of History
at
PRINCE'S GOLF CLUB

With 27 championship holes Prince's Golf Club enjoys a worldwide reputation as a traditional links of the finest quality. Individual golfers, societies and corporate golf days are warmly welcomed 7 days a week throughout the year. Residential golf break packages with the RAC 3 star Bell Hotel, Sandwich, are available at competitive rates.
Scene of Gene Sarazen's famous Open victory in 1932, Prince's has over the years played host to:
• Open Championship • Open Championship Final Qualifier 2003 • Curtis Cup • British Ladies Strokeplay • English Ladies' Open • PGA Mastercard Tour • PGA Club Pro Championship
"Britain's Finest Course"
Gene Sarazen, first professional Grand Slammer
Prince's Golf Club, Sandwich Bay, Kent CT13 9QB
Tel: 01304 611118 Fax: 01304 612000
www.princes-leisure.co.uk
e-mail: golf@princes-leisure.co.uk

SANDWICH See page 141

SANDWICH — Map 05 TR35

Prince's Prince's Dr, Sandwich Bay CT13 9QB
☎ 01304 611118 ▤ 01304 612000
e-mail: golf@princes-leisure.co.uk
With 27 championship holes, Prince's Golf Club enjoys a world wide reputation as a traditional links of the finest quality and is a venue that provides all that is best in modern links golf. The purpose built clubhouse, located at the centre of the three loops of nine, can seat 200 diners and offers panoramic views over Sandwich Bay and the course.

Dunes: 9 holes, 3343yds, Par 36, SSS 36.
Himalayas: 9 holes, 3163yds, Par 35, SSS 35.
Shore: 9 holes, 3347yds, Par 36, SSS 36.
Club membership 250.
continued

Visitors available all week, must contact in advance. **Societies** welcome all week, please contact in advance. **Green Fees** from £45-£75 (on application). **Cards** 🖮 🖮 🖮 🖮 🖮 **Prof** Derek Barbour **Course Designer** (1951 Sir Guy Campbell & J S F Morrison) **Facilities** ⊗ 〰 🖮 🖮 🖮 🖮 🖮 🖮 🖮 🖮 **Leisure** snooker, private beach area.**Conf** Max 150 Thtr 150 Class 80 Board 30 Banquet 100 **Location** 2m E via toll road, follow signs from Sandwich

Hotel ★★★ 67% San Clu Hotel, Victoria Pde, East Cliff, RAMSGATE ☎ 01843 592345 44 en suite

Knole Park Seal Hollow Rd TN15 0HJ
☎ 01732 452150 📄 01732 463159
e-mail: secretary@knolepark.fsnet.co.uk
The course is set in a majestic park with many fine trees and deer running loose. It has a wiry turf seemingly impervious to rain. Certainly a pleasure to play on. Excellent views of Knole House and the North Downs. Outstanding greens.
18 holes, 6266yds, Par 70, SSS 70, Course record 62.
Club membership 800.
Visitors must have a handicap certificate and contact the secretary in advance, may not play at weekends or bank holidays. **Societies** telephone initially. **Green Fees** £50 per day; £40 per round. **Cards** 🖮 🖮 🖮 🖮 🖮 **Prof** Phil Sykes **Course Designer** J A Abercromby **Facilities** ⊗ 〰 🖮 🖮 🖮 🖮 🖮 🖮 **Leisure** squash. **Location** SE side of town centre off B2019

Hotel ★★★ 69% Donnington Manor, London Rd, Dunton Green, SEVENOAKS ☎ 01732 462681 60 en suite

Sheerness Power Station Rd ME12 3AE
☎ 01795 662585 📄 01795 668100
e-mail: thesecretary@sheernessgc.golfagent.co.uk
Semi-links, marshland course, few bunkers, but many ditches and water hazards.
18 holes, 6460yds, Par 72, SSS 71, Course record 66.
Club membership 650.
Visitors with member only at weekends. **Societies** weekdays only, book in advance. **Green Fees** terms on application. **Prof** L Stanford **Facilities** ⊗ 〰 by prior arrangement 🖮 🖮 🖮 🖮 🖮 🖮 **Location** 1.5m E off A249

Hotel ★★★★ 75% Bridgewood Manor Hotel, Bridgewood Roundabout, Walderslade Woods, CHATHAM ☎ 01634 201333 100 en suite

Darenth Valley Station Rd TN14 7SA
☎ 01959 522944 & 522922 📄 01959 525089
e-mail: darenthvalleygolfcourse@shoreham2000.fsbusiness.co.uk
Gently undulating picturesque parkland course in a beautiful Kentish valley, with excellent well drained greens. The course has matured and developed to become a challenge to both high and low handicap golfers.
18 holes, 6302yds, Par 72, SSS 71, Course record 64.
Visitors advisable to book in advance. **Societies** contact in advance. **Green Fees** £17.50 per round (£23 weekends). **Cards** 🖮 🖮 🖮 🖮 🖮 **Prof** David J Copsey **Facilities** ⊗ by prior arrangement 〰 by prior arrangement 🖮 🖮 🖮
continued

Conf Max 100 Class 100 Board 24 Banquet 140 **Location** 3m N of Sevenoaks, off A25 between Oxford and Eynsford

Hotel ★★★ 69% Donnington Manor, London Rd, Dunton Green, SEVENOAKS ☎ 01732 462681 60 en suite

The Oast Golf Centre Church Rd, Tonge ME9 9AR
☎ 01795 473527
e-mail: range@oastgolf.freeserve.co.uk
A par 3 Approach course of 9 holes with 18 tees augmented by a 17-bay floodlit driving range and a putting green.
9 holes, 1664yds, Par 54, SSS 54.
Visitors no restrictions. **Societies** telephone in advance. **Green Fees** £7 per 18 holes; £5 per 9 holes. **Prof** D Chambers **Course Designer** D Chambers **Facilities** 🖮 🖮 🖮 🖮 🖮 🖮 **Location** 2m NE, A2 between Bapchild/Teynham

Hotel ★★★★ 75% Bridgewood Manor Hotel, Bridgewood Roundabout, Walderslade Woods, CHATHAM ☎ 01634 201333 100 en suite

Sittingbourne & Milton Regis Wormdale, Newington ME9 7PX ☎ 01795 842261 ☎ 01795 844117
e-mail: sittingbourne@golfclub.totalserve.co.uk
A downland course with pleasant vistas. There are a few uphill climbs, but the course is far from difficult. The new back nine holes are very testing.
18 holes, 6291yds, Par 71, SSS 70, Course record 63.
Club membership 670.
Visitors by prior arrangement or letter of introduction. Must contact in advance, may not play at weekends. **Societies** Tue & Thu, apply in advance. **Green Fees** £35 per 36 holes; £25 per round. **Prof** John Hearn **Course Designer** Donald Steel **Facilities** ⊗ 〰 🖮 🖮 🖮 🖮 🖮 🖮 🖮 **Location** Turn off Chestnut Street (old A249) at Danaway

Hotel ★★★★ 75% Bridgewood Manor Hotel, Bridgewood Roundabout, Walderslade Woods, CHATHAM ☎ 01634 201333 100 en suite

Upchurch River Valley Golf Centre Oak Ln, Upchurch ME9 7AY ☎ 01634 379592 📄 01634 387784
Undulating parkland course set in picturesque countryside. Testing water hazards on several holes. Excellent winter course. The 9-hole course is ideal for beginners and for those keen to sharpen up their short game.
18 holes, 6237yds, Par 70, SSS 70.
Club membership 541.
Visitors can play anytime, book for weekend 5 days in advance, weekdays 2 days in advance. **Societies** telephone 01634 360626 for details. **Green Fees** not confirmed. **Cards** 🖮 **Prof** Roger Cornwell **Course Designer** David Smart **Facilities** ⊗ 〰 🖮 🖮 🖮 🖮 🖮 🖮 🖮 **Leisure** heated outdoor swimming pool. **Location** A2 between Rainham and Newington

Hotel ★★★ 69% Russell Hotel, 136 Boxley Rd, MAIDSTONE ☎ 01622 692221 42 en suite

If the name of the club appears in *italics*, details have not been confirmed for this edition of the guide

Royal St George's

Sandwich, *Kent*   ☎ 01304 613090   Fax 01304 611245   Map 05 TR35

e-mail: secretary@royalstgeorges.com

Consistently ranked among the leading golf courses in the world, Royal St George's occupies a unique place in the history of golf, playing host, in 1894, to the first Open Championship played outside Scotland. Set among the dunes of Sandwich Bay, the Links provide a severe test for even the greatest of golfers. Only two Open winners, (Bill Rogers in 1981 and Greg Norman in 1993) have managed to be under par after the 72 holes. The undulations on the fairways, the borrows on the greens, the strategically placed bunkers and the prevailing winds, which blow on all but the rarest of occasions, soon reveal any weaknesses and there are few, over the years, who have mastered all the vagaries in one round.

Visitors must contact in advance and have a handicap certificate. All golf is two ball golf. May not play at weekends or bank holidays.

Societies Mon-Fri, must apply in writing

Green Fees 18 holes £75; 36 holes £110

Facilities ⊗ ⌇ ⌇ ⌇ ⌇ ⌇ ⌇ ⌇
Professional (A. Brooks)

Location Sandwich CT13 9PB
(1.5m E of Sandwich, signed from town)

Holes/Par/Course record 18 holes, 6930 yds, Par 70, SSS 74, Course record 63

Championship Course

SNODLAND   Map 05 TQ76

Oastpark Malling Rd ME6 5LG

☎ 01634 242661 ▤ 01634 240744

A challenging parkland course for golfers of all abilities. The course has water hazards, orchards and views across the Valley of Dean.

18 holes, 6173yds, Par 69, SSS 69, Course record 71. Club membership 300.

Visitors may book 7 days in advance. **Societies** early booking with deposits required. **Green Fees** not confirmed. **Cards** 💳 💳 💳 💳 **Prof** Nathan French **Course Designer** J D Banks **Facilities** ⊗ ⅶ ⅃ ⬛ ♀ ⚘ 🏠 ⚐ ℂ **Location** Access via junct 4 on M20

Hotel ★★★ 64% Larkfield Priory Hotel, London Rd, Larkfield, MAIDSTONE ☎ 01732 846858 52 en suite

TENTERDEN   Map 05 TQ83

Tenterden Woodchurch Rd TN30 7DR

☎ 01580 763987 (sec) & 762409 (shop) ▤ 01580 763987

e-mail: tenterden-golf-club@lineone.net

Set in tranquil undulating parkland with beautiful views, the course is challenging with several difficult holes.

18 holes, 6071yds, Par 70, SSS 69, Course record 61. Club membership 600.

Visitors contact secretary. May only play with member weekends and bank holidays. Handicap certificate required. **Societies** contact secretary, full details on request. **Green Fees** £22.50. **Prof** Kyle Kelsall **Facilities** ⊗ ⅶ ⅃ ⬛ ♀ ⚘ 🏠 🐎 🚜 ⚐ **Location** 0.75m E on B2067

Hotel ★★★🏠🏠 Kennel Holt Hotel, Goudhurst Rd, CRANBROOK ☎ 01580 712032 10 en suite

TONBRIDGE   Map 05 TQ54

Poultwood Higham Ln TN11 9QR

☎ 01732 364039 & 366180 ▤ 01732 353781

There are two public 'pay and play' parkland courses in an idyllic woodland setting. The courses are ecologically designed, over predominantly flat land offering challenging hazzards and interesting playing conditions for all standards of golfer.

Course 1: 18 holes, 5569yds, Par 68, SSS 67 or 9 holes, 1281yds, Par 28.
Course 2: 9 holes, 1218yds, Par 28, SSS 28.

Visitors non registered golfers may book up to 2 days in advance for 18 hole course, or take available tee times, pay and play system on 9 hole. **Societies** apply in advance to the clubhouse manager tel 01732 366180. **Green Fees** £12.50 per 18 holes (£18 weekends and bank holidays);£5 per 9 holes(£6.60 weekends and bank holidays). **Cards** 💳 💳 💳 💳 **Prof** Chris Miller **Course Designer** Hawtree **Facilities** ⊗ ⅶ ⅃ ⬛ ♀ ⚘ 🏠 ⚐ ⚐ **Leisure** squash. **Conf** Max 20 **Location** Off A227, 3m N of Tonbridge

Hotel ★★★ 66% Rose & Crown Hotel, 125 High St, TONBRIDGE ☎ 01732 357966 49 en suite

TUNBRIDGE WELLS (ROYAL)   Map 05 TQ53

Nevill Benhall Mill Rd TN2 5JW

☎ 01892 525818 ▤ 01892 517861

e-mail: manager@nevillgolfclub.co.uk

The county boundaries of Kent and Sussex run along the northern perimeter of the course. Open undulating ground, well-wooded with some heather and gorse for the first half. The second nine holes slope away from the clubhouse to a valley where a narrow stream hazards two holes. *continued*

18 holes, 6349yds, Par 71, SSS 70, Course record 64. Club membership 800.

Visitors must contact 48 hours in advance, handicap certificate required, permission from secretary for weekends play. **Societies** must apply in writing one month in advance. **Green Fees** £33 per day; £25 per round. **Prof** Paul Huggett **Course Designer** Henry Cotton **Facilities** ⊗ ⅶ ⅃ ⬛ ♀ ⚘ 🏠 ⚐ **Location** S of Tunbridge Wells, off forest road

Hotel ★★★ 77% The Spa Hotel, Mount Ephraim, TUNBRIDGE WELLS ☎ 01892 520331 71 en suite

Tunbridge Wells Langton Rd TN4 8XH

☎ 01892 523034 ▤ 01892 536918

Somewhat hilly, well-bunkered parkland course with lake; trees form natural hazards.

9 holes, 4725yds, Par 65, SSS 62, Course record 59. Club membership 470.

Visitors must contact in advance, limited availability weekends. **Societies** weekdays, apply in advance. **Green Fees** not confirmed. **Cards** 💳 💳 💳 **Prof** Mike Barton **Facilities** ⅃ ⬛ ♀ ⚘ 🏠 ⚐ ⚐ **Location** 1m W on A264

Hotel ★★★ 77% The Spa Hotel, Mount Ephraim, TUNBRIDGE WELLS ☎ 01892 520331 71 en suite

WESTERHAM   Map 05 TQ45

Parkwood Chestnut Av, Tatsfield TN16 2EG

☎ 01959 577744 & 577177 (pro-shop) ▤ 01959 572702

e-mail: mail@parkwoodgolf.co.uk

Situated in an area of natural beauty, flanked by an ancient woodland with superb views across Kent and Surrey. An undulating course, tree lined and with some interesting water features. Playable in all weather conditions.

18 holes, 6835yds, Par 72, SSS 72, Course record 66. Club membership 500.

Visitors telephone in advance. May not play bank holidays. **Societies** apply in writing/telephone in advance. **Green Fees** terms on application. **Cards** 💳 💳 💳 💳 💳 **Prof** Nick Terry **Facilities** ⊗ ⅶ ⅃ ⬛ ♀ ⚘ 🏠 🐎 🚜 ⚐ **Location** A25 onto B2024 Croydon Rd which becomes Clarks Lane. At Church Hill junct join Chestnut Av

Hotel ★★★ 69% Donnington Manor, London Rd, Dunton Green, SEVENOAKS ☎ 01732 462681 60 en suite

Westerham Valence Park, Brasted Rd TN16 1LJ

☎ 01959 567100 ▤ 01959 567101

e-mail: t.willison@virgin.net

Originally completely wooded forestry land with thousands of mature pines. The storms of 1987 created *continued*

natural fairways and the mature landscape makes the course both demanding and spectacular. A clubhouse with first class facilities and magnificent views.
18 holes, 6272yds, Par 72, SSS 72.
Club membership 700.
Visitors welcome but may not play Sat & Sun am. **Societies** telephone events office for details. **Green Fees** £26 per round (Mon-Thurs);£30 (Fri);£35 (weekends). **Cards** 💳 💳 💳 💳 💳 💳 **Prof** Robert Sturgeon **Course Designer** D Williams **Facilities** ⊗ ⊪ ⓛ 🐴 ♀ 🏌 🏡 🍴 🚜 💈 ┇
Location A25 between Westerham and Brasted

Hotel ★★★ 69% Donnington Manor, London Rd, Dunton Green, SEVENOAKS ☎ 01732 462681 60 en suite

WESTGATE ON SEA   Map 05 TR37

Westgate and Birchington 176 Canterbury Rd
CT8 8LT ☎ 01843 831115
A fine blend of inland and seaside holes which provide a good test of the golfer despite the apparently simple appearance of the course.
18 holes, 4926yds, Par 64, SSS 64, Course record 60.
Club membership 320.
Visitors Mon-Sat after 10am, Sun and bank holidays after 11am, must contact in advance & have handicap certificate, restricted at weekends. **Societies** must contact the secretary. **Green Fees** £15 (£17 weekends). **Prof** Roger Game **Facilities** ⊗ by prior arrangement ⊪ by prior arrangement ⓛ 🏌 ♀ 🏡 🍴 💈 **Location** E side of town centre off A28

Hotel ★★★ 64% Royal Albion Hotel, Albion St, BROADSTAIRS ☎ 01843 868071 19 en suite

WEST KINGSDOWN   Map 05 TQ56

Woodlands Manor Tinkerpot Ln, Otford TN15 6AB
☎ 01959 523806 & 524161 📠 524398
e-mail: woodlandsgolf@aol.com
Two distinct nine hole layouts with views over an area of outstanding natural beauty. The course is challenging but fair with varied and memorable holes of which the 7th, 10th and 18th stand out. Good playing conditions all year round.
18 holes, 6015yds, Par 69, SSS 69.
Club membership 600.
Visitors by prior arrangement. May not play weekends am, or Tue am. **Societies** apply in advance. **Green Fees** £21 per round, £32 per day (£27 per round weekends). **Cards** 💳 💳 💳 💳 **Prof** Philip Womack **Course Designer** Lyons/Coles **Facilities** ⊗ ⊪ ⓛ 🏌 ♀ 🏡 🍴 🚜 💈 ┇
Location Through West Kingsdown on A20, turn right opposite Portbello Inn into School Lane. Continue into Tinkerpot Lane, club house left.

Hotel ★★★ 68% Holiday Inn Maidstone, London Rd, Wrotham Heath, WROTHAM ☎ 0870 400 9054 106 en suite

WEST MALLING   Map 05 TQ65

Kings Hill Fortune Way, Discovery Dr, Kings Hill
ME19 4AG ☎ 01732 875040 📠 01732 875019
e-mail: khatkhgolf@aol.com
Set in over 200 acres of undulating terrain and features large areas of protected heath and mature woodland. USGA standard greens and tees.
18 holes, 6622yards, Par 72, SSS 72.
Club membership 530.
Visitors weekdays only, book in advance. **Societies** weekdays only, book by telephone. **Green Fees** £30

continued

(weekdays only). **Cards** 💳 💳 💳 💳 💳 💳 **Prof** David Hudspith **Course Designer** David Williams Partnership **Facilities** ⊗ ⊪ by prior arrangement ⓛ 🏌 ♀ 🏡 🍴 🚜 💈 ┇ **Location** M20 junct 4, take A228 towards Tonbridge

Hotel ⓤ Travel Inn Maidstone (Leybourne), Castle Way, LEYBOURNE ☎ 01732 521630 40 en suite

WHITSTABLE   Map 05 TR16

Chestfield (Whitstable) 103 Chestfield Rd,
Chestfield CT5 3LU ☎ 01227 794411 & 792243
📠 01227 794454
e-mail: secretary@chestfield-golfclub.co.uk
Gently undulating parkland course with sea views. The par 3 3rd is generally played into the wind and the 4th has a difficult lefthand dogleg.
18 holes, 6200yds, Par 70, SSS 70, Course record 67.
Club membership 650.
Visitors contact for times, not Sun am. **Societies** must apply in writing/telephone. **Green Fees** £22 per round;£30 per day(£25 per round weekends). **Cards** 💳 💳 💳 💳 💳 **Prof** John Brotherton **Course Designer** D Steel/James Braid **Facilities** ⊗ ⊪ ⓛ 🏌 ♀ 🏡 🍴 🚜 💈 **Conf** Max 50 **Location** 0.5m S by Chestfield Railway Station, off A2990

Hotel ★★★ 66% The Chaucer, Ivy Ln, CANTERBURY ☎ 0870 400 8106 42 en suite

Whitstable & Seasalter Collingwood Rd CT5 1EB
☎ 01227 272020 📠 01227 280822
Links course.
9 holes, 5357yds, Par 66, SSS 63, Course record 62.
Club membership 350.
Visitors weekend play by prior arrangement. **Green Fees** £15 per 18 holes;£8 per 9 holes. **Facilities** ⊗ ⓛ 🏌 ♀ 🏡 **Location** W side of town centre off B2205

Hotel ★★★ 66% The Chaucer, Ivy Ln, CANTERBURY ☎ 0870 400 8106 42 en suite

LANCASHIRE

ACCRINGTON   Map 07 SD72

Accrington & District Devon Av, Oswaldtwistle
BB5 4LS ☎ 01254 381614 📠 01254 233273
e-mail: info@accrington-golf-club.com
Moorland course with pleasant views of the Pennines and surrounding areas. The course is a real test for even the best amateur golfers and has hosted many County matches and Championships over its 100 plus years history.
18 holes, 6044yds, Par 70, SSS 69, Course record 63.
Club membership 600.
Visitors must contact in advance, handicap certificate required. **Societies** contact in advance. **Green Fees** £22 Mon-Thu (£28 Fri-Sun & bank holidays). **Prof** Bill Harling **Course Designer** J Braid **Facilities** ⊗ ⊪ ⓛ 🏌 ♀ 🏡 🍴 🚜 💈 **Location** Mid way between Accrington & Blackburn

Hotel ★★★★ 65% Dunkenhalgh Hotel, Blackburn Rd, Clayton-le-Moors, ACCRINGTON ☎ 01254 398021 53 en suite 69 annexe en suite

Looking for a driving range?
See the index at the back of the guide

Baxenden & District Top o' th' Meadow, Baxenden
BB5 2EA ☎ 01254 234555
e-mail: baxgolf@hotmail.com
Moorland course with a long par 3 to start.
9 holes, 5740yds, Par 70, SSS 68, Course record 67.
Club membership 340.
Visitors may not play Sat, Sun and bank holidays except
with member. **Societies** must contact in advance. **Green Fees**
terms on application. **Facilities** ⊗ ⅷ ⅼ ♥ ♀ ⅃ 🏠 ⅾ **Location**
1.5m SE off A680

Hotel ★★★★ 65% Dunkenhalgh Hotel, Blackburn Rd,
Clayton-le-Moors, ACCRINGTON ☎ 01254 398021
53 en suite 69 annexe en suite

Green Haworth Green Haworth BB5 3SL
☎ 01254 237580 & 382510 🖹 01254 396176
e-mail: golf@greenhaworth.freeserve.co.uk
**Moorland course dominated by quarries and difficult in
windy conditions.**
9 holes, 5522yds, Par 68, SSS 67, Course record 66.
Club membership 320.
Visitors may not play Sun, Mar-Oct. **Societies** apply in
writing. Weekdays only before 5pm. Or contact secretary on
above telephone number. **Green Fees** not confirmed.
Facilities ⊗ ⅷ ⅼ ♥ ♀ ⅃ **Location** 2m S off A680

Hotel ★★★★ 65% Dunkenhalgh Hotel, Blackburn Rd,
Clayton-le-Moors, ACCRINGTON ☎ 01254 398021
53 en suite 69 annexe en suite

BACUP
Map 07 SD82
Bacup Maden Rd OL13 8HY
☎ 01706 873170 & 877726 🖹 01706 877726
9 holes, 6008yds, Par 70, SSS 69.
Location W side of town off A671
Telephone for further details

Hotel ★★★ 68% Rosehill House Hotel, Rosehill Av,
BURNLEY ☎ 01282 453931 30 en suite

BARNOLDSWICK
Map 07 SD84
Ghyll Skipton Rd BB18 6JH ☎ 01282 842466
e-mail: secretary@ghyllgc.freeserve.com
**Excellent, parkland course with outstanding views,
especially from the 8th tee where you can see the Three
Peaks. Testing 8th hole is an uphill par 4. Eleven holes in
total nine in Yorkshire and two in Lancashire.**
9 holes, 5790yds, Par 68, SSS 66, Course record 62.
Club membership 345.
Visitors may not play Tue, Fri after 4.30pm & Sun. **Societies**
must contact in writing. **Green Fees** £14 per day (£18
weekends). **Facilities** ♥ ♀ ⅃ **Location** M65 to Colne (end
of motorway). A56 toward Skipton. Turn left after Earby on
B6252

Hotel ★★★ 67% Stirk House Hotel, GISBURN
☎ 01200 445581 40 en suite 10 annexe en suite

BICKERSTAFFE
Map 07 SD40
Mossack Hall Liverpool Rd L39 0EE
☎ 01695 421717 🖹 01695 424961
**Relatively flat parkland course with scenic views. USGA
greens and water features on 4 holes.**
18 holes, 6375yards, Par 71, SSS 70, Course record 68.
Club membership 580.
Visitors must contact in advance. **Societies** write/telephone
in advance. **Green Fees** £25 per 18 holes (£30 weekends).

Prof Phil Atkiss **Course Designer** Steve Marnoch **Facilities**
⊗ ⅷ ⅼ ♥ ♀ ⅃ 🏠 ⅾ **Location** off M58 junct 3

Hotel ★★★ 65% Quality Hotel Skelmersdale, Prescott Rd,
UPHOLLAND ☎ 01695 720401 55 en suite

BLACKBURN
Map 07 SD62
Blackburn Beardwood Brow BB2 7AX
☎ 01254 51122 🖹 01254 665578
e-mail: sec@blackburngolfclub.com
**Parkland course on a high plateau with stream and hills.
Superb views of Lancashire coast and the Pennines.**
18 holes, 6144yds, Par 71, SSS 70, Course record 62.
Club membership 550.
Visitors must contact professional in advance. **Societies**
must contact in advance. **Green Fees** £24 per day (£28
weekends & bank holidays). **Prof** Alan Rodwell **Facilities** ⊗
ⅷ ⅼ ♥ ♀ ⅃ 🏠 ⅾ ⅾ **Conf** Class 50 **Location** 1.25m NW
of town centre off A677

Hotel ★★ 75% Millstone Hotel, Church Ln, Mellor,
BLACKBURN ☎ 01254 813333 18 en suite 6 annexe en
suite

BLACKPOOL
Map 07 SD33
Blackpool North Shore Devonshire Rd FY2 0RD
☎ 01253 352054 🖹 01253 591240
e-mail: office@blackpoolnorthshoregolfclub.com
Undulating parkland course.
18 holes, 6432yds, Par 71, SSS 71, Course record 63.
Club membership 900.
Visitors may not play Thu & Sat. Advisable to contact in
advance. **Societies** must contact in advance. **Green Fees** £30
(£35 weekends & bank holidays). **Prof** Brendan Ward
Facilities ⊗ ⅷ ⅼ ♥ ♀ ⅃ 🏠 ⅾ ⅾ **Leisure** Y. **Location** on
A587 N of town centre

Hotel ★★ 68% Brabyns Hotel, 1-3 Shaftesbury Av, North
Shore, BLACKPOOL ☎ 01253 354263 & 352163
🖹 01253 352915 22 en suite

Blackpool Park North Park Dr FY3 8LS
☎ 01253 397916 🖹 01253 397916
**The golf course, situated in Stanley Park is municipal.
The golf club (Blackpool Park) is private but golfers may
use the clubhouse facilities if playing the course. An
abundance of grassy pits, ponds and open dykes.**
18 holes, 6087yds, Par 70, SSS 69, Course record 64.
Club membership 600.
Visitors may not play Saturday. Must apply to Mrs A Hirst,
Town Hall, Talbot Square, Blackpool. **Societies** must apply
in writing to Mrs A Hirst, Blackpool Borough Council, Town
Hall, Talbot Square, Blackpool. **Green Fees** £12 per round
(£13.50 weekend & bank holidays). **Prof** Brian Purdie
Course Designer Mckenzie **Facilities** ⊗ ⅷ ⅼ ♥ ♀ ⅃ 🏠
ⅾ ⅾ **Location** 1m E of Blackpool Tower

Hotel ★★★ 63% Savoy Hotel, Queens Promenade, North
Shore, BLACKPOOL ☎ 01253 352561 131 en suite

De Vere Blackpool (Herons Reach) East Park
Blackpool FY3 8LL
☎ 01253 766156 & 838866 🖹 01253 798800
e-mail: Dominik.Naughton@devere-hotels.com
**The course was designed by Peter Alliss and Clive
Clarke. There are 10 man-made lakes and several
existing ponds. Built to a links design, well mounded but
fairly easy walking. Water comes into play on 9 holes,**

continued
continued

better players can go for the carry or shorter hitters can take the safe route. The course provides an excellent and interesting challenge for golfers of all standards.
18 holes, 6628yds, Par 72, SSS 71, Course record 64. Club membership 450.

De Vere Blackpool (Herons Reach Golf Course)

Visitors may book up to 2 weeks in advance tel 01253 766156, (hotel guest/visiting society no limit to how far in advance bookings can be made). Handicap essential, etiquette and dress rules must be adhered to **Societies** telephone or write to golf sales office 01253 838866. **Green Fees** not confirmed. **Cards** 🖃 ▆▆ ▆▆ 🔲 ▆▆ ▆▆ 🗉 **Prof** Dominik Naughton **Course Designer** Peter Alliss/Clive Clark **Facilities** ⊗ ⅲ 🖢 💺 ♀ 🛆 🛍 ⬧ ⋔ ⬥ 🚜 ♂ ⚓ **Leisure** hard tennis courts, heated indoor swimming pool, squash, sauna, solarium, gymnasium, health and beauty facilities. **Location** Off A587 adjacent to Stanley Park & Zoo

Hotel ★★★★ 64% De Vere Heron's Reach, East Park Dr, BLACKPOOL ☎ 01253 838866 164 en suite

BURNLEY Map 07 SD83

Burnley Glen View BB11 3RW
☎ 01282 421045 & 451281 🗐 01282 451281
e-mail: burnleygolfclub@onthegreen.co.uk
Moorland course with hilly surrounds.
18 holes, 5939yds, Par 69, SSS 69, Course record 62. Club membership 700.
Visitors must contact in advance. May not play on Saturdays. **Societies** must apply in writing. Telephone first for details. **Green Fees** £20 per day (£25 weekends & bank holidays). **Prof** Paul McEvoy **Facilities** ⊗ ⅲ 🖢 💺 ♀ 🛆 🛍 ♂ **Location** eastbound M65 junct 9, follow Halifax signs for 3m to Glen View Rd. Westbound M65 junct 10/11 to Burnley town centre, take Manchester Rd for 1m and turn left into Glen View Rd

Hotel ★★★ 68% Rosehill House Hotel, Rosehill Av, BURNLEY ☎ 01282 453931 30 en suite

Towneley Towneley Park, Todmorden Rd BB11 3ED
☎ 01282 438473
Parkland course, with other sporting facilities.
18 holes, 5811yds, Par 70, SSS 68, Course record 67. Club membership 290.
Visitors must contact in advance. **Societies** must contact in advance in writing. **Green Fees** not confirmed. **Facilities** ⊗ ⅲ 🖢 ♀ 🛆 🛍 ♂ **Location** 1m SE of town centre on A671

Hotel ★★★ 74% Oaks Hotel, Colne Rd, Reedley, BURNLEY ☎ 01282 414141 50 en suite

CHORLEY Map 07 SD51

Charnock Richard Preston Rd, Charnock Richard PR7 5LE ☎ 01257 470707 🗐 01257 794343
Flat parkland course with plenty of Americanised water hazards. Signature hole the 6th par 5 with an island green.
18 holes, 6234yds, Par 71, SSS 70, Course record 68. Club membership 550.
Visitors strict full dress code, members time 8.30-9.30pm and 12.00-1.00pm weekdays, telephone for weekend play.
Societies contact club secretary in writing. **Green Fees** terms on application. **Cards** 🖃 ▆▆ ▆▆ 🗉 **Prof** Lee Taylor **Course Designer** Chris Court **Facilities** ⊗ ⅲ 🖢 💺 ♀ 🛆 🛍 ⬧ 🚜 ♂ **Location** On the main A49, 0.25m from Camelot Theme Park

Hotel ★★★ 69% Park Hall Hotel, Park Hall Rd, Charnock Richard, CHORLEY ☎ 01257 452090 455000 🗐 01257 451838 54 en suite 84 annexe en suite

Chorley Hall o' th' Hill, Heath Charnock PR6 9HX
☎ 01257 480263 🗐 01257 480722
e-mail: secretary@chorleygolfclub.freeserve.co.uk
A splendid moorland course with plenty of fresh air. The well-sited clubhouse affords some good views of the Lancashire coast and of Angelzarke, a local beauty spot. Beware of the short 3rd hole with its menacing out-of-bounds.
18 holes, 6269yds, Par 71, SSS 70, Course record 62. Club membership 550.
Visitors must contact in advance, must play from yellow tees and may not play weekends or bank holidays.
Societies must contact in advance. Tue-Fri only. **Green Fees** £29 per round/day. **Prof** Mark Bradley **Course Designer** J A Steer **Facilities** ⊗ 🖢 💺 ♀ 🛆 🛍 🚜 ♂ **Location** 2.5m SE on A673

Hotel ★★★ 70% Pines Hotel, 570 Preston Rd, Clayton-Le-Woods, CHORLEY ☎ 01772 338551 37 en suite

Duxbury Jubilee Park Duxbury Hall Rd PR7 4AT
☎ 01257 265380 🗐 01257 274500
A municipal parkland course set in parkland and mature woodland. The contours, elevated tees and greens, the bunkers and the water hazards on several holes give constant interest and challenge, particularly around the turn when the woods come into play. The 10th to the 12th offer the hardest challenges with the 17th not far behind.
18 holes, 6390yds, Par 71, SSS 70.
Club membership 250.
Visitors must contact 6 days in advance via Pro shop.
Societies must contact in advance by letter. **Green Fees** not confirmed. **Prof** S Middelman **Course Designer** Hawtree & Sons **Facilities** ⊗ 💺 🛆 🛍 ⋔ ♂ **Location** 2.5m S off A6

continued

Hotel ↻ Welcome Lodge, Welcome Break Services, CHORLEY ☎ 01257 791746 100 en suite

Shaw Hill Hotel Golf & Country Club

Preston Rd, Whittle-Le-Woods PR6 7PP
☎ 01257 269221 📠 01257 261223
e-mail: info@shaw-hill.co.uk
A fine heavily wooded parkland course designed by one of Europe's most prominent golf architects and offering a considerable challenge as well as tranquillity and scenic charm. Six holes are protected by water and signature holes are the 8th and the closing 18th played slightly uphill to the imposing Club House.
18 holes, 6246yds, Par 72, SSS 70, Course record 65.
Club membership 500.
Visitors Mon-Fri only, must contact in advance, denims and trainers not allowed on course or in clubhouse. **Societies** must telephone in advance. **Green Fees** Summer: £30 (£40 Fri, weekends and bank holidays). Winter: £20 (£30 Fri, weekends and bank holidays). **Cards** 🃏 ▅ 🃏 🃏 🃏 🃏 🃏 **Prof** David Clark **Course Designer** Harry Vardon **Facilities** ⊗ ⑂ ᴸ ▆ ♀ ♂ ⛿ 🏌 ⛳ 🐎 ⚹ **Leisure** heated indoor swimming pool, sauna, solarium, gymnasium, Beauty salon. **Conf** Max 200 Thtr 200 Class 200 Board 200 Banquet 200 **Location** On A6 1.5m N

Hotel ★★★ 71% Shaw Hill Hotel Golf & Country Club, Preston Rd, Whittle-le-Woods, CHORLEY ☎ 01257 269221 26 en suite 4 annexe en suite

CLITHEROE   Map 07 SD74

Clitheroe Whalley Rd, Pendleton BB7 1PP
☎ 01200 422292 📠 01200 422292
e-mail: secretary@clitheroegolfclub.com
One of the best inland courses in the country. Clitheroe is a parkland-type course with water hazards and good scenic views, particularly towards Longridge, and Pendle Hill.
18 holes, 6326yds, Par 71, SSS 71, Course record 67.
Club membership 750.
Visitors must contact in advance. **Societies** must contact in advance. **Green Fees** £33 (£39 weekends & bank holidays). **Prof** John Twissell **Course Designer** James Braid **Facilities** ⊗ ⑂ ᴸ ▆ ♀ ♂ ⛿ 🏌 ⚹ ⛳ **Location** 2m S of Clitheroe on Whalley Road

Hotel ★★ 69% Shireburn Arms Hotel, Whalley Rd, Hurst Green, CLITHEROE ☎ 01254 826518 18 en suite

COLNE   Map 07 SD84

Colne Law Farm, Skipton Old Rd BB8 7EB
☎ 01282 863391
Moorland course with scenic surroundings.
9 holes, 5961yds, Par 70, SSS 69, Course record 63.
Club membership 356.
Visitors restricted Thu. Must contact in advance. **Societies** must contact in advance. **Green Fees** not confirmed. **Facilities** ⊗ ⑂ ᴸ ▆ ♀ ♂ **Location** 1m E off A56

Hotel ★★★ 67% Stirk House Hotel, GISBURN ☎ 01200 445581 40 en suite 10 annexe en suite

Where to stay, where to eat?
Visit www.theAA.com

DARWEN   Map 07 SD62

Darwen Winter Hill BB3 0LB ☎ 01254 701287 (club) & 776370 (pro) 📠 01254 773833
First 9 holes on parkland, the second 9 on moorland.
18 holes, 5863yds, Par 69, SSS 68, Course record 63.
Club membership 600.
Visitors may not play on Tue or Sat. **Societies** must contact in advance. **Green Fees** not confirmed. **Prof** Wayne Lennon **Facilities** ⊗ ⑂ ᴸ ▆ ♀ ♂ ⛿ **Location** 1m NW

Hotel ★★★ 70% Whitehall Hotel, Springbank, Whitehall, DARWEN ☎ 01254 701595 17 en suite

FLEETWOOD   Map 07 SD34

Fleetwood Princes Way FY7 8AF
☎ 01253 873661 & 773573 📠 01253 773573
e-mail: fleetwoodgc@aol.com
Championship length, flat seaside links where the player must always be alert to changes of direction or strength of the wind.

18 holes, 6723yds, Par 72, SSS 72.
Club membership 600.
Visitors may not play on competition days or Tue. **Societies** must contact in advance. A deposit of £5 per player is required. **Green Fees** terms on application. **Prof** S McLaughlin **Course Designer** J A Steer **Facilities** ⊗ ⑂ ᴸ ▆ ♀ ♂ ⛿ ⚹ **Location** W side of town centre

Hotel ★★ 68% Brabyns Hotel, 1-3 Shaftesbury Av, North Shore, BLACKPOOL ☎ 01253 354263 & 352163 📠 01253 352915 22 en suite

GARSTANG   Map 07 SD44

Garstang Country Hotel & Golf Club

Garstang Rd, Bowgreave PR3 1YE
☎ 01995 600100 📠 01995 600950
e-mail: garstanghotel@btconnect.com
Fairly flat parkland course following the contours of the Rivers Wyre and Calder and providing a steady test of ability, especially over the longer back nine. Exceptional drainage makes the course playable all year round.
18 holes, 6050yds, Par 68, SSS 68.
Visitors tee times bookable 6 days in advance. **Societies** telephone for availability and confirm in writing. **Green Fees** not confirmed. **Cards** 🃏 ▅ 🃏 🃏 🃏 🃏 🃏 **Prof** Robert Head **Course Designer** Richard Bradbeer **Facilities** ⊗ ⑂ ᴸ ▆ ♀ ♂ ⛿ 🏌 ⚹ **Location** Situated on B6430 1m S of Garstang

Hotel ★★★ 70% Pickerings, Garstang Rd, Catterall, GARSTANG ☎ 01995 600999 12 en suite

Between Royal Birkdale And Royal Lytham

... is the Garstang Country Hotel and Golf Club. An easy 18 hole course by comparison but we aim to cook better. Quiet, peaceful, modern, ideal for Veteran Sections tours, very reasonable prices, free car parking, sheep available for insomniacs to count, gorgeous countryside, golf shop knows all the local courses

01995 600 100.
Bowgreave, Garstang, Lancs.
garstangandgolfhotel.com

GREAT HARWOOD   Map 07 SD73

Great Harwood Harwood Bar, Whalley Rd BB6 7TE
☎ 01254 884391
Flat parkland course with fine views of the Pendle region.
9 holes, 6411yds, Par 73, SSS 71, Course record 68.
Club membership 380.
Visitors must contact in advance. **Societies** welcome midweek only, apply in writing. **Green Fees** not confirmed.
Facilities ⓑ ⓦ ♀ ⚘ **Location** E side of town centre on A680

Hotel ★★★★ 65% Dunkenhalgh Hotel, Blackburn Rd, Clayton-le-Moors, ACCRINGTON ☎ 01254 398021 53 en suite 69 annexe en suite

---

HASLINGDEN   Map 07 SD72

Rossendale Ewood Ln Head BB4 6LH
☎ 01706 831339 & 213616 (Pro) ▤ 01706 228669
e-mail: rgc@golfers.net
Testing meadowland course, mainly flat, situated on a plateau with panoramic views.
18 holes, 6293yds, Par 72, Course record 64.
Club membership 700.
Visitors must contact in advance. Must play with member on Sat. **Societies** must telephone in advance & confirm in writing. **Green Fees** not confirmed. **Prof** Stephen Nicholls
Facilities ⓧ ⑩ ⓑ ⓦ ♀ (ex Mon) ⚘ ⓕ ⚐ **Location** 0.5m S off A56

Hotel ★★ 75% Millstone Hotel, Church Ln, Mellor, BLACKBURN ☎ 01254 813333
18 en suite 6 annexe en suite

HEYSHAM   Map 07 SD46

Heysham Trumacar Park, Middleton Rd LA3 3JH
☎ 01524 851011 ▤ 01524 853030
e-mail: secretary@heyshamgolf.freeserve.co.uk
Seaside parkland course, partly wooded. The 15th is a 459 yard par 4 hole nearly always played into the prevailing south west wind.
18 holes, 6266yds, Par 69, SSS 70, Course record 64.
Club membership 930.
Visitors book in advance via the professional, restricted at weekends. **Societies** must contact in advance. **Green Fees** £27 per day; £23 per round (£35 weekends & bank holidays). **Prof** Ryan Done **Course Designer** Alex Herd **Facilities** ⓧ ⑩ ⓑ ⓦ ♀ ⚘ ⓕ ⚐ **Leisure** snooker. **Location** 0.75m S off A589

Hotel ★★★ 65% Clarendon Hotel, 76 Marine Rd West, West End Promenade, MORECAMBE ☎ 01524 410180 29 en suite

---

KNOTT END-ON-SEA   Map 07 SD34

Knott End Wyreside FY6 0AA
☎ 01253 810576 ▤ 01253 813446
Pleasant, undulating parkland course on banks of River Wyre. Open to sea breezes.
18 holes, 5789yds, Par 69, SSS 68, Course record 63.
Club membership 500.
Visitors book via professional up to 7 days in advance.
Societies must contact in advance. **Green Fees** terms on application. **Prof** Paul Walker **Course Designer** Braid
Facilities ⓧ ⑩ ⓑ ⓦ ♀ ⚘ ⓕ ⚐ **Location** W side of village off B5377

Hotel ★★ 68% Brabyns Hotel, 1-3 Shaftesbury Av, North Shore, BLACKPOOL ☎ 01253 354263 & 352163 ▤ 01253 352915 22 en suite

---

LANCASTER   Map 07 SD46

Lancaster Golf Club Ashton Hall, Ashton-with-Stodday LA2 0AJ ☎ 01524 751247 ▤ 01524 752742
This course is unusual for parkland golf as it is exposed to the winds coming off the Irish Sea. It is situated on the Lune estuary and has some natural hazards and easy walking. There are however several fine holes among woods near the old clubhouse.
18 holes, 6282yds, Par 71, SSS 71, Course record 66.
Club membership 925.
Visitors must play with member or resident weekends. Must contact in advance and have a handicap certificate. **Societies** Mon-Fri only. Must contact in advance. Handicap certificate required. **Green Fees** £32 per day; £28 per round. **Cards** ▦ ▦ ▦ ▣ **Prof** David Sutcliffe **Course Designer** James Braid **Facilities** ⓧ ⑩ ⓑ ⓦ ♀ ⚘ ⓕ ⚐ ⚐ **Location** 3m S on A588

Hotel ★★★★ 69% Lancaster House Hotel, Green Ln, Ellel, LANCASTER ☎ 01524 844822 80 en suite

Lansil Caton Rd LA1 3PE ☎ 01524 61233
Challenging parkland course.
9 holes, 5523yds, Par 70, SSS 67, Course record 68.
Club membership 375.
Visitors may not play before 1pm on Sun. **Societies** weekdays only; must contact in writing. **Green Fees** not confirmed. **Facilities** ⓑ ⓦ ♀ ⚘ **Location** N side of town centre on A683

continued

147

Hotel ★★★ 67% Holiday Inn Lancaster, Waterside Park, Caton Rd, LANCASTER ☎ 0870 400 9047 157 en suite

LANGHO   Map 07 SD73

Mytton Fold Hotel & Golf Complex Whalley
Rd BB6 8AB ☎ 01254 245392 📠 01254 248119
e-mail: mytton-fold.hotel@virgin.net
The course has panoramic views across the Ribble Valley and Pendle Hill. Tight fairways and water hazards are designed to make this a challenging course for any golfer.
18 holes, 6082yds, Par 72, SSS 70, Course record 69.
Club membership 350.
Visitors weekends restricted must contact in advance. Societies telephone in advance. Green Fees £16 per round. Cards ▦ ▦ ▦ ▦ ▦ ▣ Prof Gary P Coope Course Designer Frank Hargreaves Facilities ⊗ ⊪ ⅃ ◪ ♀ ⚘ 🏠 ☕ 🐾 ☕ ♂ Conf Max 290 Thtr 290 Class 60 Board 40 Banquet 270 Del £65 to £300 * Location On A59 between Langho and Whalley

Hotel ★★★ 70% Northcote Manor, Northcote Rd, LANGHO ☎ 01254 240555 14 en suite

LEYLAND   Map 07 SD52

Leyland Wigan Rd PR5 2UD
☎ 01772 436457 📠 01772 436457
e-mail: manager@leylandgc.demon.co.uk
Parkland course, fairly flat and usually breezy.
18 holes, 6123yds, Par 69, SSS 70, Course record 64.
Club membership 650.
Visitors must contact in advance. Welcome weekdays, with member only at weekends. Societies must contact in advance. Green Fees not confirmed. Prof Colin Burgess Facilities ⊗ ⊪ ⅃ ◪ ♀ ⚘ ♂ ⚑ Location E side of town centre on A49

Hotel ★★★ 70% Pines Hotel, 570 Preston Rd, Clayton-Le-Woods, CHORLEY ☎ 01772 338551 37 en suite

LONGRIDGE   Map 07 SD63

Longridge Fell Barn, Jeffrey Hill PR3 2TU
☎ 01772 783291 📠 01772 783022
e-mail: secretary@longridgegolfclub.fsnet.co.uk
One of the oldest clubs in England, celebrating 125th anniversary in 2002. A moorland course with panoramic views of the Trough of Bowland, The Fylde coast and Welsh Mountains.
18 holes, 5975yds, Par 70, SSS 69, Course record 65.
Club membership 700.
Visitors Must contact in advance. Limited play at weekends Jul-Aug. Societies welcome by prior arrangement. Green Fees £25 per day; £16.50 per round. Prof Stephen Taylor Facilities ⊗ ⊪ ⅃ ◪ ♀ ⚘ 🏠 🐾 ⚘ ♂ Conf Max 100 Class 25 Del from £25 * Location 8m NE of Preston off B6243

Hotel ★★ 69% Shireburn Arms Hotel, Whalley Rd, Hurst Green, CLITHEROE ☎ 01254 826518 18 en suite

LYTHAM ST ANNES   Map 07 SD32

Fairhaven Lytham Hall Park, Ansdell FY8 4JU
☎ 01253 736741 (Secretary) 736976 (Pro) 📠 01253 731461
A flat, but interesting parkland links course of good standard. There are natural hazards as well as numerous bunkers and players need to produce particularly accurate second shots. An excellent test of golf for all abilities.

continued

18 holes, 6883yds, Par 74, SSS 73, Course record 64.
Club membership 750.
Visitors telephone professional in advance. Societies must contact in advance. Green Fees terms on application. Cards ▦ ▦ ▦ ▦ ▣ Prof Brian Plucknett Course Designer J A Steer Facilities ⊗ ⊪ ⅃ ◪ ♀ ⚘ 🏠 🐾 ♂ Location E side of town centre off B5261

Hotel ★★★ 65% Bedford Hotel, 307-311 Clifton Dr South, LYTHAM ST ANNES ☎ 01253 724636 35 en suite

Lytham Green Drive Ballam Rd FY8 4LE
☎ 01253 737390 737379 📠 01253 731350
e-mail: sec@greendrive.fsnet.co.uk
Green Drive provides a stern but fair challenge for even the most accomplished golfer. Tight fairways, strategically placed hazards and small tricky greens are the trade mark of this testing course which meanders through pleasant countryside and is flanked by woods, pastures and meadows. The course demands accuracy in spite of the relatively flat terrain.
18 holes, 6163yds, Par 70, SSS 69, Course record 64.
Visitors must contact in advance, weekend play by arrangement only. Societies telephone to book in advance. Green Fees £38 per day; £30 per round. Prof Andrew Lancaster Course Designer Steer Facilities ⊗ ⊪ ⅃ ◪ ♀ ⚘ 🏠 ♂ Location E side of town centre off B5259

Hotel ★★★★ 65% Clifton Arms, West Beach, Lytham, LYTHAM ST ANNES ☎ 01253 739898 48 en suite

LYTHAM ST ANNES   See Page 149

LYTHAM ST ANNES   Map 07 SD32

St Annes Old Links Highbury Rd East FY8 2LD
☎ 01253 723597 📠 01253 781506
e-mail: secretary@coastalgolf.co.uk
Seaside links, qualifying course for Open Championship; compact and of very high standard, particularly greens. Windy, very long 5th, 17th and 18th holes. Famous hole: 9th (171 yds), par 3. Excellent club facilities.

18 holes, 6616yds, Par 72, SSS 72, Course record 64.
Club membership 750.
Visitors may not play on Sat or before 9.15am & between noon-2pm weekdays. Sundays by telephoning on the day. Handicap certificate requested. Societies must contact in advance. Green Fees £38 per day. Cards ▦ ▦ ▦ ▣ Prof D J Webster Course Designer George Lowe Facilities ⊗ ⊪ ⅃ ◪ ♀ ⚘ 🏠 ♂ Location N side of town centre

Hotel ★★★ 65% Bedford Hotel, 307-311 Clifton Dr South, LYTHAM ST ANNES ☎ 01253 724636 35 en suite

Royal Lytham & St Annes

Lytham St Annes, *Lancs* ☎ 01253 724206 Fax 01253 780946 Map 07 SD32

Founded in 1886, this huge links course can be difficult, especially in windy conditions.
Unusually for a championship course it starts with a par 3, the nearby railway line and red brick houses create distractions which only add to the challenge.

The course has hosted many Open Championships with some memorable victories, amateur Bobby Jones famously won here in 1926; Bob Charles of New Zealand became the only left-hander to win the title and in 1969 Tony Jacklin helped to revive British golf with his win here.

Visitors Mon & Thu only (unless guest at Dormy House). Must contact in advance and have a handicap certificate (18 max gentlemen, 24 max ladies)

Societies must apply to Secretary in advance (large groups Thu only)

Green Fees Mon-Fri £100 per round £140 per day; weekends £140 per round (contact Secretary for Dormy rates)

Facilities ⊗ ⅷ ╚ ♚ ♀ ⌂ ♨ ⌂ ♂ ⸙

Professional (Eddie Birchenough) **Conf Banquet** 100

Location Links Gate, Lytham FY8 3LQ (0.5m E of St Annes town)

Holes/Par/Course record 54 holes. Championship Course: 18 holes, 6885 yrds, Par 71, SSS 74, Course record 64. Members Course: 18 holes, 6635yds, Par 71, SSS74, Course record 64. Visitors Course: 18 holes, 6350 yds, Par 71, SSS 72

Championship Course

WHERE TO STAY AND EAT NEARBY

Hotels
★★★★65% Clifton Arms, West Beach, Lytham. ☎ 01253 739898. 48 en suite

★★★67% Chadwick, South Promenade. ☎ 01253 720061. 75 en suite

★★★65% Bedford, 307-311 Clifton Drive South. ☎ 01253 724636. 35 en suite

★★69% Glendower, North Promenade. ☎ 01253 723241. 60 en suite

★★69% Lindum Hotel, 63-67 South Promenade. ☎ 01253 721534. 76 en suite

Restaurant
LYTHAM ST ANNES
◎◎ Green's Bistro
319 St Andrews Rd
☎ 01253 789990

MORECAMBE
Map 07 SD46

Morecambe Bare LA4 6AJ
☎ 01524 412841 🖹 01524 400088
e-mail: morecambegolf@btconnect.com
Holiday golf at its most enjoyable. The well-maintained, wind-affected seaside parkland course is not long but full of character. Even so the panoramic views across Morecambe Bay and to the Lake District and Pennines make concentration difficult. The 4th is a testing hole.
18 holes, 5770yds, Par 67, SSS 69, Course record 69.
Club membership 850.
Visitors may play from yellow tees, must contact in advance. Societies must contact in advance. Green Fees terms on application. Prof Simon Fletcher Course Designer Dr Alister Mackenzie Facilities ⊗ ⊞ ⓑ ⬛ ♥ ♀ ♣ ⬚ 🖋 Location N side of town centre on A5105

Hotel ★★★ 65% Elms Hotel, Bare Village, MORECAMBE ☎ 01524 411501 40 en suite

NELSON
Map 07 SD83

Marsden Park Townhouse Rd BB9 8DG
☎ 01282 661912
A semi-parkland course offering panoramic views of surrounding countryside, set in the foothills of Pendle Marsden Park, a testing 18 holes for golfers of all abilities.
18 holes, 5813yds, Par 70, SSS 68, Course record 66.
Club membership 298.
Visitors welcome at any time, advised to book in advance at weekends. Societies Must contact in writing. Green Fees not confirmed. Cards 🔲 ▬ 🔲 🗏 Prof Martin Ross Facilities ⊗ ⊞ ⓑ ⬛ ♥ ♀ ♣ ⬚ 🖋 🖋 Location E side of town centre off A56

Hotel ★★★ 74% Oaks Hotel, Colne Rd, Reedley, BURNLEY ☎ 01282 414141 50 en suite

Nelson King's Causeway, Brierfield BB9 0EU
☎ 01282 611834 & 617000 🖹 01282 606226
Moorland course. The late Dr. MacKenzie, who laid out the course, managed a design which does not include any wearisome climbing and created many interesting holes. Visitors will find a warm welcome and the friendliness extends to the recently refurbished clubhouse which caters to all needs and has wonderful panoramic views of the surrounding Pendle area.
18 holes, 6007yds, Par 70, SSS 69, Course record 63.
Club membership 580.
Visitors must telephone 01282 617000 in advance, may not play before 9.30am or between 12.30-1.30pm. Societies must contact in advance. Green Fees £25 per day (£30 weekends & bank holidays). Prof Nigel Sumner Course Designer Dr Mackenzie Facilities ⊗ ⊞ ⓑ ⬛ ♥ ♀ ♣ ⬚ 🖋 Location Take A682 to Brierfield, left at traffic lights into Halifax Road which becomes Kings Causeway

Hotel ★★★ 74% Oaks Hotel, Colne Rd, Reedley, BURNLEY ☎ 01282 414141 50 en suite

ORMSKIRK
Map 07 SD40

Hurlston Hall Hurlston Ln, Southport Rd, Scarisbrick
L40 8HB ☎ 01704 840400 & 841120 (pro shop)
🖹 01704 841404
e-mail: hurlston_hall@btinternet.com
Designed by Donald Steel, this gently undulating course
continued

offers fine views across the Pennines and Bowland Fells. With generous fairways, large tees and greens, two streams and seven lakes, it provides a good test of golf for players of all standards. Luxurious colonial-style clubhouse.
18 holes, 6746yds, Par 72, SSS 72, Course record 66.
Club membership 650.
Visitors welcome, but may be asked for handicap certificate or letter of introduction from own club. Preferable to book in advance. Societies registered Golf Societies and others approved by club, write or telephone for details. Green Fees £38 per day; £34 per 27 holes; £28 per round (£44/£38/£34 weekends). Cards 🔲 ▬ 🔲 🔲 🗏 Prof Jon Esclapez Course Designer Donald Steel Facilities ⊗ ⊞ ⓑ ⬛ ♥ ♀ ♣ ⬚ 🖋 🖋 🖋 ⬚ 🖋 ⓒ Leisure fishing. Conf Max 100 Thtr 100 Class 50 Board 30 Banquet 100 Del from £5 * Location Situated 6m from Southport and 2m from Ormskirk along A570

Hotel ★★★ 67% Beaufort Hotel, High Ln, Burscough, ORMSKIRK ☎ 01704 892655 20 en suite

Ormskirk Cranes Ln, Lathom L40 5UJ
☎ 01695 572227 🖹 01695 572227
e-mail: secretary@ormskirkgolfclub.mersinet.co.uk
A pleasantly secluded, fairly flat, parkland course with much heath and silver birch. Accuracy from the tees will provide an interesting variety of second shots.
18 holes, 6358yds, Par 70, SSS 71, Course record 63.
Club membership 300.
Visitors restricted Saturdays. Societies must telephone or contact in writing. Green Fees £45 per day; £35 per round (£50/£40 Weds & weekends). Prof Jack Hammond Facilities ⊗ ⊞ ⓑ ⬛ ♥ ♀ ♣ ⬚ 🖋 Location 1.5m NE

Hotel ★★★ 67% Beaufort Hotel, High Ln, Burscough, ORMSKIRK ☎ 01704 892655 20 en suite

PLEASINGTON
Map 07 SD62

Pleasington BB2 5JF
☎ 01254 202177 🖹 01254 201028
e-mail: jean@pleasington-golf.co.uk
Plunging and rising across lovely parkland and heathland turf this course tests judgement of distance through the air to greens of widely differing levels. The 11th and 4th are testing holes.
18 holes, 6417yds, Par 71, SSS 71.
Club membership 700.
Visitors may play Mon & Wed-Fri only. Societies must contact in advance. Green Fees £42 per 2 rounds; £36 per round. Prof Ged Furey Facilities ⊗ ⊞ ⓑ ⬛ ♥ ♀ ♣ ⬚ 🖋 Location J3 off M65 follow sign for Blackburn

Hotel ★★ 75% Millstone Hotel, Church Ln, Mellor, BLACKBURN ☎ 01254 813333
18 en suite 6 annexe en suite

POULTON-LE-FYLDE
Map 07 SD33

Poulton-le-Fylde Breck Rd FY6 7HJ
☎ 01253 892444 & 893150 🖹 01253 892444
A pleasant, municipal parkland course suitable for all standards of golfers.
9 holes, 4454yds, Par 71, SSS 68.
Club membership 300.
Visitors no restrictions, contact by telephone or writing. Societies contact in advance by telephone or in writing. Green Fees £13 per 18 holes; £8.50 per 9 holes (£15/£10
continued

weekends). **Cards** ⊟ ▄▄ 🔲 📶 **Prof** Lewis Ware **Course Designer** E Astbury **Facilities** ⊗ 🍺 ♀ ⚘ 🍴 ⚑ 🏌 ⛳

Location From M55 junct 3 follow A585 to Poulton, club is then signposted
....

Hotel ★★ 68% Brabyns Hotel, 1-3 Shaftesbury Av, North Shore, BLACKPOOL ☎ 01253 354263 & 352163 📄 01253 352915 22 en suite

---

PRESTON   Map 07 SD52

Ashton & Lea Tudor Av, Lea PR4 0XA
☎ 01772 726480 & 735282 📄 01772 735762
e-mail: ashtonleagolf@supanet.com
Fairly flat parkland course with pond and streams, offering pleasant walks and some testing holes for golfers of all standards. Water comes into play on seven of the last nine holes. The course has three challenging par 3s.

18 holes, 6334yds, Par 71, SSS 70, Course record 65.
Club membership 650.
Visitors must contact professional on 01772 720374 or secretary on 01772 735282. **Societies** must contact in writing or by telephone. **Green Fees** not confirmed. **Prof** M Greenough **Course Designer** J Steer **Facilities** ⊗ 〗⟆ ⮯ ⮷ 🍺 ♀ ☘ 🏠 🏌 **Location** 3m W of Preston on A5085
....

Hotel ★★★ 64% Holiday Inn Preston, Ringway, PRESTON ☎ 0870 400 9066 119 en suite

Fishwick Hall Glenluce Dr, Farringdon Park PR1 5TD
☎ 01772 798300 & 795870 📄 01772 704600
e-mail: fishwickhallgolfclub@supanet.com
Meadowland course overlooking River Ribble. Natural hazards.
18 holes, 6045yds, Par 70, SSS 69, Course record 66.
Club membership 750.
Visitors advisable to contact in advance. **Societies** must contact in advance. **Green Fees** terms on application. **Prof** Martin Watson **Facilities** ⊗ 〗⟆ ⮯ 🍺 ♀ 🏠 🏌 **Location** Off M6 junct 31
....

Hotel ★★★ 64% Holiday Inn Preston, Ringway, PRESTON ☎ 0870 400 9066 119 en suite

Ingol Tanterton Hall Rd, Ingol PR2 7BY
☎ 01772 734556 📄 01772 729815
e-mail: ingol@golfers.net
Championship designed course with natural water hazards, set in 250 acres of beautiful parkland. A good test for any calibre of golfer.
18 holes, 6294yds, Par 72, SSS 70, Course record 68.
Club membership 650.
Visitors must contact booking office in advance. **Societies** must contact. **Green Fees** £22 per round (£27 weekends). **Cards** ⊟ ▄▄ 🔲 📶 💳 **Prof** Ryan Grimshaw **Course**

continued

Designer Henry Cotton **Facilities** ⊗ 〗⟆ ⮯ 🍺 ♀ ☘ 🏠 🚜 🏌 **Leisure** squash, Snooker & Pool. **Conf** Max 135 Thtr

Ingol

120 Class 60 Board 55 Banquet 135 **Location** Junct 32 off M6, take slip road to Garstang & Preston A6, then follow signs to Ingol
....

Hotel ★★★ 64% Holiday Inn Preston, Ringway, PRESTON ☎ 0870 400 9066 119 en suite

Penwortham Blundell Ln, Penwortham PR1 0AX
☎ 01772 744630 📄 01772 740172
e-mail: penworthamgolfclub@supanet.com
A progressive golf club set close to the banks of the River Ribble. The course has tree-lined fairways, excellent greens, and provides easy walking. Testing holes include the 178-yd, par 3 third, the 480-yd, par 5 sixth, and the 398-yd par 4 sixteenth.
18 holes, 6056yds, Par 69, SSS 69, Course record 65.
Club membership 1020.   *continued*

Penwortham Golf Club

Visitors must contact in advance, restricted Tue & weekends. **Societies** must apply in writing. **Green Fees** £30 per day; £25 per round (£33 per day weekends). **Prof** Steven Holden **Facilities** ⊗ ⟁ ⓛ 🖳 ♀ ⚎ 🏠 ⚒ **Conf** Board 14 **Location** 1.5m W of town centre off A59

Hotel ★★★ 65% Tickled Trout, Preston New Rd, Samlesbury, PRESTON ☎ 01772 877671 72 en suite

Preston Fulwood Hall Ln, Fulwood PR2 8DD
☎ 01772 700011 📖 01772 794234
Pleasant inland golf at this course set in very agreeable parkland. There is a well-balanced selection of holes, undulating amongst groups of trees, and not requiring great length.
18 holes, 6312yds, Par 71, SSS 71.
Club membership 800.
Visitors may play midweek only. Must contact in advance and have a handicap certificate. **Societies** must contact in writing/telephone. **Green Fees** £35 per day/round. **Prof** Andrew Greenbank **Course Designer** James Braid **Facilities** ⊗ ⟁ ⓛ 🖳 ♀ ⚎ 🏠 ⚒ ⚑ **Location** N side of town centre

Hotel ★★★★ 67% Preston Marriott Hotel, Garstang Rd, Broughton, PRESTON ☎ 01772 864087 150 en suite

RISHTON   Map 07 SD73

Rishton Eachill Links, Hawthorn Dr BB1 4HG
☎ 01254 884442 📖 01254 726205
e-mail: msm@cwcom.net
Undulating moorland course.
9 holes, 6097yds, Par 70, SSS 69, Course record 68.
Club membership 270.
Visitors must play with member on weekends and bank holidays. **Societies** must contact in writing. **Green Fees** £15 per 18 holes. **Course Designer** Peter Alliss/Dave Thomas **Facilities** ⊗ ⟁ ⓛ 🖳 ♀ by arrangement ⚎ **Conf** Max 70 **Location** M65 junct 6/7, club 1m from junct

Hotel ★★★★ 65% Dunkenhalgh Hotel, Blackburn Rd, Clayton-le-Moors, ACCRINGTON ☎ 01254 398021 53 en suite 69 annexe en suite

SILVERDALE   Map 07 SD47

Silverdale Redbridge Ln LA5 0SP
☎ 01524 701300 📖 01524 702074
e-mail: silverdalegolfclub@ecosse.net
Challenging heathland course with rock outcrops. Excellent views.
18 holes, 5210yds, Par 69, SSS 64.
Club membership 500.

continued

Visitors telephone 01524-701300 to book tee. Sun not available April-Sept inclusive. **Societies** must contact in writing. **Green Fees** terms on application. **Facilities** ⊗ ⟁ ⓛ 🖳 ♀ ⚎ 🏠 ⚒ **Location** Opposite Silverdale Station

Hotel ★★ 65% Royal Station Hotel, Market St, CARNFORTH ☎ 01524 732033 & 733636 📖 01524 720267 13 en suite

UPHOLLAND   Map 07 SD50

Beacon Park Beacon Ln WN8 7RU
☎ 01695 622700 📖 01695 633066
18 holes, 6000yds, Par 72, SSS 69, Course record 68.
Course Designer Donald Steel **Location** S of Ashurst Beacon Hill
Telephone for further details

Hotel ★★★ 67% Beaufort Hotel, High Ln, Burscough, ORMSKIRK ☎ 01704 892655 20 en suite

Dean Wood Lafford Ln WN8 0QZ
☎ 01695 622219 📖 01695 622245
e-mail: office@dwgc.fsnet.co.uk
This parkland course has a varied terrain - flat front nine, undulating back nine. Beware the par 4, 11th and 17th holes, which has ruined many a card. If there were a prize for the best maintained course in Lancashire, Dean Wood would be a strong contender.
18 holes, 6179yds, Par 71, SSS 71, Course record 66.
Club membership 800.
Visitors must play with member Tue, Wed. **Societies** must contact in advance. **Green Fees** £30 per day (£33 weekends). **Prof** Stuart Danchin **Course Designer** James Braid **Facilities** ⊗ ⟁ ⓛ 🖳 ♀ ⚎ 🏠 ⚒ ⚑ **Location** 1m from junct 26 of M6

Hotel ★★★ 65% Quality Hotel Skelmersdale, Prescot Rd, UPHOLLAND ☎ 01695 720401 55 en suite

WHALLEY   Map 07 SD73

Whalley Long Leese Barn, Clerk Hill Rd BB7 9DR
☎ 01254 822236
Parkland course near Pendle Hill, overlooking the Ribble Valley. Superb views. Ninth hole over pond.
9 holes, 6258yds, Par 72, SSS 71, Course record 69.
Club membership 400.
Visitors must telephone 01254 822236 in advance. **Societies** must apply in writing. **Green Fees** £16 per day (£20 weekends and bank holidays). **Prof** Jamie Hunt **Facilities** ⊗ ⟁ ⓛ 🖳 ♀ ⚎ 🏠 **Location** 1m SE off A671

Hotel ★★★★ 61% Clarion Hotel & Suites Foxfields, Whalley Rd, Billington, CLITHEROE ☎ 01254 822556 44 en suite

WHITWORTH   Map 07 SD81

Lobden Lobden Moor OL12 8XJ
☎ 01706 343228 📖 01706 343228
Moorland course, with hard walking. Windy.
9 holes, 5697yds, Par 70, SSS 68, Course record 65.
Club membership 250.
Visitors May not play Sat. **Societies** must apply in writing to Secretary. **Green Fees** £12 (£15 weekends). **Facilities** ⊗ ⟁ ⓛ 🖳 ♀ ⚎ **Location** E side of town centre off A671

Hotel ★★★★ 64% Norton Grange Hotel, Manchester Rd, Castleton, ROCHDALE ☎ 01706 630788 51 en suite

WILPSHIRE   Map 07 SD63

Wilpshire Whalley Rd BB1 9LF
☎ 01254 248260 🖥 01254 248260
Parkland/moorland course with varied and interesting holes. Magnificent views of Ribble Valley, the coast and the Yorkshire Dales.
18 holes, 5971yds, Par 69, SSS 69, Course record 65.
Club membership 500.
Visitors must contact in advance. **Societies** must contact by telephone and confirm in writing. **Green Fees** not confirmed. **Cards** 🖃 💳🔲 💷 **Prof** Walter Slaven **Course Designer** James Braid **Facilities** ⊗ 🏄 🖳 💷 ♀ ⚒ 🖻 ⚑ ♂ **Location** 2m NE of Blackburn, on A666 towards Clitheroe
· ·
Hotel ★★★ 61% Sparth House Hotel, Whalley Rd, Clayton Le Moors, ACCRINGTON ☎ 01254 872263 16 en suite

---

LEICESTERSHIRE

ASHBY-DE-LA-ZOUCH   Map 08 SK31

Willesley Park Measham Rd LE65 2PF
☎ 01530 414596 🖥 01530 414596
Undulating heathland and parkland course with quick draining sandy sub-soil.
18 holes, 6304yds, Par 70, SSS 70, Course record 63.
Club membership 600.
Visitors must contact in advance. Restricted weekends. Handicap certificate required. **Societies** Wed-Fri only. Must apply in writing. **Green Fees** £30 per day/round (£35 weekends and bank holidays). **Prof** Ben Hill **Course Designer** J Braid **Facilities** ⊗ 🏄 🖳 💷 ♀ ⚒ 🖻 ♂ **Location** SW side of town centre on B5006
· ·
Hotel ★★ 65% Charnwood Arms Hotel, Beveridge Ln, Bardon Hill, COALVILLE ☎ 01530 813644 34 en suite

BIRSTALL   Map 04 SK50

Birstall Station Rd LE4 3BB
☎ 0116 267 4322 🖥 0116 267 4322
Parkland course with trees, shrubs, ponds and ditches.
18 holes, 6222yds, Par 70, SSS 70.
Club membership 650.
Visitors with member only weekends; may not play Tue, Wed & Fri after 9am. **Societies** apply in writing. **Green Fees** £30 per day; £25 per round. **Prof** David Clark **Facilities** ⊗ 🏄 🖳 💷 ♀ ⚒ 🖻 ♂ **Leisure** billiard room. **Location** 3m N of Leicester on A6
· ·
Hotel ★★ 63% Red Cow, Hinckley Rd, Leicester Forest East, LEICESTER ☎ 0116 238 7878 31 en suite

BOTCHESTON   Map 04 SK40

Forest Hill Markfield Ln LE9 9FJ
☎ 01455 824800 🖥 01455 828522
18 holes, 6039yds, Par 72, SSS 69.
Telephone for further details
· ·
Hotel ★★ 66% The Mill On The Soar, Coventry Rd, SUTTON IN THE ELMS ☎ 01455 282419 25 en suite

COSBY   Map 04 SP59

Cosby Chapel Ln, Broughton Rd LE9 1RG
☎ 0116 286 4759 🖥 0116 286 4484
e-mail: secretary@cosby-golf-club.co.uk
Undulating parkland course with a number of tricky, tight driving holes. Challenging holes include the par 4
continued

1st with an unseen meandering brook, the deceptively long par 4 3rd, the 12th from an elevated tee and the hogs-back shaped par 3 14th, both affected by the prevailing wind.
18 holes, 6410yds, Par 71, SSS 71, Course record 65.
Club membership 750.
Visitors welcome weekdays before 4pm. May not play at weekends. Recommended to telephone in advance. Handicap certificate required. **Societies** Mon-Fri only ,book with secretary in advance. **Green Fees** £29 per day; £26 per round. **Prof** Martin Wing **Course Designer** Hawtree **Facilities** ⊗ 🏄 🖳 💷 ♀ ⚒ 🖻 ⚑ ♂ **Location** S side of village
· ·
Hotel ★★★ 69% Holiday Inn Leicester - West, Braunstone Ln East, LEICESTER ☎ 0870 400 9051 0870 4009051 🖥 0116 282 3623 172 en suite

EAST GOSCOTE   Map 08 SK61

Beedles Lake 170 Broome Ln LE7 3WQ
☎ 0116 260 6759
Fairly flat parkland course, founded in 1992, with an adjoining lake and well maintained greens.
18 holes, 6625yds, Par 72, SSS 72, Course record 71.
Club membership 400.
Visitors telephone booking required for weekends. **Societies** welcome Mon-Fri **Green Fees** not confirmed. **Prof** Sean Byrne **Course Designer** D Tucker **Facilities** ⊗ 🏄 🖳 💷 ♀ ⚒ 🖻 ⚑ ♂ (**Leisure** fishing. **Location** Off A46, just N of Leicester through village of Ratcliffe on the Wreake
· ·
Hotel ★★★ 64% Rothley Court, Westfield Ln, ROTHLEY ☎ 0116 237 4141 13 en suite 21 annexe en suite

ENDERBY   Map 04 SP59

Enderby Mill Ln LE9 5HL
☎ 0116 284 9388 🖥 0116 284 9388
A gently undulating 9-hole course at which beginners are especially welcome. The longest hole is the 2nd at 407 yards and there are 5 par 3s.
9 holes, 2776yds, Par 72, SSS 71.
Club membership 150.
Visitors no restrictions. **Societies** must telephone in advance. **Green Fees** £6.50 per 18 holes; £5.30 per 9 holes (£8.75/£6.30 weekends). **Prof** Chris D'Araujo **Course Designer** David Lowe **Facilities** ⊗ 🏄 🖳 💷 ♀ ⚒ 🖻 ⚑ ♣ ♂ **Leisure** heated indoor swimming pool, squash, sauna, solarium, gymnasium. **Location** 2m S, M1 junct21 on Narborough road. Right turn off roundabout at Toby Carvery, 0.5m on left
· ·
Hotel ★★ 66% The Mill On The Soar, Coventry Rd, SUTTON IN THE ELMS ☎ 01455 282419 25 en suite

HINCKLEY   Map 04 SP49

Hinckley Leicester Rd LE10 3DR ☎ 01455 615124 & 615014 🖥 01455 890841 & 01455 615014
e-mail: proshop@hinckleygolfclub.com
Rolling parkland with lake features, and lined fairways.
18 holes, 6529yds, Par 71, SSS 71, Course record 65.
Club membership 750.
Visitors with member only weekends and bank holidays. Must contact in advance and have a handicap certificate. **Societies** Mon,wed must contact in advance. **Green Fees** not confirmed. **Cards** 🖃 💳🔲 💷 📧 **Prof** Richard Jones **Course Designer** Southern Golf Ltd **Facilities** ⊗ 🏄 🖳 💷 ♀ ⚒ 🖻 ♣ ♣⚒ ♂ **Leisure** snooker. **Location** 1.5m NE on B4668
continued

Hotel ★★★ 63% Weston Hall Hotel, Weston Ln, Weston in Arden, Bulkington, NUNEATON ☎ 024 7631 2989
40 en suite

KIBWORTH   Map 04 SP69

Kibworth Weir Rd, Beauchamp LE8 0LP
☎ 0116 279 2301 📠 0116 279 6434
e-mail: secretary@kibworthgolfclub.freeserve.co.uk
Parkland course with easy walking. A brook affects a number of fairways
18 holes, 6333yds, Par 71, SSS 70, Course record 64.
Club membership 700.
Visitors must contact in advance. With member only weekends. **Societies** must contact in advance. **Green Fees** £30 per day; £25 per round. **Prof** Bob Larratt **Facilities** ⊗ ⪫ 🍴 ⅏ ♨ ⚑ 🏌 ☂ 🏌 **Location** S side of village off A6

Hotel ★★★ 70% Three Swans Hotel, 21 High St, MARKET HARBOROUGH ☎ 01858 466644
18 en suite 43 annexe en suite

KIRBY MUXLOE   Map 04 SK50

Kirby Muxloe Station Rd LE9 2EP
☎ 0116 239 3457 📠 0116 239 3457
Pleasant parkland course with a lake in front of the 17th green and a short 18th.
18 holes, 6351yds, Par 70, SSS 70, Course record 65.
Club membership 870.
Visitors must contact in advance and a handicap certificate is required. No visitors on Tue or at weekends. **Societies** must contact in advance. **Green Fees** terms on application. **Prof** Bruce Whipham **Facilities** ⊗ ⅏ ⪫ 🍴 ⅏ ♨ 🏌 ☂ 🏌 **Location** S side of village off B5380

Hotel ★★★ 69% Holiday Inn Leicester - West, Braunstone Ln East, LEICESTER ☎ 0870 400 9051 0870 4009051
📠 0116 282 3623 172 en suite

LEICESTER   Map 04 SK50

Humberstone Heights Gypsy Ln LE5 0TB
☎ 0116 276 3680 & 299 5570 (pro) 📠 0116 2995569
Municipal parkland course with 9 hole pitch and putt and 30 bay driving range.
18 holes, 6343yds, Par 70, SSS 70, Course record 66.
Club membership 400.
Visitors must telephone in advance at weekends. **Societies** must telephone in advance. **Green Fees** £8.99 per 18 holes (£12.50 weekends); £6.99 per 9 holes. **Cards** 🗂 **Prof** Phil Highfield **Course Designer** Hawtry & Sons **Facilities** ⊗ ⪫ 🍴 ⅏ ♨ ⚑ 🏌 ☂ 🏌 **Location** 2.5m NE of city centre

Hotel ★★★ 74% Belmont House Hotel, De Montfort St, LEICESTER ☎ 0116 254 4773 77 en suite

Leicestershire Evington Ln LE5 6DJ
☎ 0116 273 8825 📠 0116 273 1900
e-mail: theleicestershiregolfclub@hotmail.com
Pleasantly undulating parkland course.
18 holes, 6329yds, Par 68, SSS 71, Course record 63.
Club membership 800.
Visitors must contact in advance. May not play Sat. Must hold a handicap certificate. **Societies** must contact in advance. **Green Fees** terms on application. **Prof** Darren Jones **Course Designer** Hawtree **Facilities** ⊗ ⅏ ⪫ 🍴 ⅏ ♨ 🏌 **Location** 2m E of city off A6030

Hotel ★★★ 62% Hermitage Hotel, Wigston Rd, Oadby, LEICESTER ☎ 0116 256 9955 56 en suite

Western Scudamore Rd, Braunstone Frith LE3 1UQ
☎ 0116 299 5566 📠 0116 299 5568
18 holes, 6518yds, Par 72, SSS 71.
Location 1.5m W of city centre off A47
Telephone for further details

Hotel ★★★ 69% Holiday Inn Leicester - West, Braunstone Ln East, LEICESTER ☎ 0870 400 9051 0870 4009051
📠 0116 282 3623 172 en suite

LOUGHBOROUGH   Map 08 SK51

Longcliffe Snell's Nook Ln, Nanpantan LE11 3YA
☎ 01509 239129 📠 01509 231286
e-mail: longcliffegolf@btconnect.com
Course of natural heathland, tree lined fairways with water in play on the 14th and 15th hole. This course is recognised by the English Golf Championship.

18 holes, 6625yds, Par 72, SSS 72, Course record 65.
Club membership 660.
Visitors must contact in advance. With member only at weekends.Handicap certificate required. **Societies** telephone in advance for availability, handicap certificate required. **Green Fees** £39 per day; £29 per round. **Cards** 🗂 🗂 📲 **Prof** David Mee **Course Designer** Williamson **Facilities** ⊗ ⅏ ⪫ 🍴 ⅏ ♨ 🏌 **Conf** Max 100 Thtr 100 Board 16 Banquet 100 **Location** 1.5m from M1 junct 23 off A512

Hotel ★★★ 64% Quality Hotel, New Ashby Rd, LOUGHBOROUGH ☎ 01509 211800 94 en suite

LUTTERWORTH   Map 04 SP58

Kilworth Springs South Kilworth Rd, North Kilworth LE17 6HJ ☎ 01858 575082 & 575974 📠 01858 575078
An 18-hole course of two loops of 9: the front 9 are links style while the back 9 are in parkland with four lakes. On a windy day it is a very challenging course and the 6th hole is well deserving of its nickname 'the Devil's Toenail'.
18 holes, 6543yds, Par 72, SSS 71, Course record 66.
Club membership 800.
Visitors welcome subject to availability. May only play after 12am at weekends. **Societies** contact in advance. **Green Fees** £18 per 18 holes; £11 per 9 holes (£21/£13 weekends).
Cards 🗂 🗂 📲 🗂 **Prof** Anders Mankert **Course Designer** Ray Baldwin **Facilities** ⊗ ⅏ ⪫ 🍴 ⅏ ♨ 🏌 ☂ ⚑ **Conf** Thtr 150 Class 100 Board 24 Banquet 120 **Location** 4m E of M1 junc 20, A4304 to Mkt Harborough

Hotel ★★ 71% The Sun Inn, Main St, MARSTON TRUSSELL ☎ 01858 465531 20 en suite

Lutterworth Rugby Rd LE17 4HN
☎ 01455 552532 🖹 01455 553586
18 holes, 6226yds, Par 70, SSS 70.
Location 0.5m S on A426
Telephone for further details
....

Hotel ★★★ 67% Brownsover Hall Hotel, Brownsover Ln, Old Brownsover, RUGBY ☎ 01788 546100
27 en suite 20 annexe en suite

MARKET HARBOROUGH   Map 04 SP78

Market Harborough Oxendon Rd LE16 8NF
☎ 01858 463684 🖹 01858 432906
A parkland course close to the town. There are wide-ranging views over the surrounding countryside. Lakes feature on four holes; challenging last three holes.
18 holes, 6070yds, Par 70, SSS 69, Course record 63.
Club membership 650.
Visitors must play with member at weekends. **Societies** must apply in writing. **Green Fees** £30 per day; £25 per round. **Prof** Frazer Baxter **Course Designer** H Swan **Facilities** ⊗ 🟊 🖪 🍺 🏌 ⚒ 🏠 🛒 **Location** 1m S on A508
....

Hotel ★★★ 70% Three Swans Hotel, 21 High St, MARKET HARBOROUGH ☎ 01858 466644
18 en suite 43 annexe en suite

Stoke Albany Ashley Rd, Stoke Albany LE16 8PL
☎ 01858 535208 🖹 01858 535505
Parkland course in the picturesque Welland Valley. Affording good views, the course should appeal to the mid-handicap golfer, and provide an interesting test to the more experienced player.
18 holes, 6132yds, Par 71, SSS 69.
Club membership 400.
Visitors welcome at all times. **Societies** please telephone secretary. **Green Fees** not confirmed. **Cards** 🎫 🟥 🟥 🟥 🟥 🟥 🟥 **Prof** Adrian Clifford **Course Designer** Hawtree **Facilities** ⊗ 🟊 🖪 🍺 🏌 ⚒ 🏠 🛒 **Location** Located N off A427 Market Harborough/Corby Road, follow Stoke Albany 500m towards Ashley village
....

Hotel ★★★ 70% Three Swans Hotel, 21 High St, MARKET HARBOROUGH ☎ 01858 466644 18 en suite 43 annexe en suite

MELTON MOWBRAY   Map 08 SK71

Melton Mowbray Waltham Rd, Thorpe Arnold LE14 4SD ☎ 01664 562118
e-mail: mmgc@le144sd.fsbusiness.co.uk
Easy walking heathland course.
18 holes, 6222yds, Par 70, SSS 70, Course record 61.
Club membership 650.
Visitors must contact professional on 01664 569629. **Societies** must contact in advance. **Green Fees** £27 per day; £20 per round (£23 per round weekends). **Prof** James Hetherington **Facilities** ⊗ 🟊 🖪 🍺 🏌 ⚒ 🏠 🛒 🏌 🍵 **Location** 2m NE of Melton Mowbray on A607
....

Hotel ★★★ 70% Sysonby Knoll Hotel, Asfordby Rd, MELTON MOWBRAY ☎ 01664 563563
23 en suite 1 annexe en suite

OADBY   Map 04 SK60

Glen Gorse Glen Rd LE2 4RF
☎ 0116 271 4159 🖹 0116 271 4159
e-mail: gggc@stayfree.co.uk

Fairly flat 18-hole parkland course with some strategically placed mature trees, new saplings and ponds affecting play on six holes. Ridge and furrow is a feature of five holes.
18 holes, 6648yds, Par 72, SSS 72, Course record 64.
Club membership 600.
Visitors must contact in advance. Must play with member at weekends. **Societies** must telephone secretary in advance. **Green Fees** £30 per day; £25 per round. **Prof** Dominic Fitzpatrick **Facilities** ⊗ 🟊 🖪 🍺 🏌 ⚒ 🏠 🛒 **Leisure** snooker room. **Location** On A6 trunk road between Oadby/Great Glen, 5m S of Leicester city centre
....

Hotel ★★★ 62% Hermitage Hotel, Wigston Rd, Oadby, LEICESTER ☎ 0116 256 9955 56 en suite

Oadby Leicester Rd LE2 4AJ ☎ 0116 270 9052
Municipal parkland course.
18 holes, 6376yds, Par 72, SSS 70, Course record 60.
Club membership 400.
Visitors no restrictions. **Societies** by arrangement contact pro shop. **Green Fees** not confirmed. **Prof** Alan Kershaw **Facilities** 🖪 🍺 🏌 ⚒ 🏠 🛒 **Location** West of Oadby, off A6
....

Hotel ★★★ 62% Hermitage Hotel, Wigston Rd, Oadby, LEICESTER ☎ 0116 256 9955 56 en suite

ROTHLEY   Map 08 SK51

Rothley Park Westfield Ln LE7 7LH
☎ 0116 230 2809 🖹 0116 230 2809
e-mail: secretary@rothleypark.co.uk
Parkland course in picturesque situation.
18 holes, 6477yds, Par 71, SSS 71, Course record 67.
Club membership 600.
Visitors must contact professional on 0116 230 3023. Weekends and bank holidays with member only. **Societies** apply in writing to secretary. **Green Fees** terms on application. **Facilities** ⊗ 🟊 🖪 🍺 🏌 ⚒ 🏠 🏌 🛒 **Location** Off A6 N of Leicester
....

Hotel ★★★ 64% Rothley Court, Westfield Ln, ROTHLEY ☎ 0116 237 4141 13 en suite 21 annexe en suite

SCRAPTOFT   Map 04 SK60

Scraptoft Beeby Rd LE7 9SJ
☎ 0116 241 9000 🖹 0116 241 9000
e-mail: info@scraptoft-golf.co.uk
A well wooded and beautiful parkland course demanding accuracy.
18 holes, 6166yds, Par 70, SSS 70.
Club membership 650.
Visitors with member only weekends. Handicap certificate required. **Societies** apply in writing/telephone. **Green Fees** £27 per day; £22 per round. **Prof** Simon Wood **Facilities** ⊗ 🟊 🖪 🍺 🏌 ⚒ 🏠 🏌 🛒 **Location** 1m NE
....

Hotel ★★★ 62% Hermitage Hotel, Wigston Rd, Oadby, LEICESTER ☎ 0116 256 9955 56 en suite

SEAGRAVE   Map 08 SK61

Park Hill Park Hill LE12 7NG
☎ 01509 815454 & 815775 (pro) 🖹 01509 816062
e-mail: mail@parkhillgolf.co.uk
Nestled in the heart of Leicestershire, overlooking the Charnwood Forest and beyond, Park Hill Golf Club boasts an 18 hole, championship length course that utilises the lands natural features to ensure that no two

continued

continued

holes are the same. The combination of water features and precisely positioned bunkers provide for a challenging, yet enjoyable course, with excellent playing conditions all year round.
18 holes, 7219yds, Par 73, SSS 75, Course record 71. Club membership 500.

Park Hill Golf Club

Visitors play after 9am weekends. **Societies** apply in advance. **Green Fees** £22 (£26 weekends). **Cards** 🃏🃏 🃏🃏🃏 **Prof** Matthew Ulyett **Facilities** ⊗ ⛾ 🛍 ☕ ♀♨🏠 ⛳ 🏌 🚶 🏊 ⚑ ₵ **Conf** Max 140 Thtr 140 Class 100 Banquet 140 **Location** 5m N of Leicester off A46 Northbound,follow signs to Seagrave

Hotel ★★★ 64% Quality Hotel, New Ashby Rd, LOUGHBOROUGH ☎ 01509 211800 94 en suite

> Entries with a green background identify courses considered to be particularly interesting

Park Hill Golf Club

Park Hill, Seagrave, Leicestershire, LE12 7NG
Tel 01509 815454   Fax 01509 816062
E-mail: mail@parkhillgolf.co.uk
www.parkhillgolf.co.uk

Nestled in the heart of Leicestershire, overlooking the Charnwood Forest and beyond, Park Hill boasts an 18 hole, Championship length course, that utilises the lands natural features to ensure that no two holes are the same, the combination of water features and precisely positioned bunkers provide for a challenging course and excellent playing conditions all year round.
Our fully licensed Clubhouse is open daily for meals and refreshments.

Ullesthorpe Frolesworth Rd LE17 5BZ
☎ 01455 209023 🖹 01455 202537
e-mail: bookings@ullesthorpecourt.co.uk
Set in 130 acres of parkland surrounding a 17th-century manor house, this championship length course can be very demanding and offers a challenge to both beginners and professionals. Excellent leisure facilities. Water plays a part on three holes.

18 holes, 6662yds, Par 72, SSS 72, Course record 67. Club membership 650.
Visitors must contact in advance. With member only Sat, no play on Sun. **Societies** contact well in advance. **Green Fees** £30 per day; £22 per round. **Cards** 🃏🃏 🃏 🃏🃏 🃏 🃏🃏 🃏🃏 🃏 **Prof** David Bowring **Facilities** ⊗ ⛾ 🛍 ☕ ♀ ♨ 🏠 ⛳ 🏌 🚶 🏊 ₵ **Leisure** hard tennis courts, heated indoor swimming pool, sauna, solarium, gymnasium, Beauty room,snooker room,steam room &jaccuzi. **Conf** Max 80 Thtr 80 Class 48 Board 30 Banquet 125 Del from £30 * **Location** 5m Lutterworth junct 20 M1

Hotel ★★★ 67% Ullesthorpe Court Country Hotel & Golf Club, Frolesworth Rd, ULLESTHORPE
☎ 01455 209023 38 en suite

Whetstone Cambridge Rd, Cosby LE9 1SJ
☎ 0116 286 1424 🖹 0116 286 1424
Easy to walk, parkland course where accuracy rather than length is required.
18 holes, 5795yds, Par 68, SSS 68, Course record 63. Club membership 500.
Visitors must contact in advance, limited times at weekends. **Societies** must contact in advance. **Green Fees** £15 (£16 weekends & bank holidays). **Cards** 🃏🃏 🃏🃏 🃏🃏 🃏 🃏🃏 🃏 **Prof** David Raitt **Course Designer** E Calloway **Facilities** ⊗ ⛾ 🛍 ☕ ♀ ♨ 🏠 🚶 🏊 ⚑ ₵ **Location** 1m S of village

Hotel ★★★ 67% Time Out Hotel & Leisure, Enderby Rd, Blaby, LEICESTER ☎ 0116 278 7898 48 en suite

Breedon Priory Green Ln DE73 1AT
☎ 01332 863081 🖹 01332 865319
A relatively short and forgiving course set in undulating countryside with magnificent views from several holes.
18 holes, 5777yds, Par 69, SSS 68, Course record 67. Club membership 779.
Visitors may play any time if tee available, must book for weekends one week in advance. **Societies** apply in writing or telephone for booking form. **Green Fees** not confirmed.
Cards 🃏🃏 🃏🃏 🃏 **Prof** Jim Broughton **Course Designer** David Snell **Facilities** ⊗ ⛾ 🛍 ☕ ♀ ♨ 🏠 🚶 🏊 ⚑ ₵ **Leisure** sauna, gymnasium. **Location** 4m W of A42/M1 junct 24
continued

Hotel ★★★ 69% The Priest House on the River, Kings Mills, Castle Donington, ☎ 01332 810649 24 en suite 19 annexe en suite

WOODHOUSE EAVES   Map 08 SK51

Charnwood Forest Breakback Ln LE12 8TA
☎ 01509 890259 🖷 01509 890925
e-mail: secretary@charnwoodforestgc.co.uk
Hilly heathland course with hard walking, but no bunkers. Play is round volcanic rock giving panoramic views over the Charnwood Forest area.
9 holes, 5960yds, Par 69, SSS 69, Course record 64.
Club membership 218.
Visitors must contact in advance, weekends restricted. **Societies** Wed & Thu only. Must contact in advance. Mon & Fri by special arrangement. **Green Fees** terms on application. **Course Designer** James Braid **Facilities** ⊗ ⅏ ㋪ ☕ ♀ ㋹ ⅋ **Location** 3m from junct 22 or 23 of M1

Hotel ★★★★ 71% Quorn Country Hotel, Charnwood House, 66 Leicester Rd, QUORN ☎ 01509 415050 23 en suite

Lingdale Joe Moore's Ln LE12 8TF
☎ 01509 890703 🖷 01509 890703
Parkland course located in Charnwood Forest with some hard walking at some holes. The par 3 (3rd) and par 5 (8th) are testing holes. Several holes have water hazards.
18 holes, 6545yds, Par 71, SSS 71, Course record 68.
Club membership 620.
Visitors must telephone professional in advance for play. **Societies** must contact in advance. **Green Fees** not confirmed. **Prof** Peter Sellears **Course Designer** David Tucker **Facilities** ⊗ ⅏ ㋪ ☕ ♀ ㋹ ㋐ ⅋ **Location** 1.5m S off B5330

Hotel ★★★★ 71% Quorn Country Hotel, Charnwood House, 66 Leicester Rd, QUORN ☎ 01509 415050 23 en suite

LINCOLNSHIRE

BELTON   Map 08 SK93

Belton Woods Hotel NG32 2LN
☎ 01476 593200 🖷 01476 574547
e-mail: devere.belton@airtime.co.uk
Two challenging 18-hole courses, a 9-hole par 3 and a driving range. The Lakes Course has thirteen lakes, while The Woodside boasts the third longest hole in Europe at 613 yards. Many leisure facilities.
The Lakes Course: 18 holes, 6831yds, Par 72, SSS 73, Course record 68.
The Woodside Course: 18 holes, 6623yds, Par 73, SSS 72, Course record 67.
Spitfire Course: 9 holes, 1010yds, Par 27, SSS 27.
Club membership 600.
Visitors book tee times in advance with exception of the Spitfire. Dress code in operation. **Societies** welcome all week, reservations to be made by telephone or letter. **Green Fees** not confirmed. **Cards** 🃏 🃏 🃏 🃏 🃏 🃏 **Prof** Steve Sayers **Facilities** ⊗ ⅏ ㋪ ☕ ♀ ㋹ ㋐ ㋐ ㋤ ⅋ ㋕ **Leisure** hard tennis courts, heated indoor swimming pool, squash, sauna, solarium, gymnasium. **Location** On A607, 2m N of Grantham

Hotel ★★★★ 75% Belton Woods Hotel, BELTON ☎ 01476 593200 136 en suite

BLANKNEY   Map 08 TF06

Blankney LN4 3AZ ☎ 01526 320263 🖷 01526 322521
Open parkland course with mature trees; fairly flat.
18 holes, 6634yds, Par 72, SSS 73, Course record 69.
Club membership 700.
Visitors must contact in advance, may not play Wed mornings, restricted at weekends. **Societies** not Wed mornings, booking required. **Green Fees** £30 per day; £24 per round (£35/£30 weekends). **Prof** Graham Bradley **Course Designer** C Sinclair **Facilities** ⊗ ⅏ ㋪ ☕ ♀ ㋐ ㋤ ㋪ ❧ ㋛ ⅋ **Leisure** snooker. **Location** 10m SW on B1188

Hotel ★★ 70% Moor Lodge Hotel, Sleaford Rd, BRANSTON ☎ 01522 791366 24 en suite

BOSTON   Map 08 TF34

Boston Cowbridge, Horncastle Rd PE22 7EL
☎ 01205 350589 🖷 01205 350589
Parkland course many water hazards in play on ten holes.
18 holes, 6490yds, Par 72, SSS 71, Course record 69.
Club membership 650.
Visitors evidence of handicap may be requested, contact in advance for tee time. **Societies** apply in writing/telephone. **Green Fees** not confirmed. **Prof** Terry Squires **Facilities** ⊗ ⅏ ㋪ ☕ ♀ ㋐ ㋤ ⅋ **Location** 2m N of Boston on B1183

Hotel ★★★ 62% New England Hotel, 49 Wide Bargate, BOSTON ☎ 01205 365255 27 en suite

Kirton Holme Holme Rd, Kirton Holme PE20 1SY
☎ 01205 290669
A young parkland course designed for mid to high handicappers. It is flat but has 2500 young trees, two natural water courses plus water hazards. The 2nd is a challenging, 386yard par 4 dogleg.
9 holes, 5778yds, Par 70, SSS 68, Course record 69.
Club membership 350.
Visitors no restrictions but booking advisable for weekends & summer evenings. **Societies** by prior arrangement. **Green Fees** £8.50 per day; £5 per 9 holes (£9.50/£6 weekends & bank holidays). **Course Designer** D W Welberry **Facilities** ⊗ ㋪ ☕ ♀ ㋐ ㋤ ⅋ **Location** 4m W of Boston off A52

Hotel ★★ 65% Comfort Inn, Donnington Rd, Bicker Bar Roundabout, BOSTON ☎ 01205 820118 55 en suite

BOURNE   Map 08 TF02

Toft Hotel Toft PE10 0JT
☎ 01778 590616 🖷 01778 590264
Parkland course on the verge of the Lincoln Edge. Includes lake and uses contours of the hills to full effect.

continued

18 holes, 6486yds, Par 72, SSS 71, Course record 63.
Club membership 450.
Visitors advisable to book for weekends. Societies apply in advance by telephone. Green Fees not confirmed. Cards 📧 📧 📧 📧 📄 Prof Mark Jackson Course Designer Roger Fitton Facilities ⊗ 洲 ⓑ ⬛ ♀ ♨ 🏠 ✿ ➤ 🛒 ✔ 𝄃 Location On A6121 Bourne/Stamford road

Hotel ★★★ 78% The George of Stamford, 71 St Martins, STAMFORD ☎ 01780 750750 & 750700 (Res) 📖 01780 750701 47 en suite

CLEETHORPES   Map 08 TA30

Cleethorpes Kings Rd DN35 0PN
☎ 01472 816110 📖 01472 814060
A mature coastal course founded in 1894. Slight undulations give variety but the flat landscape makes for easy walking. The course provides a challenge to all levels of player.

18 holes, 6356yds, Par 70, SSS 70, Course record 66.
Club membership 640.
Visitors may not play after 12.30 Wed; handicap certificate preferred, must be a member of a golf club. Societies Mon, Thu, Fri, Sun only. Must telephone in advance. Green Fees £20 per day (£25 weekends & bank holidays). Prof Paul Davies Course Designer Harry Vardon Facilities ⊗ 洲 ⓑ ⬛ ♀ ♨ 🏠 𝄃 Location 2m SE of Cleethorpes, A180/A46 from W, A16 from S

Hotel ★★★ 70% Kingsway Hotel, Kingsway, CLEETHORPES ☎ 01472 601122 49 en suite

Tetney Station Rd, Tetney DN36 5HY
☎ 01472 211644 📖 01472 211644
18-hole parkland course set at the foot of the Lincolnshire Wolds. Noted for its challenging water features.
18 holes, 6245yds, Par 71, SSS 69, Course record 65.
Club membership 450.
Visitors must contact for start time. Societies apply in writing. Green Fees £15 per day; £10 per round. Cards 📧 📧 📧 📧 📄 Prof Jason Abrams Course Designer J S Grant Facilities ⊗ 洲 ⓑ ⬛ ♀ ♨ 🏠 ✿ ➤ 🛒 ✔ 𝄃 Location 1m off A16 Louth/Grimsby road

Hotel ★★★ 70% Kingsway Hotel, Kingsway, CLEETHORPES ☎ 01472 601122 49 en suite

CROWLE   Map 08 SE71

The Lincolnshire DN17 4BU
☎ 01724 711619 📖 01724 711619
Traditional flat parkland course. Generous sized greens with discreet use of water and bunkers.
18 holes, 6283yds, Par 71, SSS 70.
Club membership 370.

continued

Visitors no restrictions. Societies welcome any time. Green Fees £11(£14 weekends). Course Designer Stubley/Byrne Facilities ⊗ 洲 ⓑ ⬛ ♀ ♨ 🏠 ✿ 𝄃 Location M180 junct 2, 1m on Crowle road

Hotel ★★ 71% Belmont Hotel, Horsefair Green, THORNE ☎ 01405 812320 23 en suite

ELSHAM   Map 08 TA01

Elsham Barton Rd DN20 0LS
☎ 01652 680291(Sec) 680432(Pro) 📖 01652 680308
e-mail: elshamgolfclub@lineone.net
Mature parkland course in a rural setting with a variety of wild life including many pheasants. Very secluded with easy walking and a reservoir to maintain irrigation.
18 holes, 6402yds, Par 71, SSS 71, Course record 67.
Club membership 600.
Visitors with member only weekends & bank holidays. Preferable to contact in advance. Societies must apply in writing. Green Fees £30 per 36 holes; £24 per 18 holes. Prof Stuart Brewer Course Designer Various Facilities ⊗ 洲 ⓑ ⬛ ♀ ♨ 🏠 ➤ 🛒 ✔ Location 2m NE of Brigg on B1206. M180 junct 5, take exit sign posted Elsham. Through village to T-junct, turn left, 1m on left

Hotel ★★★ 68% Wortley House Hotel, Rowland Rd, SCUNTHORPE ☎ 01724 842223 38 en suite

GAINSBOROUGH   Map 08 SK88

Gainsborough Thonock DN21 1PZ
☎ 01427 613088 📖 01427 810172
e-mail: gainsboroughgc.co.uk
Thonock Park course, founded in 1894 is an attractive parkland course with many deciduous trees. Karsten Lakes course is a championship course designed by Neil Coles. Set in rolling countryside the lakes and well bunkered greens provide a true test of golf. Floodlit driving range.
Thonock Park: 18 holes, 6266yds, Par 70, SSS 70, Course record 63.
Karsten Lakes: 18 holes, 6721yds, Par 72, SSS 72, Course record 65.
Club membership 700.
Visitors Thonock Park: Ladies Day Thu morning. Advance booking available. Societies must telephone in advance. Green Fees Thonock Park £28 per day, £20 per round. Karsten Lakes £35 per day, £25 per round. Cards 📧 📧 📧 📧 📄 Prof Stephen Cooper Course Designer Neil Coles Facilities ⊗ 洲 ⓑ ⬛ ♀ ♨ 🏠 ✿ ➤ 🛒 ✔ 𝄃 Conf Max 75 Thtr 75 Class 75 Board 35 Del £4.50 to £10.50 * Location 1m N off A159. Signposted off A631

Hotel ★★★ 65% West Retford Hotel, 24 North Rd, RETFORD ☎ 01777 706333 62 annexe en suite

GEDNEY HILL   Map 08 TF31

Gedney Hill West Drove PE12 0NT
☎ 01406 330922 📖 01406 330323
e-mail: d.t.h@fsddail.co.uk
Flat parkland course similar to a links course. Made testing by Fen winds and small greens. Also a 10-bay driving range.
18 holes, 5493yds, Par 70, SSS 66, Course record 67.
Club membership 200.
Visitors no restrictions. Societies telephone in advance. Green Fees not confirmed. Prof David Hutton Course Designer Monkwise Ltd Facilities ⊗ 洲 ⓑ ⬛ ♀ ♨ 🏠 ✿ ➤ 🛒 ✔ 𝄃 Location 5m SE of Spalding

continued

Hotel ★★ 66% Rose & Crown Hotel, 23/24 Market Place, WISBECH ☎ 01945 589800 20 en suite

GRANTHAM — Map 08 SK93

Belton Park Belton Ln, Londonthorpe Rd NG31 9SH
☎ 01476 567399 📋 01476 592078
e-mail: greatgolf@beltonpark
Three 9-hole courses set in classic mature parkland of Lord Brownlow's country seat, Belton House. Gently undulating with streams, ponds, plenty of trees and beautiful scenery, including a deer park. Famous holes: 5th, 12th, 16th and 18th. Combine any of the three courses for a testing 18-hole round.

Brownlow: 18 holes, 6420yds, Par 71, SSS 71, Course record 64.
Ancaster: 18 holes, 6325yds, Par 70, SSS 70.
Belmont: 18 holes, 6075yds, Par 69, SSS 69.
Club membership 850.
Visitors contact professional for suitable tee times. No green fees on Tuesday before 3pm. **Societies** apply in advance.
Green Fees £36 per day, £30 per round (£42/36 weekends).
Cards 💳 💳 **Prof** Brian McKee **Course Designer** Williamson/Allis **Facilities** ⊗ ⏶ 𝄞 ⛳ ♀ ⚐ 🏠 ⛱ ✦
Location 1.5m NE of Grantham

Hotel ★★★ 69% Kings Hotel, North Pde, GRANTHAM ☎ 01476 590800 21 en suite

Sudbrook Moor Charity St, Carlton Scroop NG32 3AT ☎ 01400 250796
A testing 9-hole parkland/meadowland course in a picturesque valley setting with easy walking.
9 holes, 4811yds, Par 66, SSS 64, Course record 69.
Club membership 600.
Visitors advisable to telephone in advance. **Green Fees** Summer: £7 per day (£9 weekends and bank holidays); Winter: £5 per day (£7 weekends and bank holidays). **Cards** 💳 💳 💳 💳 💳 **Prof** Tim Hutton **Course Designer** Tim Hutton **Facilities** 𝄞 ⛳ ♀ 🏠 ⛱ ✦ **Location** 6m NE of Grantham on A607

Hotel ★★★ 69% Kings Hotel, North Pde, GRANTHAM ☎ 01476 590800 21 en suite

GRIMSBY — Map 08 TA21

Grimsby Littlecoates Rd DN34 4LU
☎ 01472 342630 📋 01472 342630
Undulating parkland course.
18 holes, 6098yds, Par 70, SSS 69, Course record 65.
Club membership 730.
Visitors contact in advance. **Societies** by prior arrangement with secretary. **Green Fees** terms on application. **Prof** Richard Smith **Course Designer** Colt **Facilities** ⊗ ⏶ 𝄞 ⛳
♀ 🏠 ⚐ 🍴 🏌 ✦ **Location** 1m from A180 & 1m from A46

continued

Hotel ★★★ 65% Humber Royal, Littlecoates Rd, GRIMSBY ☎ 01472 240024 52 en suite

HORNCASTLE — Map 08 TF26

Horncastle West Ashby LN9 5PP ☎ 01507 526800
Parkland course with many water hazards and bunkers; very challenging. There is a 25-bay floodlit driving range.
18 holes, 5717yds, Par 70, SSS 68, Course record 71.
Club membership 200.
Visitors dress code must be adhered to, welcome anytime, may contact in advance. **Societies** apply in writing or telephone in advance. **Green Fees** £20 per day; £15 per round. **Cards** 💳 💳 **Prof** E C Wright **Course Designer** E C Wright **Facilities** ⊗ ⏶ ⛳ ♀ 🏠 ⛱ ✦ 🍴 **Leisure** fishing. **Conf** Max 250 **Location** Off A158 Lincoln/ Skegness road at Edlington, off A153 at West Ashby

Hotel ★★ 71% Admiral Rodney Hotel, North St, HORNCASTLE ☎ 01507 523131 31 en suite

HUBBERT'S BRIDGE   Map 08 TF24

Boston West Golf Centre PE20 3QX
☎ 01205 290670 ▤ 01205 290725
e-mail: info@bostonwestgolfclub.co.uk
A challenging course with water featuring on eight of the 18 large greens, these are undulating on the first nine and the mature trees/shrubs on the back nine can prove tricky. A well-drained course allowing motorised buggies and carts nearly all year.
18 holes, 6333yards, Par 72, SSS 70, Course record 70. Club membership 720.
Visitors advisable to book up to 7 days in advance - booking line 01205 290770. Dress code must be observed. Societies telephone for details. Green Fees £13 per 18 holes; £7 per 9 holes (£15/£8 weekends). Cards ▦ ▩ ▦ ▦ ▣ Prof Andrew Hare Course Designer Michael Zara Facilities ⊗ ⅶ ⓛ ♥ ♀ ⚘ ⌂ ⚐ ⚑ ⚒ ⚒ ⚐ ℓ Leisure 6 hole academy course, clay pigeon shooting. Location 2m W of Boston on crossroads of A1121/B1192

Hotel ★★★ 62% Golf Hotel, The Broadway, WOODHALL SPA ☎ 01526 353535 50 en suite

IMMINGHAM   Map 08 TA11

Immingham St Andrews Ln, off Church Ln DN40 2EU
☎ 01469 575298 ▤ 01469 577636
e-mail: admin@immgc.com
An excellent, flat parkland course noted for its numerous dykes which come into play on most holes.
18 holes, 6215yds, Par 71, SSS 70, Course record 69. Club membership 700.
Visitors telephone in advance. Societies telephone (am) to arrange date. Green Fees £12; £18 weekends; £23 bank holidays. Prof Nick Harding Course Designer Hawtree & Son Facilities ⊗ ⅶ ⓛ ♥ ♀ ⚘ ⌂ ⚐ ℓ Location 7m NW off Grimsby

Hotel ★★★ 65% Humber Royal, Littlecoates Rd, GRIMSBY ☎ 01472 240024 52 en suite

LACEBY   Map 08 TA20

Manor Barton St, Laceby Manor DN37 7EA
☎ 01472 873468(shop) & 873469(office) ▤ 01472 276706
e-mail: manorgolf@hotmail.com
The first nine holes played as a parkland course, all the fairways lined with young trees. The second nine are mainly open fairways. The 18th hole green is surrounded by water.
18 holes, 6354yds, Par 71, SSS 70. Club membership 550.
Visitors booked tee system at all times, visitors may book 6 days in advance. Societies telephone in advance. Green Fees £18 per round (£20 weekends). Cards ▦ ▩ ▦ ▦ ▣ Facilities ⊗ ⅶ ⓛ ♥ ♀ ⚘ ⌂ ⚐ ℓ Leisure fishing. Conf Max 40 Thtr 40 Class 20 Del £4 to £15 * Location A18 Barton St - Laceby/Louth

Hotel ★★★ 65% Humber Royal, Littlecoates Rd, GRIMSBY ☎ 01472 240024 52 en suite

LINCOLN   Map 08 SK97

Canwick Park Canwick Park, Washingborough Rd
LN4 1EF ☎ 01522 522166 & 542912 ▤ 01522 542912
e-mail: secretary@canwickparkgc.co.uk
Parkland course with views of Lincoln Cathedral. Testing 5th hole (200 yd par 3).
18 holes, 6160yds, Par 70, SSS 69, Course record 65. Club membership 650.

continued

Visitors with member only Sat also Sun before 3pm. Societies weekdays only by prior arrangement in writing. Green Fees not confirmed. Prof S Williamson Course Designer Hawtree & Sons Facilities ⊗ ⅶ ⓛ ♥ ♀ ⚘ ⌂ ⚐ ⚒ ℓ Location 1m E of Lincoln

Hotel ★★★ 65% Posthouse Lincoln, Eastgate, LINCOLN ☎ 0870 400 9052 70 en suite

Carholme Carholme Rd LN1 1SE
☎ 01522 523725 ▤ 01522 533733
Parkland course where prevailing west winds can add interest. Good views. First hole out of bounds left and right of fairway, pond in front of bunkered green at 5th, lateral water hazards across several fairways.
18 holes, 6243yds, Par 71, SSS 70, Course record 69. Club membership 625.
Visitors must contact in advance. Weekends may not play before 2.30pm. Societies apply in writing/telephone in advance. Green Fees not confirmed. Prof Richard Hunter Facilities ⊗ ⅶ ⓛ ♥ ♀ ⚘ ⌂ ⚐ ℓ Location 1m W of city centre on A57

Hotel ★★★ 66% The White Hart, Bailgate, LINCOLN ☎ 0870 400 8117 48 en suite

LOUTH   Map 08 TF38

Louth Crowtree Ln LN11 9LJ
☎ 01507 603681 ▤ 01507 608501
e-mail: louthgolfclub1992@btinternet.com
Undulating parkland course, fine views in an area of outstanding natural beauty.
18 holes, 6430yds, Par 72, SSS 71, Course record 64. Club membership 700.
Visitors must contact in advance to make sure tee is not reserved for competition. Societies a booking form will be sent on request. Green Fees £26 day; £20 per round (£35/£30 weekends). Cards ▦ ▩ ▦ ▦ ▣ Prof A Blundell Facilities ⊗ ⅶ ⓛ ♥ ♀ ⚘ ⌂ ⚐ ⚒ ℓ Leisure squash. Conf Max 100 Location W side of Louth between A157/A153

Hotel ★★★ 69% Beaumont Hotel, 66 Victoria Rd, LOUTH ☎ 01507 605005 16 en suite

MARKET RASEN   Map 08 TF18

Market Rasen & District Legsby Rd LN8 3DZ
☎ 01673 842319
Picturesque, well-wooded heathland course, easy walking, breezy with becks forming natural hazards. Good views of Lincolnshire Wolds.
18 holes, 6045yds, Par 70, SSS 69, Course record 66. Club membership 600.
Visitors must play with member at weekends and must contact in advance. Societies Tue & Fri only; must contact in advance. Green Fees terms on application. Prof A M Chester Facilities ⊗ ⅶ ⓛ ♥ ♀ ⚘ ⌂ ℓ Location 1m E, off A46 onto A631

Hotel ★★★ 69% Beaumont Hotel, 66 Victoria Rd, LOUTH ☎ 01507 605005 16 en suite

Market Rasen Race Course (Golf Course)
Legsby Rd LN8 3EA ☎ 01673 843434 ▤ 01673 844532
e-mail: marketrasen@rht.net
This is a public course set within the bounds of Market Rasen race course - the entire racing area is out of bounds. The longest hole is the 4th at 454yards with the

continued

race course providing a hazard over the whole length of the drive.
9 holes, 2532yds, Par 32.

Market Rasen Race Course (Golf Course)

Visitors closed racedays apart from evening meetings when open until noon. **Societies** telephone in advance to arrange. **Green Fees** £4 per round (£5 weekends). **Course Designer** Edward Stenton **Facilities** ⚑ **Conf** Thtr 300 Class 150 Board 150 Banquet 250 Del from £12 * **Location** 1m E of Market Rasen
....

Hotel ★★★ 69% Beaumont Hotel, 66 Victoria Rd, LOUTH
☎ 01507 605005 16 en suite

NORMANBY   Map 08 SE81

Normanby Hall Normanby Park DN15 9HU
☎ 01724 720226 (Pro shop) 853212 (Secretary)
e-mail: secretarydmac1066@aol.com
Well maintained course set in secluded mature parkland. A challenge to golfers of all abilities.
18 holes, 6561yds, Par 72, SSS 71, Course record 66.
Club membership 850.
Visitors book in advance by contacting professional.
Societies must contact in advance: Rachael Lennox, 01724 297860. **Green Fees** not confirmed. **Cards** 🃏 💳 **Prof** Christopher Mann **Course Designer** Hawtree & Son **Facilities** ⊗ ⽺ ⅃ ⚑ 🛒 ♨ 🏌 🛄 ♂ **Location** 3m N of Scunthorpe adj to Normanby Hall on B1130
....

Hotel ★★★ 67% Menzies Royal Hotel, Doncaster Rd, SCUNTHORPE ☎ 0870 6003013 33 en suite

SCUNTHORPE   Map 08 SE81

Ashby Decoy Burringham Rd DN17 2AB
☎ 01724 866561 📠 01724 271708
e-mail: ashby.decoy@btclick.com
Pleasant, flat parkland course to satisfy all tastes, yet test the experienced golfer.
18 holes, 6281yds, Par 71, Course record 66.
Club membership 650.
Visitors may not play Tue, weekends or bank holidays.
Handicap certificate required. **Societies** apply in advance.
Green Fees £23 per day; £18 per round. **Prof** A Miller **Facilities** ⊗ ⽺ ⅃ ⚑ ♨ 🏌 🛄 ♂ **Location** 2.5m SW on B1450 near Asda Superstore
....

Hotel ★★★ 67% Menzies Royal Hotel, Doncaster Rd, SCUNTHORPE ☎ 0870 6003013 33 en suite

Forest Pines Ermine St, Broughton DN20 0AQ
☎ 01652 650770 & 650756 📠 01652 650495
e-mail: enquiries@forestpines.co.uk
Set in 185 acres of mature parkland and open heathland

continued

and constructed in a similar design to that of Wentworth or Sunningdale, Forest Pines offers three challenging 9-hole courses - Forest, Pines and Beeches. Any combination can be played. Facilities include a 17-bay driving range and a spacious clubhouse.

Forest Pines Golf Course

Forest Course: 9 holes, 3291yds, Par 36, SSS 36.
Pines Course: 9 holes, 3591yds, Par 37, SSS 37.
Beeches: 9 holes, 3102yds, Par 35, SSS 35.
Club membership 330.
Visitors must contact in advance. **Societies** telephone in advance. **Green Fees** terms on application. **Cards** 🃏 💳 🏧 💳 🄋 **Prof** David Edwards **Course Designer** John Morgan **Facilities** ⊗ ⽺ ⅃ ⚑ ♀ ♨ 🏌 🛄 ♂ ✆ **Leisure** heated indoor swimming pool, sauna, solarium, gymnasium.**Conf** Max 250 Thtr 250 Class 100 Board 50 Banquet 200 **Location** 200yds from junct 4 M180
....

Hotel ★★★★ 70% Forest Pines Hotel, Ermine St, Broughton, SCUNTHORPE ☎ 01652 650770 86 en suite

Holme Hall Holme Ln, Bottesford DN16 3RF
☎ 01724 862078 📠 01724 862078
e-mail: tracey.curtis@btconnect.com
Heathland course with sandy subsoil. Easy walking. This course is a regular venue of both the Lincolnshire Open and amateur championships.
18 holes, 6404yds, Par 71, SSS 71, Course record 65.
Club membership 746.
Visitors must play with member at weekends & bank holidays. Must contact in advance. **Societies** must contact in advance. **Green Fees** £27 per day; £20 per round. **Prof** Richard McKiernan **Facilities** ⊗ ⽺ ⅃ ⚑ ♀ ♨ 🏌 🛄 ♂ ✆ **Location** 4m SE of Scunthorpe. M180 junct 4
....

Hotel ★★★ 67% Menzies Royal Hotel, Doncaster Rd, SCUNTHORPE ☎ 0870 6003013 33 en suite

Kingsway Kingsway DN15 7ER ☎ 01724 840945
9 holes, 1915yds, Par 29, Course record 28.
Location W side of town centre off A18
Telephone for further details
....

Hotel ★★★ 67% Menzies Royal Hotel, Doncaster Rd, SCUNTHORPE ☎ 0870 6003013 33 en suite

SKEGNESS   Map 09 TF56

North Shore Hotel & Golf Club North Shore Rd
PE25 1DN ☎ 01754 763298 📠 01754 761902
e-mail: golf@north-shore.co.uk
Part links, part parkland comprising of two out of the 9 holes situated next to the sea. A challenging course with both greens situated in front of the main bar.
18 holes, 6200yds, Par 71, SSS 71, Course record 67.
Club membership 450.

continued

North Shore Hotel & Golf Club

Visitors tee times must be booked if possible. **Societies** write or telephone in advance. **Green Fees** £33 per day; £22 per round (£45/£31 weekends). **Cards** 🖃 🖃 🖃 🖾 🖻 **Prof** J Cornelius **Course Designer** James Braid **Facilities** ⊗ ⅏ ⅃ ⚑ ☕ ⅃ ⌂ ⚑ ⚑ ♂ **Leisure** snooker. **Conf** Max 200 Thtr 200 Class 140 Board 60 Banquet 160 Del £8 to £25 * **Location** 1m N of town centre off A52, right into North Shore Holiday Centre into North Shore Road

Hotel ★★ 66% North Shore Hotel & Golf Course, North Shore Rd, SKEGNESS ☎ 01754 763298 33 en suite 3 annexe en suite

Seacroft Drummond Rd, Seacroft PE25 3AU
☎ 01754 763020 📠 01754 763020
e-mail: richard@seacroft-golfclub.co.uk
A championship seaside links traditionally laid out with tight undulations and hogsback fairways. Adjacent to Gibraltar Point Nature Reserve.

18 holes, 6479yds, Par 71, SSS 71, Course record 65.
Club membership 590.
Visitors must be a member of an affiliated golf club/society. **Societies** contact in advance. **Green Fees** £40 per day; £30 per round (£45/£35 weekends & bank holidays). **Prof** Robin Lawie **Course Designer** Tom Dunn/Willie Fernie **Facilities** ⊗ ⅏ ⅃ ⚑ ☕ ⅃ ⌂ ⚑ ♂ **Location** S side of town centre

Hotel ★★★ 64% Crown Hotel, Drummond Rd, Seacroft, SKEGNESS ☎ 01754 610760 27 en suite

SLEAFORD   Map 08 TF04

Sleaford Willoughby Rd, South Rauceby NG34 8PL
☎ 01529 488273 📠 01529 488326
e-mail: sleafordgolfclub@btinternet.com
Inland links-type course, moderately wooded and fairly flat.
18 holes, 6503yds, Par 72, SSS 71, Course record 64.
Club membership 630.

continued

Visitors contact in advance, may not play Sun in winter. **Societies** telephone enquiry to professional. Written confirmation required. **Green Fees** £27 per day; £20 per round (£36 weekends). **Prof** James Wilson **Course Designer** T Williamson **Facilities** ⊗ ⅏ ⅃ ⚑ ☕ ⅃ ⌂ ⚑ ♂ **Location** 2m W of Sleaford, off A153

Hotel ★★★ 69% Kings Hotel, North Pde, GRANTHAM ☎ 01476 590800 21 en suite

SOUTH KYME   Map 08 TF14

South Kyme Skinners Ln LN4 4AT
☎ 01526 861113 📠 01526 861113
e-mail: southkymegc@hotmail.com
A challenging fenland course described as an 'inland links' with water hazards, trees and fairway hazards.
18 holes, 6568yds, Par 72, SSS 71, Course record 67.
Club membership 470.
Visitors advisable to telephone in advance for course availability. **Societies** telephone for booking form. **Green Fees** £15 per round (£18 weekends). **Cards** 🖃 🖃 **Prof** Peter Chamberlain **Facilities** ⊗ ⅏ ⅃ ⚑ ☕ ⅃ ⌂ ⚑ ♂ **Leisure** 6 hole short course. **Location** Off B1395 in South Kyme village

Hotel ⌂ Travelodge, Holdingham, SLEAFORD ☎ 01529 414752 40 en suite

SPALDING   Map 08 TF22

Spalding Surfleet PE11 4EA
☎ 01775 680386 (office) & 680474 (pro) 📠 01775 680988
A pretty, well laid-out course in a fenland area. The River Glen runs beside the 1st, 2nd and 4th holes, and ponds and lakes are very much in play on the 9th, 10th and 11th holes. Challenging holes include the river dominated 2nd and the 10th which involves a tight drive and dog-leg left to reach a raised three-tier green.

18 holes, 6478yds, Par 72, SSS 71, Course record 62.
Club membership 750.
Visitors must contact in advance. Handicap certificate required. **Societies** write to the secretary, Societies on Thu all day and Tue pm. **Green Fees** £25 per day; £20 per round(£30 weekends & bank holidays). **Prof** John Spencer **Course Designer** Price/Spencer/Ward **Facilities** ⊗ ⅏ ⅃ ⚑ ☕ ⅃ ⌂ ⚑ ♂ **Location** 4m N of Spalding adjacent to A16

Hotel ★★ 70% Cley Hall Hotel, 22 High St, SPALDING ☎ 01775 725157 4 en suite 8 annexe en suite

STAMFORD   Map 08 TF00

Burghley Park St Martins PE9 3JX
☎ 01780 762100 & 753789 📠 01780 753789
Open parkland course with superb greens, many trees, ponds and bunkers. Situated in the grounds of Burghley House. continued on page 164

Woodhall Spa

Woodhall Spa, *Lincs* ☎ 01526 352511 Fax 01526 351817 Map 08 TF16

e-mail: flint@englishgolfunion.org

The Championship Course at Woodhall Spa, now known as the Hotchkin, is arguably the best inland course in Britain. It is a classic British heathland course with cavernous bunkers and heather-lined fairways. Golf has been played here for over 100 years and the Hotchkin has hosted most of the top national and international amateur events.

The English Golf Union acquired Woodhall Spa in 1995 to create a centre of excellence. A second course, the Bracken, has been built, together with extensive practice facilities – including one of Europe's finest short game practice areas. The English Golf Union actively encourages visitors throughout the year to The National Golf Centre to experience these facilities and to enjoy the unique ambience.

Visitors must contact in advance. Handicap certificate must be produced

Societies must apply by telephone initially

Green Fees not confirmed

Facilities ⊗ ⅷ ᵇ ᴸ ♥ ⅌ 📐 ⚲ 🏠 ⛳ ⦇ ⅔ ᵲ
Professional (C. C. Elliot)

Location The Broadway LN10 6PU
(NE side of village off B1191) Conf max 150
Banquet 200

Holes/Par/Course record 36 holes
Hotchkin: 18 holes, 7080 yds, Par 73, SSS 73,
Course record 67.
Bracken: 18 holes, 6735 yds, Par 72, SSS 74,
Course record 68

Championship Course

WHERE TO STAY AND EAT NEARBY

Hotels
WOODHALL SPA

★★★67% Petwood Hotel, Stixwould Rd.
☎ 01526 352411. 50 en suite
        See photograph on page 164
★★★62% Golf Hotel, The Broadway.
☎ 01526 353535. 50 en suite

★★65% Eagle Lodge, The Broadway.
☎ 01526 353231. 23 en suite

Restaurant
HORNCASTLE

◉◉ Magpies, 71-75 East St.
☎ 01507 527004.

18 holes, 6236yds, Par 70, SSS 70, Course record 64.
Club membership 775.
Visitors with member only weekends. Must contact in
advance & have handicap certificate. **Societies** prior
arrangement in writing, preferably by 1st Dec previous year.
Green Fees £25 per day; £15 twilight. **Prof** Glenn Davies
Course Designer Rev J Day (1938) **Facilities** ⊗ ⅏ by prior
arrangement ╠ ♥ ♀ ♨ ☎ ⊶ ♨ ✔ **Location** 1m S of
town on B1081

Hotel ★★★ 78% The George of Stamford, 71 St Martins,
STAMFORD ☎ 01780 750750 & 750700 (Res)
🗐 01780 750701 47 en suite

STOKE ROCHFORD　　　　　　Map 08 SK92

Stoke Rochford NG33 5EW
☎ 01476 530275 & 530218
**Parkland course designed by C. Turner and extended in
1936 to 18 holes by Major Hotchkin.**
18 holes, 6252yds, Par 70, SSS 70, Course record 65.
Club membership 525.
Visitors must contact Professional in advance. No visitors
before 9am weekdays, weekends by prior arrangement.
Societies contact one year in advance, in writing. **Green
Fees** £22 per round; £30 per day (£28/£40 weekends and
bank holidays). **Cards** 🔲 🔲 ⍰ **Prof** Angus Dow **Course
Designer** Major Hotchkin **Facilities** ⊗ ⅏ ╠ ♥ ♀ ♨ ☎ ❀
♨ ✔ **Location** Off A1 5m S of Grantham, right off A1
southbound signposted Stoke Rochford, U turn onto A1
northbound carriageway enter golf club via BP service
station

Hotel ★★★ 69% Kings Hotel, North Pde, GRANTHAM
☎ 01476 590800 21 en suite

SUTTON BRIDGE　　　　　　Map 09 TF42

Sutton Bridge New Rd PE12 9RQ ☎ 01406 350323
**Established in 1914 as a golf course, the nine holes are
played along, over and in a Victorian dock basin which
was abandoned as a dock in 1881. The original walls of
the dock are still intact and help to make the course one
of the most interesting courses in the region. The greens
are recognised as among the best in Lincolnshire.**
9 holes, 5724yds, Par 70, SSS 68.
Club membership 350.
Visitors may not play competition days, weekends & bank
holidays except with a member, must contact in advance.
Must have handicap certificate. **Societies** write or telephone
in advance. **Green Fees** £18 per day. **Cards** ⍰ **Prof** Alison
Johns **Facilities** ⊗ ⅏ ╠ ♥ ♀ ♨ ☎ ❀ ✔ **Location** E side
of village off A17

Hotel ★★★ 64% The Duke's Head, Tuesday Market Place,
KING'S LYNN ☎ 01553 774996 71 en suite

SUTTON ON SEA　　　　　　Map 09 TF58

Sandilands Roman Bank LN12 2RJ
☎ 01507 441432 🗐 01507 441617
**Well manicured links course next to the sea. Renowned
for the standard of its greens.**
18 holes, 6173yds, Par 71, SSS 68, Course record 59.
Club membership 200.
Visitors no restrictions. **Societies** telephone in advance.
Green Fees not confirmed. **Cards** 🔲 🔲 **Facilities** ⊗ ⅏ ╠
♥ ♀ ♨ ☎ ❀ ♨ ✔ **Leisure** hard and grass tennis
courts, gymnasium. **Location** 1.5m S off A52

Hotel ★★★ 68% Grange & Links Hotel, Sea Ln,
Sandilands, MABLETHORPE ☎ 01507 441334 23 en suite

TORKSEY　　　　　　Map 08 SK87

Lincoln LN1 2EG ☎ 01522 718721 🗐 718721
e-mail: info@lincolngc.co.uk
**A mature championship standard course offering a
variety of holes, links style to parkland.**
18 holes, 6438yds, Par 71, SSS 71, Course record 65.
Club membership 800.
Visitors no restrictions, may play at any time. **Societies**
Book in advance. **Green Fees** £32 per day; £26 per round.
Prof Ashley Carter **Course Designer** J H Taylor **Facilities**
⊗ ⅏ ╠ ♥ ♀ ♨ ☎ ❀ ♨ ✔ **Location** NE side of village,
off A156 midway between Lincoln & Gainsborough

Hotel ★★★ 66% The White Hart, Bailgate, LINCOLN
☎ 0870 400 8117 48 en suite

Millfield Laughterton LN1 2LB
☎ 01427 718255 🗐 01427 718473
e-mail: secretary@millfieldgolfclub.fsnet.co.uk
**This golf complex offers a range of facilities to suit every
golfer. The Millfield is designed to suit the more
experienced golfer and follows the natural contours of the
landscape. The Grenville Green is designed for more
casual golfers and the par 3 is suitable for beginners,
family games or for warm-up and practice play.**
*The Millfield: 18 holes, 6004yds, Par 72, SSS 69,
Course record 66.*
The Grenville Green: 18 holes, 4485yds, Par 65.
Visitors Millfield: shoes must be worn, no jeans etc.
Grenville Green no restrictions. Par 3 9 hole no restrictions.
Societies telephone in advance. **Green Fees** terms on
application. **Prof** Richard Hunter **Course Designer** C W
Watson **Facilities** ⊗ ╠ ♥ ♀ ♨ ☎ ❀ ❀ ♨ ✔ 🎾 **Leisure**
grass tennis courts. **Location** On A1133 1m N of A57

Hotel ★★★ 66% The White Hart, Bailgate, LINCOLN
☎ 0870 400 8117 48 en suite

WOODHALL SPA　　　　　　See page 163

WOODHALL SPA　　　　　　Map 08 TF16

Petwood Hotel

WOODTHORPE　　　　　　Map 09 TF48

Woodthorpe Hall LN13 0DD
☎ 01507 450000 🗐 01507 450000
e-mail: secretary@woodthorpehall.co.uk
Parkland course.
18 holes, 5140yds, Par 67, SSS 65, Course record 68.
Club membership 300.
Visitors contact in advance . **Societies** Mon-Fri, apply to the
secretary at least one month prior to visit. **Green Fees** not
confirmed. **Facilities** ⊗ ⅏ ╠ ♥ ♀ ❀ **Leisure** fishing.
Location 3m NNW of Alford on B1373

continued

Hotel ★★★ 68% Grange & Links Hotel, Sea Ln, Sandilands, MABLETHORPE ☎ 01507 441334 23 en suite

LONDON

Courses within the London Postal District area (i.e. those that have London Postcodes - W1, SW1 etc.) are listed here in postal district order, commencing East then North, South and West. Courses outside the London Postal area, but within Greater London are to be found listed under the county of **Greater London** in the gazetteer (see page 92).

LONDON

E4 CHINGFORD

Royal Epping Forest Forest Approach, Chingford E4 7AZ ☎ 020 8529 2195 ▤ 020 8559 4664
Woodland course. Red garments must be worn.
18 holes, 6342yds, Par 71, SSS 70, Course record 64. Club membership 400.
Visitors booking system in operation, telephone 0208 5295708 **Societies** must contact secretary in advance. **Green Fees** £11(£15.25 weekends). **Cards** ▦ ▦ ▦ ▦ ▦ ▦ **Prof** A Traynor **Course Designer** J G Gibson/R Bright-Thomas **Facilities** ⊗ by prior arrangement ▥ by prior arrangement ▥ by prior arrangement ▦ ♀ ♨ ☎ ♈ ♧ ⚘
Location 300 yds E of Chingford station

Hotel ★★★ 62% County Hotel Epping Forest, 30 Oak Hill, WOODFORD GREEN ☎ 020 8787 9988 99 en suite

West Essex Bury Rd, Sewardstonebury, Chingford E4 7QL ☎ 020 8529 7558 ▤ 020 8524 7870
e-mail: sec@westessexgolfclub.co.uk
Testing parkland course within Epping Forest. Notable holes are 8th (par 5), 16th (par 4), 18th (par 5).
18 holes, 6289yds, Par 71, SSS 70, Course record 63. Club membership 645.
Visitors must have handicap certificate but may not play on Tue morning, Thu afternoon & weekends. **Societies** must contact in advance. **Green Fees** £35 per day; £28 per round. **Prof** Robert Joyce **Course Designer** James Braid **Facilities** ⊗ ▥ ▦ ▦ ♀ ♨ ☎ ♧ ⚘ ♟ **Location** 1.5m N of Chingford station. Access via M25 junct 26

Hotel ★★★ 60% Roebuck Hotel, North End, BUCKHURST HILL ☎ 020 8505 4636 28 en suite

E11 LEYTONSTONE & WANSTEAD

Wanstead Overton Dr, Wanstead E11 2LW ☎ 020 8989 3938 ▤ 020 8532 9138
e-mail: wgclub@aol.com
A flat, picturesque parkland course with many trees and shrubs and providing easy walking. The par 3 16th involves driving across a lake.
18 holes, 6004yds, Par 69, SSS 69, Course record 62. Club membership 600.
Visitors must contact in advance and may only play Mon, Tue & Fri. **Societies** by prior arrangement. **Green Fees** £30 per day. **Cards** ▦ ▦ ▦ **Prof** David Hawkins **Course Designer** James Braid **Facilities** ⊗ ▥ ▦ ▦ ♀ ♨ ☎ ♧ ⚘ **Leisure** fishing. **Conf** Max 120 Banquet 120 Del £60 to £120 * **Location** From central London A12 NE to Wanstead

Hotel ★★★ 62% County Hotel Epping Forest, 30 Oak Hill, WOODFORD GREEN ☎ 020 8787 9988 99 en suite

N2 EAST FINCHLEY

Hampstead Winnington Rd N2 0TU
☎ 020 8455 0203 ▤ 020 8731 6194
Undulating parkland course with many mature trees.
9 holes, 5822yds, Par 68, SSS 68, Course record 64. Club membership 526.
Visitors restricted Tue and weekends. Contact Professional in advance on 0208 4557089. Handicap certificate required.members societies only **Green Fees** £30 per 18 holes(£35 weekends & bank holidays). **Prof** Peter Brown **Course Designer** Tom Dunn **Facilities** ⊗ ▦ ▦ ♀ ♨ ☎ ♧ ⚘ **Location** Off Hampstead Lane

Hotel ★★★ 67% Holiday Inn Hampstead, 215 Haverstock Hill, LONDON ☎ 0870 400 9037 140 en suite

N6 HIGHGATE

Highgate Denewood Rd N6 4AH
☎ 020 8340 5467 ▤ 020 8348 9152
e-mail: secretary @highgategolfclub.freeserve.co.uk
Parkland course.
18 holes, 5985yds, Par 69, SSS 69, Course record 66. Club membership 700.
Visitors may not play Wed, weekends & bank holidays. **Societies** by arrangement. **Green Fees** £30 per round;£38 per day. **Prof** Robin Turner **Course Designer** Cuthbert Butchart **Facilities** ⊗ ▥ by prior arrangement ▦ ▦ ♀ ♨ ☎ ♧ ⚘ **Conf** Board 25 **Location** A1,Bishops Avenue,Hampstead lane,Sheldon Avenue

Hotel ★★★★ 71% London Marriott Hotel Regents Park, 128 King Henry's Rd, LONDON
☎ 020 7722 7711 303 en suite

N9 LOWER EDMONTON

Lee Valley Leisure Lee Valley Leisure Centre, Meridian Way, Edmonton N9 0AS ☎ 020 8803 3611
Tricky municipal parkland course with some narrow fairways and the River Lea providing a natural hazard.
18 holes, 4962yds, Par 66, SSS 64, Course record 66. Club membership 200.
Visitors may telephone for advance bookings. **Societies** must telephone in advance. **Green Fees** £12 per round(£15 weekends). **Prof** R Gerken **Facilities** ▦ ▦ ♀ ♨ ☎ ♧ ⚘ ♟

Hotel ★★ 71% Oak Lodge Hotel, 80 Village Rd, Bush Hill Park, ENFIELD ☎ 020 8360 7082 7 en suite

N14 SOUTHGATE

Trent Park Bramley Rd, Oakwood N14 4XS
☎ 020 8367 4653 ▤ 0208 366 4581
e-mail: trentpark@americangolf.uk.com
Parkland course set in 150 acres of green belt area. Seven holes played across Merryhills brook. Testing holes are 2nd (423 yds) over brook, 190 yds from the tee, and up to plateau green; 7th (463 yds) dog-leg, over brook, par 4.
18 holes, 6381yds, Par 70, SSS 69, Course record 64. Club membership 700.
Visitors must book in advance. **Societies** must telephone in advance. **Green Fees** £13 per round(£16.50 weekends). **Cards** ▦ ▦ ▦ ▦ ▦ **Prof** R Stocker/G Harris/E Newgas **Course Designer** D McGibbon **Facilities** ⊗ ▥ ▦ ▦ ♀ ♨ ☎ ♧ ⚘ ♟ **Conf** Max 100 **Location** Opposite Oakwood underground station

Hotel ★★★★▦ 70% West Lodge Park Hotel, Cockfosters Rd, HADLEY WOOD ☎ 020 8216 3900
46 en suite 13 annexe en suite

N20 WHETSTONE

North Middlesex The Manor House, Friern Barnet Ln,
Whetstone N20 0NL
☎ 020 8445 1604 & 020 8445 3060 📠 020 8445 5023
e-mail: office@northmiddlesexgc.co.uk
Short parkland course renowned for its tricky greens.
18 holes, 5594yds, Par 69, SSS 67, Course record 64.
Club membership 580.
Visitors advisable to contact in advance. **Societies** bookings
in advance, winter offers & summer packages by prior
arrangement. **Green Fees** £23 per round;£29 per day(£29
weekends and bank holidays). reductions in winter. **Cards**
🖷 🖷 🖷 🖷 🖸 **Prof** Freddiy George **Course Designer**
Willie Park Jnr **Facilities** ⊗ ⊤ 🖳 ⯃ ♀ ⯃ 🖻 ⛳ 𝒞 **Conf**
Max 70 **Location** 5 miles S M25 junct 23
....
Hotel ★★★ 72% Edgwarebury Hotel, Barnet Ln,
ELSTREE ☎ 020 8953 8227 47 en suite

South Herts Links Dr, Totteridge N20 8QU
☎ 020 8445 2035 📠 020 8445 7569
e-mail: secretary@southherts.co.uk
**An open undulating parkland course officially in
Hertfordshire, but now in a London postal area. It is
perhaps most famous for the fact that two of the
greatest of all British professionals, Harry Vardon and
Dai Rees, CBE were professionals at the club. The
course is testing, over rolling fairways, especially in the
prevailing south-west wind.**
18 holes, 6432yds, Par 72, SSS 71, Course record 63.
Club membership 850.
Visitors must be members of recognised golf club & have
handicap certificate of 24 or less. May not play at
weekends. **Societies** Wed-Fri only, must apply in writing.
Green Fees terms on application. **Prof** Bobby Mitchell
Course Designer Harry Vardon **Facilities** ⯃ 🖻 ⛳ ↘
⯃ 𝒞 **Location** 2m E of A1 at Apex Corner
....
Hotel ★★★ 66% Holiday Inn South Mimms, SOUTH
MIMMS ☎ 0870 400 9072 143 en suite

N21 WINCHMORE HILL

Bush Hill Park Bush Hill, Winchmore Hill N21 2BU
☎ 020 8360 5738 📠 020 8360 5583
**Pleasant parkland course surrounded by trees. Contains
a large number of both fairway sandtraps and green side
bunkers. Undulating, but not too harsh.**
18 holes, 5809yds, Par 70, SSS 68.
Club membership 700.
Visitors may not play Wed mornings or weekends & bank
holidays. Handicap certificate required. **Societies** by
arrangement. **Green Fees** £35 per day; £27.50 per round.
Prof Adrian Andrews **Facilities** ⊗ 🖳 ⯃ ♀ ⯃ 𝒞 **Conf**
Max 40 Board 14 Banquet 100 **Location** M25 junct 24,1m S
of Enfield, off London road N21
....
Hotel ★★ 71% Oak Lodge Hotel, 80 Village Rd, Bush Hill
Park, ENFIELD ☎ 020 8360 7082 7 en suite

N22 WOOD GREEN

Muswell Hill Rhodes Av, Wood Green N22 7UT
☎ 020 8888 1764 📠 020 8889 9380
**Undulating parkland course with a brook running
through the centre, set in 87 acres.**
18 holes, 6438yds, Par 71, SSS 71, Course record 65.
Club membership 560.
Visitors must contact in advance, restricted weekends.

continued

Societies apply in writing or telephone. **Green Fees** £40 per
day; £30 per round(£35 per round weekends),reductions in
winter. **Prof** David Wilton **Course Designer** Braid/Wilson
Facilities ⊗ ⊤ by prior arrangement 🖳 ⯃ ♀ ⯃ 🖻 ⛳ ⯃
𝒞 **Location** Off N Circular Rd at Bounds Green
....
Guesthouse ◆◆◆◆ Raglan Hall Hotel, 8-12 Queens Av,
Muswell Hill, LONDON ☎ 020 8883 9836 48 en suite

NW4 HENDON   Map 04 TQ28

The Metro Golf Centre Barnet Copthall Sports
Centre, Gt North Way NW4 1PS
☎ 020 8202 1202 📠 020 8203 1203
e-mail: golf@metrogolf.btinternet.com
**Located just seven miles from London's West End, the
Metro Golf Centre represents a new generation of golf
facility dedicated to the development of all standards of
golfer. Facilities include a 48 bay two-tiered driving
range, a testing 9-hole par 3 course with water hazards,
pot bunkers and postage stamp greens, a short game
practice area, and a Golf Academy offering unique
teaching methods.**
9 holes, 898yds, Par 27, SSS 27, Course record 24.
Club membership 500.
Visitors welcome any time between 8am-10pm all week for
lessons, to play on the course or use driving range. **Societies**
telephone in advance. **Green Fees** not confirmed. **Cards**
🖷 🖷 🖷 🖷 🖸 **Prof** Barney Puttick **Course Designer**
Cousells **Facilities** ⊗ ⊤ 🖳 ⯃ ♀ ⯃ ⛳ ⯃ 𝒞 ⯃ **Location** Just
off A41 and A1 at junct 2 of the M1, within the Barnet
Copthall Sporting Complex
....
Hotel ★★★★ 71% London Marriott Hotel Regents Park,
128 King Henry's Rd, LONDON ☎ 020 7722 7711
303 en suite

NW7 MILL HILL

Finchley Nether Court, Frith Ln, Mill Hill NW7 1PU
☎ 020 8346 2436 & 8346 5086 📠 020 8343 4205
e-mail: secretary@finchleygolfclub.co.uk
Easy walking on wooded parkland course.

18 holes, 6411yds, Par 72, SSS 71.
Club membership 500.
Visitors must contact in advance. **Societies** must apply in
writing. **Green Fees** £25 per round;£32 per day(£34/£38
weekends). **Cards** 🖷 🖷 🖷 🖷 🖸 **Prof** David Brown
Course Designer James Braid **Facilities** ⊗ 🖳 ⯃ ♀ ⯃ 🖻
⛳ ↘ ⯃ 𝒞 **Conf** Max 50 **Location** Near Mill Hill East
Tube Station
....
Hotel ★★★ 72% Edgwarebury Hotel, Barnet Ln,
ELSTREE ☎ 020 8953 8227 47 en suite

Hendon
Ashley Walk, Devonshire Rd, Mill Hill
NW7 1DG ☎ 020 8346 6023 🖺 020 8343 1974
e-mail: hendongolf@talk21.com
Easy walking, parkland course with a good variety of trees, and providing testing golf.
18 holes, 6289yds, Par 70, SSS 70, Course record 63.
Club membership 560.
Visitors Restricted weekends & bank holidays. Must contact professional in advance on 0208 3468990 **Societies** Tue-Fri. Must contact in advance. **Green Fees** £35 per day; £30 per round (£35 per round weekends). **Cards** 🖃 🖃 🖃 🖃 🗐 **Prof** Matt Deal **Course Designer** H S Colt **Facilities** ⊗ ⅷ by prior arrangement 🖢 ♚ ♀ ♙ 🗇 ℡ ✔ **Location** 10 mins from junc 2 of M1 southbound

Hotel ★★★ 72% Edgwarebury Hotel, Barnet Ln, ELSTREE ☎ 020 8953 8227 47 en suite

Mill Hill
100 Barnet Way, Mill Hill NW7 3AL
☎ 020 8959 2339 🖺 020 8906 0731
e-mail: davidbeal@dbeal.freeserve.co.uk
Parkland course with tree and shrub lined fairways, water features strongly on holes 2, 10 and 17.

18 holes, 6247yds, Par 70, SSS 70, Course record 65.
Club membership 550.
Visitors restricted weekends & bank holidays. Must contact in advance. **Societies** must contact in advance. **Green Fees** terms on application. **Cards** 🖃 🖃 **Prof** David Beal **Course Designer** J F Abercrombie/H S Colt **Facilities** ⊗ 🖢 ♚ ♀ ♙ 🗇 ℡ ✔ 🕭 ✔ **Leisure** snooker. **Location** On A1 S bound carriageway

Hotel ★★★ 72% Edgwarebury Hotel, Barnet Ln, ELSTREE ☎ 020 8953 8227 47 en suite

SE9 ELTHAM

Eltham Warren
Bexley Rd, Eltham SE9 2PE
☎ 020 8850 4477 & 8850 1166
e-mail: secretary@elthamwarren.idps.co.uk
Parkland course with narrow fairways and small greens. The course is bounded by the A210 on one side and Eltham Park on the other.
9 holes, 5840yds, Par 69, SSS 68, Course record 63.
Club membership 440.
Visitors may not play at weekends. Must contact in advance and have a handicap certificate. **Societies** Thu only. Must book in advance. Deposit required. **Green Fees** £25 per day. **Prof** Gary Brett **Course Designer** James Braid **Facilities** ⊗ 🖢 ♚ ♀ ♙ 🗇 ✔ **Location** 0.5m from Eltham station on A210

Hotel ★★★ 73% Bromley Court Hotel, Bromley Hill, BROMLEY ☎ 020 8461 8600 116 en suite

Royal Blackheath
Court Rd SE9 5AF
☎ 020 8850 1795 🖺 020 8859 0150
e-mail: info@rbgc.com
A pleasant, parkland course of great character as befits the antiquity of the Club; the clubhouse dates from the 17th century. Many great trees survive and there are two ponds. The 18th requires a pitch to the green over a thick clipped hedge, which also crosses the front of the 1st tee.
18 holes, 6219yds, Par 70, SSS 70, Course record 65.
Club membership 720.
Visitors must contact in advance but may play mid-week only, a handicap certificate is required. **Societies** must apply in writing. **Green Fees** not confirmed. **Cards** 🖃 🖃 🗐 **Prof** Ian McGregor **Course Designer** James Braid **Facilities** ⊗ ⅷ 🖢 ♚ ♀ ♙ 🗇 ℡ ✔ 🕭 ✔ **Location** From M25 junct 3 take A20 towards London. Turn right at 2nd traffic lights to club 500yds on right

Hotel ★★★ 73% Bromley Court Hotel, Bromley Hill, BROMLEY ☎ 020 8461 8600 116 en suite

SE18 WOOLWICH

Shooters Hill
Eaglesfield Rd, Shooters Hill SE18 3DA
☎ 020 8854 6368 🖺 020 8854 0469
e-mail: shootershillgolf@netscapeonline.co.uk
Hilly and wooded parkland course with good view and natural hazards.
18 holes, 5721yds, Par 69, SSS 68, Course record 63.
Club membership 900.
Visitors must have handicap certificate and be a member of a recognised golf club but may not play at weekends, unless with member. **Societies** Tue & Thu only, by arrangement. **Green Fees** £27 per day; £22 per round. **Prof** David Brotherton **Course Designer** Willie Park **Facilities** ⊗ ⅷ 🖢 ♚ ♀ ♙ 🗇 ℡ ✔ 🕭 ✔ **Location** Shooters Hill Rd from Blackheath

Hotel ★★★ 66% Holiday Inn Bexley, Black Prince Interchange, Southwold Rd, BEXLEY ☎ 0870 400 9006 108 en suite

SE21 DULWICH

Dulwich & Sydenham Hill
Grange Ln, College Rd SE21 7LH ☎ 020 8693 3961 & 8693 8491
🖺 020 8693 2481
Parkland course overlooking London. Hilly with narrow fairways.
18 holes, 6008yds, Par 69, SSS 69, Course record 63.
Club membership 850.
Visitors must contact in advance and have a handicap certificate. May not play weekends or bank holidays. **Societies** must telephone in advance & confirm in writing. **Green Fees** terms on application. **Prof** David Baillie **Course Designer** H Colt **Facilities** ⊗ 🖢 ♚ ♀ ♙ 🗇 ℡ ✔ 🕭 ✔

Hotel ★★★ 73% Bromley Court Hotel, Bromley Hill, BROMLEY ☎ 020 8461 8600 116 en suite

SE22 EAST DULWICH

Aquarius
Marmora Rd, Honor Oak, Off Forest Hill Rd SE22 0RY ☎ 020 8693 1626
e-mail: jim.halliday@btinternet.com
Course laid out on two levels around and over covered reservoir; hazards include vents and bollards.
9 holes, 5246yds, Par 66, SSS 66, Course record 66.
Club membership 350.

continued

Visitors must be accompanied by member and have a handicap certificate. **Green Fees** terms on application. **Prof** Frederick Private **Facilities** ⓑ 🏆 ♀ 🏌 🏠

Hotel ★★★ 73% Bromley Court Hotel, Bromley Hill, BROMLEY ☎ 020 8461 8600 116 en suite

SE28 WOOLWICH

Riverside Fairway Dr, Summerton Way, Thamesmead SE28 8PP ☎ 020 8310 7975
e-mail: enquiries@thamesview-golf.fsnet.co.uk
A delightful undulating course with a mix of mature trees, new trees and water hazards. The 4th hole is a challenging 515yards down a narrow fairway.
9 holes, 5462yds, Par 70, SSS 66.
Club membership 100.
Visitors no restrictions. **Societies** book by telephone or in writing. **Green Fees** terms on application. **Cards** 🖷 🖵 🖲 🔳 🖸 **Prof** Graeme Wilson **Course Designer** Heffernan **Facilities** ⊗ ⅲ ⓑ 🏆 ♀ 🏌 🏠 ⚑ 🏌 **Location** Off A2 near Woolwich ferry

Hotel ★★★ 65% Bardon Lodge Hotel, 15-17 Stratheden Rd, Blackheath, LONDON ☎ 020 8853 7000 32 en suite

SW15 PUTNEY

Richmond Park Roehampton Gate, Priory Ln SW15 5JR ☎ 020 8876 1795 🖷 020 8878 1354
e-mail: info@gcm.com
Two public parkland courses.
Princes Course: 18 holes, 5868yds, Par 69, SSS 68, Course record 64.
Dukes Course: 18 holes, 6036yds, Par 69, SSS 68.
Visitors must contact in advance or pay and play. **Societies** must contact in advance. **Green Fees** not confirmed. **Prof** Stuart Hill & David Bown **Course Designer** Fred Hawtree **Facilities** ⊗ ⓑ 🏆 ♀ 🏌 🏠 ⚑ 🏌 🏌 **Location** Inside Richmond Park Roehampton gate

Hotel ★★★ 68% The Richmond Hill Hotel, Richmond Hill, RICHMOND UPON THAMES ☎ 020 8940 2247 138 en suite

SW18 WANDSWORTH

Central London Golf Centre Burntwood Ln, Wandsworth SW17 0AT
☎ 020 8871 2468 🖷 020 8874 7447
e-mail: clgc@aol.com
Attractive flat parkland course in the middle of London. The longest drive is the 430 yard 3rd to one of the course's superb greens. Well placed bunkers trap the careless shot and the course rewards the accurate player.
9 holes, 2277yds, Par 62, SSS 62.
Club membership 200.
Visitors must book tee-times for weekends. **Societies** telephone or write to the manager. **Green Fees** not confirmed. **Cards** 🖷 🖵 🖲 🔳 🖸 **Prof** Jeremy Robson **Course Designer** Patrick Tallock **Facilities** ⊗ ⓑ 🏆 ♀ 🏌 🏠 ⚑ 🏌 🏌 **Location** Between Garatt Lane and Trinity Road

Hotel ★★★★ 73% Cannizaro House, West Side, Wimbledon Common, LONDON ☎ 020 8879 1464 45 en suite

Looking for a driving range?
See the index at the back of the guide

SW19 WIMBLEDON

Royal Wimbledon 29 Camp Rd SW19 4UW
☎ 020 8946 2125 🖷 020 8944 8652
e-mail: secretary@royal-wimbledon-golf.co.uk
Third oldest club in England, established in 1865 and steeped in the history and traditions of the game. Mainly heathland with trees and heather, a good test of golf with many fine holes, the 12th being rated as the best.
18 holes, 6300yds, Par 70, SSS 70, Course record 66.
Club membership 1050.
Visitors must be guests of current club member or contact club in advance, weekdays only. Maximum handicap 18 and must be member of recognised club. **Societies** welcome Wed-Thu. Must apply in writing. **Green Fees** not confirmed. **Prof** Hugh Boyle **Course Designer** H Colt **Facilities** ⊗ ⅲ ⓑ 🏆 ♀ 🏌 🏠 ⚑ 🏌

Hotel ★★★★ 73% Cannizaro House, West Side, Wimbledon Common, LONDON ☎ 020 8879 1464 45 en suite

Wimbledon Common 19 Camp Rd SW19 4UW
☎ 020 8946 0294 (Pro shop) 🖷 020 8947 8697
e-mail: secretary@wcgc.co.uk
Quick-drying course on Wimbledon Common. Well wooded, with tight fairways, challenging short holes but no bunkers.The course is also played over by London Scottish Golf Club. All players must wear plain red upper garments.
18 holes, 5438yds, Par 68, SSS 66, Course record 63.
Club membership 290.
Visitors with member only at weekends. **Societies** must telephone in advance, confirm in writing. **Green Fees** £10 Mon; £16 Tue-Fri. **Prof** J S Jukes **Course Designer** Tom & Willie Dunn **Facilities** ⊗ ⅲ ⓑ 🏆 ♀ 🏌 🏠 ⚑ 🏌 **Leisure** snooker room. **Conf** Max 40 **Location** 0.5m N of Wimbledon Village

Hotel ★★★★ 73% Cannizaro House, West Side, Wimbledon Common, LONDON ☎ 020 8879 1464 45 en suite

Wimbledon Park Home Park Rd, Wimbledon SW19 7HR ☎ 020 8946 1250 🖷 020 8944 8688
e-mail: secretary@wpgc.co.uk
Easy walking on parkland course. Sheltered lake provides hazard on three holes.
18 holes, 5465yds, Par 66, SSS 66.
Club membership 700.
Visitors restricted weekends & bank holidays. Must contact in advance and have handicap certificate or letter of introduction. **Societies** must apply in writing. **Green Fees** not confirmed. **Prof** Dean Wingrove **Course Designer** Willie Park Jnr **Facilities** ⊗ ⅲ by prior arrangement ⓑ 🏆 ♀ 🏌 🏠 🏌 **Location** 400 yds from Wimbledon Park Station

Hotel ★★★ 68% The Richmond Hill Hotel, Richmond Hill, RICHMOND UPON THAMES ☎ 020 8940 2247 138 en suite

W7 HANWELL

Brent Valley 138 Church Rd, Hanwell W7 3BE
☎ 020 8567 1287
Municipal parkland course with easy walking. The River Brent winds through the course.
18 holes, 5426yds, Par 67, SSS 66.
Club membership 350.   *continued*

Visitors no restrictions. Societies one month's notice required. Green Fees terms on application. Cards 💳 💳 💳 🏌 Prof Peter Bryant Facilities ⊗ 🏌 ♀ ⚐ ⚐ 🐾 𝒞

Hotel ★★★ 65% Master Robert Hotel, 366 Great West Rd, HOUNSLOW ☎ 020 8570 6261 96 annexe en suite

MERSEYSIDE

BEBINGTON   Map 07 SJ38

Brackenwood Brackenwood Golf Course, Bracken Ln CH63 2LY ☎ 0151 608 3093
Municipal parkland course with easy walking, a very testing but fair course in a fine rural setting, usually in very good condition.
18 holes, 6285yds, Par 70, SSS 70, Course record 66.
Club membership 320.
Visitors must book for weekends one week in advance. Societies must telephone in advance. Green Fees not confirmed. Prof Ken Lamb Facilities ⚐ ⚐ 🐾 𝒞 Location 0.75m N of M53 junc 4 on B5151

Hotel ★★★★ 62% Thornton Hall Hotel, Neston Rd, THORNTON HOUGH ☎ 0151 336 3938 63 en suite

BIRKENHEAD   Map 07 SJ38

Arrowe Park Woodchurch L49 5LW
☎ 0151 677 1527
Pleasant municipal parkland course.
18 holes, 6435yds, Par 72, SSS 71, Course record 66.
Club membership 220.
Visitors no restrictions, Booking at weekends 1wk in advance. Societies must telephone in advance. Green Fees £8 per round. Cards 💳 💳 Prof Colin Disbury Facilities ⊗ 🗍 🏌 ⚐ ♀ ⚐ 🐾 𝒞 Leisure tennis courts, pitch & putt. Location 1m from M53 junc 3 on A551

Hotel ★★★ 69% Bowler Hat Hotel, 2 Talbot Rd, Prenton, BIRKENHEAD ☎ 0151 652 4931 32 en suite

Prenton Golf Links Rd, Prenton CH42 8LW
☎ 0151 608 1053 📱 0151 609 1580
Parkland course with easy walking and views of the Welsh Hills.
18 holes, 6429yds, Par 71, SSS 71.
Club membership 610.
Visitors no restrictions. Societies must telephone in advance and confirm in writing. Green Fees £30 per day. Prof Robin Thompson Course Designer James Braid Facilities ⊗ 🗍 🏌 ⚐ ♀ ⚐ 🐾 𝒞 Location M53 junct 3 off A552 towards Birkenhead

Hotel ★★★ 67% Riverhill Hotel, Talbot Rd, Prenton, BIRKENHEAD ☎ 0151 653 3773 14 en suite

Wirral Ladies 93 Bidston Rd, Oxton CH43 6TS
☎ 0151 652 1255 📱 0151 653 4323
Heathland course with heather and birch.
18 holes, 5185yds, Par 68, SSS 66.
Club membership 430.
Visitors may not play before 11am weekends or over Christmas and Easter holidays. Societies must telephone in advance. Weekdays only. Green Fees £25.50 per round. Prof Angus Law Facilities ⊗ 🗍 🏌 ⚐ ♀ ⚐ 𝒞 Leisure indoor training suite. Location W side of town centre on B5151

Hotel ★★★ 69% Bowler Hat Hotel, 2 Talbot Rd, Prenton, BIRKENHEAD ☎ 0151 652 4931 32 en suite

BLUNDELLSANDS   Map 07 SJ39

West Lancashire Hall Rd West L23 8SZ
☎ 0151 924 1076 📱 0151 931 4448
e-mail: golf@westlancashiregolf.co.uk
Challenging, traditional links with sandy subsoil overlooking the Mersey Estuary. The course provides excellent golf throughout the year. The four short holes are very fine.
18 holes, 6763yds, Par 72, SSS 73, Course record 66.
Club membership 650.
Visitors must have a handicap certificate. May not play before 9.30am Mon-Fri and on competition days and weekends only after 3.30pm. Societies must contact in advance. Green Fees £69 per day; £50 per round (£89/70 per round weekends). Cards 💳 💳 💳 💳 🏌 Prof Tim Hastings Course Designer C K Cotton Facilities ⊗ 🗍 🏌 ⚐ ♀ ⚐ 𝒞 Location N side of village, adjacent to Hall Rd station

Hotel ★★★ 64% Tree Tops Country House Restaurant & Hotel, Southport Old Rd, FORMBY ☎ 01704 572430 11 annexe en suite

BOOTLE   Map 07 SJ39

Bootle 2 Dunnings Bridge Rd L30 2PP
☎ 0151 928 1371 📱 0151 949 1815
Municipal seaside course, with prevailing north-westerly wind. Testing holes: 5th (200 yds) par 3; 7th (415 yds) par 4.
18 holes, 6362yds, Par 70, SSS 70, Course record 64.
Club membership 380.
Visitors must contact Golf Shop on 0151 928 1371 not between 9-9.45am Sat and 7.45-12 Sun. Societies must apply in writing/telephone in advance. Green Fees £7.40 per round (£9.40 weekends). Cards 💳 💳 💳 🏌 Prof Alan Bradshaw Facilities ⊗ 🏌 🏌 ⚐ ♀ ⚐ 🐾 𝒞 Leisure fishing. Location 2m NE on A5036

Hotel 🏠 Premier Lodge (Liverpool North), Dunningsbridge Rd, LIVERPOOL ☎ 0870 700 1428 62 en suite

BROMBOROUGH   Map 07 SJ38

Bromborough Raby Hall Rd CH63 0NW
☎ 0151 334 2155 📱 0151 334 7300
e-mail: sec@bromborough-golf-club.freeserve.co.uk
Parkland course.
18 holes, 6650yds, Par 72, SSS 73, Course record 67.
Club membership 800.
Visitors are advised to contact professional on 0151 334 4499 in advance. Societies normal society day Wed ; must apply in advance. Green Fees terms on application. Prof Geoff Berry Course Designer J Hassall Facilities ⊗ 🗍 🏌 🏌 ⚐ ♀ ⚐ 🐾 𝒞 Location 0.5m W of Station

Hotel ★★★ 69% Bowler Hat Hotel, 2 Talbot Rd, Prenton, BIRKENHEAD ☎ 0151 652 4931 32 en suite

CALDY   Map 07 SJ28

Caldy Links Hey Rd CH48 1NB
☎ 0151 625 5660 📱 0151 6257394
e-mail: gail@caldygolfclub.fsnet.co.uk
A parkland course situated on the estuary of the River Dee with many of the fairways running parallel to the river. Of Championship length, the course offers excellent golf all year, but is subject to variable winds
continued

169

that noticeably alter the day to day playing of each hole. There are excellent views of North Wales and Snowdonia.
18 holes, 6668yds, Par 72, SSS 72, Course record 68.
Club membership 800.
Visitors may play on weekdays only by prior arrangement. Not before 3.30pm Tue or after 12.30pm Wed. **Societies** must telephone in advance. **Green Fees** £42 per day, £37 per round. **Prof** K Jones **Course Designer** J Braid **Facilities** ⊗ ⫫ ℡ ⌘ ♀ ♈ 🔒 ♨ ♘ **Location** SE side of village, from Caldy rdbt on A540 follow signs to Caldy and golf club

Hotel ★★★★ 62% Thornton Hall Hotel, Neston Rd, THORNTON HOUGH ☎ 0151 336 3938 63 en suite

---

EASTHAM · Map 07 SJ38

Eastham Lodge 117 Ferry Rd CH62 0AP
☎ 0151 327 3003 🗎 0151 327 7574
A parkland course with many mature trees, recently upgraded to 18 holes. Most holes have a subtle dogleg to left or right. The 1st hole requires an accurate drive to open up the green which is guarded on the right by a stand of pine trees.
18 holes, 5436yds, Par 68, SSS 66.
Club membership 800.
Visitors advisable to telephone in advance to check availability, tel 0151 327 3008 professionals shop, start times available up to 2 weeks in advance, with member only at weekends. **Societies** welcome Tue. Must apply in writing. **Green Fees** £22.50 per day/round. **Prof** N Sargent **Course Designer** Hawtree/D Hemstock **Facilities** ⊗ ⫫ ℡ ⌘ ♀ ♈ 🔒 ♘ **Location** 1.5m N,off A41 to Wirral Metropolitan College & Eastham Country Park

Hotel ★★★ 66% Quality Hotel Chester, Welsh Road/Berwick Rd, Little Sutton
☎ 0151 339 5121 53 en suite

FORMBY · Map 07 SD30

Formby Golf Rd L37 1LQ
☎ 01704 872164 🗎 01704 833028
e-mail: info@formbygolfclub.co.uk
Championship seaside links through sandhills and partly through pine trees. Partly sheltered from the wind by high dunes it features firm, springy turf, fast seaside greens and natural sandy bunkers. Well drained it plays well throughout the year.

18 holes, 6701yds, Par 72, SSS 72, Course record 65.
Club membership 700.
Visitors must contact in advance, very limited on Sat & Wed. **Societies** must contact well in advance. **Green Fees**
continued

not confirmed. **Cards** 🚌 **Prof** Gary Butler **Course Designer** Park/Colt **Facilities** ⊗ ⫫ ℡ ⌘ ♀ ♈ 🔒 ♜ ⚘ ♙ **Location** N side of town

Hotel ★★★ 64% Tree Tops Country House Restaurant & Hotel, Southport Old Rd, FORMBY
☎ 01704 572430 11 annexe en suite

Formby Ladies Golf Rd L37 1YH
☎ 01704 873493 🗎 01704 873493
Seaside links - one of the few independent ladies' clubs in the country. The course has contrasting hard-hitting holes in flat country and tricky holes in sandhills and woods.
18 holes, 5374yds, Par 71, SSS 71, Course record 60.
Club membership 570.
Visitors must contact in advance and may not play Thu or before 11am Sat & Sun. **Societies** must apply in advance. Handicap certificate required. **Green Fees** terms on application. **Prof** Gary Butler **Facilities** ⊗ ℡ ⌘ ♀ ♈ 🔒 ♘ **Location** N side of town

Hotel ★★★ 64% Tree Tops Country House Restaurant & Hotel, Southport Old Rd, FORMBY ☎ 01704 572430 11 annexe en suite

---

HESWALL · Map 07 SJ28

Heswall Cottage Ln CH60 8PB
☎ 0151 342 1237 🗎 0151 342 6140
A pleasant parkland course in soft undulating country over-looking the estuary of the River Dee. There are excellent views of the Welsh hills and coastline, and a good test of golf. The clubhouse is modern and well-appointed with good facilities.
18 holes, 6492yds, Par 72, SSS 72, Course record 62.
Club membership 940.
Visitors must contact in advance. **Societies** must apply in advance. **Green Fees** terms on application. **Prof** Alan Thompson **Facilities** ⊗ ⫫ ℡ ⌘ ♀ ♈ 🔒 ♘ **Location** 1m S off A540

Hotel ★★★★ 62% Thornton Hall Hotel, Neston Rd, THORNTON HOUGH ☎ 0151 336 3938 63 en suite

---

HOYLAKE · Map 07 SJ28

Hoylake Carr Ln, Municipal Links CH47 4BG
☎ 0151 632 2956
Flat, generally windy semi-links course. Tricky fairways, with some very deep bunkers.
18 holes, 6313yds, Par 70, SSS 70, Course record 67.
Club membership 303.
Visitors tee times booked with professional, weekend bookings one week in advance **Societies** must telephone 0151 632 4883 club steward or 0151 632 2956 club professional. **Green Fees** not confirmed. **Cards** 🚌 ▆▆ 🚌 🚜 **Prof** Simon Hooton **Course Designer** James Braid **Facilities** ⊗ ⫫ ℡ ⌘ ♀ ♈ 🔒 ♜ ♨ ♘ **Location** SW side of town off A540

Hotel ★★★ 67% Leasowe Castle Hotel, Leasowe Rd, MORETON ☎ 0151 606 9191 47 en suite

---

AA Hotels that have special arrangements with golf courses are listed at the back of the guide

Royal Liverpool
Meols Dr CH47 4AL
☎ 0151 632 3101 & 632 3102 🖷 0151 632 6737
e-mail: sec@royalliverpool-golf.com
A world famous, windswept seaside links course, venue for ten Open Championships and 18 Amateur Championships.
18 holes, 6219yds, Par 72, SSS 71.
Club membership 650.
Visitors must contact in advance & have a handicap certificate. Restricted before 9.30am & between 1-2pm. No play Thu am (ladies day). Limited play weekends (pm only). **Societies** must contact in advance. **Green Fees** not confirmed. **Cards** ▨ ▦ ▩ ▤ ▦ ☑ ☑ **Prof** John Heggarty **Course Designer** R Chambers/G Morris
Facilities ⊗ ⅢⅬ ≛ ⚑ ♀ ⚑ 🏠 ⛳ ✓ ☖ **Location** SW side of town on A540

Hotel ★★★ 67% Leasowe Castle Hotel, Leasowe Rd, MORETON ☎ 0151 606 9191 47 en suite

Bowring
Roby Rd L36 4HD ☎ 0151 443 0424 489 1901
e-mail: bowringpark@knowsley.gov.uk
Flat parkland course.
Bowring Golf Club: 18 holes, 6082yds, Par 70.
Visitors no restrictions. **Societies** bookings over the phone and confirmed in writing. **Green Fees** not confirmed.
Facilities ≛ ✓ **Location** On A5080 adjacent M62 junc 5

Hotel ⇧ Premier Lodge (Liverpool South East), Roby Rd, Huyton, LIVERPOOL ☎ 0870 700 1426 53 en suite

Huyton & Prescot
Hurst Park, Huyton Ln L36 1UA
☎ 0151 489 3948 🖷 0151 489 0797
An easy walking, parkland course providing excellent golf.

18 holes, 5779yds, Par 68, SSS 68, Course record 65.
Club membership 700.
Visitors must contact in advance and be arranged with secretary, **Societies** must apply in writing. **Green Fees** not confirmed. **Prof** John Fisher **Facilities** ⊗ Ⅲ Ⓛ ≛ ⚑ ♀ ⚑ 🏠 ✓ **Location** 1.5m NE off B5199

Hotel ⇧ Travel Inn Liverpool Tarbock, Wilson Rd, Tarbock, LIVERPOOL ☎ 0151 480 9614 40 en suite

Allerton Park
Allerton Manor Golf Estate, Allerton Rd L18 3JT ☎ 0151 428 7490 🖷 428 7490
Parkland course.
18 holes, 5494yds, Par 67, SSS 66.
Visitors Must book with professional in advance for 18 hole course. **Societies** Application in writing to golf professional.

continued

Green Fees £7.30 (£8.30 weekends and bank holidays). **Prof** Barry Large **Facilities** ≛ ⚑ ⛳ ✓ **Leisure** 9 hole par 3 course. **Location** 5.5m SE of city centre off A562 and B5180

Hotel ★★★ 65% The Royal Hotel, Marine Ter, Waterloo, LIVERPOOL ☎ 0151 928 2332 25 en suite

The Childwall
Naylors Rd, Gateacre L27 2YB
☎ 0151 487 0654 🖷 0151 487 0882
e-mail: manager@childwallgc.fsnet.co.uk
Parkland golf is played here over a testing course, where accuracy from the tee is well-rewarded. The course is very popular with visiting societies for the clubhouse has many amenities. Course designed by James Braid.
18 holes, 6425yds, Par 72, SSS 71, Course record 66.
Club membership 650.
Visitors must contact in advance, no societies Tue, weekends and bank holidays. **Societies** must apply in writing. **Green Fees** £30 (£40 weekends & bank holidays). **Prof** Nigel M Parr **Course Designer** James Braid **Facilities** ⊗ Ⅲ Ⓛ ≛ ⚑ ♀ ⚑ 🏠 ⛳ ✓ **Location** 7m E of city centre off B5178

Hotel ⇧ Premier Lodge (Liverpool South East), Roby Rd, Huyton, LIVERPOOL ☎ 0870 700 1426 53 en suite

Kirkby-Liverpool Municipal
Ingoe Ln, Kirkby L32 4SS ☎ 0151 546 5435
18 holes, 6704yds, Par 72, SSS 72, Course record 68.
Location 7.5m NE of city centre on A506
Telephone for further details

Hotel ★★★ 65% The Royal Hotel, Marine Ter, Waterloo, LIVERPOOL ☎ 0151 928 2332 25 en suite

Lee Park
Childwall Valley Rd L27 3YA
☎ 0151 487 3882 🖷 0151 487 3882
18 holes, 6095yds, Par 72, SSS 69.
Course Designer G Cotton **Location** 7m E of city centre off B5178
Telephone for further details

Hotel ⇧ Premier Lodge (Liverpool South East), Roby Rd, Huyton, LIVERPOOL ☎ 0870 700 1426 53 en suite

West Derby
Yew Tree Ln, West Derby L12 9HQ
☎ 0151 254 1034 🖷 0151 259 0505
e-mail: pmilne@westderbygc.freeserve.co.uk
A parkland course always in first-class condition, and so giving easy walking. The fairways are well-wooded. Care must be taken on the first nine holes to avoid the brook which guards many of the greens. A modern well-designed clubhouse with many amenities, overlooks the course.

continued

18 holes, 6277yds, Par 72, SSS 70, Course record 65.
Club membership 550.
Visitors may not play before 9.30am. May not play
weekends and bank holidays. **Societies** may not play on
Sat, Sun & bank holidays; must contact in advance.
Green Fees £27 per round/day (£37 weekends). **Prof**
Andrew Witherup **Facilities** ⊗)Ⅲ 🖢 🖤 ♀ ⚓ 🏠 ✐
Location 4.5m E of city centre off A57

Hotel ★★★ 65% The Royal Hotel, Marine Ter,
Waterloo, LIVERPOOL ☎ 0151 928 2332 25 en suite

Woolton Doe Park, Speke Rd, Woolton L25 7TZ
☎ 0151 486 2298 📠 0151 486 1664
e-mail: keith@wooltongolf.co.uk
**Parkland course providing a good round of golf for all
standards. A members' owned course which includes two
par 5s and five par 3s.**
18 holes, 5717yds, Par 69, SSS 68, Course record 63.
Club membership 700.
Visitors must contact in advance. Restricted at weekends.
Societies must contact in advance. **Green Fees** £24 per
round (£35 weekends). **Prof** Dave Thompson **Facilities** ⊗)Ⅲ
🖢 🖤 ♀ ⚓ 🏠 ⚒ 🏌 **Leisure** Indoor teaching unit. **Conf**
Max 90 Class 45 Board 45 Banquet 90 **Location** 7m SE of
city centre off A562

Hotel ★★★ 65% The Royal Hotel, Marine Ter, Waterloo,
LIVERPOOL ☎ 0151 928 2332 25 en suite

NEWTON-LE-WILLOWS   Map 07 SJ59

Haydock Park Newton Ln WA12 0HX
☎ 01925 228525 📠 01925 228525
**A well-wooded parkland course, close to the well-
known racecourse, and always in excellent condition.
The pleasant undulating fairways offer some very
interesting golf and the 6th, 9th, 11th and 13th holes
are particularly testing. The clubhouse is very
comfortable.**
18 holes, 6058yds, Par 70, SSS 69, Course record 65.
Club membership 560.
Visitors welcome weekdays except Tue, with member
only weekends & bank holidays. Must contact in advance.
Societies must contact in advance. **Green Fees** £28 per
day. **Prof** Peter Kenwright **Course Designer** James Braid
Facilities ⊗)Ⅲ 🖢 🖤 ♀ ⚓ 🏠 ✐ **Location** 0.75m NE
off A49

Hotel ★★★ 66% Holiday Inn Haydock, Lodge Ln,
HAYDOCK ☎ 0870 400 9039 138 en suite

RAINHILL   Map 07 SJ49

Blundells Hill Blundells Ln L35 6NA
☎ 0151 4309551 (secretary) 4300100 (pro) 📠 0151 4265256
e-mail: information@blundellshill.co.uk
**Parkland course, with free-draining sandy soil, which
allows play throughout the winter.**
18 holes, 6256yds, Par 71, SSS 70, Course record 69.
Club membership 600.
Visitors may not play off white tees. **Societies** telephone for
prices and availability. **Green Fees** £35 per day; £25 per
round (£40/£30 weekends and bank holidays). **Cards** 💳
💳 💳 💳 **Prof** Richard Burbidge **Course Designer** Steve
Marnoch **Facilities** ⊗)Ⅲ 🖢 🖤 ♀ ⚓ 🏠 ⚒ 🏌 ✐ 🏌 **Leisure**
pool/snooker.**Conf** Max 160 Del £11.85 to £15.70 *
Location M62 junct 7, A57 towards Prescot, left after
garage. 2nd left into Blundells lane, on left behind trees
continued

Hotel ⇧ Premier Lodge (Liverpool East), 804 Warrington
Rd, RAINHILL ☎ 0870 700 1430 34 en suite

Eccleston Park Rainhill Rd L35 4PG
☎ 0151 493 0033 📠 0151 493 0044
e-mail: epgc@crownsportsplc.com
**A tough parkland course designed to test all golfing
abilities. Strategically placed water features, bunkers and
mounding enhance the beauty and difficulty of this
manicured course.**
18 holes, 6341yds, Par 69, SSS 71.
Club membership 650.
Visitors booking 7 days in advance. **Societies** telephone in
advance. **Green Fees** £13.50 per round (£18 weekends and
bank holidays). **Cards** 💳 💳 💳 💳 💳 **Prof** Chris
McKinney **Course Designer** Dave Thomas **Facilities** ⊗)Ⅲ
🖢 🖤 ♀ ⚓ 🏠 ⚒ ✐ **Location** M62 junct 7, follow A57
to Prescot. At hump back bridge turn right at lights, course
1m left

Hotel ⇧ Premier Lodge (Liverpool East), 804 Warrington
Rd, RAINHILL ☎ 0870 700 1430 34 en suite

ST HELENS   Map 07 SJ59

Grange Park Prescot Rd WA10 3AD
☎ 01744 26318 📠 01744 26318
e-mail: gpgc@ic24.net
**A course of Championship length set in pleasant
country surroundings - playing the course it is hard to
believe that industrial St Helens lies so close at hand.
The course is a fine test of golf and there are many
attractive holes liable to challenge all grades.**
18 holes, 6446yds, Par 72, SSS 71, Course record 65.
Club membership 730.
Visitors welcome except Tue, may not play weekends.
Advisable to contact professional in advance (01744
28785) **Societies** apply in writing **Green Fees** terms on
application. **Prof** Paul Roberts **Course Designer** James
Braid **Facilities** ⊗)Ⅲ 🖢 🖤 ♀ ⚓ 🏠 ✐ **Location** 1.5m
SW on A58

Hotel ★★ 66% Kirkfield Hotel, 2/4 Church St,
NEWTON LE WILLOWS ☎ 01925 228196 15 en suite

Houghwood Golf Billinge Hill, Crank Rd, Crank
WA11 8RL ☎ 01744 894444 & 894754 📠 01744 894754
e-mail: enquiries@houghwoodgolfclub.co.uk
**In a perfect setting Houghwood has magnificent
panoramic views over Lancashire plain and Welsh Hills.
With large USGA greens this undulating course is a
superb test of golf for all abilities.**

18 holes, 6116yds, Par 70, SSS 69, Course record 68.
Club membership 680.
Visitors no restrictions but dress code must be adhered to.
continued on page 174

The Royal Birkdale

Southport, *Merseyside*   ☎ 01704 567920   Fax 01704 562327   Map 07 SD31

e-mail: royalbirkdale@dial.pipex.com

Founded in 1889, The Royal Birkdale is considered by many to be the ultimate championship venue, having hosted every major event in the game including eight Open Championships, two Ryder Cup matches, the Walker Cup, the Curtis Cup and many major amateur events. The first hole provides an immediate taste of what is to come, requiring a well placed drive to avoid a bunker, water hazard and Out of Bounds to leave a reasonably clear view of the green. The tenth, the first of the inward nine, is unique in that it is the only hole to display the significant fairway undulations one expects from the classic links course. The twelfth is the most spectacular of the short holes on the course and is considered by Tom Watson to be one of the best par 3s in the world. Tucked away in the sandhills it has and will continue to claim a fair share of disasters. The approach on the final hole is arguably the most recognisable in golf, with the distinctive clubhouse designed to appear like an ocean cruise liner rising out of the sandhills. It is a par 5 for mere mortals, but played as a par 4 in The Open and it will provide a memorable finish to any round of golf.

Visitors must contact in advance and have a handicap certificate. Not Sat, and restricted on Sun

Societies must apply in advance

Green Fees weekdays £120 per round; £145 per day; Sunday & Bank Holidays £135 per round

Facilities ⊗ ⅷ(by prior arrangement) 🏋 ♥ ♀ ⚲ ⌂ ⛳ 𝄞 Professional (Brian Hodgkinson)

Location Waterloo Rd, Birkdale, Southport PR8 2LX (1.75m S of town centre on A565)

Holes/Par/Course record 18 holes, 6726 yds, Par 72, SSS 73

Championship Course

WHERE TO STAY AND EAT NEARBY

Hotels
SOUTHPORT

★★★66% Royal Clifton, Promenade.
☎ 01704 533771.
110 en suite

★★★69% Stutelea Hotel & Leisure Club, Alexandra Rd.
☎ 01704 544220. 20 en suite

★★★71% Scarisbrick, Lord St.
☎ 01704 543000. 90 en suite

★★71% Balmoral Lodge, 41 Queens Rd.
☎ 01704 544298. 15 en suite

Restaurant
WRIGHTINGTON

◎◎ Mulberry Tree, Wrightington Bar.
☎ 01257 451400

◎ High Moor Restaurant, Highmoor Ln (jct 27 off M6, take B5239). ☎ 01257 252364

Societies telephone enquiries welcome, deposit secures booking. **Green Fees** £17.50 per round;(£25 weekends). **Cards** ⊟ ▬ ▦ ▨ ☑ **Prof** Paul Dickenson **Course Designer** Neville Pearson **Facilities** ⊗ ⅧℐⅬ ⬛♀♣⬠🏌 ⚒ 𝄇 **Leisure** indoor golf simulator. **Conf** Max 80 Del from £20 * **Location** From M6 junct 23 follow A580 to A571 to Billinge

Hotel ★★★ 66% Holiday Inn Haydock, Lodge Ln, HAYDOCK ☎ 0870 400 9039 138 en suite

Sherdley Park Sherdley Rd WA9 5DE
☎ 01744 813149
18 holes, 5941yds, Par 70, SSS 69.
Location 2m S off A570
Telephone for further details

Hotel ★★ 66% Kirkfield Hotel, 2/4 Church St, NEWTON LE WILLOWS ☎ 01925 228196 15 en suite

SOUTHPORT See page 173

SOUTHPORT   Map 07 SD31

The Hesketh Cockle Dick's Ln, off Cambridge Rd
PR9 9QQ ☎ 01704 536897 ▤ 01704 539250
e-mail: secretary@heskethgolf.freeserve.co.uk
The Hesketh is the oldest of the six clubs in Southport, founded in 1885. Used as a final qualifying course for the Open Championship.
18 holes, 6572yds, Par 72, SSS 72, Course record 67.
Club membership 600.
Visitors welcome, with handicap certificate, at all time other than Tues am (Ladies) and 12.30-2pm daily. Must contact in advance. **Societies** please contact Martyn G Senior in advance. **Green Fees** not confirmed. **Prof** John Donoghue **Course Designer** J F Morris **Facilities** ⊗ ⅧℐⅬ ⬛♀♣⬠🏌 ⚒ 𝄇 **Location** 1m NE of town centre off A565

Hotel ★★★ 69% Stutelea Hotel & Leisure Club, Alexandra Rd, SOUTHPORT ☎ 01704 544220 20 en suite

Hillside Hastings Rd, Hillside PR8 2LU
☎ 01704 567169 ▤ 01704 563192
e-mail: hillside@ukgolfer.org
Championship links course with natural hazards open to strong wind.
18 holes, 6850yds, Par 72, SSS 74, Course record 65.
Club membership 700.
Visitors welcome except Sat, restricted on Sun & Tue (Ladies Day), must contact in advance through secretary. **Societies** must apply to secretary in advance. **Green Fees** £70 per day; £55 per round(£70 per round Sunday). **Cards** ▬ ☑ **Prof** Brian Seddon **Course Designer** Hawtree/Steel **Facilities** ⊗ ⅧℐⅬ ⬛♀♣⬠🏌 ⚒ 𝄇 **ℓ Location** 3m S of town centre on A565

Hotel ★★★ 66% Royal Clifton Hotel, Promenade, SOUTHPORT ☎ 01704 533771 110 en suite

Southport & Ainsdale Bradshaws Ln, Ainsdale
PR8 3LG ☎ 01704 578000 ▤ 01704 570896
e-mail: secretary@sandagolfclub.co.uk
'S and A', as it is known in the North is another of the fine Championship courses for which this part of the
continued

country is famed. This Club has staged many important events and offers golf of the highest order.
18 holes, 6687yds, Par 72, SSS 73, Course record 62.
Club membership 815.
Visitors welcome except Thu after 1pm, Sat after 3pm & Sun after 12 noon & bank holidays. Must contact club in advance & have handicap certificate. **Societies** must apply in advance. **Green Fees** £50 per round;£65 per day(£65 per round weekends). **Cards** ⊟ ▬ ☑ **Prof** J Payne **Course Designer** James Braid **Facilities** ⊗ ⅧℐⅬ ⬛♀ ♣⬠🏌 𝄇 **Location** 3m S off A565

Hotel ★★★ 66% Royal Clifton Hotel, Promenade, SOUTHPORT ☎ 01704 533771 110 en suite

Southport Municipal Park Rd West PR9 0JR
☎ 01704 535286
18 holes, 6400yds, Par 70, SSS 69, Course record 67.
Location N side of town centre off A565
Telephone for further details

Hotel ★★★ 66% Royal Clifton Hotel, Promenade, SOUTHPORT ☎ 01704 533771 110 en suite

Southport Old Links Moss Ln, Churchtown
PR9 7QS ☎ 01704 228207 ▤ 01704 505353
e-mail: secretary@solgc.freeserve.co.uk
Seaside course with tree-lined fairways and easy walking. One of the oldest courses in Southport, Henry Vardon won the 'Leeds Cup' here in 1922.
9 holes, 6371yds, Par 72, SSS 71, Course record 68.
Club membership 450.
Visitors advisable to contact in advance, no play Wed/Sun **Societies** apply in writing. **Green Fees** £30 per day; £22 per round (£40/£30 weekends and bank holidays). **Prof** Gary Copeman **Facilities** ⊗ ⅧℐⅬ ⬛♀♣⬠🏌 𝄇 **Location** NW side of town centre off A5267

Hotel ★★ 70% Bold Hotel, 585 Lord St, SOUTHPORT ☎ 01704 532578 23 rms (20 en suite)

WALLASEY   Map 07 SJ29

Bidston Bidston Link Rd CH44 2HR
☎ 0151 638 3412 ▤ 6306650
Parkland course, with westerly winds. Flat easy walking.
18 holes, 6233yds, Par 70, SSS 70.
Club membership 600.
Visitors groups of 4 or more should contact in advance. **Societies** must apply in writing. **Green Fees** £18.50 per 18 holes. **Prof** Neil McFallane **Facilities** ⊗ ⅧℐⅬ ⬛♀♣⬠ 🏌 ⚒ **Location** 0.5m W of M53 junc 1 entrance off A551

Hotel ★★★ 67% Leasowe Castle Hotel, Leasowe Rd, MORETON ☎ 0151 606 9191 47 en suite

Leasowe Moreton CH46 3RD
☎ 0151 677 5852 ▤ 0151 604 1448
A semi-links, seaside course which has recently undergone landscaping on the first five holes, new mounds removing the former rather flat appearance.
18 holes, 6227yds, Par 71, SSS 71.
Club membership 637.
Visitors telephone professional (0151 678 5460). Handicap certificate required. Not Sat play and not before noon on Sun. **Societies** contact in advance. **Green Fees** not confirmed. **Cards** ⊟ ▬ ▨ ▦ ▨ ☑ **Prof** Andrew Ayres **Course Designer** John Ball Jnr **Facilities** ⊗ ⅧℐⅬ ⬛♀♣⬠🏌 𝄇 **Location** 2m W on A551
continued

Hotel ★★★ 67% Leasowe Castle Hotel, Leasowe Rd,
MORETON ☎ 0151 606 9191 47 en suite

Wallasey Bayswater Rd CH45 8LA
☎ 0151 691 1024 📠 0151 638 8988
e-mail: wallaseygc@aol.com
A well-established sporting links, adjacent to the Irish
Sea, with huge sandhills and many classic holes where
the player's skills are often combined with good
fortune. Large, firm greens and fine views but not for
the faint-hearted.

18 holes, 6503yds, Par 72, SSS 72, Course record 65.
Club membership 650.
Visitors must contact one month in advance. Societies
must apply in writing or telephone. Green Fees £45 per
round(£60 weekends and bank holidays). Cards 💳 Prof
Mike Adams Course Designer Tom Morris Facilities ⊗
🎱 📠 💺 ♀ 🅿 🏠 ⛳ 🏌 ♂ Location N side of town centre
off A554

Hotel ★★★ 70% Grove House Hotel, Grove Rd,
WALLASEY ☎ 0151 639 3947 & 0151 630 4558
📠 0151 639 0028 14 en suite

Warren Grove Rd CH45 0JA ☎ 0151 639 8323
e-mail: golfer@warrengc.freeserve.co.uk
Short, undulating links course with first-class greens and
prevailing winds off the sea.
9 holes, 5854yds, Par 72, SSS 68.
Club membership 100.
Visitors welcome except Sun 7-11am. Societies contact in
advance. Green Fees terms on application. Prof Steve
Konrad Facilities 🏠 🏌 ♂ Location N side of town centre
off A554

Hotel ★★★ 67% Leasowe Castle Hotel, Leasowe Rd,
MORETON ☎ 0151 606 9191 47 en suite

NORFOLK

BARNHAM BROOM   Map 05 TG00

Barnham Broom Hotel, Golf, Conference,
Leisure Honingham Rd NR9 4DD ☎ 01603 759552
📠 01603 758224
e-mail: enquiry@barnhambroomhotel.co.uk
Valley course meanders through the River Yare
Valley, parkland and mature trees. Hill course has
wide fairways, heavily guarded greens and spectacular
views.
Valley Course: 18 holes, 6603yds, Par 72, SSS 72.
Hill Course: 18 holes, 6495yds, Par 71, SSS 71.
Club membership 500.
continued

Visitors must contact in advance on 01603 759552.
Societies must contact in advance on 01603 759393
Green Fees Apr-Oct from £30, reduced winter rate.
Cards 💳 ▬ ▬ 📠 💳 📶 🈂 Prof A Rudge Course
Designer Frank Pennink Facilities ⊗ 🎱 📠 💺 ♀ 🅿 🏠
🏌 🏠 🌳 🚣 ⛳ 🏌 Leisure hard tennis courts, heated
indoor swimming pool, squash, sauna, solarium,
gymnasium, 3 academy holes. golf school.Conf Max 300
Thtr 150 Class 120 Board 75 Banquet 150 Del £27.50 to
£127.50 * Location 1m N, S of A47

Hotel ★★★ 75% Barnham Broom Hotel & Country
Club, BARNHAM BROOM ☎ 01603 759393 52 en suite

BAWBURGH   Map 05 TG10

Bawburgh Glen Lodge, Marlingford Rd NR9 3LU
☎ 01603 740404 📠 01603 740403
e-mail: info@bawburgh.com
Undulating course, mixture of parkland and heathland.
The main feature is a large glacial swale which meanders
its way down to the River Yare creating many interesting
tee and green locations. Excellent 18th hole to finish
requiring a long accurate second shot to clear the lake in
front of the elevated green.
Course 1: 18 holes, 6231yds, Par 70, SSS 70,
Course record 65.
Course 2: 18 holes, 5968yds, Par 70, SSS 69.
Club membership 750.
Visitors must contact in advance, limited play at weekends.
Societies must contact in advance. Green Fees terms on
application. Prof Chris Potter Course Designer John
Barnard Facilities ⊗ 📠 💺 ♀ 🅿 🏠 🌳 🚣 ⛳ 🏌 Conf Max
16 Location S of Royal Norfolk Showground, on A47

Hotel ★★★ 73% Park Farm Hotel, HETHERSETT
☎ 01603 810264 5 en suite 42 annexe en suite

BRANCASTER   Map 09 TF74

Royal West Norfolk PE31 8AX
☎ 01485 210223 📠 01485 210087
If you want to see what golf courses were like years
ago, then go to the Royal West Norfolk where tradition
exudes from both clubhouse and course. Close by the
sea, the links are laid out in the grand manner and are
characterised by sleepered greens, superb cross-
bunkering and salt marshes.
18 holes, 6428yds, Par 71, SSS 71, Course record 66.
Club membership 825.
Visitors must contact well in advance. Restrictions at
weekends and in Aug. Societies must contact Secretary in
advance. Green Fees £60 per round (£70 weekends).
Reduced winter rate. Cards 💳 ▬ ▬ 📠 💳 Prof S
Rayner Course Designer Holcombe-Ingleby Facilities ⊗
🎱 📠 💺 ♀ 🅿 🏠 🏌 ♂ Location 7m E of Hunstanton. In
Brancaster village turn N at the beach/Broad Lane junct
with A149 for 1m

Hotel ★★ 73% The White Horse, Brancaster Staithe,
Norfolk ☎ 01485 210262 15 en suite

CROMER   Map 09 TG24

Royal Cromer 145 Overstrand Rd NR27 0JH
☎ 01263 512884 📠 01263 512430
e-mail: general.manager@royal-cromer.com
Seaside course set out on cliff edge, hilly and subject to
continued

wind. Challenging upland course with spectacular views out to sea and overlooking town. Strong sea breezes affect the clifftop holes, the most famous being the 14th (the Lighthouse) which has a green in the shadow of the lighthouse.
18 holes, 6508yds, Par 72, SSS 72, Course record 67. Club membership 700.
Visitors must contact in advance & have handicap certificate. **Societies** must contact in advance. **Green Fees** terms on application. **Prof** Lee Patterson **Course Designer** J H Taylor **Facilities** ⊗ ⅢⅢ ⅼⅼ ⅬⅬ Ⅱ Ⅱ Ⅱ Ⅱ Ⅱ ⅼ Ⅱ **Location** 1m E on B1159

Hotel ★★ 68% Red Lion, Brook St, CROMER
☎ 01263 514964 12 en suite

YE OLDE RED LION HOTEL

Brook Street, Cromer, Norfolk, NR27 9HD.
Tel: 01263 514964
Fax:01263 512834
www.yeolderedlionhotel.co.uk

Stands on a cliff corner overlooking the sandy beaches but close to town centre. Some rooms have seaviews as does our Edwardian Bar, which has a wide selection of real ales.
There is a snooker room and also Galleon's Restaurant with à la carte and table d'hôte menus.
Plus our newly re-furbished function room

Ryston Park PE38 0HH
☎ 01366 382133 ▤ 01366 383834
e-mail: rystonparkgc@fsnet.co.uk
Parkland course.
9 holes, 6310yds, Par 70, SSS 70, Course record 66. Club membership 330.
Visitors must contact in advance. May not play weekends or bank holidays. **Societies** must apply in writing. **Green Fees** £25 per day; £20 per round. **Prof** Alison Shead **Course Designer** James Braid **Facilities** ⊗ ⅢⅢ ⅼⅼ ⅬⅬ Ⅱ Ⅱ Ⅱ Ⅱ **Location** 0.5m S on A10

Hotel ★★ 72% Castle Hotel, High St, DOWNHAM MARKET ☎ 01366 384311 12 en suite

Dereham Quebec Rd NR19 2DS
☎ 01362 695900 ▤ 01362 695904
Parkland course.
9 holes, 6225yds, Par 71, SSS 70, Course record 64. Club membership 480.
Visitors must contact in advance. Weekends with member only. **Societies** must apply in writing or telephone in advance. **Green Fees** £17.50 per round, £22.50 per day. **Prof** Robert Curtis **Facilities** ⊗ ⅢⅢ ⅼⅼ ⅬⅬ Ⅱ Ⅱ Ⅱ Ⅱ **Location** N side of town centre off B1110

Hotel ★★★ 75% Barnham Broom Hotel & Country Club, BARNHAM BROOM ☎ 01603 759393 52 en suite

The Norfolk Golf & Country Club Hingham Rd, Reymerston NR9 4QQ ☎ 01362 850297 ▤ 01362 850614
The course meanders through more than 200 acres of rolling Norfolk countryside, including ancient ditches, hedging and woodland. Large greens are built to USGA specification.
18 holes, 6609yds, Par 72, SSS 72, Course record 69. Club membership 500.
Visitors contact Golf reception for advance bookings. **Societies** apply in writing to the Society Organiser. **Green Fees** terms on application. **Cards** ▦ ▦ ▩ ▨ **Prof** Tony Varney **Facilities** ⊗ ⅢⅢ ⅼⅼ ⅬⅬ Ⅱ Ⅱ Ⅱ Ⅱ Ⅱ Ⅱ Ⅱ
Leisure heated indoor swimming pool, sauna, solarium, gymnasium, pitch & putt. **Location** 12m W of Norwich, off B1135

Hotel ★★★ 75% Barnham Broom Hotel & Country Club, BARNHAM BROOM ☎ 01603 759393 52 en suite

Diss Stuston IP22 3JB ☎ 01379 641025 ▤ 01379 641025
18 holes, 6238yds, Par 73, SSS 70.
Location 1.5m SE on B1118
Telephone for further details

Hotel ★★★ 75% The Cornwallis Country Hotel & Restaurant, BROME ☎ 01379 870326 11 en suite 5 annexe en suite

Fakenham Gallow Sports Centre, The Race Course N21 7NY ☎ 01328 863534
A well-wooded 9-hole course.
9 holes, 6174yds, Par 71, SSS 70, Course record 65. Club membership 460.
Visitors any time with member, restricted until after noon weekends. **Societies** apply in writing or telephone. **Green**

continued

Fees not confirmed. **Cards** 🔲 ▆ ▆ 🖼 🗺 💲 **Prof**
Martyn Clarke PGA **Course Designer** Cotton(UK) **Facilities**
⊗ 🏓 🍴 💺 ♀ ⛳ ⛳ **Leisure** hard tennis courts, squash,
indoor bowling.

Hotel ★★ 68% Crown Hotel, 6 Market Place,
FAKENHAM ☎ 01328 851418 12 en suite

FRITTON   Map 05 TG40

Caldecott Hall Golf & Leisure Caldecott Hall,
Beccles Rd NR31 9EY ☎ 01493 488488 📠 01493 488561
e-mail: caldecotthall@supanet.com
Facilities at Caldecott Hall include an 18-hole course with
testing dog-leg fairways, a short par 3 9-hole course, a
floodlit driving range, and good practising areas.

Main Course: 18 holes, 6536yards, Par 72, SSS 71.
Club membership 500.
Visitors visitors always welcome, subject to availability.
Societies arrangements in advance. **Green Fees** £20 per day
(£25 weekends). **Cards** 🔲 ▆ ▆ 🖼 🗺 💲 **Prof** Syer
Shulver **Facilities** ⊗ 🏓 🍴 💺 ♀ ⛳ ⛳ 🚩 🏹 🚜 ⛳ ⛳
Leisure fishing, 9 hole par 3 course. **Conf** Max 100
Location On the A143 Beccles/Gt Yarmouth road at Fritton

Hotel ★★★ 72% Caldecott Hall Golf & Leisure, Caldecott
Hall, Beccles Rd, FRITTON ☎ 01493 488488 8 en suite

GORLESTON-ON-SEA   Map 05 TG50

Gorleston Warren Rd NR31 6JT
☎ 01493 661911 & 662103 📠 01493 661911
Cliff top course, the most easterly in the British Isles. One
of the outstanding features of the course is the 7th hole,
which was rescued from the ravages of cliff erosion about
20 years ago. The green, only eight yards from the cliff
edge, is at the mercy of the prevailing winds and club
selection is critical.
18 holes, 6391yds, Par 71, SSS 71, Course record 68.
Club membership 860.
Visitors advisable to contact in advance, must have
handicap. Dress code in operation. **Societies** must apply in
writing. **Green Fees** £25 per day (£30 weekends). **Prof** Nick
Brown **Course Designer** J H Taylor **Facilities** ⊗ 🏓 🍴 💺 ♀
💺 🚩 🚩 ⛳ **Location** Between Gt Yarmouth and
Lowestoft, signposted on the main A12 road

Hotel ★★★ 74% Cliff Hotel, Cliff Hill, Gorleston, GREAT
YARMOUTH ☎ 01493 662179 39 en suite

GREAT YARMOUTH   Map 05 TG50

Great Yarmouth & Caister Beach House,
Caister-on-Sea NR30 5TD
☎ 01493 728699 📠 01493 728831
e-mail: office@caistergolf.co.uk
This great old club, which celebrated its centenary in
continued

1982, has played its part in the development of the
game. It is a fine old-fashioned links where not many
golfers have bettered the SSS in competitions. The 468-
yard 8th (par 4), is a testing hole and the 7th is an
extremely fine short hole. A feature of the course is a
number of sleepered bunkers, a line of four bisecting
the 4th.
18 holes, 6330yds, Par 70, SSS 70, Course record 66.
Club membership 720.
Visitors must contact in advance. Restricted weekends.
Societies must apply in writing or telephone. **Green Fees**
terms on application. **Cards** ▆▆ **Course Designer** H Colt
Facilities ⊗ 🏓 🍴 💺 ♀ ⛳ ⛳ **Location** 0.5m N off
A149

Hotel ★★★ 70% Imperial Hotel, North Dr, GREAT
YARMOUTH ☎ 01493 842000 39 en suite

HUNSTANTON   Map 09 TF64

Hunstanton Golf Course Rd PE36 6JQ
☎ 01485 532811 📠 01485 532319
e-mail: hunstanton.golf@eidosnet.co.uk
A championship links course set among some of the
most natural golfing country in East Anglia. Keep out
of the numerous bunkers and master the fast greens to
play to your handicap - then you only have the wind to
contend with! Good playing conditions all year round.
18 holes, 6360yds, Par 72, SSS 70.
Club membership 675.
Visitors must contact in advance and be a club member
with current handicap certificate. Restricted at weekends
& may not play bank holiday weekends. Play in two ball
format i.e. singles or foursomes. **Societies** apply in
advance. **Green Fees** £55 (£65 weekends). Winter £35
(£45 weekends); £30/£40 after 4pm. **Prof** James Dodds
Course Designer James Braid **Facilities** ⊗ 🏓 by prior
arrangement 🍴 💺 ♀ ⛳ 🚩 🚩 🏹 🚜 ⛳ **Location** Off
A149 in Old Hunstanton Village signposted

Hotel ★★ 74% Caley Hall Motel, Old Hunstanton Rd,
HUNSTANTON ☎ 01485 533486 33 annexe en suite

KING'S LYNN   Map 09 TF62

Eagles 39 School Rd, Tilney All Saints PE34 4RS
☎ 01553 827147 📠 01553 829777
e-mail: shop@eagles-golf-tennis.co.uk
Parkland course with plenty of water hazards and
bunkers. Also par 3 course and floodlit, covered driving
range.
9 holes, 4284yds, Par 64, SSS 61, Course record 64.
Club membership 200.
Visitors must contact in advance. Dress code required.
Societies must apply in writing. **Green Fees** £11 per 18
holes; £7.50 per 9 holes (£14.50/£8.50 weekends & bank
holidays). **Cards** 🔲 ▆ ▆ 🖼 🗺 💲 **Prof** Nigel
Pickerell **Course Designer** D W Horn **Facilities** ⊗ by prior
arrangement 🍴 💺 ♀ ⛳ 🚩 🚩 ⛳ ⛳ **Leisure** hard tennis
courts. **Location** Off A47 at roundabout to Tilney All Saints
between Kings Lynn and Wisbech

Hotel ★★★ 64% The Duke's Head, Tuesday Market Place,
KING'S LYNN ☎ 01553 774996 71 en suite

AA website: www.theAA.com

King's Lynn Castle Rising PE31 6BD
☎ 01553 631654 🖥 631036
e-mail: klgc@eidosnet.co.uk
The course is set among silver birch and fir woodland and benefits, especially in the winter from well-drained sandy soil.
18 holes, 6609yds, Par 72, SSS 73, Course record 64.
Club membership 910.
Visitors must contact in advance, handicap certificate required. **Societies** apply in writing or by phone in advance. **Green Fees** £40 per day (£50 weekends). **Prof** John Reynolds **Course Designer** Thomas & Allis **Facilities** ⊗ ⅷ ⅃ ℒ ℒ ℒ ℒ ℒ **Leisure** Snooker. **Location** 4m NE off A149

Hotel ★★★ 64% The Duke's Head, Tuesday Market Place, KING'S LYNN ☎ 01553 774996 71 en suite

MATTISHALL   Map 09 TG01

Mattishall South Green NR20 3JZ ☎ 01362 850111
Mattishall has the distinction of having the longest hole in Norfolk at a very demanding 625yds.
9 holes, 3300mtrs, Par 72, SSS 69.
Club membership 120.
Visitors no restrictions. **Societies** welcome. **Green Fees** not confirmed. **Course Designer** B Todd **Facilities** ℒ ℒ ℒ ℒ **Location** 0.75m S of Mattishall Church

Hotel ★★★ 75% Barnham Broom Hotel & Country Club, BARNHAM BROOM ☎ 01603 759393 52 en suite

MIDDLETON   Map 09 TF61

Middleton Hall Hall Orchards PE32 1RH
☎ 01553 841800 🖥 01553 841800
e-mail: middleton-hall@btclick.com
The setting is one of natural undulations, and mature specimen trees, offering a most attractive environment for the game of golf. The architecturally designed course provides a challenge for the competent golfer, there is also a covered floodlit driving range and practice putting green.
18 holes, 6004yds, Par 71, SSS 69, Course record 71.
Club membership 600.
Visitors no restrictions. **Societies** must contact in advance. **Green Fees** £30 per day; £25 per round (£35/£30 weekends and bank holidays). **Cards** 🌐 🚈 🌐 **Prof** Steve White **Course Designer** D Scott **Facilities** ⊗ ⅷ ℒ ℒ ℒ ℒ ℒ **Location** 4m from King's Lynn on A47 towards Norwich

Hotel ★★★ 66% Butterfly Hotel, Beveridge Way, Hardwick Narrows, KING'S LYNN ☎ 01553 771707 50 en suite

MUNDESLEY   Map 09 TG33

Mundesley Links Rd NR11 8ES
☎ 01263 720279 & 720095 🖥 01263 720279
Parkland course, undulating with panoramic views, short but competitive. One mile from the sea.
9 holes, 5377yds, Par 68, SSS 66, Course record 64.
Club membership 500.
Visitors restricted Wed & weekends, also Tue 4-6pm, dress regulations, no sharing clubs, golf shoes must be worn, prior booking preferred. Handicap certificate required. **Societies** must contact one month in advance. **Green Fees** £18 per round (£25 weekends and bank holidays). **Prof** T G Symmons **Facilities** ⊗ ⅷ by prior arrangement ℒ ℒ ℒ ℒ ℒ **Location** W side of village off B1159
continued

Hotel ★★ 68% Red Lion, Brook St, CROMER
☎ 01263 514964 12 en suite

NORWICH   Map 05 TG20

Costessey Park Old Costessey NR8 5AL
☎ 01603 746333 & 747085 🖥 01603 746185
The course lies in the gently contoured Two River valley, providing players with a number of holes that bring the river and man-made lakes into play.
18 holes, 5820yds, Par 71, SSS 68, Course record 68.
Club membership 600.
Visitors may not play competition days, prior booking required for weekends. **Societies** welcome by prior arrangement. **Green Fees** not confirmed. **Prof** Simon Cook **Facilities** ⊗ ⅷ ℒ ℒ ℒ ℒ ℒ ℒ ℒ ℒ

Hotel ★★★ 67% Quality Hotel, 2 Barnard Rd, Bowthorpe, NORWICH ☎ 01603 741161 80 en suite

De Vere Dunston Hall Hotel Ipswich Rd
NR14 8PQ ☎ 01508 470444 🖥 01508 470689
e-mail: dhreception@devere-hotels.com
Parkland course with water features at many holes. Varied and challenging woodland setting. Floodlit driving range.
18 holes, 6300yds, Par 71, SSS 70, Course record 70.
Visitors must book in advance. **Societies** apply in writing or telephone for details. **Green Fees** not confirmed. **Cards** 🌐 🚈 🌐 🌐 **Prof** Peter Briggs **Course Designer** M Shaw **Facilities** ⊗ ⅷ ℒ ℒ ℒ ℒ ℒ ℒ ℒ ℒ ℒ **Leisure** hard tennis court, heated indoor swimming pool, sauna, solarium, gymnasium. **Location** On A140

Hotel ★★★★ 70% De Vere Dunston Hall, Ipswich Rd, NORWICH ☎ 01508 470444 130 en suite

Eaton Newmarket Rd NR4 6SF
☎ 01603 451686 & 452881 🖥 01603 451686
e-mail: administrator@eatongc.co.uk
An undulating, tree-lined parkland course with excellent trees. Easy opening par 5 followed by an intimidating par 3 that is well bunkered with deep rough on both sides. The challenging 17th hole is uphill to a small hidden green and always needs more club than expected.
18 holes, 6114yds, Par 70, SSS 70, Course record 64.
Club membership 800.
Visitors restricted before 11.30am weekends. Advised to contact in advance. **Societies** must contact in advance. **Green Fees** £30 per day (£40 weekends). **Cards** 🌐 🚈 🌐 🌐 **Prof** Mark Allen **Facilities** ⊗ ⅷ by prior arrangement ℒ ℒ ℒ ℒ ℒ **Location** 1.5m SW of city centre off A11

Hotel ★★★ 73% Park Farm Hotel, HETHERSETT ☎ 01603 810264 5 en suite 42 annexe en suite

Marriott Sprowston Manor Hotel & Country Club Wroxham Rd NR7 8RP
☎ 01603 254290 🖥 01603 788884
e-mail: sprowston.manor@marriotthotels.com
Set in 100 acres of parkland, including an impressive collection of oak trees which provide a backdrop to many holes. A very tight course, so accuracy is required for good golf. The facilities include a 27-bay driving range.
18 holes, 5763yds, Par 70, SSS 68, Course record 63.
Club membership 600.
Visitors no restrictions. Advisable to book in advance. **Societies** must contact in advance. **Green Fees** not
continued

confirmed. **Cards** 🔲🔲🔲🔲🔲🔲🔲🔲 **Prof** Guy D
Ireson **Facilities** ⊗ ⫴⪆ ⬛ ♟♀⫞⛳🏠🏌🛒♻♨
Leisure heated indoor swimming pool. **Location** 4m NE
from city centre on A1151

Hotel ★★★★ 75% Marriott Sprowston Manor Hotel &
Country Club, Sprowston Park, Wroxham Rd, Sprowston,
NORWICH ☎ 01603 410871 94 en suite

Royal Norwich Drayton High Rd, Hellesdon NR6 5AH
☎ 01603 429928 & 408459 (Pro) 📱 01603 417945
e-mail: mail@royalnorwichgolf.co.uk
**Undulating mature parkland course complimented with
gorse. Largely unchanged since the alterations carried
out by James Braid in 1924. A challenging test of golf.**
18 holes, 6506yds, Par 72, SSS 72, Course record 65.
Club membership 700.
Visitors must contact in advance. Restricted weekends &
bank holidays. **Societies** must contact in advance. **Green
Fees** £36 per day; £23 per round (£44/£29 weekends & bank
holidays). **Prof** Dean Futter **Course Designer** James Braid
Facilities ⊗ ⫴⪆ by prior arrangement ⪆ ⬛ ♟♀🏠🏌♻
Location 2.5m NW of city centre on A1067

Hotel ★★★ 67% Quality Hotel, 2 Barnard Rd, Bowthorpe,
NORWICH ☎ 01603 741161 80 en suite

Wensum Valley Hotel, Golf & Country Club
Beech Av, Taverham NR8 6HP ☎ 01603 261012
📱 01603 261664
e-mail: enqs@wensumvalley.co.uk
**An undulating, picturesque golf course situated on the
side of a valley. The greens in particular are very
undulating and always give the average golfer a testing
time. The 12th hole from a raised tee provides a blind and
windy tee shot and a very sloping green.**
*Valley Course: 18 holes, 6172yds, Par 71, SSS 69,
Course record 67.*
Wensum Course: 9 holes, 2906yds, Par 70, SSS 68.
Club membership 900.
Visitors no restrictions but advisable to book tee times at
weekends. **Societies** apply in writing or by telephone. **Green
Fees** £20 per day. **Cards** 🔲🔲🔲🔲🔲🔲🔲🔲 **Prof** Peter
Whittle **Course Designer** B Todd **Facilities** ⊗ ⫴⪆ ⬛ ♟♀
⪆🏠⫞⛳🏌🛒♻♨ **Leisure** heated indoor swimming
pool, fishing, sauna, solarium, gymnasium.**Conf** Max 150
Thtr 150 Class 40 Board 40 Banquet 40 Del £20 to £30 *
Location 5m N of Norwich, off A1067

Hotel ★★★ 68% Swallow Nelson Hotel, Prince of Wales
Rd, NORWICH ☎ 01603 760260 132 en suite

Sheringham Weybourne Rd NR26 8HG
☎ 01263 823488 & 822038 📱 01263 825189
e-mail: sgc.sec@care4free.net
**Splendid cliff-top links with gorse, good 'seaside turf'
and plenty of space. Straight driving is essential for a
low score. The course is close to the shore and can be
very windswept, but offers magnificent views.**
18 holes, 6495yds, Par 70, SSS 71, Course record 65.
Club membership 680.
Visitors must contact in advance & have handicap
certificate. Restricted weekends. **Societies** must apply in
writing. **Green Fees** £40 per day (£50 Saturdays). **Prof** M
W Jubb **Course Designer** Tom Dunn **Facilities** ⊗ ⫴⪆ ⪆
⬛ ♟♀🏠🏌♻ **Location** W side of town centre on
A149

continued

Hotel ★★ 70% Beaumaris Hotel, South St,
SHERINGHAM ☎ 01263 822370 21 en suite

Swaffham Cley Rd PE37 8AE
☎ 01760 721621(secretary) 721611(pro) 📱 01760 721621
Heathland course and designated wildlife site.
18 holes, 6539yds, Par 71, SSS 71.
Club membership 500.
Visitors must contact in advance. With member only at
weekends & not before midday. **Societies** must contact in
advance. **Green Fees** £25 per round;£30 per day. **Prof** Peter
Field **Course Designer** Jonathan Gaunt **Facilities** ⊗ ⪆ ⬛ ♟♀
⪆🏠⛳♻ **Location** 1.5m SW

Hotel ★★★ 65% George Hotel, Station Rd, SWAFFHAM
☎ 01760 721238 29 en suite

Feltwell Thor Ave, Feltwell IP26 4AY
☎ 01842 827644 📱 01842 827644
**In spite of being an inland links, this 9-hole course is still
open and windy.**
9 holes, 6488yds, Par 72, SSS 71, Course record 71.
Club membership 400.
Visitors dress restriction, no jeans, tracksuits or collarless
shirts, golf shoes to be worn. **Societies** apply in writing or
telephone in advance. **Green Fees** £15 per day(£24
weekends). **Prof** Neil Mitchell **Facilities** ⊗ ⫴⪆ ⬛ ♟♀
(closed Mon) ⪆🏠⛳♻ **Location** On B1112, next to
RAF Feltwell

Hotel ★★ 65% The Thomas Paine Hotel, White Hart St,
THETFORD ☎ 01842 755631 13 en suite

Thetford Brandon Rd IP24 3NE
☎ 01842 752169 📱 01842 766212
**This is a course with a good pedigree. It was laid out
by a fine golfer, C.H. Mayo, later altered by James
Braid and then again altered by another famous
course designer, Mackenzie Ross. It is a testing
heathland course with a particularly stiff finish.**
18 holes, 6849yds, Par 72, SSS 73, Course record 66.
Club membership 850.
Visitors pre booking advisable, may not play weekends or
bank holidays except with member. Handicap certificate
required. **Societies** must contact in advance, Wed-Fri
only. **Green Fees** £35. **Cards** 🔲🔲🔲🔲🔲 **Prof**
Gary Kitley **Course Designer** James Braid **Facilities** ⊗
⫴⪆ ⬛ ♟♀🏠⛳♻ **Location** 2m W of Thetford on
B1107

Hotel ★★ 65% The Thomas Paine Hotel, White Hart St,
THETFORD ☎ 01842 755631 13 en suite

Richmond Park Saham Rd IP25 6EA
☎ 01953 881803 📱 01953 881817
e-mail: info@richmondpark.co.uk
**Compact parkland course with mature and young trees.
These together with the Little Wissey river and other
water hazards create an interesting but not daunting
challenge.**
18 holes, 6289yds, Par 71, SSS 70, Course record 69.
Club membership 600.

continued

Richmond Park Golf Club

Visitors not before 10.30am weekends & bank holidays.
Societies must contact in advance. **Green Fees** £30 per day;
£22.50 per round (£30 weekends & bank holidays). **Cards**
⚏ ▦ ▦ ▦ ⚏ ⚏ **Prof** Alan Hemsley **Course Designer**
D Jessup/D Scott **Facilities** ⊗ ⵘ ⧫ ☕ ♀ ♨ 🏠 ⛳ 🏠 🏌
⛳ ℓ **Leisure** gymnasium. **Conf** Max 85 Board 12 Del £11.75
to £75 * **Location** 500yds NW of town centre

....

Hotel ★★★ 65% George Hotel, Station Rd, SWAFFHAM
☎ 01760 721238 29 en suite

| WESTON LONGVILLE | Map 09 TG11 |

Weston Park NR9 5JW
☎ 01603 872363 ▤ 01603 873040
e-mail: golf@weston-park.co.uk
**Testing course set in 200 acres of mature parkland with
specimen trees.**
18 holes, 6648yds, Par 72, SSS 72, Course record 69.
Club membership 400.
Visitors must telephone for tee times on 01603 872998.
Societies must telephone for prices and tee times. **Green
Fees** on application. **Cards** ⚏ ▦ ▦ ⚏ ⚏ **Prof**
Michael Few **Course Designer** Golf Technology **Facilities**
⊗ ⧫ ☕ ♀ ♨ 🏠 🏌 ⛳ **Leisure** hard tennis courts. **Conf**
Thtr 50 Board 25 Banquet 44 **Location** Follow brown signs
off A1067 or A47. 9m SW of Norwich

....

Hotel ★★★ 67% Quality Hotel, 2 Barnard Rd, Bowthorpe,
NORWICH ☎ 01603 741161 80 en suite

| WEST RUNTON | Map 09 TG14 |

Links Country Park Hotel & Golf Club
NR27 9QH ☎ 01263 838215 ▤ 01263 838264
e-mail: sales@links-hotel.co.uk
**Parkland course 500 yds from the sea, with superb views
overlooking West Runton. The hotel offers extensive
leisure facilities.**
9 holes, 4842yds, Par 66, SSS 64.
Club membership 300.
Visitors restrictions weekends. **Societies** must telephone in
advance. **Green Fees** £25 per day (£30 weekends). **Cards**
⚏ ▦ ▦ ⚏ ⚏ **Prof** Andrew Collison **Course Designer**
J.H Taylor **Facilities** ⊗ ⵘ ⧫ ☕ ♀ ♨ 🏠 🏌 🏠 🏌 ⛳
Leisure hard tennis courts, heated indoor swimming pool,
sauna, solarium. **Conf** Thtr 100 Class 50 Board 40 Banquet
150 Del from £25 * **Location** S side of village off A149

....

Hotel ★★ 70% Beaumaris Hotel, South St, SHERINGHAM
☎ 01263 822370 21 en suite

> If the name of the club appears
> in *italics*, details have not been
> confirmed for this edition of the guide

| NORTHAMPTONSHIRE |

| CHACOMBE | Map 04 SP44 |

Cherwell Edge OX17 2EN
☎ 01295 711591 ▤ 01295 713674
e-mail: cegc@ukonline.co.uk
**Parkland course over chalk giving good drainage. The
front nine is short and tight with mature trees. The back
nine is longer and more open.**

18 holes, 5956yds, Par 70, SSS 68, Course record 64.
Club membership 500.
Visitors no restrictions but golf shoes to be worn and tidy
appearance expected. Some restrictions at weekends.
Societies must apply in advance. **Green Fees** £20 per 18
holes (£25 weekends); £40 per day. **Cards** ⚏ ▦ ▦ ⚏ ⚏
Prof Jason Newman **Course Designer** R Davies **Facilities**
⊗ ⵘ ⧫ ☕ ♀ ♨ 🏠 🏌 🏠 ⛳ ℓ **Location** M40 junct 11,
0.5m S off B4525, 2m from Banbury

....

Hotel ★★★ 68% Whately Hall, Banbury Cross,
BANBURY ☎ 0870 400 8104 72 en suite

| COLD ASHBY | Map 04 SP67 |

Cold Ashby Stanford Rd NN6 6EP
☎ 01604 740548 ▤ 01604 740548
e-mail: coldashby.golfclub@virgin.net
**Undulating parkland course, nicely matured, with superb
views. The 27 holes consist of three loops of nine which
can be interlinked with each other. All three loops have
their own challenge and any combination of two loops
will give an excellent course. The start of the Elkington
loop offers five holes of scenic beauty and testing golf and
the 3rd on the Winwick loop is a 200-yard par 3 from a
magnificent plateau tee.**
*Ashby-Elkington: 18 holes, 6308yds, Par 72, SSS 70,
Course record 69.*
*Elkington-Winwick: 18 holes, 6250yds, Par 70, SSS 70,
Course record 69.*
*Winwick-Ashby: 18 holes, 6004yds, Par 70, SSS 69,
Course record 66.*
Club membership 700.
Visitors start time must be reserved at weekends. **Societies**
must contact in advance. **Green Fees** £15 per 18 holes (£17
weekends). **Cards** ⚏ ▦ ▦ ⚏ **Prof** Shane Rose **Course
Designer** David Croxton **Facilities** ⊗ ⵘ ⧫ ☕ ♀ ♨ 🏠 🏌
🏠 ⛳ ⛳ **Conf** Max 100 Thtr 100 Class 60 Board 30 Del
from £12 * **Location** Close to junct 1 A14 & junct 18 M1
midway between Rugby, Leicester & Northampton

....

Hotel ★★★ 64% Holiday Inn Rugby/Northampton, CRICK
☎ 0870 400 9059 88 en suite

COLLINGTREE — Map 04 SP75

Collingtree Park Windingbrook Ln NN4 0XN
☎ 01604 700000 & 701202 📠 01604 702600
e-mail: info@collingtreeparkgolf.com
Superb 18-hole resort course designed by former U.S. and British Open champion Johnny Miller. The American style course has water hazards on ten holes with a spectacular par 5 18th Island Green. The Golf Academy includes a driving range, practice holes, indoor video teaching room.

18 holes, 6776yds, Par 72, SSS 72, Course record 66.
Visitors must contact in advance & have handicap certificate. **Societies** contact in advance. **Green Fees** terms on application. **Cards** 🃏🃏🃏🃏🃏🃏 **Prof** G.Pook/H.Bareham/A.Carter **Course Designer** Johnny Miller **Facilities** ⊗ ⍫ 🔊 💺 ♀ 🏌 🏡 🍴 🏂 🚗 ✓ ₤ **Leisure** fishing, 3 hole Academy. indoor teaching room. **Location** M1-junc 15 on A508 to Northampton

Hotel ★★★★ 69% Northampton Marriott Hotel, Eagle Dr, NORTHAMPTON ☎ 01604 768700 120 en suite

CORBY — Map 04 SP88

Corby Public Stamford Rd, Weldon NN17 3JH
☎ 01536 260756 📠 01536 260756
Municipal course laid out on made-up quarry ground and open to prevailing wind. Played over by Priors Hall Club.
18 holes, 6677yds, Par 72, SSS 72.
Club membership 600.
Visitors are advised to book in advance. **Societies** must contact in advance. **Green Fees** £10.60 (£13.70 weekends). **Prof** Jeff Bradbrook **Course Designer** F Hawtree **Facilities** ⊗ ⍫ 🔊 💺 ♀ 🏌 🏡 🍴 🏂 🚗 ✓ **Location** 4m NE on A43

Inn ♦♦ Raven Hotel, Rockingham Rd, CORBY ☎ 01536 202313 17 rms (6 en suite)

DAVENTRY — Map 04 SP56

Daventry & District Norton Rd NN11 5LS
☎ 01327 702829
A hilly course with hard walking.
9 holes, 5812yds, Par 69, SSS 68, Course record 67.
Club membership 350.
Visitors no visitors before 11.30am Sun mornings. **Societies** contact the club secretary. **Green Fees** £10 per round (£15 weekends & bank holidays). **Facilities** 💺 ♀ 🏌 🏡 **Location** 0.5m East

Hotel ★★★★ 60% Hanover International Hotel & Club, Sedgemoor Way, DAVENTRY ☎ 01327 307000 138 en suite

HELLIDON LAKES
HOTEL, GOLF & COUNTRY CLUB

Situated in 220 acres of beautiful countryside, Hellidon lakes has a spectacular 27 hole championship course meandering through scenic lakes and valleys - a haven of peace and tranquillity yet only 20 minutes from the M1, M40, M6 and A14 as well as major rail links. Leisure facilities include a putting green, fishing, tennis, 4 lanes of ten pin bowling, indoor golf simulator, heated indoor swimming pool, 55 station gym and health studio with beauty therapists, sunbed, steam room and spa bath. 110 bedrooms with private bathrooms, award winning restaurant, bistro and bar.

2 NIGHT BREAKS - SOCIETY & CORPORATE DAYS - CONFERENCES - BANQUETS - WEDDINGS

www.marstonhotels.com
HELLIDON LAKES, HELLIDON, DAVENTRY, NORTHANTS NN11 6GG
★★★★ **TEL: 01327 262550**
FAX: 01327 262559

FARTHINGSTONE — Map 04 SP65

Farthingstone Hotel & Golf Course NN12 8AH
☎ 01327 361291 📠 01327 361645
e-mail: bookings@farthingstone.co.uk
A mature and challenging course set in picturesque countryside.
18 holes, 6299yds, Par 70, SSS 70, Course record 68.
Club membership 400.
Visitors must contact in advance. **Societies** must contact in advance. **Green Fees** 18 holes: £17 Mon-Thur; £20 Fri; £25 weekends after 10am. **Cards** 💳💳💳💳💳 **Prof** Greg Lunn **Course Designer** Don Donaldson **Facilities** ⊗ ⍫ 🔊 💺 ♀ 🏌 🏡 🍴 🏂 🚗 ✓ **Leisure** squash, Snooker room. **Location** W of M1 junct 16

Hotel ★★ 62% Globe Hotel, High St, WEEDON ☎ 01327 340336 15 en suite 3 annexe en suite

HELLIDON — Map 04 SP55

Hellidon Lakes Hotel & Country Club
NN11 6GG ☎ 01327 262550 📠 01327 262559
e-mail: stay@hellidon.demon.co.uk
Spectacular parkland course designed by David Snell.
18 holes, 6691yds, Par 72, SSS 72.
Club membership 500.
Visitors 18 hole course; must contact in advance & have handicap certificate at weekends. 9 hole; open to beginners. **Societies** must telephone in advance. **Green Fees** not confirmed. **Cards** 💳💳💳💳💳 **Prof** Gary Wills **Course Designer** D Snell **Facilities** ⊗ ⍫ 🔊 💺 ♀ 🏌 🏡 🍴 🏂 🚗 ✓ **Leisure** hard tennis courts, heated indoor swimming pool, fishing, solarium, gymnasium, golf simulator, ten pin bowling. **Location** 0.5m off A361 between Daventry & Banbury

continued

Hotel ★★★★ 67% Hellidon Lakes Hotel & Country Club, HELLIDON ☎ 01327 262550 70 en suite

Kettering Headlands NN15 6XA
☎ 01536 511104 📠 01536 511104
e-mail: kgc@ukgateway.net.
A very pleasant, mainly flat meadowland course with easy walking.
18 holes, 6081yds, Par 69, SSS 69, Course record 63.
Club membership 700.
Visitors welcome but with member only weekends & bank holidays. **Societies** Wed & Fri only, apply in writing. **Green Fees** £32 per day; £25 per round. **Prof** Kevin Theobald **Course Designer** Tom Morris **Facilities** ⊗ ⅏ ⅊ ☷ ⅋ ⅂ **🖰 ⅋ 𝒸 Location** S side of town centre

Hotel ★★★★ 73% Kettering Park Hotel, Kettering Parkway, KETTERING ☎ 01536 416666 119 en suite

Pytchley Golf Lodge Pytchley Ln NN14 1EY
☎ 01536 511527 📠 01536 790266
Nine hole course on which two ponds and 18 bunkers come into play. Plays well in winter with no temporary greens.
9 holes, 2574yards, Par 34, SSS 65, Course record 72.
Club membership 300.
Visitors pay and play **Societies** telephone in advance **Green Fees** £13 per 18 holes; £7 per 9 holes (£17/£9 weekends). **Prof** Peter Machin **Course Designer** Roger Griffiths Associates **Facilities** ⊗ ⅊ ⅊ ⅂ 🖰 ⅋ 𝒸 ⅂ **Location** off A14/A509 towards Kettering

Hotel ★★★★ 73% Kettering Park Hotel, Kettering Parkway, KETTERING ☎ 01536 416666 119 en suite

Brampton Heath Sandy Ln, Church Brampton
NN6 8AX ☎ 01604 843939 📠 01604 843885
e-mail: slawrence@bhgc.co.uk
Appealing to both the novice and experienced golfer, this beautiful, well drained heathland course affords panoramic views over Northampton. It plays like an inland links in the summer - fast running fairways, true rolling greens with the wind always providing a challenge. Excellent play all year round.
18 holes, 6366yds, Par 71, SSS 70, Course record 67.
Club membership 500.
Visitors advisable to book especially for weekends, may book up to 8 days in advance. **Societies** write or telephone for details. **Green Fees** £15 per round (£19 weekends & bank holidays). **Cards** 🖭 📇 📇 📇 📇 **Prof** Richard Hudson **Course Designer** D Snell **Facilities** ⊗ ⅏ ⅊ ⅊ ⅂ 🖰 ⅋ 🍴 ⅊ 𝒸 ⅂ **Conf** Max 100 Del from £11.50 * **Location**
continued

Signposted off old A50 Kingsthorpe to Welford road, 2m N of Kingsthorpe

Hotel ★★★ 69% Lime Trees Hotel, 8 Langham Place, Barrack Rd, NORTHAMPTON ☎ 01604 632188 27 en suite

Delapre Golf Complex Eagle Dr, Nene Valley Way NN4 7DU ☎ 01604 764036 📠 01604 706378
e-mail: ruth@delapre.northampton.gov.uk
Rolling parkland course, part of municipal golf complex, which includes two 9-hole, par 3 courses, pitch-and-putt and 40 bay floodlit driving-range.
The Oaks: 18 holes, 6269yds, Par 70, SSS 70, Course record 66.
Hardingstone Course: 9 holes, 2109yds, Par 32, SSS 32.
Club membership 700.
Visitors no restrictions but advance booking advised for weekends. **Societies** must book and pay full green fees 2 weeks in advance. **Green Fees** £12 per 18 holes; £8 per 9 holes (£16/£10 weekends and bank holidays). **Cards** 🖭 📇 📇 📇 **Prof** John Corby **Course Designer** John Jacobs/John Corby **Facilities** ⊗ ⅏ ⅊ ⅊ ⅂ 🖰 ⅋ 𝒸 ⅂ **Location** 3m from M1 junct 15 on A508/A45

Hotel ★★★ 64% Quality Hotel Northampton, Ashley Way, Weston Favell, NORTHAMPTON ☎ 01604 739955 31 en suite 35 annexe en suite

Kingsthorpe Kingsley Rd NN2 7BU
☎ 01604 710610 📠 01604 710610
e-mail: kingsthorpe.gc@lineone.net
A compact, undulating parkland course set within the town boundary. Not a long course but the undulating terrain provides a suitable challenge for golfers of all standards. While not a hilly course, the valley that runs through it ensures plenty of sloping lies. The 18th hole is claimed to be the longest 400yds in the county when played into wind and is amongst the finest finishing holes in the area.
18 holes, 5918yds, Par 69, SSS 69, Course record 63.
Club membership 600.
Visitors must contact in advance. With member only weekends. **Societies** must contact in advance. **Green Fees** £25 per day. **Prof** Paul Armstrong **Course Designer** Mr Alison/ H Colt **Facilities** ⊗ ⅏ ⅊ ⅊ ⅂ 🖰 ⅋ 𝒸 **Conf** Max 40 Class 80 Board 25 Banquet 60 **Location** N side of town centre on A5095 between the Racecourse and Kingsthorpe

Hotel ★★★ 64% Quality Hotel Northampton, Ashley Way, Weston Favell, NORTHAMPTON ☎ 01604 739955 31 en suite 35 annexe en suite

Northampton Harlestone NN7 4EF
☎ 01604 845155 📠 01604 820262
e-mail: golf@northamptongolfclub.co.uk
Parkland course with water in play on three holes.
18 holes, 6615yds, Par 72, SSS 72, Course record 66.
Club membership 750.
Visitors must contact in advance and have handicap certificate. With member only at weekends, no visitors on Wed. **Societies** must contact in advance. **Green Fees** £35 per day. **Cards** 🖭 📇 📇 📇 📇 **Prof** Kevin Dickens **Course Designer** Sinclair Steel **Facilities** ⊗ ⅏ ⅊ ⅊ ⅂ 🖰 𝒸 **Location** NW of town centre on A428

Hotel ★★★ 69% Lime Trees Hotel, 8 Langham Place, Barrack Rd, NORTHAMPTON ☎ 01604 632188 27 en suite

Northamptonshire County Golf Ln, Church
Brampton NN6 8AZ ☎ 01604 843025 🖹 01604 843463
e-mail: office@ncgc.fsworld.co.uk
A fine, traditional championship golf course situated on
undulating heathland with areas of gorse, heather and
extensive coniferous and deciduous woodland. A river
and a railway line pass through the course.
18 holes, 6505yds, Par 70, SSS 72, Course record 65.
Club membership 750.
Visitors restricted weekends. May not play on bank holidays.
Must contact in advance and have a handicap certificate.
Societies Wed/Thu only, must contact in advance. Green
Fees £45 per day. Prof Tim Rouse Course Designer H S
Colt Facilities ⊗ 〣 ⓑ ▆ ♀ ♨ 🛍 ⓣ 🏌 ✓ 🏌 Location
5m NW of Northampton, off A5199

Hotel ★★★ 64% Quality Hotel Northampton, Ashley Way,
Weston Favell, NORTHAMPTON ☎ 01604 739955
31 en suite 35 annexe en suite

Overstone Park Billing Ln NN6 0AP
☎ 01604 647666 🖹 01604 642635
e-mail: steph@overstonepark.co.uk
A testing parkland course, gently undulating within
panoramic views of local stately home. Excellent drainage
and fine greens make the course great all year round.
Water comes into play on three holes.
18 holes, 6602yds, Par 72, SSS 72, Course record 69.
Club membership 500.
Visitors contact in advance, only after 2pm at weekends.
Societies write or telephone. Green Fees not confirmed.
Cards 🖃 📇 🔢 🔳 Prof Brain Mudge Course
Designer Donald Steel Facilities ⊗ 〣 ⓑ ▆ ♀ ♨ 🛍 ⓣ ⟊
✓ Leisure hard tennis courts, heated indoor swimming pool,
fishing, sauna, solarium, gymnasium. Location Exit M1
junct 15, follow A45 to Billing Aquadrone turn off, course is
2m on Gt Billing Way

Hotel ★★★ 69% Lime Trees Hotel, 8 Langham Place,
Barrack Rd, NORTHAMPTON
☎ 01604 632188 27 en suite

Oundle Benefield Rd PE8 4EZ
☎ 01832 273267 (Gen Manager) 🖹 01832 273267
e-mail: office@oundlegolfclub.fsnet.co.uk
Undulating parkland course set in pleasant countryside.
Stream running through course in play on nine holes.
Small greens demand careful placement from tees and
accurate iron play.
18 holes, 6265yds, Par 72, SSS 70, Course record 68.
Club membership 600.
Visitors may not play before 9am or 10.30am Tue or
weekends unless with member. Societies must apply in
advance, weekdays only. Green Fees £25.50 per day; £18.50
per round (£35.50 per day/round weekends). Cards 🖃 📇
Prof Richard Keys Facilities ⊗ 〣 ⓑ ▆ ♀ ♨ 🛍 ⓣ ✓
Location 1m W on A427

Inn ♦♦ Raven Hotel, Rockingham Rd, CORBY
☎ 01536 202313 17 rms (6 en suite)

Staverton Park Staverton Park NN11 6JT
☎ 01327 302000
18 holes, 6661yds, Par 71, SSS 72, Course record 65.
Course Designer Cmdr John Harris Location 0.75m NE of
Staverton on A425
Telephone for further details   continued

Hotel ★★★★ 60% Hanover International Hotel & Club,
Sedgemoor Way, DAVENTRY ☎ 01327 307000
138 en suite

Rushden Kimbolton Rd, Chelveston NN9 6AN
☎ 01933 418511
Parkland course with brook running through the middle.

10 holes, 6335yds, Par 71, SSS 70, Course record 68.
Club membership 400.
Visitors may not play Wed afternoon. With member only
weekends. Societies must apply in writing. Green Fees
terms on application. Facilities ⊗ 〣 ⓑ ▆ ♀ ♨ Location
2m E of Higham Ferrers on Kimbolton Rd

Hotel ⌂ Travelodge Wellingborough, Saunders Lodge,
RUSHDEN ☎ 01933 57008 40 en suite

Wellingborough Great Harrowden Hall NN9 5AD
☎ 01933 677234 🖹 01933 679379
e-mail: info@wellingboroughgolfclub.org
An undulating parkland course with many trees.
The 514 yd 14th is a testing hole. The clubhouse is a
stately home.

18 holes, 6617yds, Par 72, SSS 72, Course record 68.
Club membership 820.
Visitors may not play at weekends & bank holidays or Tue
between 10am and 2.30pm. Societies must apply in writing.
Green Fees £40 per day; £35 per round. Prof David Clifford
Course Designer Hawtree Facilities ⊗ 〣 ⓑ ▆ ♀ ♨ ⓣ
🏌 ✓ Leisure outdoor swimming pool. Conf Max 60 Thtr
60 Class 50 Board 18 Banquet 80 Location 2m N of
Wellingborough on A509

Hotel ⌂ Travelodge Wellingborough, Saunders Lodge,
RUSHDEN ☎ 01933 57008 40 en suite

AA website: www.theAA.com

WHITTLEBURY   Map 04 SP64
Whittlebury Park Golf & Country Club
NN12 8XW ☎ 01327 858092 🖹 01327 858009
The 36 holes incorporate three loops of tournament-standard nines plus a short course. The 1905 Course is a reconstruction of the original parkland course built at the turn of the century, the Royal Whittlewood is a lakeland course playing around copses and the Grand Prix, next to Silverstone Motor Racing circuit has a strong links feel playing over gently undulating grassland with challenging lake features.
Grand Prix: 9 holes, 3339yds, Par 36, SSS 36.
Royal Whittlewood: 9 holes, 3323yds, Par 36, SSS 36.
1905: 9 holes, 3256yds, Par 36, SSS 36.
Club membership 320.
Visitors must contact in advance. **Societies** telephone 01327 858092 in advance. **Green Fees** terms on application. **Cards** ⊠ 🚗 📇 🔳 **Course Designer** Cameron Sinclair **Facilities** ⊗ 🏤 🍴 🏌 🏐 ♣ 🏪 🏁 🛥 ⚲ 🏌 **Location** A413 Buckingham Road

Hotel ★★★ 66% Buckingham Beales Hotel, Buckingham Ring Rd, BUCKINGHAM ☎ 01280 822622 70 en suite

NORTHUMBERLAND

ALLENDALE   Map 12 NY85
Allendale High Studdon, Allenheads Rd NE47 9DH
☎ 01434 683926 & 682809 🖹 01434 683668
e-mail: nostalgiaplus@supanet.com
Challenging and hilly parkland course set 1000 feet above sea level with superb views of Allendale. New club house.
9 holes, 4541yds, Par 66, SSS 62, Course record 69.
Club membership 270.
Visitors may not play Aug bank holiday until after 3pm. Welcome Sats. **Societies** must apply in writing to Secretary. **Green Fees** £10 per day. **Facilities** 🍴 🏐 **Location** 1.5m S on B6295

Hotel ★★★ 68% Beaumont Hotel, Beaumont St, HEXHAM ☎ 01434 602331 25 en suite

ALNMOUTH   Map 12 NU21
Alnmouth Foxton Hall NE66 3BE
☎ 01665 830231 🖹 01665 830922
e-mail: alnmouthgolfclub.com
Coastal course with pleasant views.

18 holes, 6429yds, Par 71, SSS 69, Course record 64.
Club membership 800.
Visitors Fri, weekends & bank holidays. Must contact in advance. **Societies** Mon-Thu only. **Green Fees** £32 per day (£38 weekends). **Cards** ⊟ 🚗 📇 🔳 📇 **Prof** Linzi Hardy
continued

Course Designer H S Colt **Facilities** ⊗ 🏤 🍴 🍴 🏐 ♣ 🏪 🏁 🛥 🌳 ⚲ 🏌 **Leisure** snooker room. **Location** 1m NE. 4m E of Alnwick

Hotel ★★★ 58% White Swan Hotel, Bondgate Within, ALNWICK ☎ 01665 602109 58 en suite

Alnmouth Village Marine Rd NE66 2RZ
☎ 01665 830370 🖹 01665 602096
e-mail: golf@alnmouth-village.fsnet.co.uk
Seaside course with part coastal view.
9 holes, 6090yds, Par 70, SSS 70, Course record 63.
Club membership 480.
Visitors may not play before 11am on competition days. **Societies** must contact in advance. **Green Fees** terms on application. **Course Designer** Mungo Park **Facilities** ⊗ 🏤 🍴 🏐 ♣ **Location** E side of village

Hotel ★★★ 58% White Swan Hotel, Bondgate Within, ALNWICK ☎ 01665 602109 58 en suite

ALNWICK   Map 12 NU11
Alnwick Swansfield Park NE66 1AB ☎ 01665 602632
e-mail: mail@alnwickgolfclub.co.uk
Parkland course offering a fair test of golfing skills.
18 holes, 6284yds, Par 70, SSS 70, Course record 66.
Club membership 400.
Visitors some restrictions on competition days. May play after 10am weekends **Societies** must contact secretary in advance. **Green Fees** £25 per day; £20 per round (£25/£20 weekends & bank holidays). **Course Designer** Rochester **Facilities** ⊗ 🏤 🍴 🍴 🏐 ♣ ⚲ **Location** From south left into Willowburn avenue. Over rdbt, 2nd left up Swansfield Park Rd, continue up hill to park gates bend left. 1st right

Hotel ★★★ 58% White Swan Hotel, Bondgate Within, ALNWICK ☎ 01665 602109 58 en suite

BAMBURGH   Map 12 NU13
Bamburgh Castle The Club House,
40 The Wynding NE69 7DE ☎ 01668 214378 (club) & 214321 (sec) 🖹 01668 214607
e-mail: bamburghcastlegolfclub@hotmail.com
Superb coastal course with excellent greens that are both fast and true, natural hazards of heather and whin bushes abound. Magnificent views of Farne Islands, Holy Island, Lindisfarne Castle, Bamburgh Castle and Cheviot Hils.
18 holes, 5621yds, Par 68, SSS 67, Course record 64.
Club membership 785.
Visitors must contact in advance. Restricted weekends, bank holidays and competition days. **Societies** apply in writing. Weekdays & Sun only. **Green Fees** £26.50 (£32.50 weekends). **Cards** ⊟ 🚗 📇 🔳 📇 **Course Designer** George Rochester **Facilities** ⊗ 🏤 🍴 🍴 🏐 ♣ 🛥 ⚲ **Location** 6m E of A1 via B1341 or B1342

Hotel ★★ 69% Lord Crewe Arms, Front St, BAMBURGH ☎ 01668 214243 18 rms (17 en suite)

BEDLINGTON   Map 12 NZ28
Bedlingtonshire Acorn Bank NE22 6AA
☎ 01670 822457 🖹 01670 823048
Meadowland/parkland course with easy walking. Under certain conditions the wind can be a distinct hazard.
18 holes, 6813yards, Par 73, SSS 73, Course record 64.
Club membership 800.
continued

Visitors may not play before 9.30am weekdays or before 10.30am weekends and bank holidays. Book with professional. **Societies** contact the Secretary in writing or telephone. **Green Fees** £24 per day, £17 per round (£30/£24 weekends). **Prof** Marcus Webb **Course Designer** Frank Pennink **Facilities** ⊗ ⫞ by prior arrangement ⯑ ⯑ ♀ ⯑ ⯑ ⯑ ⯑ ⯑ **Location** 1m SW on A1068

BELFORD   Map 12 NU13

Belford South Rd NE70 7DP
☎ 01668 213433 ▣ 01668 213919
An east coast parkland course. Crosswinds affect the 4th but the compensation is spectacular views over Holy Island.
9 holes, 3152yds, Par 72, SSS 70, Course record 72.
Club membership 200.
Visitors not before 10am Sun. **Societies** must contact in advance. **Green Fees** £15 per 18 holes; £10 per 9 holes (£18/£11 weekends & bank holidays). **Cards** ⯑ ⯑ ⯑ ⯑ ⯑ **Course Designer** Nigel Williams **Facilities** ⊗ ⫞ ⯑ ⯑ ♀ ⯑ ⯑ ⯑ ⯑ ⯑ **Location** Just off A1, midway between Alnwick & Berwick on Tweed

Hotel ★★★ 69% Blue Bell Hotel, Market Place, BELFORD ☎ 01668 213543 17 en suite

BELLINGHAM   Map 12 NY88

Bellingham Boggle Hole NE48 2DT
☎ 01434 220530 (Secretary) ▣ 01434 220160
e-mail: admin@bellinghamgolfclub.com
This highly regarded 18-hole golf course is situated between Hadrian's Wall and the Scottish Border. A rolling parkland course with many natural hazards. There is a mixture of testing par 3s, long par 5s and tricky par 4s.
18 holes, 6093yds, Par 70, SSS 70, Course record 65.
Club membership 500.
Visitors welcome all week, advisable to contact in advance as starting sheet in operation. **Societies** must contact in advance. **Green Fees** £20 per day/round (£25 per day/round weekends). **Course Designer** E Johnson/I Wilson **Facilities** ⊗ by prior arrangement ⫞ by prior arrangement ⯑ ⯑ ♀ ⯑ ⯑ ⯑ **Location** N side of village on B6320

Hotel ★★ 69% Riverdale Hall Hotel, BELLINGHAM ☎ 01434 220254 20 en suite

BERWICK-UPON-TWEED   Map 12 NT95

Berwick-upon-Tweed (Goswick) Goswick TD15 2RW ☎ 01289 387256 ▣ 01289 387334
e-mail: goswickgc@btconnect.com
Natural seaside links course, with undulating fairways, elevated tees and good greens.

continued

18 holes, 6465yds, Par 72, SSS 71, Course record 69.
Club membership 600.
Visitors must contact in advance for weekends, advisable at other times. **Societies** must telephone in advance (apply in writing Apr-Sep). **Green Fees** £32 per day; £27 per round (£42/32 weekends). **Cards** ⯑ ⯑ ⯑ ⯑ ⯑ **Prof** Paul Terras **Course Designer** James Braid **Facilities** ⊗ ⫞ ⯑ ⯑ ♀ ⯑ ⯑ ⯑ ⯑ ⯑ ⯑ **Location** 6m S off A1

Hotel ★★★ 69% Blue Bell Hotel, Market Place, BELFORD ☎ 01668 213543 17 en suite

Magdalene Fields Magdalene Fields TD15 1NE
☎ 01289 306384 & 306130 ▣ 01289 306384
e-mail: mail@magdalene-fields.co.uk
Seaside course with natural hazards formed by sea bays. All holes open to winds. Testing 8th hole over bay (par 3).
18 holes, 6407yds, Par 72, SSS 71, Course record 65.
Club membership 350.
Visitors must contact in advance for weekend play. **Societies** must contact in advance. **Green Fees** £19 per round (£21 weekends). **Cards** ⯑ ⯑ ⯑ ⯑ **Course Designer** Willie Park **Facilities** ⊗ ⫞ ⯑ ⯑ ♀ ⯑ ⯑ ⯑ ⯑ ⯑ **Location** 0.5m on E side of town centre

Hotel ★★★★ 74% Tillmouth Park Country House Hotel, CORNHILL-ON-TWEED ☎ 01890 882255 12 en suite 2 annexe en suite

BLYTH
Map 12 NZ38

Blyth New Delaval, Newsham NE24 4DB
☎ 01670 540110 (sec) & 356514 (pro) 🖹 01670 540134
e-mail: blythgc@lineone.net
Course built over old colliery. Parkland with water hazards.
18 holes, 6456yds, Par 72, SSS 71, Course record 63.
Club membership 860.
Visitors with member only after 4pm & at weekends before 2pm. May book up to 3 days in advance. **Societies** apply in writing/telephone. **Green Fees** £25 per day; £20 per round (£25 per round weekends). **Prof** Andrew Brown **Course Designer** Hamilton Stutt **Facilities** ⊗ ㋐ 🖢 🝙 ♀ ⚒ 🏌 🖹 ♂
Location 6m N of Whitley Bay

Hotel ★★★ 68% Windsor Hotel, South Pde,
WHITLEY BAY ☎ 0191 251 8888 70 en suite

CRAMLINGTON
Map 12 NZ27

Arcot Hall NE23 7QP
☎ 0191 236 2794 🖹 0191 217 0370
A wooded parkland course, reasonably flat.
18 holes, 6380yds, Par 70, SSS 70, Course record 62.
Club membership 695.
Visitors must contact in advance. May not play weekends. **Societies** must contact in advance. **Green Fees** terms on application. **Prof** John Metcalfe **Course Designer** James Braid **Facilities** ⊗ ㋖ 🖢 🝙 ♀ ⚒ 🖹 🏌 ♂ **Location** 2m SW off A1

Hotel ⬥ Innkeeper's Lodge Cramlington, Blagdon Ln,
CRAMLINGTON ☎ 01670 736111 18 en suite

EMBLETON
Map 12 NU22

Dunstanburgh Castle NE66 3XQ
☎ 01665 576562 🖹 01665 576562
e-mail: enquiries@dunstanburgh.com
Rolling links designed by James Braid, adjacent to the beautiful Embleton Bay. Historic Dunstansburgh Castle is at one end of the course and a National Trust lake and bird sanctuary at the other. Superb views.
18 holes, 6298yds, Par 70, SSS 69, Course record 69.
Club membership 385.
Visitors advisable to contact in advance at weekends and holiday periods. **Societies** must contact in advance. **Green Fees** £18 per day (£28 per day; £20 per round weekends and bank holidays). **Course Designer** James Braid **Facilities** ⊗ ㋖ 🖢 🝙 ♀ ⚒ 🖹 🏌 ♂ **Location** 7m NE of Alnwick off A1

Hotel ★★ 70% Dunstanburgh Castle Hotel, EMBLETON
☎ 01665 576111 17 en suite

FELTON
Map 12 NU10

Burgham Park NE65 8QP ☎ 01670 787898 (office)
& 787978 (pro shop) 🖹 01670 787164
PGA associates designed course, making the most of the gentle rolling landscape and with views to the sea and the Northumbrian Hills.
18 holes, 6751yards, Par 72, SSS 72, Course record 67.
Club membership 560.
Visitors no restrictions if tee times available. **Societies** contact secretary for advance booking. **Green Fees** £15 per round (£18 weekends). **Cards** 🖿 🖿 🖾 **Prof** Steve McNally **Course Designer** Andrew Mair **Facilities** ⊗ ㋖ 🖢 🝙 ♀ ⚒ 🖹 🏌 ♂ ╿ **Leisure** par 3 course. **Location** 5m N of Morpeth, 0.5m off A1

continued

Hotel ★★★ 73% Linden Hall Hotel, Health Spa & Golf Course, LONGHORSLEY ☎ 01670 500000 50 en suite

GREENHEAD
Map 12 NY66

Haltwhistle Wallend Farm CA6 7HN
☎ 016977 47367 🖹 01434 344311
Interesting course with panoramic views of Northumberland National Park. The 515yard par 5 14th hole is a real test of golf skill, played from the highest point of the course through an undulating fairway to a viciously sloping green. The 188yard par 3, now the 1st hole, played uphill, is particularly difficult playing into the prevailing west wind.
18 holes, 5522yds, Par 69, SSS 67, Course record 70.
Club membership 391.
Visitors no visitors Sun mornings. **Societies** apply in writing to: Hon Secretary, John Gilbertson, Parkhead Farmhouse, Bardon Mill, Northumberland NE47 7JS. **Green Fees** terms on application. **Facilities** ⊗ ㋖ 🖢 🝙 ♀ 🖢 **Location** N on A69 past Haltwhistle on Gilsland Road

Hotel ★★★ 🍴 Farlam Hall Hotel, BRAMPTON
☎ 016977 46234 11 en suite 1 annexe en suite

HEXHAM
Map 12 NY96

De Vere Slaley Hall, Golf Resort & Spa Slaley
NE47 OBY ☎ 01434 673154 🖹 01434 673152
e-mail: slaley.hall@devere-hotels.com
Measuring 7073yds from the championship tees, this Dave Thomas designed course incorporates forest, parkland and moorland with an abundance of lakes and streams. The challenging par 4 9th (452yds) is played over water through a narrow avenue of towering trees and dense rhododendrons. The Priestman course designed by Neil Coles is of equal length and standard as the Hunting course. Opened in spring 1999 it is situated in 280 acres on the western side of the estate, giving panoramic views over the Tyne Valley.
Hunting Course: 18 holes, 7073yds, Par 72, SSS 74, Course record 65.
Priestman Course: 18 holes, 7010yds, Par 72, SSS 72, Course record 67.
Club membership 350.
Visitors must contact in advance, times subject to availability. **Societies** apply in writing to bookings co-ordinator, small groups 8 or less may book by telephone. **Green Fees** Hunting Course: £65 per round; Priestman Course: £40 per round. **Cards** 🖿 🖿 🖿 🖿 🖾 **Prof** Gordon Robinson **Course Designer** Dave Thomas/Neil Coles **Facilities** ⊗ ㋖ 🖢 🝙 ♀ ⚒ 🖹 🏌 🛏 🐾 🥘 ♂ ╿ **Leisure** heated indoor swimming pool, fishing, sauna, solarium, gymnasium.**Conf** Max 250 Del from £45 * **Location** 8m S of Hexham off A68

Hotel ★★★★ 70% De Vere Slaley Hall, Slaley, HEXHAM
☎ 01434 673350 139 en suite

Hexham Spital Park NE46 3RZ
☎ 01434 603072 🖹 01434 601865
e-mail: hexham.golf.club@talk21.com
A very pretty well drained parkland course with interesting natural contours. Exquisite views from parts of the course, of the Tyne Valley below. As good a parkland course as any in the North of England.
18 holes, 6000yds, Par 70, SSS 68, Course record 64.
Club membership 700.

continued

Visitors advance booking advisable. **Societies** welcome weekdays, contact in advance. **Green Fees** £40 per day; £30 per round (£40 per round weekends). **Cards** 🔤 ▬ 🔤 🔤 🔤 **Prof** Martin Forster **Course Designer** Vardon/Caird **Facilities** ⊗)Ⅲ ⓑ ♥ ♀ ⚑ ⌂ ☂ ♘ **Leisure** squash. **Conf** Max 100 **Location** 1m NW on B6531

Hotel ★★★ 68% Beaumont Hotel, Beaumont St, HEXHAM ☎ 01434 602331 25 en suite

LONGHORSLEY   Map 12 NZ19

Linden Hall NE65 8XF
☎ 01670 500011 📠 01670 500001
e-mail: golf@lindenhall.co.uk
Set within the picturesque Linden Hall Estate on a mixture of mature woodland and parkland with established lakes and burns providing interesting water features to match the peaceful surroundings. This award winning golf course is a pleasure to play for all standards of golfer.

18 holes, 6846yds, Par 72, SSS 73.
Club membership 330.
Visitors must book in advance. **Societies** must be of reasonable standard of play, observe dress code & etiquette, preferably have handicap certificate. **Green Fees** £22.50 per round (£27.50 weekends). **Cards** 🔤 ▬ 🔤 🔤 🔤 **Prof** David Curry **Course Designer** Jonathan Gaunt **Facilities** ⊗)Ⅲ ⓑ ♥ ♀ ⚑ ⌂ ☂ ♘ ♘ ♘ **Leisure** hard tennis courts, heated indoor swimming pool, sauna, solarium, gymnasium.**Conf** Max 350 Board 30 Banquet 230 Del from £35 * **Location** From A1 N/S take A697 to Coldstream, approx 4m to Longhorsley, Linden Hall 0.5m past village

Hotel ★★★ 73% Linden Hall Hotel, Health Spa & Golf Course, LONGHORSLEY ☎ 01670 500000 50 en suite

MATFEN   Map 12 NZ07

Matfen Hall NE20 0RH
☎ 01661 886400 📠 01661 886055
e-mail: info@matfenhall.com
An 18-hole parkland course set in beautiful countryside with many natural and man-made hazards. The course is an enjoyable test for players of all abilities but it does incorporate challenging water features in the shape of a large lake and a fast flowing river. The dry stone wall presents a unique obstacle on several holes. The 4th, 9th, 12th and 14th holes are particularly testing par 4s, the dog legged 16th is the pick of the par 5s but Matfen's signature hole is the long par 3 17th with its narrow green teasingly sited just over the river.
18 holes, 6516yds, Par 72, SSS 71, Course record 67.
Club membership 500.

continued

Visitors contact in advance, restricted on weekends between 8-10am. **Societies** telephone for details. **Green Fees** £37.50 per day; £27.50 per round (£40/£30 weekends). **Cards** 🔤 🔤 🔤 🔤 🔤 🔤 **Prof** John Harrison **Course Designer** Mair/James/Gaunt **Facilities** ⊗)Ⅲ ⓑ ♥ ♀ ⚑ ⌂ ☂ ♘ ♘ **Leisure** 9 hole par 3 course.**Conf** Max 120 Thtr 120 Class 40 Board 30 Banquet 120 Del £32 * **Location** Just off B6318 Military road 15m W of Newcastle

Hotel ★★ 66% Angel of Corbridge, Main St, CORBRIDGE ☎ 01434 632119 5 en suite

MORPETH   Map 12 NZ28

Morpeth The Clubhouse NE61 2BT
☎ 01670 504942 📠 01670 504918
Parkland course with views of the Cheviots. Venue for 2000 County Match Play Championship.
18 holes, 6206yds, Par 71, SSS 69, Course record 65.
Club membership 700.
Visitors restricted weekends & bank holidays. Must contact in advance and have a handicap certificate. **Societies** apply in writing. **Green Fees** not confirmed. **Prof** Martin Jackson **Course Designer** Harry Vardon **Facilities** ⊗)Ⅲ ⓑ ♥ ♀ ⚑ ⌂ ♘ ♘ **Location** S side of town centre on A197

Hotel ★★★ 73% Linden Hall Hotel, Health Spa & Golf Course, LONGHORSLEY ☎ 01670 500000 50 en suite

NEWBIGGIN-BY-THE-SEA   Map 12 NZ38

Newbiggin-by-the-Sea Prospect Place NE64 6DW
☎ 01670 817344 📠 01670 520236
Seaside-links course.
18 holes, 6452yds, Par 72, SSS 71, Course record 65.
Club membership 620.
Visitors must contact professional on arrival and may not play before 10am. **Societies** must apply in writing. **Green Fees** £20 (£25 weekends and bank holidays). **Prof** Marcus Webb **Course Designer** Willie Park **Facilities** ⊗)Ⅲ ⓑ ♥ ♀ ⚑ ⌂ ☂ ♘ ♘ **Leisure** snooker. **Conf** Max 100 **Location** N side of town

Hotel ★★★ 73% Linden Hall Hotel, Health Spa & Golf Course, LONGHORSLEY ☎ 01670 500000 50 en suite

PONTELAND   Map 12 NZ17

Ponteland 53 Bell Villas NE20 9BD
☎ 01661 822689 📠 01661 860077
Open parkland course offering testing golf and good views.
18 holes, 6524yds, Par 72, SSS 71, Course record 66.
Club membership 720.
Visitors with member only Fri, weekends & bank holidays. **Societies** welcome Tue & Thu only. Must contact in advance. **Green Fees** £25 per day. **Cards** 🔤 🔤 **Prof** Alan Robson-Crosby **Course Designer** Harry Fernie **Facilities** ⊗)Ⅲ ⓑ ♥ ♀ ⚑ ⌂ ♘ **Location** 0.5m E on A696

Hotel ★★★ 66% Novotel Newcastle upon Tyne, Ponteland Rd, Kenton, NEWCASTLE UPON TYNE ☎ 0191 214 0303 126 en suite

PRUDHOE   Map 12 NZ06

Prudhoe Eastwood Park NE42 5DX
☎ 01661 832466 📠 01661 830710
Parkland course with natural hazards and easy walking along undulating fairways.
18 holes, 5812yds, Par 69, SSS 69, Course record 60.
Club membership 700.

continued

Visitors must contact in advance. Weekends after 4.30pm
Societies must contact in writing. Green Fees not confirmed.
Prof John Crawford Facilities ⊗ ⅷ ▙ ▀ ♀ ⚒ 🏠
Location E side of town centre off A695

Hotel ★★★ 70% Gibside Hotel, Front St, WHICKHAM
☎ 0191 488 9292 45 en suite

ROTHBURY   Map 12 NU00

Rothbury Old Race Course NE65 7TR
☎ 01669 620718 & 621271
Scenic, flat parkland course set alongside the River
Coquet and surrounded by Simonside hills and Cragside
Hall.
9 holes, 5681yds, Par 68, SSS 67, Course record 65.
Club membership 306.
Visitors weekends by arrangement only. Societies must
contact secretary in advance. Green Fees £11 per day (£16
weekends & bank holidays). Course Designer J Radcliffe
Facilities ▙ ▀ ♀ ⚒ Location SW side of town off B6342

Hotel ★★★ 58% White Swan Hotel, Bondgate Within,
ALNWICK ☎ 01665 602109 58 en suite

SEAHOUSES   Map 12 NU23

Seahouses Beadnell Rd NE68 7XT
☎ 01665 720794 🖹 01665 721994
e-mail: seahousesgolfclub@breathemail.net
Typical links course with many hazards, including the
famous 10th, 'Logans Loch', water hole.
18 holes, 5516yds, Par 67, SSS 67, Course record 63.
Club membership 750.
Visitors must contact in advance. Societies must contact in
advance. May not play Sun. Green Fees £18 per day (£25
weekends & bank holidays). Facilities ⊗ ⅷ ▙ ▀ ♀ ⚒ ♂
Location S side of village on B1340

Hotel ★★ 69% Bamburgh Castle Hotel, SEAHOUSES
☎ 01665 720283 20 en suite

STOCKSFIELD   Map 12 NZ06

Stocksfield New Ridley Rd NE43 7RE
☎ 01661 843041 🖹 01661 843046
e-mail: info@sgcgolf.co.uk
Challenging course: parkland (9 holes), woodland (9
holes). Some elevated greens and water hazards.
18 holes, 5978yds, Par 70, SSS 69, Course record 61.
Club membership 550.
Visitors welcome except Wed am & Sat until 4pm, unless
accompanied by a member. Societies must contact in
advance. Green Fees £35 per day; £30 per round(£35 per
round weekends and bank holidays). Prof David Mather
Course Designer Pennick Facilities ⊗ ⅷ by prior
arrangement ▙ ▀ ♀ ⚒ 🏠 ⚒ ♂ Leisure snooker. Location
Hexham to Newcastle A695,1.5malong New Ridley Rd at
Esso Station

Hotel ★★★ 68% Beaumont Hotel, Beaumont St,
HEXHAM ☎ 01434 602331 25 en suite

SWARLAND   Map 12 NU10

Swarland Hall Coast View NE65 9JG
☎ 01670 787010
Parkland course set in mature woodland. There are seven
par 4 holes in excess of 400 yards.
18 holes, 6335yds, Par 72, SSS 72.
Club membership 400.
Visitors restricted on competition days.Advance booking
advisable. Societies apply in advance. Green Fees £15 per
continued

round; £18 per day(£20/£25 weekends and bank holidays).
Cards ▨ ▨ ▨ ▨ ▨ ▨ Prof Wayne Tyrie Facilities ⊗
ⅷ ▙ ▀ ♀ ⚒ 🏠 ⚒ ♂ 🏠 ▙ ♂ Location Approx 1m W
of A1

Hotel ★★★ 73% Linden Hall Hotel, Health Spa & Golf
Course, LONGHORSLEY ☎ 01670 500000 50 en suite

WARKWORTH   Map 12 NU20

Warkworth The Links NE65 0SW ☎ 01665 711596
Seaside links course, with good views and alternative tees
for the back nine. The first hole is a very testing par 3 and
skill is required to avoid the out of bounds. The course is
not friendly to 'slicers' with heather and bracken on the
eastern side on the way out. The fearsome Killiecrankie
Gorge is in play four times during the 18 holes, especially
challenging when a north wind is blowing.
9 holes, 5870yds, Par 70, SSS 68, Course record 66.
Club membership 470.
Visitors welcome except Tue & Sat. Societies must contact
in advance. Green Fees not confirmed. Course Designer T
Morris Facilities ⊗ ▙ ▀ ♀ ⚒ Location 0.5m E of village
off A1068

Hotel ★★★ 58% White Swan Hotel, Bondgate Within,
ALNWICK ☎ 01665 602109 58 en suite

WOOLER   Map 12 NT92

Wooler Dod Law, Doddington NE71 6EA
☎ 01668 282135
Hilltop, moorland course with spectacular views over the
Glendale valley. Nine greens played from 18 tees. A very
challenging course when windy with one par 5 of 580
yards. The course is much under used during the week so
is always available.
9 holes, 6411yds, Par 72, SSS 71, Course record 71.
Club membership 300.
Visitors normally no restrictions. Societies by prior
arrangement with secretary. Green Fees £10 per day(£15
weekends and bank holidays). Facilities ⊗ by prior
arrangement ⅷ by prior arrangement ▙ by prior arrangement
▀ ♀ ⚒ ♂ 🏠 ♂ Location At Doddington on B6525
Wooler/Berwick Rd

Hotel ★★★ 69% Blue Bell Hotel, Market Place,
BELFORD ☎ 01668 213543 17 en suite

NOTTINGHAMSHIRE

CALVERTON   Map 08 SK64

Ramsdale Park Golf Centre Oxton Rd NG14 6NU
☎ 0115 965 5600 🖹 0115 965 4105
The High course is a challenging and comprehensive test
for any standard of golf. A relatively flat front nine is
followed by an undulating back nine that is renowned as
one of the best 9 holes of golf in the county. The Low
course is an 18 hole par 3 course gaining a reputation as
one of the best in the country.
High Course: 18 holes, 6546yds, Par 71, SSS 71,
Course record 70.
Low Course: 18 holes, 2844yds, Par 54, SSS 54.
Club membership 400.
Visitors may book up to 7 days in advance. Societies
welcome midweek, apply in writing or telephone. Green
Fees terms on application. Cards ▨ ▨ ▨ ▨ ▨ Prof Robert
Macey Course Designer Hawtree Facilities ⊗ ⅷ ▙ ▀ ♀
continued

🏔🏕⛳🎿🚵 ✂ (**Conf** Max 60 Thtr 30 Banquet 60
Location 8m NE of Nottingham, off B6386

Hotel ★★★ 67% Westminster Hotel, 312 Mansfield Rd,
Carrington, NOTTINGHAM
☎ 0115 955 5000 72 en suite

Springwater Moor Ln NG14 6FZ
☎ 0115 965 2129 & 965 4946 📠 0115 965 4946
e-mail: mooregroupltd@aol.com
**This attractive golf course, set in rolling countryside close
to Nottingham, offers an interesting and challenging
game of golf to players of all handicaps. The 18th hole is
particularly noteworthy.**
18 holes, 6262yds, Par 71, SSS 71, Course record 68.
Club membership 440.
Visitors five day advance booking by telephone, booking
available all week subject to competitions and Society/
Corporate reservations. **Societies** apply in writing or
telephone for Society Pack. **Green Fees** £15 per round (£20
weekends & bank holidays); £25 per day. **Cards** 💳 💳 💳
💳 💳 🅿 **Prof** Paul Drew **Course Designer** Neil
Footitty/Paul Wharmsby **Facilities** ⊗ 🍴 🏌 🏕 🏔 🏕
🚵 ✂ (**Leisure** short game academy.**Conf** Max 80 Thtr
80 Class 40 Board 30 Banquet 80 **Location** 600yds on left
from Moor Lane turning to Calverton off A6097, signposted

Hotel ★★★ 67% Westminster Hotel, 312 Mansfield Rd,
Carrington, NOTTINGHAM
☎ 0115 955 5000 72 en suite

EAST LEAKE   Map 08 SK52

Rushcliffe Stocking Ln LE12 5RL
☎ 01509 852959 📠 01509 852688
e-mail: rushcliffegc@netscapeonline.co.uk
Hilly, tree-lined and picturesque parkland course.
18 holes, 6013yds, Par 70, SSS 69, Course record 63.
Club membership 700.
Visitors welcome but may not play Tue and restricted
weekends & bank holidays 9.30-11am & 3-4.30pm. **Societies**
must apply in advance. **Green Fees** £30 per day; £25 per
round. **Prof** Chris Hall **Facilities** ⊗ 🍴 🏔 🏕 🏌 🏕 ✂

Hotel ★★★ 73% Best Western Yew Lodge Hotel,
Packington Hill, Kegworth,
☎ 01509 672518 63 en suite

HUCKNALL   Map 08 SK54

Leen Valley Golf Centre Wigwam Ln NG15 7TA
☎ 0115 964 2037 📠 0115 964 2724
e-mail: leen-jackbarker@btinternet.com
**An interesting and challenging parkland course,
featuring several lakes, the River Leen and the Baker
Brook. Suitable for all standards of golfers.**
18 holes, 6233yds, Par 72, SSS 70.
Club membership 750.
Visitors tee times can be booked in advance and are
advisable for Fri, Sat & Sun. **Societies** by arrangement.
Green Fees not confirmed. **Cards** 💳 💳 💳 💳 🅿 **Prof**
John Lines **Course Designer** Tom Hodgetts **Facilities** ⊗ 🍴
🏔 🏕 🏌 🏕 🚵 ✂ **Leisure** 9 hole par 3 course.
Location 0.5m from Hucknall Town Centre, follow signs for
railway station and turn right into Wigwam Lane

Hotel ★★★ 65% Bestwood Lodge, Bestwood Country
Park, Arnold, NOTTINGHAM
☎ 0115 920 3011 39 en suite

KEYWORTH   Map 08 SK63

Stanton on the Wolds Golf Rd, Stanton-on-the-
Wolds NG12 5BH
☎ 0115 937 4885 & 937 2044 📠 0115 937 4885
**Parkland course, fairly flat with stream running through
four holes.**
18 holes, 6437yds, Par 73, SSS 71, Course record 67.
Club membership 705.
Visitors must contact in advance. Must play with member at
weekends and may not play Tue. **Societies** must apply in
writing. **Green Fees** £31 per day; £23 per round. **Prof** Nick
Hernon **Course Designer** Tom Williamson **Facilities** ⊗ 🍴
by prior arrangement 🏔 🏕 🏌 🏕 ✂ **Location** E side of
village, 9m S of Nottingham off A606

Hotel ★★ 66% Rufford Hotel, 53 Melton Rd, West
Bridgford, NOTTINGHAM ☎ 0115 981 4202 34 en suite

KIRKBY IN ASHFIELD   Map 08 SK55

Notts Derby Rd NG17 7QR
☎ 01623 753225 📠 01623 753655
e-mail: nottsgolfclub@hollinwell.fsnet.co.uk
Undulating heathland Championship course.
18 holes, 7098yds, Par 72, SSS 75, Course record 64.
Club membership 450.
Visitors must contact in advance & have handicap
certificate. With member only weekends & bank holidays.
Societies must apply in advance. **Green Fees** £75 per day;
£50 per round. **Cards** 💳 💳 💳 💳 🅿 **Prof** Alasdair
Thomas **Course Designer** Willie Park **Facilities** ⊗ 🍴 🏔
🏕 🏌 🏕 🚵 🚵 ✂ (**Conf** Max 30 **Location** 2m
SE of Mansfield off A611

Hotel ★★★★ 70% Renaissance Derby/Nottingham
Hotel, Carter Ln East, SOUTH NORMANTON
☎ 01773 812000 158 en suite

MANSFIELD   Map 08 SK56

Sherwood Forest Eakring Rd NG18 3EW
☎ 01623 626689 & 627403 📠 01623 420412
e-mail: sherwood@forest43.freeserve.co.uk
**As the name suggests, the Forest is the main feature of
this natural heathland course with its heather, silver
birch and pine trees. The homeward nine holes are
particularly testing. The 11th to the 14th are notable
par 4 holes on this well-bunkered course designed by
the great James Braid.**
18 holes, 6849yds, Par 71, SSS 74, Course record 67.
Club membership 750.
Visitors weekdays only by prior arrangement with the
golf manager. **Societies** by arrangement with the golf
manager. **Green Fees** terms on application. **Prof** Ken Hall
Course Designer W S Colt/James Braid **Facilities** ⊗ 🍴
🏔 🏕 🏌 🏕 🚵 ✂ **Leisure** snooker. **Location** E of
Mansfield

Hotel ★★ 66% Pine Lodge Hotel, 281-283 Nottingham
Rd, MANSFIELD ☎ 01623 622308 20 en suite

MANSFIELD WOODHOUSE   Map 08 SK56

Mansfield Woodhouse Leeming Ln North NG19 9EU
☎ 01623 623521
9 holes, 2446yds, Par 68, SSS 64.
Course Designer A Highfield & F Horfman **Location** N side
of town centre off A60
Telephone for further details

continued

Hotel ★★ 66% Pine Lodge Hotel, 281-283 Nottingham Rd, MANSFIELD ☎ 01623 622308 20 en suite

NEWARK-ON-TRENT   Map 08 SK75

Newark Coddington NG24 2QX
☎ 01636 626282 ▤ 01636 626497
Wooded, parkland course in secluded situation with easy walking.
18 holes, 6444yds, Par 71, SSS 71, Course record 66.
Club membership 600.
Visitors must contact in advance and have handicap certificate. May not play Tue (Ladies Day). **Societies** must contact in advance. **Green Fees** terms on application. **Prof** P A Lockley **Course Designer** T Williamson **Facilities** ⊗ ⫟ ⓵ ⌂ ☜ 𝒸 **Leisure** snooker. **Location** 4m E of Newark on Sleaford Road(A17)

Hotel ★★ 74% The Grange Hotel, 73 London Rd, NEWARK ☎ 01636 703399 10 en suite 5 annexe en suite

NOTTINGHAM   Map 08 SK53

Beeston Fields Old Dr, Wollaton Rd, Beeston NG9 3DD ☎ 0115 925 7062 ▤ 0115 925 4280
e-mail: beestonfieldsgolfclub@supanet.com
Parkland course with sandy subsoil and wide, tree-lined fairways. The par 3, 14th has elevated tee and small bunker-guarded green.

18 holes, 6402yds, Par 71, SSS 71, Course record 64.
Club membership 600.
Visitors must contact professional on 0115 922 0872 for availability. **Societies** must apply in advance. **Green Fees** £26 per round (£36 weekends). **Prof** Alun Wardle **Course Designer** Tom Williamson **Facilities** ⊗ ⫟ by prior arrangement ⓵ ☜ 𝒸 ⌂ ☜ 𝒸 **Location** 400mtrs SW off A52 Nottingham/Derby road

Hotel ★★★ 65% Holiday Inn Derby/Nottingham, Bostocks Ln, SANDIACRE ☎ 0870 400 9062 93 en suite

Bramcote Hills Thoresby Rd, off Derby Rd, Bramcote NG9 3EP ☎ 0115 928 1880
A pay and play, 18-hole par 3 course, a great challenge.
18 holes, 1500yds, Par 54.
Visitors no restrictions. **Societies** telephone in advance. **Green Fees** terms on application. **Facilities** ☜ ⫟ **Location** Off A52 Derby rd

Hotel ★★★ 63% Holiday Inn Nottingham City, St James's St, NOTTINGHAM ☎ 0870 400 9061 160 en suite

Bulwell Forest Hucknall Rd, Bulwell NG6 9LQ
☎ 0115 976 3172 (pro shop) & 977 0576 (club)
▤ 0115 976 3172
Municipal heathland course with many natural hazards.
continued

Very tight fairways and subject to wind. Five challenging par 3s. Excellent drainage.
18 holes, 5616yds, Par 68, SSS 67, Course record 62.
Club membership 350.
Visitors restricted weekends. Contact pro shop 24 hours in advance. **Societies** must apply in advance. **Green Fees** £11 per round (£13 weekends & bank holidays). **Cards** ▦ ▦ 🂠 ▦ ▦ 🂠 **Prof** Lee Rawlings **Facilities** ⊗ ⓵ ☜ ♀ ⌂ ☜ 𝒸 **Leisure** hard tennis courts. **Location** 3m from junct 26 on M1. 4m NW of city centre on A611

Hotel ★★★ 65% Nottingham Gateway, Nuthall Rd, Cinderhill, NOTTINGHAM ☎ 0115 979 4949 107 en suite

Chilwell Manor Meadow Ln, Chilwell NG9 5AE
☎ 0115 925 8958 ▤ 0115 922 0575
e-mail: chilwellmanorgolfclub@barbox.net
Flat parkland course.
18 holes, 6255yds, Par 70, SSS 71, Course record 66.
Club membership 750.
Visitors with member only weekends. Must contact in advance and have a handicap certificate. **Societies** welcome Mon, must apply in advance. **Green Fees** £20 per round/day. **Cards** ▦ **Prof** Paul Wilson **Course Designer** Tom Williamson **Facilities** ⊗ ⫟ ⓵ ☜ ♀ ⌂ 𝒸 **Location** 4m SW on A6005

Hotel ★★ 64% Europa Hotel, 20-22 Derby Rd, LONG EATON ☎ 0115 972 8481 15 en suite

Edwalton Municipal Wellin Ln, Edwalton NG12 4AS
☎ 0115 923 4775
Gently sloping, 9-hole parkland course. Also 9-hole par 3 and large practice ground.
9 holes, 3336yds, Par 72, SSS 72, Course record 71.
Club membership 900.
Visitors booking system in operation. **Societies** prior booking necessary. **Green Fees** not confirmed. **Cards** ▦ ▦ ▦ 🂠 **Prof** John Staples **Facilities** ⊗ ☜ ☜ ♀ ⌂ ☜ 𝒸 **Location** S of Nottingham, off A606

Hotel ★★ 66% Rufford Hotel, 53 Melton Rd, West Bridgford, NOTTINGHAM ☎ 0115 981 4202 34 en suite

Mapperley Central Av, Plains Rd, Mapperley NG3 5RH
☎ 0115 955 6672 ▤ 0115 955 6670
Hilly meadowland course but with easy walking.
18 holes, 6303yds, Par 71, SSS 70, Course record 68.
Club membership 650.
Visitors must contact in advance. May not play Tue or Sat. **Societies** must telephone in advance. **Green Fees** terms on application. **Course Designer** John Mason **Facilities** ⊗ ⫟ ⓵ ☜ ♀ ⌂ ☜ 🐾 𝒸 **Leisure** pool room. **Location** 3m NE of city centre off B684

Hotel ★★★ 63% Holiday Inn Nottingham City, St James's St, NOTTINGHAM ☎ 0870 400 9061 160 en suite

Nottingham City Lawton Dr, Bulwell NG6 8BL
☎ 0115 927 6916 & 927 2767 ▤ 0115 927 6916
A pleasant municipal parkland course on the city outskirts.
18 holes, 6218yds, Par 69, SSS 70, Course record 65.
Club membership 425.
Visitors restricted Sat 7am-3pm. Contact professional in advance. **Societies** welcome, contact professional. **Green Fees** terms on appliaction. **Cards** ▦ ▦ ▦ 🂠 ▦ ▦ 🂠 **Prof** Cyril Jepson **Course Designer** H Braid **Facilities** ⊗ ⫟ ⓵ ☜ ♀ ⌂ ☜ 𝒸 **Location** 4m NW of city centre off A6002
continued

Hotel ★★★ 65% Nottingham Gateway, Nuthall Rd,
Cinderhill, NOTTINGHAM ☎ 0115 979 4949 107 en suite

Wollaton Park Limetree Av, Wollaton Park
NG8 1BT ☎ 0115 978 7574 ▤ 0115 970 0736
e-mail: wollatonparkgc@aol.com
A championship parkland course on slightly
undulating land set in historic deer park. Fine views of
16th century Wollaton Hall.
18 holes, 6445yds, Par 71, SSS 71, Course record 64.
Club membership 700.
Visitors may not play Wed or competition days. Societies
must apply in advance. Green Fees £39 per day; £28.50
per round (£44.50/£33.50 weekends). Prof John Lower
Course Designer W Williamson Facilities ⊗ ⟩⟨ ᴸ ⬛ ⬤ ♀
⛷ 🏠 ⛳ ♂ Location 2.5m W of city centre off
Nottingham ring road at junct with A52

Hotel ★★★ 60% Swans Hotel & Restaurant, 84-90
Radcliffe Rd, West Bridgford, NOTTINGHAM
☎ 0115 981 4042 30 en suite

OLLERTON   Map 08 SK66

Rufford Park Golf & Country Club Rufford Ln,
Rufford NG22 9DG ☎ 01623 825253 ▤ 01623 825254
e-mail: enquiries@ruffordpark.co.uk
Set in the heart of Sherwood Forest, Rufford Park is
noted for its pictuesque 18 holes with its especially
challenging par 3s. From the unique 175yard par 3 17th
over water to the riverside 641yard 13th, the course
offers everything the golfer needs from beginner to
professional.
Rufford Park Golf Centre: 18 holes, 6286yds, Par 70, SSS
70, Course record 67.
Club membership 650.
Visitors booking recommended. Societies society packages
on request, need to booked in advance. Green Fees terms on
application. Cards ▦ ▬▬ ▩ ▩ ▩ Prof John
Vaughan/James Thompson Course Designer David
Hemstock Facilities ⊗ ⟩⟨ ᴸ ⬛ ♀ ⛷ 🏠 ⛳ ♂ ⛳ Conf
Max 200 Board 20 Banquet 120 Location S Of Ollerton off
A614. Take the 'Rufford Mill' turn

Hotel ★★★ 67% Clumber Park Hotel, Clumber Park,
WORKSOP ☎ 01623 835333 48 en suite

OXTON   Map 08 SK65

Oakmere Park Oaks Ln NG25 0RH
☎ 0115 965 3545 ▤ 0115 965 5628
e-mail: oakmereenquiries@oakmerepark.co.uk
Set in rolling parkland in the heart of picturesque Robin
Hood country. The par 4 (16th) and par 5 (1st) are
notable. Twenty-bay floodlit driving range.
Admirals: 18 holes, 6617yds, Par 72, SSS 72,
Course record 68.
Commanders: 9 holes, 6407yds, Par 72, SSS 72.
Club membership 900.
Visitors correct golf attire required, please book for
weekends. Societies please apply in writing or telephone.
Green Fees Admirals: £18 per round (£24 weekends).
Commanders: £10 per round (£14 weekends). Cards ▦ ▬
▬▬ ▩ ▩ Prof Daryl St-John Jones Course Designer Frank
Pennick Facilities ⊗ ⟩⟨ ᴸ ⬛ ♀ ⛷ 🏠 ⛳ ♦ ⛳ Conf
Max 60 Location 7m NE from Nottingham on A614

Hotel ★★★ 67% Westminster Hotel, 312 Mansfield Rd,
Carrington, NOTTINGHAM ☎ 0115 955 5000 72 en suite

RADCLIFFE-ON-TRENT   Map 08 SK63

Cotgrave Place Golf Club Stragglethorpe, Nr
Cotgrave Village NG12 3HB
☎ 0115 933 3344 ▤ 0115 933 4567
e-mail: cotgrave@americangolf.com
The course now offers 36 holes of championship golf. The
front nine of the Open Course are placed around a
beautiful lake, man made ponds and the Grantham
Canal. The back nine is set in magnificent parkland with
mature trees and wide fairways. Masters has an opening
nine set amongst hedgerows and coppices. The huge
greens with their interesting shapes are a particularly
challenging test of nerve. The par 5, 17th hole is one of
the toughest in the country.

Open course: 18 holes, 6303yds, Par 71, SSS 70.
Masters course: 18 holes, 5887yds, Par 69, SSS 68.
Club membership 750.
Visitors must contact, can book 1 week in advance. Societies
telephone in advance. Green Fees terms on application.
Cards ▦ ▦ ▬▬ ▩ Prof Robert Smith Course
Designer Peter Aliss Facilities ⊗ ⟩⟨ ᴸ ⬛ ♀ ⛷ 🏠 ▶ ⛳
♂ ⛳ Conf Max 200 Thtr 200 Class 90 Board 30 Banquet
150 Del £14 to £25 * Location Off A52, 6 miles from
Nottingham

Hotel ★★★ ⚑ 72% Langar Hall, LANGAR
☎ 01949 860559 12 en suite

Radcliffe-on-Trent Dewberry Ln, Cropwell Rd
NG12 2JH ☎ 0115 933 3000 ▤ 0115 911 6991
e-mail: les.rotgc@talk21.com
Fairly flat, parkland course with three good finishing
holes: 16th (427 yds) par 4; 17th (180 yds) through
spinney, par 3; 18th (331 yds) dog-leg par 4. Excellent
views.
18 holes, 6381yds, Par 70, SSS 71, Course record 64.
Club membership 670.
Visitors must contact in advance, societies only on Wed.
Societies welcome Wed. Must contact in advance. Green
Fees £23 per day (£28 weekends and bank holidays). Prof
Craig George Course Designer Tom Williamson Facilities
⊗ ⟩⟨ ᴸ ⬛ ♀ ⛷ 🏠 ⛳ ♦ ♂ Location Take the A52 to
Nottingham, turn L at 2nd set of traffic lights, 400yds on left

Hotel ★★★ 60% Swans Hotel & Restaurant, 84-90
Radcliffe Rd, West Bridgford, NOTTINGHAM
☎ 0115 981 4042 30 en suite

RETFORD   Map 08 SK78

Retford Brecks Rd, Ordsall DN22 7UA ☎ 01777 860682
(Secretary) & 703733 (Pro) ▤ 01777 710412
A wooded, parkland course.
18 holes, 6409yds, Par 72, SSS 72, Course record 67.
Club membership 700.   continued

Visitors advisable to contact in advance, with member only at weekends and holidays. **Societies** apply in writing or telephone. Not welcome Tue morning or bank holidays, limited availability weekends. **Green Fees** not confirmed. **Prof** Craig Morris **Course Designer** Tom Williamson **Facilities** ⊗ ⵏ ⵎ ⵏ ♀ ⵏ 🖼 🍴 ⵏ ⵏ ⵏ **Location** 1.5m S A620, between Worksop & Gainsborough

Hotel ★★★ 65% West Retford Hotel, 24 North Rd, RETFORD ☎ 01777 706333 62 annexe en suite

RUDDINGTON   Map 08 SK53

Ruddington Grange Wilford Rd NG11 6NB
☎ 0115 984 6141 📠 0115 9405165
e-mail: info@ruddingtongrange.com
Undulating parkland course with water hazards on 12 holes.
18 holes, 6543yds, Par 72, SSS 72, Course record 69.
Club membership 650.
Visitors a handicap certificate is required, tee time must be booked in advance. Play may be restricted Sat & Wed mornings. **Societies** must contact in advance. **Green Fees** not confirmed. **Prof** Robert Simpson **Course Designer** E MacAusland **Facilities** ⊗ ⵏ ⵎ ⵏ ♀ ⵏ 🖼 ⵏ ⵏ **Location** 5m S of Nottingham, A60 to Ruddington

Hotel ★★★ 60% Swans Hotel & Restaurant, 84-90 Radcliffe Rd, West Bridgford, NOTTINGHAM ☎ 0115 981 4042 30 en suite

SERLBY   Map 08 SK68

Serlby Park DN10 6BA ☎ 01777 818268
Parkland course.
11 holes, 5325yds, Par 66, SSS 66, Course record 63.
Club membership 250.
Visitors must be introduced by and play with member. **Societies** apply in writing before 31 Dec for following year. **Green Fees** terms on application. **Course Designer** Viscount Galway **Facilities** ⊗ ⵏ ⵎ ⵏ ♀ ⵏ **Location** E side of village off A638

Hotel ★★★ 70% Charnwood Hotel, Sheffield Rd, BLYTH ☎ 01909 591610 34 en suite

SUTTON IN ASHFIELD   Map 08 SK45

Coxmoor Coxmoor Rd NG17 5LF
☎ 01623 557359 📠 01623 557359
e-mail: coxmoor@freeuk.com
Undulating moorland/heathland course with easy walking and excellent views. The clubhouse is traditional with a well-equipped games room. The course lies adjacent to Forestry Commission land over which there are several footpaths and extensive views.
18 holes, 6589yds, Par 73, SSS 72, Course record 65.
Club membership 700.
Visitors must play with member weekends & bank holidays. Must contact in advance. **Societies** must apply in advance. **Green Fees** £37 per 18 holes; £48 per day. **Cards** 🖿 🖿 🖿 ⵏ ⵏ **Prof** David Ridley **Facilities** ⊗ ⵏ ⵎ ⵏ ♀ ⵏ 🖼 ⵏ **Leisure** snooker. **Location** 2m SE off A611. 4m from junct 27 on M1

Hotel ★★★★ 70% Renaissance Derby/Nottingham Hotel, Carter Ln East, SOUTH NORMANTON ☎ 01773 812000 158 en suite

WORKSOP   Map 08 SK57

Bondhay Golf & Country Club Bondhay Ln, Whitwell S80 3EH ☎ 01909 723608 📠 01909 720226
The wind usually plays quite an active role in making this pleasantly undulating course testing. Signatures holes are the 10th which requires a second shot over water into a basin of trees; the 11th comes back over the same expanse of water and requires a mid to short iron to a long, narrow green; the 18th is a par 5 with a lake right in lay up distance - the dilemma is whether to lay up short or go for the carry. The par 3s are generally island-like in design, requiring accuracy to avoid the protective bunker features.
Devonshire Course: 18 holes, 6705yds, Par 72, SSS 71, Course record 67.
Family Course: 9 holes, 1118yds, Par 27, Course record 24.
Club membership 400.
Visitors must contact in advance. **Societies** must telephone in advance. **Green Fees** not confirmed. **Cards** 🖿 🖿 🖿 **Prof** Michael Ramsden **Course Designer** Donald Steel **Facilities** ⊗ ⵏ ⵎ ⵏ ♀ ⵏ 🖼 ⵏ ⵏ ⵏ **Leisure** fishing. **Location** 5m W of Worksop, off A619

Hotel ★★★ 64% Sitwell Arms Hotel, Station Rd, RENISHAW ☎ 01246 435226 30 en suite

College Pines Worksop College Dr S80 3AP
☎ 01909 501431 📠 01909 481227
This course was opened in 1994 and the par 73 layout covers 150 acres of well-drained land with heathland characteristics. It is club policy to remain open on full tees and greens all year round.
18 holes, 6716yards, Par 73, SSS 72, Course record 67.
Club membership 500.
Visitors welcome by appointment. **Societies** write/telephone in advance. Deposit required to secure booking. **Green Fees** £20 per day; £12 per round (£30/£18 weekends and bank holidays). **Prof** Charles Snell **Course Designer** David Snell **Facilities** ⊗ ⵏ ⵎ ⵏ ♀ ⵏ 🖼 ⵏ ⵏ ⵏ **Location** S of Worksop, on B6034 Edwinstowe road

Hotel ★★★ 67% Clumber Park Hotel, Clumber Park, WORKSOP ☎ 01623 835333 48 en suite

Kilton Forest Blyth Rd S81 0TL ☎ 01909 486563
Slightly undulating, parkland course on the north edge of Sherwood Forest. Includes three ponds. Excellent conditions all the year round.
18 holes, 6424yds, Par 72, SSS 71, Course record 67.
Club membership 320.
Visitors must contact in advance. May not play at weekends before 10am. **Societies** must contact in advance. **Green Fees** £9 per 18 holes(£12.40 weekends). **Prof** Stuart Betteridge **Facilities** ⊗ ⵏ ⵎ ⵏ ♀ ⵏ 🖼 ⵏ **Leisure** bowling. **Location** 1m NE of town centre on B6045

Hotel ★★★ 66% Lion Hotel, 112 Bridge St, WORKSOP ☎ 01909 477925 32 en suite

Lindrick Lindrick Common S81 8BH
☎ 01909 475282 📠 01909 488685
Heathland course with some trees and masses of gorse.
18 holes, 6486yds, Par 71, SSS 71, Course record 64.
Club membership 510.
Visitors must contact in advance. Restricted Tue &

continued

weekends. Handicap certificate required. **Societies** welcome except Tue (am) & weekends by prior arrangement with the Secretary. **Green Fees** terms on application. **Cards** 🔲 🔲 🔲 🔲 🔲 🔲 🔲 **Prof** John R King **Facilities** ⊗ ⊐⊩ ⓛ ⚏ ♀ ♨ 🏠 ♂ **Leisure** buggies for disabled only. **Location** 4m NW of Worksop on A57

Hotel ★★★ 66% Lion Hotel, 112 Bridge St, WORKSOP ☎ 01909 477925 32 en suite

Worksop Windmill Ln S80 2SQ
☎ 01909 472696 & 477731 📄 01909 477731
Adjacent to Clumber Park this course has a heathland-type terrain, with gorse, broom, oak and birch trees. Fast, true greens, dry all year round.
18 holes, 6660yds, Par 72, SSS 73.
Club membership 600.
Visitors by arrangement with professional tel: 01909 477732. **Societies** must apply in advance. **Green Fees** £32 per 18 holes;£40 per day(£40 per round weekends). **Prof** C Weatherhead **Course Designer** Tom williamson **Facilities** ⊗ ⊐⊩ ⓛ ⚏ ♀ ♨ 🏠 🦌 ♂ **Leisure** snooker. **Location** Off A57 Ringroad, B6034 to Edwinstowe

Hotel ★★★ 67% Clumber Park Hotel, Clumber Park, WORKSOP ☎ 01623 835333 48 en suite

OXFORDSHIRE

ABINGDON   Map 04 SU49

Drayton Park Steventon Rd, Drayton Village OX14
4LA ☎ 01235 550607 (Pro Shop) & 528989 (Secretary) 📄 01235 525731
Set in the heart of the Oxfordshire countryside, an 18-hole parkland course designed by Hawtree. Five lakes and sand-based greens.
18 holes, 5500yds, Par 67, SSS 67.
Club membership 500.
Visitors may phone to book, must have golf shoes, no jeans or tracksuits. **Societies** contact in advance. **Green Fees** not confirmed. **Prof** Martin Morbey **Course Designer** Hawtree **Facilities** ⊗ ⊐⊩ ⓛ ⚏ ♀ ♨ 🏠 🌾 🦌 ♂ ₵ **Leisure** 9 hole par 3 course. **Location** Between Oxford & Newbury,off A34 at Didcot

Hotel ★★★ 66% The Upper Reaches, Thames St, ABINGDON ☎ 0870 400 8101 31 en suite

BANBURY   Map 04 SP44

Rye Hill Milcombe OX15 4RU
☎ 01295 721818 📄 01295 720089
Well drained course features wide fairways, large undulating greens, water hazards on the 10th, and fine views of the surrounding countryside.
18 holes, 6919yds, Par 72, SSS 73, Course record 64.
Club membership 400.
Visitors must book in advance, especially at weekends. May not play Sat before 11am. **Societies** telephone for details of Packages available. **Green Fees** £20 per round (£25 weekends/bank holidays/Christmas week). **Cards** 🔲 🔲 🔲 🔲 **Prof** Tony Pennock **Facilities** ⊗ ⊐⊩ ⓛ ⚏ ♀ ♨ 🏠 🌾 🦌 ♂ **Leisure** fishing, 3 hole par 3 academy. **Conf** Max 200 Banquet 200 **Location** M40 junct 11, take A361 towards Chipping Norton, signed 1m out of Bloxham

Hotel ★★★ 70% Banbury House, Oxford Rd, BANBURY ☎ 01295 259361 63 en suite

BURFORD   Map 04 SP21

Burford Swindon Rd OX18 4JG
☎ 01993 822583 📄 01993 822801
Parkland with mature, treelined fairways and high quality greens.
18 holes, 6432yds, Par 71, SSS 71, Course record 64.
Club membership 750.
Visitors must contact in advance. May not play weekends. **Societies** apply in writing. **Green Fees** £36 per day. **Prof** Michael Ridge **Course Designer** John H Turner **Facilities** ⊗ ⊐⊩ ⓛ ⚏ ♀ ♨ 🏠 🌾 ♂ **Location** 0.5m S off A361

Hotel ★★ 65% Golden Pheasant Hotel, 91 High St, BURFORD ☎ 01993 823223 12 rms (11 en suite)

CHESTERTON   Map 04 SP52

Bicester Golf & Country Club OX26 1TE
☎ 01869 241204 📄 01869 240754
e-mail: bicestergolf@ukonline.co.uk
Recently reconstructed, the course has several lakes and sculptured greens. The 13th and 18th holes require shots of a very high standard.
18 holes, 6600yds, Par 71, SSS 70, Course record 68.
Club membership 700.
Visitors may pre-book up to 7 days ahead. **Societies** by appointment and in advance **Green Fees** terms on application. **Cards** 🔲 🔲 🔲 🔲 🔲 **Prof** J Goodman **Course Designer** R Stagg **Facilities** ⊗ ⊐⊩ ⓛ ⚏ ♀ ♨ 🏠 🦌 ♂ **Conf** Max 200 Thtr 200 Class 120 Board 100 Banquet 160 **Location** 0.5m W off A4095, 1m E of B430 at Weston-on-the-Green

Hotel ★★ 70% Jersey Arms Hotel, BICESTER ☎ 01869 343234 & 343505 📄 01869 343565 6 en suite 14 annexe en suite

CHIPPING NORTON   Map 04 SP32

Chipping Norton Southcombe OX7 5QH
☎ 01608 642383 📄 01608 645422
e-mail: chipping.nortongc@virgin.net
Downland course situated at 800 feet above sea level, its undulations providing a good walk. On a limestone base, the course dries quickly in wet conditions. The opening few holes provide a good test of golf made more difficult when the prevailing wind makes the player use the extremes of the course.

18 holes, 6241yds, Par 71, SSS 70, Course record 62.
Club membership 900.
Visitors with member only at weekends & bank holidays. **Societies** telephone in advance. **Green Fees** £28 per day. **Prof** Neil Rowlands **Facilities** ⊗ ⊐⊩ ⓛ ⚏ ♀ ♨ 🏠 🌾 🦌 ♂ **Location** 1.5m E on A44

continued

Hotel ★★★ 70% The Mill House Hotel & Restaurant, KINGHAM ☎ 01608 658188 21 en suite 2 annexe en suite

Wychwood Lyneham OX7 6QQ
☎ 01993 831841 🖹 01993 831775
Lyneham was designed to use the natural features. It is set in 170 acres on the fringe of the Costwolds and blends superbly with its surroundings. Lakes and streams enhance the challenge of the course with water coming into play on eight of the 18 holes. All greens are sand based, built to USGA specification.
18 holes, 6669yds, Par 72, SSS 72, Course record 67.
Club membership 725.
Visitors must contact in advance. **Societies** apply in advance. **Green Fees** £30 per day; £22 per round (£37/£26 weekends). **Cards** 🔲 🔲 🔲 💷 **Prof** James Fincher **Course Designer** D G Carpenter **Facilities** ⊗ ⁙ 🏌 ⏇ ♀ ⚑ 🏠 ⛳ 🐾 🚜 ⛳ **Location** Off A361, between Burford/Chipping Norton

Hotel ★★★ 70% The Mill House Hotel & Restaurant, KINGHAM ☎ 01608 658188 21 en suite 2 annexe en suite

Hotel ★★★ 70% The Mill House Hotel & Restaurant, KINGHAM ☎ 01608 658188 21 en suite 2 annexe en suite

DIDCOT Map 04 SU59

Hadden Hill Wallingford Rd OX11 9BJ
☎ 01235 510410 🖹 01235 511260
e-mail: info@haddenhillgolf.co.uk
A challenging course on undulating terrain with excellent drainage so visitors can be sure of playing no matter what the weather conditions have been. Two loops of nine holes.
18 holes, 6563yds, Par 71, SSS 71, Course record 65.
Club membership 400.
Visitors telephone pro shop to book tee times. **Societies** telephone to arrange times/dates & receive booking form. **Green Fees** £15 per 18 holes; £9 per 9 holes (£20/£12 weekends). **Prof** Adrian Waters **Course Designer** Michael V Morley **Facilities** ⊗ ⁙ 🏌 ⏇ ♀ ⚑ 🏠 ⛳ 🐾 🚜 ⛳ **Leisure** teaching academy. **Location** A34 Milton interchange, follow A4130, Course located 1m E of Didcot

Hotel ★★★ 66% Abingdon Four Pillars Hotel, Marcham Rd, ABINGDON ☎ 01235 553456 62 en suite

FARINGDON Map 04 SU29

Carswell Carswell SN7 8PU
☎ 01367 870422 🖹 01367 870592
An attractive course set in undulating wooded countryside close to Faringdon. Mature trees, five lakes and well placed bunkers add interest to the course. Floodlit driving range.
18 holes, 6133yds, Par 72, SSS 70.
Club membership 750.
Visitors must book 8 days in advance, no earlier for tee time. **Societies** on weekdays only telephone to check availability, deposit required, **Green Fees** not confirmed. **Cards** 🔲 🔲 🔲 💷 **Prof** Steve Parker **Facilities** ⊗ ⁙ 🏌 ⏇ ♀ ⚑ 🏠 ⛳ 🚜 ⛳ **Leisure** sauna, solarium, gymnasium. **Location** Just off the A420 between Oxford and Swindon

Hotel ★★★ 73% Sudbury House Hotel & Conference Centre, London St, FARINGDON ☎ 01367 241272 49 en suite

> An asterisk * in the Green Fees or Conference facilities indicates that prices given are for 2002

FRILFORD Map 04 SU49

Frilford Heath OX13 5NW
☎ 01865 390864 🖹 01865 390823
e-mail: secretary@frilfordheath.co.uk
54 holes in three distinctive layouts of significantly differing character. The Green course is a fully mature heathland course of some 6000 yards. The Red course is of championship length at 6800 yards with a parkland flavour and a marked degree of challenge. The Blue course is of modern design, and at 6728 yards, it incorporates water hazards and large shallow sand traps.
Red Course: 18 holes, 6884yds, Par 73, SSS 73, Course record 68.
Green Course: 18 holes, 6006yds, Par 69, SSS 69.
Blue Course: 18 holes, 6728yds, Par 72, SSS 72.
Club membership 1300.
Visitors contact in advance. Handicap certificates required. **Societies** apply in advance. **Green Fees** £50 per day(£65 weekends). **Cards** 🔲 🔲 🔲 💷 **Prof** Derek Craik **Course Designer** J Taylor/D Cotton/S Gidman **Facilities** ⊗ ⁙ 🏌 ⏇ ♀ ⚑ 🏠 ⛳ 🐾 🚜 ⛳ **Location** 3m W of Abingdon off A338 Oxford-Wantage road

Hotel ★★★ 66% Abingdon Four Pillars Hotel, Marcham Rd, ABINGDON ☎ 01235 553456 62 en suite

HENLEY-ON-THAMES Map 04 SU78

Aspect Park Remenham Hill RG9 3EH
☎ 01491 578306 🖹 01491 578306
Parkland course.
18 holes, 6557yds, Par 72, SSS 72.
Club membership 500.
Visitors must contact in advance, suitable golf attire required on course, no jeans in the clubhouse. **Societies** must contact in advance. **Green Fees** £32 per day; £20 per 18 holes; £12 per 9 holes (£37/£25/£15 weekends). **Cards** 🔲 🔲 🔲 💷 **Prof** Terry Notley **Course Designer** Tim Winsland **Facilities** ⊗ ⁙ 🏌 ⏇ ♀ ⚑ 🏠 ⛳ 🐾 🚜 ⛳ **Conf** Max 100

Hotel ★★★ 70% Red Lion Hotel, Hart St, HENLEY-ON-THAMES ☎ 01491 572161 26 en suite

Badgemore Park Badgemore RG9 4NR
☎ 01491 572206 🖹 01491 576899
e-mail: info@badgemorepark.com
Mature parkland course with easy walking. The 13th is a very difficult par 3 hole played over a valley to a narrow green and accuracy off the tee is essential.

18 holes, 6129yds, Par 69, SSS 69, Course record 64.
Club membership 700.
Visitors check for availability by contacting professional shop on 01491 574175. 48 hrs booking minimum for
continued

weekend play. Tue mornings, lady members only. **Societies** contact the Club Secretary to book. **Green Fees** £22 per round (£33 weekends & bank holidays). **Cards** 🌐 💳 📇
🌐 📠 **Prof** Jonathan Dunn **Course Designer** Robert Sandow **Facilities** ⊗ ⅷ by prior arrangement 🏌 ♟ ♀ ⅄ 🏠 ⚑ 🏸
🏹 ⛳ ♟ **Conf** Thtr 80 Class 50 Board 50 Banquet 130 **Location** From Henley head north west on B290 to Rotherfield Greys golf Club, 1.5m on right

Hotel ★★★ 70% Red Lion Hotel, Hart St, HENLEY-ON-THAMES 🕿 01491 572161 26 en suite

Henley Harpsden RG9 4HG
🕿 01491 575742 🖺 01491 412179
e-mail: henleygolfclub@btinternet.com
Undulating parkland course, with adjoining woodlands.
18 holes, 6329yds, Par 70, SSS 70, Course record 63.
Club membership 800.
Visitors must contact in advance. Weekend only with a member. **Societies** Wed & Thu, apply in writing. **Green Fees** £40 per day; £30 per round. **Prof** Mark Howell **Course Designer** James Braid **Facilities** ⊗ ⅷ 🏌 ♟ ♀ ⅄ 🏠 ♟
Location 1.25m S off A4155

Hotel ★★★ 70% Red Lion Hotel, Hart St, HENLEY-ON-THAMES 🕿 01491 572161 26 en suite

Studley Wood The Straight Mile OX33 1BF
🕿 01865 351122 & 351144 🖺 01865 351166
e-mail: admin@swgc.co.uk
Woodland course set in a former deer park with twelve lakes and specimen oak trees providing challenging natural hazards on almost all the holes.
18 holes, 6811yds, Par 73, SSS 73, Course record 65.
Club membership 700.
Visitors must play to handicap standard, tee times booked up to 4 days in advance. **Societies** contact secretary for details.
Green Fees £30 per round (£40 weekends). **Cards** 🌐
📇 🌐 📠 **Prof** Tony Williams **Course Designer** Simon Gidman **Facilities** ⊗ ⅷ 🏌 ♟ ♀ ⅄ 🏠 ⚑ 🏹 ⛳ ♟ **Conf** Max 50 **Location** 4m from Oxford follow signs for Horton-cum-Studley from Headington rdbt on Oxford ringroad

Hotel ★★★★🏅 75% Studley Priory Hotel, HORTON-CUM-STUDLEY 🕿 01865 351203 & 351254
🖺 01865 351613 18 en suite

Kirtlington OX5 3JY
🕿 01869 351133 🖺 01869 351143
e-mail: info@kirtlingtongolfclub.co.uk
A five year old inland links type course with challenging greens. The course incorporates many mature natural features and boasts 102 bunkers and a 'bye-hole', the 110 yard par 3 19th when an extra hole is required to determine a winner.
18 holes, 6107yds, Par 70, SSS 69, Course record 68.
Club membership 400.
Visitors must book for weekends and advisable to book for weekdays. Must contact in advance. **Societies** contact for Society packages. **Green Fees** £17 per 18 holes (£22 weekends & bank holidays). **Cards** 🌐 💳 📇 🌐 📠 📇
Course Designer Graham Webster **Facilities** ⊗ 🏌 ♟ ♀ ⅄
🏠 ⚑ 🏹 ⛳ ♟ **Location** on A4095 just outside village of Kirtlington

Hotel ★★★ 67% Weston Manor Hotel, WESTON-ON-THE-GREEN 🕿 01869 350621 15 en suite 20 annexe en suite

The Oxfordshire Rycote Ln OX9 2PU
🕿 01844 278300 🖺 01844 278003
Designed by Rees Jones, The Oxfordshire is considered to be one of the most exciting courses in the country. With four man-made lakes and 135 bunkers, it is a magnificent test of shot-making where almost every hole deserves special mention. Unfortunately it is only open to members and their guests.
18 holes, 7192yds, Par 72, SSS 75, Course record 64.
Club membership 600.
Visitors members' guests only, must put application in writing. **Societies** **Green Fees** terms on application.
Cards 🌐 💳 📇 🌐 📠 **Prof** Neil Pike **Course Designer** Rees Jones **Facilities** ⊗ ⅷ 🏌 ♟ ♀ ⅄ 🏠 ⚑ 🏹
⛳ ♟ **Conf** Thtr 250 Class 150 Board 50 Banquet 200 Del from £28 * **Location** 1.5m from junct 7, M40 on A329

Hotel ★★★ 76% Spread Eagle Hotel, Cornmarket, THAME 🕿 01844 213661 33 en suite

Huntercombe RG9 5SL
🕿 01491 641207 🖺 01491 642060
This heathland/woodland course overlooks the Oxfordshire plain and has many attractive and interesting fairways and greens. Walking is easy after the 3rd which is a notable hole. The course is subject to wind and grass pot bunkers are interesting hazards.
18 holes, 6301yds, Par 70, SSS 70, Course record 63.
Club membership 800.
Visitors must contact in advance and have a handicap certificate. **Societies** must contact in advance. **Green Fees** £45 per day; £30 per round (£45 per round Sun and bank holidays). **Prof** John B Draycott **Course Designer** Willy Park **Facilities** ⊗ ⅷ 🏌 ♟ ♀ ⅄ 🏠 ♟ **Location** 6m W of Henley-on-Thames off A130

Hotel ★★★ 66% Shillingford Bridge Hotel, Shillingford, WALLINGFORD 🕿 01865 858567 34 en suite 8 annexe en suite

Hinksey Heights South Hinksey OX1 5AB
🕿 01865 327775 🖺 01865 736930
e-mail: play@oxford-golf.co.uk

Set in an area of outstanding natural beauty, overlooking the incomparable "Dreaming Spires" of Oxford and the Thames Valley. The course has been designed and built as a series of interesting and distinctive holes that reward
continued

the thoughtful golfer. Several of the holes challenge you to be bold, with the inherent risk of danger, or to play safe. There is also a 9 hole par 3 course for golfers of all ages and abilities.

18 holes, 7023yds, Par 74, SSS 74.
Club membership 300.
Visitors advisable to telephone in advance. **Societies** apply in advance. **Green Fees** £25 per day; £15 per round (£33/£20 weekends). **Cards** ▦ ▦ ▦ ▦ **Prof** David Bolton **Course Designer** David Heads **Facilities** ⊗ ⌇ ⌶ ▨ ☕ ♀ △ 🏠 ⚑ �1 ⚐ ⎰ **Location** on A34 (Oxford ring road) between Abingdon and Oxford Botley junction
....

Hotel ★★★ 69% Hawkwell House, Church Way, Iffley Village, OXFORD ☎ 01865 749988 51 en suite

North Oxford Banbury Rd OX2 8EZ
☎ 01865 554924 ▤ 01865 515921
e-mail: secretary@nogc.co.uk
Gently undulating parkland course.
18 holes, 5736yds, Par 67, SSS 67, Course record 62.
Club membership 700.
Visitors at weekends & bank holidays may only play after 4pm. **Societies** must contact in advance. **Green Fees** £25 per day; £18 per round (£14 per round Mondays). **Cards** ▦ ▦ ▦ ▩ ▨ **Prof** Robert Harris **Facilities** ⊗ ⌇ ⌶ ▨ ☕ ♀ △ 🏠 ⚑ ⎰ **Location** 3m N of city centre on A4165
....

Hotel ★★★★ 66% The Oxford Hotel, Godstow Rd, Wolvercote Roundabout, OXFORD
☎ 01865 489988 173 en suite

Southfield Hill Top Rd OX4 1PF
☎ 01865 242158 ▤ 01865 242158
e-mail: southfieldgolfclub@btinternet.com
Home of the City, University and Ladies Clubs, and well-known to graduates throughout the world. A challenging course, in varied parkland setting, providing a real test for players.
18 holes, 6328yds, Par 70, SSS 70, Course record 61.
Club membership 850.
Visitors with member only at weekends. **Societies** must apply in writing. **Green Fees** £25 per day; £20 per round. **Cards** ▦ ▦ **Prof** Tony Rees **Course Designer** H S Colt **Facilities** ⊗ ⌇ ⌶ ▨ ☕ ♀ △ 🏠 ⚑ ⚐ ⎰ **Location** 1.5m SE of city centre off B480
....

Hotel ★★★ 65% Eastgate Hotel, The High, Merton St, OXFORD ☎ 0870 400 8201 64 en suite

Shrivenham Park Penny Hooks SN6 8EX
☎ 01793 783853 ▤ 01793 782999
An undulating course with excellent drainage, providing a good challenge for all standards of golfer.
18 holes, 5769yds, Par 69, SSS 69, Course record 64.
Club membership 350.
Visitors phone in advance. **Societies** phone for details.
Green Fees not confirmed. **Cards** ▦ ▦ ▦ ▦ ▨ ▩ ▨
Prof Jamie McArthur **Course Designer** Gordon Cox
Facilities ⊗ ⌇ ⌶ ▨ ☕ ♀ △ 🏠 ⚑ 🚍 ⎰ **Location** 0.5m NE of town centre
....

Hotel ★★★ 73% Sudbury House Hotel & Conference Centre, London St, FARINGDON ☎ 01367 241272 49 en suite

Tadmarton Heath OX15 5HL
☎ 01608 737278 ▤ 01608 730548
e-mail: thgc@btinternet.com
A mixture of heath and sandy land, the course, which is open to strong winds, incorporates the site of an old Roman encampment. The clubhouse is an old farm building with a 'holy well' from which the greens are watered. The 7th is a testing hole over water.
18 holes, 5917yds, Par 69, SSS 69, Course record 63.
Club membership 600.
Visitors weekday by appointment, with member only at weekends. **Societies** by arrangement with club office.
Green Fees £38 per day. **Prof** Tom Jones **Course Designer** Col Hutchinson **Facilities** ⊗ ⌶ ▨ ☕ ♀ △ 🏠 ⚑ 🚍 ⎰ **Leisure** fishing. **Location** 1m SW of Lower Tadmarton off B4035, 4m from Banbury
....

Hotel ★★★ 70% Banbury House, Oxford Rd, BANBURY ☎ 01295 259361 63 en suite

Springs Hotel Wallingford Rd, North Stoke OX10 6BE
☎ 01491 827310 ▤ 01491 827312
e-mail: golfclub@thespringshotel.com
133 acres of park land, bordered by the River Thames, within which lie three lakes and challenging wetland areas. The course has traditional features like a double green and sleepered bunker with sleepered lake edges of the typical American design.

18 holes, 6470yds, Par 72, SSS 71, Course record 67.
Club membership 580.
Visitors handicap certificate required. Dress code must be adhered to. **Societies** apply in writing,telephone/e-mail.
Green Fees £34 per round (£27.50 weekends). **Cards** ▦ ▦ ▩ ▦ ▨ **Prof** Leigh Atkins/Pete Lvil **Course Designer** Brian Hugget **Facilities** ⊗ ⌇ ⌶ ▨ ☕ ♀ △ 🏠 ⚑ 🚍 **Leisure** heated outdoor swimming pool, fishing, sauna. **Conf** Max 120 Thtr 50 Class 16 Board 22 Banquet 26 Del £40 to £50 * **Location** 15 miles SE of Oxford & 12.5 miles NW of Reading.
....

Hotel ★★★ 72% Springs Hotel, Wallingford Rd, North Stoke, WALLINGFORD ☎ 01491 836687 31 en suite

Waterstock Thame Rd OX33 1HT
☎ 01844 338093 ▤ 01844 338036
e-mail: oxfordgolf@btinternet.com
A 6,500yard course designed by Donald Steel with USGA greens and tees fully computer irrigated. Four par 3s

continued

facing North, South, East and West. A brook and hidden lake affect six holes, with doglegs being 4th and 10th holes. Five par 5s on the course, making it a challenge for players of all standards.
18 holes, 6535yds, Par 73, SSS 71, Course record 69.
Club membership 500.
Visitors no restrictions. **Societies** apply in writing or telephone. **Green Fees** £15.50 per 18 holes;£8.25 per 9 holes(£18.50/£9.75 weekends). **Cards** ▬▬ ▬ ▬ 🖭 **Prof** Paul Bryant **Course Designer** Donald Steel **Facilities** ⊗ ⥥⯊ ⮱ 🖳⯒ 🛠 ⌕ ⚲ 🏐 ♝ ⚲ ℂ **Leisure** fishing. **Location** M40 junct 8/8A east of Oxford near Wheatley.
· ·
Hotel ★★★ 76% Spread Eagle Hotel, Cornmarket, THAME ☎ 01844 213661 33 en suite

Greetham Valley Golf Club

WITNEY — Map 04 SP31

Witney Lakes Downs Rd OX8 5SY
☎ 01993 893011 📄 01993 778866
e-mail: resort@witney-lakes.co.uk
A lakeland style course with five large lakes coming into play on eight holes. An excellent test of golf that will use every club in your bag.
18 holes, 6700yds, Par 71, Course record 67.
Club membership 400.
Visitors may book 5 days in advance, weekends after 10.30 am **Societies** telephone or write in advance. **Green Fees** not confirmed. **Cards** ▬▬ ▬ ▬ 🖭 **Prof** Adam Souter **Course Designer** Simon Gidman **Facilities** ⊗ ⥥⯊ ⮱ 🖳⯒ ⚲ 🏐 ♝ ⚲ ℂ **Leisure** heated indoor swimming pool, sauna, solarium, gymnasium. **Location** 2m W of Witney town centre, off B4047 Witney/Burford road

Hotel ★★★ 70% Witney Four Pillars Hotel, Ducklington Ln, WITNEY ☎ 01993 779777 83 en suite

RUTLAND

GREAT CASTERTON — Map 08 TF00

Rutland County PE9 4AQ
☎ 01780 460330 📄 01780 460437
e-mail: pat@rutlandcounty.freeserve.co.uk
Inland links-style course with gently rolling fairways, large tees and greens. Playable all year round due to good drainage.
18 holes, 6401yds, Par 71, SSS 71, Course record 64.
Club membership 650.
Visitors must book in advance at the shop, tel 01780 460239. **Societies** contact office by phone, must be booked in advance. **Green Fees** £25 (£30 weekends & bank holidays). **Cards** ▬▬ ▬ ▬ 🖭 **Prof** James Darroch **Course Designer** Cameron Sinclair **Facilities** ⊗ ⥥⯊ ⮱ 🖳⯒ ⚲ 🏐 ♝ ⚲ ℂ **Conf** Max 20 Board 20 Banquet 50 Del £10 to £30 * **Location** 2m N of Stamford on A1
· ·
Hotel ★★ 68% The White Horse Inn, Main St, EMPINGHAM ☎ 01780 460221 & 460521
📄 01780 460521 4 en suite 9 annexe en suite

GREETHAM — Map 08 SK91

Greetham Valley Wood Ln LE15 7NP
☎ 01780 460004 📄 01780 460623
e-mail: GVGC@rutnet.co.uk
Set in 260 acres, including mature woodland, undulating natural valley, and water hazards. The complex comprises two 18 hole courses, The Lakes and The Valley. A luxurious clubhouse, 9 hole par 3, floodlit driving range and teaching academy. *continued*

Lakes: 18 holes, 6779yds, Par 72, SSS 72, Course record 68.
Valley: 18 holes, 5595yds, Par 68, SSS 67.
Club membership 1000.
Visitors must contact in advance. **Societies** must contact in advance. **Green Fees** £42 per day; £29 per 18 holes (£50/£33 weekends). **Cards** ▬▬ ▬ ▬ 🖭 **Prof** John Pengelly **Course Designer** F E Hinch **Facilities** ⊗ ⥥⯊ ⮱ 🖳⯒ ⚲ 🏐 ♝ ⚲ ℂ **Leisure** bowls green 9 hole par 3. **Location** Take the B668 Oakham road off the A1 and follow signs to the course which are clearly marked
· ·
Hotel ★★★ 75% Barnsdale Lodge Hotel, The Avenue, Rutland Water, North Shore, OAKHAM
☎ 01572 724678 45 en suite

KETTON — Map 04 SK90

Luffenham Heath PE9 3UU
☎ 01780 720205 📄 01780 722146
e-mail: jringleby@theluffenhamheathgc.co.uk
This undulating heathland course with low bushes, much gorse and many trees, lies in a conservation area for flora and fauna. From the higher part of the course there is a magnificent view across the Chater Valley. The course places a premium on accuracy with many demanding driving holes, challenging bunkers and well guarded greens. The course is not long but there are several outstanding holes.
18 holes, 6315yds, Par 70, SSS 70, Course record 64.
Club membership 550.
Visitors must contact in advance. **Societies** write or telephone in advance. **Green Fees** £50 per day; £40 per round. **Cards** ▬▬ ▬ 🖭 **Prof** Ian Burnett **Course Designer** James Braid **Facilities** ⊗ ⥥⯊ ⮱ 🖳⯒ ⚲ 🏐 ♝ ⚲ ℂ **Location** 1.5m SW of Ketton by Fosters Railway Bridge on A6121
· ·
Hotel ★★★ 78% The George of Stamford, 71 St Martins, STAMFORD ☎ 01780 750750 & 750700 (Res) 📄 01780 750701 47 en suite

SHROPSHIRE

BRIDGNORTH — Map 07 SO79

Bridgnorth Stanley Ln WV16 4SF
☎ 01746 763315 📄 01746 761381
A pleasant course laid out on parkland on the bank of the River Severn.
18 holes, 6673yds, Par 73, SSS 73, Course record 65.
Club membership 725.
Visitors must contact in advance but may not play on Wed. Restricted weekends. **Societies** must contact in writing. **Green Fees** not confirmed. **Prof** Paul Hinton **Facilities** ⊗ ⥥⯊ *continued*

🛦 ⚐ ♀ 👤 🏠 ❥ ⚷ **Leisure** fishing. **Location** 1m N off B4373, 0.5m from town centre

Hotel ★★ 64% Falcon Hotel, Saint John St, Lowtown, BRIDGNORTH ☎ 01746 763134 12 en suite

CHURCH STRETTON — Map 07 SO49

Church Stretton Trevor Hill SY6 6JH
☎ 01694 722281 🖹 01694 722633
e-mail: secretary@csgc.freeserve.co.uk
Hillside course designed by James Braid on the lower slopes of the Long Mynd.
18 holes, 5020yds, Par 66, SSS 65, Course record 63.
Club membership 450.
Visitors Tee reserved for members Sat 9-10.30 & 1-2.30, Sun prior to 10.30 & 1-2.30 (summer), 12-1.30; (winter). **Societies** must contact in advance. **Green Fees** £18 per day/round (£26 weekends & bank holidays). **Prof** J Townsend **Course Designer** James Braid **Facilities** ⊗ ∭ 🛦 ⚐ ♀ 👤 🏠 🛥 **Location** W of the town. From Cardington Valley drive up Trevor Hill, a steep, winding road

Hotel ★★ 70% Mynd House Hotel, Ludlow Rd, Little Stretton, CHURCH STRETTON ☎ 01694 722212 7 en suite

CLEOBURY MORTIMER — Map 07 SO67

Cleobury Mortimer Wyre Common DY14 8HQ
☎ 01299 271112 🖹 01299 271468
Well designed 27-hole parkland course set in undulating countryside with fine views from all holes, and offering an interesting challenge to golfers of all abilities.
Foxes Run: 9 holes, 2980yds, Par 34, SSS 34.
Badgers Sett: 9 holes, 3271yds, Par 36, SSS 36.
Deer Park: 9 holes, 3167yds, Par 35, SSS 35.
Club membership 650.
Visitors advisable to book in advance, handicap certificate may be required at weekends. **Societies** write or telephone in advance. **Green Fees** £30 per day; £20 per 18 holes (£36/£30 weekends). **Cards** 🎫 ▬ ▬ 🔀 💷 **Prof** Jon Jones/Martin Payne **Course Designer** E.G.U **Facilities** ⊗ ∭ 🛦 ⚐ ♀ 👤 🏠 🛥 ⚷ ❣ **Leisure** fishing, snooker table. **Location** 10m W of Kidderminster on A4117 1m N of Cleobury Mortimer, off B4201

Hotel ★★ 66% The Redfern Hotel, CLEOBURY MORTIMER ☎ 01299 270395
5 en suite 6 annexe rms (5 en suite)

HIGHLEY — Map 07 SO78

Severn Meadows WV16 6HZ
☎ 01746 862212
9 holes, 5258yds, Par 68, SSS 67.
Telephone for further details

Hotel ★★★★ 66% Mill Hotel & Restaurant, ALVELEY ☎ 01746 780437 21 en suite

LILLESHALL — Map 07 SJ71

Lilleshall Hall TF10 9AS
☎ 01952 603840 & 604776 🖹 01952 604776
Heavily-wooded parkland course. Easy walking.
18 holes, 5906yds, Par 68, SSS 68, Course record 65.
Club membership 650.
Visitors must contact in advance and introduced by member at weekends. **Societies** must apply in writing by Dec for the following year. **Green Fees** £22 per 18 holes. **Prof** Stuart McKane **Course Designer** H S Colt **Facilities** ⊗ ∭ 🛦 ⚐ ♀ 👤 🏠 ⚷ **Location** 3m SE

continued

....

Hotel ★★ 68% White House Hotel, Wellington Rd, Muxton, TELFORD ☎ 01952 604276 & 603603
🖹 01952 670336 32 en suite

LUDLOW — Map 07 SO57

Ludlow Bromfield SY8 2BT
☎ 01584 856366 & 856285 🖹 01584 856366
e-mail: ludlowgo@barbox.net
A long-established heathland course in the middle of the racecourse. Very flat, quick drying, with broom and gorse-lined fairways.

18 holes, 6277yds, Par 70, SSS 70, Course record 65.
Club membership 700.
Visitors advisable to contact in advance. **Societies** apply in advance. **Green Fees** £20 (£25 weekends and bank holidays). **Prof** Russell Price **Facilities** ⊗ ∭ 🛦 ⚐ ♀ 👤 🏠 ❣ ⚷ **Location** 1m N of Ludlow, off A49

Hotel ★★★ 64% The Feathers at Ludlow, Bull Ring, LUDLOW ☎ 01584 875261 40 en suite

MARKET DRAYTON — Map 07 SJ63

Market Drayton Sutton Ln TF9 2HX
☎ 01630 652266 🖹 01630 652266
e-mail: marketdraytongc@btinternet.com
Parkland course in quiet, picturesque surroundings providing a good test of golf. Bungalow on course is available for golfing holidays.
18 holes, 6290yds, Par 71, SSS 71, Course record 69.
Club membership 600.
Visitors may not play on Sun; must play with member on Sat. Must contact in advance. **Societies** welcome Mon,Wed,Thu & Fri, must contact in advance. **Green Fees** £24 per round. **Prof** Russell Clewes **Facilities** ⊗ ∭ 🛦 ⚐ ♀ 👤 🏠 ❣ ⚷ **Location** 1m SW

Hotel ★★★ 🏆 70% Goldstone Hall, Goldstone, MARKET DRAYTON ☎ 01630 661202 & 661487
🖹 01630 661585 8 en suite

MEOLE BRACE — Map 07 SJ41

Meole Brace Otely Rd SY2 6QQ ☎ 01743 364050
9 holes, 5830yds, Par 68, SSS 68, Course record 66.
Location NE side of village off A49
Telephone for further details

Hotel ★★★ 63% The Lion, Wyle Cop, SHREWSBURY ☎ 01743 353107 59 en suite

Looking for a driving range?
See the index at the back of the guide

OSWESTRY   Map 07 SJ22

Mile End Mile End, Old Shrewsbury Rd SY11 4JE
☎ 01691 671246 📠 01691 670580
e-mail: info@mileendgolfclub.co.uk
A gently undulating parkland-type course boasting
challenging holes for all standards of golfing ability.
Longest hole is par 5 14th at 540yds. A number of water
features need to be negotiated including two large ponds
on the 3rd and 17th. The course is set in 140 acres,
ensuring all holes are sufficiently isolated.
18 holes, 6194yds, Par 71, SSS 69, Course record 69.
Club membership 550.
Visitors welcome at all times please telephone in advance to
check availability. **Societies** must contact in advance,
information available. **Green Fees** £22 per day; £15 per
round (£28/£20 weekends). **Prof** Scott Carpenter **Course
Designer** Price/Gough **Facilities** ⊗ ⓑ ⟆ ♀ ⚲ 🏠 ⚘ ⫶
Location 1m SE of Oswestry, just off A5
· ·
Hotel ★★★ 70% Wynnstay Hotel, Church St, OSWESTRY
🏨 01691 655261 29 en suite

Oswestry Aston Park SY11 4JJ
☎ 01691 610535 📠 01691 610535
e-mail: secretary@oswestrygolfclub.co.uk
Gently undulating mature parkland course set in
splendid Shropshire countryside. Free draining soils
make Oswestry an ideal year round test of golf.
18 holes, 6024yds, Par 70, SSS 69, Course record 62.
Club membership 960.
Visitors must contact in advance. Must have a handicap
certificate or play with member. **Societies** must contact in
advance. **Green Fees** £30 per day, £24 per round (telephone
for weekend rates). **Prof** David Skelton **Course Designer**
James Braid **Facilities** ⊗ ⟆ ⓑ ⟆ ♀ ⚲ 🏠 ⚘ **Location** 2m
SE on A5
· ·
Hotel ★★★ 70% Wynnstay Hotel, Church St, OSWESTRY
🏨 01691 655261 29 en suite

PANT   Map 07 SJ22

Llanymynech SY10 8LB ☎ 01691 830983
Upland course on the site of an early Iron Age/Roman
hillfort with far-reaching views. 15 holes in Wales 3 holes
in England, drive off in Wales, putt out in England on 4th
hole.
18 holes, 6114yds, Par 70, SSS 69, Course record 65.
Club membership 700.
Visitors contact in advance, some weekends restricted.
Societies must contact Secretary. **Green Fees** £25 per day;
£20 per round (£25 per round weekends). **Prof** Andrew P
Griffiths **Facilities** ⊗ ⟆ ⓑ ⟆ ♀ ⚲ 🏠 ⚘ **Location** 6m S
of Oswestry on A483. In village of Pant turn at Cross Guns
Inn
· ·
Hotel ★★★ 70% Wynnstay Hotel, Church St, OSWESTRY
🏨 01691 655261 29 en suite

SHIFNAL   Map 07 SJ70

Shifnal Decker Hill TF11 8QL
☎ 01952 460330 📠 01952 461127
e-mail: secretary@shifnalgolfclub.co.uk
Well-wooded parkland course. Walking is easy and an
attractive country mansion serves as the clubhouse.
18 holes, 6468yds, Par 71, SSS 71, Course record 65.
Club membership 700.
Visitors must contact in advance, may not play at weekends
continued

or on Thursdays. **Societies** must contact in advance. **Green
Fees** £30 per day; £25 per round. **Cards** 🚦 ▦ 🚗 🏧
🅿 **Prof** Justin Flanagan **Course Designer** Pennick **Facilities**
⊗ ⟆ ⓑ ⟆ ♀ ⚲ 🏠 ⚘ **Location** 1m N of Shifnal, off
B4379
· ·
Hotel ★★★★ 66% Park House Hotel, Park St, SHIFNAL
🏨 01952 460128 38 en suite 16 annexe en suite

SHREWSBURY   Map 07 SJ41

Arscott Arscott, Pontesbury SY5 0XP
☎ 01743 860114 📠 01743 860114
At 365 feet above sea level, the views from Arscott Golf
Club, of the hills of south Shropshire and Wales are
superb. Arscott is a new course, set in mature parkland
with water features and holes demanding all sorts of club
choice. A challenge to all golfers both high and low
handicap.
18 holes, 6178yds, Par 70, SSS 69, Course record 68.
Club membership 480.
Visitors most times available by prior arrangement. **Societies**
apply in writing or telephone for tee reservation. **Green Fees**
£16 per round (£20 weekends). **Course Designer** M Hamer
Facilities ⊗ ⟆ ⓑ ⟆ ♀ ⚲ 🏠 ⫶ ⚘ **Leisure** fishing.
Location Off A488, S of Shrewsbury 3m from A5
· ·
Hotel ★★★ 63% The Lion, Wyle Cop, SHREWSBURY
🏨 01743 353107 59 en suite

Shrewsbury Condover SY5 7BL ☎ 01743 872976,
872977 (sec) & 874581 (pro) 📠 01743 874647
e-mail: p.seal@sealgolf.co.uk
Parkland course. First nine flat, second undulating with
good views of the Long Mynd Range. Several holes with
water features. Fast putting surfaces.
18 holes, 6300yds, Par 70, SSS 70.
Club membership 872.
Visitors must contact in advance, weekend restrictions and
have a handicap certificate. **Societies** must contact in writing.
Green Fees terms on application. **Prof** Peter Seal **Facilities**
⊗ ⟆ ⓑ ⟆ ♀ ⚲ 🏠 ⚘ ⫶ **Location** 4m S off A49
· ·
Hotel ★★★ 71% Prince Rupert Hotel, Butcher Row,
SHREWSBURY 🏨 01743 499955 70 en suite

TELFORD   Map 07 SJ60

The Shropshire Granville Park, Muxton TF2 8PQ
☎ 01952 677800 📠 01952 677622
e-mail: golf@theshropshire.co.uk
This 27 hole course comprises three loops of nine. Each
course has an abundance of lakes and water hazards
making club selection a vital part of the round.
Championship tees are available by pre-arrangement for
the low handicap player.
Blue: 9 holes, 3286yds, Par 35, SSS 35.
Silver: 9 holes, 3303yds, Par 36, SSS 36.
Gold: 9 holes, 3334yds, Par 36, SSS 36.
Club membership 400.
Visitors recommended to book 7 days in advance. **Societies**
must book in advance. **Green Fees** terms on application.
Cards 🚦 ▦ 🚗 🅿 🏧 🚦 🅿 **Prof** Andrew Holmes
Course Designer Martin Hawtree **Facilities** ⊗ ⟆ ⓑ ⟆ ♀
⚲ 🏠 ⟐ ⚘ ⫶ **Conf** Thtr 300 Class 150 Board 100
Banquet 200 Del from £18.50 * **Location** From M54/A5
take B5060 towards Donnington. Take 3rd exit at Granville
rdbt and continue
· ·
Hotel ★★★ 65% Telford Golf & Country Club, Great Hay
Dr, Sutton Heights, TELFORD 🏨 01952 429977 96 en suite

Telford Golf & Country Club Great Hay Dr,
Sutton Heights TF7 4DT ☎ 01952 429977 🖹 01952 586602
Rolling parkland course overlooking the Severn Gorge with tree lined fairways and easy walking. Five lakes and large sand traps are hazards to the fine greens.
18 holes, 6761yds, Par 72, SSS 72, Course record 66.
Club membership 450.
Visitors must book in advance, be a competent golfer and abide by dress regulations. Societies must telephone in advance 01952 429977 Green Fees £20 per round(£25 weekends). Cards 🔁 ▓ 🏧 💷 🔁 ▓ ◨ Prof Daniel Bateman Course Designer Harris/Griffiths Facilities ⊗ ⊐🍴 ╠ ☰ 🍷 ♨ 🏠 👕 🥢 🦐 🦀 𝄢 𝄢 Leisure heated indoor swimming pool, squash, sauna, solarium, gymnasium, snooker,pool,steam room & beauty &masseur treatments.Conf Thtr 200 Class 140 Board 60 Banquet 140 Del from £34.50 * Location 4m S of town centre off A442

Hotel ★★★ 65% Telford Golf & Country Club, Great Hay Dr, Sutton Heights, TELFORD ☎ 01952 429977 96 en suite

WELLINGTON   Map 07 SJ61

Wrekin Ercall Woods, Golf Links Ln TF6 5BX
☎ 01952 244032 🖹 01952 252906
Downland course with some hard walking but superb views.

18 holes, 5570yds, Par 67, SSS 66, Course record 64.
Club membership 675.
Visitors must contact in advance. Limited weekends & bank holidays. Societies must apply in writing/telephone. Green Fees £30 per day; £22 per round (£30 per round/day weekends). Prof K Housden Facilities ⊗ ⊐🍴 ╠ ☰ 🍷 ♨ 🏠 𝄢 Location Off junct 7 of M54,1.25m S off B5061

Hotel ★★★★ 65% Buckatree Hall Hotel, The Wrekin, Wellington, TELFORD ☎ 01952 641821 60 en suite

WESTON-UNDER-REDCASTLE   Map 07 SJ52

Hawkstone Park Hotel SY4 5UY
☎ 01939 200611 🖹 01939 200311
e-mail: info@hawkstone.co.uk
The Hawkstone Course plays through the English Heritage designated Grade I landscape of the historic park and follies providing a beautiful, tranquil yet dramatic back drop to a round of golf. The Windmill Course utilises many American-style features and extensive water hazards and is a challenging alternative.

Hawkstone Course: 18 holes, 6491yds, Par 72, SSS 71, Course record 65.
Windmill Course: 18 holes, 6476yds, Par 72, SSS 72, Course record 64.
Academy Course: 6 holes, 741yds, Par 18, SSS 18.
Club membership 650.
Visitors advance bookings recommended. Societies must contact in advance by telephone. Green Fees £32 per round (£40 weekends). Cards 🔁 ▓ 🏧 💷 🔁 ▓ ◨ Prof Anthony Roberts Course Designer J Braid Facilities ⊗ ⊐🍴 ╠ ☰ 🍷 ♨ 🏠 👕 🥢 🦐 🦀 𝄢 𝄢 Leisure 6 hole, par 3 course,snooker.Conf Max 200 Thtr 200 Class 90 Board 50 Banquet 180 Del from £29.50 * Location N side of village 0.75m E of A49

Farmhouse ◆◆◆◆Soulton Hall, Soulton, WEM ☎ 01939 232786 6 en suite

WHITCHURCH   Map 07 SJ54

Hill Valley Terrick Rd SY13 4JZ
☎ 01948 663584 & 667788 🖹 01948 665927
e-mail: info@hillvalley.co.uk
Two testing parkland courses ideally suited to the club and scratch golfer alike. The Emerald, cleverly designed by Peter Alliss and Dave Thomas, has fairways that thread their way through 160 acres of trees, lakes and streams to American-style greens trapped by sand and water. Shorter Sapphire with smaller greens requiring accurate approach shots.
Emerald: 18 holes, 6628yds, Par 73, SSS 72, Course record 64.
Sapphire: 18 holes, 4800yds, Par 66, SSS 64.
Club membership 600.
Visitors must contact in advance, deposit required. Societies must contact in advance; deposit required. Green Fees not confirmed. Cards 🔁 ▓ 🏧 💷 🔁 ▓ ◨ Prof A R Minshall & Clive Burgess Course Designer Peter Alliss/Dave Thomas Facilities ⊗ ⊐🍴 ╠ ☰ 🍷 ♨ 🏠 👕 🥢 🦐 🦀 𝄢 Leisure sauna, solarium, gymnasium. Location 1m N. Follow signs from Bypass

continued

Hotel ★★ 70% Crown Hotel & Restaurant, High St,
NANTWICH ☎ 01270 625283 18 en suite

WORFIELD   Map 07 SO79

Chesterton Valley Chesterton WV15 5NX
☎ 01746 783682
Dry course built on sandy soil giving excellent drainage.
No temporary greens and no trolley ban.
18 holes, 5671yards, SSS 67.
Club membership 450.
Societies telephone in advance. Green Fees not confirmed.
Prof Philip Hinton Course Designer Len Vanes Facilities
☕ ♀ 🅿 🏠 ⛳ ☍ Location on B4176 Dudley/Telford
road

Hotel ★★★ Old Vicarage Hotel, BRIDGWORTH
☎ 01746 716497 & 0800 0968010 📋 01746 716552
10 en suite 4 annexe en suite

Worfield Roughton WV15 5HE
☎ 01746 716372 📋 01746 716302
This undulating course with good-sized greens, well
placed bunkers and three lakes, rated highly in a golf
magazine survey. All year round golf based on sandy soil.
18 holes, 6545yds, Par 73, SSS 72, Course record 68.
Club membership 500.
Visitors must contact in advance, weekends only after 2pm.
Societies contact in advance. Green Fees £25 per day; £20
per 18 holes (£25 weekends). Cards 🔳 🔳 🔳 🔳 📖 Prof
Steve Russell Course Designer T Williams Facilities ⊗ ⟫⊞
🅱 ☕ ♀ 🏠 ⛏ 🏌 ☍ Location 3m W of Bridgnorth, off
A454

Hotel ★★★ Old Vicarage Hotel, BRIDGWORTH
☎ 01746 716497 & 0800 0968010 📋 01746 716552
10 en suite 4 annexe en suite

SOMERSET

BACKWELL   Map 03 ST46

Tall Pines Cooks Bridle Path, Downside BS48 3DJ
☎ 01275 472076 📋 01275 474869
Parkland course with views over the Bristol Channel.
18 holes, 6049yds, Par 70, SSS 69, Course record 65.
Club membership 500.
Visitors no green fees before 11am unless by prior
arrangement. Must book in advance at weekends and may
not play before noon. Societies prior arrangement by
telephone for details. Green Fees £18 per round. Prof Alex
Murray Course Designer T Murray Facilities ⊗ ⟫⊞ 🅱 ☕ ♀
🏠 🏠 ⛏ ⛳ ☍ Location Adjacent to Bristol Airport, 1m
off A38

Hotel ★★★ 64% Beachlands Hotel, 17 Uphill Rd North,
WESTON-SUPER-MARE ☎ 01934 621401 24 en suite

BATH   Map 03 ST76

Bath Sham Castle, North Rd BA2 6JG
☎ 01225 463834 📋 01225 331027
e-mail: enquiries@bathgolfclub.org.uk
Considered to be one of the finest courses in the west,
this is the site of Bath's oldest golf club. Situated on
high ground overlooking the city and with splendid
views over the surrounding countryside. The rocky
ground supports good quality turf and there are many
continued

good holes. The 17th is a dog-leg right past, or over the
corner of an out-of-bounds wall, and thence on to an
undulating green.
18 holes, 6442yds, Par 71, SSS 71, Course record 66.
Club membership 750.
Visitors advisable to contact in advance. Handicap
certificates required. Societies Wed & Fri by prior
arrangement. Green Fees £32 per day; £27 per round
(£38/£33 weekends & bank holidays). Prof Peter J
Hancox Course Designer Colt & others Facilities ⊗ ⟫⊞
🅱 ☕ ♀ 🏠 🏠 🏌 ☍ Location 1.5m SE city centre off
A36

Hotel ★★★ 70% The Francis, Queen Square, BATH
☎ 0870 400 8223 95 en suite

Entry Hill BA2 5NA ☎ 01225 834248
9 holes, 2065yds, Par 33, SSS 30.
Club membership 300.
Visitors advisable to book in advance, must wear golf shoes
or training shoes. Societies bookings required in advance.
Green Fees not confirmed. Prof Tim Tapley Facilities ☕
🏠 🏠 🏌 ☍ Location Off A367

Lansdown Lansdown BA1 9BT
☎ 01225 422138 📋 01225 339252
e-mail: admin@lansdowngolfclub.co.uk
A flat parkland course situated 800 feet above sea level,
providing a challenge to both low and high handicap
golfers.
18 holes, 6316yds, Par 71, SSS 70, Course record 63.
Club membership 700.
Visitors must contact in advance to ascertain availability and
have a handicap certificate. Societies apply in writing or
telephone in advance. Green Fees £22 per day/round (£28
weekends). Cards 🔳 🔳 🔳 🔳 📖 Prof Terry Mercer
Course Designer C A Whitcombe Facilities ⊗ ⟫⊞ 🅱 ☕ ♀
🏠 🏠 ☍ Conf Max 80 Thtr 80 Class 80 Board 80 Banquet
80 Location 6m SW of exit 18 of M4, beside Bath
racecourse

Hotel ★★★ 69% Pratt's Hotel, South Pde, BATH
☎ 01225 460441 46 en suite

BRIDGWATER   Map 03 ST23

Cannington Cannington College, Cannington TA5 2LS
☎ 01278 655050 📋 01278 655055
Nine hole golf course with 18 tees of 'links-like'
appearance, designed by Martin Hawtree of Oxford. The
4th hole is a challenging 464yard par 4, slightly up hill
and into the prevailing wind.
9 holes, 6072yds, Par 68, SSS 70.
Club membership 240.
Visitors pay & play anytime ex Wed evening. Societies
apply in writing. Green Fees not confirmed. Prof Ron
Macrow Course Designer Martin Hawtree Facilities 🏠 🏠
🏌 ☍ ☍ Leisure Cycle hire. Location 4m NW of Bridgwater
of A39

Hotel ★★ 66% Friarn Court Hotel, 37 St Mary St,
BRIDGWATER ☎ 01278 452859 16 en suite

BURNHAM-ON-SEA   Map 03 ST34

Brean Coast Rd, Brean Sands TA8 2QY
☎ 01278 752111(pro shop) 📋 01278 752111
e-mail: alex.ferguson@hru.co.uk
Level and open moorland course with water hazards.
Facilities of the adjoining Brean Leisure Park. *continued*

Brean Golf Club At Brean Leisure Park

18 holes, 5715yds, Par 69, SSS 68, Course record 66.
Club membership 350.
Visitors may not play on Sat & Sun before 11.30am. Book in advance through professional. **Societies** contact office or professional in advance. **Green Fees** £18 (£20 weekends). **Cards** 🖃 💳 **Prof** David Haines **Facilities** ⊗ ⑪ ⓛ 🍺 ♈ ⚐ 🏌️ 🏒 ⚑ 🚲 ♐ **Leisure** heated indoor plus outdoor swimming pool, fishing, fun park with 30 rides/attractions. **Conf** Max 350 Thtr 300 Class 250 Board 100 Banquet 350 **Location** 4m from junct 22 M5 on coast road

Hotel ★★★⚘ 70% Batch Country Hotel, Batch Ln, LYMPSHAM ☎ 01934 750371 10 en suite

Burnham & Berrow St Christopher's Way TA8 2PE
☎ 01278 785760 📠 01278 795440
e-mail: secretary@burnhamandberrowgc.2-golf.com
Natural championship links course with panoramic views of the Somerset hills sweeping across the famed reed beds and the Bristol Channel with the islands of Steepholm and Flatholm against the background of the Welsh coast line.
Championship Course: 18 holes, 6606yds, Par 71, SSS 73, Course record 66.
Channel Course: 9 holes, 6120yds, Par 70, SSS 69.
Club membership 900.
Visitors must contact in advance & have handicap certificate (22 or under gentlemen, 30 or under ladies) to play on the Championship course. **Societies** telephone in advance. **Green Fees** Championship Course: £40 day/round (£60 weekends); Channel Course £12. **Cards** 🖃 💳 💳 ♐ **Prof** Mark Crowther-Smith **Facilities** ⊗ ⑪ ⓛ 🍺 ♈ ⚐ 🏌️ ⚑ ♐ **Location** 1m N of town on B3140

Hotel ★★ 70% Woodlands Country House Hotel, Hill Ln, BRENT KNOLL ☎ 01278 760232 8 en suite

CHARD	Map 03 ST30

Windwhistle Golf, Squash & Country Club
Cricket St Thomas TA20 4DG
☎ 01460 30231 📠 01460 30055

continued

Parkland course at 735ft above sea level with outstanding views over the Somerset Levels to the Bristol Channel and South Wales. Major changes to the layout of the course are planned for 2002 to 2003.
East/West Course: 18 holes, 6510yds, Par 73, SSS 71, Course record 69.
Club membership 500.
Visitors must contact in advance. **Societies** by prior arrangement. **Green Fees** terms on application. **Cards** 🖃 💳 💳 ♐ **Prof** Duncan Driver **Course Designer** Braid & Taylor **Facilities** ⊗ ⓛ 🍺 ♈ ⚐ 🏌️ ⚑ ♐ **Leisure** squash. **Location** 3m E of Chard on A30

Hotel ★★★ 66% Shrubbery Hotel, ILMINSTER ☎ 01460 52108 17 en suite

CLEVEDON	Map 03 ST47

Clevedon Castle Rd, Walton St Mary BS21 7AA
☎ 01275 874057 📠 01275 341228
e-mail: clevedongc.sec@virgin.net
Situated on the cliff-top overlooking the Severn estuary and with distant views of the Welsh coast. Excellent parkland course in first-class condition. Magnificent scenery and some tremendous 'drop' holes.
18 holes, 6557yds, Par 72, SSS 72, Course record 63.
Club membership 750.
Visitors must contact in advance. No play Wed morning. **Societies** not bank holidays, telephone or apply in writing. **Green Fees** £25 per day (£40 weekends & bank holidays). **Prof** Robert Scanlan **Course Designer** S Herd **Facilities** ⊗ ⑪ ⓛ 🍺 ♈ ⚐ 🏌️ ♐ **Location** 1m NE of town centre

Hotel ★★★ 66% Walton Park Hotel, Wellington Ter, CLEVEDON ☎ 01275 874253 40 en suite

CONGRESBURY	Map 03 ST46

Mendip Spring Honeyhall Ln BS49 5JT
☎ 01934 852322 📠 01934 853021
e-mail: mendipspring@lineone.net
Set in peaceful countryside with the Mendip Hills as a backdrop, this 18-hole course includes lakes and numerous water hazards covering some 12 acres of the course. The 12th is an island green surrounded by water and there are long drives on the 7th and 13th. The 9-hole Lakeside course is an easy walking course, mainly par 4. Floodlit driving range.
Brinsea Course: 18 holes, 6334yds, Par 71, SSS 70, Course record 64.
Lakeside: 9 holes, 2392yds, Par 34, SSS 66.
Club membership 445.
Visitors must contact in advance for Brinsea course and handicap certificate required for weekends. Lakeside is play & pay anytime. **Societies** Booking in advance by arrangement. **Green Fees** terms on application. **Cards** 🖃 💳 💳 💳 ♐ **Prof** John Blackburn & Robert Moss **Facilities** ⊗ ⑪ ⓛ 🍺 ♈ ⚐ 🏌️ ⚑ 🚲 ♐ **Location** 8m E of Weston-Super-Mare between A370 and A38

Hotel ★★★⚘ 74% Daneswood House Hotel, Cuck Hill, SHIPHAM ☎ 01934 843145 & 843945 📠 01934 843824 14 en suite 3 annexe en suite

Where to stay, where to eat?
Visit www.theAA.com

ENMORE Map 03 ST23

Enmore Park TA5 2AN
☎ 01278 671481 (office) & 671519 (pro) 🖷 01278 671740
e-mail: golfclub@enmore.fsnet.co.uk
Hilly, parkland course with water features on foothills of Quantocks. Wooded countryside and views of Quantocks and Mendips. 1st and 10th are testing holes.
18 holes, 6406yds, Par 71, SSS 71, Course record 66.
Club membership 750.
Visitors phone professional for details, must have handicap certificate for weekends. Societies must contact in advance.
Green Fees £30 per day; £20 per round (£30 per round weekends). Cards 💳 🖃 🆑 🖫 🆔 Prof Nigel Wixon
Course Designer Hawtree Facilities ⊗ 沆 ╚ ♥ 𝚈 ♬ 🏠 𝑇
🕈 ♨ ℰ Location A39 to Minehead, at first set of lights turn left to Spaxton, then 1.5m to reservoir and turn left
······················
Hotel ★★★ 71% Walnut Tree Hotel, North Petherton, BRIDGWATER ☎ 01278 662255 32 en suite

FARRINGTON GURNEY Map 03 ST65

Farrington Golf & Country Club Marsh Ln
BS39 6TS ☎ 01761 451596 🖷 01761 451021
e-mail: info@farringtongolfclub.net
USGA spec greens on both challenging 9 and 18 hole courses. Newly completed 18 hole course with computerised irrigation, six lakes, four tees per hole and excellent views. Testing holes include the 12th (282yds) with the green set behind a lake at the base of a 100ft drop, and the 17th which is played between two lakes.
Executive Course: 9 holes, 3002yds, Par 54, SSS 53, Course record 54.
Main Course: 18 holes, 6335yds, Par 72, SSS 71, Course record 66.
Club membership 750.
Visitors must book starting times and have a handicap certificate to play at weekends. Societies welcome except for weekends & bank holidays, telephone or write in advance.
Green Fees Main course: £30 per day, £22 per round (£36/28 weekends; Executive course; £10 per day; £5.50 per 9 holes (£13.50/£8 weekends). Cards 💳 🖃 🆑 🖫 Prof Jon Cowgill Course Designer Peter Thompson Facilities ⊗
沆 ╚ ♥ 𝚈 ♬ 🏠 𝑇 🕈 ♨ ℰ Leisure video teaching studio.Conf Thtr 150 Class 150 Board 150 Banquet 150
······················
Hotel ★★★ 71% Centurion Hotel, Charlton Ln, MIDSOMER NORTON ☎ 01761 417711 44 en suite

FROME Map 03 ST74

Frome Golf Centre Critchill Manor BA11 4LJ
☎ 01373 453410 🖷 01373 453410
e-mail: fromegolfclub@yahoo.co.uk
Attractive parkland course, founded in 1993, situated in a picturesque valley just outside the town, complete with practice areas and a driving range.
18 holes, 5466yds, Par 69, SSS 67, Course record 64.
Club membership 360.
Visitors tee times essential at weekends and bank holidays. Societies telephone in advance. Green Fees £18.50 per day; £13.50 per 18 holes; £10.50 per 9 holes (£20/£15.50/£12.50 weekends and bank holidays). Prof Murdock McEwan Facilities ⊗ ╚ ♥ 𝚈 ♬ 🏠 𝑇 ♨ ℰ Location A361 Frome/Shepton Mallet, at Nunney Catch rdbt through Nunney, course on left before Frome
······················
Hotel ★★ 65% The George at Nunney, 11 Church St, NUNNEY ☎ 01373 836458 9 rms (8 en suite)

Orchardleigh BA11 2PH
☎ 01373 454200 & 454206 🖷 01373 454202
Originally designed by Ryder Cup golfer, Brian Huggett, as two returning nines through mature parkland. Five lakes bring water into play on seven holes.
18 holes, 6831yds, Par 72, SSS 73, Course record 67.
Club membership 500.
Visitors no visitors before 11am at weekends. Societies apply in writing or telephone in advance. Green Fees £25 per round (£32.50 weekends & bank holidays). Cards 💳
🖃 🆑 🖫 🆔 Prof Ian Ridsdale Course Designer Brian Huggett Facilities ⊗ 沆 ╚ ♥ 𝚈 ♬ 🏠 𝑇 ♨ ℰ Leisure fishing. Location 1m W of Frome on the A362
······················
Hotel ★★ 65% The George at Nunney, 11 Church St, NUNNEY ☎ 01373 836458 9 rms (8 en suite)

GURNEY SLADE Map 03 ST64

Mendip BA3 4UT ☎ 01749 840570 🖷 01749 841439
e-mail: mendipgolfclub@lineone.net
Undulating downland course offering an interesting test of golf on superb fairways and extensive views over the surrounding countryside.
18 holes, 6383yds, Par 71, SSS 71, Course record 65.
Club membership 900.
Visitors Handicap certificates required for play at weekends and bank holidays. Societies by arrangement with secretary.
Green Fees not confirmed. Prof Adrian Marsh Course Designer C K Cotton Facilities ⊗ 沆 ╚ ♥ 𝚈 ♬ 🏠 𝑇 ℰ Location 1.5m S off A37
······················
Hotel ★★★ 71% Centurion Hotel, Charlton Ln, MIDSOMER NORTON ☎ 01761 417711 44 en suite

KEYNSHAM Map 03 ST66

Stockwood Vale Stockwood Ln BS31 2ER
☎ 0117 986 6505 🖷 0117 986 8974
e-mail: stockwoodvalegc@netscapeonline.co.uk
Undulating and challenging public course in a beautiful setting with interesting well bunkered holes, in particular the beautiful and challenging 5th and 13th holes.
18 holes, 6031yds, Par 71, SSS 69.
Club membership 600.
Visitors no restrictions, but must reserve a start time. Societies telephone in advance. Green Fees £15 per round (£17 weekends). Cards 💳 🖃 🆑 🖫 🆔 Prof John Richards Facilities ⊗ 沆 ╚ ♥ 𝚈 ♬ 🏠 ℰ ℰ Location Off Hicks Gate on A4 junct with A4174
······················
Guesthouse ◆◆◆◆ Grasmere Court Hotel, 22-24 Bath Rd, KEYNSHAM ☎ 0117 986 2662 16 en suite

LANGPORT Map 03 ST42

Long Sutton Long Sutton TA10 9JU
☎ 01458 241017 🖷 01458 241022
Gentle, undulating, Pay and Play course.
18 holes, 6367yds, Par 71, SSS 70, Course record 71.
Club membership 600.
Visitors advisable to phone in advance. Societies telephone in advance. Green Fees £16 per round (£20 weekends).
Cards 💳 🖃 🆑 🖫 🆔 Prof Andrew Hayes Course Designer Patrick Dawson Facilities ⊗ 沆 ╚ ♥ 𝚈 ♬ 🏠 𝑇 🕈 ♨ ℰ
ℰ Conf Max 100 Thtr 100 Class 40 Board 30 Banquet 120
Location 10m NW of Yeovil off A372
······················
Hotel ★★★ 71% The Hollies, Bower Hinton, MARTOCK ☎ 01935 822232 32 annexe en suite

LONG ASHTON   Map 03 ST57

Long Ashton The Clubhouse, Clarken Coombe
BS41 9DW ☎ 01275 392229 🖬 01275 394395
e-mail: secretary@longashtongolfclub
Wooded parkland course with fine turf, wonderful views
of Bristol and surrounding areas and a spacious practice
area. Good testing holes, especially the back nine, in
prevailing south-west winds. The short second hole
(126yds) cut from an old quarry and played over a road
can ruin many a card! Good drainage ensures pleasant
winter golf. Two extra holes have been added, giving a
variety of course.
Ashton Course: 18 holes, 6077yds, Par 70, SSS 70.
Coombe Course: 18 holes, 6381, Par 71, SSS 71.
Club membership 700.
Visitors with recognised handicap certificate. **Societies** must
contact the secretary in advance. **Green Fees** terms on
application. **Cards** 🖭 🟥 🟥 🔲 **Prof** Mike Hart **Course
Designer** J H Taylor **Facilities** ⊗ 🝙 🏌 🟫 ♀ 🐾 🏠 ⛳
Location 0.5m N on B3128

Hotel ★★★ 67% Redwood Lodge Hotel, Beggar Bush Ln,
Failand, BRISTOL ☎ 01275 393901 112 en suite

Woodspring Golf & Country Club Yanley Ln
BS18 9LR ☎ 01275 394378 🖬 01275 394473
Avon Course: 9 holes, 2960yds, Par 35, SSS 34.
Brunel Course: 9 holes, 3320yds, Par 37, SSS 35.
Severn Course: 9 holes, 3267yds, Par 36, SSS 35.
Course Designer Clarke/Alliss/Steel **Location** Off A38
Bridgewater Road
Telephone for further details

Hotel ★★★ 67% Redwood Lodge Hotel, Beggar Bush Ln,
Failand, BRISTOL ☎ 01275 393901 112 en suite

MIDSOMER NORTON   Map 03 ST65

Fosseway Golf Course Charlton Ln BA3 4BD
☎ 01761 412214 🖬 01761 418357
e-mail: centurion@centurionhotel.co.uk
Very attractive tree-lined parkland course, not
demanding but with lovely views towards the Mendip
Hills.
9 holes, 4565yds, Par 67, SSS 61.
Club membership 300.
Visitors may not play on Wed evenings, Sun mornings &
competition days. **Societies** apply in writing or telephone.
Green Fees £15 per day. **Cards** 🖭 🟥 🔲 **Course Designer**
C K Cotton/F Pennink **Facilities** ⊗ 🝙 🏌 🟫 ♀ 🐾 🏠 🏴 ⛳
Leisure heated indoor swimming pool, sauna, gymnasium.
Conf Thtr 220 Class 60 Board 40 Banquet 120 Del £22 to
£100 * **Location** SE of town centre off A367

Hotel ★★★ 71% Centurion Hotel, Charlton Ln,
MIDSOMER NORTON ☎ 01761 417711 44 en suite

MINEHEAD   Map 03 SS94

Minehead & West Somerset The Warren
TA24 5SJ ☎ 01643 702057 🖬 01643 705095
e-mail: secretary@mineheadgolf.co.uk
Flat seaside links, very exposed to wind, with good turf
set on a shingle bank. The last five holes adjacent to
the beach are testing. The 215-yard 18th is wedged
between the beach and the club buildings and provides
a good finish.
18 holes, 6228yds, Par 71, SSS 70, Course record 65.
Club membership 620.
continued

Visitors must contact secretary in advance. **Societies**
telephone in advance. **Green Fees** £26 (£30 weekends and
bank holidays). **Cards** 🖭 🟥 🟥 🔲 **Prof** Ian
Read **Facilities** ⊗ 🝙 🏌 🟫 ♀ 🐾 🏠 ⛳ **Location** E
end of esplanade

Hotel ★★ 78% Channel House Hotel, Church Path,
MINEHEAD ☎ 01643 703229 8 en suite

SALTFORD   Map 03 ST66

Saltford Golf Club Ln BS31 3AA
☎ 01225 873513 🖬 01225 873525
Parkland course with easy walking and panoramic views
over the Avon Valley. The par 4 2nd and 13th are
notable.
18 holes, 6081yds, Par 71, SSS 71.
Club membership 800.
Visitors must contact in advance & have handicap
certificate. **Societies** must telephone in advance. **Green Fees**
£28 per day; £24 per round (£32 per round weekends). **Prof**
Dudley Millinstead **Course Designer** Harry Vardon
Facilities ⊗ 🝙 🏌 🟫 ♀ 🐾 🏠 🏴 🐾 ⛳ **Conf** Class 30
Board 18 **Location** S side of village

Hotel ★★★🏅 77% Hunstrete House Hotel, HUNSTRETE
☎ 01761 490490 25 en suite

SOMERTON   Map 03 ST42

Wheathill Wheathill TA11 7HG
☎ 01963 240667 🖬 01963 240230
A par 68 parkland course with nice views in quiet
countryside. It is flat lying with the 13th hole along the
river. There is an Academy 4-hole course and a massive
practice area.
18 holes, 5362yds, Par 68, SSS 66.
Club membership 400.
Visitors no restrictions. **Societies** telephone to arrange.
Green Fees £15 (£20 weekends). **Prof** A England **Course
Designer** J Pain **Facilities** ⊗ 🝙 🏌 🟫 ♀ 🐾 🏠 🏴 🐾 ⛳
Leisure 8 hole academy course. **Location** 5m E of Somerton
off B3153

Hotel ★★★ 62% Wessex Hotel, High St, STREET
☎ 01458 443383 50 en suite

TAUNTON   Map 03 ST22

Oake Manor Oake TA4 1BA
☎ 01823 461993 🖬 01823 461995
e-mail: golf@oakemanor.co.uk

A parkland/lakeland course situated in breathtaking
Somerset countryside with views of the Quantock,
Blackdown and Brendon Hills. Ten holes feature water
hazards such as lakes, cascades and a trout stream. The
continued

15th hole (par 5, 476yds) is bounded by water all down the left with a carry over another lake on to an island green. The course is challenging yet great fun for all standards of golfer.
18 holes, 6109yds, Par 70, SSS 69.
Club membership 600.
Visitors no restrictions but visitors must book start times in order to avoid disappointment.Phone 01823 461993. **Societies** contact professional by telephone. **Green Fees** £20 per round (£25 weekends). **Cards** **Prof** Russell Gardner **Course Designer** Adrian Stiff **Facilities** **Conf** Max 250 **Location** Exit M5 junct 26, take A38 towards Taunton and follow signs to Oake

Hotel ★★★ 71% Rumwell Manor Hotel, Rumwell, TAUNTON ☎ 01823 461902 10 en suite 10 annexe en suite

Taunton & Pickeridge Corfe TA3 7BY
☎ 01823 421537 🖹 01823 421742
e-mail: sec@taunt-pickgolfclub.sagehost.co.uk
Downland course with extensive views of the Quantock and Mendip Hills,.established in 1892. Renowned for its excellent greens.
18 holes, 5927yds, Par 69, SSS 68, Course record 63.
Club membership 600.
Visitors must have a handicap certificate **Societies** must telephone in advance. **Green Fees** £26 per day; £22 per round (£30 weekends). **Prof** Gary Milne **Facilities** **Location** 4m S off B3170

Hotel ★★★ 75% The Mount Somerset Hotel, Henlade, TAUNTON ☎ 01823 442500 11 en suite

Taunton Vale Creech Heathfield TA3 5EY
☎ 01823 412220 🖹 01823 413583
e-mail: tvgc@easynet.co.uk
An 18 hole and a 9 hole golf course in a parkland complex occupying 156 acres in the Vale of Taunton. Complex includes a floodlit driving range.

Charlton Course: 18 holes, 6167yds, Par 70, SSS 69, Course record 65.
Durston Course: 9 holes, 2004yds, Par 64, SSS 60.
Club membership 800.
Visitors telephone booking essential. Contact Professional on 01823 412880 **Societies** must book in advance. **Green Fees** 18 hole: £19 per round; £28 per day(£23/£34 weekends). 9 hole:£9 per round;£13 per day(£11/£16 weekends). **Prof** Martin Keitch **Course Designer** John Payne **Facilities** **Conf** Max 40 Del from £50 * **Location** Off A361 between juncts 24 & 25 on M5

Hotel ★★★ 75% The Mount Somerset Hotel, Henlade, TAUNTON ☎ 01823 442500 11 en suite

Vivary Park Municipal Fons George TA1 3JU
☎ 01823 333875 🖹 01823 352713
e-mail: vivary.golf.course@tauntondeane.gov.uk
A parkland course, tight and narrow with ponds.
18 holes, 4620yds, Par 63, SSS 63, Course record 59.
Club membership 700.
Visitors may play anytime except weekends before 9am, bookings can be made 8 days in advance. **Societies** apply in writing. **Green Fees** not confirmed. **Prof** Mike Steadman **Course Designer** W H Fowler **Facilities** **Leisure** hard tennis courts. **Location** S side of town centre off A38

Hotel ★★ 67% Corner House Hotel, Park St, TAUNTON ☎ 01823 284683 33 rms (27 en suite)

WEDMORE — Map 03 ST44

Isle of Wedmore Lineage BS28 4QT
☎ 01934 713649 (Office) 712452 (Pro) 🖹 01934 713696
e-mail: graham@grahamcoombegolfshops.junglelink.co.uk
Gentle undulating course designed to maintain natural environment. Existing woodland and hedgerow enhanced by new planting. Magnificent panoramic views of Cheddar Valley and Glastonbury Tor.
18 holes, 6006yds, Par 70, SSS 69, Course record 71.
Club membership 680.
Visitors telephone professional in advance. Not before 9.30am weekends. **Societies** weekdays telephone in advance,weekends subject to competitions. **Green Fees** £20. **Cards** **Prof** Graham Coombe **Course Designer** Terry Murray **Facilities** **Leisure** indoor teaching studio & custom fitting centre. **Conf** Max 120 Thtr 160 Class 80 Board 100 Banquet 120 **Location** Off B3139 between Wells & Burnham-on-Sea

Hotel ★★★ 70% Swan Hotel, Sadler St, WELLS ☎ 01749 836300 35 en suite

WELLS — Map 03 ST54

Wells (Somerset) East Horrington Rd BA5 3DS
☎ 01749 675005 🖹 01749 675005
e-mail: secretary@wellsgolfclub99.freeserve.co.uk
Beautiful wooded course with wonderful views. The prevailing SW wind complicates the 448yd 3rd.
18 holes, 6015yds, Par 70, SSS 69, Course record 66.
Club membership 700.
Visitors must contact in advance & have handicap certificate weekends. Tee times restricted at weekends to after 9.30pm **Societies** must apply in advance. **Green Fees** £20 per day/round(£25 weekends). **Prof** Adrian Bishop **Facilities** **Location** 1.5m E off B3139

Hotel ★★★ 70% Swan Hotel, Sadler St, WELLS ☎ 01749 836300 35 en suite

WESTON-SUPER-MARE — Map 03 ST36

Weston-super-Mare Uphill Rd North BS23 4NQ
☎ 01934 626968 & 633360(pro) 🖹 01934 621360
e-mail: karen@wsmgolfclub.fsnet.co.uk
A compact and interesting layout with the opening hole adjacent to the beach. The sandy, links-type course is slightly undulating and has beautifully maintained turf and greens. The 15th is a testing 455-yard, par 4.
18 holes, 6300yds, Par 70, SSS 70, Course record 65.
Club membership 800.

continued

Visitors must have handicap certificate to play. Societies apply in writing or telephone. Green Fees terms on application. Cards 🔲 🔲 📱 Prof Mike Laband Course Designer T Dunne/Dr Mackenzie Facilities ⊗ 〼 ᐧ 🍷 ♀ 占 🕋 ♂ Location S side of town centre off A370

Hotel ★★★ 64% Beachlands Hotel, 17 Uphill Rd North, WESTON-SUPER-MARE ☎ 01934 621401 24 en suite

Worlebury Monks Hill BS22 9SX
☎ 01934 625789 📋 01934 621935
e-mail: secretary@worleburygc.co.uk
Situated on the ridge of Worlebury Hill, this seaside course offers fairly easy walking and extensive views of the Severn estuary and Wales.
18 holes, 5963yds, Par 70, SSS 69, Course record 66.
Club membership 650.
Visitors must be recognised golfers, handicap certificate or proof of club membership may be required. Societies apply in writing or telephone in advance. Green Fees £22 per day(£28 weekends). Prof Gary Marks Course Designer H Vardon Facilities ⊗ 〼 ᐧ 🍷 ♀ 占 🕋 ♂ Location 2m NE off A370

Hotel ★★★ 64% Beachlands Hotel, 17 Uphill Rd North, WESTON-SUPER-MARE ☎ 01934 621401 24 en suite

Yeovil Sherborne Rd BA21 5BW
☎ 01935 422965 📋 01935 411283
e-mail: yeovilgolfclub@yeovilgc.fsnet.co.uk
On the Old Course the opener lies by the River Yeo before the gentle climb to high downs with good views. The outstanding 14th and 15th holes present a challenge, being below the player with a deep railway cutting on the left of the green. The 1st on the Newton Course is played over the river which then leads to a challenging but scenic golf course.
Old Course: 18 holes, 6150yds, Par 72, SSS 70, Course record 64.
Newton Course: 9 holes, 4891yds, Par 68, SSS 65, Course record 63.
Club membership 1000.
Visitors must contact in advance. Members only before 9.30am and 12.30-2. Handicap certificate required for Old Course. Societies telephone in advance. Green Fees Old Course: £25 per round (£30 weekends). Newton Course: £18 per round (£20 weekends). Cards 🔲 🔲 🔲 🔲 📱 Prof Geoff Kite Course Designer Fowler & Allison Facilities ⊗ 〼 ᐧ 🍷 ♀ 占 🕋 ♂ ♂ Location 1m E on A30

Hotel ★★★ 73% Yeovil Court Hotel, West Coker Rd, YEOVIL ☎ 01935 863746 15 en suite 15 annexe en suite

STAFFORDSHIRE

Brocton Hall ST17 0TH
☎ 01785 661901 📋 01785 661591
Parkland course with gentle slopes in places, easy walking.
18 holes, 6064yds, Par 69, SSS 69, Course record 66.
Club membership 665.
Visitors not competition days. Must contact in advance. Societies must apply in advance. Green Fees terms on

continued

application. Course Designer Harry Vardon Facilities ⊗ 〼 ᐧ 🍷 ♀ 占 🕋 ♂ 🚜 ♂ Location NW side of village off A34

Hotel ★★★ 65% Garth Hotel, Wolverhampton Rd, Moss Pit, STAFFORD ☎ 01785 256124 60 en suite

Branston Burton Rd, Branston DE14 3DP
☎ 01283 512211 📋 01283 566984
e-mail: sales@branston-golf-club.co.uk
Flat semi-parkland course, adjacent to River Trent, on undulating ground with natural water hazards on 13 holes. A new 9 hole course has recently been opened.

18 holes, 6697yds, Par 72, SSS 72, Course record 65.
Club membership 800.
Visitors may not play before noon or at weekends. Must contact in advance. Societies must telephone in advance. Green Fees £28 per 18 holes (£40 weekends). Cards 🔲 🔲 🔲 📱 Prof Jacob Sture Course Designer G Ramshall Facilities ⊗ 〼 ᐧ 🍷 ♀ 占 🕋 ᐧ ♂ ♂ ⌂ Leisure heated indoor swimming pool, sauna, solarium, gymnasium, 9 hole course.Conf Max 80 Thtr 24 Class 28 Board 80 Del from £22.95 * Location 1.5m SW on A5121

Hotel ★★ 67% Ye Olde Dog & Partridge Hotel, High St, TUTBURY ☎ 01283 813030 6 en suite 14 annexe en suite

Burton-upon-Trent 43 Ashby Rd East DE15 0PS
☎ 01283 544551(sec) & 562240 (pro) 📋 01283 544551
e-mail: burtongolfclub@btinternet.com
Undulating parkland course with trees a major feature. There are testing par 3s at 10th and 12th. The 18th has a lake on the approach to the green.
18 holes, 6579yds, Par 71, SSS 71, Course record 64.
Club membership 650.
Visitors must contact in advance and have a handicap certificate. Societies must contact in advance. Green Fees £38 per day; £28 per round (£40/£32 weekends). Prof Gary Stafford Course Designer H S Colt Facilities ⊗ 〼 ᐧ 🍷 ♀ 占 🕋 ᐧ ♂ Location 3m E on A511

Guesthouse ♦♦♦♦ Edgecote Hotel, 179 Ashby Rd, BURTON UPON TRENT ☎ 01283 568966 11 rms (5 en suite)

Craythorne Craythorne Rd, Stretton DE13 0AZ
☎ 01283 564329 📋 01283 511908
e-mail: admin@craythorne.co.uk
A relatively short and challenging parkland course with tight fairways and views of the Trent Valley. Excellent greens. Suits all standards but particularly good for society players. The course is now settled and in good condition after major refurbishments.
18 holes, 5525yds, Par 68, SSS 67, Course record 66.
Club membership 450.

continued

The Craythorne

Visitors must contact in advance. **Societies** apply in writing or telephone for details. **Green Fees** £30 per day; £22 per round (£35/£28 weekends & bank holidays). **Cards** 📧 ▦ 🖭 **Prof** Steve Hadfield **Facilities** ⊗ ⑄ ⓑ ♨ ♀ ⌂ 🏐 ⸙ ❦ ⨼ ⎛ **Conf** Max 120 Thtr 100 Banquet 140 Del £26.50 * **Location** Off A38 through Stretton village

Guesthouse ◆◆◆◆ Edgecote Hotel, 179 Ashby Rd, BURTON UPON TRENT ☎ 01283 568966 11 rms (5 en suite)

Hoar Cross Hall Health Spa Golf Academy
Hoar Cross DE13 8QS ☎ 01283 575671 🖹 01283 575652
e-mail: info@hoarcross.co.uk
Golf academy located in the grounds of a stately home, now a well appointed health spa resort and hotel. Driving range, bunker and practice areas.
Club membership 300.
Visitors day guests & residents. **Societies** golfing societies that are resident only. **Green Fees** terms on application. **Prof** Richard Coy **Course Designer** Geoffrey Collins **Facilities** ⌂ 🏐 ♨ 🛒 ⎛ **Leisure** hard tennis courts, heated indoor swimming pool, sauna, solarium, gymnasium. **Conf** Thtr 150 Class 65 Board 50 Banquet 70 Del £60 *

Hotel ★★ 63% Claymar Hotel, 118A Main St, ALREWAS ☎ 01283 790202 20 en suite

Beau Desert Rugeley Rd, Hazelslade WS12 5PJ
☎ 01543 422626 🖹 01543 451137
Heathland course surrounded by a forest, and used as an Open Qualifier venue.
18 holes, 6310yds, Par 70, SSS 71, Course record 64.
Club membership 500.
Visitors are advised to contact professional in advance. **Societies** must contact in advance. **Green Fees** £40 per round (£50 weekends). **Prof** Barrie Stevens **Course Designer** Herbert Fowler **Facilities** ⊗ ⑄ ⓑ 🖭 ♀ ⌂ 🏐 ⸙ ⨼ ⎛ **Conf** Max 150 Del £10 to £50 * **Location** 0.5m NE of village

Hotel ★★★ 63% Roman Way Hotel, Watling St, Hatherton, CANNOCK ☎ 01543 572121 56 en suite

Cannock Park Stafford Rd WS11 2AL
☎ 01543 578850 🖹 01543 578850
e-mail: david.dunk@18global.co.uk
Part of a large leisure centre, this parkland-type course plays alongside Cannock Chase. Good drainage, open all year.
18 holes, 5149yds, Par 67, SSS 65.
Club membership 250.
Visitors telephone pro shop on 01543 578850 to book in

continued

advance. **Societies** please telephone in advance. **Green Fees** £9 per round (£11 weekends). **Prof** David Dunk **Course Designer** John Mainland **Facilities** ⊗ ⑄ ⓑ 🖭 ♀ ⌂ 🏐 ⸙ ⎛ ❦ **Leisure** hard tennis courts, heated indoor swimming pool, sauna, solarium, gymnasium. **Location** 0.5m N of town centre on A34

Hotel ★★★ 63% Roman Way Hotel, Watling St, Hatherton, CANNOCK ☎ 01543 572121 56 en suite

Enville Highgate Common DY7 5BN
☎ 01384 872074 (Office) 🖹 01384 873396
e-mail: enville@egolfclub.freeserve.co.uk
Easy walking on two fairly flat woodland/heathland courses - the 'Highgate' and the 'Lodge'.
Highgate Course: 18 holes, 6556yds, Par 72, SSS 72, Course record 65.
Lodge Course: 18 holes, 6290yds, Par 70, SSS 70, Course record 66.
Club membership 900.
Visitors must play with member at weekends. **Societies** phone initially for details. **Green Fees** £40 per 36 holes; £30 per 18 holes. **Prof** Sean Power **Facilities** ⊗ ⑄ ⓑ 🖭 ♀ ⌂ 🏐 ❦ 🛒 **Location** From Stourbridge take A458 towards Bridgnorth, after 4.5m turn right. Golf club signposted

Hotel ★★★★ 66% Mill Hotel & Restaurant, ALVELEY ☎ 01746 780437 21 en suite

Goldenhill Mobberley Rd ST6 5SS
☎ 01782 234200 🖹 01782 234303
Rolling parkland course with water features on six of the back nine holes.
18 holes, 5957yds, Par 71, SSS 69.
Club membership 300.
Visitors advisable to contact in advance. **Societies** must apply in writing or telephone. **Green Fees** not confirmed. **Facilities** ⊗ ⑄ ⓑ 🖭 ♀ ⌂ 🏐 ⸙ ❦ ⎛ **Location** On A50, 4m N of Stoke

Hotel ★★★ 71% Manor House Hotel, Audley Rd, ALSAGER ☎ 01270 884000 57 en suite

Himley Hall Golf Centre Log Cabin, Himley Hall Park DY3 4DF ☎ 01902 895207
Parkland course set in grounds of Himley Hall Park, with lovely views. Large practice area including a pitch-and-putt.
9 holes, 6215yds, Par 72, SSS 70, Course record 65.
Club membership 200.
Visitors restricted weekends. **Societies** welcome weekday, apply in writing or telephone in advance. **Green Fees** £7 per 9 holes; £10 per 18 holes. **Prof** Jeremy Nichols **Course Designer** A Baker **Facilities** ⓑ 🖭 ⌂ ⎛ **Location** 0.5m E on B4176

Hotel ★★★ 63% Himley Country Hotel, School Rd, HIMLEY ☎ 01902 896716 73 en suite

Leek Birchall, Cheddleton Rd ST13 5RE
☎ 01538 384779 🖹 01538 384535
Undulating, challenging mainly parkland course, reputedly one of the best in the area.
18 holes, 6218yds, Par 70, SSS 70, Course record 63.
Club membership 825.

continued

Visitors must contact Professional in advance, may not play after 3pm without a member. **Societies** must apply in advance. **Green Fees** £26 per day (£32 weekends). **Prof** Ian Benson **Facilities** ⊗ ⅷ ⮂ ⬛ ♥ ♀ ⬥ ⊡ ✐ **Location** 0.75m S on A520

···

Hotel ★★★ 69% George Hotel, Swan Square, Burslem, STOKE-ON-TRENT ☎ 01782 577544 39 en suite

Westwood (Leek) Newcastle Rd ST13 7AA
☎ 01538 398385 & 398897 (Prof) 🖹 01538 382485
A challenging moorland/parkland course set in beautiful open countryside with an undulating front nine. The back nine is more open and longer with the River Churnet coming into play on several holes.
18 holes, 6207yds, Par 70, SSS 69, Course record 66.
Club membership 700.
Visitors must book in advance. **Societies** apply by phone or in writing. **Green Fees** terms on application. **Prof** Neale Hyde **Facilities** ⊗ ⅷ ⮂ ⬛ ♥ ♀ ⬥ ⊡ ✐ **Conf** Thtr 30 Class 40 Board 25 Del from £50 * **Location** On A53, S of Leek

···

Hotel ★★★ 69% George Hotel, Swan Square, Burslem, STOKE-ON-TRENT ☎ 01782 577544 39 en suite

Seedy Mill Elmhurst WS13 8HE
☎ 01543 417333 🖹 01543 418098
e-mail: s.dixon@clubhaus.com
A 27 hole course in picturesque parkland scenery. Numerous holes crossed by meandering mill streams. Undulating greens defended by hazards lie in wait for the practised approach. Well appointed clubhouse.
18 holes, 6308yds, Par 72, SSS 70, Course record 68.
Club membership 1200.
Visitors must contact at least 3 days in advance, weekend time restrictions. **Societies** apply in writing or telephone. **Green Fees** terms on application. **Cards** ▨▨ ▨▨ ▨▨ ▨▨ 🆅 **Prof** Chris Stanley **Course Designer** Hawtree & Son **Facilities** ⊗ ⅷ ⮂ ⬛ ♥ ♀ ⊡ ❣ ⛳ ✐ ℟ **Conf** Max 120 Del from £22.50 * **Location** On B5014 at Elmhurst, 2m N of Lichfield, off A515

···

Hotel ★★★ 68% Little Barrow Hotel, Beacon St, LICHFIELD ☎ 01543 414500 24 en suite

---

Whittington Heath Tamworth Rd WS14 9PW
☎ 01543 432317 🖹 01543 433962
18 magnificent holes winding their way through heathland and trees, presenting a good test for the serious golfer. Leaving the fairway can be severely punished. The dog-legs are most tempting, inviting the golfer to chance his arm. Local knowledge is a definite advantage. Clear views of the famous three spires of Lichfield Cathedral.
18 holes, 6490yds, Par 70, SSS 71, Course record 64.
Club membership 660.
Visitors must contact in advance. May not play at weekends. Handicap certificate required. **Societies** welcome Wed & Thu, must apply in writing. **Green Fees** £50 per 36 holes; £42 per 27 holes; £35 per 18 holes.
Cards ▨▨ ▨▨ ▨▨ ▨▨ 🆅 **Prof** Adrian Sadler **Course Designer** Colt **Facilities** ⊗ ⅷ ⮂ ⬛ ♥ ♀ ⬥ **Location** 2.5m SE on A51 Lichfield-Tamworth road

···

Hotel ★★★ 68% Little Barrow Hotel, Beacon St, LICHFIELD ☎ 01543 414500 24 en suite

---

Keele Golf Centre Newcastle Rd, Keele ST5 5AB
☎ 01782 627596 🖹 01782 714555
e-mail: jackbarker_keelegolfcentreltd@hotmail.com
Parkland course with mature trees and great views of Stoke-on-Trent and surrounding area.

18 holes, 6396yds, Par 71, SSS 70, Course record 64.
Club membership 300.
Visitors must contact in advance, bookings from 7 days in advance. **Societies** **Green Fees** £9 per round (£13 weekends) £7 per 9 holes. **Cards** ▨▨ ▨▨ ▨▨ ▨▨ 🆅 **Facilities** ⊗ ⅷ ⮂ ⬛ ♥ ♀ ⬥ ❣ ❦ ⛳ ✐ ℟ **Location** On A525 towards Madeley opposite Keele university

···

Hotel ★★★ 66% Holiday Inn Stoke-on-Trent, Clayton Rd, NEWCASTLE-UNDER-LYME
☎ 0870 400 9077 119 en suite

Newcastle-Under-Lyme Whitmore Rd ST5 2QB
☎ 01782 617006
Parkland course.
18 holes, 6404yds, Par 72, SSS 71.
Club membership 600.
Visitors must contact in advance. With member only weekends. **Societies** must contact in advance. **Green Fees** not confirmed. **Prof** Paul Symonds **Facilities** ⮂ ⬛ ♀ ⬥ ⊡ ❣ ✐ **Location** 1m SW on A53

···

Hotel ★★ 62% Comfort Inn, Liverpool Rd, Cross Heath, NEWCASTLE-UNDER-LYME ☎ 01782 717000 43 en suite 24 annexe en suite

Wolstanton Dimsdale Old Hall, Hassam Pde,
Wolstanton ST5 9DR ☎ 01782 622413 (Sec) & 616995
A challenging undulating suburban course incorporating six difficult par 3 holes. The 6th hole (par 3) is 233yds from the Medal Tee.
18 holes, 5807yds, Par 68, SSS 68, Course record 63.
Club membership 700.
Visitors must contact in advance. May not play Tue (Ladies Day). With member only at weekends & bank holidays. **Societies** must contact in advance. **Green Fees** terms on application. **Cards** ▨▨ ▨▨ ▨▨ ▨▨ 🆅 **Prof** Simon Arnold **Facilities** ⊗ ⅷ ⮂ ⬛ ♥ ♀ ⬥ **Location** 1.5m from town centre. Turn off A34 at MacDonalds

···

Hotel ★★★ 66% Holiday Inn Stoke-on-Trent, Clayton Rd, NEWCASTLE-UNDER-LYME ☎ 0870 400 9077 119 en suite

Onneley CW3 5QF ☎ 01782 750577 & 846759
A parkland course offering panoramic views over Cheshire and Shropshire to the Welsh hills. *continued*

13 holes, 5781yds, Par 70, SSS 68.
Club membership 410.
Visitors welcome except during competitions, but may not play on Sun and with member only Sat and bank holidays. **Societies** packages available apply in writing to secretary, or by telephone. **Green Fees** £20 per day. **Facilities** ⊗ ⅧⅢ by prior arrangement ⓑ ⚑ ♀⚒ **Location** 2m from Woore on A525

Hotel ★★★ 66% Holiday Inn Stoke-on-Trent, Clayton Rd, NEWCASTLE-UNDER-LYME ☎ 0870 400 9077 119 en suite

PATTINGHAM   Map 07 SO89

Patshull Park Hotel Golf & Country Club
WV6 7HR ☎ 01902 700100 🖺 01902 700874
e-mail: sales@patshull-park.co.uk
Picturesque course set in 280 acres of glorious Capability Brown landscaped parkland. Designed by John Jacobs, the course meanders alongside trout fishing lakes. Water comes into play alongside the 3rd hole and there is a challenging drive over water on the 13th. Wellingtonia and cedar trees prove an obstacle to wayward drives off several holes. The 12th is the toughest hole on the course and the tee shot is vital, anything wayward and the trees block out the second to the green.

Patshull Park: 18 holes, 6400yds, Par 72, SSS 71, Course record 64.
Club membership 330.
Visitors must contact in advance. **Societies** must contact in advance. **Green Fees** £30 per round (£40 weekends & bank holidays). **Cards** 🌐 ▆ 🔲 🔲 🔲 🔲 **Prof** Richard Bissell **Course Designer** John Jacobs **Facilities** ⊗ ⅧⅢ ⓑ ⚑ ♀⚒🏠⛳🏥🚗⚓ **Leisure** heated indoor swimming pool, fishing, sauna, solarium, gymnasium. **Conf** Thtr 160 Class 64 Board 44 Banquet 160 Del £25 to £35 * **Location** 1.5m W of Pattingham at Pattingham Church take the Patshull Rd, Golf club on right

Hotel ★★★ 68% Patshull Park Hotel Golf & Country Club, Patshull Park, PATTINGHAM ☎ 01902 700100 49 en suite

PERTON   Map 07 SO89

Perton Park Wrottesley Park Rd WV6 7HL
☎ 01902 380103 & 380073 🖺 01902 326219
e-mail: golf@swindonperton.fsbusiness.co.uk
Challenging inland links style course set in the picturesque Staffordshire countryside.
18 holes, 6520yds, Par 72, SSS 72, Course record 61.
Club membership 500.
Visitors must book in advance. **Societies** must telephone in advance. **Green Fees** £12 per round (£18 weekends & bank holidays). **Cards** 🌐 ▆ **Prof** Jeremy Harrold **Facilities** ⊗ ⅧⅢ ⓑ ⚑ ♀⚒🏠⛳🚗⚓⚓✶ **Leisure** hard tennis courts, bowling greens. **Location** 6m W of Wolverhampton, off A454   *continued*

Hotel ★★ 69% Ely House Hotel, 53 Tettenhall Rd, WOLVERHAMPTON ☎ 01902 311311 19 en suite

RUGELEY   Map 07 SK01

St Thomas's Priory Armitage Ln WS15 1ED
☎ 01543 492096 🖺 01543 492244
Set in 160 acres of rolling Staffordshire countryside.
18 holes, 5969yds, Par 70, SSS 70, Course record 64.
Club membership 400.
Visitors phone in advance. **Societies** telephone in advance. **Green Fees** £20 per round (£25 weekends). **Cards** 🌐 ▆ 🔲 🔲 🔲 **Prof** Richard O'Hanlon **Course Designer** P 1 Mulholland **Facilities** ⊗ ⅧⅢ ⓑ ⚑ ♀⚒🏠⛳🚗⚓⚓ **Leisure** fishing. **Location** off A51 on A513

Hotel ⟰ Travelodge, Western Springs Rd, RUGELEY ☎ 01889 570096 32 en suite

STAFFORD   Map 07 SJ92

Stafford Castle Newport Rd ST16 1BP
☎ 01785 223821
Parkland type course built around Stafford Castle.
9 holes, 6382yds, Par 71, SSS 70, Course record 68.
Club membership 400.
Visitors must contact in advance. May not play Sun morning. **Societies** must apply in writing or by telephone. **Green Fees** £16 per day (£20 weekends). **Facilities** ⊗ ⅧⅢ ⓑ ⚑ ♀⚒ **Location** SW side of town centre off A518

Hotel ★★★ 65% Garth Hotel, Wolverhampton Rd, Moss Pit, STAFFORD ☎ 01785 256124 60 en suite

STOKE-ON-TRENT   Map 07 SJ84

Burslem Wood Farm, High Ln, Tunstall ST6 7JT
☎ 01782 837006
9 holes, 5354yds, Par 66, SSS 66, Course record 66.
Location 4m N of city centre on B5049
Telephone for further details

Hotel ★★★ 69% George Hotel, Swan Square, Burslem, STOKE-ON-TRENT ☎ 01782 577544 39 en suite

Greenway Hall Stanley Rd, Stockton Brook ST9 9LJ
☎ 01782 503158 🖺 01782 504259
e-mail: jackbarker_greenwayhallgolfclub@hotmail.com
Moorland course with fine views of the Pennines.

18 holes, 5678yds, Par 68, SSS 67, Course record 65.
Club membership 350.
Visitors welcome any time. **Societies** telephone for information and availability. **Green Fees** £10(£13.50 weekends). **Cards** 🌐 ▆ 🔲 🔲 🔲 🔲 **Prof** Mark Armitage **Facilities** ⊗ ⅧⅢ ⓑ ⚑ ♀⚒🏠⛳⚓⚓✶ **Conf** Max 50 **Location** 5m NE off A53

Hotel ★★★ 69% George Hotel, Swan Square, Burslem, STOKE-ON-TRENT ☎ 01782 577544 39 en suite

Trentham 14 Barlaston Old Rd, Trentham ST4 8HB
☎ 01782 658109 📠 01782 644024
e-mail: secretary@trenthamgolf.org
Parkland course. The par 3, 4th is a testing hole reached
through a copse of trees.

18 holes, 6644yds, Par 72, SSS 72, Course record 67.
Club membership 600.
Visitors must contact in advance. Societies must contact in
advance. Green Fees terms on application. Cards 🖃 🖃 📀
Prof Sandy Wilson Course Designer Colt & Alison
Facilities ⊗ ⍫ ⅃ ⅃ 🍺 ⅄ 🏌️ 🏠 🏹 🛺 ✎ ⅃ Leisure
squash. Location 1st right off A5035 from Trentham
Gardens, A34 junct 3 m South of Newcastle under Lyme

Hotel ★★★ 66% Haydon House Hotel, Haydon St,
Basford, STOKE-ON-TRENT ☎ 01782 711311
17 en suite 6 annexe en suite

Trentham Park Trentham Park ST4 8AE
☎ 01782 658800 📠 01782 658800
e-mail: trevor-berrisford@barbox.net
Fine woodland course. Set in established parkland with
many challenging and interesting holes.
18 holes, 6425yds, Par 71, SSS 71, Course record 67.
Club membership 850.
Visitors must contact in advance. Societies Wed & Fri, must
apply in advance. Green Fees £27.50 per round(£32
weekends). Prof Brian Rimmer Facilities ⊗ ⍫ ⅃ ⍲ 🍺 ⅄ ⅃
🏠 🏹 🛺 ✎ Location Adjacent to Trentham Gardens, off
A34 3m S of Newcastle-under-Lyme

Hotel ★★★ 66% Holiday Inn Stoke-on-Trent, Clayton Rd,
NEWCASTLE-UNDER-LYME ☎ 0870 400 9077
119 en suite

Barlaston Meaford Rd ST15 8UX
☎ 01782 372795 & 372867 📠 01782 372867
e-mail: barlaston.gc@virgin.net
Picturesque meadowland course designed by Peter Alliss.
18 holes, 5800yds, Par 69, SSS 68.
Club membership 650.
Visitors may not play before 10am or after 4pm Fridays,
weekends and bank holidays after 10 am. Societies telephone
or apply in writing. Green Fees terms on application. Prof
Ian Rogers Course Designer Peter Alliss Facilities ⊗ ⍫ ⅃
🍺 ⅄ 🏠 ✎ ⅃ Location 9 miles N junct 14 & 5 miles S
junct 15 of M6.

Hotel ★★★ 68% Stone House Hotel, Stafford Rd, STONE
☎ 01785 815531 50 en suite

AA website: www.theAA.com

Izaak Walton Eccleshall Rd, Cold Norton ST15 0NS
☎ 01785 760900
A gently undulating meadowland course with streams
and ponds as features.
18 holes, 6281yds, Par 72, SSS 72, Course record 72.
Club membership 400.
Visitors must contact in advance for weekends play.
Societies must telephone in advance. Green Fees not
confirmed. Prof Julie Brown Facilities ⊗ ⍫ ⅃ 🍺 ⅄ 🏠
✎ ⅃ Location On B5026 between Stone & Eccleshall

Hotel ★★★ 68% Stone House Hotel, Stafford Rd, STONE
☎ 01785 815531 50 en suite

Stone Filleybrooks ST15 0NB ☎ 01785 813103
9-hole parkland course with easy walking and 18
different tees.
9 holes, 6299yds, Par 71, SSS 70, Course record 67.
Club membership 310.
Visitors with member only weekends & bank holidays.
Societies must apply in writing. Green Fees £20 per
day/round. Facilities ⊗ ⍫ ⅃ 🍺 ⅄ 🏠 ✎ Location 0.5m W
on A34

Hotel ★★★ 68% Stone House Hotel, Stafford Rd, STONE
☎ 01785 815531 50 en suite

Drayton Park Drayton Park, Fazeley B78 3TN
☎ 01827 251139 📠 01827 284035
Parkland course designed by James Braid. Club
established since 1897.
18 holes, 6439yds, Par 71, SSS 71, Course record 62.
Club membership 550.
Visitors with member only weekends. Must book in advance
(call either professional or secretary). Societies must apply in
writing. Green Fees £34 per day(£40 per round weekends).
Cards 🖃 🖃 🖃 📀 🖃 📀 Prof M W Passmore Course
Designer James Braid Facilities ⊗ ⍫ ⅃ 🍺 ⅄ 🏠 🛺 ✎
Location 2m S on A4091, next to Drayton Manor Leisure
Park

Hotel ★★★★ 75% The De Vere Belfry, WISHAW
☎ 01675 470301 324 en suite

Tamworth Municipal Eagle Dr, Amington B77 4EG
☎ 01827 709303 📠 01827 709304
First-class municipal, parkland course and a good test of
golf.
18 holes, 6488yds, Par 73, SSS 72, Course record 63.
Club membership 460.
Visitors must book in advance at weekends. Societies must
contact in advance. Green Fees £14. Cards 🖃 📀 Prof
Wayne Allcock Course Designer Hawtree & Son Facilities
⊗ ⍫ ⅃ 🍺 ⅄ 🏠 🏌️ 🏹 ✎ ⅃ Location 2.5m E off
B5000

Hotel ★★ 64% Angel Croft Hotel, Beacon St, LICHFIELD
☎ 01543 258737 10 rms (8 en suite) 8 annexe en suite

Manor Leese Hill, Kingstone ST14 8QT
☎ 01889 563234 📠 01889 563234
e-mail: ant-foulds@bigfoot.com
A short but tough course set in the heart of the
Staffordshire countryside with fine views of the
surrounding area.

continued

18 holes, 6060yds, Par 71, SSS 69, Course record 67.
Club membership 400.
Visitors must contact in advance. **Societies** must telephone in advance. **Green Fees** £7.50/12.50 (£12.50/20 weekends). **Cards** 💳 ▬ ▬ 🅿️ **Course Designer** Various **Facilities** ⊗)∭ ⮫ 🖐 💺 🍴 🏠 ↝ 🛒 ♂ (**Leisure** fishing. **Location** 2m from Uttoxeter on A518 towards Stafford

Hotel ★★★ 68% Stone House Hotel, Stafford Rd, STONE ☎ 01785 815531 50 en suite

Uttoxeter Wood Ln ST14 8JR
☎ 01889 564884 (Pro) & 566552 (Office) 🗎 01889 567501
Undulating, challenging course with spectacular views over the Dove valley and at times adjacent to the racecourse.
18 holes, 5710yds, Par 70, SSS 69, Course record 66.
Club membership 900.
Visitors restricted weekends and competition days. Advisable to check availability during peak periods. **Societies** must book in advance. **Green Fees** £20 per round;£25 per day(£30 per round weekends). **Cards** 💳 ▬ 🎴 Prof Adam McCandless **Course Designer** G Rothera **Facilities** ⊗)∭ ⮫ 🖐 💺 🍴 🏠 🛒 ♂ **Location** Close to A50, 0.5m beyond main entrance to racecourse

Hotel ★★★ 68% Stone House Hotel, Stafford Rd, STONE ☎ 01785 815531 50 en suite

Ingestre Park ST18 0RE
☎ 01889 270845 🗎 01889 270845
Parkland course set in the grounds of Ingestre Hall, former home of the Earl of Shrewsbury, with mature trees and pleasant views.
18 holes, 6268yds, Par 70, SSS 70, Course record 67.
Club membership 750.
Visitors with member only weekends & bank holidays. Must play before 3.30pm weekdays. Advance booking preferred. Handicap certificate required. **Societies** must apply in advance. **Green Fees** £30 per day; £25 per round. **Prof** Danny Scullion **Course Designer** Hawtree **Facilities** ⊗)∭ ⮫ 🖐 💺 🍴 🏠 🛒 ♂ **Location** 2m SE off A51

Hotel ★★★ 66% Tillington Hall Hotel, Eccleshall Rd, STAFFORD ☎ 01785 253531 91 en suite

Whiston Hall Whiston Hall ST10 2HZ
☎ 01538 266260 🗎 01538 266820
A challenging 18-hole course in scenic countryside, incorporating many natural obstacles and providing a test for all golfing abilities.
18 holes, 5742yds, Par 71, SSS 69, Course record 70.
Club membership 400.
Visitors reasonable dress on the course. Must telephone in advance at weekends. **Societies** phone for details. **Green Fees** £10 per round. **Prof** Derry Goodburn **Course Designer** T Cooper **Facilities** ⊗)∭ ⮫ 🖐 💺 🍴 🏠 ♂ **Leisure** fishing, snooker. **Location** Off A52, between Stoke-on-Trent and Ashbourne

Hotel ★★★ 69% George Hotel, Swan Square, Burslem, STOKE-ON-TRENT ☎ 01782 577544 39 en suite

---

Looking for a driving range?
See the index at the back of the guide

WENTWORTH
HOTEL ★★★
Aldeburgh, Suffolk
Tel: (01728) 452312 Fax: (01728) 454343
E-mail: stay@wentworth-aldeburgh.co.uk
Website: www.wentworth-aldeburgh.com

The Hotel has the comfort and style of a Country House. Two comfortable lounges, with open fires and antique furniture, provide ample space to relax. Each individually decorated bedroom, many with sea views, is equipped with a colour television, radio, hairdryer and tea making facilities. The Restaurant serves a variety of fresh produce whilst a light lunch can be chosen from the Bar menu, eaten outside in the sunken terrace garden. Aldeburgh is timeless and unhurried. There are quality shops, two excellent golf courses within a short distance from the hotel, long walks and some of the best birdwatching at Minsmere Bird reserve. Music and the Arts can be heard at the Internationally famous Snape Malting Concert hall. Lastly, there are miles of beach to sit upon and watch the sea!

Aldeburgh Saxmundham Rd IP15 5PE
☎ 01728 452890 🗎 01728 452937
e-mail: info@aldeburghgolfclub.co.uk
Fine heathland golf course providing a varied and interesting challenge for the handicap golfer. Additional 9 hole course suitable for golfing holiday makers.
18 holes, 6349yds, Par 68, SSS 71, Course record 65. River Course: 9 holes, 4228yds, Par 64, SSS 61, Course record 62. Club membership 900.
Visitors must contact in advance and have a handicap certificate. 2 ball/foursomes only. **Societies** must contact in advance. **Green Fees** Aldeburgh Course: £50 per day (£60 weekend). River Course: up to £15. **Prof** Keith Preston **Course Designer** various **Facilities** ⊗ ⮫ 🖐 💺 💺 🏠 🍴 ♂ **Location** 1m W of Aldeburgh on A1094

Wentworth Hotel

continued

Hotel ★★★ 74% Wentworth Hotel, Wentworth Rd,
ALDEBURGH ☎ 01728 452312 30 rms (28 en suite) 7
annexe en suite   *See photograph on page 211*

BECCLES   Map 05 TM49

Beccles The Common NR34 9YN ☎ 01502 712244
**Common course with gorse bushes, no water hazards or
bunkers.**
9 holes, 2779yds, Par 68, SSS 67.
Club membership 175.
Visitors no restrictions. **Societies** must telephone in advance.
Green Fees terms on application. **Facilities** ♀ ♨ 🖻 ✑
Location NE side of town

Hotel ★★★ 65% Hotel Hatfield, The Esplanade,
LOWESTOFT ☎ 01502 565337 33 en suite

BUNGAY   Map 05 TM38

Bungay & Waveney Valley Outney Common
NR35 1DS ☎ 01986 892337 🗎 01986 892222
e-mail: bungaygolf@aol.com
**Heathland course partly comprising Neolithic stone
workings, easy walking.**
18 holes, 6044yds, Par 69, SSS 69, Course record 64.
Club membership 730.
Visitors should contact in advance. With member only
weekends & bank holidays. **Societies** must contact in
advance. **Green Fees** not confirmed. **Cards** 💳 💳 💳
💳 🔊 **Prof** Nigel Whyte **Course Designer** James Braid
Facilities ⊗ ♨ ♛ ♀ ♨ 🖻 ⚑ 🛺 ✑ **Location** 0.5m NW
on A143

Hotel ★★★ 65% Hotel Hatfield, The Esplanade,
LOWESTOFT ☎ 01502 565337 33 en suite

BURY ST EDMUNDS   Map 05 TL86

Bury St Edmunds Tut Hill IP28 6LG
☎ 01284 755979 🗎 01284 763288
e-mail: bury.golf@talk21.com
**Undulating parkland course with easy walking and
attractive short holes, but quite long. Nine hole course
made up of five par 3s and four par 4s.**
18 holes, 6669yds, Par 72, SSS 72, Course record 68.
9 holes, 2217yds, Par 62, SSS 62.
Club membership 850.
Visitors with member only at weekends for 18 hole course.
Societies must apply in writing. **Green Fees** not confirmed.
Cards 💳 💳 💳 💳 🔊 **Prof** Mark Jillings **Course
Designer** Ted Ray **Facilities** ⊗ 🎿 by prior arrangement ♨
♛ ♀ ♨ 🖻 ⚑ ✑ **Location** 2m NW on B1106 off A14

Hotel ★★★ 71% Angel Hotel, Angel Hill, BURY ST
EDMUNDS ☎ 01284 714000 64 en suite

The Suffolk Golf & Country Club Fornham St
Genevieve IP28 6JQ ☎ 01284 706777 🗎 01284 706721
e-mail: thelodge@the-suffolk.co.uk
**A classic parkland course with the River Lark running
through it. Criss-crossed by ponds and streams with rich
fairways. Considerable upgrading of the course in recent
years and the three finishing holes are particularly
challenging.**
*The Genevieve Course: 18 holes, 6376yds, Par 72, SSS 71,
Course record 70.*
Club membership 600.
Visitors contact in advance to book tee times. **Societies**
telephone for details. **Green Fees** £25 per round (£30
continued

THE SUFFOLK GOLF AND COUNTRY CLUB

- Modern 3★★★ Hotel overlooking golf course
- All rooms en suite with Sat TV & modem ports
- Indoor Pool Spa Sauna & Steam Room • Large
air cond. Gymnasium • 18-hole Genevieve
Course • Buggy & Trolley hire • Beauty &
Hairdressing salon • Preferential green fees for
hotel guests • Golf breaks available
• 5 mins. from the A14

**Fornham St. Genevieve,
Bury St. Edmunds, Suffolk IP28 6JQ
01284-706777**
www.the-suffolk.co.uk
e-mail: thelodge@the-suffolk.co.uk

The Suffolk Golf & Country Club

weekends). **Cards** 💳 💳 **Prof** Steve Hall **Facilities** ⊗ 🎿
♨ ♛ ♀ ♨ 🖻 ⚑ ♐ 🛺 ✑ **Leisure** heated indoor
swimming pool, fishing, sauna, solarium, gymnasium. **Conf**
Max 150 Thtr 150 Board 38 Banquet 140 Del from £25 *
Location Off the A14 onto the B1106 to Fornham

Hotel ★★★★ 74% Ravenwood Hall Hotel, Rougham,
BURY ST EDMUNDS ☎ 01359 270345
7 en suite 7 annexe en suite

CRETINGHAM   Map 05 TM26

Cretingham IP13 7BA
☎ 01728 685275 🗎 01728 685037
Parkland course.
18 holes, 4968yds, Par 68, SSS 66.
Club membership 350.
Visitors booking required for weekends. **Societies** must
contact in advance. **Green Fees** £14 (£16 weekends & bank
holidays). **Cards** 💳 💳 💳 💳 🔊 **Prof** Neil Jackson
continued

Course Designer J Austin **Facilities** ⊗ 🥂 ☎ ♀ ♨ 🏠 🛥 🚗
🚲 ♂ ♈ **Leisure** hard tennis courts, outdoor swimming pool,
fishing, pitch & putt, 9 hole course.**Conf** Banquet 120
Location 2m from A1120 at Earl Soham

....

Hotel ★★ 66% Cedars Hotel, Needham Rd,
STOWMARKET ☎ 01449 612668 25 en suite

FELIXSTOWE   Map 05 TM33
Felixstowe Ferry Ferry Rd IP11 9RY
☎ 01394 286834 📄 01394 273679
e-mail: secretary@felixstowegolf.co.uk
Seaside links course, pleasant views, easy walking.
Testing 491 yd, 7th hole. 9 hole course now open.
Martello Course: 18 holes, 6272yds, Par 72, SSS 70,
Course record 66.
Kingsfleet: 9 holes, 2986yds, Par 35, SSS 35.
Club membership 900.
Visitors may play Martello Course weekends after 2.30pm
and must contact in advance. Kingsfleet course no
restrictions. **Societies** Tue, Wed & Fri. **Green Fees** Martello
£30 (£20 after 1pm); £35 after 2.30pm weekends and bank
holidays. Kingsfleet £15 per day; £10 per 9 holes. **Prof** Ian
MacPherson **Course Designer** Henry Cotton **Facilities** ⊗ 🎿
by prior arrangement 🥂 ☎ ♀ ♨ 🏠 ♂ **Location** NE
side of town centre. Signposted from A14

....

Hotel ★★★ 70% Orwell Hotel, Hamilton Rd,
FELIXSTOWE ☎ 01394 285511 58 en suite

FLEMPTON   Map 05 TL86
Flempton IP28 6EQ ☎ 01284 728291
e-mail: flempton.golf@btinternet.com
Breckland course.
9 holes, 6240yds, Par 70, SSS 70.
Club membership 250.
Visitors must contact in advance and produce handicap
certificate. With member only weekends & bank holidays.
Societies limited to small societies - must apply in writing.
Green Fees £30 per day. **Prof** Chris Aldred **Course**
Designer J H Taylor **Facilities** ⊗ 🥂 ☎ ♀ ♨ 🏠 ♂
Location 0.5m W on A1101

....

Hotel ★★★ 71% The Priory Hotel, Tollgate, BURY ST
EDMUNDS ☎ 01284 766181 9 en suite 30 annexe en suite

HALESWORTH   Map 05 TM37
Halesworth Bramfield Rd IP19 9XA
☎ 01986 875567 📄 01986 874565
A 27-hole professionally designed parkland complex of
one 18 hole membership course and a 9 hole pay and
play.
18 holes, 6580yds, Par 72, SSS 72, Course record 71.
9 holes, 2398yds, Par 33, SSS 33.
Club membership 300.
Visitors visitors welcome at all times except for Sunday
before noon on the 18 hole course. Handicap certificate
required for 18 hole course. **Societies** telephone for booking
form. **Green Fees** terms on application. **Prof** Simon Harrison
Course Designer J W Johnson **Facilities** ⊗ 🎿 🥂 ☎ ♀ ♨
🏠 🛥 🚲 ♂ ♈ **Conf** Max 40 Del £10 to £25 * **Location**
0.75m S of town, signposted on left of A144 road to
Bramfield

....

Hotel ★★★ 72% Swan Hotel, Market Place,
SOUTHWOLD ☎ 01502 722186
26 rms (25 en suite) 17 annexe en suite

HAVERHILL   Map 05 TL64
Haverhill Coupals Rd CB9 7UW
☎ 01440 761951 📄 01440 761951
e-mail: haverhillgolf@coupalsroad.fsnet.co.uk
An 18 hole course lying across two valleys in pleasant
parkland. The front nine with undulating fairways is
complimented by a saucer-shaped back nine, bisected by
the River Stour, presenting a challenge to golfers of all
standards.
18 holes, 5929yds, Par 70, SSS 69, Course record 67.
Club membership 767.
Visitors telephone to check for club competitions. **Societies**
must contact in advance. Tue & Thu only. **Green Fees** £25
per day (£32 weekends and bank holidays). **Cards** 💳 💳
💳 💳 💳 🅿️ **Prof** Nick Duc **Course Designer** P
Pilgrem/C Lawrie **Facilities** ⊗ 🎿 🥂 ☎ ♀ ♨ 🏠 ♂
Leisure chipping green. **Conf** Max 49 **Location** 1m SE off
A1017

....

Hotel ★★ 72% Four Seasons Hotel, Walden Rd,
THAXTED ☎ 01371 830129 9 en suite

HINTLESHAM   Map 05 TM04
Hintlesham Hall IP8 3NS
☎ 01473 652761 📄 01473 652750
e-mail: office@hintlefhamhallgolfclub.com
Magnificent championship length course blending
harmoniously with the ancient parkland surrounding
this exclusive hotel. The 6630yd parkland course was
designed by Hawtree and Son, one of the oldest
established firms of golf course architects in the world.
The course is fair but challenging for low and high
handicappers alike. Hotel offers beautiful
accommodation, excellent cuisine and many facilities.

18 holes, 6638yds, Par 72, SSS 72, Course record 63.
Club membership 470.
Visitors must contact 48 hours in advance. **Societies** must
telephone in advance. **Green Fees** £46 per day; £34 per
round,(£54/£42 weekends & bank holidays). **Cards** 💳
💳 💳 🅿️ **Prof** Alastair Spink **Course Designer**
Hawtree & Sons **Facilities** ⊗ 🎿 🥂 ☎ ♀ ♨ 🏠 🛥 🚗 🍴
🚲 ♂ **Leisure** hard tennis courts, heated outdoor
swimming pool, sauna, gymnasium. **Location** In village
on A1071

....

Hotel ★★★★♨ Hintlesham Hall Hotel, HINTLESHAM
☎ 01473 652334 & 652268 📄 01473 652463 33 en suite

┌─────────────────────────────────────┐
│   Prices may change during the   │
│   currency of the Guide, please   │
│   check when booking   │
└─────────────────────────────────────┘

IPSWICH — Map 05 TM14

Alnesbourne Priory Priory Park IP10 0JT
☎ 01473 727393 📄 01473 278372
e-mail: PrioryParkIpswich@msn.com
A fabulous outlook facing due south across the River Orwell is one of the many good features of this course set in woodland. All holes run among trees with some fairways requiring straight shots. The 8th green is on saltings by the river.
9 holes, 1700yds, Par 29.
Club membership 30.
Visitors closed on Tuesday. Closed 8 Jan-01 Mar. **Societies** Tue only, telephone in advance. **Green Fees** £10per day (£11 Sat; £12 Sun & bank holidays). **Facilities** ⊗ ⫫ ⤶ ⤴ 🍴 ⤳ **Location** 3m SE, off A14

Hotel ★★★ 69% Courtyard by Marriott Ipswich, The Havens, Ransomes Europark, IPSWICH ☎ 01473 272244 60 en suite

Fynn Valley IP6 9JA
☎ 01473 785267 📄 01473 785632
e-mail: enquiries@fynn-valley.co.uk
Undulating parkland course plus par 3 nine-hole and driving range.
18 holes, 6310yds, Par 70, SSS 71, Course record 67.
Club membership 700.
Visitors members only Sun until 10.30am. **Societies** must apply in advance. **Green Fees** 18 holes: £22 (£25 weekends). 9 holes £12. **Cards** ⬜ ⬜ **Prof** K Vince/ P Wilby/ A Lucas **Course Designer** Tony Tyrrell **Facilities** ⊗ ⫫ ⤶ ⤴ ⤳ ⤴ 🍴 ⤳ **Leisure** Par 3 course, practice bunker.**Conf** Max 180 Thtr 150 Class 50 Board 65 Banquet 180 Del £1.50 to £11.40 * **Location** 2m N of Ipswich on B1077

Hotel ★★★ 65% Novotel Ipswich, Greyfriars Rd, IPSWICH ☎ 01473 232400 100 en suite

Ipswich Purdis Heath IP3 8UQ
☎ 01473 728941 📄 01473 715236
e-mail: mail@ipswichgolfclub.com
Many golfers are suprised when they hear that Ipswich has, at Purdis Heath, a first-class golf course. In some ways it resembles some of Surrey's better courses; a beautiful heathland course with two lakes and easy walking.
18 holes, 6435yds, Par 71, SSS 71, Course record 64 or 9 holes, 1930yds, Par 31.
Club membership 865.
Visitors must contact in advance & have a handicap certificate for 18 hole course. **Societies** must contact in advance. **Green Fees** 18 hole course: £40 per day; £30 per round (£45/£35 weekends & bank holidays). 9 hole course: £10 per day (£12.50 weekends & bank holidays). **Cards** ⬜ ⬜ ⬜ **Prof** Stephen Whymark **Course Designer** James Braid **Facilities** ⊗ ⤶ ⤴ ⤳ ⤴ 🍴 ⤳ **Location** 3 miles E of town centre off A1156, 1m from St Augustines church on Bucklesham road

Hotel ★★★ 73% Marlborough Hotel, Henley Rd, IPSWICH ☎ 01473 226789 22 en suite

Rushmere Rushmere Heath IP4 5QQ
☎ 01473 725648 📄 01473 273852
e-mail: rushmeregolfclub@talk21.com
Heathland course with gorse and prevailing winds. A good test of golf.
continued

18 holes, 6262yds, Par 70, SSS 70, Course record 66.
Club membership 700.
Visitors not before 2.30pm weekends & bank holidays. Must have a handicap certificate. Must contact in advance.
Societies weekdays by arrangement. **Green Fees** £25 per round/day. **Cards** ⬜ ⬜ ⬜ ⬜ ⬜ **Prof** N T J McNeill **Facilities** ⊗ ⫫ ⤶ ⤴ ⤳ ⤴ 🍴 ⤳ **Location** On A1214 Woodbridge road, close to hospital, signposted

Hotel ★★★ 73% Marlborough Hotel, Henley Rd, IPSWICH ☎ 01473 226789 22 en suite

LOWESTOFT — Map 05 TM59

Rookery Park Carlton Colville NR33 8HJ
☎ 01502 560380 📄 01502 560380
Parkland course with a 9-hole, par 3 adjacent.
18 holes, 6714yds, Par 72, SSS 72.
Club membership 1000.
Visitors must have handicap certificate. **Societies** by arrangement. **Green Fees** not confirmed. **Prof** Martin Elsworthy **Course Designer** C D Lawrie **Facilities** ⊗ ⫫ ⤶ ⤴ ⤳ ⤴ 🍴 ⤳ **Location** 3.5m SW on A146

Hotel ★★★ 65% Hotel Hatfield, The Esplanade, LOWESTOFT ☎ 01502 565337 33 en suite

NEWMARKET — Map 05 TL66

Links Cambridge Rd CB8 0TG
☎ 01638 663000 📄 01638 661476
e-mail: secretary@linksgc.fsbusiness.co.uk
Gently undulating parkland.
18 holes, 6582yds, Par 72, SSS 72, Course record 66 or, Par 72.
Club membership 780.
Visitors must have handicap certificate, may not play Sun before 11.30am. **Societies** telephone secretary in advance.
Green Fees £32 per day; £24 per round (£36/£28 weekends). **Prof** John Sharkey **Course Designer** Col. Hotchkin **Facilities** ⊗ ⫫ ⤶ ⤴ ⤳ ⤴ 🍴 ⤳ **Location** 1m SW on A1034

Hotel ★★★ 68% Heath Court Hotel, Moulton Rd, NEWMARKET ☎ 01638 667171 41 en suite

NEWTON — Map 05 TL94

Newton Green Newton Green CO10 0QN
☎ 01787 377217 & 377501 📄 01787 377549
e-mail: thesecretary@newtongreengolfclub.fsnet.co.uk
Flat 18-hole course with lake. First nine holes are open with bunkers and a pond. Second nine holes are tight with ditches and gorse.
18 holes, 5960yds, Par 69, SSS 68.
Club membership 640.
Visitors must contact in advance but may not play on Tue before 12.30 or at weekends without a member. **Societies** apply in advance. **Green Fees** £20 per round; £28 per 36 holes. **Cards** ⬜ ⬜ ⬜ **Prof** Tim Cooper **Facilities** ⊗ ⫫ ⤶ ⤴ ⤳ ⤴ 🍴 ⤳ **Location** W side of village on A134

Hotel ★★★ 67% The Bull, Hall St, LONG MELFORD ☎ 01787 378494 25 en suite

RAYDON — Map 05 TM03

Brett Vale Noakes Rd IP7 5LR
☎ 01473 310718 📄 01473 312270
Brett Vale course takes you through a nature reserve and on lakeside walks, affording views over Dedham Vale. The excellent fairways demand an accurate tee
continued

and good approach shots. 1, 2, 3, 8, 10 and 15 are all affected by crosswinds, but once in the valley it is much more sheltered. Although only 5797 yards the course is testing and interesting at all levels of golf.
18 holes, 5797yds, Par 70, SSS 69, Course record 65.
Club membership 600.
Visitors must book tee times and wear appropriate clothing, soft spikes only. **Societies** apply in writing or telephone. **Green Fees** £20 (£25 weekends). **Cards** ⬜ ⬛ ⬛ ⬛ ⬛ **Prof** Paul Bate **Course Designer** Howard Swan **Facilities** ⊗ ⫙ ⬛ ⬛ ♀ ⚲ ⬛ ⬆ ⬛ ⬛ ⬛ ⬛ ⬛ **Leisure** fishing.**Conf** Max 250 Class 250 Board 80 Banquet 200 **Location** B1070 at Raydon, 2m from A12

Hotel ★★★⛊ Maison Talbooth, Stratford Rd, DEDHAM ☎ 01206 322367 10 en suite

---

SOUTHWOLD — Map 05 TM57

Southwold The Common IP18 6TB
☎ 01502 723234 & 723248
Commonland course with 4-acre practice ground and panoramic views of the sea.
9 holes, 6052yds, Par 70, SSS 69, Course record 67.
Club membership 450.
Visitors restricted on competition days (Ladies-Wed, Gents-Sun). **Societies** must contact in advance. **Green Fees** £20 per 18 holes;£35 per day (£22 per 18 holes weekends). **Prof** Brian Allen **Course Designer** J Braid **Facilities** ⊗ ⬛ ⬛ ♀ ⬆ ⬛ ⬛ **Location** From A12 - B1140 to Southwold

Hotel ★★★ 72% Swan Hotel, Market Place, SOUTHWOLD ☎ 01502 722186
26 rms (25 en suite) 17 annexe en suite

STOWMARKET — Map 05 TM05

Stowmarket Lower Rd, Onehouse IP14 3DA
☎ 01449 736473 📠 01449 736826
e-mail: mail@stowmarketgc.sagehost.co.uk
Parkland course.
18 holes, 6107yds, Par 69, SSS 69, Course record 66.
Club membership 630.
Visitors must contact in advance. **Societies** Thu or Fri, by arrangement. **Green Fees** £28(£34 weekends). **Prof** Duncan Burl **Facilities** ⊗ ⫙ ⬛ ⬛ ♀ ⬆ ⬛ ⬛ ⬛ ⬛ **Location** 2.5m SW off B1115

Hotel ★★ 66% Cedars Hotel, Needham Rd, STOWMARKET ☎ 01449 612668 25 en suite

---

THORPENESS — Map 05 TM45

Thorpeness Golf Club & Hotel IP16 4NH
☎ 01728 452176 📠 01728 453868
e-mail: info@thorpeness.co.uk

continued

Thorpeness Golf Club provides a 6271 yard coastal heathland course, designed in 1923 by James Braid. The quality of his design combined with modern green keeping techniques has resulted in an extremely challenging course for golfers at all levels. It is also one of the driest courses in the region.
18 holes, 6271yds, Par 69, SSS 71, Course record 66.
Club membership 500.
Visitors contact in advance. **Societies** telephone in advance, deposit required. **Green Fees** £32.50 per day. **Cards** ⬜ ⬛ ⬛ ⬛ ⬛ ⬛ ⬛ **Prof** Frank Hill **Course Designer** James Braid **Facilities** ⊗ ⫙ ⬛ ⬛ ♀ ⬆ ⬛ ⬛ ⬛ ⬛ **Leisure** hard tennis courts, snooker room. **Conf** Del from £25 **Location** W side of village off B1353

Hotel ★★★ 74% White Lion Hotel, Market Cross Place, ALDEBURGH ☎ 01728 452720 38 en suite

---

WALDRINGFIELD — Map 05 TM24

Waldringfield Heath Newbourne Rd IP12 4PT
☎ 01473 736768 📠 01473 736436
18 holes, 6141yds, Par 71, SSS 69, Course record 67.
Course Designer Phillip Pilgrem **Location** 3m NE of Ipswich off old A12
Telephone for further details

Hotel ★★★⛊ 76% Seckford Hall Hotel, WOODBRIDGE ☎ 01394 385678 22 en suite 10 annexe en suite

---

WOODBRIDGE — Map 05 TM24

Seckford Seckford Hall Rd, Great Bealings IP13 6NT
☎ 01394 388000 📠 01394 382818
e-mail: info@seckfordgolf.co.uk
A challenging course interspersed with young tree plantations, numerous bunkers, water hazards and undulating fairways, providing a tough test for all levels of golfer. The testing 18th is almost completely surrounded by water.
Seckford Golf Course: 18 holes, 5303yds, Par 68, SSS 66, Course record 62.
Club membership 400.
Visitors telephone in advance for tee times. **Societies** telephone in advance. Computerised booking system. **Green Fees** £17 per round(£25 weekends and bank holidays). **Cards** ⬜ ⬛ ⬛ ⬛ ⬛ ⬛ ⬛ **Prof** Simon Jay **Course Designer** J Johnson **Facilities** ⊗ ⫙ ⬛ ⬛ ♀ ⬆ ⬛ ⬛ ⬛ ⬛ **Leisure** heated indoor swimming pool, fishing, gymnasium. **Location** 1m W of Woodbridge, 0ff A12, next to Seckford Hall hotel

Hotel ★★★⛊ 76% Seckford Hall Hotel, WOODBRIDGE ☎ 01394 385678 22 en suite 10 annexe en suite

Ufford Park Hotel Golf & Leisure Yarmouth Rd, Ufford IP12 1QW ☎ 01394 383555 & 382836
📠 01394 383582
e-mail: uffordparkltd@btinternet.com
The 18-hole par 71 course is set in ancient parkland has many natural features including 11 water hazards retained from the original parkland. Free draining making it playable all year. There is also an extensive hotel and leisure complex beside the course.
18 holes, 6485yds, Par 71, SSS 71, Course record 65.
Club membership 350.
Visitors must book tee time from golf shop 01394 382836. Must adhere to dress code. Handicap certificates required for

continued

Sat/Sun mornings. **Societies** telephone or fax in advance to book tee time. **Green Fees** on application. **Cards** ⌦ ▬ ⚏ ▦ ▦ ⚏ **Prof** Stuart Robertson **Course Designer** Phil Pilgrim **Facilities** ⊗ ⫫ ⧠ ⚏ ♀ ⚭ ⊞ ⚐ ⛴ ⚒ ⚓ **Leisure** heated indoor swimming pool, sauna, solarium, gymnasium.**Conf** Thtr 200 Board 55 Banquet 170 Del from £28.50 **Location** Just off A12, on the B1438

Hotel ★★★ 72% Ufford Park Hotel Golf & Leisure, Yarmouth Rd, Ufford, IPSWICH / WOODBRIDGE ☎ 01394 383555 42 en suite 8 annexe en suite

Woodbridge Bromeswell Heath IP12 2PF
☎ 01394 382038 ▤ 01394 382392
e-mail: woodbridgegc@anglianet.co.uk
A beautiful course, one of the best in East Anglia. It is situated on high ground and in different seasons present golfers with a great variety of colour. Some say that of the many good holes the 16th is the best.
18 holes, 6299yds, Par 70, SSS 70, Course record 64.
Forest Course: 9 holes, 3191yds, Par 70, SSS 70.
Club membership 900.
Visitors Main Course: must contact in advance, handicap certificate required, with member only weekends. Forest Course: open all days and no handicap certificate required. **Societies** by prior telephone call or in writing. **Green Fees** Main Course: £34 per day/round. Forest Course: £18/ per day/round. **Prof** Adrian Hubert **Course Designer** Davie Grant **Facilities** ⊗ ⫫ ⧠ ⚏ ♀ ⚭ ⊞ ⚒ **Location** 2.5m NE off A1152

Hotel ★★★⚑ 76% Seckford Hall Hotel, WOODBRIDGE ☎ 01394 385678 22 en suite 10 annexe en suite

Royal Worlington & Newmarket IP28 8SD
☎ 01638 712216 & 717787 ▤ 01638 717787
e-mail: pinkjug@lineone.net
Inland 'links' course. Favourite 9-hole course of many golf writers.
9 holes, 3105yds, Par 35, SSS 70, Course record 67.
Club membership 325.
Visitors with member only at weekends. Must contact in advance and have a handicap certificate. **Societies** must apply in writing. **Green Fees** £50 per day; £37 after 2pm, unlimited. **Prof** Malcolm Hawkins **Course Designer** Tom Dunn **Facilities** ⊗ ⧠ ⚏ ♀ ⚭ ⊞ ⚐ ⚒ **Location** 0.5m SE of Worlington village near Mildenhall

Hotel ★★★ 76% Riverside Hotel, Mill St, MILDENHALL ☎ 01638 717274 18 en suite 11 annexe en suite

New Zealand Woodham Ln KT15 3QD
☎ 01932 345049 ▤ 01932 342891
e-mail: roger.marrett@nzgc.org
Heathland course set in trees and heather.
18 holes, 6073yds, Par 68, SSS 69, Course record 66.
Club membership 320.
Visitors must contact in advance. **Societies** telephone initially. **Green Fees** £65 per day; £50 per round (Sat £75). **Prof** Vic Elvidge **Course Designer** Muir
continued

Fergusson/Simpson **Facilities** ⊗ ⧠ ⚏ ♀ ⚭ ⊞ ⚐ ⚒ ⚓ ⛴ ⚒ **Location** 1.5m E of Woking

Hotel ★★★ 67% The Ship, Monument Green, WEYBRIDGE ☎ 01932 848364 39 en suite

Ashford Manor Fordbridge Rd TW15 3RT
☎ 01784 424644 ▤ 01784 424649
Tree lined parkland course, looks easy but is difficult.
18 holes, 6352yds, Par 70, SSS 70, Course record 64.
Club membership 700.
Visitors advisable to telephone in advance, handicap certificate required, with member only at weekends but may not play competition days. **Societies** welcome weekdays, except Thu am, must contact in advance. **Green Fees** not confirmed. **Prof** Mike Finney **Facilities** ⊗ ⫫ ⧠ ⚏ ♀ ⚭ ⊞ **Location** 2m E of Staines via A308 Staines by-pass

Hotel ★★★ 69% The Thames Lodge, Thames St, STAINES ☎ 0870 400 8121 78 en suite

Pennyhill Park Hotel & Country Club London Rd GU19 5EU ☎ 01276 471774 ▤ 01276 473217
e-mail: pennyhillpark@msn.com
A nine-hole course set in 11 acres of beautiful parkland. It is challenging to even the most experienced golfer.
9 holes, 2095yds, Par 32, SSS 32.
Club membership 100.
Visitors prior booking must be made and must be resident at hotel or day visitor using other hotel facilities.telephone in advance. **Green Fees** £15 weekdays (£25 weekends). **Cards** ⌦ ▬ ▬ ▦ ▦ ⚏ **Facilities** ⊗ ⫫ ⧠ ⚏ ♀ ⚭ ⊞ ⚐ ⚒ **Leisure** hard tennis courts, heated outdoor swimming pool, fishing, gymnasium. **Conf** Max 170 Thtr 160 Class 100 Board 57 Banquet 170 Del from £70 * **Location** Off A30 between Camberley and Bagshot

Hotel ★★★★★ 73% Pennyhill Park Hotel & Country Club, London Rd, BAGSHOT ☎ 01276 471774 26 en suite 97 annexe en suite

Windlesham Grove End GU19 5HY
☎ 01276 452220 ▤ 01276 452290
A parkland course with many demanding par 4 holes over 400 yards. Thoughtfully designed by Tommy Horton.
18 holes, 6650yds, Par 72, SSS 72, Course record 69.
Club membership 800.
Visitors no restrictions **Societies** apply in advance. **Green Fees** £25 per round (£35 weekends). **Cards** ⌦ ▬ ▬ ▦ **Prof** Lee Mucklow/Alan Barber **Course Designer** Tommy Horton **Facilities** ⊗ ⧠ ⚏ ♀ ⚭ ⊞ ⚐ ⚒ ⚒ **Conf** Max 100 **Location** Junct of A30/A322

Hotel ★★★★★ 73% Pennyhill Park Hotel & Country Club, London Rd, BAGSHOT ☎ 01276 471774 26 en suite 97 annexe en suite

Banstead Downs Burdon Ln, Belmont, Sutton SM2 7DD ☎ 020 8642 2284 ▤ 020 8642 5252
e-mail: bdgc@ukonline.co.uk
A natural downland course set on a site of botanic interest. A challenging 18 holes with narrow fairways and tight lies.
continued

18 holes, 6194yds, Par 69, SSS 69, Course record 64.
Club membership 902.
Visitors must book in advance and have handicap certificate or letter of introduction. With member only weekends. Societies Thu, by prior arrangement Green Fees £35 per day; £25 after noon (weekdays only). Prof Robert Dickman Course Designer J H Taylor/James Braid Facilities ⊗ ﹖ by prior arrangement ⅃ ⚑ ♀ ⚒ 🏠 ⚐ Location 1.5m N on A217

· ·

Hotel ★★ 63% Thatched House Hotel, 135 Cheam Rd, Sutton ☎ 020 8642 3131 32 rms (29 en suite)

Cuddington Banstead Rd SM7 1RD
☎ 020 8393 0952 ▤ 020 8786 7025
e-mail: cuddingtongc@aol.com
Parkland course with easy walking and good views.
18 holes, 6595yds, Par 71, SSS 71, Course record 66.
Club membership 694.
Visitors must contact in advance and have a handicap certificate or letter of introduction. Societies welcome Thu, must apply in advance. Green Fees £40 weekday (£50 weekends). Prof Mark Warner Course Designer H S Colt Facilities ⊗ ﹖ ⅃ ⚑ ♀ ⚒ 🏠 ⚐ Conf Max 80 Location N of Banstead station on A2022

· ·

Hotel ★★ 63% Thatched House Hotel, 135 Cheam Rd, Sutton ☎ 020 8642 3131 32 rms (29 en suite)

BRAMLEY   Map 04 TQ04
Bramley GU5 0AL ☎ 01483 892696 ▤ 01483 894673
e-mail: secretary@bramleygolfclub.co.uk
Parkland course, from the high ground picturesque views of the Wey Valley on one side and the Hog's Back. Full on course irrigation system with three reservoirs on the course.
18 holes, 5990yds, Par 69, SSS 69, Course record 63.
Club membership 850.
Visitors may not play Tue am (Ladies Morning) and must play with member at weekends & bank holidays. Must contact secretary on 01483 892696. Societies must telephone the secretary in advance. Green Fees £35 per day; £28 per round (weekdays only). Prof Gary Peddie Course Designer James Braid Facilities ⊗ ﹖ ⅃ ⚑ ♀ ⚒ 🏠 ⚐ Location 3m S of Guildford on A281

· ·

Hotel ★★★ 69% Holiday Inn Guildford, Egerton Rd, GUILDFORD ☎ 0870 400 9036 162 en suite

BROOKWOOD   Map 04 SU95
West Hill Bagshot Rd GU24 0BH
☎ 01483 474365 ▤ 01483 474252
e-mail: secretary@westhill-golfclub.co.uk
Set in the Surrey landscape of heath, heather and tree lined fairways. An interesting and challenging course with a stream which affects play on seven holes. Drives on the fairway must be precisely placed, many of the greens are subtly contoured and putts can never be taken for granted.
18 holes, 6368yds, Par 69, SSS 70, Course record 62.
Club membership 500.
Visitors must contact in advance & have handicap certificate, may not play weekends & bank holidays. Societies weekdays only (ex Wed). Telephone in advance. Green Fees £60 per day; £45 per round. Cards ▦ ▦ ▦ ▦ ▦ Prof John A Clements Course Designer C Butchart/W Parke Facilities ⊗ ﹖ by prior arrangement ⅃ ⚑ ♀ ⚒ 🏠 ⚐ 🛒 ⚐ Location E side of village on A322
continued

Hotel ★★★★★ 73% Pennyhill Park Hotel & Country Club, London Rd, BAGSHOT ☎ 01276 471774 26 en suite 97 annexe en suite

CAMBERLEY   Map 04 SU86
Camberley Heath Golf Dr GU15 1JG
☎ 01276 23258 ▤ 01276 692505
One of the great 'heath and heather' courses so frequently associated with Surrey. Several very good short holes - especially the 8th. The 10th is a difficult and interesting par 4, as is the 17th, where the drive must be held well to the left as trouble lies to the right. A fairway irrigation system has been installed.

18 holes, 6147yds, Par 72, SSS 70, Course record 65.
Club membership 600.
Visitors may not play at weekends. Must contact in advance. Societies must apply in advance. Green Fees terms on application. Cards ▦ ▦ ▦ ▦ ▦ ▦ Prof Glen Ralph Course Designer Harry S Colt Facilities ⊗ ⅃ ⚑ ♀ ⚒ 🏠 ⚐ 🛒 ⚐ ⚐ Conf Thtr 102 Class 66 Board 40 Banquet 80 Location 1.25m SE of town centre off A325

· ·

Hotel ★★★★★ 73% Pennyhill Park Hotel & Country Club, London Rd, BAGSHOT ☎ 01276 471774 26 en suite 97 annexe en suite

Pine Ridge Old Bisley Rd, Frimley GU16 9NX
☎ 01276 675444 & 20770 ▤ 01276 678837
e-mail: enquiry@pineridgegolf.co.uk
Pay and play heathland course cut through a pine forest with challenging par 3s, deceptively demanding par 4s and several birdiable par 5s. Easy walking, but gently undulating. Good corporate or society packages.
18 holes, 6458yds, Par 72, SSS 71, Course record 67.
Club membership 400.
Visitors no jeans or trainers,necessary to book for weekends. Societies apply in advance by writing/telephone, packages available to suit. Green Fees not confirmed. Cards ▦ ▦ Prof Peter Sefton Course Designer Clive D Smith Facilities ⊗ ﹖ ⅃ ⚑ ♀ ⚒ 🏠 ⚐ 🛒 ⚐ ⚐ Leisure ten pin bowling. Location Just off B3015, near A30

· ·

Hotel ★★★ 74% Frimley Hall, Lime Av, CAMBERLEY ☎ 0870 400 8224 86 en suite

CATERHAM   Map 05 TQ35
Happy Valley Rook Ln, Chaldon CR3 5AA
☎ 01883 344555 ▤ 01883 344422
e-mail: cgm.wells@virgin.net
Opened in May 1999, this American style course is set in beautiful countryside and features fully irrigated greens and fairways. It also has large practice areas. *continued*

18 holes, 6858yds, Par 72, SSS 73, Course record 73.
Club membership 750.
Visitors may play weekdays and weekends and can book in advance. **Societies** apply in writing/telephone in advance. **Green Fees** £20 per round (£25 weekends & bank holidays). **Cards** 🖃 ▆▆ ▆▆ 🅿 **Prof** David Kent **Course Designer** David Williams **Facilities** ⊗ ⅶ ┗ 💺 🏌 🏖 🍴 🍽 🛒 🚲 🍴 ⚓ **Location** M25 junct 7, M23 junct 6/A22

Hotel ★★★★ 77% Coulsdon Manor, Coulsdon Court Rd, Coulsdon, CROYDON ☎ 020 8668 0414 35 en suite

CHERTSEY — Map 04 TQ06

Laleham Laleham Reach KT16 8RP
☎ 01932 564211 🖹 01932 564448
e-mail: sec@laleham-golf.co.uk
Well-bunkered parkland/meadowland course.
18 holes, 6204yds, Par 70, SSS 70.
Club membership 600.
Visitors members guests only at weekends. **Societies** must contact in writing/telephone. **Green Fees** terms on application. **Prof** Hogan Stott **Facilities** ⊗ ⅶ ┗ 💺 🏌 🏖 🍴 🍽 **Location** M25 junct 11/A320 to Thorpe Park, at roundabout take exit to Penton Marina and follow signs to club

Hotel ★★★ 69% The Thames Lodge, Thames St, STAINES ☎ 0870 400 8121 78 en suite

CHIDDINGFOLD — Map 04 SU93

Chiddingfold Petworth Rd GU8 4SL
☎ 01428 685888 🖹 01428 685939
With panoramic views across the Surrey Downs, this challenging course offers a unique combination of lakes, mature woodland and wildlife.
18 holes, 5501yds, Par 70, SSS 67.
Club membership 325.
Visitors telephone bookings up to one week in advance. **Societies** prior telephone booking required. **Green Fees** not confirmed. **Cards** 🖃 ▆▆ ▆▆ 🅿 **Prof** Paul Creamer **Course Designer** Jonathan Gaunt **Facilities** ⊗ ⅶ ┗ 💺 🏌 🏖 🍴 🍽 🛒 🍴 **Location** A283

Hotel ★★★ 65% Lythe Hill Hotel, Petworth Rd, HASLEMERE ☎ 01428 651251 41 en suite

CHIPSTEAD — Map 04 TQ25

Chipstead How Ln CR5 3LN
☎ 01737 555781 🖹 01737 555404
e-mail: office@chipsteadgolf.freeserve.co.uk
Hilly parkland course, hard walking, good views. Testing 18th hole.
18 holes, 5504yds, Par 68, SSS 67, Course record 61.
Club membership 650.
Visitors must contact in advance. May not play weekends or Tue mornings. **Societies** must apply in writing. **Green Fees** £30 per round. **Prof** Gary Torbett **Facilities** ⊗ ⅶ ┗ 💺 🏌 🏖 🍴 🍽 🛒 🍴 **Conf** Max 90 Board 30 Banquet 90 **Location** 0.5m N of village

Hotel ★★★★ 70% Le Meridien Selsdon Park, Addington Rd, Sanderstead, CROYDON ☎ 020 8657 8811 204 en suite

> **If the name of the club appears in *italics*, details have not been confirmed for this edition of the guide**

CHOBHAM — Map 04 SU96

Chobham Chobham Rd, Knaphill GU21 2TZ
☎ 01276 855584 🖹 01276 855663
Designed by Peter Allis and Clive Clark, Chobham course sits among mature oaks and tree nurseries offering tree-lined fairways, together with six man-made lakes.
18 holes, 5959yds, Par 69, SSS 67, Course record 67.
Club membership 750.
Visitors booking in advance essential. **Societies** by prior arrangement. **Green Fees** not confirmed. **Cards** 🖃 ▆▆ 🅿 ▆▆ 🅿 **Prof** Tim Coombes **Course Designer** Peter Alliss/Clive Clark **Facilities** ⊗ ⅶ by prior arrangement ┗ 💺 🏌 🏖 🍴 🍴 **Location** A3046 between Chobham and Knaphill

Hotel ★★★ 66% Falcon Hotel, 68 Farnborough Rd, FARNBOROUGH ☎ 01252 545378 30 en suite

COBHAM — Map 04 TQ16

Silvermere Redhill Rd KT11 1EF
☎ 01932 584300 🖹 01932 584301
e-mail: sales@silvermere.freeserve.co.uk
Parkland course with many very tight holes through woodland, 17th has 170 yd carry over the lake. 18th played to a new island green. Driving range.
18 holes, 6700yds, Par 73.
Club membership 740.
Visitors may not play at weekends until 11am. Must contact in advance. **Societies** must contact by telephone. **Green Fees** £20 per 18 holes (£30 weekends). **Cards** 🖃 ▆▆ ▆▆ ▆▆ ▆▆ 🅿 **Prof** Doug McClelland **Facilities** ⊗ ⅶ ┗ 💺 🏌 🏖 🍴 🍴 **Leisure** fishing. **Conf** Max 160 Thtr 200 Class 60 Board 40 Banquet 140 Del from £19.50 * **Location** 2.25m NW off A245

Hotel ★★★★ 69% Woodlands Park Hotel, Woodlands Ln, STOKE D'ABERNON ☎ 01372 843933 59 en suite

CRANLEIGH — Map 04 TQ03

Fernfell Golf & Country Club Barhatch Ln GU6 7NG ☎ 01483 268855 🖹 01483 267251
Scenic woodland/parkland course at the base of the Surrey hills, easy walking. Clubhouse in 400-year-old barn.
18 holes, 5648yds, Par 68, SSS 67, Course record 64.
Club membership 1000.
Visitors welcome weekdays but restricted Thu am. For weekends contact professional shop in advance on 01483 277188 **Societies** telephone in advance. **Green Fees** not confirmed. **Cards** 🖃 ▆▆ ▆▆ ▆▆ 🅿 **Prof** Trevor Longmuir **Facilities** ⊗ ┗ 💺 🏌 🏖 🍴 🍽 🛒 🍴 **Leisure** hard tennis courts, heated indoor swimming pool, sauna, gymnasium. **Location** Off A281 Guildford to Horsham road, signposted Cranleigh

Hotel ★★★ 64% Gatton Manor Hotel Golf & Country Club, Standon Ln, OCKLEY ☎ 01306 627555 18 en suite

Wildwood Country Club Horsham Rd, Alfold GU6 8JE ☎ 01403 753255 🖹 01403 752005
Parkland with stands of old oaks dominating several holes, a stream fed by a natural spring winds through a series of lakes and ponds. The greens are smooth, undulating and large. The 5th and 16th are the most challenging holes.
18 holes, 6655yds, Par 72, SSS 73, Course record 65.
Club membership 500.

continued

Visitors welcome subject to availability & booking. **Societies** apply in writing or telephone for enquiries. **Green Fees** £45 per day; £30 per round (£67.50/£45 weekends & bank holidays). **Cards** 🏧 ▇▇ ▇▇ ▇▇ 🔲 **Prof** Simon Andrews **Course Designer** Hawtree & Sons **Facilities** ⊗)Ⅲ ⌐ ▆ ⚑ ♨ ⚐ 🔓 ⛳ ⌐ ⌐ ♪ ⚐ ⚐ ⛳ **Leisure** fishing, Par 3 course. **Location** Off A281, approx 9m S of Guildford

Hotel ★★★ 66% Hurtwood Inn Hotel, Walking Bottom, PEASLAKE ☎ 01306 730851 9 en suite 8 annexe en suite

CROYDON

For other golf courses in the area, please see Greater London.

DORKING   Map 04 TQ14

Betchworth Park Reigate Rd RH4 1NZ
☎ 01306 882052 🖹 01306 877462
e-mail: manager@betchworthparkgc.co.uk
Parkland course, with hard walking on southern ridge of Boxhill.
18 holes, 6266yds, Par 69, SSS 70, Course record 64.
Club membership 725.
Visitors weekend play Sun pm only. Must contact in advance. **Societies** apply in writing/telephone/fax. **Green Fees** terms on application. **Prof** Andy Tocher **Course Designer** H Colt **Facilities** ⊗)Ⅲ ⌐ ▆ ⚑ ♨ ⚐ 🔓 ⛳ ⚐ **Location** 1m E on A25

Hotel ★★★ 63% The White Horse, High St, DORKING ☎ 0870 400 8282 37 en suite 41 annexe en suite

Dorking Chart Park, Deepdene Av RH5 4BX
☎ 01306 886917
e-mail: dorkinggolfclub@ukgateway.net
Undulating parkland course, easy slopes, wind-sheltered. Testing holes: 5th 'Tom's Puddle' (par 4); 7th 'Rest and Be Thankful' (par 4); 9th 'Double Decker' (par 4).
9 holes, 5120yds, Par 66, SSS 65, Course record 62.
Club membership 392.
Visitors may not play Wed am and with member only weekends & bank holidays. Contact in advance. **Societies** Tue & Thu, telephone in advance. **Green Fees** terms on application. **Prof** Paul Napier **Course Designer** J Braid/Others **Facilities** ⊗ ⌐ ▆ ⚑ ♨ ⚐ 🔓 ⛳ ♪ ⚐ ⚐ ⚐ **Location** 1m S on A24

Hotel ★★★★ 67% The Burford Bridge, Burford Bridge, Box Hill, DORKING ☎ 0870 400 8283 57 en suite

EAST HORSLEY   Map 04 TQ05

Drift The Drift, Off Forest Rd KT24 5HD
☎ 01483 284641 & 284772(shop) 🖹 01483 284642
Woodland course with secluded fairways and picturesque setting. A challenging course that punishes the wayward shot.
18 holes, 6424yds, Par 73, SSS 72, Course record 68.
Club membership 730.
Visitors book in advance to the pro shop, Mon-Fri only, except bank holidays. **Societies** Mon-Fri, telephone in advance. **Green Fees** not confirmed. **Cards** 🏧 ▇▇ ▇▇ 🔲 **Prof** Liam Greasley/Alan Brennan **Course Designer** Robert Sandow **Facilities** ⊗ ⌐ ▆ ⚑ ♨ ⚐ 🔓 ⛳ ♪ ⚐ ⚐ ⛳ **Location** 1.5m N off B2039

Hotel ★★ 62% Bookham Grange Hotel, Little Bookham Common, Bookham, LEATHERHEAD ☎ 01372 452742 27 en suite

EFFINGHAM   Map 04 TQ15

Effingham Guildford Rd KT24 5PZ
☎ 01372 452203 🖹 01372 459959
e-mail: secretary@effinghamgolfclub.freeserve.co.uk
Easy-walking downland course laid out on 270 acres with tree-lined fairways. It is one of the longest of the Surrey courses with wide subtle greens that provide a provocative but by no means exhausting challenge. Fine views.
18 holes, 6524yds, Par 71, SSS 71, Course record 64.
Club membership 800.
Visitors contact in advance. With member only weekends & bank holidays. **Societies** Wed, Thu & Fri only and must book in advance. **Green Fees** not confirmed. **Prof** Steve Hoatson **Course Designer** H S Colt **Facilities** ⊗ ⌐ ▆ ⚑ ⚐ 🔓 ⛳ ♪ ⚐ ⚐ ⛳ **Leisure** hard tennis courts. **Location** W side of village on A246

Hotel ★★ 62% Bookham Grange Hotel, Little Bookham Common, Bookham, LEATHERHEAD ☎ 01372 452742 27 en suite

ENTON GREEN   Map 04 SU94

West Surrey GU8 5AF
☎ 01483 421275 🖹 01483 41519
e-mail: westsurreygolfclub@btinternet.com
A good parkland-type course in rolling, well-wooded setting. Some fairways are tight with straight driving at a premium. The 17th is a testing hole with a long hill walk.
18 holes, 6300yds, Par 71, SSS 70, Course record 65.
Club membership 600.
Visitors must contact in advance and have a handicap certificate. **Societies** must apply in writing. All players to have a handicap. **Green Fees** terms on application. **Prof** Alister Tawse **Course Designer** Herbert Fowler **Facilities** ⊗)Ⅲ ⌐ ▆ ⚑ ♨ ⚐ 🔓 ⚐ ⛳ **Location** S side of village

Hotel ★★★ 66% The Bush Hotel, The Borough, FARNHAM ☎ 0870 400 8225 83 en suite

EPSOM   Map 04 TQ26

Epsom Longdown Ln South KT17 4JR
☎ 01372 721666 🖹 01372 817183
e-mail: secretary@epsomgolfclub.co.uk
Traditional downland course with many mature trees and fast undulating greens. Thought must be given to every shot to play to one's handicap.
18 holes, 5701yds, Par 69, SSS 68, Course record 62.
Club membership 700.
Visitors available any day except Tue, Sat & Sun till 12.00 hrs. **Societies** telephone 01372 721666. **Green Fees** £39 per 36 holes; £29 per round,(£32 per round weekends). **Cards** ▇▇ ▇▇ ▇▇ 🔲 **Prof** Ron Goudie **Course Designer** Willie Dunne **Facilities** ⊗)Ⅲ ⌐ ▆ ⚑ ♨ ⚐ 🔓 ⛳ ⚐ **Conf** Max 70 Thtr 70 Board 40 Del £50 to £250 * **Location** SE side of town centre on B288

Hotel ★★★★ 69% Woodlands Park Hotel, Woodlands Ln, STOKE D'ABERNON ☎ 01372 843933 59 en suite

Horton Park Golf & Country Club Hook Rd
KT19 8QG ☎ 020 8393 8400 & 8394 2626
🖹 020 8394 1369
e-mail: hortonparkgc@aol.com
Parkland course in picturesque surroundings within a

continued

country park with a natural lake. The course offers a challenge to all golfers with dog-legs, water hazards and the 10th at 160yds with an island green. There is also a separate full length par 3 9 hole course.
Millennium: 18 holes, 6257yds, Par 71, SSS 70.
Club membership 450.

Horton Park Golf & Country Club

Visitors must book for weekends, recommended booking for midweek. Dress code in force. **Societies** must telephone in advance to play at weekends & bank holidays. **Green Fees** not confirmed. **Cards** ▒▒ ▒▒ 🖲 **Prof** Martyn Hirst **Course Designer** Dr Peter Nicholson **Facilities** ⊗ ⅷ ଳ ⬛ ♀ ♨ 🖻 ⊮ ⚲ ⚖ ⚲ ∎

Hotel ★★★★ 69% Woodlands Park Hotel, Woodlands Ln, STOKE D'ABERNON ☎ 01372 843933 59 en suite

ESHER   Map 04 TQ16

Moore Place Portsmouth Rd KT10 9LN
☎ 01372 463533
Public course on attractive, undulating parkland laid out some 60 years ago by Harry Vardon. Examples of most of the trees that will thrive in the UK are to be found on the course. Testing short holes at 2nd, 3rd and 9th.
9 holes, 2078yds, Par 33, SSS 30, Course record 28.
Club membership 150.
Visitors no restrictions. **Societies** must contact in advance. **Green Fees** not confirmed. **Prof** Nick Gadd **Course Designer** Harry Vardon/David Allen **Facilities** ⊗ ⅷ ଳ ⬛ ♀ ♨ 🖻 ⊮ ⚲ **Location** 0.5m from town centre on A307

Hotel ★★★ 67% The Ship, Monument Green, WEYBRIDGE ☎ 01932 848364 39 en suite

Thames Ditton & Esher Portsmouth Rd KT10 9AL
☎ 020 8398 1551
Commonland course with public right of way across the course. Although the course is not long, accuracy is essential and wayward shots are normally punished.
18 holes, 5149yds, Par 66, SSS 65, Course record 63.
Club membership 250.
Visitors may not play on Sun mornings. Advisable to telephone for availability. **Societies** must contact in advance. **Green Fees** £12 per 18 holes; £9 per 9 holes. **Cards** ▒▒ ▒▒ 🖲 **Prof** Rob Jones **Facilities** ⊗ ⅷ ଳ ⬛ ♀ ♨ 🖻 ⚲ **Location** 1m NE on A307, adjacent to Marquis of Granby pub

Hotel ⬧ Premier Lodge, Portsmouth Rd, Fairmile, COBHAM ☎ 0870 700 1432 48 en suite

FARLEIGH   Map 05 TQ36

Farleigh Court Old Farleigh Rd CR6 9PX
☎ 01883 627711 🖹 01883 627722
e-mail: fcgc@fbd-uk.u-net.com
The course occupies 350 acres of land and is surrounded
continued

by a bird sanctuary and natural woodlands. The course designer has instinctively utilised two valleys to make the course interesting and challenging.
Members: 18 holes, 6414yds, Par 72, SSS 71.
Pay & Play: 9 holes, 3281yds, Par 36.
Club membership 450.
Visitors may not play Members course before 10am at weekends. **Societies** welcome, please and ask for Society Co ordinator. **Green Fees** Members course: £30 (£40 weekends). Pay & play £9 (£12 weekends). **Cards** ▒▒ ▒▒ ▒▒ 🖲 ▒▒ 🖲 **Prof** S Graham **Course Designer** John Jacobs **Facilities** ⊗ ⅷ ଳ ⬛ ♀ ♨ 🖻 ⊮ ⚲ ⚖ ⚲ sauna. **Conf** Max 50 Thtr 45 **Location** 1.5m from Selsdon

Hotel ★★★★ 70% Le Meridien Selsdon Park, Addington Rd, Sanderstead, CROYDON ☎ 020 8657 8811 204 en suite

FARNHAM   Map 04 SU84

Blacknest Binsted GU34 4QL
☎ 01420 22888 🖹 01420 22001
Privately owned pay and play golf centre catering for all ages and levels of abilities. Facilities include a 15-bay driving range, gymnasium and a challenging 18-hole course featuring water on 14 holes.
18 holes, 6019yds, Par 69, SSS 69, Course record 65.
Club membership 450.
Visitors welcome at all times but should telephone for tee times especially weekends. No denims or collarless shirts. **Societies** prior arrangements necessary telephone or write. **Green Fees** not confirmed. **Cards** ▒▒ ▒▒ 🖲 ▒▒ 🖲 ▒▒ 🖲 **Prof** Ian Benson **Course Designer** Mr Nicholson **Facilities** ⊗ ⅷ by prior arrangement ଳ ⬛ ♀ ♨ 🖻 ⚲ ⚖ ⚲ **Leisure** sauna, solarium, gymnasium. **Location** 0.5m S of A31 at Bentley

Hotel ★★★♨ 61% Farnham House Hotel, Alton Rd, FARNHAM ☎ 01252 716908 25 en suite

Farnham The Sands GU10 1PX
☎ 01252 782109 🖹 01252 781185
e-mail: info@farnhamgolfclub.com
A mixture of meadowland and heath with quick drying sandy subsoil. Several of the earlier holes have interesting features, the finishing holes rather less.
18 holes, 6447yds, Par 72, SSS 71, Course record 66.
Club membership 700.
Visitors must contact in advance. Must be member of recognised club & have handicap certificate. With member only weekends. **Societies** must apply in writing. **Green Fees** £45 per day; £40 per round. **Prof** Grahame Cowlishaw **Course Designer** Donald Steel **Facilities** ⊗ ⅷ by prior arrangement ଳ ⬛ ♀ ♨ 🖻 ⚲ **Location** 3m E off A31

Hotel ★★★ 66% The Bush Hotel, The Borough, FARNHAM ☎ 0870 400 8225 83 en suite

Farnham Park Folly Hill, Farnham Park GU9 0AU
☎ 01252 715216
Pay & Play parkland course in Farnham Park.
9 holes, 1163yds, Par 27, SSS 48, Course record 48.
Club membership 70.
Visitors pay and play everyday. **Societies** telephone in advance. **Green Fees** £4.50 (£5 weekends). **Cards** ▒▒ ▒▒ ▒▒ 🖲 **Prof** D Bryant **Course Designer** Henry Cotton **Facilities** ⊗ ⅷ ଳ ⬛ ♀ 🖻 ⚲ **Location** N side of town centre on A287, adjacent to Farnham Castle

continued

Hotel ★★★ 66% The Bush Hotel, The Borough, FARNHAM ☎ 0870 400 8225 83 en suite

GODALMING   Map 04 SU94

Broadwater Park Guildford Rd, Farncombe GU7 3BU
☎ 01483 429955 ▤ 01483 429955
A par 3 public course with floodlit driving range.
9 holes, 1287yds, Par 54, SSS 50.
Club membership 160.
Visitors must book for weekends & bank holidays. **Societies** telephone in advance. **Green Fees** terms on application.
Cards ▭ ▭ ▧ ▨ **Prof** Kevin D Milton/Nick English **Course Designer** Kevin Milton **Facilities** ⊗ ▙ � ♀ 🏠 ⛳ ♂ ↑ **Location** 4m SW of Guildford

Hotel ★★★ 77% The Angel Posting House and Livery, 91 High St, GUILDFORD ☎ 01483 564555 11 en suite 10 annexe en suite

Hurtmore Hurtmore Rd, Hurtmore GU7 2RN
☎ 01483 426492 ▤ 01483 426121
A Peter Alliss/Clive Clark Pay and Play course with seven lakes and 85 bunkers. The 15th hole is the longest at 537yds. Played mainly into the wind there are 10 bunkers to negotiate. The 3rd hole at 448yds stroke Index 1 is a real test. A dogleg right around a lake and nine bunkers makes this hole worthy of its stroke index.
18 holes, 5530yds, Par 70, SSS 67, Course record 67.
Club membership 200.
Visitors book by telephone up to 7 days in advance. **Societies** telephone in advance. **Green Fees** £12 per 18 holes (£16 weekends);Twilight £8 (£10 weekends). **Cards** ▭ ▭ ▧ ▨ **Prof** Maxine Burton **Course Designer** Peter Alliss/Clive Clark **Facilities** ⊗ ▙ ▨ ♀ 🏠 ⛳ ↑ ♂ **Leisure** practice nets. **Location** 6m S of Guildford on the A3

Hotel ★★★ 77% The Angel Posting House and Livery, 91 High St, GUILDFORD ☎ 01483 564555 11 en suite 10 annexe en suite

Shillinglee Park Chiddingfold GU8 4TA
☎ 01428 653237 & 708158 ▤ 01428 644391
Manicured parkland course with many natural features including seven ponds. The 4th and 7th are the signature holes requiring tee shots and second shots over ponds, to well-guarded greens.
9 holes, 5032yds, Par 64, SSS 64, Course record 65.
Club membership 400.
Visitors restricted Sat, Tue and Thu morning, advisable to book any other time. **Societies** apply for details. **Green Fees** terms on application. **Cards** ▭ ▭ ▧ ▨ **Prof** Mark Dowdell **Course Designer** Roger Mace **Facilities** ⊗ ▥ by prior arrangement ▙ ▨ ♀ 🏠 ↑ ♂ **Location** 5m S of Godalming, off A283

Hotel ★★★★ 65% Lythe Hill Hotel, Petworth Rd, HASLEMERE ☎ 01428 651251 41 en suite

GUILDFORD   Map 04 SU94

Guildford High Path Rd, Merrow GU1 2HL
☎ 01483 563941 ▤ 01483 453228
e-mail: secretary@guildfordgolfclub.co.uk
The course is on typical Surrey downland bordered by attractive woodlands. Situated on chalk, it is acknowledged to be one of the best all-weather courses in the area, and the oldest course in Surrey. Although not a long course, the prevailing winds across the open
continued

downs make low scoring difficult. It is possible to see four counties on a clear day.
18 holes, 6090yds, Par 69, SSS 70, Course record 65.
Club membership 700.
Visitors must contact in advance. With member only weekends & bank holidays. **Societies** welcome Mon-Fri. Must apply in advance. **Green Fees** £45 per day; £35 per round. **Prof** P G Hollington **Course Designer** J H Taylor/Hawtree **Facilities** ⊗ ▥ ▙ ▨ ♀ 🏠 ↑ **Location** E side of town centre off A246

Hotel ★★★ 70% The Manor, Newlands Corner, GUILDFORD ☎ 01483 222624 45 en suite

Merrist Wood Coombe Ln, Worplesdon GU3 3PE
☎ 01483 238890 ▤ 01483 238896
e-mail: mwgc@merristwood-golfclub.co.uk
More parkland than heathland, Merrist Wood has a bit of everything. Water comes into play on five holes, the bunkering is fierce, the greens slope and the back nine has plenty of trees. Two holes stand out especially: the picturesque par 3 11th with a tee shot through the trees and the dastardly par 4 17th, including a 210yd carry over a lake and ditches either side of the green.
18 holes, 6600yds, Par 72, SSS 71, Course record 69.
Club membership 500.
Visitors must contact in advance, at weekends only after 11am, subject to availability. **Societies** apply in writing. **Green Fees** terms on application. **Cards** ▭ ▭ ▧ ▨ **Prof** Charles Cox **Course Designer** David Williams **Facilities** ⊗ ▥ ▙ ▨ ♀ 🏠 ♂ ↑ **Conf** Max 50 Thtr 80 Class 60 Board 30 Banquet 80 Del from £13 * **Location** 3m out of Guildford on A323 to Aldershot

Hotel ★★★ 77% The Angel Posting House and Livery, 91 High St, GUILDFORD ☎ 01483 564555 11 en suite 10 annexe en suite

Milford Station Ln, Milford GU8 5HS
☎ 01483 419200 ▤ 01483 419199
e-mail: milford@americangolf.uk.com
A Peter Alliss/Clive Clark designed course. The design has cleverly incorporated a demanding course within an existing woodland and meadow area.
18 holes, 5960yds, Par 69, SSS 68, Course record 64.
Club membership 750.
Visitors must contact in advance, tee booking system, telephone 01483 416291 up to 1 week in advance. May not play weekends until 12 noon. **Societies** telephone in advance. **Green Fees** terms on application. **Cards** ▭ ▭ ▭ ▧ ▨ **Prof** Paul Creamer **Course Designer** Peter Allis **Facilities** ⊗ ▥ ▙ ▨ ♀ 🏠 ↑ ♂ **Location** 6m SW Guildford, leave A3 at Milford, A3100 to Enton

Hotel ★★★ 77% The Angel Posting House and Livery, 91 High St, GUILDFORD ☎ 01483 564555 11 en suite 10 annexe en suite

Roker Park Rokers Farm, Aldershot Rd GU3 3PB
☎ 01483 236677 ▤ 01483 232324
A Pay and Play 9-hole parkland course. A challenging course with two par 5 holes.
9 holes, 3037yds, Par 36, SSS 72.
Club membership 200.
Visitors no restrictions, pay & play, phone for reservations. **Societies** prior arrangement with deposit at least 14 days before, minimum 12 persons. **Green Fees** not confirmed.
continued

Prof Kevin Warn **Course Designer** W V Roker **Facilities** ⊗ 🏍 ⚒ ☕ ♀ ♿ 🏡 🚩 🐟 🛶 ♂ ℓ **Location** A323, 3m from Guildford

....

Hotel ★★★ 77% The Angel Posting House and Livery, 91 High St, GUILDFORD ☎ 01483 564555
11 en suite 10 annexe en suite

HINDHEAD   Map 04 SU83

Hindhead Churt Rd GU26 6HX
☎ 01428 604614 🖹 01428 608508
An excellent example of a Surrey heath-and-heather course, and most picturesque. Players must be prepared for some hard walking. The first nine fairways follow narrow valleys requiring straight hitting; the second nine are much less restricted.
18 holes, 6356yds, Par 70, SSS 70, Course record 63.
Club membership 770.
Visitors must contact in advance and have a handicap certificate. **Societies** Wed & Thu only, contact in advance **Green Fees** £47 per day; £36 per round (£57/£46 weekends & bank holidays). **Prof** Neil Ogilvy **Course Designer** J H Taylor **Facilities** ⊗ 🏍 ⚒ ☕ ♀ ♿ 🏡 🚩 ♂ ℓ **Location** 1.5m NW of Hindhead on A287

....

Hotel ★★★★ 65% Lythe Hill Hotel, Petworth Rd, HASLEMERE ☎ 01428 651251 41 en suite

KINGSWOOD   Map 04 TQ25

Kingswood Golf and Country House Sandy Ln KT20 6NE ☎ 01737 832188 & 833920
Mature parkland course sited on a plateau with delightful views of Chipstead Valley.
Kingswood Golf and Country Club: 18 holes, 6880yds, Par 72, SSS 73.
Club membership 700.
Visitors must contact professional at least 24 hrs in advance. May not play weekend mornings. **Societies** must apply in advance. **Green Fees** £36 per round (£50 weekends). **Cards** 🖅 ▆▆ ▆▆ ▆▆ ▆▆ 🔲 **Prof** Terry Sims **Course Designer** James Braid **Facilities** ⊗ 🏍 ⚒ ☕ ♀ ♿ 🏡 🚩 🐟 🛶 ♂ ℓ **Leisure** squash, 3 snooker tables.**Conf** Max 250 Del from £24.50 * **Location** 0.5m S of village off A217

....

Hotel ★★★ 67% Reigate Manor Hotel, Reigate Hill, REIGATE ☎ 01737 240125 50 en suite

Surrey Downs Outwood Ln KT20 6JS
☎ 01737 839090 & 839092 🖹 01737 839080
e-mail: booking@surreydownsgc.co.uk
A new course on a 200 acre with spectacular views over the North Downs and home to rabbits, foxes, deer and herons.
18 holes, 6356yards, Par 71, SSS 70, Course record 67.
Visitors must contact in advance and reserve time. **Societies** apply in advance by telephone **Green Fees** £25 per round (£35 weekends). **Cards** 🖅 ▆▆ ▆▆ 🔲 ▆▆ 🔲 **Facilities** ♿ 🏡 🛶 ♂ ℓ **Location** M25 junct 8, follow signs for Sutton (A217). At 3rd roundabout take last exit to Kingswood (Bonsor Drive). Turn right at end into Waterhouse Lane and continue until it merges into Outwood Lane, Club on right after Eyhurst Park

....

Hotel ⇧ Premier Lodge (Epsom South), Brighton Rd, Burgh Heath, TADWORTH ☎ 0870 700 1438 75 en suite

LEATHERHEAD   Map 04 TQ15

Leatherhead Kingston Rd KT22 0EE
☎ 01372 843966 & 843956 🖹 01372 842241
e-mail: secretary@lgc-golf.co.uk
Undulating parkland course with tree lined fairways and strategically placed bunkers. Easy walking.
18 holes, 6203yds, Par 71, SSS 70, Course record 64.
Club membership 630.
Visitors telephone pro shop 01372 843956 up to 21 days in advance. May not play before 3pm weekends. **Societies** telephone in advance. **Green Fees** £55 per day; £37.50 per round (£47.50 per round weekends). **Cards** 🖅 ▆▆ ▆▆ ▆▆ 🔲 **Prof** Simon Norman **Facilities** ⊗ 🏍 ⚒ ☕ ♀ ♿ 🏡 🚩 🛶 ♂ **Conf** Max 120 Thtr 120 Class 48 Board 40 Banquet 100 Del £40 to £550 * **Location** 0.25m from junct 9 of M25, on A243

....

Hotel ★★★★ 69% Woodlands Park Hotel, Woodlands Ln, STOKE D'ABERNON ☎ 01372 843933 59 en suite

Pachesham Park Golf Complex Oaklawn Rd KT22 0BT ☎ 01372 843453 🖹 01372 844076
e-mail: philktaylor@hotmail.com
An undulating parkland course starting with five shorter but tight holes on one side of the wood, followed by four longer more open but testing holes to finish.
9 holes, 2805yds, Par 70, SSS 67, Course record 67.
Club membership 250.
Visitors book 2 days in advance by phone. May play weekends **Societies** apply in advance. **Green Fees** £15 per 18 holes; £9 per 9 holes (£18/£10.50 weekends & bank holidays). **Cards** 🖅 ▆▆ ▆▆ ▆▆ 🔲 **Prof** Philip Taylor **Course Designer** Phil Taylor **Facilities** ⊗ 🏍 by prior arrangement ⚒ ☕ ♀ ♿ 🏡 🚩 ♂ ℓ **Conf** Max 60 Class 12 Board 12 Banquet 60 **Location** Off A244 or A245, 0.5m from M25 junct 9

....

Hotel ★★★★ 69% Woodlands Park Hotel, Woodlands Ln, STOKE D'ABERNON ☎ 01372 843933 59 en suite

Tyrrells Wood The Drive KT22 8QP
☎ 01372 376025 🖹 01372 360836
Parkland course with easy walking.
18 holes, 6282yds, Par 71, SSS 70, Course record 65.
Club membership 700.
Visitors must contact in advance. Restricted weekends. **Societies** must apply in advance. **Green Fees** £34 per round weekdays. **Cards** 🖅 ▆▆ ▆▆ ▆▆ 🔲 **Prof** Simon Defoy **Course Designer** James Braid **Facilities** ⊗ 🏍 ⚒ ☕ ♀ ♿ 🏡 🚩 ♂ **Conf** Board 20 **Location** 2m SE of town, off A24

....

Hotel ★★★★ 67% The Burford Bridge, Burford Bridge, Box Hill, DORKING ☎ 0870 400 8283 57 en suite

LIMPSFIELD   Map 05 TQ45

Limpsfield Chart Westerham Rd RH8 0SL
☎ 01883 723405 & 722106
Tight heathland course set in National Trust land, well wooded.
9 holes, 5718yds, Par 70, SSS 68, Course record 64.
Club membership 300.
Visitors with member only or by appointment weekends & not before 3.30pm Thu (Ladies Day). **Societies** must apply in advance. **Green Fees** £18 per day (£20 weekends). **Facilities** ⚒ ♀ ♿ **Leisure** putting green, practice area. **Location** 1m E on A25 from M25 junct 6

continued

Hotel ★★★ 69% Donnington Manor, London Rd, Dunton Green, SEVENOAKS ☎ 01732 462681 60 en suite

LINGFIELD · Map 05 TQ34

Lingfield Park Lingfield Rd, Racecourse Rd RH7 6PQ
☎ 01342 832659 🖹 01342 836077
e-mail: cmorley@lingfieldpark.co.uk
Difficult and challenging, tree-lined parkland course set in 210 acres of beautiful Surrey countryside with water features and 60 bunkers.
18 holes, 6473yds, Par 71, SSS 72, Course record 69.
Club membership 700.
Visitors must be accompanied by member on Sat & Sun. Advisable to telephone first. **Societies** must telephone in advance. **Green Fees** terms on application. **Cards** 💳 ▬ ▬ ▬ ▬ ▬ 🅿 **Prof** Christopher Morley **Facilities** ⊗ ⊓ ⅃ ♨ ▬ ♀ ♨ ⌂ 🏌 ✝ ⊟ 🏐 ♨ ✔ ✆ **Leisure** squash, sauna, solarium, gymnasium. **Location** Jcnt 6 off M25 follow signs to racecourse
· ·
Hotel ★★★ 64% Woodbury House Hotel, Lewes Rd, EAST GRINSTEAD ☎ 01342 313657 13 en suite

NEWDIGATE · · · · · · · · · · · · · · · · · · · Map 04 TQ14

Rusper Rusper Rd RH5 5BX
☎ 01293 871871 (shop) & 871456 (office) 🖹 01293 871456
e-mail: jill@ruspergolfclub.co.uk
The 18-hole course is set in countryside and offers golfers of all abilities a fair and challenging test. After a gentle start the holes wind through picturesque scenery, mature woodland and natural water hazards.
18 holes, 6621yds, Par 71, SSS 72.
Club membership 220.
Visitors welcome but telephone to reserve time, some restrictions if competitions being played. **Societies** telephone in advance for details. **Green Fees** £9 per 9 holes; £13.50 per round (£12.50/£17.50 weekends and bank holidays). **Cards** 💳 ▬ ▬ 🅿 **Prof** Janice Arnold **Course Designer** A Blunden **Facilities** ⊗ ⊓ ⅃ ▬ ♀ ♨ ⌂ 🏌 ✝ ⊟ ♨ ✔ ✆ **Location** Between Newdigate/Rusper, off A24
· ·
Hotel ★★★★ 67% The Burford Bridge, Burford Bridge, Box Hill, DORKING ☎ 0870 400 8283 57 en suite

OCKLEY · Map 04 TQ14

Gatton Manor Hotel Golf & Country Club
Standon Ln RH5 5PQ ☎ 01306 627555 🖹 01306 627713
e-mail: gattonmanor@enterprise.net
Undulating parkland course through woods and over many challenging water holes.
18 holes, 6629yds, Par 72, SSS 72, Course record 68.
Club membership 300.

continued

Visitors may book up to 10 days in advance. Restricted Sun (am). Tee times to be booked through professional 01306 627557 **Societies** must apply in advance. **Green Fees** not confirmed. **Cards** 💳 ▬ ▬ 🔄 ▬ 🅿 **Prof** Rae Sargent **Course Designer** Henry Cotton **Facilities** ⊗ ⊓ ⅃ ▬ ♀ ♨ ⌂ 🏌 ✝ ⊟ ♨ ▬ ✔ ✆ **Leisure** grass tennis courts, fishing, sauna, solarium, gymnasium. **Location** 1.5m SW off A29
· ·
Hotel ★★★ 64% Gatton Manor Hotel Golf & Country Club, Standon Ln, OCKLEY ☎ 01306 627555 18 en suite

OTTERSHAW · · · · · · · · · · · · · · · · · · · Map 04 TQ06

Foxhills Club and Resort Stonehill Rd
KT16 0EL ☎ 01932 872050 🖹 01932 875200
e-mail: events@foxhills.co.uk
A pair of parkland courses designed in the grand manner with three championship courses. One course is tree-lined, the other, as well as trees, has massive bunkers and artificial lakes which contribute to the interest. Both courses offer testing golf and they finish on the same long 'double green'. Par 3 'Manor' course also available.
The Bernard Hunt Course: 18 holes, 6734yds, Par 73, SSS 72, Course record 65.
Longcross Course: 18 holes, Course record 70.
Manor Course: 9 holes.
Visitors contact sales office to reserve times. Restricted before noon weekends. **Societies** welcome Mon-Fri, must apply in advance. **Green Fees** £65 per round. **Cards** 💳 ▬ ▬ ▬ 🅿 **Prof** B Hunt/A Good/R Summerscales **Course Designer** F W Hawtree **Facilities** ⊗ ⊓ ⅃ ▬ ♨ ♀ ⌂ 🏌 ✝ ⊟ ♨ ♨ ✔ ✆ **Leisure** hard tennis courts, outdoor and indoor heated swimming pools, squash, sauna, solarium, gymnasium.**Conf** Max 100 Thtr 100 Class 60 Board 60 Banquet 200 **Location** M25 junct 11 follow signs to Woking, 2nd rdbt, 3rd exit into Foxhills road, left at T junct, 100yds right
· ·
Hotel ★★★ 64% The Crown Hotel, 7 London St, CHERTSEY ☎ 01932 564657 30 annexe en suite

PIRBRIGHT · Map 04 SU95

Goal Farm Gole Rd GU24 0PZ
☎ 01483 473183 & 473205
Beautiful lanscaped parkland 'Pay and Play' course with excellent greens.
9 holes, 1273yds, Par 54, SSS 48, Course record 69.
Club membership 300.
Visitors may not play on Sat before 4pm or Thu before 2pm. **Societies** telephone in advance. **Green Fees** £4.75 per 9 holes; £9.50 per 18 holes (£5/£10 weekends and bank holidays). **Course Designer** Bill Cox **Facilities** ⅃ ▬ ♀ ♨ ⌂ 🏌 **Location** 1.5m NW on B3012
· ·
Hotel ★★★ 69% Holiday Inn Farnborough, Lynchford Rd, FARNBOROUGH ☎ 0870 400 9029 143 en suite

PUTTENHAM · · · · · · · · · · · · · · · · · · · Map 04 SU94

Puttenham Heath Rd GU3 1AL
☎ 01483 810498 🖹 01483 810988
Picturesque tree-lined heathland course offering testing golf, easy walking.
18 holes, 6211yds, Par 71, SSS 70.
Club membership 650.

continued

Visitors weekdays by prior arrangment tel: 01483 810498, with member only weekends & public holidays. **Societies** apply in advance to secretary. **Green Fees** £35 per day; £25 per round. **Prof** Gary Simmons **Facilities** ⊗ ⓛ ♨ ♀ ♨ 🏠 ♎ **Location** 1m SE on B3000

Hotel ★★★ 66% The Bush Hotel, The Borough, FARNHAM ☎ 0870 400 8225 83 en suite

REDHILL   Map 04 TQ25

Redhill & Reigate Clarence Rd, Pendelton Rd RH1 6LB ☎ 01737 240777 📋 01737 242117
Flat well wooded parkland course.
18 holes, 5272yds, Par 68, SSS 66, Course record 65.
Club membership 600.
Visitors may not play before 11am weekends. Must contact in advance. **Societies** must apply in writing. **Green Fees** not confirmed. **Prof** Warren Pike **Course Designer** James Braid **Facilities** ⊗ ⓛ ♨ ♀ ♨ 🏠 ♎ **Location** 1m S on A23

Hotel ★★★ 67% Reigate Manor Hotel, Reigate Hill, REIGATE ☎ 01737 240125 50 en suite

REIGATE   Map 04 TQ25

Reigate Heath Flanchford Rd RH2 8QR ☎ 01737 242610 & 226793 📋 01737 226793
Gorse, heather, pine and birch trees abound on this popular 9-hole heathland course. Sandy soil gives all year round play even in the wettest winters. Clubhouse enjoys panoramic views of the North Downs and Leith Hill.
9 holes, 5658yds, Par 67, SSS 67, Course record 65.
Club membership 550.
Visitors with member only weekends & bank holidays. Must contact in advance. **Societies** must apply in writing. **Green Fees** not confirmed. **Prof** Barry Davies **Facilities** ⊗ ⏷ by prior arrangement ⓛ ♨ ♀ ♨ 🏠 ♎ **Location** 1.5m W off A25

Hotel ★★★ 67% Reigate Manor Hotel, Reigate Hill, REIGATE ☎ 01737 240125 50 en suite

Reigate Hill Gatton Bottom RH2 0TU ☎ 01737 645577 📋 01737 642650
Championship standard course with fully irrigated tees and greens. Feature holes include the 5th which is divided by four bunkers and the par 5 14th involving a tricky second shot across a lake. Very good short holes at 8th and 12th with panoramic views from the tees.
18 holes, 6175yds, Par 72, SSS 70, Course record 75.
Club membership 550.
Visitors must contact in advance to book tee time, may not play weekends until 12 noon. **Societies** welcome Mon-Fri but must book in advance. **Green Fees** terms on application.
Cards 🎴 ■■ 🎴 📃 🎴 📃 **Prof** Chris Forsyth **Course Designer** David Williams **Facilities** ⊗ ⓛ ♨ ♀ ♨ 🏠 ♎ 🏌 🏌 ♎ **Location** 1m from junct 8 of M25

Hotel ★★★ 63% Bridge House Hotel, Reigate Hill, REIGATE ☎ 01737 246801 & 244821 📋 01737 223756 39 en suite

SHEPPERTON   Map 04 TQ06

American Golf at Sunbury Charlton Ln TW17 8QA ☎ 01932 771414 📋 01932 789300
e-mail: sunbury@americangolf.uk.com
27 holes of golf catering for all standards of golfer and a 32 bay floodlit driving range.
Sunbury Golf Course: 18 holes, 5103yds, Par 68, SSS 65, Course record 60.

continued

Academy: 9 holes, 2444yds, Par 33, SSS 32.
Club membership 600.
Visitors no restrictions. **Societies** advance booking necessary. **Green Fees** not confirmed. **Cards** 🎴 ■■ 🎴 📃 **Prof** Alistair Hardaway **Facilities** ⊗ ⓛ ♨ ♀ ♨ 🏠 🏌 🏌 ♎ **Location** Off junct 1 of the M3

Hotel ★★★ 69% The Thames Lodge, Thames St, STAINES ☎ 0870 400 8121 78 en suite

SUTTON GREEN   Map 04 TQ05

Sutton Green New Ln GU4 7QF
☎ 01483 747898 📋 01483 750289
e-mail: admin@suttongreengc.co.uk
Set in the Surrey countryside, a challenging course with many water features. Excellent year round conditions with fairway watering. Many testing holes with water surrounding greens and fairways, making accuracy a premium.
18 holes, 6350yds, Par 71, SSS 70, Course record 64.
Club membership 600.
Visitors must contact in advance, play after 2pm weekends **Societies** Mon-Fri. Call for details. **Green Fees** terms on application. **Cards** 🎴 ■■ 🎴 **Prof** Paul Tedder **Course Designer** David Walker/Laura Davies **Facilities** ⊗ ⏷ ⓛ ♨ ♀ ♨ 🏠 🏌 🏌 🏌 ♎ **Conf** Max 130 Thtr 130 Class 50 Board 16 **Location** Off A320 between Woking & Guildford

Hotel ★★★★★ 73% Pennyhill Park Hotel & Country Club, London Rd, BAGSHOT ☎ 01276 471774 26 en suite 97 annexe en suite

TANDRIDGE   Map 05 TQ35

Tandridge RH8 9NQ
☎ 01883 712274 📋 01883 730537
e-mail: info@tandridge.fsnet.co.uk
A parkland course with two loops of 9 holes from the clubhouse. The first 9 is relatively flat. The second 9 undulates and reveals several outstanding views of the North Downs and the South.
18 holes, 6250yds, Par 70, SSS 70, Course record 66.
Club membership 750.
Visitors must contact in advance. May play Mon, Wed, Thu **Societies** Mon, Wed & Thu, apply in advance. **Green Fees** £52 am round/all day; £40 pm round. **Prof** Chris Evans **Course Designer** H S Colt **Facilities** ⊗ ⓛ ♨ ♀ ♨ 🏠 🏌 ♎ **Location** 2m SE junc 6 M25, 1.5m E of Godstone on A25

Hotel ★★★★ 74% Nutfield Priory, Nutfield, REDHILL ☎ 01737 824400 60 en suite

TILFORD   Map 04 SU84

Hankley Common The Club House GU10 2DD ☎ 01252 792493 📋 01252 795699
A natural heathland course subject to wind. Greens are first rate. The 18th, a long par 4, is most challenging, the green being beyond a deep chasm which traps any but the perfect second shot. The 7th is a spectacular one-shotter.
18 holes, 6438yds, Par 71, SSS 71, Course record 62.
Club membership 700.
Visitors handicap certificate required, restricted to afternoons at weekends. **Societies** apply in writing. **Green Fees** £65 per day; £50 per round (£65 per round weekends

continued

Wentworth Club

Virginia Water, *Surrey* ☎ 01344 842201 Fax 01344 842804 Map 04 TQ06

e-mail: reception@wentworthclub.com

Wentworth Club, the home of the Volvo PGA and Cisco World Match Play Championships, is a very special venue for any sporting, business or social occasion. The West Course (7047 yards) is familiar to millions of television viewers who have followed the championships here. There are two other 18-hole courses, The East Course (6188 yards) and The Edinburgh Course (7004 yards) as well as a 9-hole Par 3 executive course. The courses are Surrey heathland with woodland of pine, oak and birch trees.

The Club is renowned for its fine English food and the superb Tennis and Health centre, which includes 14 outdoor tennis courts with 4 different playing surfaces, a 25m indoor pool and further extensive leisure facilities.

Visitors must contact in advance and have a handicap certificate (men max 24, ladies max 32). May not play weekends

Societies contact in advance in writing

Green Fees West £85–£210; Edinburgh £70–£145; East £65–£115

Facilities ⊗ 〣 ᴸᴱ 🔩 ♀ 🛏 ⚖ 🏠 ⛳ 🛎 🏌 ♿ 🏌

Professional (David Rennie)

Leisure tennis and health club, squash, swimming, sauna, solarium, gymnasium **Conf** Thtr 200 Board 50 Banquet 200 Del £68

Location Wentworth Drive GU25 4LS (main gate directly opposite turning for A329 on main A30)

Holes/Par/Course record 54 holes.
West Course: 18 holes, 7047 yds, Par 73, SSS 74, Course record 63
East Course: 18 holes, 6201 yds, Par 68, SSS 70, Course record 62
Edinburgh: 18 holes, 7004 yds, Par 72, SSS 74, Course record 67

WHERE TO STAY AND EAT NEARBY

Hotels

ASCOT

★★★★⊛ 67% The Royal Berkshire, London Rd, Sunninghill. ☎ 01344 623322. 63 en suite

★★★★64% The Berystede, Bagshot Rd, Sunninghill. ☎ 0870 400 8111. 90 en suite

BAGSHOT

★★★★★🌮🌮🌮 73% Pennyhill Park, London Rd. ☎ 01276 471774. 26 en suite 7 annexe en suite

EGHAM

★★★★🌮 74% Runnymede Hotel & Spa, Windsor Rd. ☎ 01784 436171. 180 en suite

Restaurant

BRAY

🌮🌮🌮🌮🌮 Fat Duck, High Street ☎ 01628 580333

🌮🌮🌮🌮 Waterside Inn, Ferry Rd. ☎ 01628 620691

Championship Course

and bank holidays). Cards ▨ ▨ ▨ ▨ ▨ ▨ Prof
Peter Stow Facilities ⊗ 〗 ⅃ ▨ ♀ ⅄ 🛆 🛆 ♂
Location 0.75m SE of Tilford

Hotel ★★★ 66% The Bush Hotel, The Borough,
FARNHAM ☎ 0870 400 8225 83 en suite

VIRGINIA WATER See page 225

WALTON-ON-THAMES Map 04 TQ16
Burhill Burwood Rd KT12 4BL
☎ 01932 227345 ▤ 01932 267159
e-mail: info@burhillgolf-club.co.uk
A picturesque parkland course that offers a challenge
to golfers of all abilities. The 18th is a splendid par 4
requiring a well-placed drive and a long firm second.
*Old Course: 18 holes, 6479yds, Par 70, SSS 71, Course
record 65.*
New Course: 18 holes, 6597yds, Par 72, SSS 71.
Club membership 1000.
Visitors no visitors weekends or bank holidays unless
introduced by member. Must contact in advance. Societies
apply in writing. Green Fees £65 per 18 holes;£85 per
day. Cards ▨ Prof Lee Johnson Course Designer
Willie Park Facilities ⊗ 〗 ⅃ ▨ ♀ ⅄ 🛆 🛆 ♂ ♂
Location M25 junct 10 on to A3 towards London, 1st exit
(Painshill junct, towards Byfleet, Golf Club signed

Hotel ★★★ 67% The Ship, Monument Green,
WEYBRIDGE ☎ 01932 848364 39 en suite

WALTON-ON-THE-HILL See page 227

WEST BYFLEET Map 04 TQ06
West Byfleet Sheerwater Rd KT14 6AA
☎ 01932 343433 ▤ 01932 340667
e-mail: secretary@wbgc.co.uk
An attractive course set against a background of
woodland and gorse. The 13th is the famous 'pond'
shot with a water hazard and two bunkers fronting the
green. No less than six holes of 420 yards or more.
18 holes, 6211yds, Par 70, SSS 70.
Club membership 622.
Visitors must contact professional in advance, only with
member at weekends. Restricted Thu (Ladies Day).
Societies must apply in writing/telephone. Green Fees
£33 per 18 holes. Cards ▨ ▨ ▨ ▨ ▨ Prof David
Regan Course Designer C S Butchart Facilities ⊗ 〗 ⅃
▨ ♀ ⅄ 🛆 🛆 ♂ ♂ ♂ Location W side of village on
A245, from A3 take A245 towards Byfleet and West
Byfleet, after going over M25 pass through 2 sets lights,
mini rdbt turn right into Sheerwater road club left

Hotel ★★★ 70% The Manor, Newlands Corner,
GUILDFORD ☎ 01483 222624 45 en suite

WEST CLANDON Map 04 TQ05
Clandon Regis Epsom Rd GU4 7TT
☎ 01483 224888 ▤ 01483 211781
e-mail: office@clandonregis-golfclub.co.uk
High quality parkland course with challenging lake holes
on the back nine. European Tour specification tees and
greens.
18 holes, 6419yds, Par 72, SSS 71, Course record 66.
Club membership 700.   *continued*

Visitors contact in advance. Afternoon only at weekends &
bank holidays. Societies telephone in advance. Green Fees
£25 per 18 holes(£35 weekends). Cards ▨ ▨ ▨ ▨
▨ Prof Steve Lloyd Course Designer David Williams
Facilities ⊗ 〗 ⅃ ▨ ♀ ⅄ 🛆 ♂ ♂ ♂ Leisure sauna.
Location From A246 Leatherhead direction

Hotel ★★★ 70% The Manor, Newlands Corner,
GUILDFORD ☎ 01483 222624 45 en suite

WEST END Map 04 SU96
Windlemere Windlesham Rd GU24 5LS
☎ 01276 858727
A parkland course, undulating in parts with natural
water hazards. There is also a floodlit driving range.
9 holes, 2673yds, Par 34, SSS 33, Course record 30.
Visitors no restrictions. Societies advisable to contact in
advance. Green Fees not confirmed. Cards ▨ ▨ ▨ ▨
▨ Prof David Thomas Course Designer Clive Smith
Facilities ⅃ ▨ ♀ ⅄ 🛆 ♂ ♂ ♂ Location N side of village
at junct of A319/A322

Hotel ★★★★★ 73% Pennyhill Park Hotel & Country Club,
London Rd, BAGSHOT ☎ 01276 471774
26 en suite 97 annexe en suite

WEYBRIDGE Map 04 TQ06
St George's Hill Golf Club Rd, St George's Hill
KT13 0NL ☎ 01932 847758 ▤ 01932 821564
e-mail: admin@stgeorgeshillgolfclub.co.uk
Comparable and similar to Wentworth, a feature of
this course is the number of long and difficult par 4s.
To score well it is necessary to place the drive - and
long driving pays handsomely. Walking is hard on this
undulating, heavily wooded course with plentiful
heather and rhododendrons.
*Red & Blue: 18 holes, 6569yds, Par 70, SSS 71, Course
record 64.*
Green: 9 holes, 2897yds, Par 35.
Club membership 600.
Visitors must contact in advance and have a handicap
certificate. Visitors may only play Wed-Fri. Societies
apply in writing/telephone. Green Fees £95 per day; £70
per round. Prof A C Rattue Course Designer H S Colt
Facilities ⊗ ⅃ ▨ ♀ ⅄ 🛆 ♂ ♂ Location 2m S off
B374

Hotel ★★★ 67% The Ship, Monument Green,
WEYBRIDGE ☎ 01932 848364 39 en suite

WOKING Map 04 TQ05
Hoebridge Golf Centre Old Woking Rd GU22 8JH
☎ 01483 722611 ▤ 01483 740369
e-mail: info@hoebridge.co.uk
Three public courses set in parkland on Surrey sand belt.
The main course is a championship length challenge
course, Shey Copse is a 9 hole course, ideal for the
intermediate golfer and the Maybury an 18 hole par 3
course which is suited to beginners and occasional golfers.
*Main Course: 18 holes, 6536yds, Par 72, SSS 71, Course
record 68.*
Shey Course: 9 holes, 2294yds, Par 33.
Maybury Course: 18 holes, 2230yds, Par 54.
Club membership 600.
Visitors welcome every day, course and reservation desk
open dawn to dusk. Credit card reservations 6 days in
advance. Societies Mon-Fri only, telephone in advance
continued

Walton Heath

Walton on the Hill, *Surrey*   ☎ 01737 812380   Fax 01737 814225   Map 04 TQ25

Boasting two extremely challenging courses, Walton Heath is a traditional Members' Club. Enjoying an enviable international reputation, the club was founded in 1903. Walton Heath has played host to over 60 major amateur and professional championships, including the 1981 Ryder Cup, five European Open Tournaments (1991, 1989, 1987, 1980 and 1978). Many prestigious amateur events have been held here, and in 2002 Walton Heath was hosting the English Amateur. The Old Course is popular with visitors, however the New Course is very challenging, requiring subtle shots to get the ball near the hole. Straying from the fairway brings its punishment with gorse, bracken and heather to test the most patient golfer.

e-mail: mbawden@whgc.co.uk

Visitors limited play weekends. Must contact in advance and have a handicap certificate or letter of introduction

Societies must contact in advance

Green Fees from £77-£87 per round

Facilities ⊗ 🛏 💺 ♀ ⚲ 🏠 ✝ ✓
Professional (Ken MacPherson)

Location Deans Lane, Tadworth KT20 7TP (SE side of village, off B2032)

Holes/Par/Course record 36 holes. Old course: 18 holes, 6801 yds, Par 72, SSS 73, Course record 65
New course: 18 holes, 6613 yds, Par 72, SSS 72 Course record 67

Championship Course

WHERE TO STAY AND EAT NEARBY

Hotels
DORKING

★★★★67% The Burford Bridge, Burford Bridge, Box Hill (2m NE A24).
☎ 0870 400 8283. 57 en suite

REIGATE

★★★67% Reigate Manor, Reigate Hill.
☎ 01737 240125. 50 en suite

★★★63% Bridge House, Reigate Hill.
☎ 01737 246801.
39 en suite

STOKE D'ABERNON

★★★★◉◉ 69% Woodlands Park, Woodlands Ln. ☎ 01372 843933.
59 en suite

Restaurant
TADWORTH

◉◉ The Dining Room, 59a High St.
☎ 01737 226650

◉ Gemini, 28 Station Approach.
☎ 01737 812179

Green Fees Main course: £18(£22.50 weekends)Shey £10.
Cards 🖃 🖃 🖃 🖾 **Prof** Tim Powell **Course Designer**
John Jacobs **Facilities** ⊗ ⫴ 🏌 ⚑ ♀ ⚒ 🏠 ⛳ 🏐 ⛳ ⚐
Leisure gymnasium, health & fitness club. **Location** off
M25 junct 11, on B382 Old Woking to West Byfleet road
⋯⋯⋯⋯⋯⋯⋯⋯⋯⋯⋯⋯⋯⋯⋯⋯⋯

Hotel ★★★★★ 73% Pennyhill Park Hotel & Country Club,
London Rd, BAGSHOT ☎ 01276 471774 26 en suite 97
annexe en suite

Pyrford Warren Ln, Pyrford GU22 8XR
☎ 01483 723555 📄 01483 729777
e-mail: pyrford@americangolf.uk.com
This inland links style course was designed by Peter Alliss
and Clive Clark. Set between Surrey woodlands, the
fairways weave between 23 acres of water courses while
the greens and tees are connected by rustic bridges. The
signature hole is the par 5 9th at 595 yards, with a dogleg
and final approach over water and a sand shelf. Excellent
playing conditions all year round.
18 holes, 6230yds, Par 72, SSS 70, Course record 64.
Club membership 650.
Visitors must book in advance. **Societies** must contact in
advance. **Green Fees** £40 (£60 weekends before 12,£45 after
12). **Cards** 🖃 🖃 🖃 🖾 🖾 **Prof** Darren Brewer
Course Designer Peter Allis & Clive Clark **Facilities** ⊗ ⫴
🏌 ⫿ ♀ ⚒ 🏠 ⛳ 🏐 🥅 ⚐ ⛳ **Location** Off A3 Ripley to
Pyrford
⋯⋯⋯⋯⋯⋯⋯⋯⋯⋯⋯⋯⋯⋯⋯⋯⋯

Hotel ★★★★★ 73% Pennyhill Park Hotel & Country Club,
London Rd, BAGSHOT ☎ 01276 471774
26 en suite 97 annexe en suite

Traditions Pyrford Rd, Pyrford GU22 8UE
☎ 01932 350355 📄 01932 350234
e-mail: traditions@americangolf.uk.com
Situated in the heart of the Surrey countryside with a
mature setting which includes various woodland and
water features. A course with many challenges which can
be enjoyed by golfers of all levels and experience.
18 holes, 6304yds, Par 71, SSS 70, Course record 67.
Club membership 400.
Visitors no restrictions. **Societies** telephone in advance.
Green Fees £20 per 18 holes;£11 per 9 holes (£25/£13
weekends and bank holidays). **Cards** 🖃 🖃 🖃 🖾 🖾
🖾 **Prof** Nick Stoner **Course Designer** Peter Alliss **Facilities**
⊗ ⫴ 🏌 ⫿ ♀ ⚒ 🏠 ⛳ 🏐 🥅 ⚐ **Location** M25 junct 10
onto A3, follow signs to Wisley Gardens,off A3, through
village to end of road, right to Pyford road, course 0.5 miles
on right
⋯⋯⋯⋯⋯⋯⋯⋯⋯⋯⋯⋯⋯⋯⋯⋯⋯

Hotel ★★★★★ 73% Pennyhill Park Hotel & Country Club,
London Rd, BAGSHOT ☎ 01276 471774
26 en suite 97 annexe en suite

Woking Pond Rd, Hook Heath GU22 0JZ
☎ 01483 760053 📄 01483 772441
An 18-hole course on Surrey heathland with few
changes from the original course designed in 1892 by
Tom Dunn. Bernard Darwin a past Captain and
President has written ' the beauty of Woking is that
there is something distinctive about every hole'.
18 holes, 6340yds, Par 70, SSS 70, Course record 65.
Club membership 550.
Visitors must contact secretary at least 7 days prior to
playing. No visitors weekends & bank holidays. **Societies**
telephone intially then confirm in writing, normally 12
months notice. **Green Fees** not confirmed. **Prof** Carl
continued

Bianco **Course Designer** Tom Dunn **Facilities** ⊗ ⫴ 🏌 🏠
⛳ ♀ ⚒ 🏠 ⛳ ⚐ **Location** W of town centre in area
of St Johns/Hook Heath
⋯⋯⋯⋯⋯⋯⋯⋯⋯⋯⋯⋯⋯⋯⋯⋯⋯

Hotel ★★★★★ 73% Pennyhill Park Hotel & Country
Club, London Rd, BAGSHOT
☎ 01276 471774 26 en suite 97 annexe en suite

Worplesdon Heath House Rd GU22 0RA
☎ 01483 472277
The scene of the celebrated mixed-foursomes
competition. Accurate driving is essential on this
heathland course. The short 10th across a lake from
tee to green is a notable hole, and the 18th provides a
wonderfully challenging par 4 finish.
18 holes, 6440yds, Par 71, SSS 71, Course record 64.
Club membership 590.
Visitors must play with member at weekends & bank
holidays. Must contact in advance and have a handicap
certificate. **Societies** must contact in writing. **Green Fees**
not confirmed. **Cards** 🖃 🖃 🖃 🖾 🖾 **Prof** J Christine
Facilities ⊗ 🏌 ⫴ 🏠 ♀ ⚒ 🏠 ⛳ ⚐ **Location** 6m N of
Guildford, off A322
⋯⋯⋯⋯⋯⋯⋯⋯⋯⋯⋯⋯⋯⋯⋯⋯⋯

Hotel ★★★★★ 73% Pennyhill Park Hotel & Country
Club, London Rd, BAGSHOT
☎ 01276 471774 26 en suite 97 annexe en suite

WOLDINGHAM   Map 05 TQ35

North Downs Northdown Rd CR3 7AA
☎ 01883 652057 📄 01883 652832
e-mail: info@northdownsgolfclub.co.uk
Downland course, 850 ft above sea-level, with several
testing holes and magnificent views.
North Downs Golf Course: 18 holes, 5857yds, Par 69, SSS
68, Course record 65.
Club membership 550.
Visitors must play with member at weekends and bank
holidays. Must contact in advance. **Societies** must telephone
in advance and confirm in writing. **Green Fees** £35 per day;
£20 per round. **Prof** M Homewood **Course Designer**
Pennink **Facilities** ⊗ ⫴ 🏌 🏠 ⛳ ♀ ⚒ 🏠 ⛳ ⚐ **Conf** Max 80
Location 0.75m S of Woldingham village
⋯⋯⋯⋯⋯⋯⋯⋯⋯⋯⋯⋯⋯⋯⋯⋯⋯

Hotel ★★★ 69% Donnington Manor, London Rd, Dunton
Green, SEVENOAKS ☎ 01732 462681 60 en suite

Woldingham Halliloo Valley Rd CR3 7HA
☎ 01883 653501 📄 01883 653502
Located in Halliloo Valley and designed by the American
architect Bradford Benz, this pleasant course utilises all
the contours and features of the valley.

continued

18 holes, 6393yds, Par 71, SSS 70, Course record 64.
Club membership 650.
Visitors tee times should be booked in advance with pro shop. Weekends available after noon for visitors. **Societies** telephone to book. **Green Fees** £25 per round(£40 weekends). **Cards** 🔲 🔲 🔲 🔲 **Prof** Nick Carter **Course Designer** Bradford Benz **Facilities** ⊗ by prior arrangement 🏌 by prior arrangement 🏌 ♥ ♀ 👤 🏠 🎯 ♥ ⟡ 🏌 **Conf** Thtr 100 Class 60 Board 40 Banquet 40 Del from £8.50 * **Location** M25 junct 6 take A22 north towards London/Croydon. Proceed for 2 miles, at rdbt take Woldingham Exit, continue under viaduct, bear 2nd left at fork into Halliloo Valley road, entrance left.

Hotel ★★★ 69% Donnington Manor, London Rd, Dunton Green, SEVENOAKS ☎ 01732 462681 60 en suite

SUSSEX, EAST

BEXHILL   Map 05 TQ70

Cooden Beach Cooden Sea Rd TN39 4TR
☎ 01424 842040 & 843938 (Pro Shop) 📠 01424 842040
e-mail: cbgc@btconnect.com
The course is close by the sea, but is not real links in character. Despite that, it is dry and plays well throughout the year. There are some excellent holes such as the 4th, played to a built-up green, the short 12th, and three good holes to finish. There are added ponds which make the player think more about tee shots and shots to the green.

18 holes, 6500yds, Par 72, SSS 71, Course record 67.
Club membership 730.
Visitors must have a handicap certificate. Restricted at weekends. Book in advance with professional 01424 843938. **Societies** must contact in advance by telephoning secretary. **Green Fees** £32 per day/round (£35 weekends). **Cards** 🔲 🔲 **Prof** Jeffrey Sim **Course Designer** W Herbert Fowler **Facilities** ⊗ 🏌 ♥ ♀ 👤 🏠 🎯 ♥ 🏌 ⟡ **Location** 2m W on A259

Hotel ★★★⚫ 71% Powder Mills Hotel, Powdermill Ln, BATTLE ☎ 01424 775511 30 en suite 10 annexe en suite

Highwoods Ellerslie Ln TN39 4LJ
☎ 01424 212625 📠 01424 216866
e-mail: secretary@highwoodsgolfclub.co.uk
Undulating parkland course with water on six holes.
18 holes, 6218yds, Par 70, SSS 70, Course record 63.
Club membership 750.
Visitors must play with member on Sun. Must contact in advance and have an introduction from own club. Handicap required. **Societies** advance notice advised. **Green Fees** £30 per day (£35 weekends). **Prof** Mike Andrews **Course**

continued

Designer J H Taylor **Facilities** ⊗ 🏌 🏌 ♥ ♀ 👤 🏠 ⟡ **Location** 1.5m NW

Hotel ★★★ 63% Royal Victoria Hotel, Marina, St Leonards-on-Sea, HASTINGS ☎ 01424 445544 50 en suite

BRIGHTON & HOVE   Map 04 TQ30

Brighton & Hove Devils Dyke Rd BN1 8YJ
☎ 01273 556482 📠 01273 554247
e-mail: philbonsall@pgapro.freeserve.co.uk
Testing 9 hole course with glorious views over the Downs and the sea. Famous drop hole par 3.
9 holes, 5704yds, Par 68, SSS 68, Course record 64.
Club membership 300.
Visitors must contact in advance, restricted play Wed, Fri & weekends. **Societies** must contact secretary in advance. **Green Fees** £17 per 18 holes; £11 per 9 holes (£25/£15 weekends). **Cards** 🔲 🔲 🔲 🔲 **Prof** Phil Bonsall **Course Designer** James Braid **Facilities** ⊗ 🏌 🏌 ♥ ♀ 👤 🏠 🎯 ♥ 🏌 ⟡ **Conf** Max 40 **Location** 4m NW

Hotel ★★★ 69% The Old Tollgate Restaurant & Hotel, The Street, BRAMBER ☎ 01903 879494 11 en suite 20 annexe en suite

Dyke Devils Dyke, Dyke Rd BN1 8YJ
☎ 01273 857296(office) & 857260(pro shop)
📠 01273 857078
e-mail: secretary@dykegolfclub.org.uk
This downland course has some glorious views both towards the sea and inland. The best hole on the course is probably the 17th; it is one of those teasing short holes of just over 200 yards, and is played across a gully to a high green.
18 holes, 6611yds, Par 72, SSS 72, Course record 66.
Club membership 750.
Visitors advisable to contact in advance. May not play before noon on Sun. **Societies** apply by telephone or in writing. **Green Fees** terms on application. **Prof** Richard Arnold **Course Designer** Fred Hawtree **Facilities** ⊗ 🏌 🏌 ♥ ♀ 👤 🏠 🎯 ♥ 🏌 ⟡ **Location** 4m N of Brighton, between A23 & A27

Hotel ★★★ 69% The Old Tollgate Restaurant & Hotel, The Street, BRAMBER ☎ 01903 879494 11 en suite 20 annexe en suite

East Brighton Roedean Rd BN2 5RA
☎ 01273 604838 📠 01273 680277
Undulating downland course, overlooking the sea with extensive views.
18 holes, 6346yds, Par 72, SSS 70, Course record 62.
Club membership 650.
Visitors contact in advance & may only play weekends after 11am. **Societies** must contact in advance, handicap certificate required. **Green Fees** not confirmed. **Cards** 🔲 🔲 🔲 🔲 **Prof** Mark Stuart-William **Course Designer** James Braid **Facilities** ⊗ 🏌 🏌 ♥ ♀ 👤 🏠 🎯 ♥ 🏌 ⟡ **Location** 2m E of Palace Pier, overlooking marina

Hotel ★★★ 63% Quality Hotel Brighton, West St, BRIGHTON ☎ 01273 220033 138 en suite

Hollingbury Park Ditchling Rd BN1 7HS
☎ 01273 552010 (sec) 📠 01273 552010/6
e-mail: graemecrompton@sussexgolfcentre.fsnet.co.uk
Municipal course in hilly situation on the Downs, overlooking the sea.

continued

18 holes, 6500yds, Par 72, SSS 71, Course record 65.
Club membership 300.
Visitors must contact in advance. **Societies** telephone the secretary for details. **Green Fees** terms on application. **Prof** Graeme Crompton **Facilities** ⊗ 🏌 ♟ ♀ ⚐ 🏠 ⚐️ ⚐ ✆ 🐾 🚗 🏌
Location 2m N of town centre

Hotel ★★★ 63% Quality Hotel Brighton, West St, BRIGHTON ☎ 01273 220033 138 en suite

Waterhall Saddlescombe Rd BN1 8YN
☎ 01273 508658
Hilly downland course with hard walking and open to the wind. Private club playing over municipal course.
18 holes, 5773yds, Par 69, SSS 68, Course record 66.
Club membership 300.
Visitors must contact in advance. Restricted tee times Sat and Sun am. **Societies** must contact the secretary in writing or telephone. **Green Fees** not confirmed. **Prof** Paul Charman **Facilities** ⊗ 🗎 🏌 🏠 ♀ ⚐ 🏠 ⚐️ ✆ **Location** 2m NE from A27

Hotel ★★★ 69% The Old Tollgate Restaurant & Hotel, The Street, BRAMBER ☎ 01903 879494 11 en suite 20 annexe en suite

West Hove Church Farm, Hangleton BN3 8AN
☎ 01273 419738 & 413494 (pro) ▣ 01273 439988
e-mail: info@westhovegolfclub.co.uk
A downland course designed by Hawtree & Sons.
18 holes, 6216yds, Par 71, SSS 70, Course record 65.
Club membership 600.
Visitors tee times by arrangement. **Societies** by arrangement, telephone, write or e-mail. **Green Fees** £25 (£30 weekends). **Prof** Darren Cook **Course Designer** Hawtree & Sons **Facilities** ⊗ 🗎 by prior arrangement 🏌 🏠 ♀ ⚐ 🏠 ⚐️ ✆ ℂ **Location** Easy access from A27, N of Brighton

Hotel ★★★ 67% Courtlands Hotel, 15-27 The Drive, HOVE ☎ 01273 731055 60 en suite 7 annexe en suite

CROWBOROUGH   Map 05 TQ53
Crowborough Beacon Beacon Rd TN6 1UJ
☎ 01892 661511 ▣ 01892 667339
e-mail: cbgc@eastsx.fsnet.co.uk
Standing some 800 feet above sea level, this is a testing heathland course, with panoramic views of the South Downs, Eastbourne and even the sea on a clear day.

18 holes, 6279yds, Par 71, SSS 70, Course record 66.
Club membership 700.
Visitors must contact in advance & have handicap certificate but may only play at weekends & bank holidays after 2.30pm. **Societies** telephone or apply in writing to secretary. **Green Fees** £40 per day; £30 per

continued

round (£35 per round weekends). **Prof** D C Newnham **Facilities** ⊗ 🗎 🏌 ♀ ⚐ 🏠 ⚐️ ✆ **Location** 1m SW on A26

Hotel ★★★ 77% The Spa Hotel, Mount Ephraim, TUNBRIDGE WELLS ☎ 01892 520331 71 en suite

Dewlands Manor Cottage Hill, Rotherfield TN6 3JN
☎ 01892 852266 ▣ 01892 853015
A beautifully kept compact meadowland course. The short par 4 4th can be played by the brave by launching a driver over the trees, the 7th requires accurate driving on a tight fairway and the final two holes are sweeping par 5s travelling parallel to each other, a small stream guarding the front of the 9th green.
9 holes, 3186yds, Par 36, SSS 70.
Visitors must telephone in advance. **Societies** telephone for availability. **Green Fees** terms on application. **Cards** ☷ ☶ 🔳 🔳 ▣ **Prof** Nick Godin **Course Designer** R M & N M Godin **Facilities** ⊗ 🗎 🏌 ♀ ⚐ 🏠 ⚐️ ✆ 🐾 🚗 ✆ **Leisure** indoor teaching facilities with computer analysis. **Location** 0.5m S of Rotherfield

Inn ◆◆◆◆ Plough & Horses Inn, Walshes Rd, CROWBOROUGH ☎ 01892 652614 8 en suite

DITCHLING   Map 05 TQ31
Mid Sussex Spatham Ln BN6 8XJ
☎ 01273 846567 ▣ 01273 845767
e-mail: admin@midsussexgolfclub.co.uk
Mature parkland course with many trees, water hazards, strategically placed bunkers and superbly contoured greens. The 14th hole, a spectacular par 5, demands accurate shotmaking to avoid the various hazards along its length.
18 holes, 6462yds, Par 71, SSS 71, Course record 65.
Club membership 600.
Visitors telephone in advance to book tee times. After 12pm at weekends. **Societies** advance booking required. **Green Fees** £25 per round. **Cards** ☷ 🔳 ☶ 🔳 🔳 ▣ **Prof** Neil Plimmer **Course Designer** David Williams **Facilities** ⊗ 🗎 🏌 ♀ ⚐ 🏠 ⚐️ ✆ 🐾 🚗 ✆ ℂ **Conf** Max 50 **Location** 1m E of Ditchling village

Hotel ★★★ 76% Shelleys Hotel, High St, LEWES ☎ 01273 472361 19 en suite

EASTBOURNE   Map 05 TV69
Eastbourne Downs East Dean Rd BN20 8ES
☎ 01323 720827 ▣ 01323 412506
This downland course has spectacular views over the South Downs and Channel. Situated in an area of outstanding natural beauty approximately 1 mile behind Beachy Head.
18 holes, 6601yds, Par 72, SSS 72, Course record 70.
Club membership 650.
Visitors a handicap certificate is required for weekends. Visitors may not play before 9.15am weekdays and before 11am weekends except by arrangement. **Societies** contact secretary in advance for details. **Green Fees** £25 per day; £20 per round (£28/£22 weekends and bank holidays). **Cards** ☷ ☶ **Prof** T Marshall **Course Designer** J H Taylor **Facilities** ⊗ 🗎 🏌 🏠 ♀ ⚐ 🏠 ⚐️ ✆ **Location** 0.5m W of town centre on A259

Hotel ★★★ 71% Lansdowne Hotel, King Edward's Pde, EASTBOURNE ☎ 01323 725174 110 en suite

Royal Eastbourne Paradise Dr BN20 8BP
☎ 01323 729738 🖻 01323 729738
A famous club which celebrated its centenary in 1987.
The course plays longer than it measures. Testing
holes are the 8th, a par 3 played to a high green and
the 16th, a par 5 righthand dogleg.
*Devonshire Course: 18 holes, 6107yds, Par 70, SSS 69,
Course record 62.*
Hartington Course: 9 holes, 2147yds, Par 64, SSS 61.
Club membership 800.
Visitors must contact in advance, may not play weekends
except by arrangement. Handicap certificate required for
Devonshire course. Societies must apply in advance.
Green Fees not confirmed. Prof Richard Wooller Course
Designer Arthur Mayhewe Facilities ⊗ ⓛ ⚑ ♀ ⛁ 🏠 🍴
🏐 ⚲ 🛒 ⚸ Location 0.5m W of town centre

Hotel ★★★ 71% Lansdowne Hotel, King Edward's Pde,
EASTBOURNE ☎ 01323 725174 110 en suite

7 Courses to choose from!

Willingdon Southdown Rd, Willingdon BN20 9AA
☎ 01323 410981 🖻 01323 411510
e-mail: secretary@wgc.demon.co.uk
Unique, hilly downland course set in oyster-shaped
amphitheatre.
18 holes, 6118yds, Par 69, SSS 69.
Club membership 570.
Visitors no restrictions. Societies apply in advance. Green
Fees £25 per day; £20 per round (£28/22 weekends). Winter
£18 per round (£20 weekends). Cards 🖾 🟥 Prof Troy
Moore Course Designer J Taylor/Dr Mackenzie Facilities
⊗ ⓛ ⚑ ♀ ⛁ 🏠 🍴 🏐 🛒 ⚸ Location 0.5m N of town
centre off A22

Hotel ★★★ 62% Wish Tower Hotel, King Edward's Pde,
EASTBOURNE ☎ 01323 722676 54 en suite

FOREST ROW   Map 05 TQ43

Ashdown Forest Golf Hotel Chapel Ln RH18 5BB
☎ 01342 824866 🖻 01342 824869
e-mail: enquiries@ashgolf.co.uk
A natural undulating heathland and woodland course cut
out of the Ashdown Forest. No sand bunkers, just equally
testing heather dunes with the 14th hole regarded as the
best. The hotel specialises in catering for golf breaks and
societies.
West Course: 18 holes, 5606yds, Par 68, SSS 67.
Club membership 180.
Visitors must contact in advance, bookings up to 6 days in
advance. Prepayment required. Societies must telephone in
advance. Green Fees not confirmed. Cards 🖾 🟥 🟦 🟥
🟥 🔲 Prof Martyn Landsborough Facilities ⊗ 🍴 ⓛ ⚑ ♀
⛁ 🏠 🍴 🏐 ⚸ Location 4m S of East Grinstead off A22 &
B2110

Hotel ★★★ 64% Woodbury House Hotel, Lewes Rd, EAST
GRINSTEAD ☎ 01342 313657 13 en suite

Royal Ashdown Forest Chapel Ln RH18 5LR
☎ 01342 822018 🖻 01342 825211
e-mail: office@royalashdown.co.uk
Old Course on undulating heathland. No bunkers.
Long carries off the tees and magnificent views over
the Forest. Not a course for the high handicapper.
West Course on natural heathland with no bunkers.
Less demanding than Old Course although accuracy is
at a premium.
*Old Course: 18 holes, 6477yds, Par 72, SSS 71, Course
record 67.*
West Course: 18 holes, 5606yds, Par 68, SSS 67.
Club membership 450.
Visitors restricted weekends & Tue. Must have a
handicap certificate on Old Course. No restrictions on
West Course. Societies must contact in advance. Green
Fees Old Course: £550 per day; £45 per round (£60
weekends). West Course: £23 per day; £18 per round
(£28/£23 weekends). Cards 🖾 🟥 Prof Martyn
Landsborough Facilities ⊗ ⓛ ⚑ ♀ ⛁ 🏠 🍴 🏐 ⚸
Location SE side of Forest Row village, off B2110

Hotel ★★★ 64% Woodbury House Hotel, Lewes Rd,
EAST GRINSTEAD ☎ 01342 313657 13 en suite

Looking for a driving range?
See the index at the back of the guide

The Beauport Park Hotel

Hastings, Sussex TN38 8EA ★★★
Telephone: 01424 851222
Fax: 01424 852465

A Georgian country house hotel set in 38 acres of parkland with its own swimming pool, tennis courts, putting green, badminton lawn, French boules, outdoor chess, croquet lawn and country walks. Candle-lit restaurant and open log fires. Adjacent to an 18 hole and 9 hole golf course, floodlight driving range and riding stables. Convenient for East Sussex National Golf Course – and many other interesting courses.

Luxurious golf lodge now available.

Special Golfing Breaks inclusive of green fees all year. Please send for our colour brochure and tariff.

HAILSHAM   Map 05 TQ50

Wellshurst Golf & Country Club North St,
Hellingly BN27 4EE ☎ 01435 813456(pro shop) & 813636(office) 🖹 01435 812444
e-mail: info@wellshurst.com
There are outstanding views of the South Downs and the Weald Valley from this 18-hole, well-manicured, undulating course. There are varied features and some water hazards. A practice sand bunker, putting green and driving range are available to improve your golf. The clubhouse and leisure facilities are open to visitors.
18 holes, 5771yds, Par 70, SSS 68, Course record 64.
Club membership 400.
Visitors no restrictions but advisable to book. **Societies** telephone in advance to book tee times. **Green Fees** £26 per day; £18 per 18 holes (£30/£22 weekends & bank holidays).
Cards 💳 💳 🈸 **Prof** Mark Jarvis **Course Designer** The Golf Corporation **Facilities** ⊗ ⊁🗓 🖢 🖤 ♀ 🛆 🖨 🛈 🍴 🐾 🔌 ♂ ᵗ **Leisure** sauna, solarium, gymnasium. **Conf** Max 180 Thtr 180 Class 120 Board 100 Banquet 120 Del £6 to £20 * **Location** 2.5m N of Hailsham, on A267

Hotel ★★ 69% The Olde Forge Hotel & Restaurant, Magham Down, HAILSHAM ☎ 01323 842893 7 en suite

HASTINGS & ST LEONARDS   Map 05 TQ80

Hastings Beauport Park Estate, St Leonards TN37 7BP
☎ 01424 854243 🖹 01424 854244
Played over Hastings Public Course. Undulating parkland with stream and fine views.
18 holes, 6248yds, Par 71, SSS 70, Course record 70.
Club membership 400.
Visitors no restrictions. **Societies** arrangement by telephone.
continued

Green Fees £14 per 18 holes: £10 per 9 holes (£17/£12.50 weekends). **Cards** 💳 💳 🈸 🈳 💷 **Prof** Charles Giddins **Facilities** ⊗ ⊁🗓 🖢 🖤 ♀ 🛆 🖨 🛈 🍴 ♂ ᵗ **Leisure** hard tennis courts, outdoor swimming pool. **Location** 3m N of Hastings on A2100

Hotel ★★★🟂 69% Beauport Park Hotel, Battle Rd, HASTINGS ☎ 01424 851222 25 en suite

HEATHFIELD   Map 05 TQ52

Horam Park Chiddingly Rd, Horam TN21 0JJ
☎ 01435 813477 🖹 01435 813677
e-mail: angie@horamgolf.freeserve.co.uk
A pretty woodland course with lakes.
9 holes, 6237yds, Par 70, SSS 68, Course record 64.
Club membership 450.
Visitors contact for tee times. **Societies** prior booking required. **Green Fees** £15.50 per 18 holes; £10.50 per 9 holes (£17/£11 weekends). **Cards** 💳 💳 🈸 🈳 💷 **Prof** Giles Velvick **Course Designer** Glen Johnson **Facilities** ⊗ 🗓 🖢 🖤 ♀ 🛆 🖨 🛈 🐾 🔌 ♂ ᵗ **Leisure** pitch & putt. **Location** Off A267 Hailsham-Heathfield

Hotel ★★★ 66% Boship Farm Hotel, Lower Dicker, HAILSHAM ☎ 01323 844826 47 annexe en suite

HOLTYE   Map 05 TQ43

Holtye TN8 7ED
☎ 01342 850635 & 850576 🖹 01342 850576
e-mail: j.p.holmes@holtyegolfclub.fsnet.co.uk
Undulating forest/heathland course with tree-lined fairways providing testing golf. Different tees on back nine.
9 holes, 5325yds, Par 66, SSS 66, Course record 62.
Club membership 360.
Visitors may not play mornings Wed-Thu & weekends. **Societies** Tue & Fri by arrangement. **Green Fees** terms on application. **Prof** Kevin Hinton **Facilities** 🖢 🖤 ♀ 🛆 🖨 ᵗ **Location** 4m E of East Grinstead and 6m W of Tunbridge Wells on A264

Hotel ★★★ 64% Woodbury House Hotel, Lewes Rd, EAST GRINSTEAD ☎ 01342 313657 13 en suite

LEWES   Map 05 TQ41

Lewes Chapel Hill BN7 2BB
☎ 01273 483474 🖹 01273 483474
Downland course. Fine views.
18 holes, 6220yds, Par 71, SSS 70, Course record 64.
Club membership 680.
Visitors may not play at weekends before 2pm. **Societies** must contact in advance. **Green Fees** £35 per day; £25 per round (£36 per round weekends). **Prof** Paul Dobson **Course**
continued

East Sussex National

Uckfield, *East Sussex* ☎ 01825 880088 Fax 01825 880066 Map 05 TQ42

e-mail: golf@eastsussexnational.co.uk

East Sussex National offers two huge courses ideal for big-hitting professionals. The European Open has been staged here and it is home to the European Headquarters of the David Leadbetter Golf Academy, with indoor or outdoor video analysis. Bob Cupp designed the courses using 'bent' grass from tee to green, resulting in an American-style course to test everyone. The greens on both the East and West courses are immaculately maintained, the West course is reserved for members and their guests, but visitors are welcomed on the other course.

The entrance seems daunting for first-time visitors unprepared for the vast car park, huge red-brick clubhouse and suspended corridor from the reception area through to the well-stocked professional's shop.

Visitors Contact Advance Reservations 01825 880231

Societies Contact Advance Reservations 01825 880230

Green Fees not confirmed ▬ ▬ ▬ ▬ ▬ ▬ ▬

Facilities ⊗ ⌂ ▬ ▬ ♀ ▬ ⚐ ⚑ ▲ ⚘ ⚐

Professional (Phil Lewin). Golf Academy

Leisure tennis, sauna, solarium **Conf** max 160 Thtr 160 Class 90 Board 70 Banquet 170

Location Little Horsted TN22 5ES (2m S of Uckfield on A22)

Holes/Par/Course record 36 holes. East Course: 18 holes, 7138 yds, Par 72, SSS 74, Course record 63 West Course: 18 holes, 7154 yds, Par 72, SSS 74

Championship Course

WHERE TO STAY

Hotels

UCKFIELD

★★★★⊚ 67% Buxted Park Country House Hotel, Buxted. ☎ 01825 732711. 44 en suite

★★★⊚⊚ 80% Horsted Place, Little Horsted. ☎ 01825 750581. 17 en suite 3 annexe en suite

NEWICK

★★★⊚⊚ 83% Newick Park Country Estate ☎ 01825 723633. 13 en suite 3 annexe en suite

Designer Jack Rowe **Facilities** ⊗ ⅷ by prior arrangement ┗ ▦ ♀ ♙ ♓ ⛿ ♖ ⛳ **Location** E side of town centre

Hotel ★★★ 62% White Hart Hotel, 55 High St, LEWES ☎ 01273 476694 23 en suite 29 annexe en suite

NEWHAVEN   Map 05 TQ40

Peacehaven Brighton Rd BN9 9UH
☎ 01273 512571 & 514049 ▤ 01273 512571
Downland course, sometimes windy. Testing holes: 1st (par 3), 4th (par 4), 9th (par 3), 10th (par 3), 18th (par 3). Attractive views over the Sussex Downs, the River Ouse and Newhaven Harbour.
9 holes, 5488yds, Par 70, SSS 67, Course record 65.
Club membership 270.
Visitors may not play before 11am weekends. **Societies** telephone in advance. **Green Fees** £12 per 18 holes; £9 per 9 holes (£18/£12 weekends). **Cards** 🖭 🖭 🖭 🖭 ▨ **Prof** Ian Pearson **Course Designer** James Braid **Facilities** ┗ ♥ ♀ ♙ ♓ ⛳ **Location** 0.75m W of Newhaven on A259

Hotel ★★★ 68% The Star Inn, ALFRISTON ☎ 0870 400 8102 37 en suite

RYE   Map 05 TQ92

Rye New Lydd Rd, Camber TN31 7QS
☎ 01797 225241 ▤ 01797 225460
e-mail: ryelinks@btclick.com
Unique links course with superb undulating greens set amongst ridges of sand dunes alongside Rye Harbour. Fine views over Romney Marsh and towards Fairlight and Dungeness.
Old Course: 18 holes, 6317yds, Par 68, SSS 71, Course record 64.
Jubilee Course: 9 holes, 3109yds, Par 71, SSS 70.
Club membership 1100.
Visitors must be invited/introduced by a member. **Green Fees** terms on application. **Prof** Michael Lee **Course Designer** H S Colt **Facilities** ⊗ ♥ ♀ ♙ ♓ ⛿ ⛳ ♗ ♘ **Location** 2.75m SE off A259

Hotel ★★★ 63% The George, High St, RYE ☎ 01797 222114 22 en suite

SEAFORD   Map 05 TV49

Seaford Firle Rd, East Blatchington BN25 2JD
☎ 01323 892442 ▤ 01323 894113
e-mail: secretary@seafordgolfclub.co.uk
The great H. Taylor did not perhaps design as many courses as his friend and rival, James Braid, but Seaford's original design was Taylor's. It is a splendid downland course with magnificent views and some fine holes.
18 holes, 6551yds, Par 69, SSS 71.
Club membership 600.
Visitors must contact in advance. **Societies** must contact in advance. **Green Fees** £28 per round (£33 weekends and bank holidays). **Cards** 🖭 🖭 🖭 🖭 ▨ **Prof** David Mills/Clay Morris **Course Designer** J H Taylor **Facilities** ⊗ ⅷ ┗ ♥ ♀ ♙ ♓ ⛿ ♗ ♘ ⛳ **Location** Turn inland at war memorial off A259

Hotel ★★★ 68% The Star Inn, ALFRISTON ☎ 0870 400 8102 37 en suite

Seaford Head Southdown Rd BN25 4JS
☎ 01323 890139 & 894843
18 holes, 5848yds, Par 71, SSS 68, Course record 63.
Telephone for further details

Hotel ★★★ 69% Deans Place, Seaford Rd, ALFRISTON ☎ 01323 870248 36 en suite

SEDLESCOMBE   Map 05 TQ71

Sedlescombe Kent St TN33 0SD
☎ 01424 871700 ▤ 01424 871712
e-mail: golf@golfschool.co.uk
Situated in the beautiful Sussex countryside. The natural water and tree line adds to the beauty as well as making it an enjoyable round of golf.
18 holes, 6269yds, Par 72, SSS 70.
Club membership 300.
Visitors please telephone and reserve tee times.No jeans or tracksuits allowed,golf shoes must be worn on the course.Hire shoes available. **Societies** please telephone to reserve tee times. **Green Fees** not confirmed. **Cards** 🖭 🖭 🖭 ▨ **Prof** James Andrews **Facilities** ⊗ ⅷ ┗ ♥ ♀ ♙ ♓ ⛿ ♗ ♘ ♓ ⛳ ♖ **Leisure** gymnasium. **Location** A21, 4m N of Hastings

Hotel ★★★ 68% Brickwall Hotel, The Green, SEDLESCOMBE ☎ 01424 870253 26 en suite

TICEHURST   Map 05 TQ63

Dale Hill Hotel & Golf Club TN5 7DQ
☎ 01580 200112 ▤ 01580 201249
e-mail: info@dalehill.co.uk
Dale Hill is set in over 350 acres, high on the Kentish Weald in an area of 'Outstanding Natural Beauty'. Offering two 18 hole golf courses, one of which has been designed by Ian Woosnam to USGA specifications.
Dale Hill: 18 holes, 6106yds, Par 70, SSS 69.
Ian Woosnam: 18 holes, 6512yds, Par 71, SSS 71.
Club membership 950.
Visitors booking only 7 days in advance. **Societies** must contact in advance. **Green Fees** Dale Hill: £35; Ian Woosnam: £60 per round. **Cards** 🖭 🖭 🖭 ▨ **Prof** PGA approved pro **Course Designer** Ian Woosnam **Facilities** ⊗ ⅷ ┗ ♥ ♀ ♙ ♓ ⛿ ♗ ♘ ♓ ⛳ ♖ **Leisure** heated indoor swimming pool, sauna, gymnasium.**Conf** Max 60 Thtr 60 Class 40 Board 30 Del from £40 * **Location** M25 junct 5, at Flimwell A21, turn right onto B2087 left after 1 mile

Hotel ★★★★ 68% Dale Hill Hotel & Golf Club, TICEHURST ☎ 01580 200112 26 en suite

UCKFIELD See page 233

UCKFIELD   Map 05 TQ42

Piltdown Piltdown TN22 3XB
☎ 01825 722033 ▤ 01825 724192
e-mail: piltdowngolf@lineone.net
Natural heathland course with much heather and gorse. No bunkers, easy walking, fine views.
18 holes, 6070yds, Par 68, SSS 69, Course record 67.
Club membership 400.
Visitors must telephone pro shop in advance 01825 722389 and have a handicap certificate. Play on Tue, Thu and weekends is restricted. **Societies** must contact in writing. **Green Fees** £30 per round; £40 per day. **Prof** Jason Partridge **Facilities** ⊗ ⅷ ┗ ♥ ♀ ♙ ♓ ⛿ ♗ ♘ ♓ ⛳ **Location**

continued

Between Newick & Maresfield off A272, club signposted

Hotel ★★★ 80% Horsted Place, Little Horsted,
UCKFIELD ☎ 01825 750581 17 en suite 3 annexe en suite

SUSSEX, WEST

ANGMERING   Map 04 TQ00

Ham Manor BN16 4JE
☎ 01903 783288 📠 01903 850886
e-mail: secretary.ham.manor@tinyonline.co.uk
**Two miles from the sea, this parkland course has fine
springy turf and provides an interesting test in two
loops of nine holes each.**
18 holes, 6267yds, Par 70, SSS 70, Course record 64.
Club membership 780.
Visitors must have a handicap certificate. Telephone pro
shop in advance 01903 783732. **Societies** telephone for
details **Green Fees** terms on application. **Prof** Simon
Buckley **Course Designer** Harry Colt **Facilities** ⛳ 🍴 🏌️
Location Off A259

Guesthouse ◆◆◆◆ Kenmore Guest House, Claigmar Rd,
RUSTINGTON ☎ 01903 784634 7 rms (6 en suite)

ARUNDEL   Map 04 TQ00

Avisford Park Yapton Ln, Walberton BN18 0LS
☎ 01243 554611 📠 01243 555580
**A 18 hole course enjoying a country hotel complex
setting. The course opens with a real challenge as there is
out of bounds water and tree hazards the whole length of
this 414yard drive.**
18 holes, 5703yds, Par 68, SSS 66.
Club membership 100.
Visitors must contact in advance for weekend play. **Societies**
apply in writing or telephone. **Green Fees** not confirmed.
Cards 🖃 💳 💳 📇 💳 **Prof** Richard Beach **Facilities** ⛳ 🍴
🍽️ ♀ ⚒ 🏌️ 🍴 🚶 🚜 🏌️ **Leisure** hard tennis courts, outdoor
and indoor heated swimming pools. **Location** Off A27,
towards Yapton

Hotel ★★★ 66% Norfolk Arms Hotel, High St, ARUNDEL
☎ 01903 882101 21 en suite 13 annexe en suite

BOGNOR REGIS   Map 04 SZ99

Bognor Regis Downview Rd, Felpham PO22 8JD
☎ 01243 821929 (Secretary) 📠 01243 860719
e-mail: secretary@bognorgoflclub.co.uk
**This flattish, well tree lined, parkland course has more
variety than is to be found on some other South Coast
courses. The club is also known far and wide for its
enterprise in creating a social atmosphere. The course
is open to the prevailing wind and the River Rife and
many water ditches need negotiation.**
18 holes, 6238yds, Par 70, SSS 70, Course record 64.
Club membership 700.
Visitors handicap certificate required. Must contact in
advance (pro shop 01243 865209). **Societies** phone
initially. **Green Fees** terms on application. **Prof** Stephen
Bassil **Course Designer** James Braid **Facilities** ⛳ 🍴 🏌️
🍽️ ♀ ⚒ 🍴 🚶 🍴 🏌️ **Conf** Max 50 Thtr 25 Class 40 Del
£10 to £15 * **Location** 0.5m N at Felpham traffic lights on
A259

Hotel ★★ 70% Aldwick Hotel, Aldwick Rd, Aldwick,
BOGNOR REGIS ☎ 01243 821945 20 en suite

BURGESS HILL   Map 04 TQ31

Burgess Hill Cuckfield Rd RH15 8RE
☎ 01444 258585 📠 247318
e-mail: golfacademy@skynow.net
**Opened May 1998, an academy course bordered by a
tributary of the River Adur. Facilities available for public
use include a floodlit driving range and a large sweeping
putting green.**
9 holes, 1250yds, Par 27.
Visitors None. **Societies** contact in advance. **Green Fees** £9
per 9 holes (£12 including 50 balls). **Cards** 🖃 💳 💳 📇
🖃 📇 💳 **Prof** Mark Collins **Course Designer** Donald Steel
Facilities ⛳ 🍽️ 🍴 🍽️ ♀ ⚒ 🍴 🏌️ 🍴 **Leisure** pitching &
chipping green.**Conf** Max 120 **Location** N of town on
B2036

Hotel ★★★★ 72% Hilton Park Hotel, Tylers Green,
CUCKFIELD ☎ 01444 454555 11 en suite

CHICHESTER   Map 04 SU80

Chichester Hunston Village PO20 6AX
☎ 01243 533833 📠 01243 539922
e-mail: chigolfclub@mistral.co.uk
**Set amongst lush farmland, the Tower course has four
lakes which bring water into play on seven holes. Also the
Florida-style Cathedral and a 9-hole par 3 and a floodlit
driving range.**
Tower Course: 18 holes, 6175yds, Par 72, SSS 69,
Course record 67.
Cathedral Course: 18 holes, 6461yds, Par 72, SSS 71,
Course record 65.
Club membership 600.
Visitors a strict dress code is in operation. Must contact in
advance. Tee reservations up to 7 days in advance on 01243
533833. **Societies** must contact in advance. **Green Fees** not
confirmed. **Cards** 🖃 💳 💳 📇 🖃 📇 💳 **Prof** John
Slinger **Course Designer** Philip Saunders **Facilities** ⛳ 🍽️ 🍴
🍽️ ♀ ⚒ 🍴 🏌️ 🚜 🍴 🏌️ **Leisure** mini golf and par 3 course.
Location 3m S of Chichester, on B2145 at Hunston

Hotel ★★★ 70% The Ship Hotel, North St, CHICHESTER
☎ 01243 778000 36 en suite

COPTHORNE   Map 05 TQ33

Copthorne Borers Arms Rd RH10 3LL
☎ 01342 712033 & 712508 📠 01342 717682
e-mail: info@copthornegolfclub.co.uk
**Despite it having been in existence since 1892, this club
remains one of the lesser known Sussex courses. It is
hard to know why because it is most attractive with
plenty of trees and much variety**
18 holes, 6505yds, Par 71, SSS 71, Course record 67.
Club membership 550.
Visitors advised to contact in advance, may not play
weekends before 1pm. **Societies** must contact in advance.
Green Fees terms on application. **Cards** 🖃 💳 💳 **Prof**
Joe Burrell **Course Designer** James Braid **Facilities** ⛳ 🍴
🍽️ ♀ ⚒ 🍴 🏌️ 🍴 **Location** E side of village junc 10 of
M23 off A264

Hotel ★★★★ 69% Copthorne Hotel London Gatwick,
Copthorne Way, COPTHORNE ☎ 01342 348800 &
348888 📠 01342 348833 227 en suite

AA website: www.theAA.com

Effingham Park The Copthorne Hotel Effingham Park, West Park Rd RH10 3EU ☎ 01342 716528 ▤ 716039
9 holes, 1822yds, Par 30, SSS 57, Course record 28.

Course Designer Francisco Escario **Location** 2m E on B2028
Telephone for further details

Hotel ★★★★ 65% Copthorne Hotel Effingham Park Gatwick, West Park Rd, COPTHORNE
☎ 01342 714994 122 en suite

CRAWLEY   Map 04 TQ23

Cottesmore Buchan Hill, Pease Pottage RH11 9AT
☎ 01293 528256 ▤ 01293 522819
e-mail: cottesmore@americangolf.uk.com
Founded in 1974, the Griffin Course is a fine test of golfing skill with fairways lined by silver birch, pine, oak and rhododendrons. Four holes have lakes as hazards.
Griffin Course: 18 holes, 6248yds, Par 71, SSS 70, Course record 67.
Visitors dress code applies. Advisable to contact in advance. **Societies** must telephone in advance. **Green Fees** not confirmed. **Prof** Calum J Callan **Course Designer** Michael J Rogerson **Facilities** ⊗ ⅷ ⌾ 🏌 ♥ ⅄ ⚑ 🏌 ⌾ ⚑ ◑ ⚑ ∲
Leisure hard tennis courts, heated indoor swimming pool, sauna, solarium, gymnasium. **Location** 3m SW 1m W of M23 junc 11

Hotel ★★★ Alexander House Hotel, East St, TURNERS HILL ☎ 01342 714914 15 en suite

Ifield Golf & Country Club Rusper Rd, Ifield RH11 0LN ☎ 01293 520222 ▤ 01293 612973
Parkland course.
18 holes, 6330yds, Par 70, SSS 70, Course record 64.
Club membership 750.
Visitors must contact professional in advance. Must be guest of member at weekends. **Societies** apply in advance. **Green Fees** £36 per day; £26 per round weekdays. **Prof** Jonathan Earl **Course Designer** Hawtree & Taylor **Facilities** ⊗ ⅷ ⌾ 🏌 ⅄ ⚑ ♥ ⚑ ∲ **Leisure** squash. **Location** 1m W side of town centre off A23

Hotel ★★★ Alexander House Hotel, East St, TURNERS HILL ☎ 01342 714914 15 en suite

Tilgate Forest Golf Centre Titmus Dr RH10 5EU
☎ 01293 530103 ▤ 01293 523478
Designed by former Ryder Cup players Neil Coles and Brian Huggett, the course has been carefully cut through a silver birch and pine forest. It is possibly one of the most beautiful public courses in the country. The 17th is a treacherous par 5 demanding an uphill third shot to a green surrounded by rhododendrons.

continued

18 holes, 6359yds, Par 71, SSS 70, Course record 69.
Club membership 200.
Visitors public course, pay & play at all times. **Societies** telephone in advance for details. **Green Fees** terms on application. **Cards** 🖃 📰 🖾 🖎 ⚑ **Prof** Sean Trussell **Course Designer** Neil Coles/Brian Huggett **Facilities** ⊗ ⅷ ⌾ 🏌 ⚑ ⅄ ⚑ ⚑ 🏌 ⌾ ∲ **Leisure** par 3 nine hole course. **Location** 2m E of town centre

Hotel ★★★ Alexander House Hotel, East St, TURNERS HILL ☎ 01342 714914 15 en suite

EAST GRINSTEAD   Map 05 TQ33

Chartham Park Felcourt Rd, Felcourt RH19 2JT
☎ 01342 870340 & 870008 (pro shop) ▤ 01342 870719
e-mail: b.smith@clubhaus.com
Mature parkland course.
18 holes, 6680yards, Par 72, SSS 72, Course record 64.
Club membership 334.
Visitors may book up to 7 days in advance. Weekdays anytime, weekends after noon. **Societies** weekdays or weekends after noon, telephone for details. **Green Fees** £30 per round (£35 weekends). **Cards** 🖃 📰 🖾 🖎 ⚑ **Prof** David Hobbs **Course Designer** Neil Coles **Facilities** ⊗ ⅷ ⌾ 🏌 ⅄ ⚑ ⚑ 🏌 ⚑ ∲ **Location** M25 junct 6, take A22 to traffic lights, turn left. At mini-roundabout take 1st exit, next mini-roundabout take 2nd exit, club 2m on right.

Hotel ★★★ 64% Woodbury House Hotel, Lewes Rd, EAST GRINSTEAD ☎ 01342 313657 13 en suite

GOODWOOD   Map 04 SU80

Goodwood Kennel Hill PO18 0PN
☎ 01243 774968 ▤ 01243 781741
Downland course designed by the master architect, James Braid. Many notable holes, particularly the finishing ones: 17 down an avenue of beech trees and 18 along in front of the terrace. Superb views of the downs and the coast.
18 holes, 6434yds, Par 72, SSS 71.
Club membership 930.
Visitors must have handicap certificate **Societies** Wed & Thu, telephone secretary in advance. **Green Fees** terms on application. **Prof** Keith MacDonald **Course Designer** J Braid **Facilities** ⊗ ⅷ ⌾ 🏌 ⅄ ⚑ ⚑ 🏌 ♥ ⚑ **Location** 3m NE of Chichester off A27

Hotel ★★★★ 72% Marriott Goodwood Park Hotel & Country Club, GOODWOOD ☎ 01243 775537 94 en suite

Marriott Goodwood Park Hotel & Country Club PO18 0QB ☎ 01243 775537 ▤ 01243 520120
A parkland course set within the 12,000 acre Goodwood estate, home to the Dukes of Richmond for over 300 years. Fairly generous over the opening holes but gets progressively harder as you approach the turn.
18 holes, 6579yds, Par 72, SSS 71, Course record 68.
Club membership 700.
Visitors tee times are subject to availability, please book in advance. Golf course dress and etiquette must be adhered to. **Societies** telephone or write. **Green Fees** £35 per round. **Cards** 🖃 📰 🖾 🖎 ⚑ **Prof** Adrian Wratting **Course Designer** Donald Steele **Facilities** ⊗ ⅷ ⌾ 🏌 ⚑ ⅄ ⌾ 🏌 ♥ ⚑ ∲ ⚑ **Leisure** hard tennis courts, heated indoor swimming pool, sauna, solarium, gymnasium. **Conf**

continued

Max 150 Thtr 150 Class 60 Board 60 Banquet 130 Del £60 to £80 * **Location** 3m NE of Chichester, in the grounds of Goodwood House

Hotel ★★★★ 72% Marriott Goodwood Park Hotel & Country Club, GOODWOOD ☎ 01243 775537 94 en suite

HASSOCKS   Map 04 TQ31

Hassocks London Rd BN6 9NA
☎ 01273 846630 & 846990 📠 01273 846070
e-mail: hgc@hassocksgolfclub.co.uk
Set against the backdrop of the South Downs, Hassocks is an 18 hole par 70 course designed and contoured to blend naturally with the surrounding countryside. A friendly and relaxed course, appealing to golfers of all ages and abilities.
18 holes, 5754yds, Par 70, SSS 68, Course record 66.
Club membership 400.
Visitors phone Pro. Shop in advance,01273 846990.
Societies apply in writing or telephone in advance. **Green Fees** £15 per 18 holes (£19.50 weekends and bank holidays).
Cards 🖃 🎟 🔀 🔟 **Prof** Charles Ledger **Course Designer** Paul Wright **Facilities** ⊗ ⮱ 🖤 ♀ ⚲ 🖺 ⛳ 🐾 🖥 ♪
Location On the A273 between Burgess Hill and Hassocks

Hotel ★★★ 62% The Hickstead Hotel, Jobs Ln, Bolney, HICKSTEAD ☎ 01444 248023 50 en suite

HAYWARDS HEATH   Map 05 TQ32

Haywards Heath High Beech Ln RH16 1SL
☎ 01444 414457 📠 01444 458319
e-mail: haywardsheath.golfclub@virgin.net
Pleasant parkland course with several challenging par 4s and 3s.
18 holes, 6216yds, Par 71, SSS 70, Course record 66.
Club membership 770.
Visitors must have a handicap certificate. Must contact in advance. **Societies** Wed & Thu only by prior arrangement with the secretary. **Green Fees** £26 per 18 holes (£35 weekends). **Prof** Michael Henning **Facilities** ⊗ ⮱ 🖤 ♀ ⚲ 🖺 ⛳ ♪ ♪ **Location** 1.25m N of Haywards Heath off B2028

Hotel ★★★ 67% The Birch Hotel, Lewes Rd, HAYWARDS HEATH ☎ 01444 451565 51 en suite

Paxhill Park East Mascalls Ln, Lindfield RH16 2QN
☎ 01444 484467 📠 01444 482709
e-mail: johnbowen@paxhillpark.fsnet.co.uk
A relatively flat parkland course designed by Patrick Tallack. Water hazard on 5th, 13th and 14th holes,
18 holes, 6117yds, Par 70, SSS 69, Course record 67.
Club membership 320.
Visitors welcome but may not play weekend and some weekday mornings. **Societies** must contact in advance.
continued

Green Fees £18 (£22 weekends). **Cards** 🖃 🎟 🔀 🔟 **Prof** Marcus Green **Course Designer** P Tallack **Facilities** ⮱ 🖤 ♀ ⚲ 🖺 ⛳ ♪ ♪ **Leisure** snooker. **Location** Outside Lindfield village just off B2011.

Hotel ★★★ 67% The Birch Hotel, Lewes Rd, HAYWARDS HEATH ☎ 01444 451565 51 en suite

HORSHAM   Map 04 TQ13

Horsham Worthing Rd RH13 7AX
☎ 01403 271525 📠 01403 274528
A short but challenging course, with six par 4s and three par 3s, two of which are played across water. Designed for beginners and intermediates but also challenges better players with a standard scratch of six below par.
9 holes, 4122yds, Par 33, SSS 30, Course record 55.
Club membership 280.
Visitors no restrictions. **Societies** apply in advance. **Green Fees** terms on application. **Cards** 🖃 ⮱ 🎟 🔀 🔟 **Prof** Alister Fitt **Facilities** ⊗ ⽊ ⮱ 🖤 ♀ ⚲ 🖺 ⛳ ♪ ♪ **Leisure** solarium, gymnasium. **Location** Off A24 rdbt, between Horsham/Southwater, by garage on B2237

Hotel ★★ 67% Ye Olde King's Head Hotel, Carfax, HORSHAM ☎ 01403 253126 42 rms (41 en suite)

HURSTPIERPOINT   Map 04 TQ21

Singing Hills Albourne BN6 9EB
☎ 01273 835353 📠 01273 835444
Three distinct nines (Lake, River & Valley) can be combined to make a truly varied game. Gently undulating fairways and spectacular waterholes make Singing Hills a test of accurate shotmaking. The opening two holes of the River nine have long drives, while the second hole on the Lake course is an Island green where the tee is also protected by two bunkers. The Valley Course demand long, accurate tee shots.
Lake: 9 holes, 3253yds, Par 35, SSS 35.
River: 9 holes, 2861yds, Par 34, SSS 34.
Valley: 9 holes, 3362yds, Par 36, SSS 34.
Club membership 390.
Visitors no restrictions, but strict dress code observed.
Societies apply in advance. **Green Fees** £32 per day, £22 per round; (£40/£30 weekends). **Cards** 🖃 ⮱ 🎟 🔀 🔟 **Prof** Wallace Street **Course Designer** M R M Sandow **Facilities** ⊗ ⽊ ⮱ 🖤 ♀ ⚲ 🖺 ⛳ ♪ ♪ **Conf** Max 50 **Location** Off A23, on B2117

Hotel ★★★ 62% The Hickstead Hotel, Jobs Ln, Bolney, HICKSTEAD ☎ 01444 248023 50 en suite

LITTLEHAMPTON   Map 04 TQ00

Littlehampton 170 Rope Walk, Riverside West BN17 5DL ☎ 01903 717170 📠 726629
e-mail: lgc@talk21.com
A delightful seaside links in an equally delightful setting - and the only links course in the area.
18 holes, 6226yds, Par 70, SSS 70.
Club membership 500.
Visitors may not book tee times, contact Pro Shop for availability on 01903 716369. **Societies** welcome weekdays, must apply in advance. **Green Fees** not confirmed. **Prof** Guy McQuitty **Course Designer** Hawtree **Facilities** ⊗ ⽊ ⮱ 🖤 ♀ ⚲ 🖺 🐾 ♪ **Location** 1m W of Littlehampton off A259

Hotel ⽥ Travelodge Littlehampton, Worthing Rd, RUSTINGTON ☎ 01903 733150 36 en suite

LOWER BEEDING   Map 04 TQ22

Mannings Heath Hotel Winterpit Ln RH13 6LY
☎ 01403 891191 📠 01403 891499

An 8 hole practice course and a driving range, designed as an executive course for beginners and those who find it difficult to play a full 18 holes. It is very popular.
9 holes, 1529yds, Par 31.
Club membership 150.
Visitors phone for details. **Societies** telephone in advance. **Green Fees** not confirmed. **Cards** 〓 ▬ ▨ ▬ ▨ 🗂 **Prof** Jim Debenham **Facilities** ⊗ ℿ ㄥ 🖳 🖳 ⚘ ✝ 🏠 **Leisure** fishing. **Location** Located off the A281 south of Horsham

Hotel ★★★★♨ South Lodge Hotel, Brighton Rd, LOWER BEEDING ☎ 01403 891711 41 en suite
Additional hotel ★★★★♨♨South Lodge Hotel, Brighton Rd, LOWER BEEDING ☎ 01403 891711 Fax 01403 891766 41 en suite

MANNINGS HEATH   Map 04 TQ22

Mannings Heath Fullers, Hammerpond Rd
RH13 6PG ☎ 01403 210228 📠 01403 270974
e-mail: enquiries@manningsheath.com

The Waterfall is a downhill, parkland, part heathland, championship parkland course with streams and trees in abundance. It boasts three spectacular par 3s but all the holes are memorably unique. The Kingfisher course is a modern design with a lake which comes into play.
Waterfall: 18 holes, 6378yds, Par 70, SSS 70,
Course record 67.
Kingfisher: 18 holes, 6217yds, Par 70, SSS 70,
Course record 67.
Club membership 700.
Visitors may book up to 28 days in advance. **Societies** must contact in advance. **Cards** 〓 ▬ ▨ 🖳 ▬ ▨ 🗂 **Prof** Clive Tucker **Course Designer** David Williams **Facilities** ⊗ ℿ ㄥ 🖳 ♀ ㄥ 🏠 ⚘ ✝ ➘ 🏌 ✓ ✝ **Leisure** hard tennis courts, fishing, sauna, chipping practice area.**Conf** Max 100 Thtr 100 Class 70 Board 30 Banquet 100 Del £45 to £75 * **Location** M23 junct 11, take A281 from Horsham or Brighton. Club on N side of village

Hotel ★★★★♨ South Lodge Hotel, Brighton Rd, LOWER BEEDING ☎ 01403 891711 41 en suite

MIDHURST   Map 04 SU82

Cowdray Park Petworth Rd GU29 0BB
☎ 01730 813599 📠 01730 815900
e-mail: cowdray-golf@lineone.net

Undulating parkland course with scenic views of surrounding countryside, including Elizabethan ruins. The course is situated in a National Park originally designed by Capability Brown in the 18th century.
18 holes, 6212yds, Par 70, SSS 70, Course record 66.
Club membership 720.
Visitors advised to contact in advance. Handicap certificate required. **Societies** apply in writing/telephone/e-mail/fax. **Green Fees** not confirmed. **Cards** 〓 ▬ ▨ 🗂 **Prof** Richard Gough **Course Designer** Jack White **Facilities** ⊗ ℿ ㄥ 🖳 ♀ ㄥ 🏠 ⚘ ➘ ✓ **Location** 1m E of Midhurst on A272

Guesthouse ♦♦♦♦ Park House Hotel, Bepton, MIDHURST ☎ 01730 812880 19 en suite

PULBOROUGH   Map 04 TQ01

West Sussex Golf Club Ln, Wiggonholt RH20 2EN
☎ 01798 872563 📠 01798 872033
e-mail: secretary@westsussexgolf.co.uk
Heathland course.
18 holes, 6223yds, Par 68, SSS 70, Course record 61.
Club membership 850.
Visitors must contact in advance, may not play weekends except by prior agreement of the secretary, and on Fri except with a member. **Societies** Wed & Thu only, apply in writing. **Green Fees** £60 per day; £50 per round (£65/£55 weekends & bank holidays). **Prof** Tim Packham **Course Designer** Campbell/Hutcheson **Facilities** ⊗ ㄥ 🖳 ♀ ㄥ 🏠 ⚘ ➘ ✓ ✝ **Location** 1.5m E of Pulborough off A283

Hotel ★★★ 69% Roundabout Hotel, Monkmead Ln, WEST CHILTINGTON ☎ 01798 813838 23 en suite

PYECOMBE   Map 04 TQ21

Pyecombe Clayton Hill BN45 7FF
☎ 01273 845372 📠 01273 843338
e-mail: pyecombegc@btopenworld.com

Typical downland course on the inland side of the South Downs. Picturesque with magnificent views.
18 holes, 6278yds, Par 71, SSS 70, Course record 67.
Club membership 700.
Visitors must contact in advance and may only play after 9.15am weekdays and after 2.15pm weekends **Societies** telephone secretary in advance. **Green Fees** £25 per round (£30 weekends). **Prof** C R White **Facilities** ⊗ ℿ by prior arrangement ㄥ 🖳 ♀ ㄥ 🏠 ⚘ ✓ **Location** E side of village on A273

Hotel ★★★ 67% Courtlands Hotel, 15-27 The Drive, HOVE ☎ 01273 731055 60 en suite 7 annexe en suite

SELSEY   Map 04 SZ89

Selsey Golf Links Ln PO20 9DR
☎ 01243 602203 📠 01243 602722
e-mail: selsey.cc@talk21.com
Fairly difficult seaside course, exposed to wind and has natural ditches.
9 holes, 5834yds, Par 68, SSS 68, Course record 64.
Club membership 360.
Visitors must contact in advance. **Societies** must contact in advance in writing **Green Fees** £14 per 18 holes; £10 per 9 holes (£18/£11 weekends). **Prof** Peter Grindley **Course Designer** J H Taylor **Facilities** ⊗ ℿ ㄥ 🖳 ♀ ㄥ 🏠 ✓ **Leisure** hard tennis courts. **Location** 1m N off B2145

Hotel ★★★ 70% The Ship Hotel, North St, CHICHESTER ☎ 01243 778000 36 en suite

SLINFOLD   Map 04 TQ13

Slinfold Park Golf & Country Club Stane St
RH13 7RE ☎ 01403 791555 📠 01403 791465
e-mail: info@slinfoldpark.co.uk

Slinfold course enjoys splendid views among mature trees. The 10th tee is spectacularly located on the centre of one of the two large landscaped lakes. The 166-yard 16th has water running in front of of the tee and everything sloping towards it!
Championship Course: 18 holes, 6407yds, Par 72, SSS 71, Course record 64.
Academy Course: 9 holes, 1315yds, Par 28.
Club membership 611. *continued*

Slinfold Park Golf & Country Club

Visitors book 7 days in advance, restricted weekends and bank holidays. **Societies** advance booking required, weekends and bank holidays not available. **Green Fees** not confirmed. **Cards** 🔲 🔲 🔲 🔲 🔲 **Prof** T Clingan **Course Designer** John Fortune **Facilities** ⊗ 🍴 🏌 💪 ♀ ⛳ 🏡 🛺 🚜 ⌁ ᘐ **Location** 4m W on the A29

Hotel ★★★ 66% Hurtwood Inn Hotel, Walking Bottom, PEASLAKE ☎ 01306 730851 9 en suite 8 annexe en suite

WEST CHILTINGTON   Map 04 TQ01

West Chiltington Broadford Bridge Rd RH20 2YA
☎ 01798 812115 (bookings) & 813574 📠 01798 812631
The Main Course is situated on gently undulating, well-drained greens and offers panoramic views of the Sussex Downs. Three large double greens provide an interesting feature to this course. Also 9-hole short course and 13-bay driving range.
Windmill: 18 holes, 5888yds, Par 70, SSS 69, Course record 66 or 9 holes, 1360yds, Par 28.
Visitors book tee times in advance. **Societies** by prior arrangement. **Green Fees** not confirmed. **Cards** 🔲 🔲 🔲 🔲 🔲 **Prof** Barrie Aram/Ian Williams **Course Designer** Brian Barnes **Facilities** ⊗ 🏌 💪 ♀ ⛳ 🏡 🛺 ⌁ ᘐ **Location** On N side of village

Hotel ★★★ 69% Roundabout Hotel, Monkmead Ln, WEST CHILTINGTON ☎ 01798 813838 23 en suite

WORTHING   Map 04 TQ10

Hill Barn Municipal Hill Barn Ln BN14 9QE
☎ 01903 237301 📠 01903 217613
Downland course with views of both Isle of Wight and Brighton.
18 holes, 6224yds, Par 70, SSS 70.
Club membership 1000.
Visitors no restrictions, but advisable to book tee times, 7 days in advance. **Societies** must telephone in advance. **Green Fees** £14 per round (£16.50 weekends). **Cards** 🔲 🔲 🔲 🔲 🔲 **Prof** S Blanshard **Course Designer** Fred Hawtree **Facilities** ⊗ 🍴 🏌 💪 ♀ ⛳ 🏡 🛺 🚜 ⌁ **Leisure** croquet. **Conf** Max 30 **Location** N side of town at junct of A24/A27

Hotel ★★★ 64% Findon Manor Hotel, High St, Findon, WORTHING ☎ 01903 872733 11 en suite

Worthing Links Rd BN14 9QZ
☎ 01903 260801 📠 01903 694664
e-mail: worthinggolf@pavilion.co.uk
The Upper Course, short and tricky with entrancing views, will provide good entertainment. 'Lower Course' is considered to be one of the best downland courses in the country.

continued

Lower Course: 18 holes, 6530yds, Par 71, SSS 72, Course record 62.
Upper Course: 18 holes, 5243yds, Par 66, SSS 66.
Club membership 1200.
Visitors advisable to contact in advance, not weekends during GMT. **Societies** contact in advance. **Green Fees** Lower Course:£40 per 36 holes;£35 per 18 holes(£50/£40 weekends).Upper Course: £24 per 18 holes(£40 weekends). **Prof** Stephen Rolley **Course Designer** H S Colt **Facilities** ⊗ 🍴 🏌 💪 ♀ ⛳ 🏡 🛺 🚜 ⌁ ᘐ **Location** N side of town centre off A27

Hotel ★★★ 72% Ardington Hotel, Steyne Gardens, WORTHING ☎ 01903 230451 45 en suite

TYNE & WEAR

BACKWORTH   Map 12 NZ37

Backworth The Hall NE27 0AH ☎ 0191 268 1048
Parkland course with easy walking, natural hazards and good scenery.
9 holes, 5930yds, Par 71, SSS 69, Course record 63.
Club membership 480.
Visitors visitors may not play Tue (Ladies Day) & weekend mornings. Play limited Sat/Sun during Apr-Sep. Must contact in advance. **Societies** apply in writing to secretary. **Green Fees** not confirmed. **Facilities** ⊗ 🍴 by prior arrangement 🏌 💪 ♀ ⛳ **Leisure** bowling green. **Location** W side of town on B1322

Hotel ⌂ Travel Inn Newcastle-upon-Tyne Holystone, Holystone Roundabout, NEWCASTLE ☎ 0191 270 2704 40 en suite

BIRTLEY   Map 12 NZ25

Birtley Birtley Ln DH3 2LR ☎ 0191 410 2207
Parkland course.
9 holes, 5662yds, Par 67, SSS 67, Course record 63.
Club membership 270.
Visitors must play with member at weekends & bank holidays. **Societies** apply in writing, must contact 1 month in advance in summer. **Green Fees** not confirmed. **Facilities** 🏌 💪

Hotel ★★★ 67% Holiday Inn Washington, Emerson District 5, WASHINGTON ☎ 0870 400 9084 138 en suite

BOLDON   Map 12 NZ36

Boldon Dipe Ln, East Boldon NE36 0PQ
☎ 0191 536 5360 & 0191 536 4182 📠 0191 537 2270
e-mail: info@boldongolfclub.co.uk
Parkland links course, easy walking, distant sea views.
18 holes, 6362yds, Par 72, SSS 70, Course record 67.
Club membership 700.
Visitors may not play after 3.30pm at weekends & bank holidays. **Societies** must contact in advance. **Green Fees** £20 (£24 weekends and bank holidays). **Course Designer** Harry Varden **Facilities** ⊗ 🍴 🏌 💪 ♀ ⛳ 🏡 🛺 🛥 🚜 ⌁ **Leisure** snooker. **Location** S side of village off A184

Hotel ★★★ 67% Quality Hotel, Witney Way, Boldon, SUNDERLAND ☎ 0191 519 1999 82 en suite

AA website: www.theAA.com

CHOPWELL — Map 12 NZ15

Garesfield NE17 7AP
☎ 01207 561309 📠 01207 561309
e-mail: information@garesfieldgc.fsbusiness.co.uk
Undulating parkland course with good views and picturesque woodland surroundings.
18 holes, 6458yds, Par 72, SSS 70, Course record 68. Club membership 697.
Visitors weekends after 4.30pm only, unless with member. Must contact in advance. **Societies** must contact secretary in advance. May play Sun only and max of 24 players. **Green Fees** £22 per day; £18 per round (£20 weekends). **Prof** David Race **Course Designer** Harry Fernie **Facilities** ⊗ ⅏ 🖥 ☕ 🏌 ♿ 📷 🚗 ♿ **Location** From A1 take A694 to Rowlands Gill. Turn right (signed Ryton) to High Spen. Turn left for Chopwell

Hotel ★★★ 63% Quality Hotel Newcastle, Newgate St, NEWCASTLE UPON TYNE ☎ 0191 232 5025 93 en suite

FELLING — Map 12 NZ26

Heworth Gingling Gate, Heworth NE10 8XY
☎ 0191 469 4424 📠 0191 469 9898
Fairly flat, parkland course.
18 holes, 6422yds, Par 71, SSS 71. Club membership 800.
Visitors may not play Sat & before 10am Sun, Apr-Sep. **Societies** must apply in writing. **Green Fees** £18 per day. **Prof** Adrian Marshall **Facilities** ⊗ ⅏ 🖥 ☕ 🏌 ♿ 📷 🚗 ♿ **Conf** Max 100 **Location** On A195, 0.5m NW of junc with A1(M)

Hotel ★★★ 67% Holiday Inn Washington, Emerson District 5, WASHINGTON ☎ 0870 400 9084 138 en suite

GATESHEAD — Map 12 NZ26

Ravensworth Moss Heaps, Wrekenton NE9 7UU
☎ 0191 487 2843
18 holes, 5966yds, Par 69, SSS 69.
Course Designer J W Fraser **Location** 3m SE off A6127
Telephone for further details

Hotel ★★★ 65% Swallow Hotel, High West St, GATESHEAD ☎ 0191 477 1105 103 en suite

GOSFORTH — Map 12 NZ26

Gosforth Broadway East NE3 5ER
☎ 0191 285 3495 📠 0191 284 6274
Parkland course with natural water hazards, easy walking.
18 holes, 6024yds, Par 69, SSS 68, Course record 65. Club membership 500.
Visitors must contact in advance. Restricted play on competition days. **Societies** welcome in advance. **Green Fees** £24 per day/round. **Prof** G Garland **Facilities** ⊗ ⅏ 🖥 ☕ 🏌 ♿ 📷 ♿ **Location** N side of town centre off A6125

Hotel ★★★★ 78% Newcastle Marriott Hotel Gosforth Park, High Gosforth Park, Gosforth, NEWCASTLE UPON TYNE ☎ 0191 236 4111 178 en suite

Parklands Gosforth Park Golfing Complex, High
Gosforth Park NE3 5HQ ☎ 0191 236 4867 & 236 4480
Parklands course is set in pleasant parkland with challenging shots around and sometimes over attractive water hazards. The first 9 holes are easier but the second 9 test even the most experienced golfer.

continued

18 holes, 6060yds, Par 71, SSS 69, Course record 66. Club membership 600.
Visitors a daily start sheet operates with bookings taken from 4.30pm the previous day during weekdays, and from 8am Fri & Sat for weekends. **Societies** by prior arrangement with club secretary. **Green Fees** not confirmed. **Prof** Brian Rumney **Facilities** ⊗ ⅏ 🖥 ☕ 🏌 ♿ 📷 ♿ 📷 **Location** 3m N, at the end A1 Western by Pass

Hotel ★★★★ 78% Newcastle Marriott Hotel Gosforth Park, High Gosforth Park, Gosforth, NEWCASTLE UPON TYNE ☎ 0191 236 4111 178 en suite

HOUGHTON-LE-SPRING — Map 12 NZ35

Elemore Elemore Ln, Hetton-le-Hole DH5 0QB
☎ 0191 517 3061 📠 0191 517 3054
Elmore course tests a players ability in all aspects of the game, with drives over water as well as wedges. The greens are firm all year round and there are well positioned bunkers.
18 holes, 5947yds, Par 69, Course record 68. Club membership 100.
Visitors no restrictions. Phone to avoid society days. **Societies** apply in writing, telephone enquiries welcome. **Green Fees** not confirmed. **Course Designer** J Gaunt **Facilities** ⊗ 🖥 ☕ 🏌 ♿ 📷 🚩 ⚑ 🚗 ♿ **Location** 4m S of Houghton-Le-Spring on the A182

Hotel ★★ 66% Chilton Lodge Country Pub & Hotel, Black Boy Rd, Chilton Moor, Fencehouses, HOUGHTON-LE-SPRING ☎ 0191 385 2694 25 en suite

Houghton-le-Spring Copt Hill DH5 8LU
☎ 0191 584 1198 & 584 0048
Hilly, downland course with natural slope hazards.
18 holes, 6443yds, Par 72, SSS 71, Course record 64. Club membership 600.
Visitors may not play on Sun until 4pm. **Societies** must contact secretary in advance. **Green Fees** terms on application. **Prof** Kevin Gow **Facilities** ⊗ ⅏ 🖥 ☕ 🏌 ♿ 📷 **Location** 0.5m E on B1404

Hotel ★★ 66% Chilton Lodge Country Pub & Hotel, Black Boy Rd, Chilton Moor, Fencehouses, HOUGHTON-LE-SPRING ☎ 0191 385 2694 25 en suite

NEWCASTLE UPON TYNE — Map 12 NZ26

City of Newcastle Three Mile Bridge NE3 2DR
☎ 0191 285 1775 📠 0191 2840700
e-mail: info@cityofnewcastlegolfclub.com
A well-manicured parkland course in the Newcastle suburbs.
18 holes, 6528yds, Par 72, SSS 71, Course record 64. Club membership 600.
Visitors no restrictions but advisable to telephone first. **Societies** telephone in advance **Green Fees** £30 per day; £25 per round (£30 weekends). **Prof** Steve McKenna **Course Designer** Harry Vardon **Facilities** ⊗ ⅏ 🖥 ☕ 🏌 ♿ 📷 🚩 ♿ **Location** 3m N on B1318

Hotel ★★★ 65% The Caledonian Hotel, Newcastle, 64 Osborne Rd, Jesmond, NEWCASTLE UPON TYNE ☎ 0191 281 7881 89 en suite

Newcastle United Ponteland Rd, Cowgate NE5 3JW
☎ 0191 286 9998
e-mail: info@nugc.co.ul
Moorland course with natural hazards.

continued

18 holes, 6617yds, Par 72, SSS 72, Course record 66.
Club membership 650.
Visitors must play with member at weekends. **Societies** must contact in writing or telephone in advance. **Green Fees** terms on application. **Course Designer** Various **Facilities** ⊗ ⅢⅢ ᴸᴮ 🍴♀♐🏠🎯♦❄❋ **Leisure** Snooker table. **Location** 1.25m NW of city centre off A6127

Hotel ★★★ 66% Swallow Imperial Hotel, Jesmond Rd, NEWCASTLE UPON TYNE ☎ 0191 281 5511 122 en suite

Northumberland High Gosforth Park NE3 5HT
☎ 0191 236 2498 📄 0191 236 2498
Many golf courses have been sited inside racecourses, although not so many survive today. One which does is the Northumberland Club's course at High Gosforth Park. Naturally the course is flat but there are plenty of mounds and other hazards to make it a fine test of golf. It should be said that not all the holes are within the confines of the racecourse, but both inside and out there are some good holes. This is a Championship course.
18 holes, 6629yds, Par 72, SSS 72, Course record 65.
Club membership 580.
Visitors may not play at weekends or competition days. Must contact in advance. **Societies** must apply in writing or telephone. **Green Fees** £45 per day; £35 per round. **Course Designer** Colt/Braid **Facilities** ⊗ ⅢⅢ ᴸᴮ 🍴♀🏠 ♦ **Location** 4m N of city centre off A1

Hotel ★★★★ 78% Newcastle Marriott Hotel Gosforth Park, High Gosforth Park, Gosforth, NEWCASTLE UPON TYNE ☎ 0191 236 4111 178 en suite

Westerhope Whorlton Grange, Westerhope NE5 1PP
☎ 0191 286 7636 📄 0191 2146287
Attractive parkland course with tree-lined fairways, and easy walking. Good open views towards the airport.
18 holes, 6444yds, Par 72, SSS 71, Course record 64.
Club membership 778.
Visitors with member only at weekends and bank holidays.Must contact in advance. **Societies** must contact Secretary in advance. **Green Fees** not confirmed. **Cards** ⊟ ▰▰ 🔶 **Prof** Nigel Brown **Facilities** ⊗ ⅢⅢ ᴸᴮ 🍴♀🏠🎯 ➤⚙♦ **Location** 4.5m NW of city centre off B6324

Hotel ★★★★ 78% Newcastle Marriott Hotel Gosforth Park, High Gosforth Park, Gosforth, NEWCASTLE UPON TYNE ☎ 0191 236 4111 178 en suite

Ryton Clara Vale NE40 3TD
☎ 0191 413 3737 📄 0191 413 1642
e-mail: secretary@rytongolfclub.co.uk
Parkland course.
18 holes, 5950yds, Par 70, SSS 69, Course record 67.
Club membership 600.
Visitors with member only at weekends. **Societies** apply in advance. **Green Fees** £20 per day; £16 per round. **Facilities** ⊗ ⅢⅢ ᴸᴮ 🍴♀🏠 **Location** NW side of town off A695

Hotel ★★★ 70% Gibside Hotel, Front St, WHICKHAM ☎ 0191 488 9292 45 en suite

Tyneside Westfield Ln NE40 3QE
☎ 0191 413 2742 📄 0191 413 2742
Open parkland course, water hazard, hilly, practice area.
continued

---

18 holes, 6042yds, Par 70, SSS 69, Course record 65.
Club membership 641.
Visitors must contact in advance to play at weekends (after 3pm) **Societies** must apply in advance. **Green Fees** £20 per round. **Cards** ⊟ ▰▰ 🔶 **Prof** Malcolm Gunn **Course Designer** H S Colt **Facilities** ⊗ ⅢⅢ ᴸᴮ 🍴♀🏠 ♦ **Location** NW side of town off A695

Hotel ★★★ 70% Gibside Hotel, Front St, WHICKHAM ☎ 0191 488 9292 45 en suite

South Shields Cleadon Hills NE34 8EG
☎ 0191 456 8942 📄 0191 456 8942
e-mail: thesecretary@south-shields-golf.freeserve.co.uk
A slightly undulating downland course on a limestone base ensuring good conditions underfoot. Open to strong winds, the course is testing but fair. There are fine views of the coastline.
18 holes, 6174yds, Par 71, SSS 70, Course record 64.
Club membership 750.
Visitors must contact in advance. **Societies** by arrangement. **Green Fees** £22 per day (£27 weekends & bank holidays). **Prof** Gary Parsons **Course Designer** McKenzie-Braid **Facilities** ⊗ ⅢⅢ ᴸᴮ 🍴♀🏠 **Conf** Max 36 **Location** SE side of town centre off A1300

Hotel ★★★ 65% Sea Hotel, Sea Rd, SOUTH SHIELDS ☎ 0191 427 0999 32 en suite

Whitburn Lizard Ln NE34 7AF
☎ 0191 529 4944 (Sec) & 529 2144 (club) 📄 0191 529 4944
Parkland course.with sea views.
18 holes, 5899yds, Par 69, SSS 68, Course record 64.
Club membership 700.
Visitors restricted weekends & Tue. Contact professional in advance. **Societies** must apply in writing to secretary **Green Fees** terms on application. **Prof** David Stephenson **Course Designer** Colt, Alison & Morrison **Facilities** ⊗ ⅢⅢ ᴸᴮ 🍴♀ 🏠 ♦ **Location** 2.5m SE off A183

Hotel ★★★★ 70% Sunderland Marriott Hotel, Queen's Pde, Seaburn, SUNDERLAND ☎ 0191 529 2041 82 en suite

Ryhope Leechmore Way, Ryhope SR2 0DH
☎ 0191 523 7333
18 holes, 4601yds, Par 65, SSS 63.
Location 3.5m S of city centre
Telephone for further details

Hotel ★★★★ 70% Sunderland Marriott Hotel, Queen's Pde, Seaburn, SUNDERLAND ☎ 0191 529 2041 82 en suite

Wearside Coxgreen SR4 9JT
☎ 0191 534 2518 📄 0191 5346186
Open, undulating parkland course rolling down to the River Wear and beneath the shadow of the famous Penshaw Monument. Built on the lines of an Athenian temple it is a well-known landmark. Two ravines cross the course presenting a variety of challenging holes.
18 holes, 6373yds, Par 71, SSS 74, Course record 63.
Club membership 648.
Visitors may not play before 9.30am, between 12.30-1.30 or after 4pm. **Societies** must apply in writing. **Green Fees** £20 (£26 weekends). **Prof** Doug Brolls **Facilities** ⊗ ⅢⅢ ᴸᴮ 🍴♀🏠♦ **Location** 3.5m W off A183   *continued*

Hotel ★★★★ 70% Sunderland Marriott Hotel, Queen's Pde, Seaburn, SUNDERLAND ☎ 0191 529 2041
82 en suite

TYNEMOUTH   Map 12 NZ36

Tynemouth Spital Dene NE30 2ER
☎ 0191 257 4578 📠 0191 259 5193
Well-drained parkland course, not physically demanding but providing a strong challenge to both low and high handicap players.
18 holes, 6359yds, Par 70, SSS 70, Course record 66.
Club membership 800.
Visitors must play with member weekends & bank holidays. **Societies** must contact in writing. **Green Fees** £25 per day; £20 per round. **Cards** 🃏🃏🃏 **Prof** J P McKenna **Course Designer** Willie Park **Facilities** ⊗ ⊪ 🏌 ▐ 🏌 🐎 🏌 **Location** 0.5m W

Hotel ★★★ 68% Grand Hotel, Grand Pde, TYNEMOUTH ☎ 0191 293 6666 45 annexe en suite

WALLSEND   Map 12 NZ26

Wallsend Rheydt Av, Bigges Main NE28 8SU
☎ 0191 262 1973
Parkland course.
18 holes, 6608yds, Par 72, SSS 72, Course record 66.
Club membership 655.
Visitors may not play before 12.30pm weekends. Must book in advance **Societies** must apply in writing. **Green Fees** £15.50 per round(£17.50 weekends). **Prof** Ken Phillips **Course Designer** A Snowball **Facilities** ▐ 🏌 🏌 🐎 ☎ 🏌 ⟨ **Location** NW side of town centre off A193

Hotel ★★★ 66% Swallow Imperial Hotel, Jesmond Rd, NEWCASTLE UPON TYNE ☎ 0191 281 5511 122 en suite

WASHINGTON   Map 12 NZ25

George Washington Hotel Golf & Country Club Stone Cellar Rd, High Usworth, District 12 NE37 1PH ☎ 0191 402 9988 & 417 8346 📠 0191 4151166
e-mail: georgewashington@corushotel.com
A championship standard course with tree lined fairways offering a feeling of seclusion even on busy days.

18 holes, 6604yds, Par 73, SSS 72, Course record 68.
Club membership 500.
Visitors must contact in advance. May not play before 10am or between noon & 2pm at weekends. **Societies** book in advance. **Green Fees** terms on application. **Cards** 🃏🃏 🃏🃏 **Prof** David Patterson **Course Designer** Eric Watson **Facilities** ⊗ ⊪ ▐ 🏌 🏌 🐎 ☎ 🏌 🐎 ⟨ **Leisure** heated indoor swimming pool, squash, sauna, solarium, gymnasium, 9 hole par 3 course. **Conf** Max 200 Thtr 200 Class 150 Banquet 150 Del £31 * **Location** From
continued

A195 signed Washington North take last exit on rdbt, then right at mini-rdbt

Hotel ★★★ 65% George Washington Golf & Country Club, Stone Cellar Rd, District 12, High Usworth, WASHINGTON ☎ 0191 402 9988 103 en suite

WHICKHAM   Map 12 NZ26

Whickham Hollinside Park, Fellside Rd NE16 5BA
☎ 0191 488 1576 📠 0191 488 1576
Undulating parkland course with attractive panoramic views.
18 holes, 5878yds, Par 68, SSS 68, Course record 61.
Club membership 660.
Visitors must contact Professional in advance. **Societies** by arrangement. **Green Fees** £20 (£25 weekends). **Prof** Graeme Lisle **Facilities** ⊗ ⊪ by prior arrangement ▐ 🏌 🏌 🐎 ⟨ **Location** 1.5m S

Hotel ★★★ 65% Swallow Hotel, High West St, GATESHEAD ☎ 0191 477 1105 103 en suite

WHITLEY BAY   Map 12 NZ37

Whitley Bay Claremont Rd NE26 3UF
☎ 0191 252 0180 📠 0191 297 0030
An 18-hole links type course, close to the sea, with a stream running through the undulating terrain.
18 holes, 6579yds, Par 71, SSS 71, Course record 66.
Club membership 800.
Visitors may not play Sat, telephone for Sun play. Advisable to contact in advance. **Societies** telephone initially. **Green Fees** £33 per day; £24 per round. **Prof** Gary Shipley **Facilities** ⊗ ⊪ ▐ 🏌 🏌 🐎 ☎ 🐎 ⟨ **Location** NW side of town centre off A1148

Hotel ★★★ 68% Windsor Hotel, South Pde, WHITLEY BAY ☎ 0191 251 8888 70 en suite

WARWICKSHIRE

ATHERSTONE   Map 04 SP39

Atherstone The Outwoods, Coleshill Rd CV9 2RL
☎ 01827 713110 📠 01827 715686
Scenic parkland course, established in 1894 and laid out on hilly ground.
18 holes, 6006yds, Par 72, SSS 70, Course record 68.
Club membership 495.
Visitors handicap certificate required. With member only weekends and bank holidays but not Sun. Also with holder of handicap certificate by permission of Club Secretary. **Societies** contact in advance. **Green Fees** £15 per day Mondays (£25 Tues-Fri). **Course Designer** Hawtree & Gaunt Mornoch **Facilities** ⊗ ⊪ ▐ 🏌 🏌 🐎 **Location** 0.5m S on B4116

Hotel ⌂ Travelodge, Green Ln, TAMWORTH ☎ Cen Res 0800 850950 📠 01827 260145 62 en suite

BIDFORD-ON-AVON   Map 04 SP15

Bidford Grange Stratford Rd B50 4LY
☎ 01789 490319 📠 01789 490998
Designed by Howard Swan & Paul Tillman, this very long, championship standard course is built to represent a links course and is fully irrigated. There are water hazards on the first 7 holes, and particularly challenging holes on the 16th (223yds,par 3), 8th (600yds, par 5) and an uphill par 4 at the 13th.
continued

Bidford Grange Golf Club

18 holes, 7233yds, Par 72, SSS 74, Course record 66.
Club membership 200.
Visitors Telephone for tee reservations. **Societies** apply in writing or phone, minimum 12. **Green Fees** not confirmed.
Cards 🔲 🔲 🔲 🔲 🔲 🔲 **Prof** Simon Leahy **Facilities** ⊗ 🍴🍺♀⚐🏌⛳🚩🏪🚿 ♿ ♟ **Leisure** fishing.
Location 4m W of Stratford upon Avon, B439

Hotel ★★★ 73% Salford Hall Hotel, ABBOT'S SALFORD
☎ 01386 871300 14 en suite 19 annexe en suite

BRANDON   Map 04 SP47

City of Coventry-Brandon Wood Brandon Ln,
Wolston CV8 3GQ ☎ 024 76543141 🖹 024 76545108
Municipal parkland course surrounded by fields and bounded by River Avon on east side. Floodlit driving range.
18 holes, 6610yds, Par 72, SSS 71, Course record 68.
Club membership 500.
Visitors telephone for details, advance booking recommended. **Societies** telephone secretary for details
Green Fees £10.20 per round (£13.55 weekends). **Cards** 🔲 🔲 🔲 🔲 **Prof** Chris Gledhill **Facilities** ⊗ 🍺 ♀ ♿🍴🚩🚿 ♟ **Location** Off A45 southbound

Hotel ★★★ 66% The Brandon Hall, Main St, BRANDON
☎ 0870 400 8105 60 en suite

COLESHILL   Map 04 SP28

Maxstoke Park Castle Ln B46 2RD
☎ 01675 466743 🖹 01675 466743
Parkland course with easy walking. Numerous trees and a lake form natural hazards.
18 holes, 6442yds, Par 71, SSS 71, Course record 64.
Club membership 720.
Visitors with member only at weekends & bank holidays.
Societies contact in advance. **Green Fees** terms on application. **Prof** Neil McEwan **Course Designer** various
Facilities ⊗ 🍴🍺♀⚐♿🍴🚩 ♟ **Location** 3m NE of Coleshill on B4114 turn right for Maxstoke then 1m on right

Hotel ★★★ 65% Grimstock Country House Hotel, Gilson Rd, Gilson, COLESHILL ☎ 01675 462121 & 462161
🖹 01675 467646 44 en suite

HENLEY-IN-ARDEN   Map 04 SP16

Henley Golf & Country Club Birmingham Rd
B95 5QA ☎ 01564 793715 🖹 01564 795754
e-mail: enquiries@henleygcc.co.uk
This improving course is maturing well and provides a good golfing challenge for all handicaps. All facilities recently upgraded.

continued

18 holes, 6933yds, Par 73, SSS 73.
Club membership 675.
Visitors may book up to 7 days in advance. **Societies** apply in writing or telephone in advance. **Green Fees** £25 per 18 holes (£30 weekends); £6 per 9 holes par 3 course. **Cards** 🔲 🔲 🔲 🔲 🔲 🔲 **Course Designer** N Selwyn Smith
Facilities ⊗ 🍴🍺♀⚐♿🍴 ♟ **Leisure** hard tennis courts, 9 hole par 3 course.**Conf** Max 250 Thtr 250 Class 120 Board 100 Banquet 150 Del £25 to £35 * **Location** On A3400 Birmingham to Stratford road, just N of Henley-in-Arden

Hotel ★★★ 66% Quality Hotel, Pool Bank, Southcrest,
REDDITCH ☎ 01527 541511 73 en suite

KENILWORTH   Map 04 SP27

Kenilworth Crewe Ln CV8 2EA
☎ 01926 858517 🖹 01926 864453
e-mail: info@kenilworthgolfclub.fsnet.co.uk
Parkland course in open hilly situation. Club founded in 1889.
18 holes, 6400yds, Par 73, SSS 71, Course record 62.
Club membership 755.
Visitors must contact in advance. **Societies** apply in writing.
Green Fees £32 (£40 weekends). **Cards** 🔲 🔲 🔲 🔲 🔲 🔲 **Prof** Steve Yates **Course Designer** Hawtree **Facilities** ⊗ 🍴🍺♀⚐♿🍴🚩🏪 ♟ **Leisure** Par 3 chipping green.**Conf** Max 20 Del from £75 * **Location** 0.5m NE

Hotel ★★ 69% Clarendon House Hotel, Old High St,
KENILWORTH ☎ 01926 857668 22 en suite

AA website: www.theAA.com

LEA MARSTON — Map 04 SP29
Lea Marston Hotel & Leisure Complex
Haunch Ln B76 0BY ☎ 01675 470468 📠 01675 470871

The Marston Lakes course was completed in June 2000 and opened April 2001. The layout includes many water and sand hazards through undulating parkland. While short by modern standards, it is a good test for even low handicap players, requiring virtually everything in the bag. Tees and greens have been built to championship course specifications.

Marston Lakes: 9 holes, 2054yds, Par 31, SSS 30.
Club membership 150.

Visitors book in advance and dress code applies. **Societies** must telephone in advance. **Green Fees** £11.50 per 18 holes; £6.50 per 9 holes (£14/£10.95 weekends). **Cards** 🔲 🔳 🔲 💳 📇 🔳 🔲 **Prof** Darren Lewis **Facilities** ⊗ 🏌 🏪 💈 ♀ ⌂ 🍴 🚣 🐾 🏊 🏐 **Leisure** hard tennis courts, heated indoor swimming pool, sauna, solarium, gymnasium, golf simulator.**Conf** Max 140 Thtr 140 Class 50 Board 30 Banquet 140 Del £35 to £152.50 * **Location** From M42 take the A4091 to Kingsbury. Turn right after 1 mile and golf club is signposted 1.5m on right

Hotel ★★★ 72% Lea Marston Hotel & Leisure Complex, Haunch Ln, LEA MARSTON ☎ 01675 470468 82 en suite

LEAMINGTON SPA — Map 04 SP36
Leamington & County Golf Ln, Whitnash
CV31 2QA ☎ 01926 425961 📠 01926 425961
e-mail: secretary@leamingtongolf.co.uk

Undulating parkland course with extensive views.
18 holes, 6488yds, Par 71, SSS 71, Course record 65.
Club membership 802.

Visitors must contact in advance. **Societies** telephone in advance. **Green Fees** £27 per round (£40 weekends). **Prof** Julian Mellor **Course Designer** H S Colt **Facilities** ⊗ 🏌 🏪 💈 ♀ ⌂ 🍴 🐾 🏊 **Leisure** snooker. **Location** 10 mins from M40, S side of town centre

Hotel ★★★ 59% Manor House Hotel, Avenue Rd, LEAMINGTON SPA ☎ 01926 423251 53 en suite

Newbold Comyn Newbold Ter East CV32 4EW
☎ 01926 421157
Municipal parkland course with hilly front nine. The par 4, 9th is a 467-yd testing hole. The back 9 holes are rather flat but include two par 5s.
18 holes, 6315yds, Par 70, SSS 70, Course record 70.
Club membership 280.

Visitors no restrictions. **Societies** apply to professional. **Green Fees** not confirmed. **Prof** Ricky Carvell **Facilities** ⊗ 🏌 🏪 💈 ♀ ⌂ 🍴 🐾 🏊 **Leisure** heated indoor swimming pool, gymnasium. **Location** 0.75m E of town centre off B4099

continued

Lea Marston Hotel & Leisure Complex

With its newly opened beautiful Marston Lakes course, Lea Marston is a superb venue for a relaxing golf break. The new course flows across undulating parkland, featuring many beautifully designed water and sand hazards, creating an enjoyable test for golfers of all abilities. There is also a magnificent Par 3 Academy course, floodlit driving range, indoor Smart Golf Simulator and putting green. Guests can also enjoy complimentary use of the Health Club, including indoor swimming pool, sauna, and steam room.

Haunch Lane, Lea Marston, Sutton Coldfield, Warwickshire B76 0BY
Tel:01675 470468 Fax: 01675 470871
www.leamarstonhotel.co.uk
e-mail: info@leamarstonhotel.co.uk

Hotel ★★★ 59% Manor House Hotel, Avenue Rd, LEAMINGTON SPA ☎ 01926 423251 53 en suite

LEEK WOOTTON — Map 04 SP26
The Warwickshire CV35 7QT
☎ 01926 409409 📠 01926 408409
e-mail: b.fotheringham@clubhaus.com

This is an unusual championship standard course. Designed by Karl Litten, the 36 holes are laid out as four interchangeable loops of 9 holes to create six contrasting yet superb courses in a parkland and woodland setting.

East South Course: 18 holes, 7000yds, Par 72, SSS 72, Course record 68.
North West Course: 18 holes, 7421yds, Par 74, SSS 73, Course record 70.
Club membership 1500.

Visitors can book up to 7 days in advance. **Societies** apply to sales office for details. **Green Fees** terms on application.

continued

Cards 🖃 ▬ ▬ 🐼 🖩 Prof Mark Dulson Course
Designer Karl Litten Facilities ⊗ ⅻ ⅃ 🏌 ♀ ⅄ 🏠 ⚐ ↘
🚜 ☂ ⟐ Location 1m from Kenilworth on B4115

Hotel ★★★★ 67% Le Meridien Warwick, Chesford Bridge,
KENILWORTH ☎ 01926 859331
145 en suite 9 annexe en suite

NUNEATON   Map 04 SP39

Nuneaton Golf Dr, Whitestone CV11 6QF
☎ 024 7634 7810 🗎 024 7632 7563
Undulating parkland and woodland course with Silver
Birch lining the fairways. Easy walking.
18 holes, 6429yds, Par 71, SSS 71.
Club membership 700.
Visitors must produce evidence of membership of a
recognised golf club or society, with member only at
weekends. **Societies** apply in writing. **Green Fees** £33 per
day; £28 per round. **Prof** Jon Salter **Facilities** ⊗ ⅻ ⅃ 🏌 ♀
⅄ 🏠 🚜 ☂ **Conf** Max 100 **Location** 2m SE off B4114

Hotel ★★★ 63% Weston Hall Hotel, Weston Ln, Weston in
Arden, Bulkington, NUNEATON ☎ 024 7631 2989
40 en suite

Oakridge Arley Ln, Ansley Village CV10 9PH
☎ 01676 541389 & 540542 🗎 01676 542709
e-mail: admin@oakridgegolf.fsnet.co.uk
There are a number of water hazards on the back nine
which add to the natural beauty of the countryside. The
undulating course is affected by winter cross winds on
several holes. Overall it will certainly test golfing skills.
18 holes, 6242yds, Par 71, SSS 70.
Club membership 500.
Societies apply in writing or telephone in advance. **Green
Fees** terms on application. **Cards** 🖃 ▬ 🖩 **Course**
Designer Algy Jayes **Facilities** ⊗ ⅻ ⅃ 🏌 ♀ ⅄ 🏠 ⚐ ↘
🚜 ☂ Location 4m W

Hotel ★★★ 63% Weston Hall Hotel, Weston Ln, Weston in
Arden, Bulkington, NUNEATON ☎ 024 7631 2989
40 en suite

Purley Chase Pipers Ln, Ridge Ln CV10 0RB
☎ 024 7639 3118 🗎 024 7639 8015
e-mail: enquiries@purleychase.co.uk
Meadowland course with tricky water hazards on eight
holes and undulating greens. 13-bay driving range.
18 holes, 6772yds, Par 72, SSS 72, Course record 64.
Club membership 650.
Visitors welcome weekends after 12 noon and mon-fri.
Societies telephone for provisional booking (Mon-Fri only).
Green Fees terms on application. **Cards** 🖃 ▬ 🖩 **Prof**
Gary Carver **Facilities** ⊗ ⅻ ⅃ 🏌 ♀ ⅄ 🏠 ↘ 🚜 ☂ ⟐
Location 2m NW off B4114

Hotel ★★★ 63% Weston Hall Hotel, Weston Ln, Weston in
Arden, Bulkington, NUNEATON ☎ 024 7631 2989
40 en suite

RUGBY   Map 04 SP57

Rugby Clifton Rd CV21 3RD
☎ 01788 542306 (Sec) 575134 (Pro) 🗎 01788 542306
Parkland course with brook running through the middle
and crossed by a viaduct.
18 holes, 5457yds, Par 68, SSS 67, Course record 62.
Club membership 700.

continued

Visitors weekends & bank holidays with member only.
Societies apply in writing. **Green Fees** not confirmed. **Prof**
Nat Summers **Facilities** ⊗ ⅻ ⅃ 🏌 ♀ ⅄ 🏠 ⚐ ↘ ☂
Location 1m NE on B5414

Hotel ★★★ 61% Grosvenor Hotel Rugby, 81-87 Clifton
Rd, RUGBY ☎ 01788 535686 26 en suite

Whitefields Hotel Golf & Country Club
Coventry Rd, Thurlaston CV23 9JR
☎ 01788 815555 🗎 01788 817777
Whitefields has superb natural drainage. There are many
water features and the 13th has a stunning dogleg
442yard par 4 with a superb view across Draycote Water.
The 16th is completely surrounded by water and is
particularly difficult.
18 holes, 6223yds, Par 71, SSS 70, Course record 66.
Club membership 400.
Visitors advisable to book unless hotel guest, available 7
days, contact secretary on 01788 815555. **Societies** contact
secretary in advance. **Green Fees** terms on application.
Cards 🖃 ▬ ▬ 🖩 🖩 🖩 Prof Darren Price Course
Designer Reg Mason **Facilities** ⊗ ⅻ ⅃ 🏌 ♀ ⅄ 🏠 ⚐ ↔
↘ 🚜 ☂ ⟐ **Conf** Max 200 Board 12 Del £34 to £85 *
Location Junct of M45 where it meets the A45 Coventry
road, near Dunchurch

Hotel ★★ 65% Whitefields Hotel Golf & Country Club,
Coventry Rd, Thurlaston, RUGBY
☎ 01788 521800 & 522393 🗎 01788 521695 34 en suite

STONELEIGH   Map 04 SP37

Stoneleigh Deer Park The Clubhouse, The Old Deer
Park, Coventry Rd CV8 3DR
☎ 024 76639991 &76639912 🗎 024 76511533
Parkland course in old deer park with many mature
trees. The River Avon meanders through the course and
comes into play on 4 holes. Also 9-hole course.
*Tantara Course: 18 holes, 6023yds, Par 71, SSS 69,
Course record 67.*
Avon Course: 9 holes, 1251yds, Par 27.
Club membership 800.
Visitors must contact in advance. **Societies** by prior
arrangement. **Green Fees** £18 Mon-Thur; £20 Fri;(£27
weekends and bank holidays). **Cards** 🖃 ▬ 🖩 🖩 🖩 **Prof**
Marc Coulson **Facilities** ⊗ ⅻ ⅃ 🏌 ♀ ⅄ 🏠 ⚐ ↘ 🚜 ☂
Conf Banquet 120 **Location** 3m NE of Kenilworth

Hotel ★★★★ 62% De Montfort Hotel, Abbey End,
KENILWORTH ☎ 01926 855944 108 en suite

> An asterisk * in the Green Fees or
> Conference facilities indicates that
> prices given are for 2002

STRATFORD-UPON-AVON   Map 04 SP25

Stratford Oaks Bearley Rd, Snitterfield CV37 0EZ
☎ 01789 731980 📗 01789 731981
e-mail: stratford.oaks@virgin.net
American styled, level parkland course with some water features designed by Howard Swan.
18 holes, 6100yds, Par 71, SSS 69, Course record 66.
Club membership 655.
Visitors contact in advance. **Societies** telephone in advance.
Green Fees not confirmed. **Cards** 🔲 🔲 🔲 🔲 **Prof** Andrew Dunbar **Course Designer** H Swann **Facilities** ⊗ 🍴 ⬛ ⬛ ♀ ♿ 🏠 🏌 ♣ **Location** 4m N of Stratford-upon-Avon

Hotel ★★★★ 70% Stratford Manor, Warwick Rd, STRATFORD-UPON-AVON ☎ 01789 731173 104 en suite

Stratford-upon-Avon Tiddington Rd CV37 7BA
☎ 01789 205749 📗 414909
e-mail: sec@stratfordgolf.co.uk
Beautiful parkland course. The par 3, 16th is tricky and the par 5, 17th and 18th, provide a tough end.
18 holes, 6311yds, Par 72, SSS 70, Course record 63.
Club membership 750.
Visitors may not play before 11.00am weekends. Phone in advance. **Societies** must apply in advance. Tues & Thurs only. **Green Fees** £40 per day; £35 per round(£50/£40 weekends). **Prof** D Sutherland **Course Designer** Taylor **Facilities** ⊗ 🍴 ⬛ ⬛ ♀ ♿ 🏠 🏌 🛺 ♣ **Location** 0.75m E on B4086

Hotel ★★★★ 65% The Alveston Manor, Clopton Bridge, STRATFORD-UPON-AVON ☎ 0870 400 8181 114 en suite

Welcombe Hotel Warwick Rd CV37 0NR
☎ 01789 295252 📗 01789 414666
e-mail: Sales@welcombe.co.uk
Wooded parkland course of great character and boasting superb views of the River Avon, Stratford and the Cotswolds. Set within the hotel's 157-acre estate, it has two lakes and water features.
18 holes, 6274yds, Par 70, SSS 70, Course record 64.
Visitors must contact in advance. **Societies** booking via Hotel. **Green Fees** not confirmed. **Cards** 🔲 🔲 🔲 🔲 🔲 **Prof** Carl Mason **Course Designer** Thomas Macauley **Facilities** ⊗ 🍴 ⬛ ⬛ ♀ ♿ 🏠 🏌 🚡 🛺 ♣ **Leisure** hard tennis courts, fishing, solarium, gymnasium. **Location** 1.5m NE off A46

Hotel ★★★★ 74% Welcombe Hotel and Golf Course, Warwick Rd, STRATFORD-UPON-AVON ☎ 01789 295252 64 en suite

TANWORTH-IN-ARDEN   Map 07 SP17

Ladbrook Park Poolhead Ln B94 5ED
☎ 01564 742264 📗 01564 742909
e-mail: secretary@ladbrookparkgolfclub.fsnet.co.uk
Parkland course lined with trees.
18 holes, 6427yds, Par 71, SSS 71, Course record 65.
Club membership 700.
Visitors welcome weekdays, with member at weekends. Must contact in advance & have handicap certificate. **Societies** apply in advance. **Green Fees** £40 per 36 holes, £32 per 28 holes, £25 per 18 holes. **Cards** 🔲 🔲 🔲 🔲 **Prof** Richard Mountford **Course Designer** H S Colt **Facilities** ⊗ 🍴 ⬛ ⬛ ♀ ♿ 🏠 🏌 ♣ **Location** 2.5m SE of M42 junct 3   *continued*

Hotel ★★★⚑ Nuthurst Grange Country House Hotel, Nuthurst Grange Ln, HOCKLEY HEATH ☎ 01564 783972 15 en suite

UPPER BRAILES   Map 04 SP33

Brailes Sutton Ln, Lower Brailes OX15 5BB
☎ 01608 685633 📗 01608 685205
e-mail: office@brailes-golf-club.co.uk
Undulating meadowland on 130 acres of Cotswold countryside. Sutton brook passes through the course and is crossed five times. The par 5 17th offers the most spectacular view of three counties from the tee. Challenging par 3 short holes.
18 holes, 6304yds, Par 71, SSS 70, Course record 67.
Club membership 560.
Visitors advance telephone advisable to 01608 685633. **Societies** telephone or write for information to the Director of Golf. **Green Fees** terms on application. **Cards** 🔲 🔲 🔲 📘 **Prof** Alistair Brown **Course Designer** B A Hull **Facilities** ⊗ 🍴 ⬛ ⬛ ♀ ♿ 🏠 🏌 🛺 ♣ **Location** 4m E of Shipston-on-Stour, on B4035, towards Banbury

Inn ◆◆◆◆ The Red Lion Hotel, Main St, Long Compton, SHIPSTON ON STOUR ☎ 01608 684221 5 en suite

WARWICK   Map 04 SP26

Warwick The Racecourse CV34 6HW ☎ 01926 494316
Parkland course with easy walking. Driving range with floodlit bays.
9 holes, 2682yds, Par 34, SSS 66, Course record 67.
Club membership 150.
Visitors must contact in advance. May not play Sun before 12.30pm **Societies** contact in advance. **Green Fees** £5 per 9 holes (£5.50 weekends). **Prof** Mario Luca **Course Designer** D G Dunkley **Facilities** ⬛ ♀ ♿ 🏠 🏌 ♣ **Location** W side of town centre

Hotel ★★ 62% Warwick Arms Hotel, 17 High St, WARWICK ☎ 01926 492759 35 en suite

WISHAW   See page 247

WISHAW   Map 07 SP19

Wishaw Bulls Ln B76 9QW ☎ 0121 313 2110
Parkland course.
18 holes, 5481yards, SSS 70.
Club membership 270.
Visitors telephone for details **Societies** telephone to book. **Green Fees** terms on application. **Prof** Alan Partridge **Facilities** ⊗ 🍴 ⬛ ⬛ ♀ ♿ 🏠 🏌 🐾 🛺 ♣ **Location** M42 junct 9

Hotel ★★★ 72% Lea Marston Hotel & Leisure Complex, Haunch Ln, LEA MARSTON ☎ 01675 470468 82 en suite

WEST MIDLANDS

ALDRIDGE   Map 07 SK00

Druids Heath Stonnall Rd WS9 8JZ
☎ 01922 455595 (Office) 📗 01922 452887
Testing, undulating heathland course.
18 holes, 6661yds, Par 72, SSS 73, Course record 68.
Club membership 660.
Visitors contact in advance recommended. Weekend play permitted after 2pm. **Societies** phone initially. **Green Fees** £25 per day (£32 weekends after 2pm). **Prof** Glenn Williams   *continued*

The De Vere Belfry

Wishaw, *Warwickshire*   ☎ 01675 470301   Fax 01675 470178   Map 07 SP19

e-mail: enquiries@thebelfry.com

The Belfry is unique as the only venue to have staged the biggest golf event in the world, The Ryder Cup Matches, an unprecedented 4 times, most recently in 2002. The Brabazon is regarded throughout the world as a great championship course with some of the most demanding holes in golf; world famous holes like the 10th (Ballesteros's Hole) and the 18th, with its dangerous lakes and its amphitheatre around the final green. These remained intact during the £2.4million redevelopment in 1998 which made the course even more testing.

Alternatively, you can pit your wits against a new legend in the making, The PGA National Course, which has won plaudits from near and far. The Dave Thomas designed course has been used for professional competition and is already established as one of Britain's leading courses. For those who like their golf a little easier or like to get back into the swing gently, The Derby is ideal and can be played by golfers of any standard. The Bel Air night club, The De Vere Club leisure centre and The Aqua Spa with its fire and ice bio-thermal treatments offer unique experiences away from the golf course.

Visitors Handicap certificate is required for the Brabazon & PGA courses; (24 or better for gentlemen, 32 or better for ladies & juniors.) Reservations 24 hrs in advance for non-residents

Societies must telephone in advance

Green Fees Prices on application - dependent on season.

Facilities ⊗ 〠 🎱 💼 ♀ 🍴 ⛺ 🏠 ⛳ 🥏 🪝 ✂ 🏌 Professional (P. McGovern)

Leisure tennis, squash, swimming, sauna, solarium, gymnasium
Conf max 400, private dining for golf groups

Location Wishaw. Sutton Coldfield B76 9PR (exit J9 M42, 4m E on A446)

Holes/Par/Course record 54 holes.
Brabazon: 18 holes, 6724 yds, Par 72, SSS 71
Derby: 18 holes, 6057 yds, Par 69, SSS 69
PGA National: 18 holes, 6639 yds, Par 71, SSS 70

Championship Course

WHERE TO STAY NEARBY

Hotels
WISHAW

★★★★⊛🅖 75% The De Vere Belfry, B76 9PR. ☎ 01675 470301. 324 en suite

LEA MARSTON

★★★72%
Lea Marston Hotel and Leisure Complex, Haunch Lane.
☎ 01675 470468. 83 en suite

SUTTON COLDFIELD

★★★★⊛🅖 🏷 New Hall, Walmley Rd.
☎ 0121 378 2442. 60 en suite

★★★66% Quality Hotel Sutton Court, 60-66 Lichfield Rd. ☎ 0121 354 4991. 54 en suite 8 annexe en suite

Facilities ⊗ ⅢL ⊾ ⬛ ♀⚲🏳 𝒻 **Leisure** snooker. **Location** NE side of town centre off A454

Hotel ★★★ 76% The Fairlawns at Aldridge, 178 Little Aston Rd, Aldridge, WALSALL
☎ 01922 455122 50 en suite

BIRMINGHAM   Map 07 SP08

Brandhall Heron Rd, Oldbury, Warley B68 8AQ
☎ 0121 552 2195
18 holes, 5734yds, Par 70, SSS 68, Course record 66.
Location 5.5m W of Birmingham city centre off A4123
Telephone for further details

Hotel ★★★ 67% Holiday Inn Birmingham, Chapel Ln, Great Barr, BIRMINGHAM ☎ 0870 400 9009 192 en suite

Cocks Moors Woods Alcester Rd South, Kings Heath
B14 4ER ☎ 0121 464 3584 📄 0121 441 1305
Although quite short this tree-lined, parkland course has well maintained greens and offers a good test of golf.
18 holes, 5769yds, Par 69, SSS 68.
Club membership 300.
Visitors no restrictions. **Societies** must contact in advance.
Green Fees terms on application. **Prof** Steve Ellis **Facilities** ⊗ ⅢL ⊾ ⬛ ♀⚲🏳 𝒻 **Leisure** heated indoor swimming pool, solarium, gymnasium. **Location** 4m N of M42 junct 3 on A435

Hotel ★★★ 65% Holiday Inn Birmingham City, Smallbrook Queensway, BIRMINGHAM
☎ 0870 400 9008 280 en suite

Edgbaston Church Rd, Edgbaston B15 3TB
☎ 0121 454 1736 📄 0121 454 2395
e-mail: secretary@edgbastongc.co.uk
Set in 144 acres of woodland, lake and parkland, two miles from the centre of Birmingham, this delightful course utilises the wealth of natural features to provide a series of testing and adventurous holes set in the traditional double loop that starts directly in front of the Clubhouse, an imposing Georgian mansion.
18 holes, 6106yds, Par 69, SSS 69, Course record 63.
Club membership 970.
Visitors recommended to contact in advance through golf reservations, must have handicap certificate. Most weekends pm. **Societies** must apply in writing. **Green Fees** £40 per round weekday (£50 weekend). **Cards** 💳 💳 **Prof** Jamie Cundy **Course Designer** H S Colt **Facilities** ⊗ ⅢL ⊾ ⬛ ♀⚲🏳 🐾 🏌 𝒻 **Conf** Max 120 Thtr 120 Class 60 Board 60 Banquet 110 **Location** 2m S of city centre on B4217 off A38

Hotel ★★★ 63% Plough & Harrow, 135 Hagley Rd, EDGBASTON ☎ 0121 454 4111 44 en suite

Great Barr Chapel Ln, Great Barr B43 7BA
☎ 0121 357 5270
Parkland course with easy walking. Pleasant views of Barr Beacon National Park.
18 holes, 6523yds, Par 72, SSS 72, Course record 67.
Club membership 600.
Visitors no visitors at weekends. **Societies** must contact in writing. **Green Fees** not confirmed. **Prof** Richard Spragg **Facilities** ⊗ by prior arrangement Ⅲ by prior arrangement ⊾ ⬛ ♀🏳 𝒻 **Location** 6m N of city centre off A 34

Hotel ★★★ 67% Holiday Inn Birmingham, Chapel Ln, Great Barr, BIRMINGHAM ☎ 0870 400 9009 192 en suite

Handsworth 11 Sunningdale Close, Handsworth Wood
B20 1NP ☎ 0121 554 0599 & 554 3387 📄 0121 554 3387
Undulating parkland course with some tight fairways but subject to wind.
18 holes, 6267yds, Par 70, SSS 70, Course record 65.
Club membership 800.
Visitors restricted weekends, bank holidays & Xmas. Must contact in advance and have a handicap certificate. **Societies** must contact in advance. **Green Fees** £35 per day. **Prof** Lee Bashford **Facilities** ⊗ ⅢL ⊾ ⬛ ♀⚲🏳 𝒻 **Leisure** squash. **Location** 3.5m NW of city centre off A4040

Hotel ★★ 65% Sheriden House Hotel, 82 Handsworth Wood Rd, Handsworth Wood, BIRMINGHAM
☎ 0121 554 2185 & 0121 523 5960
📄 0121 551 4761 11 en suite

Harborne 40 Tennal Rd, Harborne B32 2JE
☎ 0121 427 3058 📄 0121 427 4039
e-mail: harbourne@hgolf.fsnet.co.uk
Parkland course in hilly situation, with brook running through.
18 holes, 6230yds, Par 70, SSS 70, Course record 65.
Club membership 655.
Visitors must have handicap certificate, contact in advance, may not play weekends except with member, Ladies have priority Tue. **Societies** Mon, Wed-Fri apply to secretary, by phone or letter. **Green Fees** £35 per day; £30 per round, weekdays only. **Prof** Alan Quarterman **Course Designer** Harry Colt **Facilities** ⊗ ⅢL ⊾ ⬛ ♀⚲🏳 𝒻 **Location** 3.5 m SW of city centre off A4040

Hotel ★★★ 63% Plough & Harrow, 135 Hagley Rd, EDGBASTON ☎ 0121 454 4111 44 en suite

Harborne Church Farm Vicarage Rd, Harborne
B17 0SN ☎ 0121 427 1204 📄 0121 428 3126
Parkland course with water hazards and easy walking. Some holes might prove difficult.
9 holes, 4882yds, Par 66, SSS 64, Course record 62.
Club membership 160.
Visitors must contact in advance. **Societies** must telephone in advance. **Green Fees** £8.50 per 18 holes; £6 per 9 holes (£10/£7 weekends). **Cards** 💳 💳 💳 💳 💳 **Prof** Paul Johnson **Facilities** ⊗ ⅢL ⊾ ⬛ ⚲🏳 𝒻 **Leisure** practice net. **Location** 3.5m SW of city centre off A4040

Hotel ★★★ 63% Plough & Harrow, 135 Hagley Rd, EDGBASTON ☎ 0121 454 4111 44 en suite

Hatchford Brook Coventry Rd, Sheldon B26 3PY
☎ 0121 743 9821 📄 0121 743 3420
e-mail: idt@hbgc.freeserve.co.uk
Fairly flat, municipal parkland course.
Hatchford Brook Golf Club: 18 holes, 6155yds, Par 69, SSS 70.
Club membership 350.
Visitors are restricted early Sat & Sun. **Societies** must contact in advance. **Green Fees** £9 per round (£11 weekends). **Cards** 💳 💳 💳 💳 💳 **Prof** Mark Hampton **Facilities** ⊗ ⊾ ⬛ ♀⚲🏳 𝒻 **Location** 6m E of city centre on A45

Hotel ★★★ 65% Holiday Inn Birmingham Airport, Coventry Rd, BIRMINGHAM ☎ 0870 400 9007 141 en suite

AA website: www.theAA.com

Hilltop Park Ln, Handsworth B21 8LJ ☎ 0121 554 4463
A good test of golf with interesting layout, undulating
fairways and large greens, located in the Sandwell Valley
conservation area.
18 holes, 6208yds, Par 71, SSS 70.
Club membership 400.
Visitors no restrictions but booking necessary. Societies
Mon-Fri, telephone Professional in advance. Green Fees
£9.50 per 18 holes (£11 weekends and bank holidays). Prof
Kevin Highfield Course Designer Hawtree Facilities ⊗ ⫫
▆ ⚲ 🛈 ⫙ ⚷ Location On A41, 1m from junct 1 M5
· ·
Hotel ★★ 65% Sheriden House Hotel, 82 Handsworth
Wood Rd, Handsworth Wood, BIRMINGHAM
☎ 0121 554 2185 & 0121 523 5960 ▤ 0121 551 4761
11 en suite

Lickey Hills Rosehill, Rednal B45 8RR
☎ 0121 453 3159 ▤ 0121 457 8779
18 holes, 5835yds, Par 68, SSS 68.
Location 10m SW of city centre on B4096
Telephone for further details
· ·
Hotel ★★ 68% Norwood Hotel, 87-89 Bunbury Rd,
Northfield, BIRMINGHAM ☎ 0121 411 2202 18 en suite

Moseley Springfield Rd, Kings Heath B14 7DX
☎ 0121 444 2115 ▤ 0121 441 4662
e-mail: admin@mosgolf.freeserve.co.uk
Parkland course with a lake, pond and stream to provide
natural hazards. The par 3 4th goes through a cutting in
woodland to a tree and garden-lined amphitheatre, and
the par 4 5th entails a drive over a lake to a dog-leg
fairway.

18 holes, 6300yds, Par 70, SSS 71, Course record 63.
Club membership 600.
Visitors may only play by prior arrangement, weekdays
excluding bank holidays. Societies by prior arrangement. on
certain Wed and Fri. Green Fees £37 per day. Prof Martin
Griffin Course Designer various Facilities ⊗ ⫫ ▆ ▆ ♀ ⚲
🛈 ⚷ Location 4m S of city centre on B4146 off A435
· ·
Hotel ★★ 68% Norwood Hotel, 87-89 Bunbury Rd,
Northfield, BIRMINGHAM ☎ 0121 411 2202 18 en suite

North Worcestershire Frankley Beeches Rd,
Northfield B31 5LP ☎ 0121 475 1047 ▤ 0121 476 8681
Designed by James Braid and established in 1907, this is a
mature parkland course. Tree plantations rather than
heavy rough are the main hazards.
18 holes, 5959yds, Par 69, SSS 68, Course record 64.
Club membership 600.
Visitors by prior arrangement with professional. Must play
with member at weekends. All visitors must have an official
CONGU handicap. Societies apply in advance in writing or

continued

by telephone to the professional tel: 0121 475 5721. Green
Fees not confirmed. Prof Finley Clarke Course Designer
James Braid Facilities ⚲ 🛈 ⫙ ⚷ Location 7m SW of
Birmingham city centre, off A38
· ·
Hotel ★★ 68% Norwood Hotel, 87-89 Bunbury Rd,
Northfield, BIRMINGHAM ☎ 0121 411 2202 18 en suite

Warley Woods The Pavilion, Lightswood Hill, Warley
B67 5ED ☎ 0121 429 2440 & 6862619(secretary)
▤ 0121 434 4430
Municipal parkland course in Warley Woods. New out of
bounds areas and bunkers have tightened the course
considerably with further improvement following tree
planting.
9 holes, 5346yds, Par 68, SSS 66, Course record 64.
Club membership 200.
Visitors must contact in advance. Linc card system for easier
booking. Societies booking advised, times very limited for
large parties. Green Fees not confirmed. Cards ▩ ▩ ▩
Prof David Owen Facilities ⊗ ▆ ⚲ 🛈 ⫙ ⚷ Location
4m W of city centre off A456
· ·
Hotel ★★★ 63% Plough & Harrow, 135 Hagley Rd,
EDGBASTON ☎ 0121 454 4111 44 en suite

Ansty Golf Centre Brinklow Rd, Ansty CV7 9JH
☎ 024 7662 1341 ▤ 024 7660 2568
18-hole Pay and Play course of two 9-hole loops.
Membership competitions for handicaps. Driving range
and putting green.
18 holes, 6079yds, Par 71, SSS 68, Course record 66.
Academy Course: 9 holes, 704yds, Par 27.
Club membership 400.
Visitors no restrictions. Societies welcome, telephone in
advance. Green Fees terms on application. Cards ▩ ▩
▩ ▨ Prof Simon Firkins Course Designer David Morgan
Facilities ⊗ ⫫ ▆ ▆ ♀ ⚲ 🛈 ⫙ ⤢ ⚷ ⚹ Location 1m
from M6/M69 junct 2
· ·
Hotel ★★★ 64% Novotel Coventry, Wilsons Ln,
COVENTRY ☎ 024 7636 5000 98 en suite

Coventry St Martins Rd, Finham Park CV3 6RJ
☎ 024 76414152 ▤ 024 76690131
The scene of several major professional events, this
undulating parkland course has a great deal of quality.
More than that, it usually plays its length, and thus
scoring is never easy, as many professionals have
found to their cost.
18 holes, 6601yds, Par 73, SSS 73, Course record 66.
Club membership 500.
Visitors must contact in advance. May not play at
weekends and bank holidays. Societies must apply in
writing/telephone. Green Fees not confirmed. Cards ▩
▩ ▩ ▨ Prof Philip Weaver Course Designer Vardon
Bros/Hawtree Facilities ⊗ ⫫ ▆ ▆ ♀ ⚲ 🛈 ⚷
Location 3m S of city centre on B4113, 2m from jct of
A45/A46
· ·
Hotel ★★★ 67% Hylands Hotel, Warwick Rd,
COVENTRY ☎ 024 7650 1600 61 en suite

Coventry Hearsall Beechwood Av CV5 6DF
☎ 024 76713470 ▤ 024 76691534
Parkland course with fairly easy walking. A brook
provides an interesting hazard.

continued

18 holes, 6005yds, Par 70, SSS 69.
Club membership 650.
Visitors with member only at weekends. **Societies** apply in writing to secretary. **Green Fees** £30 per day. **Prof** Mike Tarn **Facilities** ⊗ ⅷ ㄴ ♥ ♀ ⚐ ⊞ ♦ ♂ **Location** 1.5m SW of city centre off A429

Hotel ★★★ 67% Hylands Hotel, Warwick Rd, COVENTRY ☎ 024 7650 1600 61 en suite

Windmill Village Hotel Golf & Leisure Club
Birmingham Rd, Allesley CV5 9AL
☎ 024 7640 4040 ▤ 024 7640 4042
e-mail: sales@windmillvillagehotel.co.uk
An attractive 18-hole course over rolling parkland with plenty of trees and two lakes that demand shots over open water. Four challenging par 5 holes. Good leisure facilities.
18 holes, 5213yds, Par 70, SSS 67, Course record 63.
Club membership 600.
Visitors must contact in advance. Pre-payment required at peak times. May not play weekends 7-10am. **Societies** telephone for booking form. **Green Fees** terms on application. **Cards** ⊟ ▤ ▦ ⊡ ▨ ⊠ **Prof** Robert Hunter **Course Designer** Robert Hunter **Facilities** ⊗ ⅷ ㄴ ♥ ♀ ⚐ ⊞ ♦ ⚐ ♥ ♣ ♂ **Leisure** hard tennis courts, heated indoor swimming pool, sauna, solarium, gymnasium, beauty suite, practise nets. **Conf** Thtr 400 Class 150 Board 100 Banquet 220 **Location** On A45 W of Coventry

Hotel ★★★ 72% Brooklands Grange Hotel & Restaurant, Holyhead Rd, COVENTRY ☎ 024 7660 1601 30 en suite

Dudley Turner's Hill, Rowley Regis, Warley B65 9DP
☎ 01384 233877 ▤ 01384 233177
Fairly hilly parkland course.
18 holes, 5714yds, Par 69, SSS 68.
Club membership 550.
Visitors must contact in advance, may not play at weekends. **Societies** must contact in advance. **Green Fees** not confirmed. **Cards** ⊟ ▦ ⊡ **Prof** Guy Dean **Facilities** ⊗ ⅷ ㄴ ♥ ♀ ⚐ ⊞ ♂ **Location** 2m S of town centre off B4171

Hotel ★★★ 63% Himley Country Hotel, School Rd, HIMLEY ☎ 01902 896716 73 en suite

Swindon Bridgnorth Rd, Swindon DY3 4PU
☎ 01902 897031 ▤ 01902 326219
e-mail: golf@swindonperton.fsbusiness.co.uk
Attractive undulating woodland/parkland course, with spectacular views.
Old Course: 18 holes, 6121yds, Par 71, SSS 70.
Club membership 700.
Visitors must contact in advance. **Societies** must apply in writing. **Green Fees** £18 per round (£27 weekends & bank holidays). **Cards** ⊟ ▦ **Prof** Phil Lester **Facilities** ⊗ ⅷ ㄴ ♥ ♀ ⚐ ⊞ ♣ ♂ ℓ **Leisure** fishing, Par 3 9-hole course.
Location On B4176, 3m from A449 at Himley

Hotel ★★★ 63% Himley Country Hotel, School Rd, HIMLEY ☎ 01902 896716 73 en suite

Halesowen The Leasowes, Leasowes Ln B62 8QF
☎ 0121 501 3606 ▤ 0121 501 3606
e-mail: halesowen-gc@msn.com
Parkland course in convenient position within the only Grade I listed park in the Midlands.
18 holes, 5754yds, Par 69, SSS 69, Course record 66.
Club membership 625.
Visitors welcome weekdays, may only play weekends or bank holidays with member unless previously agreed. **Societies** must apply in writing/telephone. **Green Fees** terms on application. **Prof** Jon Nicholas **Facilities** ⊗ ⅷ ㄴ ♥ ♀ ㄥ ⊞ ⚐ ♂ **Location** 1m E junct 3 M5, Leasowes Lane off Manor Lane

Hotel ★★ 67% Cedars Hotel, Mason Rd, KIDDERMINSTER ☎ 01562 515595 21 en suite

Copt Heath 1220 Warwick Rd B93 9LN
☎ 01564 772650 ▤ 01564 771022
e-mail: golf@copt-heath.co.uk
Flat parkland course designed by H. Vardon.
18 holes, 6517yds, Par 71, SSS 71, Course record 64.
Club membership 700.
Visitors must contact in advance and possess official handicap certificate. May not play weekends & bank holidays. **Societies** must contact in advance. **Green Fees** £50 per day; £40 per round. **Prof** Brian J Barton **Course Designer** H Vardon **Facilities** ⊗ ⅷ ㄴ ♥ ♀ ㄥ ⊞ ♦ ♂ ℓ **Location** On A4141, 0.50m S of junct 5 of M42

Hotel ★★★★ 66% Renaissance Solihull Hotel, 651 Warwick Rd, SOLIHULL ☎ 0121 711 3000 175 en suite

North Warwickshire Hampton Ln CV7 7LL
☎ 01676 522259 (shop) & 522464 (club) ▤ 01676 522464
Parkland course with easy walking.
9 holes, 6390yds, Par 72, SSS 71, Course record 65.
Club membership 425.
Visitors must contact in advance. Must play with member at weekends. **Societies** must apply in writing to secretary. **Green Fees** £20 per 18 holes. **Prof** Andrew Bownes **Facilities** ⊗ by prior arrangement ⅷ by prior arrangement ㄴ ♥ ♀ ㄥ ⊞ ♂ **Location** 1m SW on B4102

Hotel ★★★ 74% Manor Hotel, Main Rd, MERIDEN ☎ 01676 522735 114 en suite

Stonebridge Golf Centre Somers Rd CV7 7PL
☎ 01676 522442 ▤ 01676 522447
The course is set in the beautiful landscape of the Packington estate, with mature shrubs and trees. Water features are incorporated to provide an excellent variety for a wide range of golfing abilities.
18 holes, 6240yds, Par 70, SSS 70, Course record 70.
Club membership 400.
Visitors advisable to book in advance, booking up to 9 days in advance. **Societies** apply in writing or telephone in advance. **Green Fees** not confirmed. **Cards** ⊟ ▦ ⊡ ▨ ▦ ⊠ ⊠ **Prof** Robert Grier **Course Designer** Mark Jones **Facilities** ⊗ ⅷ ㄴ ♥ ♀ ㄥ ⊞ ⚐ ♥ ♣ ♂ ℓ **Leisure** fishing.

Hotel ★★★ 74% Manor Hotel, Main Rd, MERIDEN ☎ 01676 522735 114 en suite

Marriott Forest of Arden

Meriden, *Warwickshire*   ☎ 01676 522335   Fax 01676 523711   Map 04 SP28

This is one of the finest golf destinations in the UK, with a range of facilities to impress every golfer. The jewel in the crown is the Arden course, one of the country's most spectacular challenges and host to a succession of international tournaments, including the British Masters and English Open.

The shorter Aylesford course offers a varied and enjoyable challenge which golfers of all abilities will find rewarding. Golf events are a speciality and there is a Golf Academy as well as extensive leisure facilities.

Visitors ring to book in advance

Societies by arrangement

Green Fees Arden Course £70 per round (£80 weekends); Aylesford £35 per round (£45 weekends)

Facilities ⊗ ⊮ ⧖ 🖳 ♀ 🗠 ⚲ 🖘 ⛳ 🏌 🦌
⛳ ⛳ Professional (Phillip Hoye)

Leisure tennis, swimming, fishing, sauna, solarium, gymnasium

Location Maxstoke Lane, Meriden CV7 7HR (1m SW of Meriden on B4102)

Holes/Par/Course record Arden Course: 18 holes, 7096 yds, Par 72, Aylesford Course: 18 holes, 6525 yds, Par 72

Championship Course

WHERE TO STAY AND EAT NEARBY

Hotels
MERIDEN

★★★★⊛ 72% Marriott Forest of Arden Hotel & Country Club, Maxstoke Ln.
☎ 01676 522335. 214 en suite

★★★⊛⊛ 74% Manor Hotel, Main Rd.
☎ 01676 522735. 114 en suite

SEDGLEY   Map 07 SO99

Sedgley Golf Centre Sandyfields Rd DY3 3DL
☎ 01902 880503
e-mail: info@sedgleygolf.co.uk
Public Pay and Play course. Undulating contours and
mature trees with extensive views over surrounding
countryside.
9 holes, 3147yds, Par 72, SSS 70.
Club membership 100.
Visitors booking advisable for weekends. Societies must
contact in advance. Green Fees £6 per 9 holes; £8 per 18
holes. Prof Garry Mercer Course Designer W G Cox
Facilities ⚑ ⛳ ⚒ ⚐ (Location 0.5m from town
centre off A463

Hotel ★★★ 63% Himley Country Hotel, School Rd,
HIMLEY ☎ 01902 896716 73 en suite

SOLIHULL   Map 07 SP17

Olton Mirfield Rd B91 1JH
☎ 0121 704 1936 & 0121 705 1083 📖 0121 711 2010
e-mail: mailbox@oltongolfclub.fsnet.co.uk
Parkland course with prevailing southwest wind.
18 holes, 6265yds, Par 69, SSS 71, Course record 63.
Club membership 600.
Visitors must contact in advance. No visitors at weekend.
Societies apply in writing. Green Fees £50 per day; £40 per
18 holes. Prof Charles Haynes Course Designer J H Taylor
Facilities ⊗ ⏷ ⛳ ⚑ ⚐ ⛳ ⚒ (Location Exit M42
junct 5 and take A41 for 1.5m

Hotel ★★★★ 66% Renaissance Solihull Hotel, 651
Warwick Rd, SOLIHULL ☎ 0121 711 3000 175 en suite

Robin Hood St Bernards Rd B92 7DJ
☎ 0121 706 0061 📖 0121 706 0061
e-mail: robin.hood.golf.club@dial.pipex.com
Pleasant parkland course with easy walking and open to
good views.Tree lined fairways and varied holes,
culminating in two excellent finishing holes. Modern
clubhouse.
18 holes, 6635yds, Par 72, SSS 72, Course record 68.
Club membership 650.
Visitors must contact in advance. With member only at
weekends. Societies must contact in advance. Green Fees
£30 per 18 holes;£35 per day. Prof Alan Harvey Course
Designer H S Colt Facilities ⊗ ⏷ ⛳ ⚑ ⚐ ⛳ (
Location 2m W off B4025

Hotel ★★★★ 66% Renaissance Solihull Hotel, 651
Warwick Rd, SOLIHULL ☎ 0121 711 3000 175 en suite

Shirley Stratford Rd, Monkpath, Shirley B90 4EW
☎ 0121 744 6001 📖 0121 745 8220
e-mail: shirleygolfclub@btclick.com
Fairly flat parkland course.
18 holes, 6510yds, Par 72, SSS 71.
Club membership 600.
Visitors may not play bank holidays & with member only at
weekends. Handicap certificate is required. Societies only on
Thu, must contact in advance. Green Fees £25 per 18
holes;£30 per day. Prof S Bottrill Facilities ⊗ ⏷ ⛳ ⚑ ⚐
⚒ ⛳ (Location 0.5m N of junct 4 M42 on A34

Hotel ★★★ 64% Regency Hotel, Stratford Rd, Shirley,
SOLIHULL ☎ 0121 745 6119 112 en suite

Widney Manor Saintbury Dr, Widney Manor B91 3SZ
☎ 0121 704 0704 📖 0121 704 7999
e-mail: markharrhy@aol.com
Parkland course, fairly easy walking. Many water
features and mature trees. Currently undergoing a
programme of improvements.
18 holes, 5284yds, Par 69, SSS 66, Course record 65.
Club membership 650.
Visitors may book 7 days in advance. Payment required if
booking weekend games. Societies telephone for details
Green Fees £9.95 (Sat/Sun am £14.95/pm £9.95). Cards
⚋ ⚋ ⚋ ⚋ ⚋ ⚋ Prof Tim Atkinson Facilities ⊗ ⏷
⛳ ⚑ ⚐ ⛳ ⚒ (Location M42 junct 4, follow signs
to Monkspath and Widney Manor

Hotel ★★★★ 66% Renaissance Solihull Hotel, 651
Warwick Rd, SOLIHULL ☎ 0121 711 3000 175 en suite

STOURBRIDGE   Map 07 SO98

Hagley Golf & Country Club Wassell Grove,
Hagley DY9 9JW ☎ 01562 883701 📖 01562 887518
Undulating parkland course set beneath the Clent Hills;
there are superb views. Testing 15th, par 5, 557 yards.
18 holes, 6353yds, Par 72, SSS 72, Course record 66.
Club membership 700.
Visitors welcome weekdays but restricted Wed (Ladies Day)
& with member only at weekends. Societies Mon-Fri only,
must apply in writing. Green Fees £23 per 18 holes; £28 per
day. Cards ⚋ ⚋ Prof Iain Clark Course Designer
Garratt & Co Facilities ⊗ ⏷ ⛳ ⚑ ⚐ ⛳ ⚒ Leisure
squash. Conf Max 50 Thtr 50 Class 15 Board 12 Banquet 80
Location 1m E of Hagley off A456. 2m from junct 3 On M5

Hotel ★★ 67% Cedars Hotel, Mason Rd,
KIDDERMINSTER ☎ 01562 515595 21 en suite

Stourbridge Worcester Ln, Pedmore DY8 2RB
☎ 01384 395566 📖 01384 444660
e-mail: secretary@stourbridge-golf-club.co.uk
Parkland course.
18 holes, 6231yds, Par 70, SSS 69, Course record 67.
Club membership 859.
Visitors contact secretary, no casual visitors weekends.
Ladies day Wednesday. Societies must apply in writing/by e-
mail. Green Fees terms on application. Prof M Male
Facilities ⊗ ⏷ ⛳ ⚑ ⚐ ⛳ (Location 2m from town
centre

Hotel ★★ 67% Cedars Hotel, Mason Rd,
KIDDERMINSTER ☎ 01562 515595 21 en suite

SUTTON COLDFIELD   Map 07 SP19

Boldmere Monmouth Dr B73 6JL
☎ 0121 354 3379 📖 0121 355 4534
Established municipal course with 10 par 3s and a lake
coming into play on the 16th and 18th holes.
18 holes, 4493yds, Par 63, SSS 62, Course record 57.
Club membership 300.
Visitors must contact in advance. Societies midweek only,
apply in writing. Green Fees terms on application. Cards
⚋ ⚋ ⚋ ⚋ ⚋ ⚋ Prof Trevor Short Facilities ⊗ ⛳ ⚑
⚐ ⛳ ⚒ (Location Adjacent to Sutton Park

Hotel ★★★ 74% Moor Hall Hotel, Moor Hall Dr, Four
Oaks, SUTTON COLDFIELD
☎ 0121 308 3751 82 en suite

Little Aston Streetly B74 3AN
☎ 0121 353 2942 ▐ 0121 580 8387
e-mail: manager@littleastongolf.co.uk
Parkland course.
18 holes, 6670yds, Par 72, SSS 73, Course record 64.
Club membership 350.
Visitors must contact in advance & may not play on
Saturdays. **Societies** must apply in writing. **Green Fees** £60
per day;£50 per 18 holes. **Cards** 🔲 🔳 🔲 **Prof** John
Anderson **Course Designer** H Vardon **Facilities** ⊗ ♨ ▙ ▟
♀ ⚞ ⚭ ◌ **Location** 3.5m NW of Sutton Coldfield off
A454
....
Hotel ★★★ 74%   Moor Hall Hotel, Moor Hall Dr, Four
Oaks, SUTTON COLDFIELD ☎ 0121 308 3751 82 en suite

Moor Hall Moor Hall Dr B75 6LN
☎ 0121 308 6130 ▐ 0121 308 6130
e-mail: manager@moorhallgolfclub.fsnet.co.uk
Parkland course. The 14th is a notable hole.
18 holes, 6249yds, Par 70, SSS 70.
Club membership 600.
Visitors must contact in advance. With member only
weekends & bank holidays.Ladies day Thursday am.
Societies must apply in writing/telephone in advance. **Green
Fees** £33 per 18 holes;£44 per day. **Cards** 🔲 🔳 🔲 🔳 🔳
Prof Alan Partridge **Course Designer** Hawtree & taylor
Facilities ⊗ ♨ ▙ ▟ ♀ ⚞ ⚭ ◌ **Location** 2.5m N of
town centre off A453
....
Hotel ★★★ 74%   Moor Hall Hotel, Moor Hall Dr, Four
Oaks, SUTTON COLDFIELD ☎ 0121 308 3751 82 en suite

Pype Hayes Eachel Hurst Rd, Walmley B76 1EP
☎ 0121 351 1014 ▐ 0121 313 0206
Attractive, fairly flat course with excellent greens.
18 holes, 5927yds, Par 71, SSS 69.
Club membership 400.
Visitors phone professional in advance. **Societies** contact
professional in advance. **Green Fees** terms on application.
Cards 🔳 🔲 **Prof** James Bayliss **Course Designer** Bobby
Jones **Facilities** ⊗ ♨ ▙ ▟ ⚭ ◌ **Location** 2.5m S off
B4148
....
Hotel ★★★ Marston Farm Hotel, Bodymoor Heath,
SUTTON COLDFIELD ☎ 01827 872133 37 en suite

Sutton Coldfield 110 Thornhill Rd, Streetly B74 3ER
☎ 0121 580 7878 ▐ 0121 353 5503
**A fine natural, all-weather, heathland course, with tight
fairways, gorse, heather and trees. A good challenge for
all standards of golfer.**
18 holes, 6541yds, Par 72, SSS 71, Course record 65.
Club membership 600.
Visitors must contact in advance. Restricted at weekends and
bank holidays. **Societies** must apply in writing. **Green Fees**
£40 per day;£30 per round(£40 per round weeeekends). **Prof**
Jerry Hayes **Course Designer** D McKenzie **Facilities** ⊗ ♨
▙ ▟ ♀ ⚞ ⚭ ◌ **Location** 3m NW on B4138
....
Hotel ★★★ 74%   Moor Hall Hotel, Moor Hall Dr, Four
Oaks, SUTTON COLDFIELD ☎ 0121 308 3751 82 en suite

Walmley Brooks Rd, Wylde Green B72 1HR
☎ 0121 373 0029 & 377 7272 ▐ 0121 377 7272
**Pleasant parkland course with many trees. The hazards
are not difficult.**
18 holes, 6585yds, Par 72, SSS 72, Course record 67.
Club membership 700.

continued

Visitors must contact in advance. Weekends may only play
as guest of member. **Societies** must contact in advance.
Green Fees £35 per day; £30 per round. **Prof** C J Wicketts
Facilities ⊗ ♨ ▙ ▟ ♀ ⚞ ⚭ ◌ **Location** 2m S off
A5127
....
Hotel ★★★ Marston Farm Hotel, Bodymoor Heath,
SUTTON COLDFIELD ☎ 01827 872133 37 en suite

Bloxwich Stafford Rd, Bloxwich WS3 3PQ
☎ 01922 476593 ext 20 ▐ 01922 493449
e-mail: bloxwich.golf-club@virgin.net
**Undulating parkland course with natural hazards and
subject to strong north wind.**
18 holes, 6257yds, Par 71, SSS 71, Course record 67.
Club membership 650.
Visitors may not play at weekends. **Societies** must contact in
advance. **Green Fees** £35 per day; £30 per round. **Prof**
Richard J Dance **Facilities** ⊗ ♨ ▙ ▟ ♀ ⚞ ⚭ ◌ **Conf**
Max 15 Del from £3-£15 * **Location** 3m N of town centre on
A34
....
Hotel ★★★ 76%   The Fairlawns at Aldridge, 178 Little
Aston Rd, Aldridge, WALSALL ☎ 01922 455122
50 en suite

Calderfields Aldridge Rd WS4 2JS
☎ 01922 632243 ▐ 01922 638787
Parkland course with lake.
18 holes, 6509yds, Par 73, SSS 71.
Club membership 526.
Visitors no restrictions. **Societies** telephone 01922 632243 in
advance. **Green Fees** not confirmed. **Prof** David Williams
Course Designer Roy Winter **Facilities** ⊗ ♨ ▙ ▟ ♀ ⚞ ⚭
⚭ ⚲ ⚭ ◌ ⚞ **Leisure** fishing. **Location** On A454
....
Hotel ★★★ 76%   The Fairlawns at Aldridge, 178 Little
Aston Rd, Aldridge, WALSALL ☎ 01922 455122
50 en suite

Walsall The Broadway WS1 3EY
☎ 01922 613512 ▐ 01922 616460
Well-wooded parkland course with easy walking.
18 holes, 6300yds, Par 70, SSS 70, Course record 65.
Club membership 600.
Visitors must contact in advance. May not play weekends &
bank holidays. **Societies** must apply in writing. **Green Fees**
terms on application. **Prof** Richard Lambert **Course
Designer** McKenzie **Facilities** ⊗ ♨ ▙ ▟ ♀ ⚞ ⚭ ◌
Location 1m S of town centre off A34
....
Hotel ★★★ 63%   The Boundary Hotel, Birmingham Rd,
WALSALL ☎ 01922 633609 95 en suite

Dartmouth Vale St B71 4DW ☎ 0121 588 2131
**Meadowland course with undulating but easy walking.
The 617 yd (par 5) first hole is something of a challenge.**
9 holes, 6060yds, Par 71, SSS 71, Course record 66.
Club membership 250.
Visitors with member only at weekends. May not play bank
holidays or medal weekends until after 2pm contact pro first.
Societies must apply in writing/telephone. **Green Fees** £8
per 9 holes;£15 per 18 holes. **Prof** Simon Joyce **Facilities** ⊗
♨ ▙ ▟ ♀ ⚞ ⚭ **Location** E side of town centre off A4041
....
Hotel ⚘ Express by Holiday Inn Oldbury, Birchley Park,
OLDBURY ☎ 0121 511 0000 109 en suite

Sandwell Park Birmingham Rd B71 4JJ
☎ 0121 553 4637 📄 0121 525 1651
e-mail: secretary@sandwellparkgolfclub.co.uk
A picturesque golf course wandering over wooded
heathland and utilising natural features. Each hole is
entirely separate, shielded from the others by either
natural banks or lines of trees. A course that demands
careful placing of shots that have been given a great
deal of thought. Natural undulating fairways create
difficult and testing approach shots to the greens.

18 holes, 6468yds, Par 71, SSS 73, Course record 65.
Club membership 550.
Visitors must contact in advance. May not play at
weekends. Societies must contact in advance. Green Fees
£40 per 27/36 holes;£35 per 18 holes. Prof Nigel Wylie
Course Designer H S Colt Facilities ⊗ ⽊ ⓑ 🍺 ♀ ⚲ 🏠
🏌 Leisure practice chipping area. Conf Max 120 Thtr
120 Class 120 Board 30 Banquet 120 Del from £60 *
Location On A41, 200yds from juct 1 of the M5

Hotel ⇧ Express by Holiday Inn Oldbury, Birchley Park,
OLDBURY ☎ 0121 511 0000 109 en suite

WOLVERHAMPTON   Map 07 SO99

Oxley Park Stafford Rd, Bushbury WV10 6DE
☎ 01902 425892 📄 01902 712241
Rolling parkland course with trees, bunkers and water
hazards.
18 holes, 6226yds, Par 71, SSS 70, Course record 68.
Club membership 550.
Visitors must contact in advance. Societies must contact in
advance. Green Fees not confirmed. Prof Les Burlison
Course Designer H S Colt Facilities ⊗ ⽊ by prior
arrangement ⓑ 🍺 ♀ ⚲ 🏠 🚜 🏌 Leisure snooker.
Location N of town centre off A449

Hotel ★★ 69% Ely House Hotel, 53 Tettenhall Rd,
WOLVERHAMPTON ☎ 01902 311311 19 en suite

Penn Penn Common, Penn WV4 5JN
☎ 01902 341142 📄 01902 620504
e-mail: penn-golf.freeserve.co.uk
Heathland course just outside the town.
18 holes, 6487yds, Par 70, SSS 72, Course record 68.
Club membership 650.
Visitors must play with member at weekends. Societies must
contact in advance. Green Fees £25 per day; £20 per round.
Prof B Burlison Facilities ⊗ ⽊ ⓑ 🍺 ♀ ⚲ 🏠 🏌 Location
SW side of town centre off A449

Hotel ★★★ 66% Quality Hotel Wolverhampton, Penn Rd,
WOLVERHAMPTON ☎ 01902 429216
66 en suite 26 annexe en suite

South Staffordshire Danescourt Rd, Tettenhall
WV6 9BQ ☎ 01902 751065 📄 01902 741753
A parkland course.
18 holes, 6513yds, Par 71, SSS 71, Course record 67.
Club membership 500.
Visitors must contact in advance but may not play weekends
& before 2pm Tue. Societies must apply in writing. Green
Fees not confirmed. Prof Mark Sparrow Course Designer
Harry Vardon Facilities ⊗ ⽊ ⓑ 🍺 ♀ ⚲ 🏠 🚜 🏌
Location 3m NW off A41

Hotel ★★ 69% Ely House Hotel, 53 Tettenhall Rd,
WOLVERHAMPTON ☎ 01902 311311 19 en suite

Three Hammers Short Course Old Stafford Rd,
Coven WV10 7PP ☎ 01902 790940
Well maintained short course designed by Henry Cotton
and providing a unique challenge to golfers of all
standards.
18 holes, 1438yds, Par 54, SSS 54, Course record 43.
Visitors no restrictions. Societies contact for details. Green
Fees terms on application. Course Designer Henry Cotton
Facilities ⊗ ⽊ ⓑ 🍺 ♀ 🏠 🍸 🏌 Conf Max 120
Location On A449 N of junct 2 M54

Hotel ★★★ 63% Roman Way Hotel, Watling St, Hatherton,
CANNOCK ☎ 01543 572121 56 en suite

Wergs Keepers Ln, Tettenhall WV6 8UA
☎ 01902 742225 📄 01902 744748
Open parkland course with gently undulating fairways.
18 holes, 6949yds, Par 72, SSS 73.
Club membership 150.
Visitors are advised to contact in advance. Societies must
contact in advance. Green Fees £15 per day;£9 per 9
holes(£20/£11 weekends & bank holidays). Cards 💳 💳
💳 💳 Prof Steve Weir Course Designer C W Moseley
Facilities ⊗ by prior arrangement ⓑ 🍺 ♀ ⚲ 🏠 🍸 🚜 🏌
Location From Wolverhampton take A41 towards Newport
for 2.5m then R for 0.5m then R again

Hotel ★★ 69% Ely House Hotel, 53 Tettenhall Rd,
WOLVERHAMPTON ☎ 01902 311311 19 en suite

WIGHT, ISLE OF

COWES   Map 04 SZ49

Cowes Crossfield Av PO31 8HN
☎ 01983 292303 (secretary) & 281035
Fairly level, tight parkland course with difficult par 3s
and Solent views.
9 holes, 5934yds, Par 70, SSS 68, Course record 66.
Club membership 300.
Visitors restricted Thu & Sun mornings. Societies Mon-
Wed, must contact in advance. Green Fees £15 per day (£18
weekends). Course Designer Hamilton-Stutt Facilities ⊗ ⓑ
🍺 ♀ ⚲ 🍸 🏌 Location NW side of town, next to Cowes
High School

Hotel ★★★ 68% New Holmwood Hotel, Queens Rd, Egypt
Point, COWES ☎ 01983 292508 26 en suite

EAST COWES   Map 04 SZ59

Osborne Osborne House Estate PO32 6JX
☎ 01983 295421
Undulating parkland course in the grounds of Osborne
House. Quiet and peaceful situation.
continued

9 holes, 6398yds, Par 70, SSS 70, Course record 71.
Club membership 450.
Visitors may not play Tue before 1pm, weekends before noon & bank holidays before 11am. **Societies** telephone initially. **Green Fees** £20 (£22 weekends & bank holidays). **Facilities** ⊗ 〗Ⅲ ᴸ ᴥ 🍴 ⚙ 🏠 ⚑ ✎ **Location** E side of town centre off A3021, in grounds of Osborne House

Hotel ★★★ 68% New Holmwood Hotel, Queens Rd, Egypt Point, COWES ☎ 01983 292508 26 en suite

FRESHWATER   Map 04 SZ38

Freshwater Bay Afton Down PO40 9TZ
☎ 01983 752955 📠 01983 756704
e-mail: fbgc_iow@yahoo.co.uk
A downland/seaside links with wide fairways and spectacular coastal views of the Solent and Channel.
18 holes, 5725yds, Par 69, SSS 68.
Club membership 450.
Visitors may play daily after 9.30 ex Thu & Sun (10.30). **Societies** apply to secretary. **Green Fees** not confirmed. **Course Designer** J H Taylor **Facilities** ⊗ 〗Ⅲ ᴸ ᴥ 🍴 ⚑ ✎ **Location** 0.5m E of village off A3055

Hotel ★★★ 67% Sentry Mead Hotel, Madeira Rd, TOTLAND BAY ☎ 01983 753212 14 en suite

NEWPORT   Map 04 SZ58

Newport St George's Down, Shide PO30 2JB
☎ 01983 525076
Downland course, fine views.
9 holes, 5710yds, Par 68, SSS 68.
Club membership 350.
Visitors may not play Wed noon-3.30pm or before 3pm Sat & noon Sun. **Societies** contact Secretary in advance. **Green Fees** not confirmed. **Facilities** ᴥ 🍴 ⚑ **Location** 1.5m S off A3020

Hotel ★★★ 68% New Holmwood Hotel, Queens Rd, Egypt Point, COWES ☎ 01983 292508 26 en suite

RYDE   Map 04 SZ59

Ryde Binstead Rd PO33 3NF
☎ 01983 614809 📠 01983 567418
e-mail: secretary@rydegolfclub.freeserve.co.uk
Downland course with wide views over the Solent. Very tight with out of bound areas on most holes and 5 dog legs.
9 holes, 5772yds, Par 70, SSS 70.
Club membership 575.
Visitors may not play Wed 10.30-2.30, Sun mornings or before 10.30am Sat. **Societies** must contact in writing. **Green Fees** £16 per day; £10 per round (£20 per day weekends & bank holidays). **Cards** 💳 **Course Designer** Hamilton-Stutt **Facilities** ⊗ 〗Ⅲ by prior arrangement ᴸ ᴥ 🍴 🏠 ⚑ ✎ **Location** Right out of Fishbourne ferry terminal, left at lights,1m W on A3054

Hotel ★★ 63% Yelf's Hotel, Union St, RYDE ☎ 01983 564062 30 en suite

SANDOWN   Map 04 SZ58

Shanklin & Sandown The Fairway, Lake PO36 9PR
☎ 01983 403217 (office) & 404424 (pro) 📠 01983 403217 (office)/404424 (pro)
Heathland course with some hilly holes. Mostly sandy base but some clay makes it generally playable all year.
18 holes, 6063yds, Par 70, SSS 69, Course record 64.
Club membership 640.

continued

Visitors must contact in advance & have handicap certificate. May not play before noon Sat or 9.30am Sun. **Societies** apply in writing. **Green Fees** not confirmed. **Cards** 💳 💳 💳 💳 **Prof** Peter Hammond **Course Designer** Braid **Facilities** ⊗ 〗Ⅲ ᴸ ᴥ 🍴 ⚙ 🏠 ⚑ ✎ **Location** From Sandown drive towards Shanklin past Heights Leisure Centre after 200yds R into Fairway for 1m

Hotel ★★ 67% Cygnet Hotel, 58 Carter St, SANDOWN ☎ 01983 402930 45 rms (44 en suite)

VENTNOR   Map 04 SZ57

Ventnor Steephill Down Rd PO38 1BP
☎ 01983 853326 📠 01983 853326
e-mail: ventnorgolf@lineone.net
Downland course subject to wind. Fine seascapes.
12 holes, 5767yds, Par 70, SSS 68, Course record 68.
Club membership 297.
Visitors may not play Mon noon-3pm or Sun mornings. **Societies** telephone initially. **Green Fees** £17 per day. **Facilities** ⊗ by prior arrangement 〗Ⅲ by prior arrangement ᴸ ᴥ 🍴 ⚑ ✎ **Location** 1m NW off B3327, turning at the chip shop

Hotel ★★★★ 71% The Royal Hotel, Belgrave Rd, VENTNOR ☎ 01983 852186 55 en suite

WILTSHIRE

BISHOPS CANNINGS   Map 04 SU06

North Wilts SN10 2LP
☎ 01380 860627 📠 01380 860877
e-mail: secretary@northwiltsgolfclub.fsnet.co.uk
High, downland course with fine views.
18 holes, 6401yds, Par 71, SSS 71, Course record 65.
Club membership 800.
Visitors a handicap certificate is required at weekends. **Societies** must book in advance. **Green Fees** terms on application. **Cards** 💳 💳 💳 💳 **Prof** Graham Laing **Facilities** ⊗ 〗Ⅲ ᴸ ᴥ 🍴 ⚙ 🏠 ⚑ 🏌 ⛳ ✎ **Location** 2m NW

Hotel ★★★ 64% Bear Hotel, Market Place, DEVIZES ☎ 01380 722444 24 en suite

CALNE   Map 03 ST97

Bowood Golf & Country Club Derry Hill
SN11 9PQ ☎ 01249 822228 📠 01249 822218
e-mail: golfclub@bowood.org
A championship golf course set in the beautiful surroundings of 'Capability' Brown's Great Park.

18 holes, 6890yds, Par 72, SSS 73, Course record 63.
Club membership 500.

continued

Visitors welcome except before noon on Sat and Sun. Booking essential. **Societies** booking by telephone. **Green Fees** terms on application. **Cards** 〓 ▆ ▆ ▆ ▆ ▆ ▆ **Prof** Max Taylor **Course Designer** Dave Thomas **Facilities** ⊗ ⅢⅬ ▆ ▆ ▆ ▆ ▆ ▆ ▆ ▆ ▆ **Leisure** Bowood House and Gardens.**Conf** Max 240 **Location** M4 junct 17 off A4 between Chippenham & Calne

....

Hotel ★★★ 66% Lansdowne Strand Hotel, The Strand, CALNE ☎ 01249 812488 21 en suite 5 annexe en suite

CASTLE COMBE — Map 03 ST87

Manor House SN14 7JW

☎ 01249 782982 📠 01249 782992

e-mail: teereservations@manorhousegolfclub.com

Set in a wonderful location within the wooded estate of the 14th century Manor House, this course includes five par 5s and some spectacular par 3s. A special feature is the River Bybrook, which meanders its way through many holes, the most memorable being the 17th with a breathtaking drop to the green.

18 holes, 6286yds, Par 72, SSS 71, Course record 67. Club membership 450.

Visitors must have a handicap certificate and must contact in advance. **Societies** contact in advance. **Green Fees** £70 per day; £50 per round (£90/£60 Fri-Sun & bank holidays). **Cards** ▆ ▆ ▆ ▆ ▆ ▆ **Prof** Peter Green **Course Designer** Peter Alliss/Clive Clark **Facilities** ⊗ Ⅲ Ⅼ ▆ ▆ ▆ ▆ ▆ ▆ ▆ ▆ **Leisure** hard tennis courts, heated outdoor swimming pool, fishing, sauna, snooker.**Conf** Max 120 Thtr 120 Class 80 Board 40 Banquet 120 **Location** On B4039, 5m NW of Chippenham

....

Hotel ★★★★≝ Manor House Hotel, CASTLE COMBE ☎ 01249 782206 21 en suite 26 annexe en suite

CHAPMANSLADE — Map 03 ST84

Thoulstone Park BA13 4AQ

☎ 01373 832825 📠 01373 832821

A rolling parkland course with natural lakes and mature trees. Hole 7, stroke index 1 has a second shot over a large lake to the green so a straight drive is essential.

18 holes, 6161yds, Par 70, SSS 70. Club membership 500.

Visitors play restricted until after 11am Sat & Sun. Dress code applies. **Societies** telephone in advance. **Green Fees** £15 per day; £10 per round (£20 weekends). **Cards** ▆ **Prof** Tony Isaac **Facilities** ⊗ Ⅼ ▆ ▆ ▆ ▆ ▆ ▆ **Leisure** health & fitness gym.**Conf** Max 200 **Location** On A36 between Bath/Warminster

....

Hotel ★★ 67% Woolpack Inn, BECKINGTON ☎ 01373 831244 12 en suite

CHIPPENHAM — Map 03 ST97

Chippenham Malmesbury Rd SN15 5LT

☎ 01249 652040 📠 01249 446681

Easy walking on downland course. Testing holes at 1st and 15th.

18 holes, 5559yds, Par 69, SSS 67, Course record 64. Club membership 650.

Visitors must contact in advance. **Societies** must contact in writing. **Green Fees** not confirmed. **Prof** Bill Creamer **Facilities** ▆ ▆ ▆ ▆ ▆ ▆ **Location** M4 junct 17, 1m N of Chippenham beside A350

....

Hotel ★★★★≝ Manor House Hotel, CASTLE COMBE ☎ 01249 782206 21 en suite 26 annexe en suite

CRICKLADE — Map 04 SU09

Cricklade Hotel & Country Club Common Hill SN6 6HA ☎ 01793 750751 📠 01793 751767

e-mail: info@cricklade.fsnet.co.uk

A challenging 9-hole course with undulating greens and beautiful views. Par 3 6th (128yds) signature hole from an elevated tee to a green protected by a deep pot bunker.

9 holes, 1830yds, Par 62, SSS 57. Club membership 170.

Visitors may not play weekends or bank holidays unless accompanied by a member. Must contact in advance. **Societies** apply in writing. **Green Fees** not confirmed. **Cards** ▆ ▆ ▆ ▆ ▆ ▆ **Prof** Ian Bolt **Course Designer** Ian Bolt/Colin Smith **Facilities** ⊗ Ⅲ Ⅼ ▆ ▆ ▆ ▆ ▆ ▆ **Leisure** hard tennis courts, heated indoor swimming pool, solarium, gymnasium. **Conf** Max 80 Thtr 80 Class 60 Board 40 Banquet 120 Del £49 * **Location** On the B4040 out of Cricklade, towards Malmesbury

....

Hotel ★★★ 67% Stanton House Hotel, The Avenue, Stanton Fitzwarren, SWINDON ☎ 01793 861777 86 en suite

ERLESTOKE — Map 03 ST95

Erlestoke Sands SN10 5UB

☎ 01380 831069 📠 01380 831284

e-mail: info@erlestokesands.co.uk

The course is set on the lower slopes of Salisbury Plain with distant views to the Cotswolds and Marlborough Downs. The 7th plunges from an elevated three-tiered tee, high in the woods, to a large green with a spectacular backdrop of a meandering river and hills. The course was built to suit every standard of golfer from the novice to the very low handicapper and its two tiers offer lakes and rolling downland.

18 holes, 6406yds, Par 73, SSS 71, Course record 69. Club membership 720.

Visitors phone for tee booking in advance 01380 830300. Dress rules apply. **Societies** must book in advance. **Green Fees** £30 per day; £20 per round (£35/£25 weekends and bank holidays). **Cards** ▆ ▆ ▆ **Prof** Michael Waters **Course Designer** Adrian Stiff **Facilities** ⊗ Ⅲ Ⅼ ▆ ▆ ▆ ▆ ▆ ▆ ▆ **Location** On B3098 Devizes/Westbury road

....

Hotel ★★★ 64% Bear Hotel, Market Place, DEVIZES ☎ 01380 722444 24 en suite

GREAT DURNFORD — Map 04 SU13

High Post SP4 6AT

☎ 01722 782356 📠 01722 782674

e-mail: highpostgolfclub@lineone.net

An interesting downland course on Wiltshire chalk

continued

with good turf and splendid views over the southern area of Salisbury Plain. The par 3, 17th and the two-shot 18th require good judgement. The course is noted for quality of its greens and year round playability.

High Post Golf Club

18 holes, 6305yds, Par 70, SSS 70, Course record 64. Club membership 600.
Visitors a handicap certificate is required at weekends & bank holidays. Telephone professional in advance 01722 782219. **Societies** apply by telephone to manager. **Green Fees** £40 per day; £28 per round (£45/£35 weekends). **Prof** Ian Welding **Course Designer** Hawtree & Ptrs **Facilities** ⊗ ⊤∭ ㄴ ♨ ♀ ⌂ ⊤⌐ ⟡ ₹ **Location** Midway between Sailsbury and Amesbury on A345

Hotel ★★★ 66% Rose & Crown Hotel, Harnham Rd, Harnham, SALISBURY ☎ 01722 399955 28 en suite

HIGHWORTH   Map 04 SU29

Highworth Community Golf Centre Swindon
Rd SN6 7SJ ☎ 01793 766014 ▤ 01793 766014
Public downland course, situated in a high position affording good views of the Wiltshire Downs.
9 holes, 3120yds, Par 35, SSS 35, Course record 29. Club membership 150.
Visitors no restrictions. **Societies** advisable to contact in advance. **Green Fees** £13 per 18 holes; £7.90 per 9 holes. **Cards** ▦ ▦ ▤▦ ▨▦ ▩ **Prof** Barry Sandry **Course Designer** T Watt/ B Sandry/D Lang **Facilities** ♨ ⌂ ⊤⌐ ⟡ **Leisure** 9 hole pitch & putt course. **Location** Off A361 Swindon to Lechlade

Hotel ★★★ 73% Sudbury House Hotel & Conference Centre, London St, FARINGDON
☎ 01367 241272 49 en suite

Wrag Barn Golf & Country Club Shrivenham
Rd SN6 7QQ ☎ 01793 861327 ▤ 01793 861325
e-mail: info@wragbarn.com
Listed in 'Golfs Best Top 100 UK Courses'. An outstanding course for golfers of all abilities.
18 holes, 6595yds, Par 72, SSS 71, Course record 65. Club membership 600.
Visitors no restrictions but may not play before noon at weekends. **Societies** contact in advance. **Green Fees** £37 per day; £27 per round (£32 per round weekend). **Prof** Barry Loughrey **Course Designer** Hawtree **Facilities** ⊗ ㄴ ♨ ♀ ♨ ⌂ ⊤⌐ ⟡ ⍟ ⟡ ₹ **Conf** Max 100 Thtr 90 Class 60 Board 40 Banquet 120 Del £30 to £50 * **Location** On B4000 Shrivenham Road out of Highworth. Follow signs

Hotel ★★★ 67% Stanton House Hotel, The Avenue, Stanton Fitzwarren, SWINDON ☎ 01793 861777 86 en suite

KINGSDOWN   Map 03 ST86

Kingsdown SN13 8BS
☎ 01225 742530 ▤ 01225 743472
Fairly flat, open downland course with very sparse tree cover but surrounding wood.
18 holes, 6445yds, Par 72, SSS 71, Course record 64. Club membership 650.
Visitors weekends only with a member. Handicap certificate required weekdays. **Societies** apply by letter. **Green Fees** £26 per day. **Prof** Andrew Butler **Facilities** ⊗ ⊤∭ ㄴ ♨ ♀ ♨ ⌂ ⊤⌐ ⟡ ₹ **Location** W side of village,between Corsham & Bath

Hotel ★★★★ Lucknam Park, COLERNE
☎ 01225 742777 23 en suite 18 annexe en suite

LANDFORD   Map 04 SU21

Hamptworth Golf & Country Club Hamptworth
Rd, Hamptworth SP5 2DU
☎ 01794 390155 ▤ 01794 390022
e-mail: info@hamptworthgolf.co.uk
Hamptworth enjoys ancient woodland and an abundance of wildlife in a beautiful setting on the edge of the New Forest. The 14th is one of its most challenging holes having a narrow fairway guarded by established forest oaks. The 2nd is a dogleg of 543yds and plays differently all year.

18 holes, 6516yds, Par 72, SSS 71, Course record 68. Club membership 450.
Visitors telephone to check availability. **Societies** write or telephone in advance. **Green Fees** not confirmed. **Cards** ▦ ▦ ▤▦ ▨▦ ▩ **Prof** Phil Stevens **Course Designer** Philip Sanders/Brian Pierson **Facilities** ⊗ ⊤∭ ㄴ ♨ ♀ ♨ ⌂ ⊤⌐ ⍟ ⟡ ₹ **Leisure** gymnasium, croquet lawns. **Location** 1m NW, A36/B3079

Hotel ★★★ 71% Bartley Lodge, Lyndhurst Rd, CADNAM
☎ 023 8081 2248 31 en suite

MARLBOROUGH   Map 04 SU16

Marlborough The Common SN8 1DU
☎ 01672 512147 ▤ 01672 513164
e-mail: contactus@marlboroughgolfclub.co.uk
Downland course with extensive views over the Og Valley and Marlborough Downs.
18 holes, 6491yds, Par 72, SSS 71, Course record 61. Club membership 900.
Visitors restricted at certain times. Must have a handicap certificate at weekends. Must contact in advance. **Societies** must contact in advance. **Green Fees** £34 per day; £26 per round (£42/£31.50 weekends). **Cards** ▦ ▦ ▤▦ ▨▦ ▩ **Prof** S Amor **Facilities** ⊗ ⊤∭ ㄴ ♨ ♀ ♨ ⌂ ⟡ ⍟ ⟡ ⟡ **Conf** Thtr 55 Class 40 Board 25 Del £21 to £75 * **Location** N side of town centre on A346   *continued*

Hotel ★★★ 68% The Castle & Ball, High St,
MARLBOROUGH ☎ 01672 515201 34 en suite

OAKSEY   Map 03 ST99

Oaksey Park Golf & Leisure SN16 9SB
☎ 01666 577995 ▤ 01666 577174
9 holes, 3100yds, Par 70, SSS 69, Course record 66.
Course Designer Chapman & Warren **Location** On B road
connecting A419 & A429, on outskirts of village of Oaksey.
S of Cirencester
Telephone for further details

Hotel ★★★ 69% Stratton House Hotel, Gloucester Rd,
CIRENCESTER ☎ 01285 651761 41 en suite

OGBOURNE ST GEORGE   Map 04 SU27

Ogbourne Downs SN8 1TB
☎ 01672 841327 ▤ 01672 841101
Downland turf and magnificent greens. Wind and slopes
make this one of the most challenging courses in
Wiltshire. Extensive views.
18 holes, 6363yds, Par 71, SSS 70, Course record 65.
Club membership 800.
Visitors phone in advance. Handicap certificate required.
Societies must apply for booking form in advance. **Green
Fees** £25 per day. **Cards** 🖃 🔳 🔳 **Prof** Andrew Kirk
Course Designer J H Taylor **Facilities** ⊗ ⅃ ♥ ♀ 숟 🖬 ⊤
🕈 ♣ ☌ **Location** N side of village on A346

Hotel ★★★ 72% Ivy House Hotel, High St,
MARLBOROUGH ☎ 01672 515333 28 en suite

SALISBURY   Map 04 SU12

Salisbury & South Wilts Netherhampton SP2 8PR
☎ 01722 742645 ▤ 01722 742645
e-mail: mail@salisburygolf.co.uk
Gently undulating and well drained parkland courses in
country setting with panoramic views of the cathedral
and surrounding countryside. Never easy with six
excellent opening holes and four equally as testing closing
holes. A joy to play.
*Main Course: 18 holes, 6485yds, Par 71, SSS 71,
Course record 61.*
Bibury Course: 9 holes, 2837yds, Par 34.
Club membership 1150.
Visitors advisable to telephone in advance. **Societies**
telephone,write or e-mail for information park. **Green Fees**
terms on application. **Prof** John Cave/Geraldine Teschner
Course Designer J H Taylor/S Gidman **Facilities** ⊗ ⅃ ⅃
♥ ♀ 숟 🖬 ⊤ 🕈 ♣ ☌ **Conf** Max 150 Banquet 150
Location 2m SW of Salisbury,on A3094

Hotel ★★★ 66% Rose & Crown Hotel, Harnham Rd,
Harnham, SALISBURY
☎ 01722 399955 28 en suite

SWINDON   Map 04 SU18

Broome Manor Golf Complex Pipers Way
SN3 1RG ☎ 01793 532403 ▤ 01793 433255
Two courses and a 34-bay floodlit driving range.
Parkland with water hazards, open fairways and short
cut rough. Walking is easy on gentle slopes.
18 holes, 6283yds, Par 71, SSS 70, Course record 62.
Broom Manor Golf complex: 9 holes, Par 33.
Club membership 800.
Visitors pre-booking advised for 18 hole course, payment of
green fee is required at the time of booking by credit card.
continued

Societies must be prebooked. **Green Fees** not confirmed.
Cards 🖃 🔳 🔳 🔳 🔳 ☑ **Prof** Barry Sandry **Course
Designer** Hawtree **Facilities** ⊗ ⅃ ⅃ ♥ ♀ 숟 🖬 ⊤ ☌ ☗
Location 1.75m SE of town centre off B4006

Hotel ★★★★ 65% Swindon Marriott Hotel, Pipers Way,
SWINDON ☎ 01793 512121 155 en suite

TIDWORTH   Map 04 SU24

Tidworth Garrison Bulford Rd SP9 7AF
☎ 01980 842301 ▤ 01980 842301
e-mail: tidworth@garrison-golfclub.fsnet.co.uk
**A breezy, dry downland course with lovely turf, fine
trees and views over Salisbury Plain and the
surrounding area. The 4th and 12th holes are notable.
The 565-yard 14th, going down towards the clubhouse,
gives the big hitter a chance to let fly.**
18 holes, 6320yds, Par 70, SSS 70, Course record 63.
Club membership 850.
Visitors must contact in advance, weekend & bank
holiday bookings may not be made until Thursday prior,
handicap certificate required. **Societies** Tue & Thu,
bookings required 12-18 months in advance. **Green Fees**
£29 per round/day. **Prof** Terry Gosden **Course Designer**
Donald Steel **Facilities** ⊗ ⅃ ⅃ ♥ ♀ 숟 🖬 ⊤ ♣ ☌
Location W side of village off A338

Hotel ★★★ 63% Quality Hotel Andover,
Micheldever Rd, ANDOVER ☎ 01264 369111
13 en suite 36 annexe en suite

TOLLARD ROYAL   Map 03 ST91

Rushmore Park Golf Club SP5 5QB
☎ 01725 516326 ▤ 01725 516437
Peaceful and testing parkland course situated on
Cranborne Chase with far-reaching views. An undulating
course with avenues of trees and well drained greens.
With water on 7 out of 18 holes, it will test the most
confident of golfers.
*Rushmore Park Golf Club: 18 holes, 6172yds,
Par 71, SSS 69.*
Club membership 470.
Visitors Must book in advance. Strict dress code enforced.
Societies welcome by appointment, apply in writing. **Green
Fees** £20 per 18 holes(£24 weekends). **Cards** 🖃 🔳
🔳 ☑ **Prof** Sean McDonagh **Course Designer** David
Pottage/John Jacobs Developments **Facilities** ⊗ ⅃ by prior
arrangement ⅃ ♥ ♀ 숟 🖬 ⊤ ☌ ☗ **Location** 16m SW of
Salisbury, entrance off the B3081 between Sixpenny
Handley and Tollard Royal

Hotel ★★★ 67% Royal Chase Hotel, Royal Chase
Roundabout, SHAFTESBURY
☎ 01747 853355 35 en suite

UPAVON   Map 04 SU15

Upavon Douglas Av SN9 6BQ
☎ 01980 630787 & 630281 ▤ 01980 630787
Downland course set on sides of infamous valley, with
some wind affecting play. Includes a par 5 of 602 yards
and finishing hole of 170 yards across a ravine.
18 holes, 6402yds, Par 71, SSS 71, Course record 69.
Club membership 600.
Visitors must contact in advance and may not play before
noon at weekends. **Societies** telephone in advance. **Green**
continued

Upavon Golf Club

Fees £22 per round (£25 weekends). **Cards** ▦ ▭ ▭ ▭
🔲 **Prof** Richard Blake **Course Designer** Richard Blake
Facilities ⊗ ℍ by prior arrangement ᒪ ☕ ♀ ⚑ 🏌 🛺 🛒
♂ **Location** 1.5m SE of Upavon on A342 Andover road

Hotel ★★★ 64% Bear Hotel, Market Place, DEVIZES
☎ 01380 722444 24 en suite

WARMINSTER   Map 03 ST84

West Wilts Elm Hill BA12 0AU
☎ 01985 213133 🖹 01985 219809
A hilltop course among the Wiltshire downs on
downland turf. Free draining, short, but a very good
test of accurate iron play. Excellent greens and
clubhouse facilities.
18 holes, 5709yds, Par 70, SSS 68, Course record 62.
Club membership 650.
Visitors must contact in advance. Handicap certificate
required. **Societies** apply by letter. **Green Fees** not
confirmed. **Prof** Andrew Lamb **Course Designer** J H
Taylor **Facilities** ⊗ ℍ ᒪ ☕ ♀ ⚑ 🏌 ♂ **Location** N
side of town centre off A350

Hotel ★★★★ 74% Bishopstrow House,
WARMINSTER ☎ 01985 212312 32 en suite

WOOTTON BASSETT   Map 04 SU08

Brinkworth Longmans Farm, Brinkworth SN15 5DG
☎ 01666 510277
18 holes, 5884yds, Par 70, SSS 70.
Course Designer Jullian Sheppard **Location** Just off B4042
between Malmesbury/Wootton Bassett
Telephone for further details

Hotel ★★★ 70% Marsh Farm Hotel, Coped Hall,
WOOTTON BASSETT ☎ 01793 848044
11 en suite 27 annexe en suite

Wiltshire Vastern SN4 7PB
☎ 01793 849999 🖹 01793 849988
e-mail: tracey@the-wiltshire.co.uk
A Peter Alliss/Clive Clark design set in rolling Wiltshire
downland countryside. A number of lakes add a challenge
for both low and high handicappers.
The Wiltshire Golf Club: 18 holes, 6666yds, Par 72, SSS 72,
Course record 67.
Club membership 800.
Visitors must contact in advance. **Societies** contact in
advance. **Green Fees** £20 per 18 holes(£30 weekends and
bank holidays). **Cards** ▦ ▭ ▭ ▭ 🔲 **Prof** Paul Gravell
Course Designer Peter Allis & Clive Clark **Facilities** ⊗ ℍ
ᒪ ☕ ♀ ⚑ 🏌 ⚑ 🛺 🛒 ♂ ⛳ **Conf** Max 50 **Location** Leave
continued

M4 at junc 16, on A3102, follow Wootton Bassett. Left at
2nd rdbt through town, approx 1.5 miles course left opposite
Vastern Manor
· ·

Hotel ★★★ 70% Marsh Farm Hotel, Coped Hall,
WOOTTON BASSETT ☎ 01793 848044 11 en suite 27
annexe en suite

WORCESTERSHIRE

ALVECHURCH   Map 07 SP07

Kings Norton Brockhill Ln, Weatheroak B48 7ED
☎ 01564 826706 & 826789 🖹 01564 826955
e-mail: info@kingsnortongolfclub.co.uk
A 27 hole Championship venue, 18 hole course
7000yds par 72 plus 12 hole par 3 course. Parkland
with water hazards.
Weatheroak: 18 holes, 6748yds, Par 72, SSS 72, Course
record 65.
Brockhill: 18 holes, 6648yds, Par 72, SSS 72.
Wythall: 18 holes, 6612yds, Par 72, SSS 72.
Club membership 1000.
Visitors must contact in advance. No visitors at
weekends. **Societies** must telephone in advance. **Green
Fees** £40 per day; £32 per round. **Cards** ▦ ▭ ▭ ▭
▭ 🔲 **Prof** Kevin Hayward **Course Designer** F Hawtree
Facilities ⊗ ℍ ᒪ ☕ ♀ ⚑ 🏌 🛺 🛒 ♂ **Conf** Max
200 **Location** M42 junct3, off A435

Hotel ★★★★ 65% Hanover International Hotel & Club,
Kidderminster Rd, BROMSGROVE
☎ 01527 576600 114 en suite

BEWDLEY   Map 07 SO77

Little Lakes Golf and Country Club Lye Head
DY12 2UZ ☎ 01299 266385 🖹 01299 266398
e-mail: info@littlelakes.co.uk
A pleasant undulating 18 hole parkland course. A
challenging test of golf with stunning views of the
Worcestershire countryside.

18 holes, 6278yds, Par 71, SSS 70, Course record 68.
Club membership 400.
Visitors advisable to telephone in advance. **Societies** must
telephone in advance. **Green Fees** £16 per day (£21 per
round weekends and bank holidays). **Cards** ▦ ▭ ▭ ▭
🔲 **Prof** Mark A Laing **Course Designer** M Laing **Facilities**
⊗ by prior arrangement ℍ by prior arrangement ᒪ by prior
arrangement ☕ by prior arrangement ♀ ⚑ 🏌 🛺 🛒 ♂
Leisure hard tennis courts, heated outdoor swimming pool,
fishing. **Conf** Max 40 Board 12 **Location** 2.25m W of
Bewdley off A456
continued

Hotel ★★ 64% The George Hotel, Load St, BEWDLEY
☎ 01299 402117 11 en suite

Wharton Park Longbank DY12 2QW
☎ 01299 405222 & 405163 ▤ 01299 405121
18-hole championship-standard course in 140 acres of countryside. Some long par 5s eg the 9th (594yds) as well as superb par 3 holes at 3rd, 10th, 15th make this a very challenging course.

18 holes, 6603yds, Par 72, SSS 71, Course record 66.
Club membership 500.
Visitors must contact in advance. May not play weekend mornings. **Societies** prior booking required. **Green Fees** not confirmed. **Cards** ▦ ■ ▦ ▧ ▨ ▨ **Prof** Angus Hoare **Course Designer** Harold Swan **Facilities** ⊗ ⅲ ▙ ■ ♀ ㅅ ▨ ♦ ♣ ♂ ☾ **Location** Off A456 Bewdley bypass

Hotel ★★ 64% The George Hotel, Load St, BEWDLEY
☎ 01299 402117 11 en suite

BISHAMPTON   Map 03 SO95

Vale Golf Club Hill Furze Rd WR10 2LZ
☎ 01386 462781 ▤ 01386 462597
e-mail: tvgcc@crownsportsplc
This course offers an American-style layout, with large greens, trees and bunkers and several water hazards. Its rolling fairways provide a testing round, as well as superb views of the Malvern Hills. Picturesque and peaceful.
International Course: 18 holes, 7174yds, Par 74, SSS 74, Course record 72.
Lenches Course: 9 holes, 5518yds, Par 70, SSS 66.
Club membership 650.
Visitors booking up to one week in advance. Some weekend restrictions on International course. **Societies** must apply in advance. Some weekend restrictions. **Green Fees** not confirmed. **Cards** ▦ ■ ▦ ▧ ▨ ▨ **Prof** Caroline Griffiths **Course Designer** Bob Sandon **Facilities** ⊗ ⅲ ▙ ■ ♀ ㅅ ▨ ♦ ♣ ♂ ☾ **Location** Signposted off A4538, between Evesham & Worcester

Hotel ★★★ 64% The Star Hotel, Foregate St, WORCESTER ☎ 01905 24308 45 en suite

BLAKEDOWN   Map 07 SO87

Churchill and Blakedown Churchill Ln DY10 3NB
☎ 01562 700018 & 700200
Pleasant course on hilltop with extensive views.
9 holes, 6488yds, Par 72, SSS 71.
Club membership 400.
Visitors with member only weekends & bank holidays. Handicap certificate required. **Societies** by arrangement through secretary. **Green Fees** terms on application.
Facilities ⊗ ⅲ ▙ ■ ♀ ㅅ ▨ ♦ ☾ **Location** W side of village off A456

continued

Hotel ★★★★ 67% Stone Manor Hotel, Stone, KIDDERMINSTER ☎ 01562 777555
52 en suite 5 annexe en suite

BROADWAY   Map 04 SP03

Broadway Willersey Hill WR12 7LG
☎ 01386 853683 ▤ 01386 858643
e-mail: beta.broadwaygolfclub@care4free.net
At the edge of the Cotswolds this downland course lies at an altitude of 900 ft above sea level, with extensive views. Natural contours and man made hazards mean that drives have to be placed, approaches carefully judged and the greens expertly read.
18 holes, 5970yds, Par 72, SSS 70, Course record 65.
Club membership 850.
Visitors may not play Sat between Apr-Sep before 3pm. Restricted play Sun. Must contact in advance. **Societies** Wed-Fri, must contact in advance. **Green Fees** £37 per day; £30 per round (£37 weekends & bank holidays). **Cards** ▦ ▦ ▨ **Prof** Martyn Freeman **Course Designer** James Braid **Facilities** ⊗ ⅲ ▙ ■ ♀ ㅅ ▨ ♦ ♣ ♂ ☾ **Location** 1.5m E on A44

Hotel ★★★ 76% Dormy House Hotel, Willersey Hill, BROADWAY ☎ 01386 852711
25 en suite 23 annexe en suite

BROMSGROVE   Map 07 SO97

Blackwell Agmore Rd, Blackwell B60 1PY
☎ 0121 445 1994 ▤ 0121 445 4911
Pleasantly undulating parkland with a variety of trees. Laid out in two 9-hole loops.
18 holes, 6080yds, Par 70, SSS 71.
Club membership 365.
Visitors must contact in advance, must have handicap certificate, may not play at weekends, **Societies** must contact in advance. **Green Fees** £50 per 18 holes (£60 per 27/36 holes). **Prof** Nigel Blake **Course Designer** Harry Colt **Facilities** ⊗ by prior arrangement ⅲ by prior arrangement ▙ ■ ♀ ㅅ ▨ ♦ ♣ ♂ ☾ **Location** 2m W of Alvechurch. M42 junct 1 westbound, then B4096 or M5 junct.4, then take A38 towards Bromsgrove and B4096 to Burcot, club signed

Hotel ★★★★ 65% Hanover International Hotel & Club, Kidderminster Rd, BROMSGROVE
☎ 01527 576600 114 en suite

Bromsgrove Golf Centre Stratford Rd B60 1LD
☎ 01527 575886 & 570505 ▤ 01527 570964
e-mail: enquiries@bromsgrovegolf.f9.co.uk
Gently undulating parkland course with large contoured greens, generous tee surfaces and superb views over Worcestershire. Tricky par 3 16th across a lake. Also 41

continued

bay floodlit driving range, floodlit practice bunker and clubhouse with conference facilities.

18 holes, 5969yds, Par 68, SSS 69.

Club membership 900.

Visitors dress restriction, no T-shirts, jeans, tracksuits etc. 7 day booking facilities available. **Societies** packages available, apply in writing or telephone. **Green Fees** £9 per 9 holes; £15.50 per 18 holes (£12.50/£20.50 weekends & bank holidays). **Cards** ⟷ ▦ ▧ 🔛 **Prof** Graeme Long/Danny Wall **Course Designer** Hawtree & Son **Facilities** ⊗ ⅏ ⅃ 🌭 ⅄ ⌯ 🏠 ⛻ 🏌 ⚘ ⓒ **Conf** Max 70 Thtr 70 Class 40 Board 30 Banquet 70 **Location** 1m from Bromsgrove town centre at junct of A38/A448

Hotel ★★★★ 65% Hanover International Hotel & Club, Kidderminster Rd, BROMSGROVE ☎ 01527 576600 114 en suite

DROITWICH   Map 03 SO86

Droitwich Ford Ln WR9 0BQ
☎ 01905 774344 📠 01905 797290
Undulating parkland course.
18 holes, 5976yds, Par 70, SSS 69, Course record 62.
Club membership 732.
Visitors with member only weekends & bank holidays. **Societies** must apply by telephone and letter. **Green Fees** not confirmed. **Prof** C Thompson **Course Designer** J Braid/G Franks **Facilities** ⊗ ⅏ ⅃ 🌭 ⅄ ⌯ 🏠 ⛻ **Leisure** snooker. **Location** Off A38 Droitwich to Bromsgrove road, midway between Droitwich and M5 junct 5

Hotel ★★★★ 67% Chateau Impney Hotel, DROITWICH SPA ☎ 01905 774411 67 en suite 53 annexe en suite

Gaudet Luce Middle Ln, Hadzor WR9 7DP
☎ 01905 796375 📠 01905 797245
e-mail: info@gaudet-luce.co.uk
A challenging 18-hole course with two contrasting 9-hole loops. The front nine are long and fairly open, the back nine are tight and compact requiring good positional and approach play. Water features on several holes.
18 holes, 5887yds, Par 70, SSS 68.
Club membership 500.
Visitors welcome, advisable to telephone in advance, proper golfing attire required at all times. **Societies** telephone for details. **Green Fees** not confirmed. **Cards** ⟷ ▦ ▨ 🔛 ▧ **Prof** Phil Cundy **Course Designer** M A Laing **Facilities** ⊗ ⅏ ⅃ 🌭 ⅄ ⌯ 🏠 ⛻ ⚘ ⛳ **Location** M5 junct 5, left at Tagwell road into Middle Lane, 1st driveway on left to clubhouse

Hotel ★★★★ 67% Chateau Impney Hotel, DROITWICH SPA ☎ 01905 774411 67 en suite 53 annexe en suite

Ombersley Bishops Wood Rd, Lineholt, Ombersley WR9 0LE ☎ 01905 620747 📠 01905 620047
Undulating course in beautiful countryside high above the edge of the Severn Valley. Covered driving range and putting green.
18 holes, 6139yds, Par 72, SSS 69, Course record 67.
Club membership 750.
Visitors suitable dress expected, no jeans, shirts must have a collar. **Societies** telephone in advance. **Green Fees** not confirmed. **Cards** ▧ **Prof** Graham Glenister **Course Designer** David Morgan **Facilities** ⊗ ⅏ ⅃ 🌭 ⅄ ⌯ 🏠 ⛻ ⚓ ⛳ ⓒ **Location** 3m W of Droitwich, off A449. At Mitre Oak pub, take A4025 to Stourport, signposted 400yds on left

continued

Hotel ★★★★ 65% Raven Hotel, Victoria Square, DROITWICH SPA ☎ 01905 772224 72 en suite

FLADBURY   Map 03 SO94

Evesham Craycombe Links, Old Worcester Rd WR10 2QS ☎ 01386 860395 📠 861356
e-mail: eveshamgolfclub@talk21.com
Parkland, heavily wooded, with the River Avon running alongside 5th and 14th holes. Good views. Nine greens played from eighteen different tees.
9 holes, 6415yds, Par 72, Course record 65.
Club membership 450.
Visitors must contact in advance, and have a handicap certificate. **Societies** must apply by in advance by phone or writing. **Green Fees** £20. **Prof** Dan Cummins **Facilities** ⊗ ⅏ ⅃ 🌭 ⅄ ⌯ 🏠 ⛻ **Location** 0.75m N on A4538

Hotel ★★★ 71% The Evesham Hotel, Coopers Ln, Off Waterside, EVESHAM ☎ 01386 765566 & 0800 716969 (Res) 📠 01386 765443 39 en suite 1 annexe en suite

HOLLYWOOD   Map 07 SP07

Gay Hill Hollywood Ln B47 5PP
☎ 0121 430 8544 & 474 6001 (pro) 📠 0121 436 7796
A meadowland course, some 7 miles from Birmingham.
18 holes, 6406yds, Par 72, SSS 72, Course record 64.
Club membership 740.
Visitors must contact in advance. **Societies** telephone in advance. **Green Fees** £30. **Prof** Andrew Potter **Facilities** ⊗ ⅏ ⅃ 🌭 ⅄ ⌯ 🏠 ⛻ ⛳ **Location** N side of village

Hotel ★★★ 64% Regency Hotel, Stratford Rd, Shirley, SOLIHULL ☎ 0121 745 6119 112 en suite

KIDDERMINSTER   Map 07 SO87

Habberley Low Trimpley DY11 5RG
☎ 01562 745756 📠 01562 745756
Very hilly, wooded parkland course.
9 holes, 5401yds, Par 69, Course record 62.
Club membership 230.
Visitors may only play weekends with a member, weekdays by prior arrangement. **Societies** telephone initially. **Green Fees** not confirmed. **Facilities** ⊗ ⅏ ⅃ 🌭 ⅄ ⌯ **Location** 2m NW of Kidderminster

Hotel ★★★★ 67% Stone Manor Hotel, Stone, KIDDERMINSTER ☎ 01562 777555 52 en suite 5 annexe en suite

Kidderminster Russell Rd DY10 3HT
☎ 01562 822303 📠 01562 827866
e-mail: kidderminstergolfclub@hotmail.com
Parkland course with natural hazards and some easy walking.
18 holes, 6405yds, Par 72, SSS 71, Course record 65.
Club membership 860.
Visitors with member only weekends & bank holidays. Must have a handicap certificate. **Societies** weekdays only apply in advance. **Green Fees** terms on application. **Prof** Nick Underwood **Facilities** ⊗ ⅏ ⅃ 🌭 ⅄ ⌯ 🏠 ⛻ 🏌 ⛳ **Location** 0.5m SE of town centre, signposted off A449

Hotel ★★★★ 67% Stone Manor Hotel, Stone, KIDDERMINSTER ☎ 01562 777555 52 en suite 5 annexe en suite

Wyre Forest Zortech Av DY11 7EX

☎ 01299 822682 🖷 01299 879433
e-mail: simon@wyreforestgolf.com
Making full use of the existing contours, this interesting
and challenging course is bounded by woodland and gives
extensive views over the surrounding area. Well drained
fairways and greens.
18 holes, 5790yds, Par 70, SSS 68, Course record 68.
Club membership 397.
Visitors must telephone in advance. Societies brochure on
request, deposit secures date, write or telephone. Green Fees
£12 per 18 holes (£16 weekends); £9.50 per 9 holes (£12.50
weekends). Cards ══ ▆▆ ▆▆ ▆▆ 🖸 Prof Simon Price
Facilities ┗ ♀ ⚘ 🖻 ↑ ↘ ⊶ ⌀ ⎰ Location Halfway
between Kidderminsterm & Stourport, on A451

Hotel ★★★★ 71% Menzies Stourport Manor, Hartlebury
Rd, STOURPORT-ON-SEVERN
☎ 0870 600 3013 68 en suite

MALVERN WELLS   Map 03 SO74

Worcestershire Wood Farm, Wood Farm Rd

WR14 4PP ☎ 01684 575992 🖷 01684 893334
e-mail: thesecretary@theworcestershiregolfclub.co.uk
Fairly easy walking on windy downland course with trees,
ditches and other natural hazards. Outstanding views of
Malvern Hills and Severn Valley. 17th hole (par 5) is
approached over small lake.
18 holes, 6500yds, Par 71, SSS 72.
Club membership 750.
Visitors handicap certificate required. Societies Apply in
advance by telephone. Green Fees terms on application.
Prof Richard Lewis Course Designer J H Taylor Facilities
⊗ ⏍ ┗ ⛳ ♀ ⚘ 🖻 ↘ ⌀ Location 2m S of Gt Malvern
on B4209

Hotel ★★★♨♨ 74% The Cottage in the Wood Hotel,
Holywell Rd, Malvern Wells, MALVERN
☎ 01684 575859 8 en suite 12 annexe en suite

REDDITCH   Map 07 SP06

Abbey Hotel Golf & Country Club Dagnell End

Rd, Hither Green Ln B98 9BE
☎ 01527 406600 & 406500 🖷 01527 406514
e-mail: info@theabbeyhotel.co.uk
Young parkland course with rolling fairways. A 'Site of
Special Scientific Interest', the course includes two
fishing lakes and is pleasant to play.
18 holes, 6561yds, Par 72, SSS 72.
Club membership 500.
Visitors must contact in advance, dress code applies.
Societies must apply in writing/by telephone. Green Fees
£16 per round (£22 Fridays, weekends & bank holidays).
Cards ══ ▆▆ ▆▆ 🖸 ▆▆ ▆▆ 🖸 Prof R Davies Facilities ⊗

continued

Set amidst a beautiful undulating
landscape in North Worcestershire.
The course offers a variety of
challenges from wooded areas to
water early in your round but
many holes offer welcome relief
with their spacious fairways.
A £4 million extension programme was
completed in September 2001 making the Abbey
the ideal venue to stay and play. All guests have
complimentary use of the health club which
includes swimming pool and gymnasium.

**Hither Green Lane, Dagnell End Road,
Redditch, Worcestershire B98 9BE
Tel: 01527 406600 Fax: 01527 470871
www.theabbeyhotel.co.uk**

⏍ ┗ ⛳ ♀ ⚘ 🖻 ↑ 🖂 ↘ ⊶ ⌀ ⎰ Leisure heated indoor
swimming pool, fishing, sauna, solarium, gymnasium. Conf
Thtr 150 Class 60 Board 30 Banquet 140 Del £35 to
£152.50* Location from M42 junct 2 take A441 to Redditch
for approx 2m. Turn left at 1st roundabout, after approx
0.75m turn left at traffic lights, signposted Besley (B4101)
and then right into Hither Green Lane.

Hotel ★★★★ 65% The Abbey Hotel Golf & Country Club,
Hither Green Ln, Dagnell End Rd, Bordesley, REDDITCH
☎ 01527 406600 72 en suite

Pitcheroak Plymouth Rd B97 4PB

☎ 01527 541054 🖷 01527 65216
Woodland course, hilly in places. There is also a putting
green and a practice ground.
9 holes, 4561yds, Par 65, SSS 62.
Club membership 150.

continued

Visitors no restrictions. **Societies** telephone to book. **Green Fees** £8.65 per 18 holes; £6.65 per 9 holes (£10/£7.35 weekends). **Cards** ⬜ 🟥 🟥 🟥 🟥 💲 **Prof** David Stewart **Facilities** ⊗ ⫫ ⓛ ⅃ 🍴 △ 🏠 ⬧ ⌀ **Location** SW side of town centre off A448

Hotel ★★★ 66% Quality Hotel, Pool Bank, Southcrest, REDDITCH ☎ 01527 541511 73 en suite

Redditch Lower Grinsty, Green Ln, Callow Hill B97 5PJ
☎ 01527 5430799(sec) & 543079 📠 01527 547413
Parkland course, the hazards including woods, ditches and large ponds. The par 4, 14th is a testing hole.
18 holes, 6671yds, Par 72, SSS 72, Course record 68.
Club membership 650.
Visitors with member only weekends & bank holidays, no visitors on competition days, advisable to telephone in advance. **Societies** apply in writing to secretary. **Green Fees** £35 per day; £28 per round. **Prof** David Down **Course Designer** F Pennick **Facilities** ⊗ ⫫ ⓛ ⅃ 🍴 △ 🏠 ⬧ 🛒 ⌀ **Location** 2m SW

Hotel ★★★ 66% Quality Hotel, Pool Bank, Southcrest, REDDITCH ☎ 01527 541511 73 en suite

Cadmore Lodge Hotel & Country Club St
Michaels, Berrington Green WR15 8TQ
☎ 01584 810044 📠 01584 810044
e-mail: info@cadmorelodge.demon.co.uk
A picturesque 9-hole course in a brook valley. Challenging holes include the 1st and 6th over the lake, 8th over the valley and 9th over hedges.
9 holes, 5132yds, Par 68, SSS 65.
Club membership 200.
Visitors no restrictions but check availability. **Societies** telephone in advance. **Green Fees** £10 per day(£14 weekends). **Cards** ⬜ 🟥 🟥 💲 🟥 💲 **Facilities** ⊗ ⫫ ⓛ ⅃ △ 🏠 ⌀ **Leisure** hard tennis courts, heated indoor swimming pool, fishing, sauna, gymnasium, pool table. **Conf** Thtr 100 Class 50 Board 30 Banquet 100 Del £8.50 to £12.75 * **Location** From Tenbury take A4112 to Leominster, after approx 2m turn right for Berrington, 0.75 on left

Hotel ★★ 67% Cadmore Lodge Hotel & Country Club, Berrington Green, St Michaels, TENBURY WELLS ☎ 01584 810044 15 rms (14 en suite)

Bank House Hotel Golf & Country Club
Bransford WR6 5JD ☎ 01886 833545 📠 01886 832461
e-mail: info@bransfordclub.co.uk
The Bransford course is designed as a 'Florida' style course with fairways weaving between water courses, 13 lakes and sculptured mounds with colouful plant displays. The 6,204yd course has doglegs, island greens and tight fairways to challenge all standards of player. The 10th, 16th and 18th (The Devil's Elbow) are particularly tricky.
Bransford Course: 18 holes, 6204yds, Par 72, SSS 71, Course record 65.
Club membership 380.
Visitors all tee times must be booked, no play before 9.30am. **Societies** contact the golf secretary, all tee times must be booked in advance. **Green Fees** £20 per 18 holes (£25 weekends),reductions in winter. **Cards** ⬜ 🟥 🟥 💲 🟥 🟥 💲 **Prof** Scott Fordyce **Course Designer** Bob Sandow **Facilities** ⊗ ⫫ ⓛ ⅃ 🍴 △ 🏠 🍴 🛒 ⬧ 🛒 ⌀ 🍴 **Leisure**
continued

outdoor swimming pool, sauna, solarium, gymnasium, spa pool.**Conf** Max 400 Thtr 400 Class 150 Board 70 Banquet 250 Del from £35 * **Location** 3m S of Worcester, A4103

Hotel ★★★ 70% Bank House Hotel Golf & Country Club, Bransford, WORCESTER ☎ 01886 833551 68 en suite

Worcester Golf & Country Club Boughton Park
WR2 4EZ ☎ 01905 422555 📠 01905 749090
18 holes, 6251yds, Par 70, SSS 70, Course record 67.
Course Designer Dr A Mackenzie **Location** 1.5m from city centre on A4103
Telephone for further details

Hotel ★★★ 59% The Gifford Hotel, High St, WORCESTER ☎ 01905 726262 103 en suite

Fulford Heath Tanners Green Ln B47 6BH
☎ 01564 824758 📠 01564 822629
A mature parkland course encompassing two classic par threes. The 11th, a mere 149 yards, shoots from an elevated tee through a channel of trees to a well protected green. The 16th, a 166 yard par 3, elevated green, demands a 140 yard carry over an imposing lake.
18 holes, 5959yds, Par 70, SSS 69.
Club membership 750.
Visitors with member only weekend & bank holidays. Handicap certificate required. **Societies** must apply in advance. **Green Fees** £35. **Prof** Mike Herbert **Course Designer** Braid/Hawtree **Facilities** ⊗ ⫫ ⓛ ⅃ 🍴 △ 🏠 🛒 ⌀ **Location** 1m SE off A435

Hotel ★★★★ 66% Renaissance Solihull Hotel, 651 Warwick Rd, SOLIHULL ☎ 0121 711 3000 175 en suite

Oaks Aughton Common YO42 4PW
☎ 01757 288577 & 288007 📠 01757 289029
e-mail: oaksgolfclub@hotmail.com
Built amongst mature woodland and six lakes in the picturesque Derwent Ings and further enhanced by thousands of specimen trees. Greens are built with substantial moulding.
The Oaks: 18 holes, 6743yds, Par 72, SSS 72.
Club membership 680.
Visitors weekdays only. **Societies** may play weekdays. Telephone in advance. **Green Fees** £35 per day; £22 per round (weekdays only). **Cards** ⬜ 🟥 💲 🟥 🟥 💲 **Prof** Joe Townhill **Course Designer** Julian Covey **Facilities** ⊗ ⫫ ⓛ ⅃ 🍴 △ 🏠 🍴 🛒 🛒 ⌀ 🍴 **Leisure** 3 self-catering
continued

cottages with own putting greens. **Location** 1m N of Bubwith on B1228

Hotel ★★★ 73% The Parsonage Country House Hotel, York Rd, ESCRICK ☎ 01904 728111 12 en suite 9 annexe en suite

BEVERLEY Map 08 TA03

Beverley & East Riding The Westwood HU17 8RG
☎ 01482 868757 🖷 01482 868757

Picturesque parkland course with some hard walking and natural hazards - trees and gorse bushes. Also cattle (spring to autumn); horse-riders are an occasional hazard in the early morning.

Westwood: 18 holes, 6127yds, Par 69, SSS 69, Course record 65.
Club membership 530.

Visitors must contact in advance. **Societies** telephone 01482 868757, then written confirmation. **Green Fees** £20 per day; £15 per round (£25/£20 weekends). **Prof** Alex Ashby **Facilities** **Location** 1m SW on B1230

Hotel ★★★ 67% Beverley Arms Hotel, North Bar Within, BEVERLEY ☎ 01482 869241 56 en suite

BRANDESBURTON Map 08 TA14

Hainsworth Park Burton Holme YO25 8RT
☎ 01964 542362 🖷 01964 542362
e-mail: hainsworth@hemscott.net

A parkland course based on sand and gravel giving excellent drainage. Demands straight driving due to mature trees.

18 holes, 6435yds, Par 71, SSS 71.
Club membership 500.

Visitors contact in advance. **Societies** telephone initially. **Green Fees** not confirmed. **Cards** **Prof** Paul Binnington **Facilities** **Leisure** grass tennis courts, fishing. **Location** SW side of village on A165

Hotel ★★ 68% Burton Lodge Hotel, BRANDESBURTON ☎ 01964 542847 7 en suite 2 annexe en suite

BRIDLINGTON Map 08 TA16

Bridlington Belvedere Rd YO15 3NA
☎ 01262 606367 🖷 01262 606367

Clifftop, seaside course, windy at times, with hazards of bunkers, ponds, ditches and trees.

18 holes, 6638yds, Par 72, SSS 72, Course record 66.
Club membership 600.

Visitors must contact in advance, professional 01262 674721 limited at weekends. **Societies** telephone bookings in advance. **Green Fees** terms on application. **Prof** Anthony Howarth **Course Designer** James Braid **Facilities** **Location** 1m S off A165

Hotel ★★★ 70% Revelstoke Hotel, 1-3 Flamborough Rd, BRIDLINGTON ☎ 01262 672362 25 en suite

Bridlington Links Flamborough Rd, Marton YO15 1DW ☎ 01262 401584 🖷 01262 401702

Coastal links type course with large greens, numerous water hazards and splendid views towards Flamborough Head. When the wind blows off the sea, the course becomes a challenging test of golf for even the experienced golfer.

Main: 18 holes, 6719yds, Par 72, SSS 72, Course record 70.
Club membership 350.

continued

Visitors telephone to book tee times. **Societies** telephone for booking. **Green Fees** Summer: £15 per round (£20 weekends and bank holidays). Winter: £12 (£15 weekends). **Cards** **Prof** Steve Raybould **Course Designer** Swan **Facilities** **Conf** Max 100 Thtr 100 Class 100 Board 40 Banquet 100 **Location** On the B1255 between Bridlington and Flamborough

Hotel ★★★ 67% Expanse Hotel, North Marine Dr, BRIDLINGTON ☎ 01262 675347 48 en suite

BROUGH Map 08 SE92

Brough Cave Rd HU15 1HB
☎ 01482 667291 🖷 01482 669873
e-mail: gt@brough-golfclub.co.uk

Parkland course, where accurate positioning of the tee ball is required for good scoring.

18 holes, 6075yds, Par 68, SSS 69, Course record 64.
Club membership 700.

Visitors must have handicap certificate and contact in advance. **Societies** apply by letter. **Green Fees** £45 per day: £32 per round (£60/£45 weekends and bank holidays). **Prof** Gordon Townhill **Facilities** **Location** 0.5m N

Hotel ★★★ 65% The Humber Crown Hotel, Ferriby High Rd, NORTH FERRIBY ☎ 01482 645212 95 en suite

COTTINGHAM Map 08 TA03

Cottingham Parks Golf & Country Club
Woodhill Way HU16 5RZ
☎ 01482 846030 🖷 01482 845932
e-mail: jane@cottinghamgolf.totalserve.co.uk

Gently undulating parkland course incorporating many natural features, including lateral water hazards, several ponds on the approach to greens, and rolling fairways.

18 holes, 6459yds, Par 72, SSS 71, Course record 66.
Club membership 600.

Visitors may book by telephone in advance, times available weekdays and weekends. **Societies** deposit required and confirmation in writing. After 2pm weekends. **Green Fees** £24 per day; £16 per round (£36/24 weekends). **Cards** **Prof** Chris Gray **Course Designer** Terry Litten **Facilities** **Leisure** heated indoor swimming pool, sauna, gymnasium, Jacuzzi. **Conf** Thtr 90 Class 60 Board 60 **Location** 4m from A63/M62 on A164. Turn off to Cottingham on B1233, in 100yds turn left into Woodhill Way

Hotel ★★ 68% The Rowley Manor Hotel, Rowley Rd, LITTLE WEIGHTON ☎ 01482 848248 16 en suite

AA website: www.theAA.com

DRIFFIELD (GREAT)   Map 08 TA05

Driffield Sunderlandwick YO25 9AD
☎ 01377 253116 📠 01377 240599
An easy walking, mature parkland course set within the beautiful Sunderlandwick Estate.
18 holes, 6215yds, Par 70, SSS 69, Course record 67.
Club membership 693.
Visitors must book in advance and adhere to club dress rule.
Societies apply in writing or telephone. **Green Fees** £25 per day,£20 per round;(£40/£30 weekends). **Prof** Kenton Wright **Facilities** ⊗ ⊪ ﹒ ♥ ♀ ♨ ﹩ ℰ **Leisure** fishing. **Location** 2m S off A164

Hotel ★★★ 71%   Bell Hotel, 46 Market Place, DRIFFIELD
☎ 01377 256661 16 en suite

FLAMBOROUGH   Map 08 TA27

Flamborough Head Lighthouse Rd YO15 1AR
☎ 01262 850333 & 850417 & 850683 📠 01262 850279
e-mail: secretary@flamboroughheadgolfclub.co.uk
Undulating cliff top course on the Flamborough headland.
18 holes, 6189yds, Par 69, SSS 69, Course record 70.
Club membership 500.
Visitors welcome but may not play; before 1pm Sun, Wed between 10.30 & 1.30, Sat between 11.30 & 12.30. **Societies** must contact in advance. **Green Fees** £20 (£25 weekends & bank holidays). **Prof** Paul Harrison **Facilities** ⊗ ⊪ ﹒ ♥ ♀ ♨ ﹩ ﹩ ℰ **Location** 2m E off B1259

Hotel ★★ 67%   Flaneburg Hotel & Restaurant, North Marine Rd, FLAMBOROUGH ☎ 01262 850284 14 en suite

HESSLE   Map 08 TA02

Hessle Westfield Rd, Raywell HU16 5YL
☎ 01482 650171 & 650190 (Prof) 📠 01482 652679
e-mail: secretary@hessle-golf-club.co.uk
Well-wooded downland course with easy walking. The greens, conforming to USGA specification, are large and undulating with excellent drainage, enabling play throughout the year.
18 holes, 6604yds, Par 72, SSS 72, Course record 68.
Club membership 720.
Visitors not Tue between 9-1 and may not play before 11am on Sat & Sun. **Societies** by prior arrangement. **Green Fees** £30 per day; £25 per round (£32 per round weekends). **Cards** ⬛ ⬛ ⬛ 🖃 **Prof** Grahame Fieldsend **Course Designer** D Thomas/P Allis **Facilities** ⊗ ⊪ ﹒ ♥ ♀ ♨ ﹩ ℰ **Conf** Max 20 Del from £30 * **Location** 3m SW of Cottingham

Hotel ★★★ 65%   The Humber Crown Hotel, Ferriby High Rd, NORTH FERRIBY ☎ 01482 645212 95 en suite

HORNSEA   Map 08 TA14

Hornsea Rolston Rd HU18 1XG
☎ 01964 532020 📠 01964 532080
e-mail: hornseagolfclub@aol.com
Flat, parkland course with good greens.
18 holes, 6685yds, Par 72, SSS 72, Course record 66.
Club membership 600.
Visitors with member only at weekends until 3pm Sats, 2pm Sun. Must contact in advance. **Societies** contact Secretary in advance. **Green Fees** £30 per day; £22 per round (£30 per round weekends). **Prof** Stretton Wright **Facilities** ⊗ ⊪ by prior arrangement ﹒ ♥ ♀ ♨ ﹩ ﹩ ℰ **Location** 1m S on B1242, follow signs for Hornsea Freeport

continued

Hotel ★★★ 67%   Beverley Arms Hotel, North Bar Within, BEVERLEY ☎ 01482 869241 56 en suite

HOWDEN   Map 08 SE72

Boothferry Park Spaldington Ln DN14 7NG
☎ 01430 430364 📠 01430 430567
Pleasant meadowland course in the Vale of York with interesting natural dykes creating challenge on some holes. The par 3 5th over water will test your nerve.
18 holes, 6651yds, Par 73, SSS 72, Course record 64.
Club membership 500.
Visitors must contact in advance, tee times bookable.
Societies must contact for booking form. **Green Fees** £10 per 18 holes (£15 weekends). **Prof** Nigel Bundy **Course Designer** Donald Steel **Facilities** ⊗ ⊪ ﹒ ♥ ♀ ♨ ﹩ 🍴 ﹩ ℰ ℭ **Location** M62. junct 37, 2.5m N of Howden off B1228

Hotel ★★ 68%   Clifton Hotel, 155 Boothferry Rd, GOOLE
☎ 01405 761336 9 en suite

HULL   Map 08 TA02

Ganstead Park Longdales Ln, Coniston HU11 4LB
☎ 01482 817754 📠 01482 817754
e-mail: secretary@gansteadpark.co.uk
Parkland course, easy walking, with water features.
18 holes, 6801yds, Par 72, SSS 73, Course record 62.
Club membership 500.
Visitors contact in advance. **Societies** telephone in advance.
Green Fees terms on application. **Prof** Michael J Smee
Course Designer P Green **Facilities** ⊗ ⊪ ﹒ ♥ ♀ ♨ ﹩ 🍴 ♥ ﹩ ℰ **Location** 6m NE on A165

Hotel ★★★ 65%   Quality Hotel Hull, 170 Ferensway, HULL ☎ 01482 325087 155 en suite

Hull The Hall, 27 Packman Ln HU10 7TJ
☎ 01482 658919 📠 01482 658919
Parkland course.
18 holes, 6242yds, Par 70, SSS 70.
Club membership 840.
Visitors only weekdays. Contact professional 01482 653074.
Societies Mon Tue Thu & Fri by prior arrangement. **Green Fees** £32 per day; £26.50 per round. **Prof** David Jagger
Course Designer James Braid **Facilities** ⊗ ⊪ ﹒ ♥ ♀ ♨ ﹩ ℰ **Location** 5m W of city centre off A164

Hotel ★★★ 72%   Willerby Manor Hotel, Well Ln, WILLERBY ☎ 01482 652616 51 en suite

Springhead Park Willerby Rd HU5 5JE
☎ 01482 656309
18 holes, 6402yds, Par 71, SSS 71.
Location 5m W off A164
Telephone for further details

Hotel ★★★ 72%   Willerby Manor Hotel, Well Ln, WILLERBY ☎ 01482 652616 51 en suite

Sutton Park Salthouse Rd HU8 9HF
☎ 01482 374242 📠 01482 701428
Municipal parkland course.
18 holes, 6251yds, Par 70, SSS 69, Course record 67.
Club membership 300.
Visitors no restrictions. **Societies** prior arrangement via club, telephone and confirm in writing. **Green Fees** terms on application. **Prof** To be appointed **Facilities** ⊗ by prior arrangement ⊪ by prior arrangement ﹒ ♥ ♀ ♨ ﹩ 🍴 ♥ ﹩ **Location** 3m NE on B1237 off A165

continued

Hotel ★★★ 65% Quality Hotel Hull, 170 Ferensway,
HULL ☎ 01482 325087 155 en suite

POCKLINGTON   Map 08 SE84

Kilnwick Percy Kilnwick Percy YO42 1UF
☎ 01759 303090
Parkland course on the edge of the Wolds above
Pocklington combines a good walk with interesting golf.
Undulating fairways, mature trees, water hazards and
breathtaking views from every hole.
18 holes, 6214yards, Par 70, SSS 70.
Club membership 300.
Visitors telephone to book tee. May only play after 10am
weekends/bank holidays Societies telephone for details of
society packages. Green Fees £21 per day; £15 per 18 holes;
£10 per 9 holes (£25/£18/£12 weekends). Prof Joe Townhill
Course Designer John Day Facilities ⊗ ┗ 🖤 ♀ 占 🏠 ☂
🎱 ✆ Location 1m E of Pocklington, off B1246

Hotel ★★ 64% Feathers Hotel, 56 Market Place,
POCKLINGTON ☎ 01759 303155
6 en suite 6 annexe en suite

SOUTH CAVE   Map 08 SE93

Cave Castle Hotel & Country Club Church Hill,
South Cave HU15 2EU
☎ 01430 421286 & 422245 🗐 01430 421118
An undulating meadow and parkland course at the foot
of the Wolds, with superb views. Golf breaks are
available.
18 holes, 6500yds, Par 73, SSS 72, Course record 71.
Club membership 450.
Visitors must contact in advance, may not play before 11am
weekends/bank holidays. Societies by arrangement with
professional or golf administrator. Green Fees terms on
application. Cards ▦ 🛒 💷 Prof Stephen MacKinder
Course Designer Mrs N Freling Facilities ⊗ 𝍫 ┗ 🖤 ♀ 占
🏠 ☂ 🎱 🎱 ✆ Leisure heated indoor swimming pool,
fishing, sauna, solarium, gymnasium. Conf Max 200 Thtr
200 Banquet 200 Del from £21.50 * Location 1m from A63

Hotel ★★★ 65% The Humber Crown Hotel, Ferriby High
Rd, NORTH FERRIBY ☎ 01482 645212 95 en suite

WITHERNSEA   Map 08 TA32

Withernsea Chesnut Av HU19 2PG ☎ 01964 612078
Exposed seaside links with narrow, undulating fairways,
bunkers and small greens.
9 holes, 6207yds, Par 72, SSS 69.
Club membership 300.
Visitors with member only at weekends before 3pm.
Societies apply in writing/telephone Green Fees £12. Prof
Paul Rushworth Facilities ⊗ 𝍫 ┗ 🖤 ♀ 占 🏠 Leisure
senior/junior coaching. Location S side of town centre off
A1033, sign post in Victoria Avenue, through residential
estate. Course signposted

Hotel ★★★ 65% Quality Hotel Hull, 170 Ferensway,
HULL ☎ 01482 325087 155 en suite

YORKSHIRE, NORTH

ALDWARK   Map 08 SE46

Aldwark Manor YO61 1UF
☎ 01347 838353 🗐 01347 830007
An easy walking, scenic 18-hole parkland course with
holes both sides of the River Ure. The course surrounds
continued

the Victorian Aldwark Manor Golf Hotel. A warm
welcome to society and corporate days.
18 holes, 6154yds, Par 71, SSS 70, Course record 69.
Club membership 400.

Aldwark Manor

Visitors must contact in advance, restricted weekends.
Societies must telephone in advance. Green Fees £35 per
day; £25 per round (£40/£30 weekends & bank holiday).
Cards ▦ ■ 🛒 💷 🛒 💷 Facilities ⊗ 𝍫 ┗ 🖤 ♀ 占 🏠
☂ 🎱 ✆ Leisure heated indoor swimming pool,
fishing, sauna, gymnasium. Conf Thtr 100 Board 30
Banquet 70 Del £39 to £100 * Location 5m SE of
Boroughbridge off A1, 12m NW of York off A19

Hotel ★★★ 70% Aldwark Manor Hotel, Golf & Country
Club, ALDWARK ☎ 01347 838146 & 838251
🗐 01347 838867 25 en suite 3 annexe rms (2 en suite)

BEDALE   Map 08 SE28

Bedale Leyburn Rd DL8 1EZ ☎ 01677 422451 (sec) &
422568 (clubhouse) 🗐 01677 427143
e-mail: bedalegolfclub@aol.com
One of North Yorkshires most picturesque and
interesting golf courses. An 18 hole course set in a
parkland landscape with mature trees, water hazards and
strategically placed bunkers. Easy walking, no heavy
climbs.
18 holes, 6610yds, Par 72, SSS 72, Course record 69.
Club membership 600.
Visitors welcome, contact in advance. Societies must
acontact secretary for details. Green Fees £22 per day (£33
weekends & bank holidays). Prof Tony Johnson Facilities
⊗ 𝍫 ┗ 🖤 ♀ 占 🏠 ☂ 🎱 🎱 ✆ Location From A1 take
A684 at Leeming Bar to Bedale

Hotel ★ 69% Buck Inn, THORNTON WATLASS
☎ 01677 422461 7 rms (5 en suite)

BENTHAM   Map 07 SD66

Bentham Robin Ln LA2 7AG ☎ 01524 262455
Moorland course with glorious views.
9 holes, 5760yds, Par 70, SSS 69, Course record 69.
Club membership 480.
Visitors no restrictions. Societies must apply in advance.
Green Fees terms on application. Facilities ⊗ 𝍫 ┗ 🖤 ♀
占 Location N side of High Bentham

Guesthouse ◆◆◆◆ Ferncliffe Country Guest House, 55 Main
St, INGLETON ☎ 015242 42405 5 en suite

CATTERICK GARRISON   Map 08 SE29

Catterick Leyburn Rd DL9 3QE
☎ 01748 833268 🗐 01748 833268
Scenic parkland/moorland course of Championship
continued

standard, with good views of the Pennines and Cleveland hills. Testing 1st and 6th holes.
18 holes, 6329yds, Par 71, SSS 70, Course record 64.
Club membership 700.
Visitors tee reservation system in operation telephone professional shop 01748 833671. May not play before 10am Tue/Thu/weekends and bank holidays. **Societies** by arrangement. **Green Fees** £27 per day; £24 per round (£33 day/round weekends& bank holidays). **Prof** Andy Marshall **Course Designer** Arthur Day **Facilities** ⊗)Ⅲ ᗷ ■ ♀ ㊂ 🏠 ⚐ ⬥ 🛺 ✆ **Conf** Max 50 **Location** 0.5m W of Catterick Garrison Centre

Hotel ★★ 68% King's Head Hotel, Market Place, RICHMOND ☎ 01748 850220 26 en suite 4 annexe en suite

COPMANTHORPE   Map 08 SE54

Pike Hills Tadcaster Rd YO23 3UW
☎ 01904 700797 🖩 01904 700797
Parkland course surrounding nature reserve. Level terrain.
18 holes, 6146yds, Par 71, SSS 70, Course record 63.
Club membership 750.
Visitors welcome weekdays, with member only weekends & bank holidays. **Societies** must apply in advance. **Green Fees** terms on application. **Cards** 🖭 ▆▆ 🗿 **Prof** Ian Gradwell **Facilities** ⊗)Ⅲ ᗷ ■ ♀ ㊂ 🏠 ⚐ ⬥ 🛺 ✆ **Location** 3m SW of York on A64

Hotel ★★★★ 66% York Marriott Hotel, Tadcaster Rd, YORK ☎ 01904 701000 108 en suite

EASINGWOLD   Map 08 SE56

Easingwold Stillington Rd YO61 3ET
☎ 01347 821964 (Pro) & 822474 (Sec) 🖩 01347 822474
e-mail: brian@easingwold-golf-club.fsnet.co.uk
Parkland course with easy walking. Trees are a major feature and on six holes water hazards come into play.
18 holes, 6550yds, Par 74, SSS 72.
Club membership 750.
Visitors prior enquiry essential. **Societies** prior application in writing essential. **Green Fees** £30 per day; £25 per round (£30 weekends). **Prof** John Hughes **Course Designer** Hawtree **Facilities** ⊗)Ⅲ ᗷ ■ ♀ ㊂ 🏠 🛺 ✆ ⚐ **Location** 1m S of Easingwold, 12m N of York

Hotel ★★ 68% George Hotel, Market Place, EASINGWOLD ☎ 01347 821698 15 en suite

FILEY   Map 08 TA18

Filey West Av YO14 9BQ
☎ 01723 513293 🖩 01723 514952
e-mail: info@fileygolf.freeserve.co.uk
Parkland course with good views. Stream runs through course. Testing 9th and 13th holes.
18 holes, 6112yds, Par 70, SSS 69, Course record 64.
Club membership 900.
Visitors must telephone to reserve tee time. **Societies** contact by telephone. **Green Fees** £29 per day; £23 per round (£32/30 weekends). Reduced winter rates. 9 hole course £5 all year. **Prof** Gary Hutchinson **Course Designer** Braid **Facilities** ⊗)Ⅲ ᗷ ■ ♀ ㊂ 🏠 ⚐ ⬥ 🛺 ✆ **Location** 0.5m S of Filey

Hotel ★★ 68% Wrangham House Hotel, 10 Stonegate, HUNMANBY ☎ 01723 891333 8 en suite 4 annexe en suite

AA website: www.theAA.com

Rudding Park
🄷 O T E L & G O L F

● Award winning four star hotel
● 18 hole, par 72, Parkland Golf Course
● Corporate and Society Days welcome
● 18 bay floodlit, covered Driving Range

RUDDING PARK, FOLLIFOOT, HARROGATE,
NORTH YORKSHIRE HG3 1JH
TEL: 01423 871350 • FAX: 01423 872286
e-mail: sales@ruddingpark.com
www.ruddingpark.com

GANTON   Map 08 SE97

Ganton YO12 4PA
☎ 01944 710329 🖩 01944 710922
Championship course, heathland, gorse-lined fairways and heavily bunkered; variable winds. The opening holes make full use of the contours of the land and the approach to the second demands the finest touch. The fourth is considered as one of the best holes on the outward half with its shot across a valley to a plateau green, the surrounding gorse punishing anything less than a perfect shot. Hosts for the Walker Cup in September 2003.
18 holes, 6734yds, Par 72, SSS 73, Course record 65.
Club membership 500.
Visitors by prior arrangement. Restricted play at weekends. **Societies** prior arrangement in writing. **Green Fees** £60 per round/day (£70 weekends & bank holidays). **Cards** 🖭 ▆▆ ▆▆ 🗿 **Prof** Gary Brown **Course Designer** Dunn/Vardon/Braid/Colt **Facilities** ㊂ 🏠 ⚐ ⬥ 🛺 ✆ **Location** 11m SW of Scarborough on A64

Hotel ★★★ 63% East Ayton Lodge Country House, Moor Ln, Forge Valley, EAST AYTON ☎ 01723 864227 10 en suite 20 annexe en suite

HARROGATE   Map 08 SE35

Harrogate Forest Ln Head, Starbeck HG2 7TF
☎ 01423 862999 🖩 01423 860073
e-mail: hon.secretary@harrogate-gc.co.uk
One of Yorkshire's oldest and best courses was designed in 1897 by 'Sandy' Herd. A perfect example of golf architecture, its greens and fairways offer an
continued

interesting but fair challenge. The undulating parkland course once formed part of the ancient Forest of Knaresborough. Excellent clubhouse.
18 holes, 6241yds, Par 69, SSS 70, Course record 64. Club membership 650.
Visitors advisable to contact professional in advance, weekend play limited. **Societies** must contact in writing or intially by telephone. **Green Fees** not confirmed. **Cards** 🌐 💳 📇 📠 📶 💲 **Prof** Paul Johnson **Course Designer** Sandy Herd **Facilities** ⊗ ⊪ 🍴 ♨ ♀ ⛳ 🏠 🛒 ⚷ **Leisure** snooker. **Location** 2.25m N on A59

Hotel ★★★ 71% Grants Hotel, 3-13 Swan Rd, HARROGATE ☎ 01423 560666 42 en suite

Oakdale Oakdale Glen HG1 2LN
☎ 01423 567162 & 567188 ▤ 01423 536030
A pleasant, undulating parkland course which provides a good test of golf for the low handicap player without intimidating the less proficient. A special feature is an attractive stream which comes in to play on four holes. Excellent views from the clubhouse which has good facilities.
18 holes, 6456yds, Par 71, SSS 71, Course record 61. Club membership 1034.
Visitors no party bookings weekends. **Societies** telephone followed by letter. **Green Fees** not confirmed. **Prof** Clive Dell **Course Designer** Dr McKenzie **Facilities** ⊗ 🍴 ♨ ♀ ♿ 🏠 🛒 🚬 ⚷ **Location** N side of town centre off A61

Hotel ★★★ 71% Grants Hotel, 3-13 Swan Rd, HARROGATE ☎ 01423 560666 42 en suite

Rudding Park Hotel and Golf Rudding Park,
Follifoot HG3 1JH ☎ 01423 872100 ▤ 01423 873400
e-mail: sales@ruddingpark.com
The course provides panoramic views over the surrounding countryside and good drainage makes it playable for most of the year. Societies are particularly welcome.
18 holes, 6871yds, Par 72, SSS 73, Course record 65. Club membership 329.

Visitors handicap certificate required, tee reservation available 7 days in advance. **Societies** apply by telephone in advance. **Green Fees** £22.50 per 18 holes (£27.50 weekends). **Cards** 🌐 💳 📇 📠 📶 💲 **Prof** M & N Moore/P Jones **Course Designer** Martin Hawtree **Facilities** ⊗ ⊪ 🍴 ♨ ♀ ♿ 🏠 🛒 🎣 🗑 🚬 ⚷ **Leisure** heated outdoor swimming pool.**Conf** Max 250 Thtr 250 Class 150 Board 36 Banquet 240 Del from £48 * **Location** 2m SE of Harrogate town centre, off A658 follow brown tourist signs

continued

Hotel ★★★★ 78% Rudding Park Hotel & Golf, Rudding Park, Follifoot, HARROGATE ☎ 01423 871350 50 en suite

KIRKBYMOORSIDE   Map 08 SE68

Kirkbymoorside Manor Vale YO62 6EG
☎ 01751 431525 ▤ 01751 433190
e-mail: info@kirkbymoorsidegolf.co.uk
Hilly parkland course with narrow fairways, gorse and hawthorn bushes. Beautiful views.
18 holes, 6101yds, Par 69, SSS 69, Course record 65. Club membership 650.
Visitors are advised to contact in advance, may not play before 9.30 or between 12.30-1.30. **Societies** must apply in advance. **Green Fees** not confirmed. **Cards** 🌐 💳 📇 📠 📶 **Prof** Chris Tyson **Facilities** ⊗ ⊪ 🍴 ♨ ♀ 🏠 🛒 ⚷ **Leisure** gymnasium. **Location** N side of village

Hotel ★★ 66% George & Dragon Hotel, 17 Market Place, KIRKBYMOORSIDE ☎ 01751 433334
11 en suite 7 annexe en suite

KNARESBOROUGH   Map 08 SE35

Knaresborough Boroughbridge Rd HG5 0QQ
☎ 01423 862690 ▤ 01423 869345
e-mail: knaresboroughgolfclub@btopenworld.com
Pleasant and well presented parkland course in rural setting with excellent views on the back nine.
18 holes, 6413yds, Par 70, SSS 71, Course record 65. Club membership 802.
Visitors restricted start times summer weekends. **Societies** apply by telephone or letter. **Green Fees** £35.50 per day; £28.50 per round (£40.50/£35.50 weekends). **Prof** Gary J Vickers **Course Designer** Hawtree **Facilities** ⊗ ⊪ 🍴 ♨ ♀ ♿ 🏠 🚬 ⚷ **Location** 1.25 N on A6055

Hotel ★★★ 70% Dower House Hotel, Bond End, KNARESBOROUGH ☎ 01423 863302
28 en suite 3 annexe en suite

MALTON   Map 08 SE77

Malton & Norton Welham Park, Norton YO17 9QE
☎ 01653 697912 ▤ 01653 697912
e-mail: maltonandnorton@btconnect.com
Parkland course, consisting of 3 nine hole loops, with panoramic views of the moors. Very testing 1st hole (564 yds dog-leg, left) on the Welham course.
Welham Course: 18 holes, 6456yds, Par 72, SSS 71.
Park Course: 18 holes, 6251yds, Par 72, SSS 70.
Derwent Course: 18 holes, 6295yds, Par 72, SSS 70.
Club membership 825.
Visitors anytime except during competitions, no parties on Saturdays. **Societies** telephone and confirm in writing. **Green Fees** £25 per day/round (£30 weekends & bank holidays). **Cards** 🌐 💳 📇 📠 📶 💲 **Prof** S Robinson **Facilities** ⊗ ⊪ 🍴 ♨ ♀ ♿ 🏠 🛒 🎣 🗑 ⚷ **Location** Approx 20m E of York/0.75m of Malton

Hotel ★★★🔺 72% Burythorpe House Hotel, Burythorpe, MALTON ☎ 01653 658200 11 en suite 5 annexe en suite

MASHAM   Map 08 SE28

Masham Burnholme, Swinton Rd HG4 4HT
☎ 01765 688054 ▤ 01765 688054
Flat parkland course crossed by River Burn, which comes into play on several holes.
9 holes, 6068yds, Par 70, SSS 69, Course record 73. Club membership 327.

continued

Visitors must play with member at weekends & bank holidays. **Societies** write or telephone well in advance. **Green Fees** not confirmed. **Facilities** ⊗ by prior arrangement ⵊ by prior arrangement ⵊ by prior arrangement ♥ by prior arrangement ♀⌂ **Location** 8m from junction of B6267 off A1 signposted Thirsk/Masham. Then 1m SW off A6108

Hotel ★ 69% Buck Inn, THORNTON WATLASS
☎ 01677 422461 7 rms (5 en suite)

<hr/>

MIDDLESBROUGH   Map 08 NZ41

Middlesbrough Brass Castle Ln, Marton TS8 9EE
☎ 01642 311515 ▤ 01642 319607
e-mail: golf@brass45.fsbusiness.co.uk
Undulating wooded parkland course, prevailing winds. Testing 6th, 12th and 15th holes.
18 holes, 6278yds, Par 70, SSS 70, Course record 63.
Club membership 780.
Visitors restricted Tue & Sat. **Societies** Wed, Thu & Fri only. Must contact the club in advance. **Green Fees** £35 (£40 weekends). **Prof** Don Jones **Course Designer** Baird **Facilities** ⊗ ⵊ ⵊ ♥ ♀ ⌂ ⛳ ⛳ **Leisure** snooker table. **Conf** Max 40 Del £20 to £30* **Location** 4m S off A172

Hotel ★★★ 71% Parkmore Hotel, 636 Yarm Rd, Eaglescliffe, STOCKTON-ON-TEES
☎ 01642 786815 55 en suite

Middlesbrough Municipal Ladgate Ln TS5 7YZ
☎ 01642 315513 ▤ 01642 300726
Parkland course with good views. The front nine holes have wide fairways and large, often well-guarded greens while the back nine demand shots over tree-lined water hazards and narrow entrances to subtly contoured greens. Driving range.
18 holes, 6333yds, Par 71, SSS 70, Course record 67.
Club membership 630.
Visitors book on the day weekdays, 7days in advance for weekends & bank holidays. **Societies** apply in writing giving at least 2 weeks in advance. **Green Fees** terms on application. **Prof** Alan Hope **Course Designer** Shuttleworth **Facilities** ⵊ ♥ ♀ ⌂ ⛳ ⛳ ♥ ⛳ ♥ ⛳ **Location** 2m S of Middlesbrough on the A174

Hotel ★★★ 71% Parkmore Hotel, 636 Yarm Rd, Eaglescliffe, STOCKTON-ON-TEES
☎ 01642 786815 55 en suite

<hr/>

NORTHALLERTON   Map 08 SE39

Romanby Yafforth Rd DL7 0PE
☎ 01609 779988 ▤ 01609 779084
e-mail: grant@romanbygolf.co.uk
Set in natural undulating terrain with the River Wiske meandering through the course it offers a testing round of golf for all abilities. In addition to the river, two lakes come into play on the 2nd, 5th and 11th holes. 12-bay floodlit driving range.
18 holes, 6663yds, Par 72, SSS 72, Course record 72.
Club membership 575.
Visitors welcome everyday please book tee time in advance. **Societies** contact Grant McDonnell for details, tel 01609 778855. **Green Fees** £30 per day; £25 per round (£36/£30 weekends). **Cards** ▭ ▭ ▭ ▭ **Prof** Tim Jenkins **Course Designer** Will Adamson **Facilities** ⊗ ⵊ ⵊ ♥ ♀ ⌂ ⌂ ♥ ♥ ⛳ ♥ ⛳ **Leisure** 6 hole par 3 academy course. **Conf** Max 90 Thtr 90 Class 60 Board 40 Banquet 108 Del £5 to £20 * **Location** On the main Northallerton/Richmond road B6271, 1m W of Northallerton

Hotel ★★ 64% The Golden Lion, High St, NORTHALLERTON ☎ 01609 777411 25 en suite

<hr/>

PANNAL   Map 08 SE35

Pannal Follifoot Rd HG3 1ES
☎ 01423 872628 ▤ 01423 870043
e-mail: secretary@pannalgc.co.uk
Fine championship course. Moorland turf but well-wooded with trees closely involved with play. Excellent views enhance the course.
18 holes, 6622yds, Par 72, SSS 72, Course record 62.
Club membership 780.
Visitors preferable to contact in advance, weekends limited. **Societies** apply in advance. **Green Fees** £51 per day; £41 per round (£51 per round weekends & bank holidays). **Cards** ▭ ▭ ▭ ▭ ▭ **Prof** David Padgett **Course Designer** Sandy Herd **Facilities** ⊗ ⵊ ⵊ ♥ ♀ ⌂ ⌂ ♥ ⛳ ♥ ⛳ **Leisure** snooker. **Location** E side of village off A61

Hotel ★★★ 68% The Imperial, Prospect Place, HARROGATE ☎ 01423 565071 83 en suite

<hr/>

RAVENSCAR   Map 08 NZ90

Raven Hall Hotel Golf Course YO13 0ET
☎ 01723 870353 ▤ 01723 870072
9 holes, 1894yds, Par 32, SSS 32.
Location Situated on cliff top
Telephone for further details

Hotel ★★★ 66% Raven Hall Country House Hotel & Golf Course, RAVENSCAR ☎ 01723 870353 53 en suite

<hr/>

REDCAR   Map 08 NZ62

Cleveland Majuba Rd TS10 5BJ
☎ 01642 471798 ▤ 01642 471798
e-mail: peterfletcher@clevelandgolf.fa.co.uk
The oldest golf club in Yorkshire playing over the only links championship course in Yorkshire. A true test of traditional golf, especially when windy. Flat seaside links with easy walking.
18 holes, 6700yds, Par 72, SSS 72, Course record 67.
Club membership 820.
Visitors advisable to book in advance. **Societies** initially telephone for details. **Green Fees** terms on application. **Prof** Craig Donaldson **Facilities** ⊗ ⵊ ⵊ ♥ ♀ ⌂ **Location** 8m E of Middlesborough, at N end of Redcar

Hotel ★★★🌢 71% Grinkle Park Hotel, EASINGTON ☎ 01287 640515 20 en suite

Wilton Wilton TS10 4QY ☎ 01642 465265 (Secretary) & 452730 (Prof) ▤ 01642 465463
Parkland course with some fine views.
18 holes, 6126yds, Par 70, SSS 69, Course record 64.
Club membership 750.
Visitors telephone professional 01642 452730 to check availability, no visitors Saturday, Ladies competition have priority Tuesday, tee off 10am or later. **Societies** must telephone secretary in advance. **Green Fees** not confirmed. **Prof** P D Smillie **Facilities** ⊗ ⵊ by prior arrangement ⵊ ♥ ♀ ⌂ ⌂ ♥ **Leisure** snooker. **Location** 3m W of Redcar, on A174

Hotel ★★★🌢 71% Grinkle Park Hotel, EASINGTON ☎ 01287 640515 20 en suite

continued

Hunley Hall Golf Club & Hotel

BROTTON,
SALTBURN,
NORTH
YORKSHIRE
TS12 2QQ

Modern hotel situated amid rolling countryside by the Heritage Coast with unrivalled panoramic views and overlooking our own 27 hole golf course. The course incorporates lakes and ponds to provide exciting and challenging courses giving players of all levels and abilities a rewarding and enjoyable game. Golf breaks from £138.00 including two nights D,B&B and three days unlimited mid-week golf.

**For reservations/enquiries please call
01287 676216 Fax: 01287 678250
E-mail: enquiries@hunleyhall.co.uk
website www.hunleyhall.co.uk**

RICHMOND Map 07 NZ10

Richmond Bend Hagg DL10 5EX
☎ 01748 823231(Secretary) 📠 01748 821709
Undulating parkland course. Ideal to play 27 holes, not too testing but very interesting.
18 holes, 5886yds, Par 70, SSS 68, Course record 63.
Club membership 600.
Visitors may not play before 3.30am on Sun. Societies must contact in writing or telephone 01748 822457. Green Fees £22 per day; £20 per round (£30/25 weekends). Prof Paul Jackson Course Designer P Pennink Facilities ⊗ 🎿 🍴 ⛳ 🏌 ⚑ 🏌 🖧 🏌 Location 0.75m N, 4 miles from Scotch Corner.
....
Hotel ★★ 68% King's Head Hotel, Market Place, RICHMOND ☎ 01748 850220 26 en suite 4 annexe en suite

RIPON Map 08 SE37

Ripon City Palace Rd HG4 3HH
☎ 01765 603640 📠 01765 692880
e-mail: office@ripongolf.com
Moderate walking on undulating parkland course; two testing par 3's at 5th and 14th.
18 holes, 6084yds, Par 70, SSS 69, Course record 66.
Club membership 750.
Visitors book with professional. No play Saturdays,limited play Sundays. Societies contact in writing or telephone. Green Fees terms on application. Prof S T Davis Course Designer H Varden Facilities ⊗ 🎿 🍴 ⛳ 🏌 🏌 🖧 🏌 🏌 Location 1m NW on A6108
....
Hotel ★★★ 69% Ripon Spa Hotel, Park St, RIPON ☎ 01765 602172 40 en suite

SALTBURN-BY-THE-SEA Map 08 NZ62

Hunley Hall Golf Club & Hotel Ings Ln, Brotton TS12 2QQ ☎ 01287 676216 📠 01287 678250
e-mail: enquiries@hunleyhall.co.uk
A picturesque 27 hole coastal course with panoramic views of the countryside and coastline, providing a good test of golf and a rewarding game for all abilities.
Morgans: 18 holes, 6918yds, Par 73, SSS 73, Course record 67.
Millennium: 18 holes, 5948yds, Par 68, SSS 68, Course record 67.
Jubilee: 18 holes, 6292yds, Par 71, SSS 70, Course record 66.
Club membership 500.
Visitors tee off times must be reserved in advance, times available between 9.30-11.30am and after 1pm. Societies telephone for information and availability. Green Fees £20 per day (£30 weekends & bank holidays). Cards 🖃 🖃 💳 🖃 🖃 🖃 Prof Andrew Brook Course Designer John Morgan Facilities ⊗ 🎿 🎿 🍴 ♀ 🏌 🍴 🏌 🏌 ⚑ 🏌 🖧 🏌 🏌 Conf Max 110 Thtr 70 Class 50 Board 24 Banquet 110 Del £5 to £11.35 * Location From A174 in Brotton take St Margarets Way,700 yds to club
....
Hotel ★★ 63% Hunley Hall Golf Club & Hotel, Ings Ln, Brotton, SALTBURN ☎ 01287 676216 8 en suite

Saltburn by the Sea Hob Hill, Guisborough Rd TS12 1NJ ☎ 01287 622812 📠 01287 625988
Undulating meadowland course surrounded by woodland. Particularly attractive in autumn. There are fine views of the Cleveland Hills and of Tees Bay.
18 holes, 5846yds, Par 70, SSS 68, Course record 62.
Club membership 900.
Visitors telephone in advance, no visitors on Saturday. Societies apply in writing. Green Fees not confirmed. Prof Mike Nutter Course Designer J Braid Facilities 🎿 🍴 ♀ 🏌 🍴 🏌 Location 0.5m out of Saltburn on Guisborough road
....
Hotel ★★★🏌 71% Grinkle Park Hotel, EASINGTON ☎ 01287 640515 20 en suite

SCARBOROUGH Map 08 TA08

Scarborough North Cliff North Cliff Av YO12 6PP
☎ 01723 360786 📠 01723 362134
Seaside course beginning on cliff top overlooking North bay and castle winding inland through parkland with stunning views of the North Yorkshire Moors.
18 holes, 6425yds, Par 71, SSS 71, Course record 66.
Club membership 895.
Visitors must be member of a club with handicap certificate. May not play before 10.30am Sun. Societies prior booking with secretary for parties of 8-40. Green Fees £28 per day; £22 per round (£30/£25 weekends and bank holidays). Prof
continued

Simon N Deller **Course Designer** James Braid **Facilities** ⊗
〣 ⊾ ♨ ♀ ♨ 🏠 ⚑ ↘ ⚏ **Location** 2m N of town centre
off A165

· ·

Hotel ★★★ 65% Esplanade Hotel, Belmont Rd,
SCARBOROUGH ☎ 01723 360382 73 en suite

Scarborough South Cliff Deepdale Av YO11 2UE
☎ 01723 374737
Parkland/seaside course designed by Dr McKenzie.
18 holes, 6039yds, Par 70, SSS 69, Course record 66.
Club membership 700.
Visitors contact in advance may not play before 9.30am
Mon-Fri, 10am Sat and 10.30am Sun. **Societies** must contact
Secretary in advance. **Green Fees** terms on application. **Prof**
Tony Skingle **Course Designer** McKenzie **Facilities** ⊗ 〣 ⊾
♨ ♀ ♨ 🏠 ⚑ ⚏ **Location** 1m S on A165

· ·

Hotel ★★ 65% Bradley Court Hotel, Filey Rd, South Cliff,
SCARBOROUGH ☎ 01723 360476 40 en suite

Selby Brayton Barff YO8 9LD
☎ 01757 228622 📠 01757 228622
e-mail: selbygolfclub@hotmail.com
Mainly flat, links-type course; prevailing SW wind.
Testing holes including the 3rd, 7th and 16th.
18 holes, 6374yds, Par 71, SSS 71, Course record 63.
Club membership 840.
Visitors contact professional on 01757 228785, members
and guests only at weekends. **Societies** welcome Mon-Fri,
must apply in advance. **Green Fees** terms on application.
Prof Andrew Smith **Course Designer** J Taylor & Hawtree
Facilities ⊗ 〣 ⊾ ♨ ♀ ♨ 🏠 ⚑ ⚏ **Location** Off A19 at
Brayton

· ·

Hotel ★★★🏨 70% Monk Fryston Hall Hotel, MONK
FRYSTON ☎ 01977 682369 30 en suite

Settle Buckhaw Brow, Giggleswick BD24 0DH
☎ 01729 825288 📠 01729 825288
Picturesque parkland course with stream affecting play
on four holes.
9 holes, 5414yds, Par 68, SSS 66, Course record 59.
Club membership 380.
Visitors may not play before 4pm on Sun. **Societies** apply in
writing or telephone 4 weeks in advance. **Green Fees** not
confirmed. **Course Designer** Tom Vardon **Facilities** ♨
Location 1m N on A65

· ·

Inn ♦♦♦♦ Golden Lion, 5 Duke St, SETTLE
☎ 01729 822203 12 rms (10 en suite)

Skipton Off North West By-Pass BD23 3LF
☎ 01756 795657 📠 01756 796665
e-mail: enquiries@skiptongolfclub.co.uk
Undulating parkland course with some water hazards
and panoramic views.
18 holes, 6049yds, Par 70, SSS 69, Course record 67.
Club membership 800.
Visitors welcome by prior arrangement,may not play
weekends **Societies** must apply in writing. **Green Fees** £24
per day (£26 weekends). **Prof** Peter Robinson **Facilities** ⊗
〣 ⊾ ♨ ♀ ♨ 🏠 ⚑ ⚏ **Leisure** snooker. **Location** 1m N of
Skipton on A59

continued

Hotel ★★★ The Devonshire Arms Country House Hotel,
BOLTON ABBEY ☎ 01756 710441 41 en suite

Cocksford Cocksford, Stutton LS24 9NG
☎ 01937 834253 📠 01937 834253
e-mail: enquiries@cocksfordgolfclub.freeserve.co.uk
The course is set on undulating meadowland with the
famous Cock Beck featuring on 8 of the original 18 holes.
Whatever combination you choose the course is relatively
short featuring a number of drivable par 4s, but beware
danger surrounds many of the greens!
Old Course: 18 holes, 5570yds, Par 71, SSS 69,
Course record 68.
Club membership 450.
Visitors welcome, contact pro shop. **Societies** telephone the
secretary. **Green Fees** terms on application. **Prof** Graham
Thompson **Facilities** ⊗ 〣 ⊾ ♨ ♀ ♨ 🏠 ⚑ ⚏ **Location**
Between York & Leeds, adjacent to the village of Stutton

· ·

Hotel ★★★🏨 73% Wood Hall Hotel, Trip Ln, Linton,
WETHERBY ☎ 01937 587271
15 en suite 27 annexe en suite

Scarthingwell Scarthingwell LS24 9PF
☎ 01937 557864 (pro) 557878 (club) 📠 01937 557909
Testing water hazards and well placed bunkers and trees
provide a challenging test of golf for all handicaps at this
scenic parkland course.
18 holes, 6771yds, Par 72, SSS 72.
Club membership 500.
Visitors dress code must be adhered to. May play anytime
midweek and sundays,after 2.00pm saturdays. **Societies** golf
packages available, book one month in advance. **Green Fees**
terms on application. **Prof** Steve Footman **Facilities** ⊗ 〣 ⊾
♨ ♀ ♨ 🏠 ⚏ **Conf** Banquet 90 **Location** 4m S of
Tadcaster on the A162 Tadcaster/Ferrybridge road, approx
2m from the A1

· ·

Hotel ★★★ 77% Hazlewood Castle, Paradise Ln,
Hazlewood, TADCASTER ☎ 01937 535353
9 en suite 12 annexe en suite

Thirsk & Northallerton Thornton-le-Street
YO7 4AB ☎ 01845 522170 & 525115 📠 01845 525115
The course has good views of the nearby Hambleton Hills
to the east and Wensleydale to the west. Testing course,
mainly flat land.
18 holes, 6495yds, Par 72, SSS 71.
Club membership 500.
Visitors must telephone in advance, and have handicap
certificate. No play Sun unless with member. **Societies** must
apply in writing. **Green Fees** £28 per day; £22 per round
(£33/£28 weekends). **Prof** Robert Garner **Course Designer**
ADAS **Facilities** ⊗ 〣 ⊾ ♨ ♀ ♨ 🏠 ⚑ ⚒ ⚏ **Location**
2m N on A168

· ·

Hotel ★★ 62% Three Tuns Hotel, Market Place, THIRSK
☎ 01845 523124 10 en suite

Whitby Low Straggleton, Sandsend Rd YO21 3SR
☎ 01947 600660 📠 01947 600660
e-mail: whitby-golf-club@compuserve.com
Seaside course with 4 holes along cliff tops and over
ravines. Good views and fresh sea breeze.

continued

18 holes, 6134yds, Par 71, Course record 66.
Club membership 800.
Visitors may not play on competition days, parties must contact in advance. Societies must contact in writing. Green Fees not confirmed. Prof Tony Mason Facilities ⊗ ⽶ ⅃ ♨ ♀ ♣ ⌂ ⚑ ⚬ Location 1.5m NW on A174

Hotel ★★ 68% White House Hotel, Upgang Ln, West Cliff, WHITBY ☎ 01947 600469 10 en suite

YORK   Map 08 SE65

Forest of Galtres Moorlands Rd, Skelton YO32 2RF
☎ 01904 766198 📠 01904 769400
Level parkland course in the heart of the ancient Forest of Galtres with mature oak trees and interesting water features coming into play on the 6th, 14th and 17th holes. Views towards York Minster.
18 holes, 6412yds, Par 72, SSS 70, Course record 62.
Club membership 450.
Visitors telephone to book, may play anytime. Societies not Sat, booking system, telephone for forms. Green Fees £25 per day; £20 per round (£32/£27 weekends & bank holidays). Prof Phil Bradley Course Designer Simon Gidman Facilities ⊗ ⽶ by prior arrangement ⅃ ♨ ♀ ♣ ⌂ ⚑ ⚬ ♣ Location 0.5m from the York ring road B1237, just off A19 Thirsk road through the village of Skelton

Hotel ★★ 70% Beechwood Close Hotel, 19 Shipton Rd, Clifton, YORK ☎ 01904 658378 14 en suite

Forest Park Stockton-on-the-Forest YO32 9UW
☎ 01904 400425 & 400688 📠 01904 400717
A parkland/meadowland course with natural features including a stream and mature and new trees.
Old Foss Course: 18 holes, 6600yds, Par 71, SSS 72, Course record 73.
The West Course: 9 holes, 3186yds, Par 70, SSS 70.
Club membership 600.
Visitors welcome, subject to tee availability. Advisable to contact club in advance. Societies by prior arrangement. Green Fees terms on application. Cards ▨ ▦ ▢ Facilities ⊗ ⅃ ♨ ♀ ♣ ⌂ ⚑ ⚬ ♣ Location 4m NE of York, 1.5m from end of A64, York bypass

Hotel ★★★ 72% York Pavilion Hotel, 45 Main St, Fulford, YORK ☎ 01904 622099 57 en suite

> ### Fulford Heslington Ln YO10 5DY
> ☎ 01904 413579 📠 01904 416918
> e-mail: info@fulfordgolfclub.co.uk
> A flat, parkland/moorland course well-known for the superb quality of its turf, particularly the greens, and now famous as the venue for some of the best golf tournaments in the British Isles, in past years.
> 18 holes, 6775yds, Par 72, SSS 72, Course record 62.
> Club membership 775.
> Visitors must contact in advance. Societies not Tue am, book with the manager. Green Fees £48 per day; £37 per round. Prof Martin Brown Course Designer Dr Mckenzie Facilities ⊗ ⽶ ⅃ ♨ ♀ ♣ ⌂ ⚑ ⚬ Location 2m S of York off A19
>
> Hotel ★★★★ 66% York Marriott Hotel, Tadcaster Rd, YORK ☎ 01904 701000 108 en suite

Heworth Muncaster House, Muncastergate YO31 9JY
☎ 01904 422389 📠 01904 426156
e-mail: golf@heworth-gc.fsnet.co.uk
12-hole parkland course, easy walking. Holes 3 to 7 and 9 played twice from different tees.   continued

12 holes, 6141yds, Par 70, SSS 69, Course record 68.
Club membership 550.
Visitors advisable to telephone the professional in advance, no catering Mondays Societies apply in writing/telephone professional 01904 422389 Green Fees £18 per day; £14 per round (£20/£18 weekends). Prof Stephen Burdett Course Designer B Cheal Facilities ⊗ ⽶ ⅃ ♨ ♀ ♣ ⌂ ⚑ ⚬ Location 1.5m NE of city centre on A1036

Hotel ★★★ 66% Monkbar Hotel, Monkbar, YORK ☎ 01904 638086 99 en suite

Swallow Hall Crockey Hill YO19 4SG
☎ 01904 448889 📠 01904 448219
e-mail: jtscores@hotmail.com
A small 18-hole, par 3 course with 2 par 4s. Attached to a caravan park and holiday cottages.
18 holes, 3600yds, Par 56, SSS 56, Course record 58.
Club membership 100.
Visitors no restrictions. Societies must telephone in advance. Green Fees not confirmed. Course Designer Brian Henry Facilities ⊗ ⽶ ⅃ ♨ ♀ ♣ ⌂ ⚑ ⛳ ♣ ♣ Leisure hard tennis courts. Location Off A19, signposted to Wheldrake

Hotel ★★★ 72% York Pavilion Hotel, 45 Main St, Fulford, YORK ☎ 01904 622099 57 en suite

York Lords Moor Ln, Strensall YO32 5XF
☎ 01904 491840 (Sec) 490304 (Pro) 📠 01904 491852
e-mail: secretary@yorkgolfclub.co.uk
A pleasant, well-designed, heathland course with easy walking. The course is of good length but being flat the going does not tire. The course is well bunkered with excellent greens and there are two testing pond holes.
18 holes, 6301yds, Par 70, SSS 70, Course record 66.
Club membership 750.
Visitors with member only weekends, must contact in advance. Societies initial enquiry through professional. Green Fees £30 per 18 holes;£35 per 27 holes;£40 per 36 holes(£40 per 18 holes;£45 per 27 holes weekends and bank holidays). Prof A P Hoyles Course Designer J H Taylor Facilities ⊗ ⽶ ⅃ ♨ ♀ ♣ ⌂ ⚬ Location 6m NE of York, E of Strensall village

Hotel ★★★ 75% Dean Court Hotel, Duncombe Place, YORK ☎ 01904 625082 39 en suite

YORKSHIRE, SOUTH

BARNSLEY   Map 08 SE30

Barnsley Wakefield Rd, Staincross S75 6JZ
☎ 01226 382856 📠 01226 382856
Undulating municipal parkland course with easy walking apart from last 4 holes. Testing 8th and 18th holes.
18 holes, 5951yds, Par 69, SSS 69, Course record 64.
Club membership 450.
Visitors booking advisable, telephone professional on 01226 380358. Societies by arrangement,contact club professional at 01226 380358 Green Fees terms on application. Prof Shaun Wyke Facilities ⊗ by prior arrangement ⽶ by prior arrangement ⅃ by prior arrangement ♨ ♀ ♣ ⌂ ⚑ ⚬ Location 3m N on A61

Hotel ★★★ 72% Ardsley House Hotel & Health Club, Doncaster Rd, Ardsley, BARNSLEY ☎ 01226 309955 74 en suite

Sandhill Middlecliffe Ln, Little Houghton S72 0HW
☎ 01226 753444 📠 01226 753444
The course is reasonably flat with generously wide fairways laid out between and amongst 25 acres of newly planted woodlands. Holes of note are the 4th which is a 311 yard par 4 to a horseshoe green around a 9-foot deep bunker; the 7th par 3 to blind reverse Mackenzie Green and the 11th 416 yard par 4 dogleg where the brave can take on the out of bounds.
18 holes, 6257yds, Par 71, SSS 70, Course record 69.
Club membership 375.
Visitors welcome by prior booking. **Societies** telephone for availability, write to confirm. **Green Fees** not confirmed.
Cards 💳 💳 💳 💳 💳 **Course Designer** John Royston
Facilities ⊗ ⅄ 🏌 🍷 ♨ 🏠 🏧 **Location** 5m E of Barnsley, off A635
· ·
Hotel ★★★ 72% Ardsley House Hotel & Health Club, Doncaster Rd, Ardsley, BARNSLEY
☎ 01226 309955 74 en suite

Bawtry Golf & Country Club Cross Ln, Austerfield DN10 6RF ☎ 01302 710841 📠 01302 710850
Championship moorland course featuring the 618 yard 7th and the Postage Stamp 8th. Well drained and easy walking with attached driving range.
18 holes, 6900yds, Par 73, SSS 73, Course record 67.
Club membership 500.
Visitors no restrictions. **Societies** must contact in advance.
Green Fees £14 (£18 weekends and bank holidays). **Prof** Selby-Green **Facilities** ⊗ ⅄ 🏌 🍷 ♨ 🏠 🏐 🏧 🏧 **Conf** Max 150 Banquet 150 **Location** 2m from Bawtry on A614
· ·
Hotel ★★★ 63% The Crown Hotel, High St, BAWTRY
☎ 01302 710341 57 en suite

Crookhill Park Municipal Carr Ln DN12 2AH
☎ 01709 862979 📠 01709 866455
A naturally sloping parkland course with many holes featuring tight dog-legs and small, undulating greens. The signature hole (11th) involves a fearsome tee shot over a ditch onto a sloping fairway and final shot to an elevated green surrounded by tall trees and deep bunkers.
18 holes, 5849yds, Par 70, SSS 68, Course record 64.
Club membership 350.
Visitors booking system for general play. **Societies** bookings taken in advance, deposits taken through booking system.
Green Fees £9.70 (£10.95 weekends). **Prof** Richard Swaine **Facilities** 🏌 🍷 ♨ 🏠 🏧 **Location** 1.5m SE on B6094
· ·
Hotel ★★★ 65% Danum Hotel, High St, DONCASTER
☎ 01302 342261 66 en suite

Doncaster 278 Bawtry Rd, Bessacarr DN4 7PD
☎ 01302 865632 📠 01302 865994
e-mail: doncastergolf@aol.com
Pleasant undulating heathland course with wooded surroundings. Quick drying, ideal all year round course.
18 holes, 6220yds, Par 69, SSS 70, Course record 66.
Club membership 500.
Visitors must contact in advance for both weekdays and weekends. **Societies** must contact in advance. **Green Fees** £36 per day; £30 per round. **Prof** Graham Bailey **Course Designer** Mackenzie/Hawtree **Facilities** ⊗ ⅄ 🏌 🍷 ♨ 🏠 🏐 🏧 **Location** 4m SE on A638
continued

· ·
Hotel ★★★ 73% Mount Pleasant Hotel, Great North Rd, ROSSINGTON ☎ 01302 868696 & 868219
📠 01302 865130 42 en suite

Doncaster Town Moor Bawtry Rd, Belle Vue DN4 5HU ☎ 01302 535286 & 533167 📠 01302 533778
e-mail: dtmgc@townmoorgolfclub.fsbusiness.co.uk
Easy walking, but testing, heathland course with good true greens. Friendly club. Notable hole is 11th (par 4), 464 yds. Situated in centre of racecourse.
18 holes, 6072yds, Par 69, SSS 69, Course record 63.
Club membership 520.
Visitors may not play on Sun morning. Contact in advance.
Societies must contact in advance. **Green Fees** £18 per 18 holes, £22 per 36 holes (£20 per 18 holes weekend). **Prof** Steven Shaw **Facilities** ⊗ ⅄ 🏌 🍷 ♨ 🏠 🏧 **Conf** Max 70 **Location** 1.5m E, at racecourse, on A638
· ·
Hotel ★★★ 65% Danum Hotel, High St, DONCASTER
☎ 01302 342261 66 en suite

Owston Park Owston Ln, Owston DN6 8EF
☎ 01302 330821
e-mail: will@owstonpark.fsnet.co.uk
A flat easy walking course surrounded by woodland. A lot of mature trees and a few ditches in play. A practice putting green and chipping area.
9 holes, 2866yds, Par 35, SSS 70.
Visitors no restrictions. **Societies** telephone in advance.
Green Fees terms on application. **Cards** 💳 💳 💳 💳 💳 **Prof** Mike Parker **Course Designer** M Parker **Facilities** 🍷 ♨ 🏠 🏐 🏧 **Location** 5m N of Doncaster off A19
· ·
Hotel ★★★ 65% Danum Hotel, High St, DONCASTER
☎ 01302 342261 66 en suite

Thornhurst Park Holme Ln, Owston DN5 0LR
☎ 01302 337799 📠 01302 721495
e-mail: info@thornhurst.co.uk
Surrounded by Owston Wood, this scenic parkland course has numerous strategically placed bunkers, and a lake comes into play at the 7th and 8th holes.
18 holes, 6490yds, Par 72, SSS 72, Course record 72.
Club membership 160.
Visitors must wear trousers, shirt with collar and golf shoes, can contact 2 days in advance. **Societies** telephone or write in advance. **Green Fees** £10 per 18 holes; £5 per 9 holes (£12/£6 weekends & bank holidays). **Cards** 💳 💳 💳 💳 💳 **Prof** Kevin Pearce **Facilities** ⊗ ⅄ 🏌 🍷 ♨ 🏐 🏧 **Conf** Max 100 **Location** On the A19 between Bentley/Askern, easy access from M62 and A1(M)
· ·
Hotel ★★★ 65% Danum Hotel, High St, DONCASTER
☎ 01302 342261 66 en suite

Wheatley Armthorpe Rd DN2 5QB
☎ 01302 831655 📠 01302 812736
Fairly flat well-bunkered, lake-holed, parkland course. Well-drained, in excellent condition all year round.
18 holes, 6405yds, Par 71, SSS 71, Course record 64.
Club membership 600.
Visitors Must contact in advance. **Societies** must contact professional in advance. **Green Fees** £27 per round (£35 weekends). **Cards** 💳 💳 💳 💳 💳 **Prof** Steven Fox **Course Designer** George Duncan **Facilities** ⊗ ⅄ 🏌 🍷 ♨ 🏠 🏧 **Location** NE side of town centre off A18
continued

Hotel ★★★ 66% Regent Hotel, Regent Square, DONCASTER ☎ 01302 364180 50 en suite

HATFIELD   Map 08 SE60

Kings Wood Thorne Rd DN7 6EP ☎ 01405 741343
A flat course with ditches that come into play on several holes, especially on the testing back nine. Notable holes are the 12th par 4, 16th and par 5 18th. Water is a prominent feature with several large lakes strategically placed.
18 holes, 6002yds, Par 70, SSS 69, Course record 69.
Club membership 100.
Visitors visitors are welcome any time. **Societies** or telephone in advance. **Green Fees** £7 per 18 holes; £4 per 9 holes(£8/£4.50 weekends). **Cards** 🔳 🔳 🔳 🔳 🔳 🌀 **Prof** Jonathan Drury **Course Designer** John Hunt **Facilities** 🔳 🏠 ⛳ ℐ **Location** 2m SW of junct 1 of M180, take A614 to Thorne, then Thorne road to Hatfield

Hotel ★★ 71% Belmont Hotel, Horsefair Green, THORNE ☎ 01405 812320 23 en suite

HICKLETON   Map 08 SE40

Hickleton Lidgett Ln DN5 7BE
☎ 01709 896081 🗎 01709 896083
e-mail: hickleton@hickletongolfclub.freeserve.co.uk
Undulating, picturesque parkland course designed by Neil Coles and Brian Huggett offering a good test of golf.
18 holes, 6434yds, Par 71, SSS 71, Course record 68.
Club membership 625.
Visitors weekdays after 9am & weekends after 2.30pm. Must contact in advance. **Societies** must contact in advance. **Green Fees** not confirmed. **Prof** Paul J Audsley **Course Designer** Huggett/Coles **Facilities** ⊗ 🔳 🏠 🔳 ♀ ℒ 🏠 ⛳ 🐾 ℐ **Location** 0.5m W on B6411

Hotel ★★★ 65% Danum Hotel, High St, DONCASTER ☎ 01302 342261 66 en suite

HIGH GREEN   Map 08 SK39

Tankersley Park S35 4LG
☎ 0114 246 8247 🗎 0114 245 7818
Rolling parkland course that demands accuracy rather than length. Lush fairways. A good test of golf.
18 holes, 6212yds, Par 69, SSS 70, Course record 64.
Club membership 634.
Visitors must contact in advance. **Societies** must apply in writing. **Green Fees** £36 per day; £27 per round. **Cards** 🔳 🔳 🔳 🔳 🔳 **Prof** Ian Kirk **Course Designer** Hawtree **Facilities** ⊗ 🔳 🏠 🔳 ♀ ℒ 🏠 ⛳ 🐾 ℐ **Location** Off A61/M1 onto A616, Stocksbridge bypass

Hotel ★★★ 69% Tankersley Manor, Church Ln, TANKERSLEY ☎ 01226 744700 70 en suite

RAWMARSH   Map 08 SK49

Wath Abdy Ln S62 7SJ
☎ 01709 878609 🗎 01709 877097
e-mail: wathgolf@aol.com
Parkland course, not easy in spite of its length; 17th hole (par 3) is a difficult 244yds with narrow driving area.
18 holes, 6123yds, Par 70, SSS 69.
Club membership 680.
Visitors must play with member at weekends. Must contact in advance and have a handicap certificate. **Societies** must contact in writing, may not play at weekends. **Green Fees**

continued

£25 per day; £18 per round. **Prof** Chris Bassett **Facilities** ⊗ 🔳 🏠 🔳 ♀ ℒ 🏠 🐾 🔩 ℐ **Location** 2m N of Rotherham on B6089

Hotel ★★★ 60% Carlton Park Hotel, 102/104 Moorgate Rd, ROTHERHAM ☎ 01709 849955 76 en suite

ROTHERHAM   Map 08 SK49

Grange Park Upper Wortley Rd S61 2SJ
☎ 01709 559497
e-mail: crowncourt@bun.com
Parkland/meadowland course, with panoramic views especially from the back nine. The golf is testing, particularly at the 1st, 4th and 18th holes (par 4), and 8th, 12th and 15th (par 5).
18 holes, 6421yds, Par 71, SSS 71, Course record 65.
Club membership 214.
Visitors no restrictions. **Societies** apply in writing to professional. **Green Fees** not confirmed. **Prof** Eric Clark **Course Designer** Fred Hawtree **Facilities** ⊗ 🔳 🏠 🔳 ♀ ℒ 🏠 ⛳ ℐ 𝄆 **Location** 3m NW off A629

Hotel ★★★ 69% Tankersley Manor, Church Ln, TANKERSLEY ☎ 01226 744700 70 en suite

Phoenix Pavilion Ln, Brinsworth S60 5PA
☎ 01709 363634 & 382624 🗎 01709 363788
Undulating meadowland course with variable wind.
18 holes, 6182yds, Par 71, SSS 70, Course record 66.
Club membership 1100.
Visitors must contact in advance. **Societies** must apply in writing. **Green Fees** £24 per day; £18 per round (£32/£24 weekends and bank holidays). **Prof** M Roberts **Course Designer** C K Cotton **Facilities** ⊗ 🔳 🏠 🔳 ♀ ℒ 🏠 ⛳ ℐ 𝄆 **Leisure** hard tennis courts, squash, fishing, gymnasium.**Conf** Max 100 Del £5 to £18 * **Location** E from M1 junct 34 for 0.75m, SW side of town centre off A630

Hotel ★★★ 60% Carlton Park Hotel, 102/104 Moorgate Rd, ROTHERHAM ☎ 01709 849955 76 en suite

Rotherham Golf Club Ltd Thrybergh Park, Doncaster Rd, Thrybergh S65 4NU
☎ 01709 859500 🗎 01709 859517
Parkland course with easy walking along tree-lined fairways.
18 holes, 6324yds, Par 70, SSS 70, Course record 65.
Club membership 500.
Visitors must contact in advance. **Societies** must contact secretary in advance. **Green Fees** terms on application. **Prof** Simon Thornhill **Facilities** ⊗ 🔳 🏠 🔳 ♀ ℒ 🏠 🐾 🔩 ℐ **Location** 3.5m E on A630

Hotel ★★★ 68% Best Western Elton Hotel, Main St, Bramley, ROTHERHAM ☎ 01709 545681 13 en suite 16 annexe en suite

Sitwell Park Shrogswood Rd S60 4BY
☎ 01709 541046 🗎 01709 703637
Parkland course with easy walking.
18 holes, 6229yds, Par 71, SSS 70, Course record 61.
Club membership 450.
Visitors must contact in advance. May not play on Sat. **Societies** must contact in advance. **Green Fees** £30 per day; £25 per round (£35/£30 Sundays). **Prof** Nic Taylor **Course Designer** A MacKenzie **Facilities** ⊗ 🔳 🏠 🔳 ♀ ℒ 🏠 ⛳ 🐾 ℐ

Hotel ★★★★ 64% Hellaby Hall Hotel, Old Hellaby Ln, Hellaby, ROTHERHAM ☎ 01709 702701 52 en suite

SHEFFIELD   Map 08 SK38

Abbeydale Twentywell Ln, Dore S17 4QA
☎ 0114 236 0763 🖹 2360762
e-mail: abbeygolf@compuserve.com
Undulating parkland course set in the Beauchief Estate.
18 holes, 6407yds, Par 72, SSS 71, Course record 64.
Club membership 640.
Societies larger groups must apply in writing, smaller groups
by telephone. **Green Fees** £40 per day; £30 per round (£45
per round/day weekends, £35 after 2.30pm). **Prof** Nigel
Perry **Course Designer** Herbert Fowler **Facilities** ⊗ ⅲ ⓛ
♨ ♀ ♨ ⓔ ♋ ♒ ♒ *Conf* Max 90 **Location** 4m SW of
city centre off A621

Hotel ★★★ 71% Beauchief Hotel, 161 Abbeydale Rd
South, SHEFFIELD ☎ 0114 262 0500 50 en suite

Beauchief Public Abbey Ln S8 0DB
☎ 0114 236 7274
**Pay and play course with natural water hazards. The
rolling land looks west to the Pennines and a 12th-century
abbey adorns the course.**
18 holes, 5469yds, Par 67, SSS 66, Course record 65.
Club membership 450.
Visitors are advised to book in advance. **Societies** telephone
golf reception manager for advice. **Green Fees** £8.50 per
round (£10 weekends & bank holidays). **Cards** ☷ ☷ ☷
☷ ☷ ☷ ☷ **Prof** M C Trippett **Facilities** ⊗ ⅲ ⓛ ♨ ♀ ♨
♨ ⓔ ♋ ♒ ♒ *Conf* Max 50 **Location** 4m SW of city
centre off A621

Hotel ★★★ 71% Beauchief Hotel, 161 Abbeydale Rd
South, SHEFFIELD ☎ 0114 262 0500 50 en suite

Birley Wood Birley Ln S12 3BP ☎ 0114 264 7262
**Undulating meadowland course with well-varied features,
easy walking and good views. Practice range and putting
green.**
*Fairway course: 18 holes, 5647yds, Par 68, SSS 67,
Course record 64.*
Birley Course: 18 holes, 5037, Par 66, SSS 65.
Club membership 300.
Visitors apply in advance. **Societies** apply in advance.
Green Fees £10 per round. **Prof** Peter Ball **Facilities** ♀ ♨
♋ **Location** 4.5m SE of city centre off A616

Hotel ★★★ 66% Mosborough Hall Hotel, High St,
Mosborough, SHEFFIELD ☎ 0114 248 4353 23 en suite

Concord Park Shiregreen Ln S5 6AE
☎ 0114 257 7378
**Hilly municipal parkland course with some fairways
wood-flanked, good views, often windy. Seven par 3 holes.**
18 holes, 4872yds, Par 67, SSS 64, Course record 57.
Club membership 150.
Visitors no restrictions. **Societies** pay & play **Green Fees** £8
per round. **Prof** W Allcroft **Facilities** ⊗ ⅲ ♨ ♀ ♨ ⓔ ♋ ♒
♒ ♒ *Leisure* hard tennis courts, heated indoor swimming
pool, squash, gymnasium. **Location** 3.5m N of city centre on
B6086 off A6135

Hotel ★★★ 61% Holiday Inn Sheffield - West, Manchester
Rd, Broomhill, SHEFFIELD ☎ 0870 400 9071 136 en suite

Dore & Totley Bradway Rd, Bradway S17 4QR
☎ 0114 2366 844 🖹 0114 2366 844
Flat parkland course.
18 holes, 6265yds, Par 70, SSS 70, Course record 65.
Club membership 580.

Visitors must contact in advance a handicap certificate may
be requested, may not play weekends. **Societies** must apply
in writing. **Green Fees** £28 per day; £26 per round (£30
Sunday after 1). **Prof** Gregg Roberts **Facilities** ⊗ ⅲ ⓛ ♨ ♀
♨ ⓔ ♒ ♋ **Location** 7m S of city centre on B6054 off A61

Hotel ★★★ 61% Holiday Inn Sheffield - West, Manchester
Rd, Broomhill, SHEFFIELD ☎ 0870 400 9071 136 en suite

Hallamshire Golf Club Ltd Sandygate S10 4LA
☎ 0114 230 2153 🖹 0114 230 2153
18 holes, 6359yds, Par 71, SSS 71, Course record 63.
Course Designer Various **Location** Off A57 at Crosspool
onto Sandygate Rd, clubhouse 0.75m on right
Telephone for further details

Hotel ★★★ 61% Holiday Inn Sheffield - West,
Manchester Rd, Broomhill, SHEFFIELD
☎ 0870 400 9071 136 en suite

Hillsborough Worrall Rd S6 4BE
☎ 0114 234 9151 (Secretary) & 233 2666 (Pro)
🖹 0114 234 9151
e-mail: admin@hillsboroughgolfclub.co.uk
**Beautiful moorland/woodland course 500 ft above sea-
level, reasonable walking. Challenging first four holes
into a prevailing wind and a tight, testing 14th hole.**
18 holes, 6216yards, Par 71, SSS 70, Course record 64.
Club membership 650.
Visitors contact professional in advance. May not play Tue
(Ladies Day), Thu and weekends before 2pm without prior
arrangement. **Societies** must apply in writing to secretary.
Green Fees £30 per round (£35 weekends). **Prof** Lewis
Horsman **Facilities** ⊗ ⅲ ⓛ ♨ ♀ ♨ ⓔ ♋ ♒ ♒ ♒ ♒
Location 3m NW of city centre off A616

Hotel ★★★ 65% Rutland Hotel, 452 Glossop Rd,
SHEFFIELD ☎ 0870 6003013
63 en suite 13 annexe en suite

Lees Hall Hemsworth Rd, Norton S8 8LL
☎ 0114 255 4402
18 holes, 6171yds, Par 71, SSS 70, Course record 63.
Location 3.5m S of city centre off A6102
Telephone for further details

Hotel ★★★ 61% Holiday Inn Sheffield - West, Manchester
Rd, Broomhill, SHEFFIELD ☎ 0870 400 9071 136 en suite

Rother Valley Golf Centre Mansfield Rd, Wales Bar
S26 5PQ ☎ 0114 247 3000 🖹 0114 247 6000
e-mail: rother@jack-barker.co.uk
**The challenging Blue Monster parkland course features a
variety of water hazards. Notable holes include the 7th,
with its island green fronted by water and dominated by
bunkers to the rear. Lookout for the water on the par 5
18th.**
18 holes, 6602yds, Par 72, SSS 72, Course record 70.
Club membership 500.
Visitors 2 days in advance booking format. **Societies** apply
in writing or telephone in advance. **Green Fees** not
confirmed. **Cards** ☷ ☷ ☷ ☷ **Prof** Jason Ripley
Course Designer Michael Shattock & Mark Roe **Facilities**
⊗ ⅲ ⓛ ♨ ♀ ♨ ⓔ ♋ ♒ ♒ ♒ ♒ **Location** Off junct 31 of
the M1, follow signs to Rother Valley Country Park

Hotel ★★★ 66% Mosborough Hall Hotel, High St,
Mosborough, SHEFFIELD ☎ 0114 248 4353 23 en suite

continued

Tinsley Park Municipal Golf High Hazels Park, Darnall S9 4PE ☎ 0114 2037435
e-mail: tinsleyparkgc@hotmail.com
Undulating meadowland course with plenty of trees and rough. A test for all categories of golfer.
18 holes, 6064yds, Par 70, SSS 68, Course record 66.
Club membership 150.
Visitors prior booking essential. **Societies** apply to professional shop on 0114 2037435 **Green Fees** £10 per round. **Cards** 🖃 🄳 **Prof** A P Highfield **Facilities** ⊗ ⅷ 🏔 🍷 ♀ ♨ 🏠 ⛳ ♂ **Leisure** hard tennis courts. **Location** 4m E of city centre off A630

Hotel ★★★ 66% Mosborough Hall Hotel, High St, Mosborough, SHEFFIELD ☎ 0114 248 4353 23 en suite

Silkstone Field Head, Elmhirst Ln S75 4LD
☎ 01226 790328 🗎 01226 792653
Parkland/downland course, fine views over the Pennines. Testing golf.
18 holes, 6069yds, Par 70, SSS 70, Course record 64.
Club membership 530.
Visitors with member only at weekends. **Societies** contact in advance. **Green Fees** terms on application. **Prof** Kevin Guy **Facilities** ⊗ ⅷ 🏔 🍷 ♀ ♨ 🏠 🕭 🏌 ♂ **Location** 1m E off A628

Hotel ★★★ 72% Ardsley House Hotel & Health Club, Doncaster Rd, Ardsley, BARNSLEY
☎ 01226 309955 74 en suite

Stocksbridge & District Royd Ln, Deepcar S36 2RZ
☎ 0114 288 2003 (office) & 288 2779 (pro)
🗎 0114 283 1460
Hilly moorland course.
18 holes, 5200yds, Par 65, SSS 65, Course record 60.
Club membership 470.
Visitors contact the professional. **Societies** apply to secretary. **Green Fees** terms on application. **Prof** Timothy Brookes **Course Designer** Dave Thomas **Facilities** ⊗ ⅷ 🏔 🍷 ♀ ♨ 🏠 ♂ **Location** S side of town centre

Hotel ★★★ 61% Holiday Inn Sheffield - West, Manchester Rd, Broomhill, SHEFFIELD ☎ 0870 400 9071 136 en suite

Thorne Kirton Ln DN8 5RJ
☎ 01405 812084 🗎 01405 741899
Picturesque parkland course with 6000 newly planted trees. Water hazards on 11th, 14th & 18th holes.
18 holes, 5366yds, Par 68, SSS 66, Course record 62.
Club membership 300.
Visitors no restrictions. **Societies** telephone in advance.
Green Fees not confirmed. **Cards** 🖃 🄲 📷 🄳 **Prof** Edward Highfield **Course Designer** R D Highfield **Facilities** ⊗ ⅷ 🏔 🍷 ♀ ♨ 🏠 🏌 🕭 🕭 ♂ **Location** 8m E of Doncaster

Hotel ★★ 71% Belmont Hotel, Horsefair Green, THORNE ☎ 01405 812320 23 en suite

Wortley Hermit Hill Ln S35 7DF
☎ 0114 288 8469 🗎 0114 288 8469
Well-wooded, undulating parkland course sheltered from prevailing wind.

continued

---

18 holes, 6028yds, Par 69, SSS 68, Course record 62.
Club membership 510.
Visitors may not play between 11.30am and 1pm. Must contact professional in advance and hold a handicap certificate. **Societies** telephone in advance and confirm in writing with deposit. **Green Fees** not confirmed. **Cards** 🖃 🄲 **Prof** Ian Kirk **Facilities** ⊗ ⅷ 🏔 🍷 ♀ ♨ 🏠 🏌 ♂ **Location** 0.5m NE of village off A629

Hotel ★★★ 61% Holiday Inn Sheffield - West, Manchester Rd, Broomhill, SHEFFIELD ☎ 0870 400 9071 136 en suite

Alwoodley Wigton Ln LS17 8SA
☎ 0113 268 1680 🗎 0113 293 9458
e-mail: julie@alwoodleygolfclub.freeserve.co.uk
A fine heathland course with length, trees and abundant heather. Many attractive situations - together a severe test of golf.
18 holes, 6666yds, Par 72, SSS 72.
Club membership 460.
Visitors must contact Secretary in advance. **Societies** must apply in advance. **Green Fees** £60 per day/round (£75 weekends). **Cards** 🖃 🄲 📷 🄳 **Prof** John R Green **Course Designer** Dr Alistair Mackenzie **Facilities** ⊗ ⅷ 🏔 🍷 ♀ ♨ 🏠 🏌 ♂ **Location** 5m N off A61

Hotel ★★★ 66% The Merrion, Merrion Centre, LEEDS ☎ 0113 243 9191 109 en suite

Baildon Moorgate BD17 5PP
☎ 01274 584266 🗎 01274 530551
e-mail: sec@baildongolfclub.freeserve.co.uk
Moorland course set out in links style with outward front nine looping back to clubhouse. Panoramic views with testing short holes in prevailing winds.

18 holes, 6225yds, Par 70, SSS 70, Course record 63.
Club membership 750.
Visitors contact in advance, restricted Tue & weekends.
Societies large numbers apply in writing, small numbers check with the professional. **Green Fees** terms on application. **Prof** Richard Masters **Course Designer** Tom Morris **Facilities** ⊗ ⅷ 🏔 🍷 ♀ ♨ 🏠 🏌 ♂ **Leisure** snooker tables practice net. **Location** 3m N of Bradford, off A6038 at Shipley

Hotel ★★★★ 70% Marriott Hollins Hall Hotel & Country Club, Hollins Hill, Baildon, SHIPLEY ☎ 01274 530053 122 en suite

BINGLEY — Map 07 SE13

Bingley St Ives Golf Club House, St Ives Estate, Harden
BD16 1AT ☎ 01274 562436 📠 01274 511788
e-mail: bingleyst-ives@harden.freeserve.co.uk
Parkland/moorland course.

18 holes, 6485yds, Par 71, SSS 71, Course record 69.
Club membership 450.
Visitors contact professional on 01274 562506, no green fees
Sat. **Societies** telephone in advance, the professional 01274
562506. **Green Fees** £30 per day; £25 per round. **Cards** 💳
💳 💳 🎫 **Prof** Ray Firth **Course Designer** Alastair
Mackenzie **Facilities** ⊗ ⊞ ⅃ 🍺 ♀ 🏌 🖕 🛒 ♣ ✆ **Location**
0.75m W off B6429

Hotel ★★ 64% Dalesgate Hotel, 406 Skipton Rd, Utley,
KEIGHLEY ☎ 01535 664930 20 en suite

Shipley Beckfoot Ln BD16 1LX ☎ 01274 568652
(Secretary) & 563674 (Pro) 📠 01274 567739
e-mail: office@shipleygc.co.uk
Well established parkland course, founded in 1922,
featuring six good par 3s
18 holes, 6235yds, Par 71, SSS 70, Course record 65.
Club membership 600.
Visitors may play Mon, Wed-Fri & Sun, but Tue only after
2.30pm & Sat after 4pm. **Societies** initial enquiry by phone
to professional 01274 563674 and or by letter. **Green Fees**
not confirmed. **Cards** 💳 💳 💳 🎫 **Prof** J R Parry
Course Designer Colt, Allison, Mackenzie, Braid **Facilities**
⊗ ⊞ ⅃ 🍺 ♀ 🏌 🖕 ♣ ✆ **Location** 6m N of Bradford
on A650

Hotel ★★ 64% Dalesgate Hotel, 406 Skipton Rd, Utley,
KEIGHLEY ☎ 01535 664930 20 en suite

BRADFORD — Map 07 SE13

Bradford Moor Scarr Hall, Pollard Ln BD2 4RW
☎ 01274 771716 & 771693
Moorland course with tricky undulating greens.
9 holes, 5900yds, Par 70, SSS 68, Course record 65.
Club membership 330.
Visitors no visitors at weekends except with member.
Societies can book starting times by application in writing.
Green Fees £10 before 1.30pm, thereafter £12. **Facilities** ⅃
♀ 🏌 🖕 ✆ **Location** 2m NE of city centre off A658

Hotel ★★ 68% Park Drive Hotel, 12 Park Dr, BRADFORD
☎ 01274 480194 11 en suite

Clayton Thornton View Rd, Clayton BD14 6JX
☎ 01274 880047
Parkland course, difficult in windy conditions.
9 holes, 5407yds, Par 68, SSS 67.
Club membership 250.

Visitors may not play before 4pm on Sun. **Societies** apply in
writing to the Secretary or Captain. **Green Fees** terms on
application. **Facilities** ⊗ ⊞ ⅃ 🍺 ♀ 🏌 **Location** 2.5m SW
of city centre on A647

Hotel ★★★ 63% Novotel Bradford, 6 Roydsdale Way,
Euroaw Estate, BRADFORD ☎ 01274 683683 127 en suite

East Bierley South View Rd, East Bierley BD4 6PP
☎ 01274 681023 📠 01274 683666
e-mail: rjwelch@hotmail.com
Hilly moorland course with narrow fairways. Two par 3
holes over 200 yds.
9 holes, 4700yds, Par 64, SSS 63, Course record 59.
Club membership 300.
Visitors restricted Sat (am), Sun & Mon evening. Must
contact in advance. **Societies** must apply in writing. **Green**
Fees not confirmed. **Facilities** ⊗ ⅃ 🍺 ♀ 🏌 **Location** 4m
SE of city centre off A650

Hotel ★★★ 63% Novotel Bradford, 6 Roydsdale Way,
Euroaw Estate, BRADFORD ☎ 01274 683683 127 en suite

Headley Headley Ln, Thornton BD13 3LX
☎ 01274 833481 📠 01274 833481
Hilly moorland course, short but very testing, windy, fine
views.
9 holes, 5140yds, Par 65, SSS 65, Course record 57.
Club membership 443.
Visitors must contact in advance. **Societies** must contact in
advance. **Green Fees** not confirmed. **Facilities** ⊗ ⊞ ⅃ 🍺 ♀
🏌 **Location** 4m W of city centre off B6145 at Thornton

Hotel ★★ 68% Park Drive Hotel, 12 Park Dr, BRADFORD
☎ 01274 480194 11 en suite

Queensbury Brighouse Rd, Queensbury BD13 1QF
☎ 01274 882155 & 816864
Undulating woodland/parkland course.
9 holes, 5024yds, Par 66, SSS 65, Course record 63.
Club membership 380.
Visitors preferable to telephone in advance, restricted at
weekends. **Societies** apply in writing. **Green Fees** terms on
application. **Prof** David Delaney **Course Designer** Jonathan
Gaunt **Facilities** ⊗ ⊞ ⅃ 🍺 ♀ 🏌 🖕 ✆ **Location** 4m from
Bradford on A647

Hotel ★★ 68% Park Drive Hotel, 12 Park Dr, BRADFORD
☎ 01274 480194 11 en suite

South Bradford Pearson Rd, Odsal BD6 1BH
☎ 01274 673346 (pro shop) & 679195 (sec)
Hilly course with good greens, trees and ditches.
Interesting short 2nd hole (par 3) 200 yds, well-bunkered
and played from an elevated tee.
9 holes, 6068yds, Par 70, SSS 68, Course record 65.
Club membership 300.
Visitors must contact professional in advance. Weekends
contact for availability. Tuesday Ladies Day. **Societies** must
apply in writing to the secretary. **Green Fees** £16 per day
(£24 weekends). **Cards** 💳 **Prof** Paul Cooke **Facilities** ⊗
⊞ ⅃ 🍺 ♀ 🏌 🖕 ✆ **Conf** Max 40 Banquet 40 **Location**
2m S of city centre off A638

Hotel ★★★ 63% Novotel Bradford, 6 Roydsdale Way,
Euroaw Estate, BRADFORD
☎ 01274 683683 127 en suite

continued

West Bowling Newall Hall, Rooley Ln BD5 8LB
☎ 01274 393207 (office) & 728036 (pro) ▤ 01274 393207
Undulating, tree-lined parkland course. Testing hole: 'the Coffin' short par 3, very narrow.
18 holes, 5769yds, Par 69, SSS 67, Course record 65.
Club membership 500.
Visitors must apply in writing, very limited at weekends.
Societies must apply in writing/telephone in advance. Green Fees terms on application. Prof Ian A Marshall Facilities ⊗
🎳 🛒 🍴 ♀ 🏆 🏠 ✐ Location Corner of M606 & A638 (east)

· ·

Hotel ★★★★ 64% Hanover International Hotel & Club, Mayo Av, Off Rooley Ln, BRADFORD
☎ 01274 406606 & 406601 ▤ 01274 406600 131 en suite

West Bradford Chellow Grange Rd BD9 6NP
☎ 01274 542767 ▤ 01274 482079
Parkland course, windy, especially 3rd, 4th, 5th and 6th holes. Hilly but not hard.
18 holes, 5741yds, Par 69, SSS 68.
Club membership 440.
Visitors restricted Sat & Sun. Tuesday is Ladies day, can play if available, advisable to telephone 01274 542102 to reserve a time. Societies must contact in advance. Green Fees £21 per day/round. Prof Nigel M Barber Facilities ⊗
by prior arrangement 🎳 by prior arrangement 🛒 🍴 ♀ 🏠
✐ Leisure snooker room. Location W side of city centre off B6144

· ·

Hotel ★★★★ 70% Marriott Hollins Hall Hotel & Country Club, Hollins Hill, Baildon, SHIPLEY
☎ 01274 530053 122 en suite

BRIGHOUSE Map 07 SE12

Willow Valley Golf & Country Club Highmoor Ln, Clifton HD6 4JB ☎ 01274 878624 ▤ 01274 852805
e-mail: julian@wrgc.co.uk
A championship length 18-hole course offering a unique golfing experience, featuring island greens, shaped fairways and bunkers, and multiple teeing areas. The 9-hole course offers an exciting challenge to less experienced golfers.
South: 18 holes, 6496yds, Par 72, SSS 74, Course record 69.
North: 9 holes, 2039yds, Par 62, SSS 60.
Club membership 350.
Visitors tee times may be booked by phone on payment of green fee by credit/debit card. Societies telephone in advance for availability and booking form. Green Fees South: £23 (£28 weekends & bank holidays). North: £7 (£8 weekends & bank holidays). Cards 💳 💳 💳 🏦 ▨ Prof Julian Haworth Course Designer Jonathan Gaunt Facilities ⊗ 🎳
🛒 🍴 ♀ 🏠 🍴 🛒 ✐ ♨ Leisure 3 hole floodlit academy course. Location Junct 25 of M62 follow A644 towards Brighouse, at small rdbt right, A643, course is 2m on right

· ·

Hotel ★★ 72% Healds Hall Hotel, Leeds Rd, Liversedge, DEWSBURY ☎ 01924 409112 24 en suite

CLECKHEATON Map 08 SE12

Cleckheaton & District Bradford Rd BD19 6BU
☎ 01274 851266 ▤ 01274 871382
e-mail: info@cleckheatongolf.fsnet.co.uk
Parkland course with gentle hills.
18 holes, 5769yds, Par 71, SSS 68.
Club membership 550.
Visitors parties must arrange in advance, Sun by arrangement. Societies weekdays only; must contact in

advance, Sun by prior arrangement. Green Fees terms on application. Prof Mike Ingham Facilities ⊗ 🎳 🛒 🍴 ♀ 🏠
🏠 🍴 🛒 ✐ Location 1.5m NW on A638 junc 26 M62

· ·

Hotel ★★★ 70% Gomersal Park Hotel, Moor Ln, GOMERSAL ☎ 01274 869386 52 en suite

DEWSBURY Map 08 SE22

Hanging Heaton White Cross Rd WF12 7DT
☎ 01924 461606 ▤ 01924 430100
Arable land course, easy walking, fine views. Testing 4th hole (par 3).
9 holes, 5836yds, Par 69, SSS 68.
Club membership 500.
Visitors must play with member at weekends & bank holidays. Must contact in advance. Societies must telephone in advance. Green Fees not confirmed. Prof Gareth Moore Facilities ⊗ 🎳 🛒 🍴 ♀ 🏠 Location 0.75m NE off A653

· ·

Hotel ★★ 72% Healds Hall Hotel, Leeds Rd, Liversedge, DEWSBURY ☎ 01924 409112 24 en suite

ELLAND Map 07 SE12

Elland Hammerstones, Leach Ln HX5 0TA
☎ 01422 372505 & 374886 (pro)
9 hole parkland course played off 18 tees.
9 holes, 5498yds, Par 66, SSS 67, Course record 68.
Club membership 450.
Visitors welcome. Societies must contact in writing.
Green Fees £15 (£25 weekends & bank holidays).
Prof N Krzywicki Facilities ⊗ 🎳 🛒 🍴 ♀ 🏠 ✐
Location 1m SW

· ·

Hotel ★★★ 67% The Rock Inn Hotel, Holywell Green, HALIFAX ☎ 01422 379721 30 en suite

FENAY BRIDGE Map 08 SE11

Woodsome Hall HD8 0LQ
☎ 01484 602739 ▤ 01484 608260
A parkland course with good views and an historic clubhouse.
18 holes, 6096yds, Par 70, SSS 69, Course record 67.
Club membership 800.
Visitors must contact in advance. Jacket and tie required in all rooms except casual bar. Societies must apply in writing.
Green Fees not confirmed. Cards 💳 💳 ▨ Prof M Higginbotton Facilities ⊗ 🎳 🛒 🍴 ♀ 🏠 ✐ Location 1.5m SW off A629

· ·

Hotel ★★★ 67% Bagden Hall, Wakefield Rd, Scissett, HUDDERSFIELD ☎ 01484 865330 17 en suite

GARFORTH Map 08 SE43

Garforth Long Ln LS25 2DS
☎ 0113 286 2021 ▤ 0113 286 3308
Parkland course with fine views, easy walking.
18 holes, 6005yds, Par 69, SSS 69.
Club membership 500.
Visitors must contact in advance and have handicap certificate. With member only weekends & bank holidays.
Societies must apply in advance. Green Fees not confirmed.
Prof Ken Findlater Facilities ⊗ 🎳 🛒 🍴 ♀ 🏠 🍴 🛒 ✐ ♨
Location 1m N

· ·

Hotel ★★★ 72% Milford Lodge Hotel, A1 Great North Rd, Peckfield, LEEDS ☎ 01977 681800 47 en suite

continued

GUISELEY   Map 08 SE14

Bradford (Hawksworth) Hawksworth Ln LS20 8NP
☎ 01943 875570 & 873719 (Pro) 📠 01943 875570
Moorland course with eight par 4 holes of 360 yds or
more. The course is a venue for county championship
events.
18 holes, 6259yds, Par 71, SSS 71, Course record 66.
Club membership 650.
Visitors must have a handicap certificate and contact in
advance. May not play Sat. **Societies** make prior
arrangements with manager. **Green Fees** not confirmed. **Prof**
Sydney Weldon **Course Designer** W H Fowler **Facilities** ⊗
)Ⅲ ㎐ ♨ ♀ ♨ 🏠 ✎ **Location** SW side of town centre off
A6038

Hotel ★★★★ 70% Marriott Hollins Hall Hotel & Country
Club, Hollins Hill, Baildon, SHIPLEY
☎ 01274 530053 122 en suite

HALIFAX   Map 07 SE02

Halifax Union Ln, Ogden HX2 8XR
☎ 01422 244171 📠 01422 241459
Hilly moorland course crossed by streams, natural
hazards, and offering fine views. Testing 172-yd 17th
(par 3).
18 holes, 6037yds, Par 70, SSS 70, Course record 69.
Club membership 700.
Visitors contact professional for tee times, 01422 240047.
Limited play weekend. **Societies** contact secretary for dates.
Green Fees £25 per day. **Prof** Michael Allison **Course**
Designer A Herd/J Braid **Facilities** ⊗)Ⅲ ㎐ ♨ ♀ ♨ 🏠 ✎
✎ **Location** A629 Halifax/Keighley, 4 miles from Halifax

Hotel ★★★ 77% Holdsworth House Hotel, Holdsworth,
HALIFAX ☎ 01422 240024 40 en suite

Lightcliffe Knowle Top Rd, Lightcliffe HX3 8SW
☎ 01422 202459 204081
Heathland course.
9 holes, 5388mtrs, Par 68, SSS 68.
Club membership 460.
Visitors Must contact in advance. **Societies** Must apply in
writing. **Green Fees** terms on application. **Prof** Robert
Kershaw **Facilities** ⊗)Ⅲ ㎐ ♨ ♀ ♨ 🏠 ✎ **Location** 3.5m E
of Halifax on A58

Hotel ★★★ 77% Holdsworth House Hotel, Holdsworth,
HALIFAX ☎ 01422 240024 40 en suite

West End Paddock Ln, Highroad Well HX2 0NT
☎ 01422 341878 📠 01422 341878
e-mail: info@westendgc.co.uk
Semi-moorland course. Tree lined. Two ponds.
18 holes, 5951yds, Par 69, SSS 69, Course record 62.
Club membership 560.
Visitors contact in advance. **Societies** must apply in writing
to Secretary. **Green Fees** £30 per day; £25 per round (£30
per round sunday). **Prof** David Rishworth **Facilities** ⊗)Ⅲ ㎐
♨ ♀ ♨ 🏠 ✎ **Location** W side of town centre off A646

Hotel ★★★ 77% Holdsworth House Hotel, Holdsworth,
HALIFAX ☎ 01422 240024 40 en suite

HEBDEN BRIDGE   Map 07 SD92

Hebden Bridge Mount Skip, Wadsworth HX7 8PH
☎ 01422 842896 & 842732
Moorland course with splendid views.

continued

9 holes, 5242yds, Par 68, SSS 67, Course record 61.
Club membership 300.
Visitors weekends after 4pm only. **Societies** contact in
advance. **Green Fees** £12 (£15 weekends). **Facilities** ⊗)Ⅲ ㎐
♨ ♀ ♨ **Location** 1.5m E off A6033

Hotel ★★★ 66% Carlton Hotel, Albert St, HEBDEN
BRIDGE ☎ 01422 844400 16 en suite

HOLYWELL GREEN   Map 07 SE01

Halifax Bradley Hall HX4 9AN ☎ 01422 374108
Moorland/parkland course, tightened by tree planting,
easy walking.
18 holes, 6138yds, Par 70, SSS 70, Course record 65.
Club membership 500.
Visitors contact in advance. **Societies** must apply in advance.
Green Fees £20 per round. **Prof** Peter Wood **Facilities** ⊗)Ⅲ
㎐ ♨ ♀ ♨ 🏠 ✎ **Location** S on A6112

Hotel ★★★ 67% The Rock Inn Hotel, Holywell Green,
HALIFAX ☎ 01422 379721 30 en suite

HUDDERSFIELD   Map 07 SE11

Bagden Hall Hotel & Golf Course Wakefield Rd,
Scissett HD8 9LE ☎ 01484 865330 📠 01484 861001
e-mail: info@bagdenhall.demon.co.uk.
Well maintained tree-lined course set in idyllic
surroundings and offering a challenging test of golf for all
levels of handicap. Lake guarded greens require pin-
point accuracy.
9 holes, 3002yds, Par 56, SSS 55, Course record 60.
Club membership 200.
Visitors anytime. **Societies** company day packages available,
telephone Director of golf. **Green Fees** £10 per 18 holes (£13
weekends). **Cards** 💳 💳 💳 💳 💳 **Course Designer** F
O'Donnell/R Braithwaite **Facilities** ⊗)Ⅲ ㎐ ♨ ♀ ♨ ✎ 🏠
Conf Max 90 Thtr 90 Class 30 Board 30 Banquet 76 Del
from £30 * **Location** A636 Wakefield-Denby Dale

Hotel ★★★ 67% Bagden Hall, Wakefield Rd, Scissett,
HUDDERSFIELD ☎ 01484 865330 17 en suite

Bradley Park Off Bradley Rd HD2 1PZ
☎ 01484 223772 📠 01484 451613
e-mail: parnellreilly@tinyworld.co.uk
Parkland course, challenging with good mix of long and
short holes. Also 14-bay floodlit driving range and 9-hole
par 3 course, ideal for beginners. Superb views.
18 holes, 6284yds, Par 70, SSS 70, Course record 65.
Club membership 300.
Visitors may book by phone for weekends and bank holidays
from the preceeding Thu. No restrictions on other days.
Societies welcome midweek, apply in writing to
professional. **Green Fees** £13.50(£15.50 weekends). **Cards**
💳 💳 💳 💳 **Prof** Parnell E Reilly **Course Designer**
Cotton/Pennick/Lowire & Ptnrs **Facilities** ⊗)Ⅲ ㎐ ♨ ♀ ♨
🏠 ✎ ♨ ♨ ✎ ♨ **Leisure** 9 hole par 3 course. **Location**
2.5m from junct 25 of M62

Hotel ★★★ 66% The George Hotel, St George's Square,
HUDDERSFIELD ☎ 01484 515444 60 en suite

Crosland Heath Felk Stile Rd, Crosland Heath
HD4 7AF ☎ 01484 653216 📠 01484 461079
Moorland course with fine views over valley.
18 holes, 6007yds, Par 70, SSS 69.
Club membership 550.
Visitors welcome, but advisable to check with professional.
May not play Sat. **Societies** must telephone in advance.

continued

279

Green Fees terms on application. **Prof** James Coverley **Facilities** ⊗ ⅲ 🏌 ⚑ ♀ ♨ 🖚 ♂ **Conf** Max 30 **Location** SW off A62

....

Hotel ★★★ 66% The George Hotel, St George's Square, HUDDERSFIELD ☎ 01484 515444 60 en suite

Huddersfield Fixby Hall, Lightridge Rd, Fixby
HD2 2EP ☎ 01484 426203 📱 01484 424623
e-mail: secretary@huddersfield-golf.co.uk
A testing heathland course of championship standard laid out in 1891.
18 holes, 6432yds, Par 71, SSS 71, Course record 63.
Club membership 759.
Visitors must book tee times with professional. **Societies** welcome Mon & Wed-Fri, prior arrangement required. **Green Fees** £37 per round (£47 weekends and bank holidays). **Prof** Paul Carman **Facilities** ⊗ ⅲ 🏌 ⚑ ♀ ♨ 🖚 🖚 ♂ 🏌 **Location** 2m N off A641

....

Hotel ★★★ 66% The George Hotel, St George's Square, HUDDERSFIELD ☎ 01484 515444 60 en suite

Longley Park Maple St, Off Somerset Rd HD5 9AX
☎ 01484 422304
Lowland course, surrounded by mature woodland.
9 holes, 5212yds, Par 66, SSS 66, Course record 61.
Club membership 440.
Visitors by arrangement with professional, must have handicap certificate, restricted Thu & weekends. No catering Mon. **Societies** must apply in writing to secretary. **Green Fees** terms on application. **Prof** Nick Leeming **Facilities** ⊗ ⅲ 🏌 ⚑ ♀ ♨ 🖚 🖚 ♂ **Location** 0.5m SE of town centre off A629

....

Hotel ★★★ 66% The George Hotel, St George's Square, HUDDERSFIELD ☎ 01484 515444 60 en suite

ILKLEY   Map 07 SE14

Ben Rhydding High Wood, Ben Rhydding LS29 8SB
☎ 01943 608759
Moorland/parkland course with splendid views over the Wharfe valley. A compact but testing course.
9 holes, 4611yds, Par 65, SSS 63, Course record 64.
Club membership 290.
Visitors contact in advance. May only play at weekend as guest of member. **Societies** advance notice in writing. In view of limited resources requests considered by monthly committee meeting. **Green Fees** £12 per day (£17 weekends & bank holidays). **Course Designer** William Dell **Facilities** ♀ ♨ **Location** SE side of town, up Wheatley lane beyond Wheatley Hotel, fork left at bottom of steep section along Wheatley grove, left into High Wood. Clubhouse drive 50 yds left

....

Hotel ★★★ 73% Rombalds Hotel & Restaurant, 11 West View, Wells Rd, ILKLEY ☎ 01943 603201 15 en suite

Ilkley Nesfield Rd, Myddleton LS29 0BE
☎ 01943 600214 📱 01943 816130
e-mail: honsec@ilkleygolfclub.co.uk
This beautiful parkland course is situated in Wharfedale and the Wharfe is a hazard on each of the first seven holes. In fact, the 3rd is laid out entirely on an island in the middle of the river.
18 holes, 5953yds, Par 69, SSS 70, Course record 66.
Club membership 450.

continued

Visitors advisable to contact in advance. **Societies** apply in writing. **Green Fees** £37 per day (£42 weekends & bank holidays). **Prof** John L Hammond **Course Designer** Mackenzie **Facilities** ⊗ ⅲ 🏌 ⚑ ♀ ♨ 🖚 🏌 ♂ Leisure fishing. **Location** W side of town centre off A65

....

Hotel ★★★ 73% Rombalds Hotel & Restaurant, 11 West View, Wells Rd, ILKLEY ☎ 01943 603201 15 en suite

KEIGHLEY   Map 07 SE04

Branshaw Branshaw Moor, Oakworth BD22 7ES
☎ 01535 643235 (sec) & 647441 (pro) 📱 01535 648011
Picturesque moorland course with fairly narrow fairways and good greens. Extensive views.
18 holes, 5823yds, Par 69, SSS 68, Course record 64.
Club membership 500.
Visitors welcome most times, restrictions at weekends advisable to ring. **Societies** apply in writing to Professional. **Green Fees** £20 per day (£30 weekends). **Prof** Mark Tyler **Course Designer** James Braid **Facilities** ⊗ ⅲ 🏌 ⚑ ♀ ♨ 🖚 ♂ **Location** 2m SW on B6149

....

Hotel ★★ 64% Dalesgate Hotel, 406 Skipton Rd, Utley, KEIGHLEY ☎ 01535 664930 20 en suite

Keighley Howden Park, Utley BD20 6DH
☎ 01535 604778 📱 01535 604833
e-mail: golf@keighleygolfclub.fsnet.co.uk
Parkland course is good quality and has great views down the Aire Valley. The 17th hole has been described as 'one of the most difficult and dangerous holes in Yorkshire golf' by Yorkshire champion Phil Wood.
18 holes, 6141yds, Par 69, SSS 70, Course record 64.
Club membership 600.
Visitors restricted Sat & Sun. Must contact in advance. Ladies day on Tuesday. **Societies** must apply in advance. **Green Fees** £32 per day; £28 per round (£38/£32 weekends & bank holidays). **Cards** 💳 💳 💳 💳 💳 💳 **Prof** Mike Bradley **Facilities** ⊗ ⅲ 🏌 ⚑ ♀ ♨ 🖚 🖚 ♂ Leisure Snooker table. **Location** 1m NW of town centre off B6143, turn N at Roebuck pub and follow signs

....

Hotel ★★ 64% Dalesgate Hotel, 406 Skipton Rd, Utley, KEIGHLEY ☎ 01535 664930 20 en suite

LEEDS   Map 08 SE33

Brandon Holywell Ln, Shadwell LS17 8EZ
☎ 0113 273 7471
An 18-hole links type course enjoying varying degrees of rough, water and sand hazards.
18 holes, 4000yds, Par 63.
Visitors pay & play course booking not usually necessary. **Societies** telephone or write in advance. **Green Fees** £6.50 per 18 holes; £4.50 per 9 holes (£7.50/£5.50 weekends). **Prof** Carl Robinson **Course Designer** William Binner **Facilities** 🏌 ⚑ ♀ ♨ 🖚 🖚 ♨ 🖚 ♂ **Location** From Leeds-Wetherby Rd turn left to Shadwell left again up Main St, right at Red Lion Pub

....

Hotel ★★★★TH 70% Haley's Hotel & Restaurant, Shire Oak Rd, Headingley, LEEDS ☎ 0113 278 4446 22 en suite 7 annexe en suite

Where to stay, where to eat?
Visit www.theAA.com

Cookridge Hall Golf & Country Club

Cookridge Ln LS16 7NL
☎ 0113 2300641 🖷 0113 203 0198
e-mail: cookridgehall@americangolf.uk.com
American-style course designed by Karl Litten. Expect plenty of water hazards, tees for all standards. Large bunkers and fairways between mounds and young trees.
18 holes, 6788yds, Par 72, SSS 72.
Club membership 520.
Visitors must contact in advance. Strict dress code applies. Soft spikes preferred. **Societies** telephone in advance. **Green Fees** £30 per day; £20 per round. **Cards** 🖼🖼🖼🖼 **Prof** Mark Pearson **Course Designer** Karl Liiten **Facilities** ⊗ 🍴 🛅 🍺 ♀ 🏌 🖻 ⛳ 🏐 🚲 ℓ 🏌 **Location** On Otley Old Road, off A660, 6m NW of Leeds

Hotel ★★★★TH 70% Haley's Hotel & Restaurant, Shire Oak Rd, Headingley, LEEDS ☎ 0113 278 4446
22 en suite 7 annexe en suite

Gotts Park Armley Ridge Rd LS12 2QX

☎ 0113 231 1896 & 231 0492
e-mail: maurice.gill@lineone.net
Municipal parkland course; hilly and windy with narrow fairways. Some very steep hills to some greens. A challenging course requiring accuracy rather than length from the tees.
18 holes, 4960yds, Par 65, SSS 64, Course record 63.
Club membership 200.
Visitors no restrictions.apply directley to Leeds leisure services. **Green Fees** £7.50 per round (£9 weekends and bank holidays). **Prof** John Marlor **Facilities** ⊗ 🍴 ♀ 🖻 🏌 **Location** 3m W of city centre off A647

Hotel ★★★★ 68% Le Meridien Queen's, City Square, LEEDS ☎ 0113 243 1323 & 0870 4008696
🖷 0113 242 5154 199 en suite

Headingley Back Church Ln, Adel LS16 8DW

☎ 0113 267 9573 🖷 0113 281 7334
e-mail: headingley-golf@talk21.com
An undulating course with a wealth of natural features offering fine views from higher ground. Its most striking hazard is the famous ravine at the 18th. Leeds's oldest course, founded in 1892.
18 holes, 6298yds, Par 69, SSS 70, Course record 64.
Club membership 700.
Visitors must contact in advance, restricted at weekends. **Societies** must telephone in advance and confirm in writing. **Green Fees** £35 per day; £30 per round (£40 per day/round weekends & bank holidays). **Course Designer** Dr Mackenzie **Facilities** ⊗ 🍴 🛅 🍺 ♀ ⚖ 🖻 ⛳ ℓ **Location** 5.5m N of city centre off A660. Take A660 to Skipton, right at lights junct Farrar lane/Church lane. Follow Eccup signs

Hotel ★★★ 70% Holiday Inn Leeds Bradford Airport, Leeds Rd, BRAMHOPE ☎ 0113 284 2911 124 en suite

Horsforth Layton Rise, Layton Rd, Horsforth LS18 5EX

☎ 0113 258 6819 & 258 5200(pro) 🖷 0113 258 6819
Moorland/parkland course overlooking airport.
18 holes, 6243yds, Par 71, SSS 70, Course record 65.
Club membership 750.
Visitors restricted Sat & with member only Sun. **Societies** must apply in writing. **Green Fees** terms on application. **Prof** Dean Stokes/Simon Booth **Facilities** ⚖ 🖻 ℓ **Location** 6.5m NW of city centre off A65

continued

Hotel ★★★ 70% Holiday Inn Leeds Bradford Airport, Leeds Rd, BRAMHOPE ☎ 0113 284 2911 124 en suite

Leeds Elmete Ln LS8 2LJ

☎ 0113 265 8775 🖷 0113 232 3369
e-mail: leedsgccobble@btconnect.com
Parkland course with pleasant views.
18 holes, 6097yds, Par 69, SSS 69, Course record 63.
Club membership 600.
Visitors with member only weekends. Must book in advance weekdays. **Societies** must apply in writing. **Green Fees** terms on application. **Prof** Simon Longster **Facilities** ⊗ 🍴 🛅 🍺 ♀ ⚖ 🖻 🏌 ℓ **Location** 5m NE of city centre on A6120 off A58

Hotel ★★★★TH 70% Haley's Hotel & Restaurant, Shire Oak Rd, Headingley, LEEDS ☎ 0113 278 4446
22 en suite 7 annexe en suite

Leeds Golf Centre Wike Ridge Ln, Shadwell

LS17 9JW ☎ 0113 288 6000 🖷 0113 288 6185
Two courses - the 18-hole Wike Ridge, a traditional heathland course designed by Donald Steel. The sand-based greens are constructed to USGA specification and there are an excellent variety of holes with some very challenging par 5s. The 12-hole Oaks is complemented by a floodlit driving range and other practice facilities. The course is the home of the Leeds Golf Academy.
Wike Ridge Course: 18 holes, 6482yds, Par 72, SSS 71.
Oaks: 12 holes, 1610yds, Par 36.
Club membership 500.
Visitors no restrictions, telephone booking advisable. **Societies** tee reservation available in advance. **Green Fees** not confirmed. **Cards** 🖼🖼🖼🖼🖼 **Prof** Neil Harvey **Course Designer** Donald Steel **Facilities** ⊗ 🍴 🛅 🍺 ♀ ⚖ 🖻 🏌 🏐 🚲 ℓ 🏌 **Location** 5m N,take A58 course on N side of Shadwell

Hotel ★★★★TH 70% Haley's Hotel & Restaurant, Shire Oak Rd, Headingley, LEEDS ☎ 0113 278 4446
22 en suite 7 annexe en suite

Middleton Park Municipal Middleton Park,

Middleton LS10 3TN ☎ 0113 270 0449 🖷 0113 270 0449
e-mail: lynn@ratcliffel.fsnet.co.uk
Parkland course.
18 holes, 5263yds, Par 68, SSS 66, Course record 63.
Club membership 280.
Visitors may only use the club 6 times in one year, must contact in advance and may not play weekends. **Societies** write or email secretary. **Green Fees** £10.50 per round. **Cards** 🖼🖼 **Prof** Jim Pape **Facilities** 🛅 🍺 ♀ ⚖ 🖻 **Location** 3m S off A653

Hotel ★★★★ 68% Le Meridien Queen's, City Square, LEEDS ☎ 0113 243 1323 & 0870 4008696
🖷 0113 242 5154 199 en suite

Moor Allerton Coal Rd, Wike LS17 9NH

☎ 0113 266 1154 🖷 0113 237 1124
e-mail: info@moorallerton.demon.co.uk
The Moor Allerton Club, established in 1923, has 27 holes set in 220 acres of undulating parkland, with testing water hazards and magnificent views extending across the Vale of York. The Championship Course was designed by Robert Trent Jones, the famous

continued

American course architect, and provides a challenge to both high and low handicapped golfers.
Lakes Course: 18 holes, 6470yds, Par 71, SSS 72.
Blackmoor Course: 18 holes, 6673yds, Par 71, SSS 73.
High Course: 18 holes, 6841yds, Par 72, SSS 74.
Club membership 900.

Moor Allerton Golf Club

Visitors contact professional (0113 266 5209). **Societies** must apply in advance. **Green Fees** £50 per day; £45 per round (£65 weekends). **Cards** ⊞ ▆▆ 🅴 **Prof** Richard Lane **Course Designer** Robert Trent Jones **Facilities** ⊗ 〗Ⅱ ㄴ 🍺 ♀ ♨ 🏠 ⟟ 🐾 🏌 ♂ 𝄢 **Leisure** sauna. **Conf** Max 50 Del £75 to £100 * **Location** 5.5m N of city centre on A61

Hotel ★★★ 66% The Merrion, Merrion Centre, LEEDS ☎ 0113 243 9191 109 en suite

Moortown Harrogate Rd, Alwoodley LS17 7DB
☎ 0113 268 6521 📠 0113 268 0986
e-mail: secretary@moortown-gc.co.uk
Championship course, tough but fair. Springy moorland turf, natural hazards of heather, gorse and streams, cunningly placed bunkers and immaculate greens. Original home of Ryder Cup in 1929.
18 holes, 6782yds, Par 72, SSS 73, Course record 66.
Club membership 568.
Visitors contact in advance. **Societies** apply in writing in advance. **Green Fees** £55 per day/round (£65 weekends & bank holidays). **Prof** Bryon Hutchinson **Course Designer** A McKenzie **Facilities** ⊗ 〗Ⅱ ㄴ 🍺 ♀ ♨ 🏠 ⟟ 🐾 𝄢 **Location** 6m N of city centre on A61

Hotel ★★★ 66% The Merrion, Merrion Centre, LEEDS ☎ 0113 243 9191 109 en suite

Oulton Park Rothwell LS26 8EX
☎ 0113 282 3152 📠 0113 282 6290
27-hole championship-length municipal course. Although municipal, a dress rule is applied. 22-bay floodlit driving range. Two tier putting. Host to the City of Leeds Cup (PGA) each July.
Hall Course: 9 holes, 3286yds, Par 36, SSS 36.
Park Course: 9 holes, 3184yds, Par 35, SSS 35.
Royds Course: 9 holes, 3169yds, Par 35, SSS 35.
Club membership 450.
Visitors must apply up to 5 days in advance. Dress code in operation. **Societies** Mon-Fri. Must contact in advance. **Green Fees** not confirmed. **Cards** ⊞ ▆▆ ▆▆ 🅴 **Prof** Stephen Gromett **Course Designer** Dave Thomas **Facilities** ⊗ 〗Ⅱ ㄴ 🍺 ♀ ♨ 🏠 ⟟ 🐾 𝄢 **Leisure** heated indoor swimming pool, squash, fishing, sauna, solarium, gymnasium. **Location** Junc 30 on M62

continued

Hotel ★★★★ 62% Oulton Hall Hotel, Rothwell Ln, Oulton, LEEDS ☎ 0113 282 1000 152 en suite

Roundhay Park Ln LS8 2EJ ☎ 0113 266 2695
Attractive municipal parkland course, natural hazards, easy walking.
9 holes, 5223yds, Par 70, SSS 65, Course record 61.
Club membership 250.
Visitors must contact professional at all times. **Societies** telephone or write to the professional. **Green Fees** terms on application. **Prof** James Pape **Facilities** ♀ ♨ 🏠 ⟟ 𝄢 **Location** 4m NE of city centre off A58

Hotel ★★★★TH 70% Haley's Hotel & Restaurant, Shire Oak Rd, Headingley, LEEDS ☎ 0113 278 4446 22 en suite 7 annexe en suite

Sand Moor Alwoodley Ln LS17 7DJ
☎ 0113 268 5180 📠 0113 266 1105
e-mail: sandmoorgolf@btclick.com
A beautiful, inland course situated next to Eccup reservoir on the north side of Leeds. It has been described as the finest example of golfing paradise being created out of a barren moor. With magnificent views of the surrounding countryside, the course with its sandy soil drains exceptionally well.
18 holes, 6414yds, Par 71, SSS 71, Course record 63.
Club membership 600.
Visitors restricted weekends & bank holidays. **Societies** must apply in advance. **Green Fees** £48 per day; £38 per round (£48 per round weekends). **Prof** Peter Tupling **Course Designer** Dr A Mackenzie **Facilities** ⊗ 〗Ⅱ ㄴ 🍺 ♀ ♨ 🏠 ⟟ 𝄢 **Location** 5m N of city centre off A61

Hotel ★★★ 70% Holiday Inn Leeds Bradford Airport, Leeds Rd, BRAMHOPE ☎ 0113 284 2911 124 en suite

South Leeds Gipsy Ln, Beeston LS11 5TU
☎ 0113 277 1676 & 270 0479 (club)
e-mail: sec@slgc.freeserve.co.uk
Parkland course, windy, hard walking, good views.
18 holes, 5769yds, Par 69, SSS 68, Course record 64.
Club membership 500.
Visitors welcome weekdays except competition time, may not play weekends. **Societies** must apply in advance. **Green Fees** £18 per day/round (£26 weekends & bank holidays). **Prof** Mike Lewis **Facilities** ⊗ 〗Ⅱ ㄴ 🍺 ♀ ♨ 🏠 𝄢 **Location** 3m S of city centre off A653

Hotel ★★★★ 68% Le Meridien Queen's, City Square, LEEDS ☎ 0113 243 1323 & 0870 4008696 📠 0113 242 5154 199 en suite

Temple Newsam Temple-Newsam Rd LS15 0LN
☎ 0113 264 5624
Two parkland courses. Testing long 13th (563 yds) on second course.
Lord Irwin: 18 holes, 6460yds, Par 68, SSS 71, Course record 66.
Lady Dorothy: 18 holes, 6299yds, Par 70, SSS 70, Course record 67.
Club membership 520.
Visitors no restrictions. **Societies** must apply in advance in writing. **Green Fees** not confirmed. **Prof** Alan Swaine **Facilities** ⊗ 〗Ⅱ by prior arrangement 🍺 ♀ ♨ 🏠 ⟟ 𝄢 **Location** 3.5m E of city centre off A63

continued

Hotel ★★★★TH 70% Haley's Hotel & Restaurant, Shire Oak Rd, Headingley, LEEDS ☎ 0113 278 4446 22 en suite 7 annexe en suite

MARSDEN   Map 07 SE01

Marsden Mount Rd, Hemplow HD7 6NN
☎ 01484 844253
Moorland course with good views, natural hazards, windy.
9 holes, 5702yds, Par 68, SSS 68, Course record 65.
Club membership 200.
Visitors must play with member at weekends but not before 4pm Sat. **Societies** Mon-Fri; must contact in advance. **Green Fees** terms on application. **Prof** Nick Krzywicki **Course Designer** Dr McKenzie **Facilities** ⊗ ⅷ ㄥ ♥ ♀ ㄥ 🛍
Leisure hard tennis courts. **Location** S side off A62

Hotel ★★ 65% Old Bridge Hotel, HOLMFIRTH
☎ 01484 681212 20 en suite

MELTHAM   Map 07 SE01

Meltham Thick Hollins Hall HD9 4DQ
☎ 01484 850227 ▤ 01484 859051
e-mail: meltham@thegolfcourse.co.uk
Parkland course with good views. Testing 548 yd, 13th hole (par 5).
18 holes, 6396yds, Par 71, SSS 70, Course record 67.
Club membership 720.
Visitors may not play Sat & Wed (Ladies Day), contact professional in advance. **Societies** apply in writing/telephone. Application form on website. **Green Fees** £27 per day; £22 per round (£32/£27 weekends & bank holidays). **Prof** Paul Davies **Course Designer** Alex Herd **Facilities** ⊗ ⅷ ㄥ ♥ ♀ ㄥ 🛍 ⚑ ♂ **Location** From Huddersfield take A616 signed Sheffield, ahead at 3rd set of traffic lights on B6108 to Meltham. Left on B6107, 0.5m up hill, club entrance ahead

Hotel ★★★ 66% The George Hotel, St George's Square, HUDDERSFIELD ☎ 01484 515444 60 en suite

MIRFIELD   Map 08 SE21

Dewsbury District Sands Ln WF14 8HJ
☎ 01924 492399 & 496030 ▤ 01924 492399
Heathland/parkland course with panoramic views and hard walking. Ponds in middle of 3rd fairway, left of 5th green and 17th green.
18 holes, 6360yds, Par 71, SSS 71.
Club membership 600.
Visitors At weekends only after 2.30pm on Sundays.Telephone in advance. **Societies** telephone bookings. **Green Fees** £24 per day; £18 per round. **Prof** Nigel P Hirst **Course Designer** Old Tom Morris/ Peter Alliss **Facilities** ⊗ ⅷ by prior arrangement ㄥ ♥ ♀ ㄥ 🛍 ⚑ ♂
Leisure snooker tables. **Location** Off A644, 6m from junct 25 on M62

Hotel ★★★ 66% The George Hotel, St George's Square, HUDDERSFIELD ☎ 01484 515444 60 en suite

MORLEY   Map 08 SE22

Howley Hall Scotchman Ln LS27 0NX
☎ 01924 350100 ▤ 01924 350104
e-mail: info@howleyhall.co.uk
Parkland course with easy walking and superb views of the Pennines and Calder Valley.
18 holes, 6346yds, Par 71, SSS 71, Course record 66.
Club membership 700.

continued

Visitors play from yellow markers. May not play Sat. Societies contact for details. Green Fees £35 per day; £29 per round (£39 per day/round weekends & bank holidays). Prof Gary Watkinson Facilities ⊗ ⅷ ㄥ ♥ ♀ ㄥ 🛍 ♂ Location 1.5m S on B6123

Hotel ★★ 70% Alder House Hotel, Towngate Rd, Healey Ln, BATLEY ☎ 01924 444777 20 en suite

NORMANTON   Map 08 SE32

Normanton Snydale Rd WF6 1PN
☎ 01924 892943 ▤ 01924 220134
9 holes, 5288yds, Par 66, SSS 66.
Location 0.5m SE on B6133
Telephone for further details

Hotel ★★★ 64% Chasley Hotel, Queen St, WAKEFIELD ☎ 01924 372111 64 en suite

OSSETT   Map 08 SE22

Low Laithes Parkmill Ln, Flushdyke WF5 9AP
☎ 01924 274667 & 266067 ▤ 01924 266067
Testing parkland course.
18 holes, 6463yds, Par 72, SSS 71, Course record 65.
Club membership 600.
Visitors may not play before 9.30am and 12.30-1.30 weekdays and before 10am and 12-2 weekends/bank holidays. **Societies** by prior arrangement. **Green Fees** not confirmed. **Prof** Paul Browning **Course Designer** Dr Mackenzie **Facilities** ⊗ ⅷ ㄥ ♥ ♀ ㄥ 🛍 🚗 ♂ **Location** Leave M1 at jct 40 then signposted on Dewsbury road 0.5m from M1

Hotel ★★★ 66% Heath Cottage Hotel & Restaurant, Wakefield Rd, DEWSBURY
☎ 01924 465399 23 en suite 6 annexe en suite

OTLEY   Map 08 SE24

Otley Off West Busk Ln LS21 3NG
☎ 01943 465329 ▤ 01943 850387
e-mail: office@otley-golfclub.co.uk
An expansive course with magnificent views across Wharfedale. It is well-wooded with streams crossing the fairway. The 4th is a fine hole which generally needs two woods to reach the plateau green. The 17th is a good short hole. A test of golf as opposed to stamina.
18 holes, 6245yds, Par 70, SSS 70, Course record 62.
Club membership 700.
Visitors telephone to check tee time. May not play Tue morning or Sat. **Societies** telephone enquiries welcome, bookings in writing. **Green Fees** £36 per day; £29 per round (£42/35 weekends). **Cards** ▭ ▭ ▭ ▭ ▭ ▭ **Prof** Steven Tomkinson **Facilities** ⊗ ⅷ ㄥ ♥ ♀ ㄥ 🛍 ⚑ ♂ **Conf** Thtr 60 Class 60 Board 60 Banquet 60 **Location** 1m W of Otley off A6038

Hotel ★★★ 70% Holiday Inn Leeds Bradford Airport, Leeds Rd, BRAMHOPE ☎ 0113 284 2911 124 en suite

OUTLANE   Map 07 SE01

Outlane Slack Ln, Off New Hey Rd HD3 3YL
☎ 01422 311789 & 374762 ▤ 01422 311789
18 hole moorland course with undulating fairways. Four par 3 holes with an 8th hole of 249 yards and a 15th regarded as the hardest par 3 in Yorkshire. The three par 5s may be reachable on a good day in two strokes but in

continued

adverse conditions will take more than three. Smaller than average greens on some holes, which makes for accurate second shots.
18 holes, 6015yds, Par 71, SSS 70, Course record 66.
Club membership 600.
Visitors telephone in advance, must be correctly equipped and attired. No play Sat, limited Sun morning. Societies apply in writing. Green Fees not confirmed. Prof David Chapman Facilities ⊗ ⅷ 占 ☎ ♀ 占 ☎ ㏐ ⌀ Location S side of village off A640

Hotel ★★★ 71% Old Golf House Hotel, New Hey Rd, Outlane, HUDDERSFIELD ☎ 01422 379311 52 en suite

PONTEFRACT — Map 08 SE42

Mid Yorkshire Havercroft Ln, Darrington WF8 3BP
☎ 01977 704522 🖹 01977 600823
An 18-hole championship-standard course opened in 1993, and widely considered to be one of the finest new courses in Yorkshire.
18 holes, 6500yds, Par 72, SSS 71, Course record 68.
Club membership 500.
Visitors tee times bookable by telephone, visitors after 12 noon at weekends. Societies apply in writing to the secretary. Green Fees £15 per round (£20 weekends). Cards 🖃 🖃 🖃 Prof Alistair Cobbett Course Designer Steve Marnoch Facilities ⊗ ⅷ 占 ☎ ♀ 占 ㏐ ㏑ ⌀ 🥄 Conf Max 100 Del from £16.95 * Location On the A1, 0.5m south intersection of A1/M62

Hotel ★★★ 72% Wentbridge House Hotel, WENTBRIDGE ☎ 01977 620444
14 en suite 4 annexe en suite

Pontefract & District Park Ln WF8 4QS
☎ 01977 792241 🖹 01977 792241
e-mail: manager@pdgc.co.uk
Undulating parkland course, some elevated tees.
18 holes, 6227yds, Par 72, SSS 70.
Club membership 800.
Visitors welcome except Wed & weekends, advisable to contact in advance. Societies welcome except Wed & weekends, apply in writing or telephone. Green Fees £28 per day; £22 per round. Prof Nick Newman Course Designer A McKenzie Facilities ⊗ ⅷ 占 ☎ ♀ 占 ㏐ ⌀ Location M62 junct 32, through 1st traffic lights, filter left following B6134 signs North Featherstone/Aketon. Club 1m on right

Hotel ★★★ 72% Wentbridge House Hotel, WENTBRIDGE ☎ 01977 620444
14 en suite 4 annexe en suite

PUDSEY — Map 08 SE23

Calverley Golf Club Woodhall Ln LS28 5QY
☎ 0113 256 9244 🖹 0113 256 4362
Parkland course on gently undulating terrain where accurate approach shots are rewarded to small greens.
18 holes, 5590yds, Par 68, SSS 67, Course record 63.
Club membership 565.
Visitors advisable to book 18 hole course in advance and may not play weekend morning. 9 hole course, pay and play at all times. Societies contact in writing or telephone. Green Fees £12 per round (£15 weekends and bank holidays).
Cards 🖃 🖃 🖃 Prof Neil Wendel-Jones Facilities ⊗ ⅷ 占 ☎ ♀ 占 ☎ ㏐ 🥄 ⌀ Location Signposted Calverley from A647 Leeds/Bradford road

Hotel ★★ 68% Park Drive Hotel, 12 Park Dr, BRADFORD ☎ 01274 480194 11 en suite

Fulneck LS28 8NT ☎ 0113 256 5191
Picturesque parkland course.
9 holes, 5456yds, Par 66, SSS 67, Course record 65.
Club membership 250.
Visitors with member only weekends & bank holidays. Societies must apply in writing. Green Fees not confirmed. Facilities 占 Location Pudsey, between Leeds/Bradford

Hotel ★★★ 63% Novotel Bradford, 6 Roydsdale Way, Euroway Estate, BRADFORD ☎ 01274 683683 127 en suite

Woodhall Hills Calverley LS28 5UN
☎ 0113 255 4594
Meadowland course, prevailing SW winds, fairly hard walking. Testing holes: 14th, 377 yds (par 4); 15th, 206 yds (par 3).
18 holes, 6184yds, Par 71, SSS 70, Course record 61.
Club membership 550.
Visitors any day advise manager/professional in advance,sat after 16.30;sun after 9.30am. Societies telephone in advance. Green Fees £20.50 per round (£25.50 weekends). Prof Warren Lockett Facilities ⊗ ⅷ 占 ☎ ♀ 占 ⌀ Conf Thtr 100 Class 20 Board 20 Banquet 60 Location 1m NW off A647

Hotel ★★ 68% Park Drive Hotel, 12 Park Dr, BRADFORD ☎ 01274 480194 11 en suite

RAWDON — Map 08 SE23

Rawdon Golf & Lawn Tennis Club Buckstone Dr LS19 6BD ☎ 0113 250 6040
Undulating parkland course.
9 holes, 5980yds, Par 72, SSS 69, Course record 65.
Club membership 600.
Visitors must contact in advance & have handicap certificate. With member only. Societies must contact in advance. Green Fees not confirmed. Facilities ⊗ ⅷ 占 ☎ ♀ 占 占 ⌀ Leisure hard and grass tennis courts. Location Nw of Leeds off A65

Hotel ★★★ 67% Apperley Manor, Apperley Ln, Apperley Bridge, BRADFORD ☎ 0113 250 5626 13 en suite

RIDDLESDEN — Map 07 SE04

Riddlesden Howden Rough BD20 5QN
☎ 01535 602148
Undulating moorland course with prevailing west winds, some hard walking and beautiful views. Ten par 3 holes and spectacular 6th and 15th holes played over old quarry sites.
18 holes, 4295yds, Par 63, SSS 61.
Club membership 350.
Visitors restricted before 2pm weekends. Societies apply by telephone or in writing. Green Fees terms on application. Facilities ⊗ ⅷ 占 ☎ ♀ 占 Location 1m NW

Hotel ★★ 64% Dalesgate Hotel, 406 Skipton Rd, Utley, KEIGHLEY ☎ 01535 664930 20 en suite

SCARCROFT — Map 08 SE34

Scarcroft Syke Ln LS14 3BQ
☎ 0113 289 2311 🖹 0113 289 3835
e-mail: sge@cwcomm.net
Undulating parkland course with prevailing west wind and easy walking.

continued

18 holes, 6426yds, Par 71, SSS 69.
Club membership 667.
Visitors must contact in advance. Handicap certificate required. **Societies** must contact in advance. **Green Fees** terms on application. **Cards** 〓 〓 〓 〓 🖪 **Prof** Darren Tear **Course Designer** Charles Mackenzie **Facilities** ⊗ 🎍 🖫 ♬ 🖣 🖧 🏠 ⛳ ♂ **Conf** Max 50 **Location** 0.5m N of village off A58

....

Hotel ★★★ 66% The Merrion, Merrion Centre, LEEDS
☎ 0113 243 9191 109 en suite

SHIPLEY — Map 07 SE13

Marriott Hollins Hall Hotel & Country Club
Hollins Hill, Otley Rd BD17 7QW
☎ 01274 534212 & 534211 📄 01274 534220
Set in natural heathland amongst the beautiful Yorkshire moors and dales. The course is majestic, challenging and classically designed in the spirit of the game.
18 holes, 6671yds, Par 71, SSS 71, Course record 66.
Club membership 350.
Visitors must contact in advance, restrictions at weekend may apply, handicap certificate required. **Societies** telephone in advance 01274 530053. **Green Fees** Summer: £35 (£50 weekends); Winter: £25 (£35 weekends). **Cards** 〓 〓 〓 〓 🖪 **Prof** Gordon J Brand (touring) **Course Designer** Ross McMurray **Facilities** ⊗ 🎍 🖫 ♬ 🖣 🖧 🏠 🐂 ♂ 🌾 **Leisure** heated indoor swimming pool, sauna, solarium, gymnasium. **Conf** Thtr 175 Class 90 Board 60 Banquet 125 Del £45 to £155 * **Location** 3m N on the A6038 Otley road

Hotel ★★★★ 70% Marriott Hollins Hall Hotel & Country Club, Hollins Hill, Baildon, SHIPLEY
☎ 01274 530053 122 en suite

Northcliffe High Bank Ln BD18 4LJ
☎ 01274 596731 📄 01274 596731
e-mail: northcliffe@bigfoot.com
Parkland course with magnificent views of moors. Testing 1st hole, dog-leg left over a ravine. The 18th hole is one of the most picturesque and difficult par 3s in the country, with a green 100 feet below the tee and protected by bunkers, water and trees.
18 holes, 6104yds, Par 71, SSS 70, Course record 64.
Club membership 700.
Visitors limited access at weekend. **Societies** book via secretary in advance, weekdays only. **Green Fees** £30 per day; £25 per round (£30 per round weekend and bank holidays). **Prof** M Hillas **Course Designer** James Braid **Facilities** ⊗ 🎍 🖫 ♬ 🖣 🖧 🏠 🐂 ♀ ♂ **Location** 1.25m SW of Shipley, off A650

Hotel ★★★★ 70% Marriott Hollins Hall Hotel & Country Club, Hollins Hill, Baildon, SHIPLEY
☎ 01274 530053 122 en suite

SILSDEN — Map 07 SE04

Silsden Brunthwaite Ln, Brunthwaite BD20 0ND
☎ 01535 652998 📄 01535 654273
e-mail: info@silsdengolfclub.co.uk
Tight downland course which can be windy. Good views of the Aire Valley. A new clubhouse offers day-long facilities and the course is currently being redesigned.
18 holes, 5259yds, Par 67, SSS 66, Course record 62.
Club membership 350.
Visitors telephone in advance for weekend bookings. **Societies** telephone in advance or apply in writing. **Green Fees** not confirmed. **Facilities** ⊗ 🎍 🖫 ♬ 🖣 🖧 **Location** entering Silsden from direction of Aire Valley trunk road, turn immediately right after canal bridge

....

Hotel ★★ 64% Dalesgate Hotel, 406 Skipton Rd, Utley, KEIGHLEY ☎ 01535 664930 20 en suite

SOWERBY — Map 07 SE02

Ryburn The Shaw, Norland HX6 3QP ☎ 01422 831355
Moorland course, easy walking.
9 holes, 4984yds, Par 66, SSS 64, Course record 64.
Club membership 200.
Visitors must contact in advance. **Societies** apply in writing. **Green Fees** not confirmed. **Facilities** ⊗ 🎍 🖫 ♬ 🖣 🖧 **Location** 1m S of Sowerby Bridge off A58

....

Hotel ★★★ 67% The Rock Inn Hotel, Holywell Green, HALIFAX ☎ 01422 379721 30 en suite

TODMORDEN — Map 07 SD92

Todmorden Rive Rocks, Cross Stone Rd OL14 8RD
☎ 01706 812986
Pleasant moorland course.
9 holes, 5902yds, Par 68, SSS 68, Course record 67.
Club membership 240.
Visitors restricted Thu & weekends. Advisable to contact in advance. **Societies** must apply in writing. **Green Fees** terms on application. **Facilities** ⊗ by prior arrangement 🎍 by prior arrangement 🖫 ♬ 🖣 🖧 **Location** NE off A646

....

Hotel ★★★ 66% Carlton Hotel, Albert St, HEBDEN BRIDGE ☎ 01422 844400 16 en suite

WAKEFIELD — Map 08 SE32

City of Wakefield Horbury Rd WF2 8QS
☎ 01924 360282
Mature, level parkland course.
18 holes, 6319yds, Par 72, SSS 70, Course record 64.
Club membership 600.
Visitors restricted weekends. **Societies** must apply in advance to stewardess 01924 367242. **Green Fees** terms on application. **Cards** 〓 〓 〓 〓 🖪 **Prof** Roger Holland **Course Designer** J S F Morrison **Facilities** ⊗ 🎍 🖫 ♬ 🖣 🖧 🏠 🐂 ♂ **Location** 1.5m W of city centre on A642

....

Hotel ★★★ 68% Holiday Inn Wakefield, Queen's Dr, Ossett, WAKEFIELD ☎ 0870 400 9082 99 en suite

Painthorpe House Painthorpe Ln, Painthorpe, Crigglestone WF4 3HE ☎ 01924 274527 & 255083
📄 01924 252022
Undulating meadowland course, easy walking.
9 holes, 4544yds, Par 62, SSS 62, Course record 63.
Club membership 150.
Visitors pay and play Mon-Sat, after 2.30pm on Sun. **Societies** must telephone in advance. **Green Fees** terms on application. **Cards** 〓 🖪 **Facilities** ⊗ 🎍 🖫 ♬ 🖣 🖧

continued

Leisure bowling green. **Conf** Max 400 Class 30 Banquet 400 **Location** 2m S off A636, 0.5m from jct 39 M1

Hotel ★★★ 68% Holiday Inn Wakefield, Queen's Dr, Ossett, WAKEFIELD ☎ 0870 400 9082 99 en suite

Wakefield Woodthorpe Ln, Sandal WF2 6JH
☎ 01924 258778 (sec) & 255380 (pro) 📠 01924 242752
A well-sheltered meadowland/heath course with easy walking and good views.
18 holes, 6653yds, Par 72, SSS 72, Course record 66.
Club membership 540.
Visitors contact must be made in advance. Visitors Wed, Thu and Fri only. **Societies** must apply in writing. **Green Fees** terms on application. **Prof** Ian M Wright **Course Designer** A McKenzie/S Herd **Facilities** ⊗ ⅷ ♭ 🏌 ♀ ♧ 🏠 ♂ **Location** 3m S of Wakefield, off A61

Hotel ★★★ 68% Holiday Inn Wakefield, Queen's Dr, Ossett, WAKEFIELD ☎ 0870 400 9082 99 en suite

Wetherby Linton Ln LS22 4JF
☎ 01937 580089 📠 01937 581915
e-mail: info@wetherbygolfclub.fsnet.co.uk
Parkland course with fine views.
18 holes, 6235yds, Par 71, SSS 70, Course record 63.
Club membership 650.
Visitors may not play Mon & Tues morning. **Societies** apply in writing,email or telephone in advance. **Green Fees** £28 per round;£35 per day(£40 per round/day weekends). **Prof** Mark Daubney **Facilities** ⊗ ⅷ ♭ 🏌 ♀ ♧ 🏠 ♂ 🎣 ♂ ♧ **Conf** Max 100 Board 15 **Location** 1m W off A661

Hotel ★★★♨ 73% Wood Hall Hotel, Trip Ln, Linton, WETHERBY ☎ 01937 587271
15 en suite 27 annexe en suite

The Village Golf Course Backstone Gill Ln
LS17 9JU ☎ 0113 273 7471
A 9 hole pay and play course in an elevated position enjoying long panoramic views. The holes are par 3, 4 and 5s and include water hazards and shaped large greens.
11 holes, 5700yds, Par 72, SSS 68, Course record 66.
Visitors smart casual wear **Societies** contact in advance by letter/telephone **Green Fees** £10 per 18 holes; £7 per 11 holes (£12/£8 weekends). **Course Designer** William Binner **Facilities** ⊗ ⅷ ♭ 🏌 ♂ ♧ **Leisure** fishing. **Location** signposted, 1m off A61, 2m off A58

Hotel ★★ 75% Aragon Hotel, 250 Stainbeck Ln, LEEDS ☎ 0113 275 9306 12 en suite 5 annexe en suite

CHANNEL ISLANDS
ALDERNEY

Alderney Route des Carrieres GY9 3YD
☎ 01481 822835
Undulating seaside course with sea on all sides, offering magnificent views from its high tees and greens. Course designed by Frank Pennink.
9 holes, 5006yds, Par 64, SSS 65, Course record 65.
Club membership 400.
Visitors may not play before 10am at weekends. Advisable
continued

---

to contact in advance. **Societies** must contact in advance. **Green Fees** not confirmed. **Cards** 💳 💳 💳 💳 💳 **Facilities** ⊗ by prior arrangement ♭ 🏌 ♀ ♧ 🏠 ♂ ♧ **Location** 1m E of St Annes

GUERNSEY

Royal Guernsey GY3 5BY
☎ 01481 246523 📠 01481 243960
e-mail: r-g-g-c@lineone.net
Not quite as old as its neighbour Royal Jersey, Royal Guernsey is a sporting course which was re-designed after World War II by Mackenzie Ross, who has many fine courses to his credit. It is a pleasant links, well-maintained, and administered by the States of Guernsey in the form of the States Tourist Committee. The 8th hole, a good par 4, requires an accurate second shot to the green set amongst the gorse and thick rough. The 18th, with lively views, needs a strong shot to reach the green well down below. The course is windy, with hard walking. There is a junior section.
18 holes, 6215yds, Par 70, SSS 70, Course record 64.
Club membership 934.
Visitors must have a handicap certificate; may not play on Thu, Sat afternoons & Sun. **Green Fees** not confirmed. **Prof** Norman Wood **Course Designer** Mackenzie Ross **Facilities** ⊗ ⅷ ♭ 🏌 ♀ ♧ 🏠 ♂ ♧ ♗ **Location** 3m N of St Peter Port

Hotel ★★★★ 70% St Pierre Park Hotel, Rohais, ST PETER PORT ☎ 01481 728282 131 en suite

La Grande Mare Vazon Bay GY5 7LL
☎ 01481 253544 📠 01481 255197
This hotel and golf complex is set in over 120 acres of land. The Hawtree designed parkland course opened in 1994 and was originally designed around 14 holes with four double greens. The course was extended to a full 18 holes in 2001. Practice areas are now in place along with a teaching area.
18 holes, 4517yards, Par 64, SSS 63, Course record 65.
Club membership 800.
Visitors may book a tee time up to 2 days in advance. **Societies** must book in advance. **Green Fees** Mon-Thurs £27 per 18 holes; £19 per 9 holes. Fri-Sun £29/£21. **Cards** 💳 💳 💳 💳 💳 **Prof** Matt Groves **Course Designer** Hawtree **Facilities** ⊗ ⅷ ♭ 🏌 ♀ ♧ 🏠 ♂ 🏠 ♂ ♧ ♗ **Leisure** hard tennis courts, outdoor and indoor heated swimming pools, fishing, sauna, gymnasium, sports massage.

Hotel ★★ 77% Hotel Hougue du Pommier, Hougue du Pommier Rd, CATEL ☎ 01481 256531 43 en suite

St Pierre Park Golf Club Rohais GY1 1FD
☎ 01481 728282 📠 01481 712041
e-mail: stppark@itl.net
Par 3 parkland course with delightful setting, with lakes, streams and many tricky holes.
9 holes, 2610yds, Par 54, SSS 50, Course record 52.
Club membership 200.
Visitors must book tee times. Strict dress code, contact club
continued

in advance for datails. **Societies** must contact in advance. **Green Fees** terms on application. **Cards** **Prof** Roy Corbet **Course Designer** Jacklin **Facilities** **Leisure** hard tennis courts, heated indoor swimming pool, sauna, solarium, gymnasium. **Conf** Thtr 200 Class 130 Board 25 Banquet 400 Del £30 to £170 * **Location** 1m W off Rohais Rd

Hotel ★★★★ 70% St Pierre Park Hotel, Rohais, ST PETER PORT ☎ 01481 728282 131 en suite

JERSEY

GROUVILLE Map 16

Royal Jersey Le Chemin au Greves JE3 9BD
☎ 01534 854416 📠 01534 854684
e-mail: thesecretary@royaljersey.com
A seaside links, historic because of its age: its centenary was celebrated in 1978. It is also famous for the fact that Britain's greatest golfer, Harry Vardon, was born in a little cottage on the edge of the course and learned his golf here.
18 holes, 6100yds, Par 70, SSS 70, Course record 63. Club membership 1209.
Visitors restricted to 10am-noon & 2pm-4pm Mon-Fri & after 2.30pm weekends & bank holidays. **Societies** welcome Mon-Fri. Must apply in writing. **Green Fees** £50 per round. **Cards** **Prof** David Morgan **Facilities**
Location 4m E of St Helier off coast rd

Hotel ★★★ 68% Old Court House Hotel, GOREY ☎ 01534 854444 58 en suite

LA MOYE Map 16

La Moye La Route Orange JE3 8GQ
☎ 01534 743401 📠 01534 747289
Seaside championship links course (venue for the Jersey Seniors Open) situated in an exposed position on the south western corner of the island overlooking St Ouens Bay. Offers spectacular views, two start points, full course all year - no temporary greens.
18 holes, 6664yds, Par 72, SSS 72, Course record 68. Club membership 1300.
Visitors must contact course ranger in advance 01534 747166. Visitors may play after 2.30pm weekends and bank holidays. **Societies** apply in writing. **Green Fees** £45 per round (£50 weekends & bank holidays). **Cards** **Prof** Mike Deeley **Course Designer** James Braid **Facilities**
Location W side of village off A13

Hotel ★★★★ 83% The Atlantic Hotel, Le Mont de la Pulente, ST BRELADE ☎ 01534 744101 50 en suite

ST CLEMENT Map 16

St Clement Jersey Recreation Grounds JE2 6PN
☎ 01534 21938
9 holes, 2244yds, Par 30.
Location E side of St Helier on A5
Telephone for further details

Hotel ★★★★ Longueville Manor Hotel, ST SAVIOUR ☎ 01534 725501 32 en suite

ST OUEN Map 16

Les Mielles Golf & Country Club JE3 7FQ
☎ 01534 482787 📠 01534 485414
e-mail: enquiry@lesmielles.co.je
Challenging seaside parkland course with bent grass greens, dwarf rye fairways and picturesque ponds situated in the Island's largest conservation area within St Ouen's Bay.
18 holes, 5770yds, Par 70, SSS 68, Course record 59. Club membership 1500.
Visitors welcome all times, prior booking recommended. **Societies** write in advance to avoid disappointment. **Green Fees** £34.50 per day; £23 per 18 holes; £15 per 9 holes (£38.50/£26/£17 weekends). **Cards** **Prof** Lee Elstone/Wayne Osmand **Course Designer** J Le Brun/R Whitehead **Facilities** **Leisure** Laser clay pigeon shooting. **Conf** Max 150
Location Centre of St Ouen's Bay

Hotel ★★★ 70% Silver Springs, La Route des Genets, ST BRELADE ☎ 01534 746401 88 en suite

ISLE OF MAN

CASTLETOWN Map 06 SC26

Castletown Golf Links Fort Island, Derbyhaven IM9 1UA
☎ 01624 822201 & 822211 (pro shop) 📠 01624 824633
e-mail: fowlds@enterprise.net
Set on the Langness Peninsula, this superb Championship course is surrounded on three sides by the sea, and holds many surprises from its Championship tees. The hotel offers many leisure facilities.

18 holes, 6750yds, Par 72, SSS 72, Course record 64. Club membership 600.
Visitors contact in advance. Sat reserved for hotel residents and club members. Ladies only Wed morning **Societies** must telephone in advance. **Green Fees** £50 per day (non-resident). **Cards** **Prof** Murray Crowe **Course Designer** McKenzie Ross **Facilities** **Leisure** heated indoor swimming pool, sauna. **Conf** Max 200 Thtr 200 Class 40 Board 20 Banquet 200 Del from £30

Hotel ★★★ 68% Castletown Golf Links Hotel, Fort Island, CASTLETOWN ☎ 01624 822201 58 en suite

DOUGLAS Map 06 SC37

Douglas Pulrose Park IM2 1AE ☎ 01624 675952
e-mail: mikevipondgolf@aol.com
Hilly, parkland and moorland course under the control of Douglas Corporation.

continued

18 holes, 5937yds, Par 69, SSS 69, Course record 62.
Club membership 330.
Visitors no restrictions. **Societies** telephone to book tee time.
Green Fees terms on application. **Prof** Mike Vipond **Course**
Designer Dr A Mackenzie **Facilities** ⊗ ⊪ ↳ ♥ ♀ ⚲ 🏠 ☂
♟ **Location** 1m outside Douglas on the Castletown Road on
the Pulrose Estate ··

Hotel ★★★ 67% The Empress Hotel, Central Promenade,
DOUGLAS ☎ 01624 661155 102 en suite

Mount Murray Hotel & Country Club Mount
Murray, Santon IM4 2HT
☎ 01624 661111 ▤ 01624 611116
e-mail: hotel@mountmurray.com
A challenging course with many natural features, lakes,
streams etc. Six par 5s, five par 3s and the rest par 4. Fine
views over the whole island.
18 holes, 6664yds, Par 73, SSS 73, Course record 69.
Club membership 378.
Visitors must contact in advance. Visitors may not play
before 9.30am weekends **Societies** telephone in advance.
Green Fees £25 (£30 weekends). **Cards** ▤ ▤ ▤ ▤ ▤
▤ **Prof** Andrew Dyson **Course Designer** Bingley Sports
Research **Facilities** ⊗ ⊪ ↳ ♥ ♀ ⚲ 🏠 ☂ ⟋ ▥ ⚲ ♟ ☂
Leisure hard tennis courts, heated indoor swimming pool,
squash, sauna, solarium, gymnasium. **Conf** Max 300 Thtr
300 Del from £32.50 * **Location** Located on main road 5m
from Douglas towards airport ·······································

Hotel ★★★★ 70% Mount Murray Hotel & Country Club,
Santon, DOUGLAS ☎ 01624 661111 90 en suite

ONCHAN	Map 06 SC47

King Edward Bay Golf & Country Club
Howstrake, Groudle Rd IM3 2JR ☎ 01624 672709
e-mail: mail@kebgc.com
Club plays over King Edward Bay course. Hilly seaside
links course with natural hazards and good views.
18 holes, 5485yds, Par 67, SSS 66, Course record 59.
Club membership 350.
Visitors must have a handicap certificate. **Societies** must
contact in advance. **Green Fees** £13 per day (£15 weekends).
Prof Donald Jones **Course Designer** Tom Morris **Facilities**
⊗ ⊪ ↳ ♥ ♀ ⚲ 🏠 ☂ ⟋ **Conf** Max 150 Banquet 100
Location E side of town off A11 ·······························

Hotel ★★★★ 69% Sefton Hotel, Harris Promenade,
DOUGLAS ☎ 01624 645500 104 en suite

PEEL	Map 06 SC28

Peel Rheast Ln IM5 1BG
☎ 01624 842227 & 843456 ▤ 01624 843456
e-mail: lcullen@peelgolfclub.idps.co.uk
Moorland course, with natural hazards and easy walking.

continued

Good views. The drop down to the 12th and climb back
up to the 13th interrupt an otherwise fairly level course.
The long, dog-legged 11th hole is an outstanding par 4,
where the gorse must be carried to get a good second shot
to the green. Most notable of the short holes are the 10th
and 17th where an errant tee shot finds bunker, gorse or
thick rough.
18 holes, 5850yds, Par 69, SSS 69, Course record 64.
Club membership 856.
Visitors must contact in advance. Limited availability
weekends. **Societies** apply in writing/telephone **Green Fees**
£20 per day (£27.50 weekends & bank holidays). **Cards** ▤
▤ ▤ ▤ ▤ **Prof** Murray Crowe **Course Designer** James
Braide **Facilities** ⊗ ⊪ by prior arrangement ↳ ♥ ♀ ⚲ 🏠 ☂
▧ ♟ **Leisure** snooker. **Location** SE side of town centre on A1
··

Hotel ★★★ 67% The Empress Hotel, Central Promenade,
DOUGLAS ☎ 01624 661155 102 en suite

PORT ERIN	Map 06 SC16

Rowany Rowany Dr IM9 6LN
☎ 01624 834108 or 834072 ▤ 01624 834072
Undulating seaside course with testing later holes, which
cut through gorse and rough. However, those familiar
with this course maintain that the 7th and 12th holes are
the most challenging.
18 holes, 5840yds, Par 70, SSS 69, Course record 66.
Club membership 550.
Visitors must contact in advance. **Societies** telephone in
advance. **Green Fees** not confirmed. **Course Designer** G
Lowe **Facilities** ⊗ ⊪ by prior arrangement ↳ ♥ ♀ ⚲ 🏠 ☂
▧ ♟ **Location** N side of village off A32
··

Hotel ★★★ 67% Ocean Castle Hotel, The Promenade,
PORT ERIN ☎ 01624 836399 40 en suite

PORT ST MARY	Map 06 SC26

Port St Mary Kallow Point Rd ☎ 01624 834932
Slightly hilly course with beautiful scenic views over Port
St Mary and the Irish Sea.
9 holes, 5702yds, Par 68, SSS 67, Course record 62.
Club membership 324.
Visitors anytime except between 8-10.30 weekends.
Societies contact for details. **Green Fees** £11.50 per
round/day. **Cards** ▤ ▤ ▤ ▤ **Course Designer** George
Duncan **Facilities** ⊗ ⊪ ↳ ♥ ♀ ⚲ 🏠 ☂ ♟ **Leisure** hard
tennis courts, Croquet lawn. **Location** Signposted on
entering Port St Mary ·······························

Hotel ★★★ 67% Ocean Castle Hotel, The Promenade,
PORT ERIN ☎ 01624 836399 40 en suite

RAMSEY	Map 06 SC49

Ramsey Brookfield IM8 2AH
☎ 01624 812244 ▤ 01624 815833
e-mail: ramsey.golfclub@iofm.net
Parkland course, with easy walking. Windy. Good views.
Testing holes: 1st, par 5; 18th, par 3.
18 holes, 5960yds, Par 70, SSS 69, Course record 63.
Club membership 1000.
Visitors contact in advance, visitors may not play before
10am weekdays. **Societies** must apply in advance. **Green**
Fees £23 per day(£26 per round weekends). **Cards** ▤ ▤
Prof Calum Wilson **Course Designer** James Braid **Facilities**
⊗ ⊪ ↳ ♥ ♀ ⚲ 🏠 ☂ ⟋ **Location** SW side of town
·······································

Hotel ★★★ 67% The Empress Hotel, Central Promenade,
DOUGLAS ☎ 01624 661155 102 en suite

Scotland

SCOTLAND

ABERDEEN CITY

ABERDEEN   Map 15 NJ90

Auchmill Bonnyview Rd, West Heatheryfold AB16 7FQ
☎ 01224 714577 📄 01224 648693
This course is definitely not for beginners - the fairways
are tree-lined and very tight on most holes. Three holes
are quite hilly and although the remainder is flat there
are nice views over Aberdeen. The course is not
recommended for anyone over 22 handicap unless they
have plenty of golf balls!
18 holes, 5123metres, Par 70, SSS 67, Course record 67.
Club membership 300.
Visitors members have priority Sat & Wed for club
competitions. **Societies** apply in writing to Art and
Recreation Dept, Aberdeen City Council. **Green Fees** £9 per
round. **Course Designer** Neil Coles/Brian Hugget **Facilities**
⊗ ⽚ ⭢ 🏌 ♀ ⛏ ⚑ **Location** Outskirts Aberdeen, A96
Aberdeen/Inverness

Hotel ★★★ 66% The Craighaar, Waterton Rd, Bankhead,
ABERDEEN ☎ 01224 712275 55 en suite

Balnagask St Fitticks Rd AB11 3QT
☎ 01224 876407 📄 01224 648693
Links course. Used by the Nigg Bay Club.
18 holes, 5986yds, Par 70, SSS 69.
Visitors book in person on day of play. **Societies** apply to
council tel 01224 522000. **Green Fees** not confirmed.
Facilities ⊗ ⽚ ⭢ 🏌 ♀ ⛏ ⚑ **Leisure** 9 hole pitch & putt
course. **Location** 2m E of city centre

Hotel ★★★ 67% Maryculter House Hotel, South Deeside
Rd, Maryculter, ABERDEEN ☎ 01224 732124 23 en suite

Craibstone Golf Centre Craibstone Estate,
Bucksburn AB21 9YA ☎ 01224 716777 📄 01224 711298
e-mail: s.may@absac.ac.uk
Course comprises two halves of quite different character
and appearance in its mixture of heath and parkland.
The wide fairways make drives look tempting and the
11th to 15th present a trio of holes that would fit into
many of the great parkland courses. The greens are top
quality despite their early years.
18 holes, 5613yards, Par 69, SSS 68, Course record 66.
Club membership 375.
Visitors seven day booking system. 50% of prime times for
visitors. **Societies** telephone in advance **Green Fees** £16 per
round (£20 weekends). **Cards** ▭ ▬ 🆔 **Facilities** ⊗ ⽚ ⭢
🏌 ♀ ⛏ ⚑ ⛳ ⛏ ⚑ **Leisure** sauna, gymnasium.
Location NW of city off A96 Aberdeen-Inverness road.
Take A96 through Bucksburn village and out of town past
research institute on right. Before the next roundabout take
turning left signed 'Forrit Brae' . At top of road there is a
sign for golf club.

Hotel ★★★★ 70% Aberdeen Marriott Hotel, Overton
Circle, Dyce, ABERDEEN ☎ 01224 770011 155 en suite

Deeside Golf Rd, Bieldside AB15 9DL
☎ 01224 869457 📄 01224 869457
e-mail:dgc@bieldside28.freeserve.co.uk
An interesting riverside course with several tree-lined
fairways. A stream comes into play at nine of the 18 holes
on the main course.
Deeside Golf Club-Haughton: 18 holes, 6286yds, Par 70,
SSS 71.   *continued*

Deeside Golf Club-Blairs: 9 holes, 5889yds, Par 70, SSS 67.
Club membership 1000.
Visitors must contact in advance, may not play competition
days. **Societies** apply in writing. **Green Fees** £45 per round
(£60 weekends and bank holidays). **Cards** ▭ ▬ ▬ 🆔
Prof Frank J Coutts **Facilities** ⊗ ⽚ ⭢ 🏌 ♀ ⛏ 🏠 ⚑
Location 3m W of city centre off A93

Hotel ★★★★ 73% Ardoe House, South Deeside Rd, Blairs,
ABERDEEN ☎ 01224 860600 112 en suite

Hazelhead Public Hazlehead AB1 8BD
☎ 01224 321830 📄 01224 648693
Both No 1 and No 2 courses are tree-lined. The 9 hole
course is open but surrounded by trees.
No 1 Course: 18 holes, 6211yds, Par 70, SSS 70.
No 2 Course: 18 holes, 5742yds, Par 67, SSS 67.
Visitors no restrictions. **Societies** must contact in advance.
Green Fees not confirmed. **Prof** A Smith/G Taylor/C Nelson
Facilities ⛏ 🏠 ⚑ ⚑ **Leisure** 9 hole pitch & putt course.
Location 4m W of city centre off A944

Hotel ★★★★ 73% Ardoe House, South Deeside Rd, Blairs,
ABERDEEN ☎ 01224 860600 112 en suite

Kings Links AB24 1RZ ☎ 01224 632269
📄 01224 648693
A typical links course with no tree lines and plenty of
bunkers.The 14th hole is tricky - a long par 4 with a
raised green and not much fairway round the green. The
course is playable all year. Nearby there is a 6-hole
course. The Bon Accord Club, Caledonian Club and
Northern Club play over this course.
18 holes, 6384yds, Par 72, SSS 71.
Visitors contact starters box on 01224 632269 regarding
booking of tee times. **Societies** write to the Arts &
Recreation Dept, St Nicholas House, Broad Street, Aberdeen.
Green Fees not confirmed. **Facilities** ⛏ **Location** 0.75m
NE of city centre

Hotel ★★★ 65% Grampian Hotel, Stirling St, ABERDEEN
☎ 01224 589101 49 en suite

Murcar Bridge of Don AB23 8BD
☎ 01224 704354 📄 01224 704354
e-mail: murcar-golf-club@lineone.net
Seaside links course, prevailing SW wind, hard-walking.
Testing 4th and 14th holes.
Murcar: 18 holes, 6287yds, Par 71, SSS 72,
Course record 64.
Strabathie: 9 holes, 2680yds, Par 35, SSS 35.
Club membership 850.
Visitors must contact in advance. **Societies** advance booking
required. **Green Fees** Murcar: £65 per day; £45 per round
(£75/£55 weekends and bank holidays). Strabathie: £20 per
day; £8 per 18 holes (£30/£12 weekends and bank holidays).
Cards ▭ ▬ ▬ 🆔 **Prof** Gary Forbes **Course Designer**
Archie Simpson **Facilities** ⊗ ⽚ ⭢ 🏌 ♀ ⛏ 🏠 ⚑ ⚑
Location 5m NE of city centre off A90

Hotel ★★★ 66% The Craighaar, Waterton Rd, Bankhead,
ABERDEEN ☎ 01224 712275 55 en suite

Royal Aberdeen Links Rd, Balgownie, Bridge of Don
AB23 8AT ☎ 01224 702571 📄 01224 826591
Championship links course with undulating dunes.
Windy, easy walking.
Balgownie Course: 18 holes, 6372yds, Par 71, SSS 71,
Course record 63.   *continued*

Silverburn Course: 18 holes, 4066yds, Par 60, SSS 60.
Club membership 500.
Visitors times for visitors 10-11.30 and 2-3.30pm weekdays,
after 3.30pm weekends. Must contact in advance. **Societies**
apply in writing. **Green Fees** £65 per round;£90 per
day(£75/£120 weekends). **Cards** 🖃 💳 **Prof** Ronnie
MacAskill **Course Designer** Baird & Simpson **Facilities** ⊗
🔥 💪 ♈ ⚒ 🏠 ✦ 🐾 **Location** 2.5m N of city centre off A92

Hotel ★★★ 65% Grampian Hotel, Stirling St, ABERDEEN
🕿 01224 589101 49 en suite

Westhill Westhill Heights, Westhill AB32 6RY
🕿 01224 742567 & 740159
📄 01224 749124&01224 740159
e-mail: WGolfclub@aol.com
A relatively new course, it is now maturing and has been
altered and improved since its opening.
18 holes, 5921yds, Par 69, SSS 69, Course record 65.
Club membership 808.
Visitors welcome except Saturdays. **Societies** telephone in
advance. **Green Fees** £14 per round(£20 weekends). **Cards**
🖃 💳 📶 💷 **Prof** George Bruce **Course Designer** Charles
Lawrie **Facilities** ⊗ 🍴 🔥 💪 ♈ ⚒ 🏠 ✦ 🐾 **Location** 7m
NW of city centre off A944

Hotel ★★★ 69% Westhill Hotel, Westhill, ABERDEEN
🕿 01224 740388 38 en suite

Peterculter Oldtown, Burnside Rd AB14 0LN
🕿 01224 734994(shop) & 735245(office) 📄 01224 735580
e-mail: info@petercultergolfclub.co.uk
The course is a tight par 68 (from Yellow tees) with a
beautiful par 2 2nd and two par 5 holes in excess of
500yds. Five new holes were brought into play in 2001.
Surrounded by wonderful scenery and bordered by the
River Dee, a variety of birds, deer and foxes may be seen
on the course, which also has superb views up the Dee
Valley.
18 holes, 6207yds, Par 71, SSS 70, Course record 64.
Club membership 1035.
Visitors contact 3 days in advance, welcome between 9am-
4pm weekdays.9.30am-6pm weekends. **Societies** contact up
to 7 days in advance. **Green Fees** £18 per round;£24 per
day(£20/£26 weekends). **Cards** 🖃 💳 📶 💷 **Prof** Dean
Vannet **Course Designer** Greens of Scotland **Facilities** ⊗ 🍴
🔥 💪 ♈ ⚒ 🏠 ✦ 🐾 ♺ 🐾 **Location** On A93

Hotel ★★★ 69% Westhill Hotel, Westhill, ABERDEEN
🕿 01224 740388 38 en suite

Aboyne Formaston Park AB34 5HP
🕿 013398 86328 📄 013398 87592
e-mail: aboynegolf@btinternet.com
Beautiful parkland with outstanding views. Two lochs on
course.
18 holes, 5975yds, Par 68, SSS 69, Course record 62.
Club membership 930.
Visitors no restrictions. Advisable to contact in advance.
Societies prior booking essential. **Green Fees** terms on
application. **Cards** 🖃 💳 **Prof** Stephen Moir **Facilities**
⊗ 🍴 🔥 💪 ♈ ⚒ 🏠 ✦ 🐾 **Location** E side of village,
N of A93

continued

Hotel ★★ 70% Loch Kinord Hotel, Ballater Rd, Dinnet,
BALLATER 🕿 013398 85229 11 rms (9 en suite)

Alford Montgarrie Rd AB33 8AE
🕿 019755 62178 📄 019755 62178
e-mail: golf@alford.co.uk
A flat parkland course in scenic countryside. Divided into
sections by a road, a narrow-gauge railway and a burn.
18 holes, 5483yds, Par 69, SSS 65, Course record 64.
Club membership 600.
Visitors advisable to contact in advance. **Societies**
telephone/e-mail in advance. **Green Fees** £19 per day; £13
per round (£26/£20 weekends). **Cards** 🖃 💳 **Facilities** ⊗
🍴 🔥 💪 ♈ ⚒ 🏠 ✦ 🐾 **Location** In the centre of the village
on A944

Hotel ★★ 63% Gordon Arms Hotel, The Square, HUNTLY
🕿 01466 792288 13 en suite

Auchenblae AB30 1WQ 🕿 01561 320002
Picturesque, small, undulating parkland course offering
good views, currently being upgraded to allow safer play
and longer, more spacious greens and tees.
9 holes, 2226yds, Par 33, SSS 61, Course record 59.
Club membership 450.
Visitors restricted Wed & Fri evenings during peak season
but telephone to confirm. **Societies** must telephone in
advance. **Green Fees** £9 per day(£12 weekends). **Course
Designer** Robin Hiseman **Facilities** 💪 🐾 🐾 **Location**
0.5m NE

Hotel ★★ 66% County Hotel & Leisure Club, Arduthie Rd,
STONEHAVEN 🕿 01569 764386 14 en suite

Ballater Victoria Rd AB35 5QX
🕿 013397 55567 📄 013397 55057
e-mail: ballater@ifb.co.uk
Heather covered course with testing long holes and
beautiful scenery.
18 holes, 5638yds, Par 67, SSS 67, Course record 62.
Club membership 750.
Visitors advisable to contact in advance. **Societies** prior
booking recommended. **Green Fees** terms on application.
Cards 🖃 💳 📶 💷 **Prof** Bill Yule **Facilities** ⊗ 🍴 🔥 💪 ♈
🐾 🏠 ✦ 🐾 🐾 🐾 **Leisure** hard tennis courts, fishing,
snooker. **Location** W side of town

Hotel ★★★ 77% Darroch Learg Hotel, Braemar Rd,
BALLATER 🕿 013397 55443 13 en suite 5 annexe en suite

East Aberdeenshire Golf Centre Millden
AB23 8YY 🕿 01358 742111 📄 01358 742123
e-mail: info@eagolf.com
Designed as two loops of 9 holes each, starting and
finishing outside the clubhouse. Skilful use of 130 acres of
rolling Buchan farmland has resulted in a challenging
course of 6276 yards in length. Even in the short history
of the course, the par 3 holes have gained the reputation
of being on an equal with any in the North of Scotland.
18 holes, 6276yards, Par 71, SSS 71, Course record 69.
Club membership 400.
Visitors telephone pro shop to book tee time on 01358
742111 ext 21 **Societies** write/telephone to Sandra Watson.

continued

Green Fees £16 (£20 weekends and bank holidays). **Cards** ▦ ▦ ▦ Ⓟ **Prof** Ian Bratton **Course Designer** Ian Cresswell **Facilities** ⊗ ⅷ ዬ ♥ ♀ ♨ 🏠 ⛳ ⅄ ⚑ ⚒ ⚐ ⟋ ⟊

Hotel ★★★ 65% Holiday Inn Aberdeen, Claymore Dr, Bridge of Don, ABERDEEN ☎ 0870 400 9046 123 en suite

BANCHORY   Map 15 NO69

Banchory Kinneskie Rd AB31 5TA
☎ 01330 822365 🗎 01330 822491
Sheltered parkland course situated beside the River Dee, with easy walking and woodland scenery. Twelfth and 13th holes are testing.
18 holes, 5781yds, Par 69, SSS 68, Course record 65.
Club membership 975.
Visitors must contact in advance, telephone for details on 01330 822447 **Societies** must book in advance. **Green Fees** £28 per day, £20 per round (£23 per round weekends). **Cards** ▦ ▦ ▦ Ⓟ **Prof** David Naylor **Facilities** ⊗ ⅷ ዬ ♥ ♀ ⅄ 🏠 ⚑ ⚒ ⚐ **Location** A93, 300 yds from W end of High St

Hotel ★★★★♨ 75% Banchory Lodge Hotel, BANCHORY ☎ 01330 822625 22 en suite

Inchmarlo Golf Centre Inchmarlo AB31 4BQ
☎ 01330 822557 🗎 01330 822557
e-mail: info@inchmarlo.com
The Laird's (18 hole course) is laid out on the gentle parkland slopes of the Inchmarlo Estate and the designer has take advantage of the natural contours of the land and its many mature trees. The nine hole facility is a tricky and testing course with ponds, meandering burns and dry stone wall combined with the more traditional bunkers to test the skill of even the most accomplished player.
Laird's Course: 18 holes, 6218yards, Par 71, SSS 71.
9 holes, 1996yards, Par 32, SSS 32.
Club membership 650.
Visitors booking in advance preferred. **Societies** must book in advance **Green Fees** Laird's Course: £30 per round (£35 weekends). 9 hole course: £15 per 18 holes; £10 per 9 holes (£17/£11 weekends. **Cards** ▦ ▦ ▦ Ⓟ ▦ ▦ Ⓟ **Prof** Patrick Lovie **Course Designer** Graeme Webster **Facilities** ⊗ ⅷ ዬ ♥ ♀ ⅄ 🏠 ⚑ ⚒ ⚐ ⟋ ⟊ **Location** 0.5m from A93 Aberdeen-Braemar road

Hotel ★★★ 78% Tor-na-Coille Hotel, BANCHORY ☎ 01330 822242 22 en suite

BANFF   Map 15 NJ66

Duff House Royal The Barnyards AB45 3SX
☎ 01261 812062 🗎 01261 812224
e-mail: duff-house-royal@btinternet.com
Well-manicured flat parkland, bounded by woodlands and River Deveron. Well bunkered and renowned for its large, two-tier greens. The river is a hazard for those who wander off the tee at the 7th, 16th and 17th holes.
18 holes, 6161yds, Par 68, SSS 70, Course record 63.
Club membership 1000.
Visitors telephone professional in advance, handicap certificate is preferred. Restrictions at weekends during summer. **Societies** must apply in writing. **Green Fees** £24 per day; £18 per round (£30/£25 weekends). **Cards** Ⓟ **Prof** Bob Strachan **Course Designer** Dr McKenzie **Facilities** ⊗ ⅷ ዬ ♥ ♀ ⅄ 🏠 ⟋ **Location** 0.5m S on A98

continued

BANFF SPRINGS
H O T E L

AA
★★★

Overlooking the golden sands of the Moray Firth. Superb choice of golf courses nearby. Close to whisky and castle trails.
Banff enjoys lower than average rainfall levels and reasonable green fees – what a boost to the avid golfer! Superb restaurant and bar facilities with the Taste of Scotland award. 31 ensuite bedrooms and resident fitness suite.
Come, relax and enjoy!

Banff Springs Hotel,

Golden Knowes Road,

Banff AB45 2JE.

Tel: (01261) 812881.

Fax: (01261) 815546.

www.banffspringhotel.co.uk

Hotel ★★★ 68% Banff Springs Hotel, Golden Knowes Rd, BANFF ☎ 01261 812881 31 en suite

BRAEMAR   Map 15 NO19

Braemar Cluniebank Rd AB35 5XX
☎ 013397 41618 🗎 013397 41400
Flat course, set amid beautiful countryside on Royal Deeside, with River Clunie running through several holes. The 2nd hole is one of the most testing in the area.
18 holes, 5000yds, Par 65, SSS 64, Course record 59.
Club membership 450.
Visitors are advised to book 24 hours in advance to play on weekends. Tee reserved until 12.30 on Sat for members only. **Societies** must contact secretary in advance 01224 704471. **Green Fees** £20 per day;£15 per round(£26/£18 weekends). **Course Designer** Joe Anderson **Facilities** ⊗ ⅷ ዬ ♥ ♀ ⅄ 🏠 ⚑ ⟋ **Location** 0.5m S

Hotel ★★★ 66% The Invercauld Arms, BRAEMAR ☎ 013397 41605 68 en suite

CRUDEN BAY
Map 15 NK03

Cruden Bay Aulton Rd AB42 0NN
☎ 01779 812285 ▤ 01779 812945
e-mail: cbaygc@aol.com
A typical links course which epitomizes the old fashioned style of rugged links golf. The drives require accuracy with bunkers and protecting greens, blind holes and undulating greens. The 10th provides a panoramic view of half the back nine down at beach level, and to the east can be seen the outline of the spectacular ruin of Slains Castle featured in Bram Stoker's Dracula. The figure eight design of the course is quite unusual.
Main Course: 18 holes, 6395yds, Par 70, SSS 72, Course record 65.
St Olaf Course: 9 holes, 5106yds, Par 64, SSS 65.
Club membership 1100.
Visitors welcome on weekdays, at weekends only when there are no competitions, advisable to contact for details. Societies weekdays only telephone in advance. Green Fees terms on application. Cards ▤▤ ▤▤ ▤▤ ▤ Prof Robbie Stewart Course Designer Thomas Simpson Facilities ⊗ 〕Ⅲ ﾋ ♥ ♀ ♧ ⇲ 〒 ✔ 〔 Location SW side of village on A975

Hotel ★★ 70% Red House Hotel, Aulton Rd, CRUDEN BAY ☎ 01779 812215 6 rms (5 en suite)

ELLON
Map 15 NJ93

McDonald Hospital Rd AB41 9AW
☎ 01358 720576 ▤ 01358 720001
e-mail: mcdonald.golf@virgin.net
Tight, parkland course with streams.
18 holes, 5986yds, Par 70, SSS 70.
Club membership 710.
Visitors advisable to book in advance Societies telephone in advance. Green Fees £15 per round;£21 per day(£18/£26 weekends). Cards ▤▤ ▤▤ ▤▤ ▤ Prof Ronnie Urquhart Facilities ⊗ 〕Ⅲ ﾋ ♥ ♀ ♧ 〒 ✔ Location 0.25m N on A948

Hotel ★★ 72% Udny Arms Hotel, Main St, NEWBURGH ☎ 01358 789444 26 en suite

FRASERBURGH
Map 15 NJ96

Fraserburgh AB43 8TL
☎ 01346 516616 & 518287 ▤ 01346 516616
e-mail: fburghgolf@aol.com
Testing seaside course, natural links. An extremely scenic course, surrounded and protected by substantial sand dunes.
Corbie: 18 holes, 6278yds, Par 70, SSS 70, Course record 65.
Rosehill: 9 holes, 2400yds, Par 66, SSS 66.
Club membership 650.
Visitors no restrictions but advised to check availability. Societies must contact in advance. Green Fees Corbie: £22 per day; £17 per round (£27/£22 weekends). Rosehill: £10 per day;£5 per 9 holes (£12/£6 weekends). Course Designer James Braid Facilities ⊗ 〕Ⅲ ﾋ ♥ ♀ ♧ 〒 ✔ Leisure Various open competitions throughout the year. Location 1m SE on B9033

Hotel ★★★★ 64% Waterside Inn, Fraserburgh Rd, PETERHEAD ☎ 01779 471121
69 en suite 40 annexe en suite

HUNTLY
Map 15 NJ53

Huntly Cooper Park AB54 4SH ☎ 01466 792643
18 holes, 5399yds, Par 67, SSS 66.
Location N side of Huntly, turn off A96 at bypass roundabout
Telephone for further details
....

Hotel ★★ 63% Gordon Arms Hotel, The Square, HUNTLY ☎ 01466 792288 13 en suite

INSCH
Map 15 NJ62

Insch Golf Ter AB52 6JY
☎ 01464 820363 ▤ 01464 820363
e-mail: inschgolf@euphony.net
A challenging 18 hole course, a mixture of flat undulating parkland, with trees, stream and pond. The most challenging hole of the course is the 9th, a testing par 5 of 536 yards requiring long and accurate play. This follows the par 3 8th, a hole which demands a well positioned tee shot played over a large water hazard to a long narrow green. Although a relatively short course, the natural woodland, water hazards and large contoured greens require accurate play.
18 holes, 5350yds, Par 69, SSS 67.
Club membership 400.
Visitors restricted during club competitions and Tee times, ie Mon - Ladies night, Tue - Mens night, Wed - juniors, telephone clubhouse 01464 820363 for information. Pre-booking is advised. Societies apply in writing or telephone, bookings accepted. Green Fees £16 per round. Course Designer Greens of Scotland Facilities ⊗ by prior arrangement 〕Ⅲ by prior arrangement ﾋ ♥ ♀ ♧ ⇲ ✔
Location A96
....

Hotel ★★★ 67% Strathburn Hotel, Burghmuir Dr, INVERURIE ☎ 01467 624422 25 en suite

INVERALLOCHY
Map 15 NK06

Inverallochy Whitelink AB43 8XY ☎ 01346 582000
Seaside links course with natural hazards, tricky par 3s and easy walking.
18 holes, 5351yds, Par 66, SSS 66, Course record 57.
Club membership 600.
Visitors restricted at weekends and competition days, contact for availability. Societies apply in writing/telephone in advance. Green Fees not confirmed. Facilities ⊗ 〕Ⅲ ﾋ ♥ ♀ ♧ Location E side of village off B9107
....

Hotel ★★★★ 64% Waterside Inn, Fraserburgh Rd, PETERHEAD ☎ 01779 471121
69 en suite 40 annexe en suite

INVERURIE
Map 15 NJ72

Inverurie Blackhall Rd AB51 5JB
☎ 01467 624080 ▤ 01467 621051
e-mail: administrator@inveruriegc.co.uk
Parkland course, part of which is through a wooded area.
18 holes, 5711yds, Par 69, SSS 68, Course record 63.
Club membership 750.
Visitors book tee time through shop up to 24 hrs in advance 01467 620193. Societies telephone administrator. Green Fees £20 per day; £16 per round (£26/£20 weekends). Cards ▤▤ ▤▤ ▤▤ ▤ Prof Mark Lees Facilities ⊗ 〕Ⅲ ﾋ ♥ ♀ ♧ 〒 ✔ Location accessible from Blackhall rdbt off A96 bypass
....

Hotel ★★★ 67% Strathburn Hotel, Burghmuir Dr, INVERURIE ☎ 01467 624422 25 en suite

KEMNAY   Map 15 NJ71

Kemnay Monymusk Rd AB51 5RA
☎ 01467 642225 shop & 643746 office 📠 01467 643746
A parkland course with stunning views, incorporating
both tree lined and open fairways and a stream crossing
four holes. The course is not physically demanding but a
challenge is presented to every level of golfer due to the
diverse characteristics of each hole.
18 holes, 6342yds, Par 71, SSS 71, Course record 67.
Club membership 800.
Visitors telephone shop for booking. Societies must
telephone in advance. Green Fees £24 per day;£18 per
round(£24/£22 weekends). Prof Ronnie McDonald Course
Designer Greens of Scotland Facilities ⊗ ⅷ ⅃ 🖤 ♀ ♨ 🏠
🏌 🥅 🏧 ✓ Location W side of village on B993

Hotel ★★★ 69% Westhill Hotel, Westhill, ABERDEEN
☎ 01224 740388 38 en suite

KINTORE   Map 15 NJ71

Kintore Balbithan AB51 0UR
☎ 01467 632631 📠 01467 632995
e-mail: kintoregolfclub@lineone.net
The course covers a large area of ground from the Don
Basin, near the clubhouse, to mature woodland at the far
perimeter. The 1st is one of the toughest opening holes in
the North East and the 7th requires an accurate drive
followed by second shot over a burn which runs
diagonally across the front of the green. The 11th is the
longest hole on the course, made longer by the fact that it
slopes upwards all the way to the green. The final holes
are short, relatively hilly and quite tricky but offer
spectacular views to the Bennachie and Grampian ranges
of hills.
18 holes, 6019yds, Par 70, SSS 69, Course record 62.
Club membership 700.
Visitors during season booking system is in operation &
slots for visitors are available. Other times can be booked 24
hours in advance. Societies apply in writing or telephone.
Green Fees terms on application. Facilities ⊗ ⅷ ⅃ 🖤 ♀
♨ 🥅 ✓ Location 1m from village centre on B977

Hotel ★★ 66% Torryburn Hotel, School Rd, KINTORE
☎ 01467 632269 9 rms (8 en suite)

MACDUFF   Map 15 NJ76

Royal Tarlair Buchan St AB44 1TA
☎ 01261 832897 📠 01261 833455
e-mail: info@royaltarlair.co.uk
Seaside clifftop course. Testing 13th, 'Clivet' (par 3).
18 holes, 5866yds, Par 71, SSS 68, Course record 62.
Club membership 520.
Visitors no restrictions. Societies apply in writing. Green
Fees £15 per round(£20 per day). Facilities ⊗ ⅷ ⅃ 🖤 ♀ ♨
🏠 🏌 ✓ Location 0.75m E off A98

Hotel ★★★ 68% Banff Springs Hotel, Golden Knowes Rd,
BANFF ☎ 01261 812881 31 en suite

NEWBURGH   Map 15 NJ92

Newburgh on Ythan Beach Rd AB41 6BE
☎ 01358 789058
e-mail: secretary@newburgh-on-ythan.co.uk
This seaside course was founded in 1888 and is adjacent
to a bird sanctuary. The course was extended in 1996 and
the nine new holes, the outward half, are characterised by
undulations and hills, with elevated tees and greens

continued

requiring a range of shot making. The original inward
nine demands accurate golf from tee to green. Testing
550yd dog-leg (par 5).
18 holes, 6162yds, Par 72, SSS 70, Course record 68.
Club membership 800.
Visitors must contact in advance, may not play Sat am.
Societies apply in advance. Green Fees terms on application.
Cards 💳 💳 💳 💳 Facilities ⊗ ⅷ ⅃ 🖤 ♀ ♨ 🏠 ✓ 🏧
Leisure hard tennis courts. Location 10 miles of Aberdeen
on A975 (off A90)

Hotel ★★ 72% Udny Arms Hotel, Main St, NEWBURGH
☎ 01358 789444 26 en suite

NEWMACHAR   Map 15 NJ81

Newmachar Swailend AB21 7UU
☎ 01651 863002 📠 01651 863055
e-mail: newmachargolfclub@compuserve.com
Hawkshill is a championship-standard parkland course
designed by Dave Thomas. Several lakes affect five of the
holes and there are well developed birch and Scots pine
trees. Swailend is a parkland course, also designed by
Dave Thomas and opened in 1997. It provides a test all of
its own with some well positioned bunkering and testing
greens.
Hawkshill Course: 18 holes, 6623yds, Par 72, SSS 74,
Course record 67.
Swailend Course: 18 holes, 6338yds, Par 72, SSS 71,
Course record 67.
Club membership 900.
Visitors contact in advance & must have handicap certificate
for Hawkshill course. Societies apply in writing. Green Fees
Hawkshill;£30 per round;£45 per day(£40 weekends per
round) Swailend:£15 per round;£25 per day(£20/£30
weekends). Cards 💳 💳 💳 💳 Prof Gordon Simpson
Course Designer Dave Thomas/Peter Allis Facilities ⊗ ⅷ
⅃ 🖤 ♀ ♨ 🏠 🏌 🥅 🏧 ✓ 🏧 Conf max 120 Location 2m N
of Dyce, off A947

Hotel ★★★ 67% Strathburn Hotel, Burghmuir Dr,
INVERURIE ☎ 01467 624422 25 en suite

OLDMELDRUM   Map 15 NJ82

Old Meldrum Kirk Brae AB51 0DJ
☎ 01651 872648 📠 01651 873555
Parkland course with tree-lined fairways and superb
views. Challenging 196yd, par 3, 11th over two ponds to a
green surrounded by bunkers.
18 holes, 5988yds, Par 70, SSS 69, Course record 66.
Club membership 700.
Visitors may not play during Club competitions. Societies
apply in writing to secretary Green Fees £14 per day/round
(£24 per day; £20 per round weekends). Prof Hamish Love
Course Designer Various Facilities ⊗ ⅷ ⅃ 🖤 ♀ ♨ 🏠 🏌
🥅 ✓ Location E side of village off A947

Hotel ★★★ 67% Strathburn Hotel, Burghmuir Dr,
INVERURIE ☎ 01467 624422 25 en suite

PETERHEAD   Map 15 NK14

Peterhead Craigewan Links, Riverside Dr AB42 1LT
☎ 01779 472149 & 480725 📠 01779 480725
e-mail: phdgc@freenetname.co.uk
The Old Course is a natural links course bounded by the
sea and the River Ugie. Varying conditions of play
depending on wind and weather. The New Course is more
of a parkland course.
Old Course: 18 holes, 6173yds, Par 70, SSS 71,
Course record 64.

continued

New Course: 9 holes, 2228yds, Par 31.
Club membership 650.
Visitors welcome any day apart from Saturdays, restricted times on the Old Course. Telephone for details. **Societies** apply in writing, restricted availablility on Saturdays **Green Fees** terms on application. **Cards** 💳 **Course Designer** W Park/ L Auchterconie/J Braid **Facilities** ⊗)⊞ ⛳ 🛒 ♀ ♨ ⚐ ⚑ *Location* N side of town centre off A90

Hotel ★★★★ 64% Waterside Inn, Fraserburgh Rd, PETERHEAD ☎ 01779 471121 69 en suite 40 annexe en suite

PORTLETHEN   Map 15 NO99

Portlethen Badentoy Rd AB12 4YA
☎ 01224 782575 & 781090 🖹 01224 781090
18 holes, 6707yds, Par 72, SSS 72, Course record 63.
Course Designer Cameron Sinclair **Location** Off A90 S of Aberdeen
Telephone for further details

Hotel ★★ 66% County Hotel & Leisure Club, Arduthie Rd, STONEHAVEN ☎ 01569 764386 14 en suite

STONEHAVEN   Map 15 NO88

Stonehaven Cowie AB39 3RH
☎ 01569 762124 🖹 01569 765973
Challenging meadowland course overlooking sea with three gullies and splendid views.
18 holes, 5103yds, Par 66, SSS 65, Course record 61.
Club membership 850.
Visitors prefer prior booking, may not play before 4pm Sat. **Societies** telephone or fax in advance to W A Donald. **Green Fees** £20 per day;£15 per round(£25/£22 weekends). **Cards** 💳 💳 💳 💷 **Course Designer** C Simpson **Facilities** ⊗)⊞ ⛳ 🛒 ♀ ♨ 🏠 ⚐ ⚑ **Leisure** snooker. **Location** 1m N off A92

Hotel ★★ 66% County Hotel & Leisure Club, Arduthie Rd, STONEHAVEN ☎ 01569 764386 14 en suite

TARLAND   Map 15 NJ40

Tarland Aberdeen Rd AB34 4TB
☎ 013398 81000 🖹 013398 81000
Difficult upland course, but easy walking. Some spectacular holes, mainly 4th (par 4) and 5th (par 3) and fine scenery.
9 holes, 5888yds, Par 67, SSS 68, Course record 65.
Club membership 406.
Visitors must contact in advance. **Societies** must telephone in advance. **Green Fees** £15 per day (£20 weekends). **Course Designer** Tom Morris **Facilities** ⊗)⊞ ⛳ 🛒 ♀ ♨ 🏠 ⚐ **Location** E side of village off B9119

Hotel ★★ 70% Loch Kinord Hotel, Ballater Rd, Dinnet, BALLATER ☎ 013398 85229 11 rms (9 en suite)

TORPHINS   Map 15 NJ60

Torphins Bog Rd AB31 4JU
☎ 013398 82115 & 82402 (Sec) 🖹 013398 82402
e-mail: stuart@macgregor5.fsnet.co.uk
Heathland/parkland course built on a hill with views of the Cairngorms.
9 holes, 4800yds, Par 64, SSS 64, Course record 63.
Club membership 380.
Visitors Restricted on competition days (alternate Sat and Sun).No visitors on Tuesday evenings. **Societies** apply in advance. **Green Fees** terms on application. **Facilities** ⊗ ⛳ 🛒 ♨ **Location** 0.25m W of village off A980 *continued*

Hotel ★★★ 78% Tor-na-Coille Hotel, BANCHORY
☎ 01330 822242 22 en suite

TURRIFF   Map 15 NJ74

Turriff Rosehall AB53 4HD
☎ 01888 562982 🖹 01888 568050
e-mail: grace@turriffgolf.sol.co.uk
A well-maintained parkland course alongside the River Deveron in picturesque surroundings. Sixth and 12th particularly challenging in a testing course.
18 holes, 6107yds, Par 70, SSS 69, Course record 64.
Club membership 860.
Visitors may not play before 10am weekends. Must contact in advance. **Societies** apply in writing to the secretary. **Green Fees** terms on application. **Prof** John Black **Facilities** ⊗)⊞ ⛳ 🛒 ♀ ♨ 🏠 ⚐ **Location** 1m W off B9024

Hotel ★★★ 68% Banff Springs Hotel, Golden Knowes Rd, BANFF ☎ 01261 812881 31 en suite

ANGUS

ARBROATH   Map 12 NO64

Arbroath Elliot DD11 2PE
☎ 01241 872069 & 875837 🖹 01241 875837
e-mail: golfshop@fsmail.net
This predominantly flat course with its wide undulating fairways and controlled rough 'flatters to deceive'. Sea breezes combined with fast greens and difficult approaches catch out the unwary, as will the subtly positioned bunkers.
18 holes, 6185yds, Par 70, SSS 69, Course record 64.
Club membership 550.
Visitors contact professional 01241 875837. **Societies** contact professional 01241 875837. **Green Fees** £18 per round;£24 per day(£24/£32 weekends). **Prof** Lindsay Ewart **Course Designer** Braid **Facilities** ⊗)⊞ ⛳ 🛒 ♀ ♨ 🏠 ⚐ ⚑ **Location** 2m SW on A92

Hotel ★★ 65% Hotel Seaforth, Dundee Rd, ARBROATH ☎ 01241 872232 19 en suite

Letham Grange Colliston DD11 4RL
☎ 01241 890373 & 809377 🖹 01241 890725
e-mail: lethamgrange@sol.co.uk
Often referred to as the 'Augusta of Scotland', the Old Course provides championship standards in spectacular surroundings with attractive lochs and burns. The Glens Course is less arduous and shorter using many natural features of the estate.

Old Course: 18 holes, 6632yds, Par 73, SSS 73, Course record 68.

continued

Glens Course: 18 holes, 5528yds, Par 68, SSS 68,
Course record 63.
Club membership 850.
Visitors no visitors weekends before 9.30am, Old Course
before 10am Tue & Glens Course before 10am Fri. **Societies**
telephone in advance. **Green Fees** Old Course: £35 (£40
weekends). Glens Course: £18 (£22.50 weekends). **Cards**
〓 ■■ ⚏ ⚏ ▨ ⚏ **Prof** Steven Moir **Course Designer**
G K Smith/Donald Steel **Facilities** ⊗ ⅷ ⅃ ⚏ ♀ ♨ ⚐ ⚑
⚏ ⚏ ⚏ **Location** 4m N on A933

Hotel ★★★ 64% The Letham Grange Mansion House
Hotel, Colliston, ARBROATH ☎ 01241 890373
19 en suite 22 annexe en suite

BARRY   Map 12 NO53

Panmure Burnside Rd DD7 7RT
☎ 01241 855120 ▤ 01241 859737
e-mail: secretary@panmuregolfclub.co.uk
A nerve-testing, adventurous course set amongst
sandhills - its hazards belie the quiet nature of the
opening holes. This tight links has been used as a
qualifying course for the Open Championship, and
features Ben Hogan's favourite hole, the dog-leg 6th,
which heralds the toughest stretch, around the turn.
18 holes, 6317yds, Par 70, SSS 71, Course record 62.
Club membership 700.
Visitors may not play Tuesday am,Saturday before 4pm.
Parties of 5 or more must contact in advance. **Societies**
must contact secretary in advance. **Green Fees** £60 per
day; £45 per round. **Cards** 〓 ■■ ⚏ ▨ **Prof** Neil
Mackintosh **Facilities** ⊗ ⅷ ⅃ ⚏ ♀ ♨ ⚐ ⚑ ⚏ ⚏ ⚏
Location S side of village off A930

BRECHIN   Map 15 NO56

Brechin Trinity DD9 7PD
☎ 01356 622383 ▤ 01356 626925
Rolling parkland course, with easy walking and good
views of Strathmore Valley and Grampian Mountains.
18 holes, 6092yds, Par 72, SSS 70, Course record 66.
Club membership 850.
Visitors contact Professional on 01356 625270 in advance.
Restricted weekends. **Societies** must contact club steward in
advance. **Green Fees** £28 per day; £20 per round (£33/£25
weekends). **Prof** Stephen Rennie **Course Designer** James
Braid (partly) **Facilities** ⊗ ⅷ ⅃ ⚏ ♀ ♨ ⚐ ⚑
Leisure squash. **Location** 1m N on B966

Hotel ★★ 64% Northern Hotel, 2/4 Clerk St, BRECHIN
☎ 01356 625505 16 en suite

LETHAM GRANGE
RESORT
HOTEL

AA
★★★★
Colliston by
Arbroath
Angus DD11 4RL
Tel: 01241 890373 Fax: 01241 890725
E-mail: lethamgrange@sol.co.uk
Situated in the heart of Angus countryside
with many sporting and leisure pursuits on
the estate, Letham Grange offers a tranquil
oasis in which to recharge.
The main house is a beautifully restored
Victorian mansion and the Golf Estate rooms
set in the grounds offer a good quality. Friendly,
efficient staff serving a mix of Scottish and
French cuisine.
Taste of Scotland Recommended

CARNOUSTIE See page 297   Map 12 NO53

EDZELL   Map 15 NO66

Edzell High St DD9 7TF
☎ 01356 647283 (Secretary) ▤ 01356 648094
e-mail: secretary@edzellgolfclub.demon.co.uk
This delightful course is situated in the foothills of the
Scottish Highlands and provides good golf as well as
conveying a feeling of peace and quiet to everyone who
plays there. The village of Edzell is one of the most
picturesque in Scotland.
18 holes, 6348yds, Par 71, SSS 71, Course record 62.
9 holes, 2057yds, Par 32, SSS 31.
Club membership 855.
Visitors may not play 4.45-6.15 weekdays & 7.30-10, 12-
2 weekends. Not before 2pm on 1st Sat each month.
Societies must contact secretary at least 14 days in
advance. **Green Fees** £34 per day; £24 per round
(£44/£30 weekends).Westwater;£10 per 9 holes;£15 per
18 holes. **Cards** 〓 ■■ ▨ **Prof** A J Webster **Course
Designer** Bob Simpson **Facilities** ⊗ ⅷ ⅃ ⚏ ♀ ♨ ⚐ ⚑
⚏ ⚏ ⚏ **Location** N of Brechin on A90, take B966
signposted Edzell, continue 3.5 miles

Hotel ★★★ 65% Glenesk Hotel, High St, EDZELL
☎ 01356 648319 24 en suite

FORFAR   Map 15 NO45

Forfar Cunninghill, Arbroath Rd DD8 2RL
☎ 01307 463773 ▤ 01307 468495
e-mail: forfargolfclub@uku.co.uk
Moorland course with wooded, undulating fairways,
excellent greens and fine views.   *continued*

Carnoustie Golf Links

Carnoustie, *Angus* ☎ **01241 853789** Fax **01241 852720** Map **12 NO53**

e-mail: administrator@carnoustiegolflinks.co.uk

This Championship Course has been voted the top course in Britain by many golfing greats and described as Scotland's ultimate golfing challenge. The course developed from origins in the 1560s; James Braid added new bunkers, greens and tees in the 1920s. The Open Championship was played here six times between 1931 and 1999. Carnoustie hosted the Scottish Open in 1995 and 1996.

The Burnside Course is shorter and tighter than the Championship Course and has been used for Open Championship qualifying rounds. The Buddon Course has been extensively remodelled making it ideal for mid to high handicappers. It features two ponds which come into play at four holes.

Visitors must contact in advance, Sat after 2pm, Sun after 11.30am. Must have handicap certificate for Championship Course

Societies must contact in advance

Green Fees Championship £80; Burnside £25; Buddon £20 ▬ ▓▓ ▭▭ ▓▓ ▚▚ ▣

Facilities ⛴ 🏠 🍴 Professional (Lee Vannet)

Leisure swimming, sauna, solarium, gym

Location Links Parade, Carnoustie DD7 7JE (11 miles from Dundee on A92 SW side of town, off A930) **Conf** Thtr 300 Class 80 Board 50 Banquet 200 Del £30–£42

Holes/Par/Course record 54 holes. Championship Course: 18 holes, 6936 yds, Par 72, SSS 75, Course record 64
Burnside Course: 18 holes, 6020 yds, Par 68, SSS 69
Buddon Links: 18 holes, 5420 yds, Par 66, SSS 67

Championship Course

---

18 holes, 6066yds, Par 69, SSS 70, Course record 61.
Club membership 850.
Visitors may not play before 2.30pm Sat. Advance booking required. **Societies** must contact in advance. **Green Fees** £28 per day; £22 per round (£35/£28 weekends). **Cards** ▦▬ ▦ ▦ ▦ ▦ **Prof** Peter McNiven **Course Designer** James Braid **Facilities** ⊗ 🏌 🏧 ⬛ 🍴 ♨ 🏠 ⛳ 🏑 🔔 **Location** 1.5m E of Forfar on A932

Hotel ★★★♨ 68% Idvies House Hotel, Letham, FORFAR ☎ 01307 818787 11 en suite

Kirriemuir Shielhill Rd, Northmuir DD8 4LN
☎ 01575 573317 📠 01575 574608
e-mail: kirriemuirgc@aol.com
Parkland and heathland course set at the foot of the Angus glens, with good view.
18 holes, 5553yds, Par 68, SSS 67, Course record 62.
Club membership 750.
Visitors must play with member at weekends. **Societies** must apply in advance, may not play weekends. **Green Fees** £26 per day; £20 per round(£35/£26 weekends). **Cards** ▦▬ ▦ ▦ **Prof** Karyn Dallas **Course Designer** James Braid **Facilities** ⊗ 🏌 🏧 ⬛ 🍴 ♨ 🏠 ⛳ **Location** 1m N off B955

Hotel ★★★♨ 68% Idvies House Hotel, Letham, FORFAR ☎ 01307 818787 11 en suite

Monifieth Princes St DD5 4AW ☎ 01382 532767 (Medal) & 532967 (Ashludie) 📠 01382 535553
The chief of the two courses at Monifieth is the Medal Course. It has been one of the qualifying venues for the Open Championship on more than one occasion. A seaside links, but divided from the sand dunes by a railway which provides the principal hazard for the first few holes. The 10th hole is outstanding, the 17th is excellent and there is a delightful finishing hole. The other course here is the Ashludie, and both are played over by a number of clubs who share the links.
Medal Course: 18 holes, 6655yds, Par 71, SSS 72, Course record 63.
Ashludie Course: 18 holes, 5123yds, Par 68, SSS 66.
Club membership 1750.
Visitors must contact in advance. Restricted to after 2pm Sat, 10am Sun & after 9.30pm Mon-Fri. **Societies** must contact in advance by telephone or writing to Medal Starter's Box, Princes St, Monifieth. **Green Fees** terms on application. **Cards** ▦▬ ▦ ▦ ▦ **Prof** Ian McLeod **Facilities** ⊗ 🏌 by prior arrangement 🏧 ⬛ 🍴 ♨ 🏠 ⛳ 🏑 **Location** NE side of town on A930

Hotel ★★ 68% Carlogie House Hotel, Carlogie Rd, CARNOUSTIE ☎ 01241 853185
12 en suite 4 annexe en suite

Montrose Links Trust Traill Dr DD10 8SW
☎ 01674 672932 📠 01674 671800
e-mail: secretary@montroselinks.co.uk
The links at Montrose like many others in Scotland are on commonland and are shared by three clubs. The Medal course at Montrose - the fifth oldest in the world - is typical of Scottish seaside links, with narrow, undulating fairways and problems from the first hole to the last. The Broomfield course is flatter and easier.

continued

5TH OLDEST GOLF COURSE IN THE WORLD   MONTROSE GOLF COURSES   15   62   "A magnificent stretch of marvellously natural ground which defies less the game was born."   Ben Crenshaw

Two links courses: MEDAL COURSE (Par 71, SSS72) BROOMFIELD COURSE (Par 66, SSS 63)
AN INVITATION TO COME AND PLAY OUR HISTORIC LINKS WHICH WAS A FINAL QUALIFYING COURSE FOR THE OPEN IN 1999.
RANKED FIFTH OLDEST IN THE WORLD
VISITORS VERY WELCOME
Individual Round and Day Tickets Available on Both Courses
All Visitors and Parties Very Welcome.
Special packages available including catering and in conjunction with local hotels
Enquiries to: Mrs M Stewart, Secretary,
Montrose Links Trust, Traill Drive,
Montrose, Angus DD10 8SW.
Tel: 01674 672932
Fax: 01674 671800
E-mail: secretary@montroselinks.co.uk
Website: www.montroselinks.co.uk

Medal Course: 18 holes, 6495yds, Par 71, SSS 72, Course record 63.
Broomfield Course: 18 holes, 4800yds, Par 66, SSS 63.
Club membership 1300.

Montrose Links Trust

Visitors may not play on the Medal Course on Sat before 2.30pm & before 10am on Sun. Must have a handicap certificate for Medal Course. Contact in advance. No restrictions on Broomfield Course. Must contact in advance. **Societies** must contact secretary in advance. **Green Fees** Medal: £42 per day; £32 per round (£50/£36 weekends). Broomfield: £16 per round(£18 weekends). **Cards** ▦▬ ▦ ▦ ▦ ▦ **Prof** Jason J Boyd **Course Designer** W Park/Tom Morris **Facilities** ⊗ 🏌 🏧 ⬛ 🍴 ♨ 🏠 ⛳ 🏑 🔔 ⛳ **Location** NE side of town off A92

Hotel ★★★ 66% Montrose Park Hotel, 61 John St, MONTROSE ☎ 01674 663400
54 en suite 5 annexe en suite

continued

Additional hotel ★★★ 72% Links Hotel, Mid Links, MONTROSE ☎ 01674 671000 Fax 01674 672698 25 en suite

ARGYLL & BUTE

CARDROSS   Map 10 NS37

Cardross Main Rd G82 5LB
☎ 01389 841754 📄 01389 842162
e-mail: golf@cardross.com
Undulating, testing parkland course with good views.
18 holes, 6469yds, Par 71, SSS 72, Course record 64.
Club membership 800.
Visitors may not play at weekends unless introduced by member. Contact professional in advance 01359 841350. **Societies** must contact in writing. **Green Fees** £40 per day; £28 per round. **Cards** 🔲 🔲 **Prof** Robert Farrell **Course Designer** James Braid **Facilities** ⊗ ⫪ ⊾ 🍴 ♀ ♨ 🏠 ⭐ ✓ **Location** In centre of village on A814

Hotel ★★★★★ 64% Cameron House Hotel, BALLOCH ☎ 01389 755565 96 en suite

CARRADALE   Map 10 NR83

Carradale The Arch PA28 6QT ☎ 01583 431321
Pleasant seaside course built on a promontory overlooking the Isle of Arran. Natural terrain and small greens are the most difficult natural hazards. Described as the most sporting 9-hole course in Scotland. Testing 7th hole (240 yds), par 3.
9 holes, 2358yds, Par 65, SSS 64, Course record 62.
Club membership 320.
Visitors no restrictions,advisable to contact at weekends during summer months. **Societies** contact in advance. **Green Fees** terms on application. **Facilities** ♨ ✓ **Location** S side of village, on B842

Hotel ★★ 68% Seafield Hotel, Kilkerran Rd, CAMPBELTOWN ☎ 01586 554385
3 en suite 6 annexe en suite

DALMALLY   Map 10 NN12

Dalmally Old Saw Mill PA33 1AE
☎ 01838 200370
e-mail: golfclub@lock-awe.com
A 9-hole flat parkland course bounded by the River Orchy and surrounded by mountains. Many water hazards and bunkers.
9 holes, 2257yds, Par 64, SSS 63, Course record 64.
Club membership 130.
Visitors no visitors on Sun between 9-10 & 1-2. **Societies** telephone in advance. **Green Fees** £10 per day. **Course Designer** MacFarlane Barrow Co **Facilities** ⊗ by prior arrangement ⊾ by prior arrangement ♨ by prior arrangement ♀ by arrangement ♨ ⭐ ✓ **Location** On A85, 1.5m W of Dalmally

Hotel ★★ 60% Polfearn Hotel, TAYNUILT ☎ 01866 822251 14 en suite

DUNOON   Map 10 NS17

Cowal Ardenslate Rd PA23 8LT
☎ 01369 705673 📄 01369 705673
e-mail: Info@cowalgolfclub.co.uk
Moorland course. Panoramic views of Clyde Estuary and surrounding hills. *continued*

18 holes, 6063yds, Par 70, SSS 70, Course record 63.
Club membership 900.
Visitors advisable to book in advance. **Societies** must telephone in advance. **Green Fees** £24 per round(£34 weekends). **Prof** Russell Weir **Course Designer** James Braid **Facilities** ⊗ ⫪ ⊾ ♨ ♀ ♨ 🏠 ⭐ ✓ **Location** 1m N

Hotel ★★ 77% Enmore Hotel, Marine Pde, Kirn, DUNOON ☎ 01369 702230 10 en suite

ERISKA   Map 10 NM94

Isle of Eriska PA37 1SD
☎ 01631 720371 📄 01631 720531
e-mail: gc@eriska-hotel.co.uk
This remote and well-maintained 6 hole course, set around the owners hotel, is gradually being upgraded to a testing 9 hole challenge, complete with stunning views.
6 holes, 1588yds, Par 22.
Club membership 40.
Visitors contact in advance. **Green Fees** £10 per day. **Cards** 🔲 🔲 🔲 🔲 **Course Designer** H Swan **Facilities** ⊗ ⊾ ♨ ♀ ♨ ⭐ 🏠 ✓ ℂ **Leisure** hard tennis courts, heated indoor swimming pool, sauna, gymnasium. **Location** A828 Connel/Fort William, signposted 4m from North of Benderloch village

Hotel ★★★★♨♨ Isle of Eriska, Eriska, Ledaig, BY OBAN ☎ 01631 720371 17 en suite

GIGHA ISLAND   Map 10 NR64

Gigha PA41 7AA ☎ 01583 505242 📄 01583 505244
A 9-hole course with scenic views of the Sound of Gigha and Kintyre. Ideal for the keen or occasional golfer.
9 holes, 5042yds, Par 66, SSS 65.
Club membership 40.
Visitors no restrictions. **Societies** telephone for details. **Green Fees** £10 per day/round. **Course Designer** Members **Facilities** ♨ ⭐ **Location** 0.5m from ferry terminal beside main road

HELENSBURGH   Map 10 NS28

Helensburgh 25 East Abercromby St G84 9HZ
☎ 01436 674173 📄 01436 671170
e-mail: thesecretary@helensburghgolfclub.org.uk
Sporting moorland course with superb views of Loch Lomond and River Clyde.
18 holes, 6104yds, Par 69, SSS 70, Course record 64.
Club membership 880.
Visitors may not play at weekends. **Societies** weekdays only, must contact in writing. **Green Fees** £35 per day; £25 per round. **Prof** David Fotheringham **Course Designer** Old Tom Morris **Facilities** ⊗ ⫪ ⊾ ♨ ♀ ♨ 🏠 ✓ **Location** NE side of town off B832

Hotel ★★★★★ 64% Cameron House Hotel, BALLOCH ☎ 01389 755565 96 en suite

INNELLAN   Map 10 NS17

Innellan Knockamillie Rd PA23 7SG
☎ 01369 830242 & 702573
9 holes, 4683yds, Par 64, SSS 64, Course record 63.
Location 4m S of Dunoon
Telephone for further details

Hotel ★★ 70% Royal Marine Hotel, Hunters Quay, DUNOON ☎ 01369 705810 31 en suite 10 annexe en suite

INVERARAY   Map 10 NN00

Inveraray North Cromalt PA32 8XT ☎ 01499 302140
**Testing parkland course with beautiful views overlooking
Loch Fyne.**
*9 holes, 5790yds, Par 70, SSS 68, Course record 69.
Club membership 178.*
Visitors no restrictions. **Societies** write or telephone to the
secretary. **Green Fees** not confirmed. **Facilities** ⛳
Location 1m S of Inveraray

Hotel ★★★ 68% Loch Fyne Hotel, INVERARAY
☎ 01499 302148 80 en suite

LOCHGILPHEAD   Map 10 NR88

Lochgilphead Blarbuie Rd PA31 8LE
☎ 01546 602340
**A varied and challenging scenic course with a spectacular
par 3 finishing hole.**
*9 holes, 2242yds, Par 64, SSS 63, Course record 58.
Club membership 250.*
Visitors restricted during weekend club competitions.
Societies apply in advance, restricted wekends. **Green Fees**
£15 per 18 holes. **Course Designer** Dr I McCamond
Facilities ⓑ ⛳ ♀ ⛳ 🏠 ♂ **Location** Adjacent to the
hospital. Signposted from the village.

Hotel ★★ 62% Stag Hotel & Restaurant, Argyll St,
LOCHGILPHEAD ☎ 01546 602496 18 en suite

LUSS   Map 10 NS39

Loch Lomond Rossdhu House G83 8NT
☎ 01436 655555 📠 01436 655500
e-mail: info@lochlomond.com
**This exclusive club is strictly members only and
getting to play here is notoriously difficult. Nick Faldo
called it the finest new course in Europe. It was
designed by two Americans, Jay Morrish and Tom
Weiskopf and was founded in 1993. There is a putting
green, practice area and driving range. The clubhouse
used to be the home of the chiefs of Clan Colquhoun.
We are told that it boasts a Chinese Drawing Room
with portraits in oil and beautiful ceilings. There are
conference facilities as well as a gym and private
fishing.**
18 holes, 7060yds, Par 71, Course record 62.
Visitors strictly members only.no visitors strictly private.
Green Fees not confirmed. **Prof** Colin Campbell **Course
Designer** Tom Weiskopf **Facilities** ⛳ 🏠 ♂ 🍴 **Leisure**
fishing, gymnasium. **Location** Off A82 at Luss

Hotel ★★★★★ 64% Cameron House Hotel, BALLOCH
☎ 01389 755565 96 en suite

MACHRIHANISH   Map 10 NR62

Machrihanish PA28 6PT
☎ 01586 810213 📠 01586 810221
e-mail: machrihanishgolf@ic24.net
**Magnificent natural links of championship status. The
1st hole is the famous drive across the Atlantic. Sandy
soil allows for play all year round. Large greens, easy
walking, windy. Fishing.**
*18 holes, 6225yds, Par 70, SSS 71.
Club membership 1200.*
Visitors no restrictions. **Societies** apply in writing. **Green
Fees** terms on application. **Cards** ▭ ▤ ▥ 🖪 **Prof** Ken
Campbell **Course Designer** Tom Morris **Facilities** ⊗ ⅷ

continued

ⓑ ⛳ ♀ ⛳ 🏠 ♂ **Location** 5m W of Campbeltown
on B843

Hotel ★★ 68% Seafield Hotel, Kilkerran Rd,
CAMPBELTOWN ☎ 01586 554385 3 en suite 6 annexe
en suite

OBAN   Map 10 NM83

Glencruitten Glencruitten Rd PA34 4PU
☎ 01631 564604
**There is plenty of space and considerable variety of
hole on this downland course - popular with
holidaymakers. In a beautiful, isolated situation, the
course is hilly and testing, particularly the 1st and 12th
(par 4s) and 10th and 15th (par 3s).**
*18 holes, 4452yds, Par 61, SSS 63, Course record 55.
Club membership 500.*
Visitors restricted Thu & weekends. **Societies** must
contact in writing. **Green Fees** £16 per day/round(£19
weekends). **Course Designer** James Braid **Facilities**
ⓑ ⛳ ♀ ⛳ 🏠 🍴 ♂ **Location** NE side of town centre
off A816

Hotel ★★★ 66% Alexandra Hotel, Corran Esplanade,
OBAN ☎ 01631 562381 64 en suite

SOUTHEND   Map 10 NR60

Dunaverty PA28 6RW
☎ 01586 830677 📠 01586 830677
e-mail: dunavertygc@aol.com
**Undulating, seaside course with spectacular views of
Ireland and the Ayrshire coast.**
*18 holes, 4799yds, Par 66, SSS 63, Course record 59.
Club membership 400.*
Visitors limited Sat, contact in advance. **Societies** apply in
advance. **Green Fees** not confirmed. **Facilities** ⊗ ⅷ ⓑ ⛳
⛳ 🏠 🍴 ♂ **Leisure** fishing. **Location** 10m S of
Campbeltown on B842

Hotel ★★ 68% Seafield Hotel, Kilkerran Rd,
CAMPBELTOWN ☎ 01586 554385
3 en suite 6 annexe en suite

TARBERT   Map 10 NR86

Tarbert PA29 6XX ☎ 01546 606896
**Beautiful moorland course. Four fairways crossed by
streams.**
9 holes, 4460yds, Par 66, SSS 63, Course record 62.
Visitors may not play Sat pm. **Societies** apply in writing.
Green Fees £10 per day. **Location** N1m W on B8024

Hotel ★★★♨ 71% Stonefield Castle Hotel, TARBERT
☎ 01880 820836 33 en suite

TIGHNABRUAICH   Map 10 NR97

Kyles of Bute PA21 2EE ☎ 01700 811603
**Moorland course which is hilly and exposed to wind. Fine
mountain and sea views.**
*9 holes, 4778yds, Par 66, SSS 64, Course record 62.
Club membership 150.*
Visitors may not play Wed 6pm or Sun am. **Societies**
telephone in advance. **Green Fees** terms on application.
Facilities ⛳ 🍴 ♂ **Location** 1.25m S off B8000

Hotel ★★ 74% Royal Hotel, Shore Rd,
TIGHNABRUAICH ☎ 01700 811239 11 en suite

CITY OF EDINBURGH

EDINBURGH   Map 11 NT27

Baberton 50 Baberton Av, Juniper Green EH14 5DU
☎ 0131 453 4911 ▤ 0131 453 4678
e-mail: babertongolfclub@btinternet.com
Parkland course offering the golfer a variety of
interesting and challenging holes. The outward half
follows the boundary of the course and presents some
demanding par 3 and 4 holes over the undulating terrain.
The inward half has some longer, equally challenging
holes contained within the course and presents some
majestic views of the Pentland Hills and the Edinburgh
skyline.
18 holes, 6129yds, Par 69, SSS 70, Course record 64.
Club membership 900.
Visitors may play at weekdays up to 3.30pm and weekends
after 1pm. Contact professional in advance on 0131 453
3555. Societies must contact in advance. Green Fees £25 per
round;£35 per day(£28/£38 weekends). Cards ▭ ▬ Prof
Ken Kelly Course Designer Willie Park Jnr Facilities ⊗ ⫫
⊾ ⚑ ♀ ⚘ ⚑ ⚐ Location 5m W of city centre off A70

Hotel ★★★★ 62% Edinburgh Marriott Hotel, 111 Glasgow
Rd, EDINBURGH ☎ 0131 334 9191 245 en suite

Braid Hills Braid Hills Approach EH10 6JZ
☎ 0131 447 6666 ▤ 0131 557 5170
Municipal heathland course with superb views of
Edinburgh and the Firth of Forth, quite challenging.
Course No 1: 18 holes, 5390yds, Par 70, SSS 68.
Course No 2: 18 holes, 4602yds, Par 65.
Visitors two courses Braids 1 & Braids 2 operate from Apr-
Sep, one course only during winter. Braids 1 is closed on
Sun. Societies telephone 0131 557 5457 or apply in writing
to Edinburgh Leisure, 23 Waterloo Place, Edinburgh EH1
3BH Green Fees not confirmed. Course Designer Peter
McEwan & Bob Ferguson Facilities ⚘ ⚑ ⚘ Location
2.5m S of city centre off A702

Hotel ★★★ 70% Braid Hills Hotel, 134 Braid Rd,
EDINBURGH ☎ 0131 447 8888 67 en suite

Bruntsfield Links Golfing Society 32 Barnton Av
EH4 6JH ☎ 0131 336 1479 ▤ 0131 336 5538
e-mail: secretary@bruntsfield.sol.co.uk
Mature parkland course with magnificent views over the
Firth of Forth and to the west. Greens and fairways are
generally immaculate. Challenging for all categories of
handicap.
18 holes, 6407yds, Par 71, SSS 71, Course record 64.
Club membership 1100.
Visitors must telephone in advance. 0131 336 4050 or 0131
continued

THE BRAID HILLS HOTEL

134 Braid Road, Edinburgh, EH10 6JD
Magnificently situated only two miles from the
city centre, yet a world away from the noise
and congestion of the centre itself, the Braid
Hills Hotel is your ideal choice when visiting
Edinburgh.
To make your reservation in this
independently owned hotel

 Tel: 0131 447 8888
Fax: 0131 452 8477

336 1479 Societies apply in writing. Green Fees £60 per
day; £42 per round (£65/£47 weekends). Cards ▭ ▬ ▬ ▬
Prof Brian Mackenzie Course Designer Willie Park Jr,A
Mackenzie, Hawtree Facilities ⊗ ⫫ ⚑ ♀ ⊾ ⚐ ⚑ ⚘ ⚑
Location 4m NW of city centre off A90

Hotel ★★★ 63% The Barnton, Queensferry Rd, Barnton,
EDINBURGH ☎ 0131 339 1144 50 en suite

Carrick Knowe Carrick Knowe, Glendevon Park
EH12 5UZ ☎ 0131 337 1096 & 557 5457(bookings)
▤ 0131 557 5170
Flat parkland course. Played over by two clubs, Carrick
Knowe and Carrick Vale.
18 holes, 5697yds, Par 70, SSS 69.
Visitors may be restricted at weekends. Societies telephone
0131 557 5457 or write to Edinburgh Leisure, 23 Waterloo
Place EH1 3BH. Green Fees not confirmed. Facilities ⚘ ⚑
⚘ Location 3m W of city centre, S of A8

Hotel ★★★ 73% Holiday Inn Edinburgh, Corstorphine Rd,
EDINBURGH ☎ 0870 400 9026 303 en suite

Craigentinny Fillyside Rd EH7 6RG
☎ 0131 554 7501 & 557 5457(bookings) ▤ 0131 557 5170
To the north east of Edinburgh, Craigentinny course is
between Leith and Portobello. It is generally flat although
there are some hillocks with gentle slopes. The famous
Arthur's Seat dominates the southern skyline.
18 holes, 5205yds, Par 67, SSS 65.
Visitors must contact in advance. Societies telephone 0131
557 5457 or apply in writing to: Edinburgh Leisure, 23
Waterloo Place EH1 3BH. Green Fees not confirmed.
Facilities ⚘ ⚑ ⚘ Location NE side of city, between Leith
& Portobello
continued

Hotel ★★★ 67% Kings Manor, 100 Milton Rd East, EDINBURGH ☎ 0131 669 0444 66 en suite

Craigmillar Park 1 Observatory Rd EH9 3HG
☎ 0131 667 0047
Parkland course, with good views.
18 holes, 5851yds, Par 70, SSS 69, Course record 63.
Club membership 750.
Visitors must contact in advance, welcome Monday-Friday and Sunday afternoons **Societies** must contact in writing. **Green Fees** not confirmed. **Prof** B McGhee **Course Designer** James Braid **Facilities** ⊗ ⊤⊤ ⛳ ▣ ♀ ⚘ 🏠 ⊤ ⛟ ✐ **Location** 2m S of city centre off A7

Hotel ★★ 68% Allison House Hotel, 15/17 Mayfield Gardens, EDINBURGH ☎ 0131 667 8049
23 rms (21 en suite)

Duddingston Duddingston Rd West EH15 3QD
☎ 0131 661 7688 🗋 0131 652 6057
e-mail: generalmanager@duddingston-golf-club.com
Parkland course with burn as a natural hazard. Testing 11th hole. Easy walking and windy.
18 holes, 6473yds, Par 72, SSS 72.
Club membership 700.
Visitors may not play at weekends. **Societies** Tue & Thu only. Must contact in advance. **Green Fees** £45 per day; £35 per round. **Cards** 🖭 ▣ **Prof** Alastair McLean **Course Designer** Willie Park Jnr **Facilities** ⊗ ⊤⊤ ⛳ ▣ ♀ ⚘ 🏠 ⊤ ⛟ ✐ **Location** 2.5m SE of city centre off A1

Hotel ★★★ 67% Kings Manor, 100 Milton Rd East, EDINBURGH ☎ 0131 669 0444 66 en suite

Kingsknowe 326 Lanark Rd EH14 2JD
☎ 0131 441 1145 (Secretary) & 441 1144 (Club)
🗋 0131 441 2079
e-mail: kingsknowe.golfclub@virgin.net
Picturesque parkland course set amidst gently rolling hills.
18 holes, 5981yds, Par 69, SSS 69, Course record 63.
Club membership 800.
Visitors contact in advance and subject to availability of tee times. **Societies** apply in writing or telephone secretary. **Green Fees** £30 per day; £20 per round(£35/£20 weekends after 3pm). **Prof** Chris Morris **Course Designer** A Herd/James Braid **Facilities** ⊗ ⊤⊤ ⛳ ▣ ♀ ⚘ 🏠 ⛟ ✐ **Conf** Max 50 **Location** 4m SW of city centre on A70

Hotel ★★★ 75% Bruntsfield Hotel, 69/74 Bruntsfield Place, EDINBURGH ☎ 0131 229 1393 75 en suite

Liberton 297 Gilmerton Rd EH16 5UJ
☎ 0131 664 3009 (sec) & 664 1056 (pro) 🗋 0131 666 0853
Undulating, wooded parkland course.
18 holes, 5306yds, Par 67, SSS 67, Course record 61.
Club membership 675.
Visitors must contact in advance. **Societies** must contact in writing. **Green Fees** terms on application. **Cards** 🖭 **Prof** Iain Seath **Facilities** ⊗ ⊤⊤ ⛳ ▣ ♀ ⚘ 🏠 ✐ **Location** 3m SE of city centre on A7

Hotel ★★★ 77% Dalhousie Castle And Spa, Bonnyrigg, EDINBURGH ☎ 01875 820153
27 en suite 5 annexe en suite

Lothianburn 106A Biggar Rd, Fairmilehead EH10 7DU
☎ 0131 445 2206 & 0131 445 5067
Situated to the south west of the city of Edinburgh, on the slopes of the Pentland Hills, the course rises from the clubhouse approximately 300ft to its highest point at the 13th green. There is only one real climb of note, after playing the 2nd shot to the 9th green. The course in noted for its excellent greens and the challenging holes include the 5th, where one drives for position in order to pitch at almost right angles to a plateau green and the 14th, longest hole on the course, three-quarters of which is downhill with out of bounds on both sides of the fairway.
18 holes, 5662yds, Par 71, SSS 68, Course record 66.
Club membership 850.
Visitors weekends after 3.30pm contact professional, weekdays up to 4pm. **Societies** apply to the secretary or telephone in the first instance. **Green Fees** £22.50 per day; £16.50 per round (£27.50/£22 .50 weekends). **Prof** Kurt Mungall **Course Designer** J Braid (re-designed 1928) **Facilities** ⊗ ⊤⊤ ⛳ ▣ ♀ ⚘ 🏠 ⊤ ✐ **Location** 4.5m S of city centre on A702

Hotel ★★★ 70% Braid Hills Hotel, 134 Braid Rd, EDINBURGH ☎ 0131 447 8888 67 en suite

EDINBURGH See page 303 Map 11 NT27

Merchants of Edinburgh 10 Craighill Gardens EH10 5PY ☎ 0131 447 1219 🗋 0131 446 9833
e-mail: admin@merchantsgolf.com
Testing hill course with fine views over the city and the surrounding countryside.
18 holes, 4889yds, Par 65, SSS 64, Course record 59.
Club membership 1000.
Visitors must contact Secretary in advance. **Societies** must contact secretary in writing/telephone 48 hours in advance. **Green Fees** £16 per round;£24 per day(£20/£30 weekends). **Prof** Neil Colquhoun **Course Designer** R G Ross **Facilities** ⊗ ⊤⊤ ⛳ ▣ ♀ ⚘ 🏠 ⊤ ♥ ⛟ ✐ **Leisure** snooker room. **Location** 2m SW of city centre off A702

Hotel ★★★ 70% Braid Hills Hotel, 134 Braid Rd, EDINBURGH ☎ 0131 447 8888 67 en suite

Mortonhall 231 Braid Rd EH10 6PB
☎ 0131 447 6974 🗋 0131 447 8712
Moorland/parkland course with views over Edinburgh.
18 holes, 6502yds, Par 72, SSS 72, Course record 66.
Club membership 525.
Visitors advisable to contact by phone. **Societies** may not play at weekends. Must contact in writing. **Green Fees** not confirmed. **Cards** 🖭 **Prof** Douglas Horn **Course Designer** James Braid/F Hawtree **Facilities** ⊗ ⛳ ▣ ♀ ⚘ 🏠 ⊤ ✐ **Location** 3m S of city centre off A702

Hotel ★★★ 70% Braid Hills Hotel, 134 Braid Rd, EDINBURGH ☎ 0131 447 8888 67 en suite

Murrayfield 43 Murrayfield Rd EH12 6EU
☎ 0131 337 3478 🗋 0131 313 0721
Parkland course on the side of Corstorphine Hill, with fine views.
18 holes, 5725yds, Par 70, SSS 69.
Club membership 815.
Visitors contact in advance, may not play at weekends. **Societies** apply in writing **Green Fees** £35 per day; £30 per round. **Prof** J J Fisher **Facilities** ⊗ ⛳ ▣ ♀ ⚘ 🏠 ⊤ ✐ **Location** 2m W of city centre off A8

continued

Marriott Dalmahoy Hotel

Kirknewton, *Edinburgh* ☏ 0131 3358010 Fax 0131 3353577 Map 11 NT27

e-mail: golf.dalmahoy@marriotthotels.co.uk

The Championship East Course has hosted many major events including the Solheim Cup, The Scottish Seniors Open Championship and the PGA Championship of Scotland. The greens are large with immaculate putting surfaces and many of the long par 4 holes offer a serious challenge to the golfer. The short holes are well bunkered and the 15th hole in particular, known as the 'Wee Wrecker' will test your nerve and skill.

The shorter West Course offers a different test with small greens requiring accuracy from the player's short game, however, the finishing holes with the Gogar Burn meandering through the fairways creates a tough finish.

Visitors welcome Mon-Fri, weekend by application. Call in advance to book tee times, subject to availability

Societies (Mon-Fri only) telephone or write for details

Green Fees East Course £69 per round (£85 weekends and public holidays); West Course £49 (£65 weekends) Special rates also for hotel residents — 🍴 🔒 💺 🏌 🎌

Facilities ⊗ 🍴 🛍 💺 ♀ 🛏 ⛺ 🏠 🏌 ⛏ ⛳ ⚑

Professional (Neal Graham)

Leisure tennis, swimming, sauna, solarium, gymnasium, beauty salon, fitness studio, jogging trail **Conf** max 360 Thtr 350 Class 150 Board 90 Banquet 360

Location Kirknewton EH27 8EB (7m W of city centre on A71)

Holes/Par/Course record East Course: 18 holes, 6651 yds, Par 72, SSS 72, Course record 62

West Course: 18 holes, 5168 yds, Par 68, SSS 66, Course record 60

WHERE TO STAY AND EAT NEARBY

Hotels
EDINBURGH

★★★★ ◎◎ 74% Marriott Dalmahoy Hotel & Country Club
☏ 0131 333 1845.
43 en suite, 172 annexe en suite

★★★★ 62% Edinburgh Marriott, 111 Glasgow Rd. ☏ 0131 334 9191.
245 en suite

UPHALL

★★★★ ◎◎ 67% Houstoun House
EH52 6JS. ☏ 01506 853831. 25 en suite
47 annexe en suite

Restaurant
LINLITHGOW

◎◎ Champany Inn EH49 7LU.
☏ 01506 834532

◎◎ Livingston's Restaurant, 52 High St.
☏ 01506 846565

Championship Course

Hotel ★★★ 73% Holiday Inn Edinburgh, Corstorphine Rd, EDINBURGH ☎ 0870 400 9026 303 en suite

Portobello Stanley St EH15 1JJ
☎ 0131 669 4361 & 557 5457(bookings) 📠 0131 557 5170
Public parkland course, easy walking.
9 holes, 2252yds, Par 32, SSS 32.
Visitors advanced booking recommended. Contact Edinburgh Leisure. **Societies** contact in advance, telephone 0131 557 5457 or write to Edinburgh Leisure, 23 Waterloo Place EH1 3BH. **Green Fees** not confirmed.
Facilities ⚒ ⚐ ♂ **Location** 3m E of city centre off A1

Hotel ★★★ 67% Kings Manor, 100 Milton Rd East, EDINBURGH ☎ 0131 669 0444 66 en suite

Prestonfield 6 Priestfield Rd North EH16 5HS
☎ 0131 667 9665 📠 0131 667 9665
e-mail: prestonfield@btclick.com
Parkland course with beautiful views.
18 holes, 6212yds, Par 70, SSS 70, Course record 66.
Club membership 850.
Visitors contact secretary in advance. May not play Sat before 10.30am or between 12pm-1.30pm & Sun before 11.30am. **Societies** must contact secretary. **Green Fees** terms on application. **Cards** 💳 💳 **Prof** John Macfarlane **Course Designer** James Braid **Facilities** ⊗ ⅲ ⓛ ⚑ ♀ ⚒ 🏠 ⚐ ⚒
♂ **Location** 1.5m S of city centre off A68

Hotel ★★★ 67% Kings Manor, 100 Milton Rd East, EDINBURGH ☎ 0131 669 0444 66 en suite

Ravelston 24 Ravelston Dykes Rd EH4 3NZ
☎ 0131 315 2486 📠 0131 315 2486
Parkland course.
9 holes, 5230yds, Par 66, SSS 65, Course record 64.
Club membership 610.
Visitors must contact in advance but may not play at weekends & bank holidays. **Green Fees** terms on application. **Course Designer** James Braid **Facilities** ⓛ ⚑
⚒ **Location** 3m W of city centre off A90

Hotel ★★★ 73% Holiday Inn Edinburgh, Corstorphine Rd, EDINBURGH ☎ 0870 400 9026 303 en suite

Royal Burgess 181 Whitehouse Rd, Barnton
EH4 6BY ☎ 0131 339 2075 📠 0131 339 3712
e-mail: secretary@royalburgess.co.uk
No mention of golf clubs would be complete without mention of the Royal Burgess, which was instituted in 1735, thus being the oldest golfing society in the world. Its course is a pleasant parkland, and one with very much variety. A club which all those interested in the history of the game should visit.
18 holes, 6111yds, Par 68, SSS 69.
Club membership 620.
Visitors must contact in advance, may not play at weekend. **Societies** must contact in advance. **Green Fees** £55 per day; £42 per round. **Cards** 💳 💳 💳 💳 💳 **Prof** Steven Brian **Course Designer** Tom Morris
Facilities ⊗ ⓛ ⚑ ♀ ⚒ 🏠 ⚐ ♂ **Location** 5m W of city centre off A90

Hotel ★★★ 63% The Barnton, Queensferry Rd, Barnton, EDINBURGH ☎ 0131 339 1144 50 en suite

Silverknowes Silverknowes, Parkway EH4 5ET
☎ 0131 336 3843 & 557 5457(bookings) 📠 0131 557 5170
Public links course on coast overlooking the Firth of Forth with magnificent views.
18 holes, 6070yds, Par 71, SSS 70.
Visitors advanced booking recommended in summer, contact Edinburgh Leisure. **Societies** telephone 0131 557 5457 or apply in writing to: Edinburgh Leisure, 23 Waterloo Place, Edinburgh EH1 3BH. **Green Fees** not confirmed. **Facilities** ⚒ ⚐ ♂ **Location** 4m NW of city centre, easy access from city by-pass

Hotel ★★★ 63% The Barnton, Queensferry Rd, Barnton, EDINBURGH ☎ 0131 339 1144 50 en suite

Swanston 111 Swanston Rd, Fairmilehead EH10 7DS
☎ 0131 445 2239
Hillside course with steep climb at 12th & 13th holes.
18 holes, 5024yds, Par 66, SSS 65, Course record 63.
Club membership 600.
Visitors contact in advance. Weekends restricted. **Societies** must contact in advance. **Green Fees** terms on application. **Prof** Richard Fyvie **Course Designer** Herbert More **Facilities** ⊗ ⅲ ⓛ ⚑ ♀ ⚒ 🏠 ⚐ ⚒ ♂ **Location** 4m S of city centre off B701

Hotel ★★★ 70% Braid Hills Hotel, 134 Braid Rd, EDINBURGH ☎ 0131 447 8888 67 en suite

Torphin Hill Torphin Rd, Colinton EH13 0PG
☎ 0131 441 1100 📠 0131 441 7166
e-mail: info@torphinhillgc.saefhost.co.uk
Beautiful hillside, heathland course, with fine views of Edinburgh and the Forth Estuary.
18 holes, 4580mtrs, Par 67, SSS 66, Course record 63.
Club membership 550.
Visitors must contact in advance, limited access Sat & Sun (only after 2pm) **Societies** must contact in advance. **Green Fees** terms on application. **Cards** 💳 **Prof** Jamie Browne **Facilities** ⊗ ⅲ ⓛ ⚑ ♀ ⚒ 🏠 ♥ **Location** 5m SW of city centre S of A720

Hotel ★★★ 70% Braid Hills Hotel, 134 Braid Rd, EDINBURGH ☎ 0131 447 8888 67 en suite

Turnhouse 154 Turnhouse Rd EH12 0AD
☎ 0131 339 1014 📠 0131 339 1844
e-mail: secretary@turnhousegc.com
Hilly, parkland/heathland course, good views over the Pentland Hills and Forth Valley.
18 holes, 6171yds, Par 69, SSS 70, Course record 62.
Club membership 800.
Visitors with member only at weekends, and no visitors Wed or Medal days. Must contact professional in advance. **Societies** must contact in writing to secretary. **Green Fees** terms on application. **Prof** John Murray **Course Designer** J Braid **Facilities** ⊗ ⅲ ⓛ ⚑ ♀ ⚒ 🏠 ⚐ ♂ **Location** 6m W of city centre N of A8

Hotel ★★★ 63% The Barnton, Queensferry Rd, Barnton, EDINBURGH ☎ 0131 339 1144 50 en suite

RATHO   Map 11 NT17

Ratho Park EH28 8NX
☎ 0131 335 0069 & 335 0068 📠 0131 333 1752
e-mail: secretary.rpgc@btinternet.com
Flat parkland course.
18 holes, 5900yds, Par 69, SSS 68, Course record 62.
Club membership 850.

continued

Visitors must contact in advance. Societies must contact in writing. Only able to play Tue-Thu Green Fees £35 per day £25 per round (£35 per round weekends). Cards ⊞ ▆ ⑨ Prof Alan Pate Course Designer James Braid Facilities ⊗ ⊞ � ▉ ♀ ⌂ 🏠 ⭢ 🚜 ⚐ Location 0.75m E, N of A71

Hotel ★★★ 73% Holiday Inn Edinburgh, Corstorphine Rd, EDINBURGH ☎ 0870 400 9026 303 en suite

SOUTH QUEENSFERRY　　　　　　　　Map 11 NT17

Dundas Parks Dundas Estate EH30 9SS
☎ 0131 319 1347 📋 0131 319 1347
e-mail: christine.wood@euphony.net
Parkland course situated on the estate of Dundas Castle, with excellent views. For 18 holes, the 9 are played twice.
9 holes, 6024yds, Par 70, SSS 69, Course record 64.
Club membership 500.
Visitors must contact in advance. May not play at weekends. Societies must contact in writing. Green Fees £10 per round.
Facilities ⌂ Location 0.5m S on A8000

Hotel ⌂ Travel Inn Edinburgh Queensferry, Builyeon Rd, SOUTH QUEENSFERRY ☎ 0131 331 5056 46 en suite

CITY OF GLASGOW

GLASGOW　　　　　　　　　　　　　　Map 11 NS56

Alexandra Alexandra Park, Alexandra Pde G31 8SE
☎ 0141 556 1294
Parkland course, hilly with some woodland. Many bunkers and a barrier of trees between 1st and 9th fairway.
9 holes, 2800yds, Par 31, Course record 25.
Club membership 85.
Visitors no restrictions. Societies telephone 24 hrs in advance or by writing one week in advance. Green Fees terms on application. Course Designer G McArthur Facilities ⌂ Leisure bowling green. Location 2m E of city centre off M8/A8

Hotel ★★★ 71% Holiday Inn, 161 West Nile St, GLASGOW ☎ 0141 352 8300 113 en suite

Cowglen Barrhead Rd G43 1AU
☎ 0141 632 0556 📋 01505 503000
Undulating and challenging parkland course with good views over the Clyde Valley to the Campsie Hills. Club and line selection is most important on many holes due to the strategic placing of copses on the course.
18 holes, 6079yds, Par 69, SSS 69, Course record 63.
Club membership 805.
Visitors play on shorter course. Must contact secretary for times in advance and have a handicap certificate. No visitors Tue, Fri and weekends. Societies must be booked in writing through the secretary. Green Fees £35 per day; £25 per round. Prof Simon Payne Course Designer David Adams/James Braid Facilities ⊗ ⊞ ㄥ ▉ ♀ ⌂ ⓕ Location M77 South from Glasgow, take Pollok/Barrhead slip road, left at lights club 0.5 miles right

Hotel ★★★ 71% Dalmeny Park Country House Hotel, Lochlibo Rd, BARRHEAD ☎ 0141 881 9211 20 en suite

Haggs Castle 70 Dumbreck Rd, Dumbreck G41 4SN
☎ 0141 427 1157 📋 0141 427 1157
Wooded, parkland course where Scottish National Championships and the Glasgow and Scottish Open have been held. Quite difficult.
continued

18 holes, 6426yds, Par 72, SSS 71, Course record 63.
Club membership 900.
Visitors may not play at weekends. Must contact in advance. Societies apply in writing. Green Fees £40 per round; £50 per day. Cards ⊞ ▆ ▨ ⑨ Prof Jim McAlister Course Designer James Braid Facilities ⊗ ⊞ ㄥ ▉ ♀ ⌂ 🏠 ⭢ ➤ 🚜 ⚐ Location 2.5m SW of city centre off M77 junct 1

Hotel ★★★ 68% Swallow Hotel, 517 Paisley Rd West, GLASGOW ☎ 0141 427 3146 117 en suite

Kirkhill Greenless Rd, Cambuslang G72 8YN
☎ 0141 641 8499 📋 0141 641 8499
Meadowland course designed by James Braid.
18 holes, 6030yds, Par 70, SSS 70, Course record 63.
Club membership 650.
Visitors must play with member at weekends. Societies must contact in advance. Green Fees not confirmed. Prof Duncan Williamson Course Designer J Braid Facilities ⊗ ⊞ ㄥ ▉ ♀ ⌂ 🏠 🚜 Location 5m SE of city centre off A749

Hotel ★★★ 65% Stuart Hotel, 2 Cornwall Way, Town Centre, EAST KILBRIDE ☎ 01355 221161 38 en suite

Knightswood Lincoln Av G13 5QZ ☎ 0141 959 6358
Flat parkland course within easy reach of city. Two dog-legs.
9 holes, 5586yds, Par 68, SSS 67.
Club membership 40.
Visitors reserved tee Wed and Fri am bookings 1 day in advance, no other restrictions. Societies welcome, must book 1 day in advance. Green Fees £3.60 per 9 holes. Facilities ⌂ Location 4m W of city centre off A82

Hotel ★★★ 64% Jurys Glasgow Hotel, Great Western Rd, GLASGOW ☎ 0141 334 8161 136 en suite

Lethamhill 1240 Cumbernauld Rd, Millerston G33 1AH
☎ 0141 770 6220 📋 1041 770 0520
Municipal parkland course.
18 holes, 5859yds, Par 70, SSS 69.
Visitors must contact in advance. Societies must contact in advance. Green Fees not confirmed. Facilities ⌂ Location 3m NE of city centre on A80

Hotel ★★★★ 73% Millennium Hotel Glasgow, George Square, GLASGOW ☎ 0141 332 6711 117 en suite

Linn Park Simshill Rd G44 5EP ☎ 0141 633 0377
Municipal parkland course with six par 3s in outward half.
18 holes, 4952yds, Par 65, SSS 65, Course record 61.
Visitors must contact in advance. Societies advance booking in writing Green Fees not confirmed. Facilities ⌂ Location 4m S of city centre off B766

Hotel ★★★ 70% Bruce Hotel, Cornwall St, EAST KILBRIDE ☎ 01355 229771 65 en suite

Pollok 90 Barrhead Rd G43 1BG
☎ 0141 632 4351 & 632 1080 📋 0141 649 1398
e-mail: pollok.gc@lineone.net
Parkland course with woods and river.
18 holes, 6254yds, Par 71, SSS 70, Course record 62.
Club membership 620.
Visitors Members only until 2pm weekends. Must contact in advance. Ladies only as part of visiting parties Societies
continued

must contact in writing **Green Fees** £42 per day; £32 per round(£50/£40 weekends). **Course Designer** James Braid **Facilities** ⊗ ℐ by prior arrangement ⅃ ⚑ ♀ ☆ **Location** 4m SW of city centre on A762

Hotel ★★★ 60% The Tinto Firs, 470 Kilmarnock Rd, GLASGOW ☎ 0141 637 2353 27 en suite

Williamwood Clarkston Rd G44 3YR
☎ 0141 637 1783 ▤ 0141 571 0166
Undulating parkland course with mature woodlands.
18 holes, 5878yds, Par 68, SSS 69, Course record 61.
Club membership 800.
Visitors apply in writing to secretary, no weekend play. **Societies** midweek bookings only, apply in writing to secretary. **Green Fees** not confirmed. **Cards** ▨ ▦ ▨ **Prof** Stewart Marshall **Course Designer** James Braid **Facilities** ⊗ ℐ ⅃ ⚑ ♀ ☆ ⌂ ✔ **Location** 5m S of city centre on B767

Hotel ★★★ 70% Bruce Hotel, Cornwall St, EAST KILBRIDE ☎ 01355 229771 65 en suite

CLACKMANNANSHIRE

ALLOA   Map 11 NS89

Alloa Schawpark, Sauchie FK10 3AX
☎ 01259 724476 ▤ 01259 724476
e-mail: bellville51@hotmail.com
Set amongst 150 acres of rolling parkland beneath the Ochil hills, this course will challenge the best golfers whilst offering great enjoyment to the average player. The challenging finishing holes, 15th to 18th, consist of two long par 3s split by two long and demanding par 4s which will test any golfer's ability. Privacy provided by mature tree lined fairways.
18 holes, 6229yds, Par 69, SSS 71, Course record 63.
Club membership 910.
Visitors 7 day booking system through professional. Advised to book especially at weekends. **Societies** apply in writing/telephone. **Green Fees** £26 per round;£36 per day(£30/£40 weekends). **Cards** ▨ ▦ ▦ ▨ **Prof** Bill Bennett **Course Designer** James Braid **Facilities** ⊗ ℐ ⅃ ⚑ ♀ ☆ ⌂ ⚐ ✔ ✔ **Location** 1.5m NE on A908

Hotel ★★ 65% Terraces Hotel, 4 Melville Ter, STIRLING ☎ 01786 472268 17 en suite

Braehead Cambus FK10 2NT ☎ 01259 725766
Attactive parkland course at the foot of the Ochil Hills, and offering spectacular views.
18 holes, 6086yds, Par 70, SSS 69, Course record 64.
Club membership 800.
Visitors advisable to telephone in advance. **Societies** must contact the clubhouse manager in advance tel 01259 725766. **Green Fees** terms on application. **Cards** ▨ ▦ ▦ **Course Designer** Robert Tait **Facilities** ⊗ ℐ ⅃ ⚑ ♀ ☆ ⌂ ⚐ ✔ **Location** 1m W on A907

Hotel ★★ 65% Terraces Hotel, 4 Melville Ter, STIRLING ☎ 01786 472268 17 en suite

ALVA   Map 11 NS89

Alva Beauclerc St FK12 5LD ☎ 01259 760431
A 9-hole course at the foot of the Ochil Hills which gives it its characteristic sloping fairways and fast greens.
9 holes, 2423yds, Par 66, SSS 64, Course record 63.
Club membership 318.

Visitors may not play during medal competitions or Thu evening (Ladies night). **Societies** apply in writing or telephone in advance. **Green Fees** not confirmed. **Facilities** ⅃ ⚑ ♀ ☆ **Location** 7m from Stirling,A91 Stirling/St Andrews rd

Hotel ★★★ 69% Royal Hotel, Henderson St, BRIDGE OF ALLAN ☎ 01786 832284 32 en suite

DOLLAR   Map 11 NS99

Dollar Brewlands House FK14 7EA
☎ 01259 742400 ▤ 01259 743497
e-mail: dollargc@brewlandshousefreeserve.co.uk
Compact hillside course with magnificent views along the Ochil Hills.
18 holes, 5242yds, Par 69, SSS 66, Course record 62.
Club membership 450.
Visitors weekdays course available but restricted Wed ladies day, weekends advised to contact in advance. **Societies** write or telephone in advance. **Green Fees** £17.50 per day; £13.50 per round (£22 day/round weekends). **Course Designer** Ben Sayers **Facilities** ⊗ ℐ ⅃ ⚑ ♀ ☆ ⚐ ✔ **Leisure** snooker table. **Location** 0.5m N off A91

Hotel ★★★ 69% Royal Hotel, Henderson St, BRIDGE OF ALLAN ☎ 01786 832284 32 en suite

MUCKHART   Map 11 NO00

Muckhart FK14 7JH
☎ 01259 781423 & 781493 ▤ 01259 781544
e-mail: enquiries@muckhart-golf-club.co.uk
Scenic heathland/downland course comprising 27 holes in three combinations of nine, all of which start and finish close to the clubhouse. Each of the nine holes requires a different approach demanding tactical awareness and a skilful touch with all the clubs in the bag. There are superb views from the courses many vantage points including the aptly named 5th 'Top of the World'.
Muckhart Course-Cowden: 9 holes, 3251yds, Par 36.
Naemoor Course: 9 holes.
Club membership 750.
Visitors telephone to book - 01259 781423 or professional 01259 781493.Correct attire to be worn at all times. **Societies** booking by prior arrangement. **Green Fees** £30 per day; £27.50 per 27 holes; £20 per round (£35/£32/£25 weekends). **Cards** ▨ ▦ ▨ **Prof** Keith Salmoni **Facilities** ⊗ ℐ ⅃ ⚑ ♀ ☆ ⌂ ⚐ ✔ **Location** S of village between A91& A823

Hotel ★★★ 66% Gartwhinzean Hotel, POWMILL ☎ 01577 840595 23 en suite

TILLICOULTRY   Map 11 NS99

Tillicoultry Alva Rd FK13 6BL
☎ 01259 750124 ▤ 01259 750124
e-mail: tillygc@stirling.co.uk
Parkland course at foot of the Ochil Hills entailing some hard walking but affording fine views.
9 holes, 5004metres, Par 68, SSS 67, Course record 64.
Club membership 400.
Visitors must contact in advance. **Societies** apply to the secretary. **Green Fees** £12 per 18 holes(£17 weekends and bank holidays). **Facilities** ⅃ ⚑ ♀ ☆ **Location** A91, 9m E of Stirling

Hotel ★★★ 69% Royal Hotel, Henderson St, BRIDGE OF ALLAN ☎ 01786 832284 32 en suite

continued

306

DUMFRIES & GALLOWAY

CASTLE DOUGLAS — Map 11 NX76

Castle Douglas Abercromby Rd DG7 1BB
☎ 01556 502801 & 502877
Parkland course, one severe hill.
9 holes, 2704yds, Par 68, SSS 66.
Club membership 500.
Societies apply by writing to secretary. **Green Fees** terms on application. **Facilities** ⊗ ⓑ ♥ ♀ ♤ 🏠 ☂ ᧔ **Location** W side of town

Hotel ★★ 66% Imperial Hotel, 35 King St, CASTLE DOUGLAS ☎ 01556 502086 12 en suite

COLVEND — Map 11 NX85

Colvend Sandyhills DG5 4PY
☎ 01556 630398 & 610878 (Sec) 📠 01556 630495
e-mail: thesecretary@colvendgolfclub.co.uk
**Picturesque and challenging course on Solway coast.
Superb views.**
18 holes, 5250yds, Par 68, SSS 67, Course record 64.
Club membership 490.
Visitors restricted Apr-Sep on Tue, 1st tee reserved for weekly Medal 1-1.30 & 4-6pm and some weekends for open competitions. **Societies** must telephone in advance. **Green Fees** £22 per day. **Course Designer** Allis & Thomas **Facilities** ⊗ ᧒ ⓑ ♥ ♀ ♤ ᧔ 🏴 ♨ 🚜 ᧔ **Location** 6m from Dalbeattie on A710 Solway Coast Rd

Hotel ★★ 68% Clonyard House Hotel, COLVEND
☎ 01556 630372 15 en suite

CUMMERTREES — Map 11 NY16

Powfoot DG12 5QE
☎ 01461 700276 📠 01461 700276
This British Championship Course is on the Solway Firth, playing at this delightfully compact semi-links seaside course is a scenic treat. Lovely holes include the 2nd, the 8th and the 11th, also 9th with World War II bomb crater.
18 holes, 6283yds, Par 71, SSS 70, Course record 63.
Club membership 950.
Visitors contact in advance. May not play before 9am between 11am-1pm and after 3.30pm weekdays, no visitors Sat or before 1pm Sun. **Societies** must book in advance. **Green Fees** not confirmed. **Cards** ▭ ⬜ **Prof** Gareth Dick **Course Designer** J Braid **Facilities** ⊗ ᧒ ⓑ ♥ ♀ ♤ 🏠 ᧔ **Location** 0.5m off B724

Hotel ★★ 65% Queensberry Arms Hotel, 47 High St, ANNAN ☎ 01461 202024 24 en suite

DALBEATTIE — Map 11 NX86

Dalbeattie 60 Maxwell Park DG5 4LS
☎ 01556 610311 & 611421
e-mail: arthurhowatson@aol.com
This 9 hole course provides an excellent challenge for golfers of all abilities. There are a few gentle slopes to negotiate but compensated by fine views along the Urr Valley. The 363 yard 4th hole is a memorable par 4. A good straight drive is required to the corner of the course where a right angle dog-leg is taken for a pitch to a smallish green.
9 holes, 5710yds, Par 68, SSS 68.
Club membership 300.

continued

Cally Palace

★★★★ GATEHOUSE OF FLEET, SOUTH WEST SCOTLAND — AA ROSETTE FOR FOOD

The Cally Palace has its own private 18 hole golf course, exclusive to hotel guests. Spacious lounges, large conservatory, indoor swimming pool, jacuzzi, sauna and billiards room compliment the Cally facilities. There are excellent golf packages available.

Tel 01557 814 341

FOR LATEST NEWS AND SEASONAL OFFERS VISIT
www.callypalace.co.uk

Visitors welcomed any day, effort made to accomodate on club competitions days **Societies** apply in writing to Secretary or telephone 01556 610311 **Green Fees** £15 per 18 holes;£10 per 9 holes;£50 for 7 day weekly ticket. **Facilities** ⊗ ⓑ ♥ ♀ ♤ 🏴 🚜 **Location** Signposted off B794

Hotel ★★ 65% King's Arms Hotel, St Andrew's St, CASTLE DOUGLAS ☎ 01556 502626 10 rms (9 en suite)

DUMFRIES — Map 11 NX97

Dumfries & County Nunfield, Edinburgh Rd DG1 1JX ☎ 01387 253585 📠 01387 253585
e-mail: dumfriescounty@netscapeonline.co.uk
Parkland course alongside River Nith, with views over the Queensberry Hills.
Nunfield: 18 holes, 5928yds, Par 69, SSS 69, Course record 61.
Club membership 800.
Visitors must contact professional in advance on 01387 268918 but may not play Saturdays and during competitions on Sundays **Societies** telephone professional in advance **Green Fees** £26 per round;£30 per day. **Prof** Stuart Syme **Course Designer** William Fernie **Facilities** ⊗ ᧒ ⓑ ♥ ♀ ♤ 🏠 ᧔ ♨ ᧔ **Conf** Max 60 **Location** 1m NE of Dumfries on A701

Hotel ★★★ 67% Station Hotel, 49 Lovers Walk, DUMFRIES ☎ 01387 254316 32 en suite

Dumfries & Galloway 2 Laurieston Av DG2 7NY
☎ 01387 263848 📠 01387 263848
e-mail: joe@golfclub.fsnet.co.uk
Attractive parkland course, a good test of golf but not physically demanding.

continued

18 holes, 6309yds, Par 70, SSS 71.
Club membership 800.
Visitors may not play on competition days. Must contact in advance. No visitors on Saturdays during season. Some Sundays not available. **Societies** apply in writing. **Green Fees** £27 per day/round (£33 weekends). **Prof** Joe Fergusson **Course Designer** W Fernie **Facilities** ⊗ ⅷ Ⅼ ☒ ♀ ⌂ 🏠 ⚐ ⚙ **Location** W side of town centre on A75

Hotel ★★★ 69% Cairndale Hotel & Leisure Club, English St, DUMFRIES ☎ 01387 254111 91 en suite

GATEHOUSE-OF-FLEET   Map 11 NX55
Gatehouse Laurieston Rd DG7 2BE
☎ 01644 450260 ▧ 01644 450260
Set against a background of rolling hills with scenic views of Fleet Bay and the Solway Firth.
9 holes, 2521yds, Par 66, SSS 66, Course record 62.
Club membership 300.
Visitors restricted Sun before 11.30am. **Societies** telephone in advance. **Green Fees** £10 per day. **Course Designer** Tom Fernie **Facilities** ⚐ **Location** 0.25m N of town

Hotel ★★★★⚐ 70% Cally Palace Hotel, GATEHOUSE OF FLEET ☎ 01557 814341 55 en suite

See advertisement on page 307

GLENLUCE   Map 10 NX15
Wigtownshire County Mains of Park DG8 0NN
☎ 01581 300420
e-mail: enquiries@wigtownshirecountygolfclub.com
Seaside links course on the shores of Luce Bay, easy walking but affected by winds. The 12th hole, a dogleg with out of bounds to the right, is named after the course's designer, Gordon Cunningham.
18 holes, 5843yds, Par 70, SSS 68, Course record 66.
Club membership 450.
Visitors may play any day by prior arrangement ex competition days. **Societies** must contact in advance. **Green Fees** £26 per day; £20 per round (£28/£22weekends). **Course Designer** W Gordon Cunningham **Facilities** ⊗ ⅷ ⅬⅬ ☒ ♀ ⚐ ⌂ ⚙ **Location** 1.5m W off A75, 200 yds off A75 on shores of Luce Bay

Hotel ★★★★ 68% North West Castle Hotel, STRANRAER ☎ 01776 704413 70 en suite 3 annexe en suite

GRETNA   Map 11 NY36
Gretna Kirtle View DG16 5HD
☎ 01461 338464 ▧ 01461 337362
e-mail: georgebirnie@aol.co.uk
A nice parkland course on gentle hills. It offers a good test of skill.
9 holes, 3214yds, Par 72, SSS 71, Course record 71.
Club membership 250.   *continued*

Visitors no restrictions. **Societies** telephone in advance. **Green Fees** not confirmed. **Course Designer** N Williams **Facilities** ⚐ ⚙ **Location** 0.5m W of Gretna on B721, signposted

Hotel ★★★ 66% Garden House Hotel, Sarkfoot Rd, GRETNA ☎ 01461 337621 21 en suite

KIRKCUDBRIGHT   Map 11 NX65
Brighouse Bay Brighouse Bay, Borgue DG6 4TS
☎ 01557 870409 ▧ 01557 870409
e-mail: complex@gillespieleisure.fsnet.co.uk
A beautifully situated scenic maritime course on free draining coastal grassland and playable all year. Making use of many natural features - water, gullies and rocks - it provides a testing challenge to golfers of all handicaps.
18 holes, 6602yds, Par 74, SSS 73.
Club membership 170.
Visitors pay as you play - payment at adjacent Golf & Leisure Club. Phoning in advance recommended. Parties over 8 must book in advance. **Societies** prior arrangement necessary. **Green Fees** £18. **Cards** 💳 **Course Designer** D Gray **Facilities** ⊗ ⅷ ⅬⅬ ☒ ♀ ⚐ ⌂ ⚙ **Leisure** heated indoor swimming pool, fishing, sauna, solarium, gymnasium, Turkish steam room, jacuzzi, pool tables.**Conf** Max 100 **Location** 3m S of Borgue off B727

Hotel ★★★ 72% Selkirk Arms Hotel, Old High St, KIRKCUDBRIGHT ☎ 01557 330402 13 en suite 3 annexe en suite

Kirkcudbright Stirling Crescent DG6 4EZ
☎ 01557 330314 ▧ 01557 330314
e-mail: david@kirkcudbrightgolf.co.uk
Parkland course. Hilly, with good views over the Harbour town of Kirkcudbright and the Dee Estuary.
18 holes, 5739yds, Par 69, SSS 69, Course record 63.
Club membership 500.
Visitors advisable to contact in advance. **Societies** contact in advance. **Green Fees** £23 per day; £18 per round. **Facilities** ⊗ ⅷ ⅬⅬ ☒ ♀ ⚐ ⌂ ⚙ **Location** NE side of town off A711

Hotel ★★★ 72% Selkirk Arms Hotel, Old High St, KIRKCUDBRIGHT ☎ 01557 330402 13 en suite 3 annexe en suite

LANGHOLM   Map 11 NY38
Langholm Whitaside DG13 0JR
☎ 013873 80673 & 81247
e-mail: golf@langholmgolfclub.co.uk
Hillside course with fine views, easy to medium walking.
9 holes, 6180yds, Par 70, SSS 70, Course record 65.
Club membership 200.
Visitors restricted Sat & Sun. **Societies** apply in writing to secretary. **Green Fees** not confirmed. **Facilities** ⊗ by prior arrangement ⅷ by prior arrangement ⅬⅬ by prior arrangement ♀ **Location** E side of village off A7

Guesthouse ♦♦♦ The Reivers Rest, 81 High St, LANGHOLM ☎ 01387 381343 5 en suite

LOCHMABEN   Map 11 NY08
Lochmaben Castlehillgate DG11 1NT ☎ 01387 810552
Attractive parkland course surrounding the Kirk Loch, excellent views on this well maintained course.
18 holes, 5357yds, Par 67, SSS 66, Course record 60.
Club membership 850.   *continued*

Visitors advised to contact in advance, 01387 810552,
visitors weekdays up to 5pm weekends available **Societies**
must contact in advance, on 01387 810552 **Green Fees** £22
per day; £18 per round (£30/£25 weekends). **Course
Designer** James Braid **Facilities** ⊗ ⟩Ⅷ ⅃ ⬦ ⚑ ♀ ☖ ⚒ ♂
Leisure fishing. **Location** S side of village off A709

Hotel ★★★ 72% The Dryfesdale Country House Hotel,
Dryfebridge, LOCKERBIE ☎ 01576 202427 15 en suite

LOCKERBIE   Map 11 NY18

Lockerbie Corrie Rd DG11 2ND
☎ 01576 203363 🖹 01576 203363
**Parkland course with fine views and featuring the only
pond hole in Dumfriesshire. Pond comes into play at
three holes.**
18 holes, 5614yds, Par 68, SSS 67, Course record 64.
Club membership 620.
Visitors restricted Sun. Advisable to book in advance.
Societies must contact secretary in advance. **Green Fees** £16
per 18 holes (£18 weekends). **Course Designer** James Braid
Facilities ⊗ ⬦ ⚑ ♀ ☖ ♈ ♂ **Location** E side of town
centre off B7068

Hotel ★★★ 72% The Dryfesdale Country House Hotel,
Dryfebridge, LOCKERBIE ☎ 01576 202427 15 en suite

MOFFAT   Map 11 NT00

Moffat Coatshill DG10 9SB
☎ 01683 220020 🖹 01683 221802
e-mail: moffatgolfclub@onetel.net.uk
**Scenic moorland course overlooking the town, with
panoramic views of southern uplands.**
18 holes, 5259yds, Par 69, SSS 67, Course record 60.
Club membership 350.
Visitors advised to contact in advance, no visitors after 12
noon on Wed. **Societies** apply in writing/telephone the
clubmaster. **Green Fees** £19 per round;£23 per day(£26/£32
weekends and bank holidays). **Cards** ▭▬☰ ▦▬
Course Designer Ben Sayers **Facilities** ⊗ ⟩Ⅷ ⬦ ⚑ ♀ ☖
♈ ♂ **Leisure** snooker. **Location** From A74(M) junct 15, 1m
on A701 to Moffat, course signposted

Hotel ★★★ 74% Moffat House Hotel, High St, MOFFAT
☎ 01683 220039 21 en suite

MONREITH   Map 10 NX34

St Medan DG8 8NJ ☎ 01988 700358
**Links course with panoramic views of the Solway and Isle
of Man.**
9 holes, 4608yds, Par 64, SSS 63, Course record 60.
Club membership 300.
Visitors no restrictions. **Societies** apply in advance by
telephone or writing **Green Fees** £20 per day; £15 per 18
holes; £10 per 9 holes. **Course Designer** James Braid
Facilities ⊗ ⟩Ⅷ ⬦ ⚑ ♀ ☖ ♈ ♂ **Location** 1m SE off A747

Hotel ★★ 67% Kelvin House Hotel, 53 Main St,
GLENLUCE ☎ 01581 300303 6 rms (5 en suite)

NEW GALLOWAY   Map 11 NX67

New Galloway High St DG7 3RN
☎ 01644 420737 & 450685 🖹 01644 450685
**Set on the edge of the Galloway Hills and overlooking
Loch Ken, the course has excellent tees and first class
greens. The course rises through the first two fairways to
a plateau with all round views that many think
unsurpassed.**
continued

9 holes, 5006yds, Par 68, SSS 67, Course record 64.
Club membership 350.
Visitors restricted on Sun (competition days). All visitors
play off yellow markers. Contact Secretary in advance.
Smart/casual dress. **Societies** contact secretary in advance.
Green Fees £13 per day. **Course Designer** James Braid
Facilities ⬦ ⚑ ♀ ☖ ♈ ♂ **Location** S side of town on
A762

Hotel ★★ 70% Douglas Arms, King St, CASTLE
DOUGLAS ☎ 01556 502231 24 en suite

NEWTON STEWART   Map 10 NX46

Newton Stewart Kirroughtree Av, Minnigaff DG8 6PF
☎ 01671 402172 🖹 01671 402172
**Parkland course in picturesque setting. A good test for all
standards of golfers with a variety of shots required.**
18 holes, 5903yds, Par 69, SSS 70, Course record 66.
Club membership 380.
Visitors must contact in advance. **Societies** must contact in
advance. **Green Fees** £25 per day;£22 per round(£29/£25
weekends and bank holidays). **Facilities** ⊗ ⬦ ⚑ ♀ ☖ ☖ ♈
⚒ ♂ **Location** 0.5m N of town centre off A75

Hotel ★★ 74% Creebridge House Hotel, NEWTON
STEWART ☎ 01671 402121 19 en suite

PORTPATRICK   Map 10 NX05

Portpatrick Golf Course Rd DG9 8TB
☎ 01776 810273 🖹 01776 810811
e-mail: enquiries@portpatrickgolfclub.com
**Seaside links-type course, set on cliffs overlooking the
Irish Sea, with magnificent views.**
*Dunskey Course: 18 holes, 5908yds, Par 70, SSS 69,
Course record 63.*
*Dinvin Course: 9 holes, 1504yds, Par 27, SSS 27,
Course record 23.*
Club membership 750.
Visitors must contact in advance. £5 deposite required
Societies must contact in advance. **Green Fees** Dunskey: £35
per day; £25 per round (£40/£30 weekends) Dinvin:£10 per
round;£15 per day. **Cards** ▭▬☰ ▦▬ ▯ **Course Designer**
Charles Hunter **Facilities** ⊗ ⟩Ⅷ ⬦ ⚑ ♀ ☖ ☖ ♈ ♂ ⚒ ♂
Location On entering village fork right at War Memorial,
300yds signposted

Hotel ★★★ 73% Fernhill Hotel, Heugh Rd,
PORTPATRICK ☎ 01776 810220
14 en suite 9 annexe en suite

SANQUHAR   Map 11 NS70

Sanquhar Euchan Golf Course, Blackaddie Rd DG4 6JZ
☎ 01659 50577 & 66095
e-mail: douglas@nithb.freeserve.co.uk
**Parkland course, fine views, easy walking. A good test for
all standards of golfer.**
9 holes, 5594yds, Par 70, SSS 68, Course record 66.
Club membership 200.
Visitors no restrictions. **Societies** must pre-book. **Green
Fees** £12 per day (£15 weekends). **Course Designer** Willie
Fernie **Facilities** ♀ ☖ ♈ **Leisure** snooker,pool. **Location**
0.5m SW off A76

Hotel ★★ 65% Blackaddie House Hotel, Blackaddie Rd,
SANQUHAR ☎ 01659 50270 9 en suite

AA website: www.theAA.com

SOUTHERNESS   Map 11 NX95

Southerness DG2 8AZ
☎ 01387 880677 📄 01387 880644
e-mail: admin@southernessgc.sol.co.uk
Natural links, Championship course with panoramic views. Heather and bracken abound.
18 holes, 6566yds, Par 69, SSS 73, Course record 65.
Club membership 830.
Visitors must have handicap certificate and contact in advance. May only play from yellow markers. **Societies** must contact in advance. **Green Fees** £35 per 18 holes (£45 weekends & bank holidays). **Cards** 💳 💳 **Course Designer** McKenzie Ross **Facilities** ⊗ ⅢⅡ ⅃ ⅃ ⅃ ⅃ ⅃ **Location** 3.5m S of Kirkbean off A710

Hotel ★★ 68% Clonyard House Hotel, COLVEND ☎ 01556 630372 15 en suite

STRANRAER   Map 10 NX06

Stranraer Creachmore by Stranraer DG9 0LF
☎ 01776 870245 📄 01776 870445
e-mail: stranraergolf@btclick.com
Parkland course with beautiful views overlooking Loch Ryan to Ailsa Craig, Arran and beyond. Several notable holes including the 3rd, a winding burn is crossed three times to a green set between a large bunker and a steep bank sloping down to the burn, the scenic 5th with spectacular views, the 11th requiring a demanding tee shot with trees and out of bounds to the left then a steep rise to very fast green. The 15th is a difficult par 3 where accuracy is paramount with ground sloping away either side of the green.
18 holes, 6308yds, Par 70, SSS 72, Course record 66.
Club membership 700.
Visitors must contact in advance. Members times reserved throughout year. **Societies** must telephone in advance. **Green Fees** terms on application. **Cards** 💳 💳 **Course Designer** James Braid **Facilities** ⊗ ⅢⅡ ⅃ ⅃ ⅃ ⅃ ⅃ **Location** 2.5m NW on A718 from Stranraer

Hotel ★★★★ 68% North West Castle Hotel, STRANRAER ☎ 01776 704413 70 en suite 3 annexe en suite

THORNHILL   Map 11 NX89

Thornhill Blacknest DG3 5DW ☎ 01848 330546
Moorland/parkland course with fine views over the southern uplands.
18 holes, 6085yds, Par 71, SSS 70, Course record 67.
Club membership 600.
Visitors apply in advance, restricted competition days. **Societies** apply in writing. **Green Fees** terms on application. **Facilities** ⊗ ⅢⅡ ⅃ ⅃ ⅃ ⅃ **Location** 1m E of town off A76

Hotel ★★ 74% Trigony House Hotel, Closeburn, THORNHILL ☎ 01848 331211 8 en suite

WIGTOWN   Map 10 NX45

Wigtown & Bladnoch Lightlands Ter DG8 9EF
☎ 01988 403354
Slightly hilly parkland course with fine views over Wigtown Bay to Galloway Hills.
9 holes, 5462yds, Par 68, SSS 67, Course record 62.
Club membership 150.

continued

Visitors advisable to contact in advance for weekend play. Course closed to visitors during open competitions. **Societies** contact secretary in advance. **Green Fees** terms on application. **Course Designer** W Muir **Facilities** ⅃ **Location** SW on A714

Hotel ★★ 74% Creebridge House Hotel, NEWTON STEWART ☎ 01671 402121 19 en suite

DUNDEE CITY

DUNDEE   Map 11 NO43

Caird Park Mains Loan DD4 9BX
☎ 01382 438871 📄 01382 433211
e-mail: la.bookings@dundeecity.gov.uk
A pay-as-you-play course situated in extensive parkland in the heart of Carnoustie countryside. A reasonably easy start belies the difficulty of the middle section (holes 7-13) and the back nine cross the Gelly Burn four times.
18 holes, 6280yds, Par 72, SSS 69, Course record 67.
Club membership 1800.
Visitors no restrictions. **Societies** must contact in advance 01382 438871. **Green Fees** £18 per round; £26 per day. **Prof** J Black **Facilities** ⅃ ⅃ ⅃ ⅃ ⅃ ⅃ **Location** From Kingsway (A90) take Forfar Road, turn left onto Claverhouse Road, 1st left into Caird Park

Hotel ★★★ 70% Swallow Hotel, Kingsway West, Invergowrie, DUNDEE ☎ 01382 641122 107 en suite

Camperdown Camperdown Park, Coupar Angus Rd DD2 4TF ☎ 01382 432688
A beautiful course located within the Camperdown Country Park with undulating, tree lined fairways.which meander through avenues of mature trees surrounding the imposing Camperdown House.
18 holes, 6548yds, Par 71, SSS 72.
Club membership 1600.
Visitors telephone in advance to be assured of a tee time. **Societies** must contact in advance. **Green Fees** not confirmed. **Prof** Roddy Brown **Facilities** ⊗ ⅢⅡ ⅃ ⅃ ⅃ ⅃ **Leisure** hard tennis courts. **Location** Kingsway (A90), turn off at Coupar Angus Road (A923) then turn left into Camperdown Park

Hotel ★★ 73% The Shaftesbury, 1 Hyndford St, DUNDEE ☎ 01382 669216 12 en suite

Downfield Turnberry Av DD2 3QP
☎ 01382 825595 📄 01382 813111
e-mail: downfieldgc@aol.com
A 1999 Open Qualifying venue. A course with championship credentials providing an enjoyable test for all golfers.
18 holes, 6803yds, Par 73, SSS 73, Course record 65.
Club membership 750.
Visitors must contact in advance, no visitors at weekends. **Societies** must contact in advance. **Green Fees** £48 per day; £34per round(£36 per round Sunday). **Cards** 💳 💳 💳 💳 **Prof** Kenny Hutton **Course Designer** James Braid **Facilities** ⊗ ⅢⅡ ⅃ ⅃ ⅃ ⅃ ⅃ **Leisure** snooker room. **Location** N of city centre, signposted on A90 Perth/Aberdeen road at junct with A923

Hotel ★★ 73% The Shaftesbury, 1 Hyndford St, DUNDEE ☎ 01382 669216 12 en suite

EAST AYRSHIRE

GALSTON   Map 11 NS53

Loudoun Edinburgh Rd KA4 8PA
☎ 01563 821993 & 820551 📠 01563 820011
e-mail: secretary@loudgowf.sol.co.uk
Pleasant, fairly flat parkland course with many mature trees, located in the Irvine valley in the rural heart of Ayrshire.
18 holes, 5773yds, Par 68, SSS 68, Course record 61.
Club membership 850.
Visitors must contact in advance. Weekdays only, must play with member at weekends/public holidays **Societies** telephone in advance. **Green Fees** £31 per day; £21 per round. **Facilities** ⊗ ⫼ ⮭ ⬛ ♥ ♀ ⚲ 🏠 ⚒ ⟋ **Location** NE side of town on A71

Hotel ★★★ 72% Strathaven Hotel, Hamilton Rd, STRATHAVEN ☎ 01357 521778 22 en suite

KILMARNOCK   Map 10 NS43

Annanhill Irvine Rd KA1 2RT
☎ 01563 521644 & 521512
Municipal, tree-lined parkland course played over by private clubs.
18 holes, 6269yds, Par 71, SSS 70, Course record 66.
Club membership 394.
Visitors must book at starters office, 01563 521512.
Societies apply in writing. **Green Fees** terms on application.
Course Designer Jack McLean **Facilities** ⚲ **Location** 1m N on A71

Caprington Ayr Rd KA1 4UW
☎ 01563 523702 & 521915 (Gen Enq)
Municipal parkland course.
18 holes, 5810yds, Par 68, SSS 68.
Club membership 400.
Visitors may not play on Sat. **Societies** must contact in advance. **Green Fees** terms on application. **Facilities** ⊗ by prior arrangement ⫼ ⮭ ⬛ ♥ ♀ ⚲ ⟋ **Location** 1.5m S on B7038

Hotel ⌂ Travelodge, Kilmarnock By Pass, KILMARNOCK ☎ 01563 573810 40 en suite

MAUCHLINE   Map 11 NS42

Ballochmyle Catrine Rd KA5 6LE
☎ 01290 550469 📠 01290 550469
e-mail: secretary@ballochmyle.freeserve.co.uk
Wooded parkland course.
18 holes, 5972yds, Par 70, SSS 69, Course record 64.
Club membership 730.
Visitors welcome. May not play Sat. **Societies** apply in writing/telephone. **Green Fees** £30 per day; £20 per round (£35/£25 Sun). **Cards** 🔲 🔳 💳 **Facilities** ⊗ ⫼ ⮭ ⬛ ♥ ♀ ⚲ 🏠 ⟋ **Leisure** snooker. **Location** 1m SE on B705

Hotel ⌂ Travelodge, Kilmarnock By Pass, KILMARNOCK ☎ 01563 573810 40 en suite

NEW CUMNOCK   Map 11 NS61

New Cumnock Lochhill, Cumnock Rd KA18 4PN
☎ 01290 338848
Parkland course.
9 holes, 5176yds, Par 68, SSS 68, Course record 63.
Club membership 280.
Visitors restricted on Sun competition days. After 4 pm only
continued

Societies apply in writing. **Green Fees** not confirmed.
Course Designer Willie Fernie **Facilities** ⊗ ⫼ ⮭ ⬛ ♥ ♀ ⚲ 🏠 **Leisure** fishing. **Location** 0.75m N on A76

Hotel ★★ 65% Blackaddie House Hotel, Blackaddie Rd, SANQUHAR ☎ 01659 50270 9 en suite

PATNA   Map 10 NS41

Doon Valley Hillside Park KA6 7JT ☎ 01292 531607
Established parkland course located on an undulating hillside.
9 holes, 5886yds, Par 70, SSS 70, Course record 56.
Club membership 100.
Visitors no restrictions mid week, advisable to contact in advance for weekends. **Societies** telephone to arrange. **Green Fees** £10 per 18 holes. **Facilities** ⚲ **Leisure** fishing.
Location 10m S of Ayr on the A713

Hotel ★★ Ladyburn, MAYBOLE
☎ 01655 740585 8 rms (7 en suite)

EAST DUNBARTONSHIRE

BALMORE   Map 11 NS57

Balmore Golf Course Rd G64 4AW
☎ 01360 620284 📠 01360 622742
e-mail: secretary@balmoregolfclub.co.uk
Parkland course with fine views.
18 holes, 5530yds, Par 66, SSS 67, Course record 62.
Club membership 700.
Visitors must contact in advance,may not play at weekends **Societies** apply in writing. **Green Fees** £40 per day; £30 per round. **Prof** Kevin Craggs **Course Designer** James Braid
Facilities ⊗ ⫼ ⮭ ⬛ ♥ ♀ ⚲ 🏠 ⟋ **Location** N off A807

Hotel ★★★ 65% Patio Hotel, 1 South Av, Clydebank Business Park, CLYDEBANK ☎ 0141 951 1133 82 en suite

BEARSDEN   Map 11 NS57

Bearsden Thorn Rd G61 4BP ☎ 0141 942 2351
Parkland course, with 16 greens and 11 teeing grounds. Easy walking and views over city.
9 holes, 6014yds, Par 68, SSS 69, Course record 67.
Club membership 600.
Visitors must be accompanied by and play with member.
Societies apply by writing. **Green Fees** £15 per 18 holes; £20 per day. **Facilities** ⊗ ⫼ ⮭ ⬛ ♥ ♀ ⚲ **Location** 1m W off A809

Hotel ★★★ 65% Patio Hotel, 1 South Av, Clydebank Business Park, CLYDEBANK ☎ 0141 951 1133 82 en suite

Douglas Park Hillfoot G61 2TJ
☎ 0141 942 2220 (Clubhouse) 942 0985 (Secretary)
📠 0141 942 0985
Parkland course with wide variety of holes.
18 holes, 5962yds, Par 69, SSS 69, Course record 64.
Club membership 900.
Visitors must be accompanied by member or must contact in advance, Wednesdays and Thursdays for visiting parties only. **Societies** Wed & Thu. Must telephone in advance.
Green Fees £31 per day; £23 per round. **Prof** David Scott
Course Designer Willie Fernie **Facilities** ⊗ ⫼ by prior arrangement ⮭ ⬛ ♥ ♀ ⚲ 🏠 ⚒ ⟋ **Location** E side of town on A81

Hotel ★★★ 65% Patio Hotel, 1 South Av, Clydebank Business Park, CLYDEBANK ☎ 0141 951 1133 82 en suite

Windyhill Baljaffray Rd G61 4QQ
☎ 0141 942 2349 🖹 0141 942 5874
e-mail: secretary@windyhill.co.uk
Interesting parkland/moorland course with panoramic views of Glasgow and beyond; testing 12th hole.
18 holes, 6254yds, Par 71, SSS 70, Course record 64.
Club membership 800.
Visitors may not play at weekends. Must contact professional in advance. Must have a handicap certificate. Societies must apply in writing. **Green Fees** £30 per day; £20 per round. **Prof** Chris Duffy **Course Designer** James Braid **Facilities** ⊗ 〗Ⅲ ᄂ ♨ ♀ ♨ 🏠 ⛳ ♂ **Location** 2m NW off B8050, 1.5 miles from Bearsden cross,just off Drymen road

Hotel ★★★ 65% Patio Hotel, 1 South Av, Clydebank Business Park, CLYDEBANK ☎ 0141 951 1133 82 en suite

BISHOPBRIGGS   Map 11 NS67

Bishopbriggs Brackenbrae Rd G64 2DX
☎ 0141 772 1810 772 8938 🖹 7622532
e-mail: bgcsecretary@dial.pipex.com
Parkland course with views to Campsie Hills.
18 holes, 6041yds, Par 69, SSS 69, Course record 63.
Club membership 800.
Visitors Must contact in advance. May not play at weekends. Societies apply in writing in advance. **Green Fees** not confirmed. **Course Designer** James Braid **Facilities** ⊗ 〗Ⅲ ᄂ ♨ ♀ ♨ 🏠 **Location** 0.5m NW off A803

Hotel ★★★ 65% Patio Hotel, 1 South Av, Clydebank Business Park, CLYDEBANK ☎ 0141 951 1133 82 en suite

Cawder Cadder Rd G64 3QD
☎ 0141 761 1281 🖹 0141 761 1281
e-mail: secretary@cawdergolfclub.org.uk
Two parkland courses; Cawder Course is hilly, with 5th, 9th, 10th, 11th-testing holes. Keir Course is flat.
Cawder Course: 18 holes, 6295yds, Par 70, SSS 71, Course record 63.
Keir Course: 18 holes, 5877yds, Par 68, SSS 68.
Club membership 1150.
Visitors must contact in advance & may play on weekdays only. Societies must contact in writing, not on Bank Holidays **Green Fees** £40 per day; £30 per round. **Cards** ⊷ ⊟ ⊠ 🖹 **Prof** Ken Stevely **Course Designer** James Braid **Facilities** ⊗ 〗Ⅲ ᄂ ♨ ♀ ♨ 🏠 ⛳ ♂ **Conf** Banquet 100 **Location** 5 m NE off A803

Hotel ★★★ 65% Patio Hotel, 1 South Av, Clydebank Business Park, CLYDEBANK ☎ 0141 951 1133 82 en suite

Littlehill Auchinairn Rd G64 1UT ☎ 0141 772 1916
Municipal parkland course.
18 holes, 6240yds, Par 70, SSS 70.
Visitors must contact in advance. Societies advance bookings required in writing **Green Fees** not confirmed. **Facilities** ♨ ᄉ **Location** 3m NE of Glasgow city centre on A803

Hotel ★★★ 60% Rosslea Hall Country House Hotel, Ferry Rd, RHU ☎ 01436 439955 29 en suite 5 annexe en suite

KIRKINTILLOCH   Map 11 NS67

Hayston Campsie Rd G66 1RN
☎ 0141 776 1244 & 775 0723 (Sec) 🖹 0141 7769030
An undulating, tree-lined course with a sandy subsoil.
18 holes, 6042yds, Par 70, SSS 70, Course record 60.
Club membership 800.
continued

Visitors must apply in advance, may not play weekends. Societies Tue & Thu, apply in writing **Green Fees** £37 per day; £27per round. **Prof** Steven Barnett **Course Designer** James Braid **Facilities** ⊗ 〗Ⅲ ᄂ ♨ ♀ ♨ ♂ **Location** 1m NW off A803

Hotel ★★★★ 66% Westerwood Hotel Golf & Country Club, 1 St Andrews Dr, Westerwood, CUMBERNAULD ☎ 01236 457171 49 en suite

Kirkintilloch Campsie Rd G66 1RN
☎ 0141 776 1256 & 775 2387 🖹 0141 775 2424
Parkland course in rural setting.
18 holes, 5860yds, Par 70, SSS 69.
Club membership 650.
Visitors must be introduced by member. Societies apply in writing. **Green Fees** on application to secretary. **Course Designer** James Braid **Facilities** ⊗ 〗Ⅲ ᄂ ♨ ♀ ♨ 🏠 **Location** 1m NW off A803

Hotel ★★★★ 66% Westerwood Hotel Golf & Country Club, 1 St Andrews Dr, Westerwood, CUMBERNAULD ☎ 01236 457171 49 en suite

LENNOXTOWN   Map 11 NS67

Campsie Crow Rd G66 7HX ☎ 01360 310244
Scenic hillside course.
18 holes, 5507yds, Par 70, SSS 68, Course record 69.
Club membership 620.
Visitors preferred weekdays. Weekends only by prior arrangment, contact professional 01360 310920. Societies written application. **Green Fees** not confirmed. **Prof** Mark Brennan **Course Designer** W Auchterlonie **Facilities** ⊗ 〗Ⅲ ᄂ ♨ ♀ ♨ 🏠 ⛳ **Location** 0.5m N on B822

Hotel ★★★★ 66% Westerwood Hotel Golf & Country Club, 1 St Andrews Dr, Westerwood, CUMBERNAULD ☎ 01236 457171 49 en suite

LENZIE   Map 11 NS67

Lenzie 19 Crosshill Rd G66 5DA ☎ 0141 776 1535 & 812 3018 🖹 0141 777 7748 or 0141 812 3018
e-mail: scottdavidson@lenziegolfclub.demon.co.uk
The course is parkland and prominent features include the old beech trees which line some of the fairways together with thorn hedges and shallow ditches. Extensive larch and fir plantations have also been created. The course is relatively flat apart from a steep hill to the green at the 5th hole.
18 holes, 5984yds, Par 69, SSS 69, Course record 64.
Club membership 890.
Visitors must contact in advance. Societies apply in writing/telephone in advance. **Green Fees** £30 per day; £24 per round. **Prof** Jim McCallum **Facilities** ⊗ 〗Ⅲ ᄂ ♨ ♀ ᄉ 🏠 ⛱ ♂ **Conf** Max 90 Board 50 Banquet 80 **Location** N of Glasgow, approx 15 mins from Glasgow city centre, Kirkintilloch turn off M80

Hotel ★★★★ 66% Westerwood Hotel Golf & Country Club, 1 St Andrews Dr, Westerwood, CUMBERNAULD ☎ 01236 457171 49 en suite

MILNGAVIE   Map 11 NS57

Clober Craigton Rd G62 7HP
☎ 0141 956 1685 🖹 0141 955 1416
e-mail: secretary@clober.co.uk
Parkland course. Testing 5th hole, par 3.
18 holes, 4824yds, Par 66, SSS 65, Course record 61.
Club membership 600.
continued

Visitors may not play after 4pm Mon-Fri. Must play with member weekends and bank holidays. **Societies** must contact in advance. **Green Fees** terms on application. **Prof** C Elliott **Facilities** ⊗ ╫ ⅃ ⅃ ♀ ⅃ 🖾 ♂ **Location** NW side of town

Hotel ★★★ 65% Patio Hotel, 1 South Av, Clydebank Business Park, CLYDEBANK ☎ 0141 951 1133 82 en suite

Esporta, Dougalston Strathblane G62 8HJ
☎ 0141 955 2404 & 955 2434 📱 0141 955 2406
A golf course of tremendous character set in 300 acres of beautiful woodland dotted with drumlins, lakes and criss-crossed by streams and ditches. The course makes excellent use of the natural features to create mature, tree-lined fairways. The course is currently being upgraded to improve drainage and introduce three new holes as well as clearing shrubbery to widen some others.
18 holes, 6225yds, Par 71, SSS 72, Course record 68.
Club membership 800.
Visitors contact in advance. May not play on Sat, tee times may be booked 3 days in advance. Sun-Fri all subject to availability of tee times. **Societies** weekdays only. **Green Fees** not confirmed. **Cards** ▭▭ ▭▭ 🖾 **Prof** Craig Everett **Course Designer** Commander Harris **Facilities** ⊗ ╫ ⅃ ♥ ♀ ⅃ 🖾 ♂ ♂ **Leisure** heated indoor swimming pool, sauna, solarium, gymnasium. **Location** NE side of town on A81

Hotel ★★★ 65% Patio Hotel, 1 South Av, Clydebank Business Park, CLYDEBANK ☎ 0141 951 1133 82 en suite

Hilton Park Auldmarroch Estate, Stockiemuir Rd G62 7HB ☎ 0141 956 4657 📱 0141 956 4657
e-mail: info@hiltonparkgolfclub.fsnet.co.uk
Moorland courses set amidst magnificent scenery.
Hilton Course: 18 holes, 6054yds, Par 70, SSS 70, Course record 65.
Allander Course: 18 holes, 5487yards, Par 69, SSS 67, Course record 65.
Club membership 1200.
Visitors must contact in advance but may not play at weekends. **Societies** apply in advance to secretary. **Green Fees** £25 per round;£35 per day. **Prof** W McCondichie **Course Designer** James Braid **Facilities** ⊗ ╫ ⅃ ♥ ♀ ⅃ 🖾 ♂ ➤ ♂ **Location** 3m NW of Milngavie, on A809

Hotel ★★★ 65% Patio Hotel, 1 South Av, Clydebank Business Park, CLYDEBANK ☎ 0141 951 1133 82 en suite

Milngavie Laighpark G62 8EP
☎ 0141 956 1619 📱 0141 956 4252
Very scenic moorland course, which plays its full length, challenging SSS, testing 1st hole followed by many others.
18 holes, 5818yds, Par 68, SSS 68, Course record 59.
Club membership 700.
Visitors must contact in advance, may not play weekends. **Societies** apply in writing. **Green Fees** not confirmed. **Course Designer** The Auchterlonie Brothers **Facilities** ⊗ ╫ ⅃ ♥ ♀ ⅃ **Location** 1.25m N

Hotel ★★★ 65% Patio Hotel, 1 South Av, Clydebank Business Park, CLYDEBANK ☎ 0141 951 1133 82 en suite

Prices may change during the currency of the Guide, please check when booking

---

EAST LOTHIAN

ABERLADY   Map 12 NT47

Kilspindie EH32 0QD
☎ 01875 870358 📱 01875 870358
Traditional Scottish seaside links, short but tight and well-bunkered. Situated on the shores of the River Forth.
Kilspindie: 18 holes, 5480yds, Par 69, SSS 66, Course record 59.
Club membership 750.
Visitors must contact in advance, preferred days for visitors Mon-Fri,but some tee times available at weekends. **Societies** contact secretary in advance. **Green Fees** £44 per day; £27.50 per round (£55/£33 weekends). **Prof** Graham J Sked **Course Designer** Various **Facilities** ⊗ ╫ ⅃ ♥ ♀ ⅃ 🖾 ♂ ♨ ♂ **Conf** Banquet 70 **Location** N side of village off A198, private road access located at Eastern end of village of Aberlady

Hotel ★★★♨ Greywalls Hotel, Muirfield, GULLANE ☎ 01620 842144 17 en suite 5 annexe en suite

Luffness New EH32 0QA
☎ 01620 843336 📱 01620 842933
Links course, National Final Qualifying Course for Open Championship.
18 holes, 6122yds, Par 69, SSS 70, Course record 62.
Club membership 700.
Visitors must contact in advance and may not play at weekends & public holidays. **Societies** telephone for application form. **Green Fees** £55 per day; £37.50 per round. **Course Designer** Tom Morris **Facilities** ⊗ ╫ ♥ ♀ ⅃ 🖾 ♂ **Location** 1m E of Aberlady on A198

Hotel ★★★♨ Greywalls Hotel, Muirfield, GULLANE ☎ 01620 842144 17 en suite 5 annexe en suite

BROXBURN   Map 11 NT07

Niddry Castle Castle Rd, Winchburgh EH52 6RQ
☎ 01506 891097
A 9-hole parkland course. While not very long, it requires accurate golf to score well.
9 holes, 5615yds, Par 70, SSS 67, Course record 64.
Club membership 600.
Visitors advisable to contact at weekends, restricted during competition time. **Societies** must contact in advance. **Green Fees** not confirmed. **Facilities** ╫ ⅃ ♥ ♀ ⅃ **Location** 9m W of Edinburgh on B9080

DUNBAR   Map 12 NT67

Dunbar East Links EH42 1LL
☎ 01368 862317 📱 01368 865202
Another of Scotland's old links. It is said that it was some Dunbar members who first took the game of golf to the North of England. A natural links course on a narrow strip of land, following the contours of the sea shore, there is a wall bordering one side and the shore on the other side making this quite a challenging course for all levels of player. The wind, if blowing from the sea, is a problem.
18 holes, 6406yds, Par 71, SSS 71, Course record 64.
Club membership 1000.
Visitors may not play Thu, between 12.30-2 weekdays, 12-2 weekends or before 9.30am any day. **Societies** telephone in advance. **Green Fees** £45 per day; £32 per round (£50/£37 weekends). **Cards** ▭▭ ▭▭ 🖾 ▭▭ 🖾 🖾 **Prof** Jacky Montgomery **Course Designer** Tom Morris **Facilities** ⊗ ╫ ⅃ ♥ ♀ ⅃ 🖾 ♨ ♂ **Location** 0.5m E off A1087

Winterfield North Rd EH42 1AU
☎ 01368 863562 🗐 01368 863562
e-mail: kevinphillips@tiscali.co.uk
Seaside course with superb views.
18 holes, 5155yds, Par 65, SSS 64, Course record 61.
Club membership 350.
Visitors contact in advance. Weekends from 10am-12 noon
& 2pm-4pm **Societies** must arrange in advance through
professional, telephone or email **Green Fees** £20 per day;
£15 per round (£25/£17 weekends). **Prof** Kevin Phillips
Facilities ⊗ 〲 ㄴ ♨ ♀ 占 ☎ ➴ ☞ ♂ **Location** W side
of town off A1087

Gifford Edinburgh Rd EH41 4JE
☎ 01620 810267 & 810591
e-mail: thesecretary@giffordgolfclub.fsnet.co.uk
Parkland course, with easy walking.

9 holes, 6243yds, Par 71, SSS 70, Course record 69.
Club membership 600.
Visitors may not play on the 1st Sun of the month during
Apr-Oct. Telephone Starter on 01620 810 591 to book tee
times. **Societies** contact in advance. **Green Fees** £15 per 18
holes; £10 per 9 holes. **Course Designer** W Wood **Facilities**
ㄴ ♨ 占 ♂ **Location** 1m SW off B6355

Gullane West Links Rd EH31 2BB
☎ 01620 842255 🗐 01620 842327
e-mail: bookings@gullanegolfclub.com
**Gullane is a delightful village and one of Scotland's
great golf centres. Gullane club was formed in 1882.
There are three Gullane courses and the No 1 is of
championship standard. It differs from most Scottish
courses in as much as it is of the upland links type and
really quite hilly. The first tee is literally in the village.
The views from the top of the course are magnificent
and stretch far and wide in every direction - in fact, it
is said that 14 counties can be seen from the highest
spot.**
*Course No 1: 18 holes, 6466yds, Par 71, SSS 72,
Course record 66.*
Course No 2: 18 holes, 6244yds, Par 71, SSS 70.
Course No 3: 18 holes, 5252yds, Par 68, SSS 66.
Club membership 1200.
Visitors advance booking recommended. **Societies**
advance booking advised. **Green Fees** terms on
application. **Cards** 🌣 ▦ ▦ ▦ ▦ **Prof** Jimmy
Hume **Course Designer** Various **Facilities** ⊗ 〲 ㄴ ♨ ♀
占 ☎ ➴ ☞ ♂ ☏ **Location** At west end of village on
A198

Hotel ★★★🏵 Greywalls Hotel, Muirfield, GULLANE
☎ 01620 842144 17 en suite 5 annexe en suite

Haddington Amisfield Park EH41 4PT
☎ 01620 🗐 01620 822727
e-mail: hadd.golg1@tesco.net
**Slightly undulating parkland course, within the grounds
of a former country estate running alongside the River
Tyne.**
18 holes, 6317yds, Par 71, SSS 70, Course record 68.
Club membership 650.
Visitors may not play between 7am-10am & noon-2pm at
weekends. Must contact in advance. **Societies** must contact
in advance; deposits required. **Green Fees** not confirmed.
Prof John Sandilands **Facilities** ⊗ 〲 ㄴ ♨ ♀ 占 ☎ ➴
♂ **Location** E side off A613 off A1,17 miles E of
Edinburgh

Hotel ★★★🏵 Greywalls Hotel, Muirfield, GULLANE
☎ 01620 842144 17 en suite 5 annexe en suite

Longniddry Links Rd EH32 0NL
☎ 01875 852141 & 01875 852228 🗐 01875 853371
e-mail: longniddrygolfclub.co.uk
**Undulating seaside links and partial parkland course
with no par 5s. One of the numerous courses which
stretch east from Edinburgh right to Dunbar. The
inward half is more open than the wooded outward
half, but can be difficult in prevailing west wind.**
18 holes, 6260yds, Par 68, SSS 70, Course record 63.
Club membership 1140.
Visitors may book tee times up to 7 days in advance, but
deposit required.may not play on competition days.
Societies Mon-Thu, apply in writing, handicap certificate
required. **Green Fees** £50 per day; £35 per round (£45 per
round weekends). **Cards** 🌣 ▦ ▦ **Prof** John Gray
Course Designer H S Colt **Facilities** ⊗ 〲 ㄴ ♨ ♀ 占 ☎
➴ ☞ ♂ **Conf** Banquet 50 **Location** N side of village
off A198

Hotel ★★★🏵 Greywalls Hotel, Muirfield, GULLANE
☎ 01620 842144 17 en suite 5 annexe en suite

Musselburgh Monktonhall EH21 6SA
☎ 0131 665 2005
e-mail: secretary@themusselburghgolfclub.com
**Testing parkland course with natural hazards including
trees and a burn, easy walking.**
18 holes, 6725yds, Par 71, SSS 73, Course record 65.
Club membership 1000.
Visitors must contact in advance. **Societies** must contact in
advance. **Green Fees** £30 per day; £20 per round (£35/£25
weekends). **Prof** Fraser Mann **Course Designer** James Braid
Facilities ⊗ 〲 ㄴ ♨ ♀ 占 ☎ ➴ ☞ ♂ **Location** 1m S
on B6415

Guesthouse ♦♦♦♦ Arden House, 26 Linkfield Rd,
Musselburgh, EDINBURGH ☎ 0131 665 0663 &
07957 867512 🗐 0131 665 0663 4 en suite

Where to stay, where to eat?
Visit www.theAA.com

(Honourable Company of Edinburgh Golfers) *Muirfield*

Gullane, *East Lothian*   ☎ 01620 842123   Fax 01620 842977   Map 12 NT48

e-mail: hceg@btinternet.com

The course at Muirfield was designed by Old Tom Morris in 1891 and is generally considered to be one of the top ten courses in the world. The club itself has an excellent pedigree, it was founded in 1744, making it just ten years older than the Royal & Ancient but not as old as Royal Blackheath.

Muirfield has staged some outstanding Open Championships, perhaps one of the most memorable in 1972 when Lee Trevino, the defending champion, seemed to be losing his grip, until a spectacular shot brought him back to beat Tony Jacklin, who subsequently never won an Open again.

Visitors Tue and Thu only. Must contact in advance and have a handicap certificate. (18 gentlemen, 24 ladies)

Societies Tue & Thu with handicap limits (18 gentlemen, 24 ladies). Must be members of recognised golf course. Up to 12 in a group.

Green Fees £90 one round; £120 two rounds

Facilities ⊗ ☐ ☐ ♀ ♨ ✎ ♂

Location Muirfield, Gullane EH31 2EG (NE side of village)

Holes/Par/Course record 18 holes, 6601 yds, Par 70, SSS 73, Course record 63

WHERE TO STAY AND EAT NEARBY

Hotels
DIRLETON

★★★71% ⊙ The Open Arms.
☎ 01620 850241. 10 en suite

GULLANE

★★★ ⊙⊙ ♨♨ Greywalls, Muirfield.
☎ 01620 842144. 17 en suite
5 annexe en suite

NORTH BERWICK

★★★67% The Marine, Cromwell Rd.
☎ 0870 400 8129. 83 en suite

★64% Nether Abbey, 20 Dirleton Ave.
☎ 01620 892802. 14 en suite

Championship Course

Musselburgh Links, The Old Golf Course
The Starter's Hut, Balcarres Rd EH21 7SD
☎ 0131 665 5438 (Starter) 665 4861(secretary)
▤ 0131 665 5438
e-mail: info@musselburgholdlinks.co.uk
A delightful nine hole links course weaving in and out of the famous Musselburgh Race Course. This course is steeped in the history and tradition of golf. Mary Queen of Scots reputedly played golf at the old course in 1567, but documentary evidence dates back to 1672. The 1st hole is a par 3 and the next three holes play eastward from the grandstand at the racecourse. The course turns north west towards the sea then west for the last four holes. Designed by nature and defined over the centuries by generations of golfers, the course boasts many natural features and hazards.
9 holes, 2874yds, Par 34, SSS 34.
Club membership 250.
Visitors must book in advance, ring starter 0131 665 5438 **Societies** must contact in advance in writing or by telephone. **Green Fees** £8.50 per 9 holes;£16 per 18 holes. **Cards** ▤
▨▨▧ ▧ **Facilities** ▾ ♀ ♨ ⚐ ♂ **Conf** Max 40 **Location** 1m E of town off A1

Guesthouse ◆◆◆◆ Arden House, 26 Linkfield Rd, Musselburgh, EDINBURGH ☎ 0131 665 0663 & 07957 867512 ▤ 0131 665 0663 4 en suite

Glen East Links, Tantallon Ter EH39 4LE
☎ 01620 892726 ▤ 01620 895447
e-mail: secretary@glen.gowf.net
An interesting course with a good variety of holes including the famous 13th. The views of the town, the Firth of Forth and the Bass Rock are breathtaking.
18 holes, 6043yds, Par 69, SSS 69, Course record 64.
Club membership 650.
Visitors booking advisable. **Societies** advance booking recommended. **Green Fees** not confirmed. **Course Designer** Ben Sayers/James Braid **Facilities** ⊗ ⁾⊩ ㊑ ▾ ♀ ♨ ⚐ ♂ **Location** 1m E of B198

Hotel ★★ 64% Nether Abbey Hotel, 20 Dirleton Av, NORTH BERWICK ☎ 01620 892802 14 en suite

North Berwick Beach Rd EH39 4BB
☎ 01620 892135 ▤ 01620 893274
e-mail: northberwichgc@aol.com
Another of East Lothian's famous courses, the links at North Berwick is still popular. A classic championship links, it has many hazards including the beach, streams, bunkers, light rough and low walls. The great hole on the course is the 15th, the famous 'Redan'. Used by both the Tantallon and Bass Rock Golf Clubs.
West Links: 18 holes, 6420yds, Par 71, SSS 71, Course record 64.
Club membership 730.
Visitors must contact in advance 01620 892135 (beyond 7 days) or 01620 892666 (within 7 days). **Societies** must contact in advance. **Green Fees** £65 per day; £42 per round (£80/£65weekends). **Cards** ▤ ▨▨ ▧ ▨ **Prof** D Huish **Facilities** ⊗ ⁾⊩ ㊑ ▾ ♀ ♨ ⚐ ♂ **Location** W side of town on A198

Hotel ★★★ 67% The Marine, Cromwell Rd, NORTH BERWICK ☎ 0870 400 8129 83 en suite

Whitekirk Whitekirk EH39 5PR
☎ 01620 870300 ▤ 01620 870330
e-mail: countryclub@whitekirk.com
Scenic coastal course with lush green fairways, gorse covered rocky banks and stunning views. Natural water hazards and strong sea breezes make this well designed course a good test of golf.
18 holes, 6526yds, Par 72, SSS 72, Course record 64.
Club membership 400.
Visitors no restrictions. **Societies** apply in writing or telephone. **Green Fees** £30 per day, £20 per round (£45/£28 weekends). **Cards** ▤ ▨▨ ▧ ▨ **Prof** Paul Wardell **Course Designer** Cameron Sinclair **Facilities** ⊗ ⁾⊩ ㊑ ▾ ♀ ♨ ⚐ ♂ ♨ ♂ ⚑ **Location** 3m off the main A1 Edinburgh/Berwick-upon-Tweed road A198 North Berwick

Hotel ★★ 64% Nether Abbey Hotel, 20 Dirleton Av, NORTH BERWICK ☎ 01620 892802 14 en suite

Royal Musselburgh Prestongrange House EH32 9RP
☎ 01875 810276 ▤ 01875 810276
e-mail: royalmusselburgh@btinternet.com
Tree-lined parkland course overlooking Firth of Forth. Well maintained and providing an excellent challenge. The final third of the course can make or break a score. The tough four hole stretches from the long par four 13th including 'The Gully', a par three 14th where to be short is to court disaster, followed by the par four 15th huddled tight beside trees to the left. A precision drive is required to find the rollercoaster fairway and from there a long iron or fairway wood is played over an uphill approach to a tilting green.
18 holes, 6237yds, Par 70, SSS 70, Course record 64.
Club membership 1000.
Visitors must contact professional in advance, restricted Fri afternoons & weekends. **Societies** should contact in advance through Management secretary **Green Fees** £35 per day;£35 per 18 holes(£35 per 18 holes weekends). **Prof** John Henderson **Course Designer** James Braid **Facilities** ⊗ ⁾⊩ ㊑ ▾ ♀ ♨ ⚐ ♂ ♨ ♂ **Conf** Max 50 **Location** W side of town centre on B1361 Prestonpans to North Berwick rd

Guesthouse ◆◆◆◆ Arden House, 26 Linkfield Rd, Musselburgh, EDINBURGH ☎ 0131 665 0663 & 07957 867512 ▤ 0131 665 0663 4 en suite

Fereneze Fereneze Av G78 1HJ
☎ 0141 880 7058 ▤ 0141 881 7149
e-mail: ferenezegc@lineone.net
Hilly moorland course, with a good view at the end of a hard climb to the 3rd, then levels out.
18 holes, 5962yds, Par 71, SSS 69, Course record 66.
Club membership 750.
Visitors must contact in advance but may not play at weekends. **Societies** apply in writing. **Green Fees** £22 per round;£25 per day. **Prof** Stuart Kerr **Facilities** ⊗ ⁾⊩ ㊑ ▾ ♀ ♨ ⚐ ♂ **Location** NW side of town off B774

Hotel ★★★ 71% Dalmeny Park Country House Hotel, Lochlibo Rd, BARRHEAD ☎ 0141 881 9211 20 en suite

CLARKSTON Map 11 NS55
Cathcart Castle Mearns Rd G76 7YL
☎ 0141 638 9449 🖹 0141 638 1201
18 holes, 5832yds, Par 68, SSS 68.
Location 0.75m SW off A726
Telephone for further details

Hotel ⛉ Premier Lodge, Eaglesham Rd, EAST KILBRIDE ☎ 0870 700 1398 40 en suite

EAGLESHAM Map 11 NS55
Bonnyton Kirktonmoor Rd G76 0QA
☎ 01355 302781 🖹 01355 303151
Dramatic moorland course offering spectacular views beautiful countryside as far as snow-capped Ben Lomond. Tree-lined fairways, plateau greens, natural burns and well situated bunkers and a unique variety of holes offer golfers both challenge and reward.
18 holes, 6255yds, Par 72, SSS 71.
Club membership 960.
Visitors welcome Mon & Thu. Must contact in advance. **Societies** must telephone in advance. **Green Fees** £40 per day. **Prof** Kendal McWade **Facilities** ⊗ �🗖 ⅃ ⚑ ♨ ♀ ᛤ 🏌 ♨ **Location** 0.25m SW off B764

Hotel ★★★ 70% Bruce Hotel, Cornwall St, EAST KILBRIDE ☎ 01355 229771 65 en suite

NEWTON MEARNS Map 11 NS55
East Renfrewshire Pilmuir G77 6RT
☎ 01355 500256 🖹 01355 500323
e-mail: david@eastrengolfclub.demon.co.uk
Undulating moorland with loch; prevailing SW wind.
18 holes, 6097yds, Par 70, SSS 70, Course record 63.
Club membership 900.
Visitors must contact professional in advance **Societies** Tues & Thur only, must contact in advance. **Green Fees** £40 per day; £30 per round. **Prof** Stewart Russell **Course Designer** James Braid **Facilities** ⊗ �🗖 ⅃ ⚑ ♀ ᛤ 🏌 **Location** 3m SW off Newton Mearns on A77

Hotel ★★★ 71% Dalmeny Park Country House Hotel, Lochlibo Rd, BARRHEAD ☎ 0141 881 9211 20 en suite

Eastwood Muirshield, Loganswell G77 6RX
☎ 01355 500285 🖹 01355 500280
e-mail: secretary@eastwoodgolfclub.demon.co.uk
An undulating moorland course situated in a scenic setting.
18 holes, 5662yds, Par 68, SSS 68, Course record 62.
Club membership 900.
Visitors contact in advance. No visitors at weekends. **Societies** must contact in advance. **Green Fees** £30 per day; £24 per round. **Cards** ⊟ ▧ ▨ Ⓔ **Prof** Iain J Darroch **Course Designer** Theodore Moone **Facilities** ⊗ �🗖 ⅃ ⚑ ♀ ᛤ 🏌 **Location** 2.5m S of Newton Mearns, on A77

Hotel ★★★ 71% Dalmeny Park Country House Hotel, Lochlibo Rd, BARRHEAD ☎ 0141 881 9211 20 en suite

Whitecraigs 72 Ayr Rd G46 6SW
☎ 0141 639 4530 & 0141 639 2140 pro 🖹 0141 639 4530
e-mail: wcraigsgc@aol.com
Beautiful parkland course only twenty minutes from the centre of Glasgow.
18 holes, 6230yds, Par 70, SSS 70, Course record 63.
Club membership 1078.

continued

Visitors must contact professional in advance and have a handicap certificate. **Societies** apply in advance. **Green Fees** not confirmed. **Prof** Alistair Forrow **Facilities** ⊗ ⅃ 🗖 ⚑ ♀ **Location** 1.5m NE on A77

Hotel ★★★ Dalmeny Park Country House Hotel, Lochlibo Rd, BARRHEAD ☎ 0141 881 9211 20 en suite

UPLAWMOOR Map 10 NS45
Caldwell G78 4AU ☎ 01505 850366 (Secretary) & 850616 (Pro) 🖹 01505 850604
e-mail: caldwellgolfclub@aol.com
Parkland course.
18 holes, 6294yds, Par 71, SSS 70, Course record 63.
Club membership 600.
Visitors must be with member at weekends & bank holidays. Must contact professional in advance. **Societies** writing to Secretary. **Green Fees** terms on application. **Prof** Stephen Forbes **Course Designer** W. Fernie **Facilities** ⊗ ⅃ 🗖 ⚑ ♀ **Location** 5m SW of Barrhead on A736 Irvine road

Hotel ★★★ 71% Dalmeny Park Country House Hotel, Lochlibo Rd, BARRHEAD ☎ 0141 881 9211 20 en suite

---

FALKIRK

FALKIRK Map 11 NS88
Falkirk Carmuirs, 136 Stirling Rd, Camelon FK2 7YP
☎ 01324 611061 (club) 🖹 01324 639573 (Sec)
e-mail: carmuirs.fgc@virgin.net
Parkland course with trees, gorse and streams.
18 holes, 6230yds, Par 71, SSS 70, Course record 66.
Club membership 800.
Visitors telephone starter 01324 611061, visiting parties may not play Sat. **Societies** telephone 01324 611061 in advance. **Green Fees** £30 per day; £20 per round (£40/£30 Sun). **Cards** ⊟ ▧ ▨ Ⓔ **Prof** Stewart Craig **Course Designer** James Braid **Facilities** ⊗ ⅃ 🗖 ⚑ ♀ ᛤ 🏌 **Location** 1.5m W on A9

Hotel ★★★★ 70% Inchyra Grange Hotel, Grange Rd, POLMONT ☎ 01324 711911 109 en suite

LARBERT Map 11 NS88
Falkirk Tryst 86 Burnhead Rd FK5 4BD
☎ 01324 562054 & 562415
Links-type course, fairly level with trees and broom, well-bunkered. Winds can affect play.
18 holes, 6053yds, Par 70, SSS 69, Course record 62.
Club membership 850.
Visitors must contact in advance no play at weekends. **Societies** visitors welcome Mon-Fri must book or telephone. **Green Fees** not confirmed. **Prof** Steven Dunsmore **Facilities** ⊗ 🗖 ⚑ ♀ ᛤ 🏌 **Location** On A88 between A9 and A905

Hotel ★★★★ 70% Inchyra Grange Hotel, Grange Rd, POLMONT ☎ 01324 711911 109 en suite

Glenbervie Clubhouse Stirling Rd FK5 4SJ
☎ 01324 562605 🖹 01324 551054
Parkland course with good views.
Glenbervie: 18 holes, 6423yds, Par 71, SSS 71, Course record 64.
Club membership 600.
Visitors Mon to Fri till 4pm, parties Tues & Thurs only **Societies** Tue & Thu only. Apply in writing. **Green Fees** not
continued

confirmed. **Cards** ⬛⬛⬛ **Prof** John Chillas **Course Designer** James Braid **Facilities** ⊗ 🏐 💺 ♀🏔 🏠 ⛳
Location 2m NW on A9

Hotel ★★★★ 70% Inchyra Grange Hotel, Grange Rd, POLMONT ☎ 01324 711911 109 en suite

POLMONT   Map 11 NS97

Grangemouth Polmont Hill FK2 0YE
☎ 01324 503840 📄 01324 503841
Windy parkland course. Testing holes: 3rd, 4th (par 4s); 5th (par 5); 7th (par 3) 216 yds over reservoir (elevated green); 8th, 9th, 18th (par 4s).
18 holes, 6314yds, Par 71, SSS 71, Course record 65.
Club membership 800.
Visitors must contact 24 hours in advance.Must have own golf shoes and clubs, Sats after 4pm. **Societies** must contact in writing. **Green Fees** £14 per round (£17.50 weekends). **Prof** Greg McFarlane **Facilities** ⊗ 〽 🏐 💺 ♀🏔 🏠 ⛳
Location On unclass rd 0.5m N of M9 junc 4

Hotel ★★★★ 70% Inchyra Grange Hotel, Grange Rd, POLMONT ☎ 01324 711911 109 en suite

Polmont Manuelrigg, Maddiston FK2 0LS
☎ 01324 711277 📄 01324 712504
Parkland course, hilly with few bunkers. Views of the River Forth and Ochil Hills.
9 holes, 3073yds, Par 72, SSS 69, Course record 66.
Club membership 300.
Visitors no visitors on Sat from Apr-Sep, Mon-Fri must tee of before 5pm. **Societies** apply in writing to club secretary. **Green Fees** £8 per 18 holes (£15 weekends). **Facilities** ⊗ 〽 🏐 💺 ♀🏔 **Location** A805 from Falkirk, 1st right after fire brigade headquarters

Hotel ★★★★ 70% Inchyra Grange Hotel, Grange Rd, POLMONT ☎ 01324 711911 109 en suite

---

FIFE

ABERDOUR   Map 11 NT18

Aberdour Seaside Place KY3 0TX
☎ 01383 860080 📄 01383 860050
e-mail: aberdourgc@aol.com
Parkland course with lovely views over Firth of Forth.

18 holes, 5460yds, Par 67, SSS 66, Course record 63.
Club membership 800.
Visitors must contact in advance, may not play Saturdays. **Societies** telephone or write to secretary in advance **Green Fees** £28 per day; £17 per round (£35 per day/round Sundays). **Prof** Gordon McCallum **Facilities** ⊗ 〽 🏐 💺 ♀ 🏔 🏠 ⛳ **Location** S side of village   *continued*

Hotel ★★ 70% Woodside Hotel, High St, ABERDOUR
☎ 01383 860328 20 en suite

ANSTRUTHER   Map 12 NO50

Anstruther Marsfield, Shore Rd KY10 3DZ
☎ 01333 310956 📄 01333 312283
Seaside links course with some excellent par 3 holes; always in good condition.
9 holes, 2266yds, Par 62, SSS 63, Course record 59.
Club membership 550.
Visitors advised to phone in advance. **Societies** welcome except Jun-Aug. Must apply in writing. **Green Fees** £14 per 18 holes; £9 per 9 holes (£16/£10 weekends). **Course Designer** Tom Morris **Facilities** 🏐 💺 ♀🏔 ⛳ **Location** SW off A917

Hotel ★★ 65% Smugglers Inn, High St East, ANSTRUTHER ☎ 01333 310506 9 en suite

BURNTISLAND   Map 11 NT28

Burntisland Golf House Club Dodhead, Kirkcaldy Rd KY3 9LQ ☎ 01592 874093 (Manager) & 872116 (Pro) 📄 01592 874093
e-mail: wktbghc@aol.com
A lush, testing course offering magnificent views over the Forth Estuary.

18 holes, 5965yds, Par 70, SSS 70, Course record 62.
Club membership 800.
Visitors weekend play may be restricted. Book by telephoning professional or manager. **Societies** apply in writing to manager. **Green Fees** not confirmed. **Cards** ⬛⬛ ⬛⬛ 🔳 ⬛⬛ 🔳 **Prof** Paul Wytrazek **Course Designer** Willie Park Jnr **Facilities** ⊗ 〽 🏐 💺 ♀🏔 🏠 🛠 ⛳ **Location** 1m E on B923

Hotel ★★ 68% Inchview Hotel, 69 Kinghorn Rd, BURNTISLAND ☎ 01592 872239 12 en suite

CARDENDEN   Map 11 NT29

Auchterderran Woodend Rd KY5 0NH
☎ 01592 721579
9 holes, 5250yds, Par 66, SSS 66, Course record 63.
Location N end Cardenden, Kirkcaldy/Glenrothes road
Telephone for further details

Hotel ★★★ 67% Dean Park Hotel, Chapel Level, KIRKCALDY ☎ 01592 261635
34 en suite 12 annexe en suite

> If the name of the club appears in *italics*, details have not been confirmed for this edition of the guide

COWDENBEATH
Map 11 NT19

Cowdenbeath Seco Place KY4 8PD ☎ 01383 511918
A parkland-based 18 hole golf course.
Dora Course: 18 holes, 6201yds, Par 70, SSS 70, Course record 68.
Club membership 250.
Visitors no restrictions. **Societies** Apply in advance by phone or write to secretary. **Green Fees** terms on application. **Facilities** ⊗ ⓑ ♨ ♀ ♨ ♂ **Location** Turn off A92 into Cowdenbeath. Take 2nd right and follow signs to course.

....

Hotel ★★ 70% Woodside Hotel, High St, ABERDOUR ☎ 01383 860328 20 en suite

CRAIL
Map 12 NO60

Crail Golfing Society Balcomie Clubhouse, Fifeness KY10 3XN
☎ 01333 450686 & 450960 📋 01333 450416
e-mail: crailgolfs@aol.com
Perched on the edge of the North Sea, the Crail Golfing Society's course at Balcomie is picturesque and sporting. Crail Golfing Society began its life in 1786 and the course is highly thought of by students of the game both for its testing holes and the standard of its greens. Craighead Links has panoramic seascape and country views. With wide sweeping fairways and large greens it is a testing but fair challenge, be warned there are hungry bunkers a plenty! This second links at Fifeness is set to join Balcomie as one of Scotlands's 'must play' courses.

Balcomie Links: 18 holes, 5922yds, Par 69, SSS 69, Course record 64.
Craighead Links: 18 holes, 6700yds, Par 71, SSS 73, Course record 69.
Club membership 1735.
Visitors must contact in advance, restricted 10am-noon & 2-4.30pm. **Societies** must contact in advance, as much notice as possible for weekend play. **Green Fees** £43 per day; £30 per round (£55/£35 weekends and bank holidays). **Cards** 🟦🟦🟦🟦🟦 **Prof** Graeme Lennie **Course Designer** Tom Morris **Facilities** ⊗ ⋙ ⓑ ♨ ♀ ♨ ⊟ ♔ ☖ ♨ ♂ **Location** 2m NE off A917

....

Hotel ★★ 65% Balcomie Links Hotel, Balcomie Rd, CRAIL ☎ 01333 450237 15 rms (13 en suite)
Additional Guesthouse ◆◆◆◆ The Spindrift, Pittenweem Rd, ANSTRUTHER ☎ 01333 310573 Fax 01333 310573 8 en suite

AA website: www.theAA.com

CUPAR
Map 11 NO31

Cupar Hilltarvit KY15 5JT ☎ 01334 653549
e-mail: secretary@cupargolfclub.freeserve.co.uk
Hilly parkland course with fine views over north east Fife. 5th/14th hole is most difficult - uphill and into the prevailing wind.
9 holes, 5074yds, Par 68, SSS 65, Course record 61.
Club membership 400.
Visitors welcome except Sat. **Societies** must contact in advance. **Green Fees** £15 per day. **Course Designer** Allan Robertson **Facilities** ⊗ ⋙ ⓑ ♨ ♀ ♨ ♔ ♨ ♂ **Location** 0.75m S off A92

....

Hotel ★★ 69% Eden House Hotel, 2 Pitscottie Rd, CUPAR ☎ 01334 652510 9 en suite 2 annexe en suite

DUNFERMLINE
Map 11 NT08

Canmore Venturefair Av KY12 0PE
☎ 01383 724969 📋 01383 731649
Parkland course with excellent turf, moderate in length but a good test of accuracy demanding a good short game. Ideal for 36 hole play, and suitable for all ages.
18 holes, 5376yds, Par 67, SSS 66, Course record 61.
Club membership 710.
Visitors Sat not usually available. Limited Sun. Must contact professional in advance (01383 728416). **Societies** apply in writing to secretary. **Green Fees** £22 per day: £16 per round (£32/£21 weekends). **Prof** David Gemmell **Course Designer** Ben Sayers & others **Facilities** ⊗ ⋙ ⓑ ♨ ♀ ♨ ☖ ♂ **Location** 1m N on A823

....

Hotel ★★★ 62% Pitfirrane Arms, Main St, Crossford, DUNFERMLINE ☎ 01383 736132 40 en suite

Dunfermline Pitfirrane, Crossford KY12 8QW
☎ 01383 723534 & 729061
e-mail: pitfirrane@aol.com
Gently undulating parkland course with interesting contours. Five par 5s, five par 3s. No water hazards.
18 holes, 6121yds, Par 72, SSS 70, Course record 65.
Club membership 950.
Visitors may not play weekends. Contact to check times. **Societies** must contact in advance. **Green Fees** not confirmed. **Prof** Steve Craig **Course Designer** J R Stutt **Facilities** ⊗ ⋙ ⓑ ♨ ♀ ♨ ⊟ ♂ **Location** 2m W of Dunfermline on A994

....

Hotel ★★★ 62% Pitfirrane Arms, Main St, Crossford, DUNFERMLINE ☎ 01383 736132 40 en suite

Pitreavie Queensferry Rd KY11 8PR
☎ 01383 722591 📋 01383 722591
Picturesque woodland course with panoramic view of the River Forth Valley. Testing golf.
continued

18 holes, 6086yds, Par 70, SSS 69, Course record 64.
Club membership 700.
Visitors welcome except for competition days. **Societies** must write or telephone in advance. **Green Fees** £26.50 per day: £19.50 per round(£38.50/£24.50). **Prof** Paul Brookes **Course Designer** Dr Alaistair McKenzie **Facilities** ⊗ 🏌 🛒 🍴 ♥ **Location** SE side of town on A823

Hotel ★★★ 63% King Malcolm, Queensferry Rd, DUNFERMLINE ☎ 01383 722611 48 en suite

ELIE   Map 12 NO40

Golf House Club KY9 1AS
☎ 01333 330301 📠 01333 330895
One of Scotland's most delightful holiday courses with panoramic views over the Firth of Forth. Some of the holes out towards the rocky coastline are splendid. This is the course which has produced many good professionals, including the immortal James Braid.
18 holes, 6273yds, Par 70, SSS 70, Course record 62.
Club membership 600.
Visitors advisable to contact in advance, limited availability Sat May-Sep and no visitors Sun May-Sep, ballot in operation for tee times during July and August. **Societies** must contact in advance. **Green Fees** not confirmed. **Cards** 🔲 🔲 💳 **Prof** Robin Wilson **Course Designer** James Braid **Facilities** ⊗ 🏌 🛒 ♥ ♀ 🛒 🍴 ♥ **Leisure** hard tennis courts. **Location** W side of village off A917

Hotel ★★ 73% The Inn at Lathones, Largoward, ST ANDREWS ☎ 01334 840494 14 annexe en suite

FALKLAND   Map 11 NO20

Falkland The Myre KY15 7AA ☎ 01337 857404
A flat, well kept course with excellent greens and views of East Lomond Hill and Falkland Palace.
9 holes, 5216yds, Par 68, SSS 65, Course record 62.
Club membership 300.
Visitors parties must make prior arrangements, please check availability at weekends. **Societies** must contact in advance. **Green Fees** not confirmed. **Facilities** ⊗ by prior arrangement 🏌 by prior arrangement 🛒 ♥ ♀ 🍴 ♥ **Location** N side of town on A912

Hotel ★★ 67% Lomond Hills Hotel, Parliament Square, FREUCHIE ☎ 01337 857329 & 857498 📠 01337 858180 24 en suite

GLENROTHES   Map 11 NO20

Glenrothes Golf Course Rd KY6 2LA ☎ 01592 754561
Mature parkland, challenging back nine with burn crossing four fairways. Wide fairways offer opportunities for long hitters and birdy chances for those with good short game.
18 holes, 6444yds, Par 71, SSS 71, Course record 67.
Club membership 750.
Visitors no restrictions except for some times at weekends . Bookings for parties can be made in advance. **Societies** write to secretary. **Green Fees** not confirmed. **Course Designer** J R Stutt **Facilities** ⊗ 🏌 🛒 ♥ ♀ 🍴 **Location** W side of town off B921

Hotel ★★★★🏌 Balbirnie House, Balbirnie Park, MARKINCH ☎ 01592 610066 30 en suite

KINCARDINE   Map 11 NS98

Tulliallan Alloa Rd FK10 4BB
☎ 01259 730798 📠 01259 730798
e-mail: enquiries@tulliallangc.f9.co.uk
Pleasant parkland course with easily negotiable slopes, a meandering burn and scenic views.
18 holes, 5965yds, Par 69, SSS 69, Course record 63.
Club membership 600.
Visitors restricted at weekends, must contact professional shop. **Societies** may not play on Sat; must contact in advance. **Green Fees** £30 per day, £16.50 per round (£39/£21 weekends). **Prof** Steven Kelly **Facilities** ⊗ 🏌 🛒 ♥ ♀ 🍴 🍴 ♥ **Location** 1m NW on A977

Hotel ★★★ 68% Dall Lodge Country House Hotel, Main St, KILLIN ☎ 01567 820217 10 en suite

KINGHORN   Map 11 NT28

Kinghorn Macduff Cres KY3 9RE
☎ 01592 890345 & 890978
Municipal course, 300 ft above sea level with views over Firth of Forth and North Sea. Undulating and quite testing. Facilities shared by Kinghorn Ladies.
18 holes, 5269yds, Par 65, SSS 67, Course record 62.
Club membership 190.
Visitors may only play between 7.30am-10.30am & 12pm-3pm Sat. **Societies** must contact in writing. **Green Fees** not confirmed. **Course Designer** Tom Morris **Facilities** ♥ **Location** S side of town on A921

Hotel ★★★ 67% Dean Park Hotel, Chapel Level, KIRKCALDY ☎ 01592 261635 34 en suite 12 annexe en suite

KIRKCALDY   Map 11 NT29

Dunnikier Park Dunnikier Way KY1 3LP
☎ 01592 261599
Parkland, rolling fairways, not heavily bunkered, views of Firth of Forth.
18 holes, 6036metres, Par 72, SSS 72, Course record 65.
Club membership 720.
Visitors visitors must contact course starter in person. **Societies** apply in writing. **Green Fees** not confirmed. **Prof** Gregor Whyte **Course Designer** R Stutt **Facilities** ⊗ 🏌 🛒 ♥ ♀ 🍴 🚜 ♥ **Location** 2m N on B981

Hotel ★★★ 67% Dean Park Hotel, Chapel Level, KIRKCALDY ☎ 01592 261635 34 en suite 12 annexe en suite

Kirkcaldy Balwearie Rd KY2 5LT
☎ 01592 205240 & 203258 (Pro Shop) 📠 01592 205240
e-mail: enquiries@kirkcaldygolfclub.sol.co.uk
Challenging parkland course in rural setting, with beautiful views. On-course watering ensures good conditions all season.
18 holes, 6004yds, Par 71, SSS 69, Course record 65.
Club membership 822.
Visitors limited play Sat. Advised to contact pro-shop 01592 203258. **Societies** apply in writing/telephone. **Green Fees** £24 per round; £30 per day(£30/£36 weekends). **Cards** 🔲 🔲 **Prof** Anthony Caira **Course Designer** Tom Morris **Facilities** ⊗ 🏌 🛒 ♥ ♀ 🍴 🍴 ♥ 🦊 🚜 ♥ **Conf** Board 16 **Location** SW side of town off A910

Hotel ★★★ 67% Dean Park Hotel, Chapel Level, KIRKCALDY ☎ 01592 261635 34 en suite 12 annexe en suite

LADYBANK   Map 11 NO30

Ladybank Annsmuir KY15 7RA
☎ 01337 830814 📠 01337 831505
e-mail: ladybankgc@aol.com
Picturesque parkland/heathland course, popular with visitors. Qualifying course for the British Open and venue for the Ladies Amateur Championship 2001.

18 holes, 6601yds, Par 71, SSS 72, Course record 63.
Club membership 1000.
Visitors advance booking essential, restricted times at weekends. **Societies** must telephone or write in advance.
Green Fees £45 per day; £35 per round (£40 per round weekends). **Cards** 🖂 💳 💳 💳 **Prof** Martin Gray **Course Designer** Tom Morris **Facilities** ⊗ ⅷ 🖿 🖳 ♀ ⚐ 🖻 ⚐ ⚑ ⬥ ☌ ⚐ ⚐ **Location** Take Kirkcaldy Rd for 0.5miles,at A91/A92 intersection.

....

Hotel ★★★ 65% Fernie Castle, Letham, CUPAR
☎ 01337 810381 20 en suite

LESLIE   Map 11 NO20

Leslie Balsillie Laws KY6 3EZ ☎ 01592 620040
Challenging parkland course.
9 holes, 4686yds, Par 63, SSS 64, Course record 63.
Club membership 230.
Visitors contact secretary in writing. **Societies** letter to the Secretary. **Green Fees** terms on application. **Course Designer** Tom Morris **Facilities** 🖳 ♀ ⚑ **Location** N side of town off A911

....

Hotel ★★★ 61% Balgeddie House Hotel, Balgeddie Way, GLENROTHES ☎ 01592 742511 19 en suite

LEUCHARS   Map 12 NO42

Drumoig Hotel & Golf Course Drumoig
KY16 0BE ☎ 01382 541800 📠 01382 542211
e-mail: drumoig@sol.co.uk
A developing but challenging young championship course. Set in a parkland environment, the course is links-like in places. Features include Whinstone Quarries and views over to St Andrews and Carnoustie. Water features are demanding, especially on the 9th where the fairway runs between Drumoig's two mini-lochs.
18 holes, 6784yds, Par 71, SSS 72.
Club membership 200.
Visitors advisable to telephone in advance. **Societies** telephone in advance. **Green Fees** not confirmed. **Cards** 🖂 💳 💳 💳 💳 💳 **Facilities** ⊗ ⅷ 🖿 🖳 ♀ ⚐ ⚐ 🖻 ⚐ ☌ ⚐ **Leisure** Scottish National Golf Centre in grounds. **Location** On the A914 between St Andrews and Dundee.

....

Hotel ★★★ Drumoig Golf Hotel, Drumoig,
LEUCHARS ☎ 01382 541800
5 en suite 24 annexe en suite

St Michaels KY16 0DX
☎ 01334 839365 & 838666 📠 01334 838666
e-mail: stmichaelsgc@btclick.com
Parkland course with open views over Fife and Tayside. The undulating course weaves its way through tree plantations. The short par 4 17th, parallel to the railway and over a pond to a stepped green, poses an interesting challenge.
18 holes, 5802yds, Par 70, SSS 68, Course record 67.
Club membership 550.
Visitors may not play on Sun before noon. **Societies** must apply in writing, limited weekends **Green Fees** not confirmed. **Cards** 🖂 💳 💳 💳 **Facilities** ⊗ ⅷ by prior arrangement 🖿 🖳 ♀ ⚐ ⚐ **Location** NW side of village on A919

....

Hotel ★★ 69% Eden House Hotel, 2 Pitscottie Rd, CUPAR
☎ 01334 652510 9 en suite 2 annexe en suite

LEVEN   Map 11 NO30

Leven Links The Promenade KY8 4HS
☎ 01333 428859 & 421390 📠 01333 428859
Leven has the classic ingredients which make up a golf links in Scotland; undulating fairways with hills and hallows, out of bounds and a 'burn' or stream. A top class championship links course used for British Open final qualifying stages, it has fine views over Largo Bay.
18 holes, 6436yds, Par 71, SSS 70, Course record 62.
Club membership 1000.
Visitors contact in advance. Limited availability Fri pm & Sat, contact for these times no more than 5 days in advance. **Societies** apply in advance. **Green Fees** not confirmed. **Course Designer** Tom Morris **Facilities** ⊗ ⅷ 🖿 🖳 ♀ ⚐ 🖻 ⚐ ⚐

....

Hotel ★★★ 77% Old Manor Hotel, Leven Rd, LUNDIN LINKS ☎ 01333 320368 24 en suite

---

Scoonie North Links KY8 4SP
☎ 01333 423437(Starter) & 307007 (Club)
e-mail: manager@scooniegc.fsnet.co.uk
A pleasant inland links course suitable for all ages.
18 holes, 4979mtrs, Par 65, SSS 65, Course record 63.
Club membership 200.
Visitors no restrictions. **Societies** apply in writing. **Green Fees** not confirmed. **Facilities** ⊗ ⅷ 🖿 🖳 ♀ ⚐

....

Hotel ★★★ 77% Old Manor Hotel, Leven Rd, LUNDIN LINKS ☎ 01333 320368 24 en suite

LOCHGELLY   Map 11 NT19

Lochgelly Cartmore Rd KY5 9PB ☎ 01592 780174
Parkland course with easy walking and often windy.
18 holes, 5491yds, Par 68, SSS 67, Course record 62.
Club membership 650.
Visitors no restrictions, parties must book in advance by writing. **Societies** must apply in writing. **Green Fees** terms on application. **Prof** Martin Goldie **Course Designer** Ian Marchbanks **Facilities** ⊗ ⅷ 🖿 🖳 ♀ ⚐ 🖻 ⚐ **Location** W side of town off A910

....

Hotel ★★★ 67% Dean Park Hotel, Chapel Level,
KIRKCALDY ☎ 01592 261635
34 en suite 12 annexe en suite

Where to stay, where to eat?
Visit www.theAA.com

Lochore Meadows
Lochore Meadows Country Park, Crosshill, Lochgelly KY5 8BA
☎ 01592 414300 🖹 01592 414345
Lochside course with natural stream running through, and woodland nearby. Country park offers many leisure facilities.
9 holes, 3207yds, Par 72, SSS 71.
Club membership 240.
Visitors no restrictions. **Societies** must contact in advance.
Green Fees £9 per 18 holes; £6 per 9 holes (£12/£8 weekends). **Facilities** ⊗ 🍺 ⛾ **Leisure** fishing, outdoor education centre, childrens play park. **Conf** Board 60
Location 2m N off B920

Hotel ★★★ 73% Green Hotel, 2 The Muirs, KINROSS
☎ 01577 863467 46 en suite

LUNDIN LINKS   Map 12 NO40
Lundin Golf Rd KY8 6BA
☎ 01333 320202 🖹 01333 329743
e-mail: secretary@lundingolfclub.co.uk
The Leven Links and the course of the Lundin Club adjoin each other. The course is part seaside and part inland. The holes are excellent but those which can be described as seaside holes have a very different nature from the inland style ones. The par 3 14th looks seawards across the Firth of Forth towards Edinburgh and the old railway line defines out of bounds at several holes. A number of burns snake across the fairways.
18 holes, 6394yds, Par 71, SSS 71, Course record 63.
Club membership 850.
Visitors visitors welcome weekdays 9-3.30 (3pm Fridays) and Sat after 2.30pm, limited times on Sun. Book well in advance. **Societies** book well in advance by telephoning Secretary (mornings). **Green Fees** £45 per day; £35 per round. (£45 per round weekends). **Cards** 🔲 🔲 💳 **Prof** David Webster **Course Designer** James Braid **Facilities** ⊗ 🍴 🗄 🍺 ⛾ 🗄 ⚷ **Location** W side of village off A915

Hotel ★★★ 77% Old Manor Hotel, Leven Rd, LUNDIN LINKS ☎ 01333 320368 24 en suite

Lundin Ladies
Woodielea Rd KY8 6AR
☎ 01333 320832
e-mail: lundinladies@madasafish.com
Short, lowland course with Roman stones on the second fairway, and coastal views.
9 holes, 2365yds, Par 68, SSS 67, Course record 66.
Club membership 375.
Visitors contact in advance. Competition days Wed and some weekends. **Societies** telephone secretary. **Green Fees** £12 per day;£7.50 per 9 holes (£15/£9 weekend). **Course Designer** James Braid **Facilities** 🍺 ⛾ ⚷ **Location** W side of village off A915

Hotel ★★★ 77% Old Manor Hotel, Leven Rd, LUNDIN LINKS ☎ 01333 320368 24 en suite

MARKINCH   Map 11 NO20
Balbirnie Park Balbirnie Park KY7 6NR
☎ 01592 612095 & 752006 (tee times) 🖹 01592 612383
A fine example of the best in traditional parkland design, with natural contours the inspiration behind the layout.
18 holes, 6214yds, Par 71, SSS 70, Course record 62.
Club membership 900.

continued

Balbirnie Park Golf Club

Visitors must contact in advance. Numbers restricted weekends and visitors must play from yellow tees, smart but casual dress code. **Societies** booking forms sent out on request by asst secretary. **Green Fees** £35 per day; £27 per round (£45/£33 weekends). **Cards** 🔲 🔲 🔲 💳 **Prof** Craig Donnelly **Facilities** ⊗ 🍴 🗄 🍺 ⛾ 🗄 🍴 🏠 🛒 ⚷
Location 2m E of Glenrothes

Hotel ★★★★ 🍴 Balbirnie House, Balbirnie Park, MARKINCH ☎ 01592 610066 30 en suite

ST ANDREWS   Map 12 NO51
British Golf Museum ☎ 01334 460046 (situated opposite Royal & Ancient Golf Club) The museum, which tells the history of golf from its origins to the present day, is of interest to golfers and non-golfers alike. Themed galleries and interactive displays explore the history of the major championships and the lives of the famous players, and trace the development of golfing equipment. An audio-visual theatre shows historic golfing moments.
Open: Etr-mid Oct, daily 9.30am-5.30pm (mid Oct-Etr Thu-Mon 11am-3pm, closed Tue & Wed. **Admission:** There is a charge. ☎ for details.

Dukes Course Craigtoun KY16 8NS
☎ 01334 474371 🖹 01334 479456
e-mail: jkelly@oldcoursehotel.co.uk
Blending the characteristics of a links course with an inland course, Dukes offers rolling fairways, undulating greens and a testing woodland section, and magnificent views over St Andrews Bay towards Carnoustie.
18 holes, 6749yds, Par 72, SSS 73, Course record 71.
Club membership 500.
Visitors booking should be in advance to avoid disappointment through the hotel resort reservations team. **Societies** apply in writing or fax in advance. **Green Fees** not confirmed. **Cards** 🔲 🔲 🔲 🔲 💳 **Prof** John Kelly **Course Designer** Peter Thomson **Facilities** ⊗ 🍴 🗄 🍺 ⛾

continued on page 324

St Andrews Links Trust

St Andrews, *Fife*   ☎ 01334 466666   Fax 01334 479555 Map 12 NO51

e-mail: linkstrust@standrews.org.uk

G olf was first played here around 1400AD and the Old Course is acknowledged world-wide as the Home of Golf. The Old has played host to the greatest golfers in the world and many of golf's most dramatic moments.

The New Course (6604 yards) opened in 1895, having been laid out by Old Tom Morris. The Jubilee opened in 1897, the championship Jubilee Course is 6805 yards long from the medal tees. A shorter version of the Jubilee Course is also available, known as the Bronze Course, measuring 5674 yards. There is no handicap limit for the shorter course and it is best for lower/middle handicap golfers.

The Eden opened in 1914 and is recommended for middle to high handicap golfers. The Strathtyrum has a shorter, less testing layout best for high handicap golfers. The Balgove nine hole course, upgraded and re-opened in 1993, is best for beginners and children. The extent of facilities and courses here make this the largest golf complex in Europe.

Visitors must telephone in advance and have handicap certificate. Old Course closed Sun. Advance booking two years for Old Course, one month New. 24 hr booking on Jubilee/Eden/Strath. No advance booking Sat.

Societies must book at least a month in advance

Green Fees Old Course £90; New Course £45; Jubilee £40; Eden £28; Strathtyrum £20; Balgove £10 (9 holes)

Facilities ⊗ ⫙ 🍴 ☕ ♀ ⚐ 🏠 🎯 🏌 🎣 ✓ 🏇

Location Pilmour House, St Andrews KY16 9SF (NW of town, off A91)

Holes/Par/Course record Old Course: 18 holes, 6566 yds, Par 72, SSS 72, Course record 67
New (West Sands Rd): 18 holes, 6604 yds, Par 71, SSS 71
Jubilee (West Sands Rd): 18 holes, 6805 yds, Par 72, SSS 72
Eden (Dundee Rd): 18 holes, 6162 yds, Par 70, SSS 70
Strathtyrum: 18 holes, 5094 yds, Par 69, SSS 69

Championship Course

WHERE TO STAY AND EAT NEARBY

Hotels
GLENFARG

★★ 67% Glenfarg, Main St.
☎ 01577 830241. 17 en suite

ST ANDREWS

★★★★★ 🏵🏵 72% Old Course St Andrews, Old Station Rd.
☎ 01334 474371. 146 en suite

★★★ 🏵🏵 77% St Andrews Golf, 40 The Scores. ☎ 01334 472611. 22 en suite

★★★ 66% Scores, 76 The Scores.
☎ 01334 472451. 30 en suite

Restaurant
CUPAR

🏵🏵🏵 Ostlers Close, Bonnygate.
☎ 01334 655574

⛺🏠🚩🏨🛥️🏑🏌️🎣 **Leisure** heated indoor swimming pool, sauna, solarium, gymnasium, computer swing analyses. **Location** Follow M90 from Edinburgh onto A91 to Cupar then to St Andrew turning off for Strathkiness

Hotel ★★★★★ 72% The Old Course Hotel Golf Resort & Spa, ST ANDREWS ☎ 01334 474371 146 en suite
Additional hotel ★★ 67% The Glenfarg Hotel & Restaurant, Main St, GLENFARG ☎ 01577 830241 Fax 01577 830665 17 rms (16 en suite)
Additional Guesthouse ◆◆◆◆ Riverview Guest House, Edenside, ST ANDREWS ☎ 01334 838009 Fax 01334 839944 7 en suite

ST ANDREWS See page 323

Hotel ★★★ 77% ST Andrews Golf Hotel, 40 The Scores ☎ 01334 472611 22 en suite

SALINE   Map 11 NT09

Saline Kinneddar Hill KY12 9LT ☎ 01383 852591
Hillside parkland course with excellent turf and panoramic view of the Forth Valley.
9 holes, 5302yds, Par 68, SSS 66, Course record 62.
Club membership 400.
Visitors advisable to contact in advance and may not play Sat, some restrictions Sun. **Societies** contact in advance. **Green Fees** terms on application. **Facilities** ⊗ 〗 Ꮟ ♨ ♀ ⛺🏌️ **Location** Junct 4 of M90, 0.5m E at junc B913/914

Hotel ★★★ 63% King Malcolm, Queensferry Rd, DUNFERMLINE ☎ 01383 722611 48 en suite

TAYPORT   Map 12 NO42

Scotscraig Golf Rd DD6 9DZ
☎ 01382 552515 🗎 01382 553130
e-mail: scotscraig@scottishgolf.com
An Open qualifying links course with more trees in evidence than most, giving a heathland feel.
18 holes, 6550yds, Par 71, SSS 72, Course record 62.
Club membership 950.
Visitors restricted at weekends and weekdays, contact in advance . **Societies** advance booking. **Green Fees** £35 per day £25 after 2pm (£40 weekends £30 after 2.30pm.)
Cards 🟰 💳 💳 **Prof** S J Campbell **Course Designer** James Braid **Facilities** ⊗ 〗 Ꮟ ♨ ♀ ⛺🏠🚩🏑🏌️🎣
Location S side of village off B945

Hotel ★★★ 66% Sandford Country House Hotel, Newton Hill, Wormit, (Nr St Andrews), DUNDEE ☎ 01382 541802 16 en suite

THORNTON   Map 11 NT29

Thornton Station Rd KY1 4DW
☎ 01592 771111 🗎 01592 774955
e-mail: johntgc@ic24.net
A relatively flat, lightly tree-lined, parkland course bounded on three sides by a river which comes into play at holes 14-16.
18 holes, 6155yds, Par 70, SSS 69, Course record 64.
Club membership 700.
Visitors restricted at weekends before 10am & between 12.30-2pm, also Tue 1-1.30 & Thu 9-10. Booking in advance recommended. **Societies** apply in advance. **Green Fees** £27 per day; £17 per round (£35/£25 weekends). **Facilities** ⊗ 〗 Ꮟ ♨ ♀ ⛺ 🏌️ **Location** 1m E of town off A92

Hotel ★★★★⚘ Balbirnie House, Balbirnie Park, MARKINCH ☎ 01592 610066 30 en suite

HIGHLAND

ALNESS   Map 14 NH66

Alness Ardross Rd IV17 0QA ☎ 01349 883877
e-mail: info@alnessgolfclub.co.uk
A testing, parkland course with beautiful views over the Cromarty Firth and the Black Isle.
18 holes, 4886yds, Par 67, SSS 64, Course record 62.
Club membership 300.
Visitors telephone in advance for weekend play, parties must telephone for booking **Societies** must contact in advance. **Green Fees** £13 per round:£16 per day(£15/£18 weekends). **Facilities** Ꮟ ♨ ♀ ⛺ 🚩 🏌️ **Leisure** fishing. **Location** 0.5m N off A9

continued

Hotel ★★★ 72% Morangie House Hotel, Morangie Rd,
TAIN ☎ 01862 892281 26 en suite

ARISAIG   Map 13 NM68

Traigh Traigh PH39 4NT
☎ 01687 450337 📠 01678 450293
According to at least one newspaper Traigh is 'probably
the most beautifully sited nine-hole golf course in the
world'. Whether that is true or not, Traigh lies by the sea
alongside sandy beaches with views to Skye and the Inner
Hebrides. The feature of the course is a line of grassy
hills, originally sand dunes, that rise to some 60 feet, and
provide a challenge to the keenest golfer.

9 holes, 2456yds, Par 68, SSS 65, Course record 67.
Club membership 150.
Visitors no restrictions. **Societies** contact in advance. **Green
Fees** £14 per day. **Course Designer** John Salvesen 1994
Facilities 🏌 🏠 ⛳ ♂ **Location** On A830 6 miles S of
Mallaig,2Miles N of Arisaig

Hotel ★★ 72% Arisaig Hotel, ARISAIG
☎ 01687 450210 13 en suite

BOAT OF GARTEN   Map 14 NH91

Boat of Garten PH24 3BQ
☎ 01479 831282 📠 01479 831523
e-mail: boatgolf@enterprise.net
This heathland course was cut out from a silver birch
forest though the fairways are adequately wide. There
are natural hazards of broom and heather, good views
and walking is easy. A round provides great variety.
18 holes, 5866yds, Par 69, SSS 69, Course record 67.
Club membership 650.
Visitors must contact in advance. Handicap certificate
required. Play restricted to 10am-4pm weekends &
9.20am-7pm weekdays **Societies** must telephone in
advance. **Green Fees** £30 per day; £25 per round
(£35/£30 weekends). **Cards** 💳 💳 💳 💳 **Course
Designer** James Braid **Facilities** ⊗ ⊪ 🏋 🏌 ♀ 🏠 🏠 ⛳
🛒 ♂ **Leisure** hard tennis courts. **Location** E side of
village

Hotel ★★★ 70% Boat Hotel, BOAT OF GARTEN
☎ 01479 831258 32 en suite

BONAR BRIDGE   Map 14 NH69

Bonar Bridge-Ardgay Migdale Rd IV24 3EJ
☎ 01863 766750
Wooded moorland course with picturesque views of hills
and loch.
9 holes, 5284yds, Par 68, SSS 66.
Club membership 250.

Visitors no restrictions. **Societies** apply in writing. **Green
Fees** terms on application. **Course Designer** Various
Facilities 🏌 🏠 ⛳ ♂ **Location** 0.5m E

Guesthouse ◆◆◆ Kyle House, Dornoch Rd, BONAR BRIDGE
☎ 01863 766360 6 rms (3 en suite)

BRORA   Map 14 NC90

Brora Golf Rd KW9 6QS
☎ 01408 621417 📠 01408 622157
e-mail: secretary@broragolf.co.uk
Typical seaside links with little rough and fine views.
Some testing holes including the 17th Tarbatness, so
called because of the lighthouse which gives the line; the
elevated tee is one of the best driving holes in Scotland.
18 holes, 6110yds, Par 69, SSS 69, Course record 61.
Club membership 704.
Visitors advisable to book in advance May-Oct. **Societies**
advisable to book in advance. **Green Fees** terms on
application. **Cards** 💳 💳 **Course Designer** James Braid
Facilities ⊗ ⊪ 🏋 🏌 ♀ 🏠 🏠 ⛳ ♂ **Location** E side of
village. Follow signs to Beach Car Park

Hotel ★★★ 72% Royal Marine Hotel, Golf Rd, BRORA
☎ 01408 621252 22 en suite

CARRBRIDGE   Map 14 NH92

Carrbridge Inverness Rd PH23 3AU
☎ 01479 841623
e-mail: enquiries@carrbridgegolf
Short but challenging part-parkland, part-moorland
course with magnificent views of the Cairngorms.
9 holes, 5402yds, Par 71, SSS 68, Course record 64.
Club membership 650.
Visitors during May-Sep, course not open to visitors after
5pm Wed & before 4pm most Sun. **Societies** small parties
welcome, apply in writing. **Green Fees** £12-£13 per day; £15
weekends (reductions after 6.30pm). **Facilities** 🏌 🏠 ⛳ ♂
Location N side of village

Hotel ★★★ 68% Dalrachney Lodge Hotel, CARRBRIDGE
☎ 01479 841252 11 en suite

DORNOCH   Map 14 NH78

The Carnegie Club Skibo Castle IV25 3RQ
☎ 01862 894600 📠 01862 894601
e-mail: skibo@carnegieclubs.com
Set within the grounds of an enchanting castle, with
the sea on three sides and the hills of Sutherland and
Ross-shire all around, this splendid course enjoys a
magnificent position. Although not long by modern
standards, strong and fickle winds will test even the
most experienced golfer. Excellent leisure facilities.
18 holes, 6403yds, Par 71, SSS 71.
Club membership 550.
Visitors weekdays only by written application to the
secretary. Tee times between 11am & 12pm. **Societies** by
prior arrangement **Green Fees** not confirmed. **Prof** David
Thomson **Course Designer** J Sutherland/Donald Steel
Facilities ⊗ by prior arrangement 🏌 ♀ 🏠 🏠 ⛳ 🍴 ♂ ♂
Leisure hard tennis courts, heated indoor swimming pool,
fishing, sauna, solarium, gymnasium. **Location** Off A9
3m before Dornoch

Hotel ★★ 68% Burghfield House Hotel, DORNOCH
☎ 01862 810212 13 en suite 15 annexe en suite

continued

Royal Dornoch Golf Rd IV25 3LW
☎ 01862 810219 📠 01862 810792
e-mail: bookings@royaldornoch.com
The Championship course was recently rated 9th amongst Britain's top courses and is a links of rare subtlety. It appears amicable but proves very challenging in play. The 18 hole Struie links course provides, in a gentler style, an enjoyable test of a golfer's accuracy.

Championship: 18 holes, 6514yds, Par 70, SSS 73, Course record 62.
Struie Course: 18 holes, 5438yds, Par 69, SSS 66.
Club membership 1600.
Visitors must have a handicap of 24 for gentlemen (ladies 39) on Championship Course. Recommended to contact in advance. Societies must apply in advance. Green Fees Championship course: £45-£60 per round (£50-£70 sundays). Struie course: £12-25 per day; £9-18 per round. Cards 🟦🟥🟦🟥 🟦 Prof A Skinner Course Designer Tom Morris Facilities ⊗ ⫴ ⤬ 🍺 ☕ ♀ ⚒ 🏠 ⛳ 🏌 🛺 ♂ Leisure hard tennis courts. Location E side of town

Hotel ★★★ 71% Royal Golf Hotel, The 1st Tee, DORNOCH ☎ 01862 810283 25 en suite

DURNESS   Map 14 NC46
Durness Balnakeil IV27 4PG
☎ 01971 511364 📠 01971 511321
e-mail: mackenziedurness@aol.com
A 9-hole course set in tremendous scenery overlooking Balnakeil Bay. Part links and part inland with water hazards. Off alternative tees for second 9 holes giving surprising variety. Tremendous last hole played across the sea to the green over 100 yards away.
9 holes, 5555yds, Par 70, SSS 67, Course record 69.
Club membership 150.
Visitors restricted 10am-12.30 on Sun during Jun-Sep. Societies must telephone in advance 01971 511364 (ex Sun). Green Fees £15 per day(£40 per week). Course Designer F Keith Facilities ⊗ 🍺 ⚒ ⛳ ♂ Leisure fishing. Location 1m W of village overlooking Balnakeil Bay

Guesthouse ◆◆◆◆ Port-Na-Con House, Loch Eriboll, LAIRG ☎ 01971 511367 3 en suite

FORT AUGUSTUS   Map 14 NH30
Fort Augustus Markethill PH32 4DP
☎ 01320 366660 & 366758
e-mail: jmm@conifers.fslife.co.uk
Moorland course, with narrow fairways and good views. Bordered by the tree-lined Caledonian Canal to the north and heather clad hills to the south.

continued

9 holes, 5379yds, Par 67, SSS 67, Course record 67.
Club membership 170.
Visitors may not play Sat 1.30-4 & occasional Sun. Societies telephone in advance. Green Fees £10 per day. Course Designer Colt Facilities ♀ ⛳ ♂ Location 1m SW on A82

FORTROSE   Map 14 NH75
Fortrose & Rosemarkie Ness Rd East IV10 8SE
☎ 01381 620529 📠 01381 621328
e-mail: secretary@fortrosegolfclub.co.uk
Seaside links course, set on a peninsula with sea on three sides. Easy walking, good views. Designed by James Braid; the club was formed in 1888.

18 holes, 5883yds, Par 71, SSS 69, Course record 64.
Club membership 770.
Visitors restricted 8.45-10.15am & 1-2.15 then 4.45-6.30pm. Societies must telephone in advance. Green Fees £33 per day; £22 per round(£38/£27 weekends). Cards 🟦🟥🟦 🟦 Course Designer James Braid Facilities ⊗ 🍺 🍺 ♀ ⚒ 🏠 ⛳ 🛺 ♂ Location E side of town centre

Hotel ★★★★ 71% Inverness Marriott Hotel, Culcabock Rd, INVERNESS ☎ 01463 237166 76 en suite 6 annexe en suite

FORT WILLIAM   Map 14 NN17
Fort William Torlundy PH33 7SN ☎ 01397 704464
Spectacular moorland location looking onto the cliffs of Ben Nevis. Tees and greens are in excellent condition following and major drainage improvements to the fairways.
18 holes, 6500yds, Par 72, SSS 71, Course record 67.
Club membership 420.
Visitors no restrictions. Societies must contact in writing. Green Fees terms on application. Cards 🟦🟥🟦🟦 🟦 Course Designer Hamilton Stutt Facilities 🍺 🍺 ♀ ⚒ ⛳ ♂ Location 3m NE on A82

Hotel ★★★ 73% Moorings Hotel, Banavie, FORT WILLIAM ☎ 01397 772797 27 en suite

GAIRLOCH   Map 14 NG87
Gairloch IV21 2BE ☎ 01445 712407 📠 01445 712407
e-mail: secretary@gairlochgc.freeserve.co.uk
Fine seaside links course running along Gairloch Sands with good views over the sea to Skye. In windy conditions each hole is affected. The par 5 eighth hole is described by one of Scotland's teaching professionals as one of the best natural par 5s in the country.
9 holes, 4514yds, Par 63, SSS 64, Course record 64.
Club membership 275.
Visitors must be competent golfer and member of a recognised club. Societies apply in writing to secretary. Green Fees terms on application. Cards 🟦 Course Designer Capt Burgess Facilities ⊗ 🍺 ♀ ⚒ 🏠 ⛳ ♂ Location 1m S on A832

continued

Hotel ★★★ 67% Creag Mor Hotel, Charleston, GAIRLOCH ☎ 01445 712068 17 en suite

GOLSPIE
Map 14 NH89

Golspie Ferry Rd KW10 6ST
☎ 01408 633266 📠 01408 633393
e-mail: golspie-golf-club.co.uk
Founded in 1889, Golspie's seaside course offers easy walking and natural hazards including beach heather and whins. Spectacular scenery.
18 holes, 5890yds, Par 68, SSS 68, Course record 64.
Club membership 300.
Visitors contact in advance. **Societies** contact in advance.
Green Fees terms on application. **Cards** 💳 **Course Designer** James Braid **Facilities** ⊗ ⅷ ⅃ 🖤 ♀ ⚲ 🏠 ⚐ ♂
Location 0.5m S off A9

Hotel ★★★ 72% Royal Marine Hotel, Golf Rd, BRORA ☎ 01408 621252 22 en suite

GRANTOWN-ON-SPEY
Map 14 NJ02

Grantown-on-Spey Golf Course Rd PH26 3HY
☎ 01479 872079 (Apr-Oct) 📠 01479 873725
e-mail: secretary@grantownonspeygolfclub.co
Parkland and woodland course. Part easy walking, remainder hilly. The 7th to 13th really sorts out the golfers.
18 holes, 5710yds, Par 70, SSS 68, Course record 60.
Club membership 800.
Visitors advisable to contact in advance. No visitors before 10am weekends. **Societies** clubhouse open Apr-Oct, apply in advance to secretary. **Green Fees** £20 per round/day (£25 weekends). **Cards** 💳 💳 **Course Designer** A Brown/W Park/J Braid **Facilities** ⊗ ⅷ by prior arrangement ⅃ 🖤 ♀ ⚲ 🏠 ⚐ 🏌 ♂ **Location** NE side of town centre

Hotel ★★ 77% Culdearn House Hotel, Woodlands Ter, GRANTOWN ON SPEY ☎ 01479 872106 9 en suite

HELMSDALE
Map 14 ND01

Helmsdale Golf Rd KW8 6JA ☎ 01431 821063
Sheltered, undulating course following the line of the Helmsdale River.
9 holes, 1860yds, Par 62, SSS 61.
Club membership 45.
Visitors no restrictions. **Societies** apply in writing or telephone in advance. **Green Fees** £10 per 18 holes.
Facilities ⚲ **Location** NW side of town on A896

Hotel ★★★ 72% Royal Marine Hotel, Golf Rd, BRORA ☎ 01408 621252 22 en suite

INVERGORDON
Map 14 NH76

Invergordon King George St IV18 0BD
☎ 01349 852715 📠 01349 852715
e-mail: info@invergordongolf.com
Fairly easy but windy 18-hole parkland course, with woodland, wide fairways and good views over Cromarty Firth. Very good greens and a fair challenge, especially if the wind is from the west.
18 holes, 6030yds, Par 69, SSS 69, Course record 65.
Club membership 240.
Visitors advised to avoid Tue & Thu 4.30-6, Mon & Wed 5-6 and Sat 8.30-10 & 1-2pm. **Societies** must contact in advance, call 01349 852715. **Green Fees** £25 per day; £20 per round. **Course Designer** A Rae **Facilities** ⅃ 🖤 ♀ ⚲ ⚐ ♂ **Location** W side of town centre on B817

continued

Hotel ★★★ 72% Morangie House Hotel, Morangie Rd, TAIN ☎ 01862 892281 26 en suite

INVERNESS
Map 14 NH64

Inverness Culcabock IV2 3XQ
☎ 01463 239882 📠 01463 239882
e-mail: igc@freeuk.com
Fairly flat parkland course with burn running through and alongside several of the holes and acting as a lateral water hazard and out of bounds at several of the holes. Considered short by modern day standards, it is an excellent test of golf rewarding straight drives and accurate iron play to well manicured greens.
18 holes, 6256yds, Par 69, SSS 70, Course record 62.
Club membership 1100.
Visitors restricted at weekends. Prior booking required.
Handicap certificate required. Limited play on Sat. **Societies** must telephone in advance. **Green Fees** £29 per round;£39 per day. **Cards** 💳 💳 💳 **Prof** Alistair P Thomson **Facilities** ⊗ ⅷ ⅃ 🖤 ♀ ⚲ 🏠 ⚐ ♂ **Location** 1 mile from town centre on Culcabock road.

Hotel ★★★★ 71% Inverness Marriott Hotel, Culcabock Rd, INVERNESS ☎ 01463 237166 76 en suite 6 annexe en suite

Loch Ness Fairways Leisure, Castle Heather IV2 6AA
☎ 01463 713335 📠 01463 712695
e-mail: info@golflochness.com
Challenging parkland course with superb views over Inverness, the Beauly Firth and the Black Isle. Built on a gentle slope but none of the holes play uphill. With a base of mature farmland, this lush and green course rewards straight and long hitters but its tricky approach play can challenge even those with a skilful short game.
18 holes, 6772yds, Par 73, SSS 72, Course record 71.
Club membership 500.
Visitors welcome **Societies** telephone for details. **Green Fees** £25 per day (£30 weekends). **Cards** 💳 💳 💳 **Prof** Martin Piggot **Course Designer** Caddies **Facilities** ⊗ ⅷ ⅃ 🖤 ♀ ⚲ 🏠 ⚐ 🏌 🏌 ♂ **Leisure** indoor bowls,target archery. **Conf** Max 80 Thtr 80 Class 40 Board 30 Del from £10.95 * **Location** SW outskirts of Inverness, along new bypass

Hotel ★★★ 66% Loch Ness House Hotel, Glenurquhart Rd, INVERNESS ☎ 01463 231248 22 en suite

Torvean Glenurquhart Rd IV3 8JN ☎ 01463 711434
(Starter) & 225651 (Secretary) 📠 01463 225651
Municipal parkland course, easy walking, good views. Boasts one of the longest par 5s in the North at 565 yards. Three ponds come into play at the 8th, 15th and 17th holes.
18 holes, 5784yds, Par 69, SSS 68, Course record 64.
Club membership 400.
Visitors Advance booking advisable especially at weekends. **Societies** advance bookings through The Highland Council, Town House, Inverness. **Green Fees** not confirmed.
Course Designer Hamilton **Facilities** ⅃ 🖤 ♀ ⚲ ⚐ ♂
Location 1.5m SW on A82

Hotel ★★★ 66% Loch Ness House Hotel, Glenurquhart Rd, INVERNESS ☎ 01463 231248 22 en suite

AA website: www.theAA.com

KINGUSSIE — Map 14 NH70

Kingussie Gynack Rd PH21 1LR
☎ 01540 661600 ▤ 01540 662066
e-mail: kinggolf@globalnet.co.uk
Upland course with natural hazards and magnificent
views. Stands about 1000ft above sea level at its highest
point, and the River Gynack, which runs through the
course, comes into play on five holes.
18 holes, 5500yds, Par 67, SSS 68, Course record 63.
Club membership 800.
Visitors advisable to book in advance. **Societies** must contact
in advance. **Green Fees** terms on application. **Course
Designer** Vardon/Herd **Facilities** ⓑ ▬ ♀ ♨ ⬡ ⚐ ♨ ⚌ ℓ
Location 0.25m N off A86

Hotel ★★ 74% The Scot House Hotel, Newtonmore Rd,
KINGUSSIE ☎ 01540 661351 9 en suite

LOCHCARRON — Map 14 NG83

Lochcarron IV54 8YU ☎ 01520 766211
Seaside links course with some parkland with an
interesting 2nd hole. A short course but great accuracy is
required.
9 holes, 3575yds, Par 62, SSS 60, Course record 60.
Club membership 130.
Visitors restricted Sat 2-5pm. **Societies** welcome but
restricted Sat 2-5pm. **Green Fees** £10 per day. **Facilities** ⚐
Location By A896,1 mile E of Lochcarron village

Hotel ★★ 68% Lochcarron Hotel, Main St,
LOCHCARRON ☎ 01520 722226 10 rms (9 en suite)

LYBSTER — Map 15 ND23

Lybster Main St KW3 6AE ☎ 01593 721308
Picturesque, short heathland course, easy walking.
9 holes, 1896yds, Par 62, SSS 61, Course record 59.
Club membership 140.
Visitors no restrictions. **Societies** must contact in advance.
Green Fees £10 per day. **Facilities** ♨ ⚐ **Location** E side
of village

Hotel ★★ 69% Mackay's Hotel, Union St, WICK
☎ 01955 602323 27 rms (19 en suite)

MUIR OF ORD — Map 14 NH55

Muir of Ord Great North Rd IV6 7SX
☎ 01463 870825 ▤ 01463 871867
e-mail: muirgolf@supanet.com-email
Old established (1875), heathland course with tight fairways and easy walking. Testing 13th, 'Castle Hill' (par 3).
18 holes, 5596yds, Par 68, SSS 68, Course record 61.
Club membership 730.
Visitors may not play during competitions. Booking required
for weekends. **Societies** write to secretary or telephone golf
shop on 01463 871311. **Green Fees** £16 per round;£18 per
day(£20/£22 weekends). **Course Designer** James Braid
Facilities ⊗ by prior arrangement ⚋ by prior arrangement ⓑ
▬ ♀ ♨ ⬡ ⚐ ♦ ⚌ ℓ **Location** S side of village on A862

Hotel ★★★ 72% Priory Hotel, The Square, BEAULY
☎ 01463 782309 34 en suite

NAIRN — Map 14 NH85

Nairn Seabank Rd IV12 4HB
☎ 01667 453208 ▤ 01667 456328
e-mail: secretary@nairngolfclub.co.uk
Championship, seaside links founded in 1887 and
created from a wilderness of heather and whin.
continued

Designed by Archie Simpson, old Tom Morris and
James Braid. Opening holes stretch out along the
shoreline with the turn for home at the 10th. Regularly
chosen for national championships.
18 holes, 6430yds, Par 71, SSS 73, Course record 64.
Newton: 9 holes, 3542yds, Par 58, SSS 57.
Club membership 1150.
Visitors book in advance through secretary, may not play
between 8-11.00 am & 12-2.30 pm (Sat & Sun). **Societies**
subject to availability bookings through secretary's office.
Green Fees terms on application. **Cards** ▭ ▬ ▬ ▣
Prof Robin P Fyfe **Course Designer** A Simpson/Old Tom
Morris/James Braid **Facilities** ⊗ ⚋ ⓑ ▬ ♀ ♨ ⬡ ⚐ ℓ
♟ **Leisure** snooker. **Location** 16m E of Inverness on A96

Hotel ★★★★ 68% Golf View Hotel & Leisure Club,
Seabank Rd, NAIRN ☎ 01667 452301 48 en suite

Nairn Dunbar Lochloy Rd IV12 5AE
☎ 01667 452741 ▤ 01667 456897
e-mail: secretary@nairndunbar.com
Links course with sea views and testing gorse-and whin-
lined fairways. Testing hole: 'Long Peter' (527 yds).
18 holes, 6720yds, Par 72, SSS 73, Course record 64.
Club membership 1200.
Visitors Weekends restricted, contact in advance. **Societies**
must contact in advance. **Green Fees** £45 per day; £35 per
round (£56/£42 weekends). **Cards** ▭ ▬ ▣ **Prof** David
Torrance **Facilities** ⊗ ⚋ ⓑ ▬ ♀ ♨ ⬡ ⚐ ♦ ⚌ ℓ **Conf**
Max 50 **Location** E side of town off A96

Hotel ★★ 64% Alton Burn Hotel, Alton Burn Rd, NAIRN
☎ 01667 452051or 453325 ▤ 01667 456697 23 en suite

NETHY BRIDGE — Map 14 NJ02

Abernethy PH25 3EB
☎ 01479 821305 ▤ 01479 821 305
e-mail: info@abernethygolfclub.com
Traditional Highland course built on natural moorland
surrounded by pine trees and offering a great variety of
shot making for the low handicapped or casual visitor.
The 2nd hole, although very short is played across
bogland and a B class road to a two-tiered green. The
small and fast greens are the most undulating and tricky
in the valley. The Abernethy forest lies on the boundary
and from many parts of the course there are splendid
views of Strathspey.
9 holes, 2551yds, Par 66, SSS 66.
Club membership 480.
Visitors contact in advance. **Societies** must contact in
advance. **Green Fees** £13 per day (£16 weekends). **Facilities**
⊗ ⓑ ▬ ♨ ⚐ ℓ **Location** N side of village on B970

Hotel ★★★ 69% Muckrach Lodge Hotel, DULNAIN
BRIDGE ☎ 01479 851257 9 en suite 4 annexe en suite

NEWTONMORE — Map 14 NN79

Newtonmore Golf Course Rd PH20 1AT
☎ 01540 673328 & 673878 ▤ 01540 673878
e-mail: secretary@newtonmoregolf.com
Inland course beside the River Spey. Beautiful views and
easy walking. Testing 17th hole (par 3).
18 holes, 6029yds, Par 70, SSS 69, Course record 68.
Club membership 420.
Visitors contact in advance. **Societies** apply in writing to
secretary. **Green Fees** terms on application. **Prof** Robert
Henderson **Facilities** ⊗ ⚋ ⓑ ▬ ♀ ♨ ⬡ ⚐ ♦ ⚌ ℓ
Location E side of town off A9
continued

328

Hotel ★★ 74% The Scot House Hotel, Newtonmore Rd, KINGUSSIE ☎ 01540 661351 9 en suite

REAY   Map 14 NC96

Reay KW14 7RE ☎ 01847 811288 🖹 01847 894189
e-mail: info@reaygolfclub.co.uk
Picturesque seaside links with natural hazards, following the contours of Sandside Bay. Most northerly 18 hole links on the British mainland. The course opens and closes with a par 3. The 581 yard par 5 4th hole 'Sahara' requires a solid tee shot and fairway wood to set up an approach to a sheltered green protected by a burn. The 196 yard par 3 7th 'Pilkington' is a beautiful short hole played across Reay burn to a raised green. The two tiered 18th protected by its greenside bunkers provides a formidable finishing hole.
18 holes, 5831yds, Par 69, SSS 69, Course record 64. Club membership 368.
Visitors restricted competition days **Societies** apply to the secretary in advance. **Green Fees** £20 per day/round. **Course Designer** Braid **Facilities** ⊗ by prior arrangement ⅷ by prior arrangement ⅘ by prior arrangement ⬛ ♀ ☺ ⛳ 🏌 🏐 ⚷ **Leisure** see web site. **Location** 11 miles W of Thurso on A836

Hotel ★★★ 60% Royal Hotel, Traill St, THURSO ☎ 01847 893191 102 en suite

STRATHPEFFER   Map 14 NH45

Strathpeffer Spa IV14 9AS
☎ 01997 421219 & 421011 🖹 01997 421011
e-mail: mail@strathpeffergolf.co.uk
Upland course with many natural hazards (only three sand bunkers), hard walking and fine views. Testing 3rd hole (par 3) across loch.
18 holes, 4792yds, Par 65, SSS 64, Course record 60. Club membership 500.
Visitors advisable to contact in advance. **Societies** apply in writing. **Green Fees** £21 per day; £15 per round. **Cards** ☒ ☒ ☒ ☒ **Prof** Gary Lister **Course Designer** Willie Park/Tom Morris **Facilities** ⬛ ⚐ ♀ ☺ ⛳ 🏌 ⚷ **Location** 0.25m N of village off A834

Hotel ★★ 72% Achilty Hotel, CONTIN ☎ 01997 421355 8 en suite 4 annexe en suite

TAIN   Map 14 NH78

Tain Chapel Rd IV19 1JE
☎ 01862 892314 🖹 01862 892099
e-mail: info@tain-golfclub.co.uk
Heathland/links course with river affecting three holes; easy walking, fine views.
18 holes, 6404yds, Par 70, SSS 71, Course record 68. Club membership 500.
Visitors no restrictions. **Societies** must book in advance. **Green Fees** £30 per round; £36 per day (£36/£46 weekends). **Cards** ☒ ☒ ☒ ☒ **Course Designer** Tom Morris **Facilities** ⊗ ⅷ ⬛ ⚐ ♀ ☺ ⛳ 🏌 🏐 ♨ ⚷ **Location** E side of town centre off B9174

Hotel ★★★ 72% Morangie House Hotel, Morangie Rd, TAIN ☎ 01862 892281 26 en suite

THURSO   Map 15 ND16

Thurso Newlands of Geise KW14 7XD ☎ 01847 893807
Parkland course, windy, but with fine views of Dunnet Head and the Orkney Islands. Tree-lined fairways but 4th and 16th holes are testing into the prevailing wind.
continued

The 13th is a short par 4 but has a testing drive over a burn with heather on left and punishing rough on right.
18 holes, 5853yds, Par 69, SSS 69, Course record 63. Club membership 230.
Visitors may not play 9-10.30 Sat or 1-1.30 Sat. **Societies** apply in advance. **Green Fees** £15 per day. **Course Designer** W S Stewart **Facilities** ⬛ ⚐ ♀ ☺ 🏌 **Location** 2m SW of Thurso on B874

Hotel ★★★ 60% Royal Hotel, Traill St, THURSO ☎ 01847 893191 102 en suite

WICK   Map 15 ND35

Wick Reiss KW1 4RW
☎ 01955 602726 🖹 01955 604418
e-mail: wickgolfclub@hotmail.com
Typical seaside links course, fairly flat, easy walking. 9 holes straight out and straight back. Normally breezy.
18 holes, 6123yds, Par 69, SSS 70, Course record 63. Club membership 352.
Visitors no restrictions. **Societies** apply in writing or telephone in advance. **Green Fees** £20 per round/day. **Course Designer** James Braid **Facilities** ⬛ ⚐ ♀ ☺ 🏌 ⚷ **Location** 3.5m N off A9

Hotel ★★ 69% Mackay's Hotel, Union St, WICK ☎ 01955 602323 27 rms (19 en suite)

INVERCLYDE

GOUROCK   Map 10 NS27

Gourock Cowal View PA19 1HD
☎ 01475 631001 🖹 01475 638307
e-mail: adt@gourockgolfclub.freeserve.co.uk
Moorland course with hills and dells. Testing 8th hole, par 5. Magnificent views over Firth of Clyde.
18 holes, 6408yds, Par 73, SSS 72, Course record 64. Club membership 720.
Visitors must have handicap certificate or letter of introduction. May not play Sat. **Societies** welcome weekdays, must contact in advance. **Green Fees** £27 per day; £20 per round (£27 per round weekends). **Prof** Graham Clark **Course Designer** J Braid/H Cotton **Facilities** ⊗ ⅷ ⬛ ⚐ ♀ ☺ ⛳ 🏌 ⚷ **Location** SW side of town off A770

Hotel ⇧ Express by Holiday Inn, Cartsburn, GREENOCK ☎ 01475 786666 72 en suite

GREENOCK   Map 10 NS27

Greenock Forsyth St PA16 8RE
☎ 01475 720793 🖹 01475 791912
Testing moorland course with panoramic views of Clyde Estuary.
18 holes, 5838yds, Par 69, SSS 69. Club membership 700.
Visitors may not play Sat. Must contact in advance and have a handicap certificate. **Societies** must telephone in advance. **Green Fees** £28 per day; £20 per round (£35/£25 weekends). **Prof** Paul Morrison **Course Designer** James Braid **Facilities** ⊗ ⅷ ⬛ ⚐ ♀ ☺ ⛳ ⚷ **Location** SW side of town off A770

Hotel ⇧ Express by Holiday Inn, Cartsburn, GREENOCK ☎ 01475 786666 72 en suite

Looking for a driving range?
See the index at the back of the guide

Greenock Whinhill Beith Rd PA16 9LN
☎ 01475 724694 evenings & weekends only
18 holes, 5504yds, Par 68, SSS 68, Course record 64.
Location 1.5m SW off B7054
Telephone for further details
....
Hotel ⌂ Express by Holiday Inn, Cartsburn, GREENOCK
☎ 01475 786666 72 en suite

KILMACOLM   Map 10 NS36

Kilmacolm Porterfield Rd PA13 4PD
☎ 01505 872139 📠 01505 874007
e-mail: secretary@kilmacolmgolf.sagehost.co.uk
Moorland course, easy walking, fine views. Testing 7th, 13th and 14th holes.
18 holes, 5961yds, Par 69, SSS 69, Course record 64.
Club membership 850.
Visitors must contact in advance, visitors welcome Tuesday, Wednesday & Thursday. **Societies** apply in writing. **Green Fees** not confirmed. **Prof** Iain Nicholson **Course Designer** Willie Campbell **Facilities** ⛳ 🏠 🛒 *𝄋* **Location** SE side of town off A761
....
Hotel ★★★★⚐ 67% Gleddoch House Hotel, LANGBANK ☎ 01475 540711 39 en suite

PORT GLASGOW   Map 10 NS37

Port Glasgow Devol Rd PA14 5XE
☎ 01475 704181 & 791214 (Sec)
A moorland course set on a hilltop overlooking the Clyde, with magnificent views to the Cowal hills.
18 holes, 5712yds, Par 68, SSS 68.
Club membership 390.
Visitors may not play on Sat. By prior arrangement or with member Sun. **Societies** apply in writing/telephone in advance. **Green Fees** £20 per day; £15 per round(£30/£20 Sundays). **Cards** 🖾 💳 🛒 **Facilities** ⛳ 🍳 🏠 🍺 🍴 🛒 **Location** 1m S
....
Hotel ★★★★⚐ 67% Gleddoch House Hotel, LANGBANK ☎ 01475 540711 39 en suite

MIDLOTHIAN

BONNYRIGG   Map 11 NT36

Broomieknowe 36 Golf Course Rd EH19 2HZ
☎ 0131 663 9317 📠 0131 663 2152
e-mail: administrator@broomieknowe.com
Easy walking mature parkland course laid out by Ben Sayers and extended by James Braid. Elevated site with excellent views.
18 holes, 6150yds, Par 70, SSS 70, Course record 65.
Visitors must contact in advance. **Societies** contact for details. **Green Fees** £19 per round:£25 per day(£25 per round weekends). **Prof** Mark Patchett **Course Designer** Ben Sayers/Hawtree **Facilities** ⛳ 🍳 🏠 🍺 🍴 🛒 🏠 *𝄋*
Location 0.5m NE off B704
....
Hotel ★★★ 77% Dalhousie Castle And Spa, Bonnyrigg, EDINBURGH ☎ 01875 820153 27 en suite 5 annexe en suite

DALKEITH   Map 11 NT36

Newbattle Abbey Rd EH22 3AD
☎ 0131 663 2123 & 0131 663 1819 📠 0131 654 1810
Gently undulating parkland course, dissected by the River South Esk and surrounded by woods.
continued

18 holes, 6025yds, Par 69, SSS 69, Course record 61.
Club membership 700.
Visitors Mon-Fri ex public holidays, before 4pm. **Societies** welcome weekdays ex public holidays, before 4pm. **Green Fees** £30 per day; £20 per round. **Prof** Scott McDonald **Course Designer** S Colt **Facilities** ⛳ 🍳 🏠 🍺 🍴 🛒 🏠 🛒 *𝄋* **Location** SW side of town off A68
....
Hotel ★★★ 77% Dalhousie Castle And Spa, Bonnyrigg, EDINBURGH ☎ 01875 820153
27 en suite 5 annexe en suite

GOREBRIDGE   Map 11 NT36

Vogrie Vogrie Estate Country Park EH23 4NU
☎ 01875 821716
A 9-hole municipal course located within a country park. The wide fairways are particularly suited to beginners.
9 holes, 2530yds, Par 33.
Visitors book by telephone 24 hrs in advance. **Green Fees** not confirmed. **Facilities** 🍺 🛒 **Location** Off B6372

PENICUIK   Map 11 NT25

Glencorse Milton Bridge EH26 0RD
☎ 01968 677189 📠 01968 674399
Picturesque parkland course with burn affecting ten holes. Testing 5th hole (237 yds) par 3.

18 holes, 5217yds, Par 64, SSS 66, Course record 60.
Club membership 700.
Visitors contact secretary, unable to play during club competitions **Societies** contact secretary for details. **Green Fees** £20 per round(£26 weekends and bank holidays). **Prof** Cliffe Jones **Course Designer** Willie Park **Facilities** ⛳ 🍳 🏠 🍺 🍴 🛒 🏠 *𝄋* **Location** 9m S of Edinburgh on A701 Pebbles Road. 1.5m N of Penicuik on A701
....
Hotel ★★ 65% Roslin Glen Hotel, 2 Penicuik Rd, ROSLIN ☎ 0131 440 2029 7 en suite

MORAY

BUCKIE   Map 15 NJ46

Buckpool Barhill Rd, Buckpool AB56 1DU
☎ 01542 832236 📠 01542 832236
Links course with superlative view over Moray Firth, easy walking.
18 holes, 6257yds, Par 70, SSS 70, Course record 64.
Club membership 430.
Visitors parties please apply in advance. **Societies** apply in advance. **Green Fees** terms on application. **Facilities** ⛳ 🍳 🏠 🍺 🍴 🛒 *𝄋* **Leisure** squash, snooker. **Location** Off A98
....
Hotel ★★ 65% Mill House Hotel, Tynet, BUCKIE ☎ 01542 850233 16 en suite

Strathlene Portessie AB56 2DJ ☎ 01542 831798
Raised seaside links course with magnificent view. A
special feature of the course is approach shots to raised
greens (holes 4, 5, 6 & 13).
18 holes, 5980yds, Par 69, SSS 69, Course record 65.
Club membership 370.
Visitors booking essential at weekends. **Societies** telephone
for Mon-Fri & apply in writing for weekends. **Green Fees**
not confirmed. **Facilities** ⊗ ⅃ ▆ ♀ ♙ ♂ **Location** 2m E
of Buckie on A942

Hotel ★★ 65% Mill House Hotel, Tynet, BUCKIE
☎ 01542 850233 16 en suite

CULLEN   Map 15 NJ56

Cullen The Links AB56 4WB
☎ 01542 840685 ▤ 01542 841977
e-mail: cullengolfclub@btinternet.com
Interesting links on two levels with rocks and ravines
offering some challenging holes. Spectacular scenery.
18 holes, 4610yds, Par 63, SSS 62, Course record 58.
Club membership 600.
Visitors no restrictions but during summer club medal
matches given preference on Mon/Wed/Sat. **Societies**
advance applications advisable. **Green Fees** £18 per day; £12
per round (£22/£16 weekends). **Course Designer** Tom
Morris/Charlie Neaves **Facilities** ⊗ ⅄▆ ▆ ♀ ♙ ♂
Location 0.5m W off A98

Hotel ★★ 65% Mill House Hotel, Tynet, BUCKIE
☎ 01542 850233 16 en suite

DUFFTOWN   Map 15 NJ33

Dufftown Tomintoul Rd AB55 4BS
☎ 01340 820325 ▤ 01340 820325
e-mail: marion_dufftowngolfclub@yahoo.com
A short and undulating inland course with spectacular
views. The tee of the highest hole, the 9th, is over 1200 ft
above sea level.
18 holes, 5308yds, Par 67, SSS 67, Course record 64.
Club membership 250.
Visitors tee reserved Tue & Wed 4.30-6.30 & Sun 7.30-9 &
12.30-2. Prior booking recommended. **Societies** apply in
writing or by telephone **Green Fees** £15 per day; £12 per
round. **Cards** ▦ ▤ **Course Designer** Members **Facilities**
⊗ by prior arrangement ⅄ by prior arrangement ⅃ ▆ ♀ ♙
♈ ♂ **Conf** Max 20 **Location** 0.75m SW off B9009

Hotel ★★★ 76% Craigellachie Hotel, CRAIGELLACHIE
☎ 01340 881204 26 en suite

ELGIN   Map 15 NJ26

Elgin Hardhillock, Birnie Rd, New Elgin IV30 8SX
☎ 01343 542338 ▤ 01343 542341
e-mail: secretary@elgingolfclub.com
Possibly the finest inland course in the north of
Scotland, with undulating greens and compact holes
that demand the highest accuracy. There are thirteen
par 4s and one par 5 hole on its parkland layout.
18 holes, 6163yds, Par 68, SSS 69, Course record 63.
Club membership 1000.
Visitors must contact in advance, weekend play only by
prior arrangement. **Societies** telephone secretary for
details. **Green Fees** £35 per day; £26 per round. **Cards**
▦ ▤ ▦ ▦ ▣ **Prof** Kevin Stables **Course**
Designer John Macpherson **Facilities** ⊗ ⅄▆ ▆ ♀ ♙
▤ ♈ ⤫ ♂ ♈ **Location** 1m S on A941
continued

Hotel ★★★ 76% Mansion House Hotel, The Haugh,
ELGIN ☎ 01343 548811 23 en suite

FORRES   Map 14 NJ05

Forres Muiryshade IV36 2RD
☎ 01309 672250 ▤ 01309 672250
e-mail: sandy@forresgolfclub.fsnet.co.uk
An all-year parkland course laid on light, well-drained
soil in wooded countryside. Walking is easy despite
some hilly holes. A test for the best golfers.
18 holes, 6240yds, Par 70, SSS 70, Course record 60.
Club membership 1000.
Visitors welcome although club competitions take
priority. Weekends may be restricted in summer. **Societies**
advised to telephone 2-3 weeks in advance. **Green Fees**
£24 per round;£30 per day. **Cards** ▦ ▦ ▣ **Prof** Sandy
Aird **Course Designer** James Braid/Willie Park **Facilities**
⊗ ⅄▆ ▆ ▆ ♀ ♙ ▤ ♈ ⤫ ⤫ ♂ **Location** SE side of
town centre off B9010

Hotel ★★★ 67% Ramnee Hotel, Victoria Rd, FORRES
☎ 01309 672410 20 en suite

GARMOUTH   Map 15 NJ36

Garmouth & Kingston Spey St IV32 7NJ
☎ 01343 870388 ▤ 01343 870388
e-mail: garmouthgolfclub@aol.com
Flat seaside course with several parkland holes and tidal
waters. The 8th hole measures only 328 yards from the
medal tee but the fairway is bounded by a ditch on either
side, the left hand one being out of bounds for the entire
length of the hole. The par 5 17th 'Whinny Side' has
gorse bordering on both sides of the fairway which can be
intimidating to any level of golfer.
18 holes, 5905yds, Par 69, SSS 69, Course record 66.
Club membership 560.
Visitors must contact in advance. **Societies** advisable to
phone in advance. **Green Fees** terms on application. **Course**
Designer George Smith **Facilities** ⊗ ⅄▆ ▆ ▆ ♀ ♙ ♈ ♂
Leisure fishing. **Location** In village on B9015

Hotel ★★★ 76% Mansion House Hotel, The Haugh,
ELGIN ☎ 01343 548811 23 en suite

HOPEMAN   Map 15 NJ16

Hopeman Clubhouse IV30 5YA
☎ 01343 830578 ▤ 01343 830152
e-mail: hopemangc@aol.com
Links-type course with beautiful views over the Moray
Firth. The 12th hole, called the Priescach, is a short hole
with a drop of 100 feet from tee to green. It can require
anything from a wedge to a wood depending on the wind.
18 holes, 5590yds, Par 68, SSS 67.
Club membership 700.
Visitors must contact in advance, restricted tee times at
weekend and between 12:45-1:45 weekdays **Societies**
contact in advance. **Green Fees** £15 per round;£20 per
day(£20/£25 weekends). **Cards** ▦ ▦ ▦ ▣ **Facilities** ⊗
⅄▆ ▆ ▆ ♀ ♙ ▤ ♈ ♂ **Location** E side of village off
B9040

Hotel ★★★ 76% Mansion House Hotel, The Haugh,
ELGIN ☎ 01343 548811 23 en suite

KEITH　　　　　　　　　　　　　Map 15 NJ45

Keith Fife Park AB55 5DF
☎ 01542 882469 🖹 01542 888176
Parkland course, with natural hazards over first 9 holes.
Testing 7th hole, 232 yds, par 3.
18 holes, 5767yds, Par 69, SSS 68.
Club membership 500.
Visitors no restrictions except competitions. **Societies** by
arrangement with outings secretary (01542 886742) **Green
Fees** £15 per day; £12 per round (£20/£15 weekends).
Facilities ⚑ ♀ ⚲ ↘ ♂ **Location** NW side of town centre
off A96, onto B9014 and first right

Hotel ★★★ 76% Craigellachie Hotel, CRAIGELLACHIE
☎ 01340 881204 26 en suite

LOSSIEMOUTH　　　　　　　　Map 15 NJ27

Moray IV31 6QS ☎ 01343 812018 🖹 01343 815102
e-mail: secretary@moraygolf.co.uk
**Two fine Scottish Championship links courses, known
as Old and New (Moray), and situated on the Moray
Firth where the weather is unusually mild.**
*Old Course: 18 holes, 6643yds, Par 71, SSS 73,
Course record 65.*
*New Course: 18 holes, 6004yds, Par 69, SSS 69,
Course record 62.*
Club membership 1550.
Visitors must contact in advance 01343 812018
Secretary. **Societies** Contact in advance. **Green Fees** not
confirmed. **Cards** 🔲 🔲 🔲 🟦 **Prof** Alistair
Thomson **Course Designer** Tom Morris **Facilities** ⊗)∭
🔓 ⚑ ♀ ⚲ 🏠 ⚑ ⚇ **Location** N side of town

Hotel ★★★ 76% Mansion House Hotel, The Haugh,
ELGIN ☎ 01343 548811 23 en suite

ROTHES　　　　　　　　　　　Map 15 NJ24

Rothes Blackhall AB38 7AN
☎ 01340 831443 (evenings) 🖹 01340 831443
e-mail: rothesgolfclub@netscapeonline.co.uk
A hilly course on an elevated site overlooking the remains
of Rothes castle and the Spey valley. The 2nd fairway and
most of the 3rd are sheltered by woodland. The ground
alongside the 5th & 6th falls away steeply.
9 holes, 4972yds, Par 68, SSS 64.
Club membership 350.
Visitors course reserved Mon 5-6.30 & Tue 5-
7.30.Telephone to confirm bookings. **Societies** apply in
writing to secretary. **Green Fees** £12 (£15 weekends).
Course Designer John Souter **Facilities** ⊗ 🔓 ⚑ ♀ ⚲
Location 9m S of Elgin on A941

Hotel ★★★ 76% Craigellachie Hotel, CRAIGELLACHIE
☎ 01340 881204 26 en suite

SPEY BAY　　　　　　　　　　Map 15 NJ36

Spey Bay IV32 7PJ ☎ 01343 820424 🖹 01343 829282
e-mail: info@speybay.com
Seaside links course over gently undulating banks and
well-drained ground. Good views along Moray coast.
Driving range.
18 holes, 6182yds, Par 70, SSS 69, Course record 65.
Club membership 350.
Visitors telephone for details (especially for Sun) **Societies**
book by telephone. **Green Fees** £20 per round (£22
weekends). **Cards** 🔲 🔲 🟦 **Course Designer** Ben
continued

Spey Bay Golf Course

Sayers **Facilities** ⊗)∭ 🔓 ⚑ ♀ ⚲ ⚑ 🏠 ↘ ⚒ ⚇ ⚑
Leisure hard tennis courts.**Conf** Thtr 150 Class 20 Board 20
Banquet 100 Del from £17.50 * **Location** 4.5m N of
Fochabers on B9104, off main Aberdeen/Inverness
road A96

Hotel ★★ 65% Mill House Hotel, Tynet, BUCKIE
☎ 01542 850233 16 en suite

NORTH AYRSHIRE

BEITH　　　　　　　　　　　　Map 10 NS35

Beith Threepwood Rd KA15 2JR
☎ 01505 503166 & 506814 🖹 01505 506814
Hilly course, with panoramic views over 7 counties.
18 holes, 5616yds, Par 68, SSS 68.
Club membership 420.
Visitors contact for details. **Societies** apply in writing to
secretary at least 1 month in advance. **Green Fees** £15 per
round(£20 weekends). **Course Designer** Members **Facilities**
⊗)∭ 🔓 ⚑ ♀ ⚲ **Location** Hilly course with panoramic
views over 7 counties

Hotel ★★★ 68% Bowfield Hotel & Country Club,
HOWWOOD ☎ 01505 705225 23 en suite

GT CUMBRAE ISLAND (MILLPORT) Map 10 NS15

Millport Golf Rd KA28 OHB
☎ 01475 530305 (Prof) & 530306 (Sec) 🖹 01475 530306
e-mail: secretary@millportgolfclub.co.uk
Pleasantly situated on the west side of Cumbrae looking
over Bute to Arran and the Mull of Kintyre. Exposure
means conditions may vary according to wind strength
and direction. A typical seaside resort course welcoming
visitors.
18 holes, 5828yds, Par 68, SSS 69, Course record 64.
Club membership 525.
Visitors advisable to phone and book tee times especially in
summer months. **Societies** telephone or write in advance.
Green Fees £25 per day; £20 per round (£31/£25 weekends).
Cards 🔲 🔲 🔲 🟦 **Prof** William Haldane Lee **Course Designer**
James Braid **Facilities** ⊗)∭ 🔓 ⚑ ♀ ⚲ 🏠 ⚇ **Location**
Approx 4m from ferry slip

Hotel ★★★ 72% Brisbane House, 14 Greenock Rd,
Esplanade, LARGS ☎ 01475 687200 23 en suite

IRVINE　　　　　　　　　　　Map 10 NS33

Glasgow Gailes KA11 5AE
☎ 0141 942 2011 🖹 0141 942 0770
e-mail: secretary@glasgow-golf.com
A lovely seaside links. The turf of the fairways and all
continued

the greens is truly glorious and provides tireless play. Established in 1882, and is a qualifying course for the Open Championship.
18 holes, 6535yds, Par 71, SSS 72, Course record 63.
Club membership 1200.
Visitors prior booking through secretary reccomended, no visitors before 2.30pm Sat & Sun. **Societies** initial contact by telephone. **Green Fees** £60 per day; £45 per round (£55 per round weekends). **Cards** 🖂 💳 💳 💳 **Prof** J Steven **Course Designer** W Park Jnr **Facilities** ⊗ ⊪ 🕯 by prior arrangement ⅃ 🛄 ♀ ☖ 🖓 🍴 ⚘ 🚜 ⚷ **Location** Off A78 at Newhouse junct, S of Irvine
....
Hotel ★★★ 75% Montgreenan Mansion House Hotel, Montgreenan Estate, KILWINNING
☎ 01294 557733 21 en suite

Irvine Bogside KA12 8SN ☎ 01294 275979
Testing links course; only two short holes.
18 holes, 6400yds, Par 71, SSS 73, Course record 65.
Club membership 450.
Societies are welcome weekdays and pm weekends, telephone in advance. **Green Fees** terms on application. **Prof** Keith Erskine **Course Designer** James Braid **Facilities** ☖ 🖃 🍴 ⚷ **Location** N side of town off A737
....
Hotel ★★★ 75% Montgreenan Mansion House Hotel, Montgreenan Estate, KILWINNING
☎ 01294 557733 21 en suite

Irvine Ravenspark 13 Kidsneuk Ln KA12 8SR
☎ 01294 271293
e-mail: secretary@irgc.co.uk
Parkland course.
18 holes, 6457yds, Par 71, SSS 71, Course record 65.
Club membership 600.
Visitors may not play Sat before 2pm. **Societies** not allowed Sat, contact club steward in advance. **Green Fees** terms on application. **Prof** Peter Bond **Facilities** ⊗ ⊪ ⅃ 🛄 ♀ ☖ 🖃 ⚷ **Location** N side of town on A737
....
Hotel ★★★ 75% Montgreenan Mansion House Hotel, Montgreenan Estate, KILWINNING
☎ 01294 557733 21 en suite

Western Gailes Gailes by Irvine KA11 5AE
☎ 01294 311649 🖃 01294 312312
e-mail: secretary@westerngailes.com
A magnificent seaside links with glorious turf and wonderful greens. The view is open across the Firth of Clyde to the neighbouring islands. It is a well-balanced course crossed by 3 burns. There are 2 par 5s, the 6th and 14th, and the 11th is a testing 445-yd, par 4, dog-leg.
18 holes, 6639yds, Par 71, SSS 73, Course record 65.
Visitors welcome Mon, Wed, Fri. Must contact in advance and have a handicap certificate.Limited number of times on Sundays pm must reserve in advance **Societies** Mon/Wed/Fri,Sun pm must contact in advance. **Green Fees** £115 per day; £85 per round including complimentary lunch (£90 Sun). **Cards** 🖂 💳 💳 💳 **Facilities** ⊗ ⊪ by prior arrangement ⅃ 🛄 ♀ ☖ 🖃 ⚷ **Location** 2m S off A737
....
Hotel ★★★ 75% Montgreenan Mansion House Hotel, Montgreenan Estate, KILWINNING
☎ 01294 557733 21 en suite

KILBIRNIE   Map 10 NS35

Kilbirnie Place Largs Rd KA25 7AT
☎ 01505 684444 & 683398
Easy walking parkland course.
18 holes, 5543yds, Par 69, SSS 67, Course record 65.
Club membership 578.
Visitors must contact in advance, may not play Sat or on competition days. **Societies** must apply in writing in advance. **Green Fees** £17 per round, £25 per day (£25/£35 Sun). **Facilities** ⊗ ⊪ 🕯 🛄 ♀ ☖ **Location** 1m W from Kilbirnie Cross on A760
....
Hotel ★★★ 72% Priory House Hotel, Broomfields, LARGS
☎ 01475 686460 21 en suite

LARGS   Map 10 NS25

Largs Irvine Rd KA30 8EU
☎ 01475 673594 🖃 01475 673594
e-mail: secretary@largsgolfclub.co.uk
A parkland, tree-lined course with views to the Clyde coast and Arran Isles.
18 holes, 6115yds, Par 70, SSS 71, Course record 63.
Club membership 850.
Visitors may not play competition days. Other times by arrangement with secretary. **Societies** apply in writing. **Green Fees** £30 per round;£40 per day(£30/40 per round weekends. **Prof** Kenneth Docherty **Course Designer** H Stutt **Facilities** ⊗ ⊪ 🕯 🛄 ♀ ☖ 🖃 🍴 ⚷ **Location** 1m S of town centre on A78
....
Hotel ★★★ 72% Priory House Hotel, Broomfields, LARGS
☎ 01475 686460 21 en suite

Routenburn Routenburn Rd KA30 8QA
☎ 01475 673230
18 holes, 5675yds, Par 68, SSS 68.
Course Designer J Braid **Location** 1m N off A78
Telephone for further details
....
Hotel ★★ 69% Willowbank Hotel, 96 Greenock Rd, LARGS ☎ 01475 672311 & 675435
🖃 01475 689027 30 en suite

SKELMORLIE   Map 10 NS16

Skelmorlie Beithglass PA17 5ES ☎ 01475 520152
Parkland/moorland course with magnificent views over Firth of Clyde. Designed by James Braid.
18 holes, 5030yds, Par 65, SSS 65.
Club membership 450.
Visitors no visitors before 3pm Sat. **Societies** apply by telephone. **Green Fees** terms on application. **Course Designer** James Braid **Facilities** ⊗ by prior arrangement ⊪ by prior arrangement 🕯 by prior arrangement 🛄 ♀ ☖ 🍴 **Leisure** fishing. **Location** E side of village off A78
....
Hotel ★★ 69% Willowbank Hotel, 96 Greenock Rd, LARGS ☎ 01475 672311 & 675435
🖃 01475 689027 30 en suite

STEVENSTON   Map 10 NS24

Ardeer Greenhead KA20 4LB
☎ 01294 464542 & 465316 🖃 01294 465316
e-mail: peter@ardeergolfclub.netlineuk.net
Parkland course with natural hazards.
18 holes, 6401yds, Par 72, SSS 72, Course record 66.
Club membership 650.
Visitors may not play Sat. **Societies** must contact in advance.

continued

Green Fees not confirmed. **Course Designer** Stutt **Facilities** ⊗)Ⅲ ⓛ ♥ ♀ ⚐ ⚒ ♂ **Location** 0.5m N off A78

Hotel ★★★ 75% Montgreenan Mansion House Hotel, Montgreenan Estate, KILWINNING ☎ 01294 557733 21 en suite

WEST KILBRIDE   Map 10 NS24

West Kilbride 33-35 Fullerton Dr, Seamill KA23 9HT
☎ 01294 823911 🖹 01294 829573
e-mail: golf@westkilbridegolfclub.com
Seaside links course on Firth of Clyde, with fine views of Isle of Arran from every hole.
18 holes, 5974yds, Par 70, SSS 70, Course record 63.
Club membership 840.
Visitors may not play at weekends or bank holidays, must contact in advance. **Societies** Tue & Thu only; must contact in advance. **Green Fees** £27 per round;£38 per day. **Prof** Graham Ross **Course Designer** James Braid **Facilities** ⊗)Ⅲ ⓛ ♥ ♀ ⚐ ⚒ ♂ **Location** W side of town off A78

Hotel ★★★ 72% Priory House Hotel, Broomfields, LARGS ☎ 01475 686460 21 en suite

NORTH LANARKSHIRE

AIRDRIE   Map 11 NS76

Airdrie Rochsoles ML6 0PQ ☎ 01236 762195
Picturesque parkland course with good views.
18 holes, 6004yds, Par 69, SSS 69, Course record 63.
Club membership 450.
Visitors must contact in advance. With member only weekends & bank holidays. **Societies** apply in writing. **Green Fees** not confirmed. **Prof** G Monks **Course Designer** J Braid **Facilities** ⊗)Ⅲ ⓛ ♥ ♀ ⚐ ♂ **Location** 1m N on B802

Hotel ★★★★ 66% Westerwood Hotel Golf & Country Club, 1 St Andrews Dr, Westerwood, CUMBERNAULD ☎ 01236 457171 49 en suite

Easter Moffat Mansion House, Station Rd, Plains ML6 8NP ☎ 01236 842878 🖹 01236 842904
e-mail: gordonmiller@emgc.freeserve.co.uk
A challenging moorland/parkland course which enjoys good views of the Campsie and Ochil hills. Although fairways are generous, accurate placement from the tee is essential on most holes. The signature hole on the course, the 18th is a truly memorable par 3, played from an elevated tee, to a receptive green in front of the club house.
18 holes, 6221yds, Par 72, SSS 70, Course record 66.
Club membership 500.
Visitors may only play on weekdays. **Societies** must contact in advance. **Green Fees** £30 per day; £20 per round. **Prof** Graham King **Facilities** ⊗)Ⅲ ⓛ ♥ ♀ ⚐ ⚒ ♂ **Location** 2m E of Airdrie on A89

Hotel ★★★★ 66% Westerwood Hotel Golf & Country Club, 1 St Andrews Dr, Westerwood, CUMBERNAULD ☎ 01236 457171 49 en suite

BELLSHILL   Map 11 NS76

Bellshill Community Rd, Orbiston ML4 2RZ
☎ 01698 745124 🖹 01698 292576
Tree lined 18 holes situated in the heart of Lanarkshire near Strathclyde Park. First opened for play in 1905 and

extended in 1970. The 2nd hole has recently been redesigned by Mark James and Andrew Mair. The first 5 holes are extremely demanding but are followed by the gentler 'birdie alley' where shots can be recovered. The signature hole is the 17th, a par 3 which involves a tricky tee shot from an elevated tee to small well bunkered green with out of bounds on the right.
18 holes, 6264yds, Par 71, SSS 70.
Club membership 500.
Visitors apply in writing in advance, may not play on competition Sat & Sun. **Societies** apply in writing in advance. **Green Fees** £16 per round;£24 per day(£20/£30 weekends). **Facilities** ⊗)Ⅲ ⓛ ♥ ♀ ⚐ **Location** 1m SE off A721

Hotel ⇧ Travel Inn Glasgow Bellshill, Belziehill Farm, BELLSHILL ☎ 01698 740180 40 en suite

COATBRIDGE   Map 11 NS76

Drumpellier Drumpellier Av ML5 1RX
☎ 01236 424139 🖹 01236 428723
18 holes, 6227yds, Par 71, SSS 70, Course record 60.
Course Designer W Fernie **Location** 0.75m W off A89
Telephone for further details

Hotel ★★★ 67% Bothwell Bridge Hotel, 89 Main St, BOTHWELL ☎ 01698 852246 90 en suite

CUMBERNAULD   Map 11 NS77

Dullatur 1A Glen Douglas Dr G68 0DW
☎ 01236 723230 🖹 01236 727271
Dullatur Carrickstone is a parkland course, with natural hazards and wind. Dullatur Antonine, designed by Dave Thomas, is a modern course,
Carrickstone: 18 holes, 6204yds, Par 70, SSS 70,
Course record 68.
Antonine: 18 holes, 5875yds, Par 69, SSS 68.
Club membership 700.
Visitors telephone for availability. **Societies** must apply in writing to secretary. **Green Fees** terms on application. **Cards** ▭ ▬ ▣ **Prof** Duncan Sinclair **Course Designer** James Braid **Facilities** ⊗)Ⅲ ⓛ ♥ ♀ ⚐ ⚒ ⚑ ♂ **Leisure** hard tennis courts, sauna, solarium, gymnasium, bowling green. **Conf** Board 50 **Location** 1.5m N of A80 at Cumbernauld

Hotel ★★★★ 66% Westerwood Hotel Golf & Country Club, 1 St Andrews Dr, Westerwood, CUMBERNAULD ☎ 01236 457171 49 en suite

Palacerigg Palacerigg Country Park G67 3HU
☎ 01236 734969 & 721461 🖹 01236 721461
e-mail: palacerigg-golfclub@lineone.net
Well wooded parkland course set in Palacerigg Country Park with good views to the Campsie Hills.
18 holes, 6444yds, Par 72, SSS 71, Course record 65.
Club membership 350.
Visitors anytime except club competitions, advance booking advisable. **Societies** apply in writing to the Secretary. **Green Fees** £7.50 per round(£8.20 per round weekends). **Course Designer** Henry Cotton **Facilities** ⊗)Ⅲ ⓛ ♥ ♀ ⚐ **Location** 2m S of Cumbernauld on Palacerigg road off Lenziemill road B8054

Hotel ★★★★ 66% Westerwood Hotel Golf & Country Club, 1 St Andrews Dr, Westerwood, CUMBERNAULD ☎ 01236 457171 49 en suite

continued

Westerwood Hotel Golf & Country Club
1 St Andrews Dr, Westerwood G68 0EW
☎ 01236 725281 🖹 01236 860730
e-mail: westerwood@mortonhotels.com
Undulating parkland/woodland course designed by Dave Thomas and Seve Ballesteros. Holes meander through silver birch, firs, heaths and heathers, and the spectacular 15th, 'The Waterfall', has its green set against a 40ft rockface. Buggie track. Hotel facilities.
18 holes, 6616yds, Par 72, SSS 72, Course record 65.
Club membership 1200.
Visitors advised to book 48 hrs in advance. **Societies** all bookings in advance to 01236 725281. **Green Fees** £27.50(£30 weekends)reductions in winter. **Cards** 🖭 🖃 🖭 🖭 **Prof** Alan Tait **Course Designer** Seve Ballesteros/Dave Thomas **Facilities** ⊗ ⫠ 🖫 🖳 ♀ 🖦 🛝 🖡 🎯 🖞 🍴 ⛳ **Leisure** hard tennis courts, heated indoor swimming pool, solarium, gymnasium, Beauty salon. **Location** Adjacent to A80, 14m from Glasgow City Centre

Hotel ★★★★ 66% Westerwood Hotel Golf & Country Club, 1 St Andrews Dr, Westerwood, CUMBERNAULD ☎ 01236 457171 49 en suite

GARTCOSH   Map 11 NS66
Mount Ellen Johnston Rd G69 8EY
☎ 01236 872277 🖹 01236 872249
Downland course with 73 bunkers. Testing hole: 10th ('Bedlay'), 156 yds, par 3.
18 holes, 5525yds, Par 68, SSS 67, Course record 67.
Club membership 500.
Visitors may play Mon-Fri 9am-4pm. Must contact in advance. **Societies** must contact in advance. **Green Fees** not confirmed. **Prof** Iain Bilsborough **Facilities** 🖫 🖳 ♀ 🖦 🖡 🍴 ⛳ **Location** 0.75m N off A752

Hotel ★★★★ 73% Millennium Hotel Glasgow, George Square, GLASGOW ☎ 0141 332 6711 117 en suite

KILSYTH   Map 11 NS77
Kilsyth Lennox Tak Ma Doon Rd G65 0RS
☎ 01236 824115 🖹 01236 823089
18 holes, 5912yds, Par 70, SSS 70, Course record 66.
Location N side of town off A803
Telephone for further details

Hotel ★★★★ 66% Westerwood Hotel Golf & Country Club, 1 St Andrews Dr, Westerwood, CUMBERNAULD ☎ 01236 457171 49 en suite

MOTHERWELL   Map 11 NS75
Colville Park New Jerviston House, Jerviston Estate, Merry St ML1 4UG
☎ 01698 265779 (pro) 🖹 01698 230418
Parkland course. First nine, tree-lined, second nine, more exposed. Testing 10th hole par 3, 16th hole par 4.
18 holes, 6250yds, Par 71, SSS 70, Course record 63.
Club membership 875.
Visitors must contact in advance in writing. Smart dress code. **Societies** apply in writing. **Green Fees** not confirmed. **Prof** John Curriet **Course Designer** James Braid **Facilities** ⊗ ⫠ 🖫 🖳 ♀ 🖦 🖡 **Location** 1.25m NE on A723 from Motherwell town centre

Hotel ★★★ 67% Bothwell Bridge Hotel, 89 Main St, BOTHWELL ☎ 01698 852246 90 en suite

MUIRHEAD   Map 11 NS66
Crow Wood Garnkirk House, Cumbernauld Rd G69 9JF
☎ 0141 779 4954 🖹 0141 779 9148
e-mail: crowwood@golfclub.fsbusiness.co.uk
Parkland course.
18 holes, 6261yds, Par 71, SSS 71, Course record 62.
Club membership 800.
Visitors must contact in advance but may not play weekends, bank holidays or competition days. **Societies** apply in advance in writing. **Green Fees** terms on application. **Cards** 🖭 🖃 **Prof** Brian Moffat **Course Designer** James Braid **Facilities** ⊗ ⫠ 🖫 🖳 ♀ 🖦 🖡 🎯 **Leisure** snooker,pool. **Conf** Banquet 40 **Location** 6 miles from Glasgow city centre, off A80 to Stirling, between villages of Stepps and Muirhead

Hotel ★★★ 75% Malmaison, 278 West George St, GLASGOW ☎ 0141 572 1000 72 en suite

SHOTTS   Map 11 NS86
Shotts Blairhead ML7 5BJ
☎ 01501 822658 🖹 01501 822650
Moorland course with fine panoramic views. A good test for all abilities.
18 holes, 6205yds, Par 70, SSS 70, Course record 63.
Club membership 800.
Visitors visitors by arrangement on Sun. **Societies** apply in writing. **Green Fees** not confirmed. **Prof** John Strachan **Course Designer** James Braid **Facilities** ⊗ ⫠ 🖫 🖳 ♀ 🖦 🖡 🎯 **Location** 2m from M8 off Benhar Road

Hotel ★★★ 65% The Hilcroft Hotel, East Main St, WHITBURN ☎ 01501 740818 31 en suite

WISHAW   Map 11 NS75
Wishaw 55 Cleland Rd ML2 7PH ☎ 01698 372869 (club house) & 357480 (office) 🖹 01698 357480
e-mail: craig.innes@virgin.net
Parkland course with many tree-lined areas. Bunkers protect 17 of the 18 greens.
18 holes, 5999yds, Par 69, SSS 69, Course record 64.
Club membership 984.
Visitors must contact secretary in advance. May not play Sat but may play alternate Sun. **Societies** apply in writing. **Green Fees** £30 per day;£20 per round(£35/£25 Sunday). **Prof** Stuart Adair **Course Designer** James Braid **Facilities** ⊗ ⫠ 🖫 🖳 ♀ 🖦 🖡 🎯 **Location** NW side of town off A721

Hotel ★★★ 70% Popinjay Hotel, Lanark Rd, ROSEBANK ☎ 01555 860441 38 en suite

PERTH & KINROSS

ABERFELDY   Map 14 NN84
Aberfeldy Taybridge Rd PH15 2BH
☎ 01887 820535 🖹 01887 820535
e-mail: abergc@supanet.com.uk
Founded in 1895, this flat, parkland course is situated by River Tay near the famous Wade Bridge and Black Watch Monument and enjoys some splendid scenery. The new layout will test the keen golfer.
18 holes, 5283yds, Par 68, SSS 66, Course record 62.
Club membership 250.
Visitors are advised to book in advance especially at weekends. **Societies** must contact in advance. **Green Fees**
continued

335

£26 per day; £16 per round (£29/£21weekends and bank holidays). **Cards** 🖊 ▆ ▆ ▆ ▆ **Course Designer** Soutars **Facilities** ⊗ 🏬 🛍 💺 ♀ ⏚ 🖕 🛒 ⌖ **Location** N side of town centre

Hotel ★★💺 72% Guinach House Hotel, By The Birks, Urlar Rd, ABERFELDY ☎ 01887 820251 7 en suite

ALYTH   Map 15 NO24

Alyth Pitcrocknie PH11 8HF
☎ 01828 632268 📠 01828 633491
e-mail: mansec@alythgolf.freeserve.co.uk
Windy, heathland course with easy walking.
18 holes, 6205yds, Par 71, SSS 71, Course record 65.
Club membership 1000.
Visitors advance booking advisable, handicap certificate required and dress etiquette must be observed. **Societies** must telephone in advance. **Green Fees** not confirmed. **Prof** Tom Melville **Course Designer** James Braid **Facilities** ⊗ 🏬 🛍 💺 ♀ ⏚ 🖕 🍴 🛒 ⌖ **Location** 1m E on B954

Hotel ★★★ 62% Angus Hotel, 46 Wellmeadow, BLAIRGOWRIE ☎ 01250 872455 81 en suite

Strathmore Golf Centre Leroch PH11 8NZ
☎ 01828 633322 📠 01828 633533
e-mail: enquiries@strathmoregolf.com
The Rannaleroch course is set on rolling parkland and heath with splendid views over Strathmore. The course is laid out in two loops of nine which both start and finish at the clubhouse. Among the challenging holes is the 480yard 5th with a 180yard carry over water from a high tee position. The nine hole Leitfie Links has been specially designed with beginners, juniors and older golfers in mind.

Rannaleroch Course: 18 holes, 6454yds, Par 72, SSS 72, Course record 68.
Leitfie Links: 9 holes, 1719yds, Par 29, SSS 29.
Club membership 400.
Visitors no restrictions, advised to book in advance. **Societies** phone enquiry recommended. **Green Fees** Rannaleroch: £20 per round (£26 weekends) Leltfie links;£8 per day(£10 weekends). **Cards** 🖊 ▆ ▆ ▆ **Prof** Colin Smith **Course Designer** John Salvesen **Facilities** ⊗ 🏬 🛍 💺 ♀ ⏚ 🖕 🛒 ⌖ **Location** 2m SE of Alyth, off B954 at Meigle onto A926

Hotel ★★ 70% Altamount House Hotel, Coupar Angus Rd, BLAIRGOWRIE ☎ 01250 873512 7 en suite

AUCHTERARDER See page 337

AUCHTERARDER   Map 11 NN91

Auchterarder Orchil Rd PH3 1LS ☎ 01764 662804 (Secretary) 663711(pro) 📠 01764 662804(sec),663711(pro)
Flat parkland course, part woodland with pine, larch and silver birch. It may be short but tricky with cunning doglegs and guarded greens that require accuracy rather than sheer power. The 14th 'Punchbowl' hole is perhaps the trickiest. A blind tee shot needs to be hit accurately over the left edge of the cross bunker to a long and narrow green - miss and you face a difficult downhill chip shot from deep rough.
18 holes, 5775yds, Par 69, SSS 68, Course record 61.
Club membership 765.
Visitors must contact professional/secretary in advance. **Societies** must contact in advance. **Green Fees** terms on application. **Prof** Gavin Baxter **Course Designer** Ben Sayers **Facilities** ⊗ 🏬 🛍 💺 ♀ ⏚ 🖕 ⌖ **Location** 0.75m SW on A824

Hotel ★★★★★ The Gleneagles Hotel, AUCHTERARDER ☎ 01764 662231 216 en suite

BLAIR ATHOLL   Map 14 NN86

Blair Atholl Invertilt Rd PH18 5TG
☎ 01796 481407 📠 01796 481292
Parkland course, river runs alongside 3 holes, easy walking.
9 holes, 5816yds, Par 70, SSS 68, Course record 65.
Club membership 460.
Visitors apply in advance to avoid competition times. **Societies** apply in writing. **Green Fees** £15 per day(£17 weekends). **Course Designer** Morriss **Facilities** 🛍 💺 ♀ ⏚ 🖕 ⌖ **Location** 0.5m S off B8079

Hotel ★★ 70% Atholl Arms Hotel, Old North Rd, BLAIR ATHOLL ☎ 01796 481205 30 en suite

BLAIRGOWRIE   Map 15 NO14

Blairgowrie Rosemount PH10 6LG
☎ 01250 872622 📠 01250 875451
e-mail: admin@blairgowrie-golf.co.uk
Two 18-hole heathland courses, also a 9-hole course.
Rosemount Course: 18 holes, 6229yds, Par 72, SSS 73, Course record 64.
Lansdowne Course: 18 holes, 6802yds, Par 72, SSS 73, Course record 67.
Wee Course: 9 holes, 4704yds, Par 64, SSS 63.
Club membership 1550.
Visitors must contact in advance & have handicap certificate, restricted Wed, Fri & weekends. **Societies** must contact in advance. **Green Fees** terms on application. **Cards** 🖊 ▆ ▆ ▆ **Prof** Charles Dernie **Course Designer** J Braid/P Allis/D Thomas/Old Tom
continued

The Gleneagles Hotel

Auchterarder, *Perth & Kinross* ☎ 01764 662231 Fax 01764 662134 Map 11 NN91

e-mail: resort.sales@gleneagles.com

The PGA Centenary Course, designed by Jack Nicklaus and launched in style in May 1993, boasts an American/Scottish layout with many water hazards, elevated tees and raised contoured greens. It is the selected venue for the Ryder Cup 2014. It boasts a five-tier tee structure, making it both the longest and shortest playable course at the resort, as well as the most accommodating to all standards of golfer. The King's Course with its abundance of heather, gorse, raised greens and plateau tees, is set within the valley of Strathearn with the Grampian mountains spectacularly in view to the north. The shorter Queen's course, with its Scots Pine lined fairways and water hazards, is set within a softer landscape and considered an easier test of golf. You can improve your game at The Golf Academy at Gleneagles, where the philosophy is that golf should be fun and fun in golf comes from playing better.

Visitors advance booking essential, 8 weeks notice; full payment in advance to secure tee times.

Societies contact for details.

Green Fees Visitors £50-£110, reductions for residents.

Facilities Professional (Sandy Smith). Golf Academy

Leisure tennis, squash, swimming, sauna, solarium, gymnasium, riding, shooting, fishing, falconry, off-road driving Conf Max 360 Thtr 360 Class 240 Board 60 Banquet 240 Del c.£72 *

Location Auchterarder PH3 1NF (2m SW of A823)

Holes/Par/Course record 54 holes.
Kings: 18 holes, 6471 yds, Par 70, SSS 73; course record 60
Queens: 18 holes, 5965 yds, Par 68, SSS 70; course record 62
PGA Centenary: 18 holes, 6551 yds, Par 72, SSS 73; course record 63

Championship Course

WHERE TO STAY NEARBY

Hotels
AUCHTERARDER
★★★★★ The Gleneagles Hotel
☎ 01764 662231. 216 en suite

★★★ 77%
Auchterarder House
☎ 01764 663646. 15 en suite

★★ 77%
Cairn Lodge, Orchil Rd
☎ 01764 662634. 11 en suite

Restaurants
PERTH
Lets Eat 77/79 Kinnoall St
☎ 01738 643377

Seafood Restaurant 168 South St
☎ 01738 449777

Morris **Facilities** **Location** Off A93 Rosemount

Hotel ★★★ Kinloch House Hotel, BLAIRGOWRIE
☎ 01250 884237 20 en suite

KINLOCH HOUSE HOTEL

AA ★★★

By Blairgowrie, Perthshire, PH10 6SG
Telephone: Blairgowrie (01250) 884 237
Fax: (01250) 884 333
E-mail: info@kinlochhouse.com

Kinloch House is an award winning, family run, Country house hotel in the heart of Sporting Perthshire. Located approximately 1½ hours from Glasgow, Edinburgh, Inverness and Aberdeen, the hotel has 30 golf courses within an hour's drive, including many Championship ones. Full drying facilities for clothes and equipment are available, we would be delighted to help plan your golf and book your tee times.

Please write, e-mail or telephone for a brochure

David and Sarah Shentall

COMRIE Map 11 NN72

Comrie Laggan Braes PH6 2LR ☎ 01764 670055
Scenic highland course with two tricky par 3 holes.
9 holes, 6040yds, Par 70, SSS 70, Course record 62.
Club membership 350.
Visitors apply in advance (for party bookings) **Societies** must contact in advance. **Green Fees** £20 per day; £16 per 18 holes; £10 per 9 holes(£25/£20/£12 weekends and bank holidays).
Course Designer Col. Williamson **Facilities**
Leisure fishing. **Location** E side of village off A85

Guesthouse ♦♦♦♦ Mossgiel Guest House, Burrell St, COMRIE ☎ 01764 670567 3 en suite

CRIEFF Map 11 NN82

Crieff Ferntower, Perth Rd PH7 3LR
☎ 01764 652909 01764 655096
e-mail: bookings@crieffgolf.co.uk
Set in the dramatic countryside of Perthshire, Crieff Golf Club was established in 1891. The Ferntower championship course has magnificent views over the Strathearn Valley and offers all golfers an enjoyable round. The short 9 hole Dornoch course, which incorporates some of the James Braid designed holes from the orginal 18 holes, provides an interesting challenge for juniors, beginners and others short of time.

Ferntower Course: 18 holes, 6427yds, Par 71, SSS 72, Course record 65.
Dornock Course: 9 holes, 2372yds, Par 32.
Club membership 720.
Visitors must contact professional in advance. **Societies** must contact professional in advance. **Green Fees** terms

continued

on application. **Cards** **Prof** David Murchie
Course Designer James Braid **Facilities** **Location** 0.5m NE on A85

Hotel ★★ 65% Locke's Acre Hotel, 7 Comrie Rd, CRIEFF ☎ 01764 652526 7 rms (4 en suite)

DUNKELD Map 11 NO04

Dunkeld & Birnam Fungarth PH8 0HU
☎ 01350 727524 01350 728660
Interesting and challenging course with spectacular views of the surrounding countryside. The original 9 hole heathland course is now augmented by an additional 9 holes of parkland character close to the Loch of the Lowes.
18 holes, 5508yds, Par 70, SSS 67.
Club membership 540.
Visitors must contact in advance at weekends,public holidays,or large parties during the week. **Societies** apply in writing/telephone. **Green Fees** £28 per day; £20 per round(£28/£25 weekends and bank holidays). **Cards** **Course Designer** D A Tod **Facilities** **Location** 1m N of village on A923

Hotel ★★★ Kinnaird, Kinnaird Estate, DUNKELD
☎ 01796 482440 9 en suite

DUNNING Map 11 NO01

Dunning Rollo Park PH2 0RH ☎ 01764 684747
Parkland course with a series of stone built bridges crossing a burn meandering over a large part of the course.

continued

9 holes, 4836yds, Par 66, SSS 63, Course record 62.
Club membership 580.
Visitors Gents competitions Saturday, Ladies Tue, otherwise no restrictions. **Societies** must contact in advance in writing. **Green Fees** £14 per round/day. **Facilities** 🏌 ⛳ 🏁
Location 1.5m off A9, 4m N of Auchterarder

••

Hotel ★★★ 68% Lovat Hotel, 90 Glasgow Rd, PERTH
☎ 01738 636555 30 en suite

Whitemoss Whitemoss Rd PH2 0QX
☎ 01738 730300 📄 01738 730300
18 holes, 5595yds, Par 68, SSS 68, Course record 63.

Course Designer Whitemoss Leisure **Location** Turn off A9 at Whitemoss Road junct, 3m N of Gleneagles **Telephone for further details**

•••••••••••••••••••••••••••••

Hotel ★★ 77% Cairn Lodge, Orchil Rd, AUCHTERARDER ☎ 01764 662634 & 662431 📄 01764 664866 11 en suite

Dalmunzie Dalmunzie Estate PH10 7QG
☎ 01250 885226 📄 01250 885225
e-mail: dalmunzie@aol.com
Well maintained Highland course with difficult walking. Testing short course with small but good greens.
9 holes, 2099yds, Par 30, SSS 30.
Club membership 78.
Visitors restricted Sun 10.30-11.30am. **Societies** advance contact preferred. **Green Fees** £11 per day. **Course Designer** Alistair Campbell **Facilities** ⊗ 🍴 🏌 🏁 ⛳ 🏁 **Leisure** hard tennis courts, fishing. **Conf** Max 20 Thtr 20 Class 20 Board 20 Del £3 to £30 * **Location** 2m NW of Spittal of Glenshee

•••••••••••••••••••••••••••••

Hotel ★★▲ 70% Dalmunzie House Hotel, SPITTAL OF GLENSHEE ☎ 01250 885224 18 rms (16 en suite)

Kenmore PH15 2HN
☎ 01887 830226 📄 01887 830211
e-mail: golf@taymouth.co.uk
Testing course in mildly undulating natural terrain. Beautiful views in tranquil setting by Loch Tay. The par 5 4th is 560 yards and only one of the par 4s, the 2nd, is under 400 yards - teeing up hitting out of a mound of trees down a snaking fairway which banks, encouraging the ball to keep on the fairway. The slightly elevated green is surrounded by banks to help hold the ball on the green. The fairways are generous and the rough short which tends to encourage an unhindered round.
9 holes, 6052yds, Par 70, SSS 69, Course record 69.
Club membership 200.

continued

Visitors advance booking advisable. **Societies** telephone in advance. **Green Fees** £13 per 18 holes; £9 per 9 holes (£14/£10 weekends). **Cards** 💳 💳 **Course Designer** Robin Menzies **Facilities** ⊗ 🍴 🏌 🏌 ⛳ 🏁 ⛳ 🏁 ⛳ 🏁 ♂
Leisure fishing. **Location** On A827, beside Kenmore Bridge

Hotel ★★★ 66% Kenmore Hotel, The Square, KENMORE
☎ 01887 830205 27 en suite 15 annexe en suite

Taymouth Castle Taymouth Castle Estate PH15 2NT
☎ 01887 830228 📄 01887 830830
e-mail: taymouth@fishingnet.com
Parkland course set amidst beautiful mountain and loch scenery. Easy walking. Fishing.
18 holes, 6066yds, Par 69, SSS 69, Course record 62.
Club membership 250.
Visitors parties must book in advance to avoid busy times. **Societies** should contact in advance. **Green Fees** not confirmed. **Prof** Alex Marshall **Course Designer** James Braid **Facilities** ⊗ 🍴 🏌 🏌 ⛳ 🏁 ⛳ 🏁 ⛳ 🏁 ♂
Leisure hard tennis courts, fishing. **Location** 1m E on A827, 5m W of Aberfeldy

••••••••••••••••••••••••••••••

Hotel ★★★ 66% Kenmore Hotel, The Square, KENMORE
☎ 01887 830205 27 en suite 15 annexe en suite

Green Hotel 2 The Muirs KY13 8AS
☎ 01577 863407 📄 01577 863180
e-mail: golf@green-hotel.com
Two interesting and picturesque parkland courses, with easy walking. Many of the fairways are bounded by trees and plantations. A number of holes, particularly on the Blue Course, have views over Loch Leven to the hills

continued

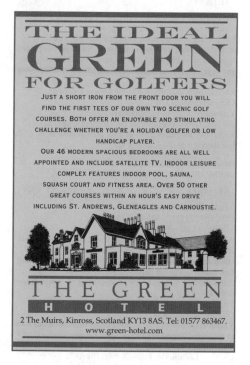

beyond. The 4th is a really challenging par 3. Some holes have burns or ditches to catch the unwary while those playing the 6th on the Red Course have to negotiate a difficult pond, and the Blue's 11th fairway has a pond on the left.
Red Course: 18 holes, 6256yds, Par 73, SSS 71.
Blue Course: 18 holes, 6438yds, Par 71, SSS 72.
Club membership 600.
Visitors Large parties should contact in advance. **Societies** must contact in advance. **Green Fees** £27 per day, £17 per round (£37/27 weekends). **Cards** ▭ ▭ ▭ ▭ **Prof** Stuart Geraghty **Course Designer** Sir David Montgomery **Facilities** ⊗ ⋙ ⌶ ▪ ♀ ⚲ 🕿 🏴 ⛟ ▷ ⚷ **Leisure** hard tennis courts, heated indoor swimming pool, squash, fishing, sauna, 4 sheet curling rink. **Conf** Max 120 Thtr 120 Class 75 Board 60 Banquet 100 Del £24 to £29.50 * **Location** NE side of town on B996

Hotel ★★★ 73% Green Hotel, 2 The Muirs, KINROSS ☎ 01577 863467 46 en suite

Milnathort South St KY13 9XA ☎ 01577 864069
e-mail: milnathortgolf@ukgateway.net
Undulating inland course with lush fairways and excellent greens for most of the year. Strategically placed copses of trees require accurate tee shots. Different tees and greens for some holes will make for more interesting play.
9 holes, 5969yds, Par 71, SSS 69, Course record 65.
Club membership 575.
Visitors no restrictions. **Societies** advisable to book in advance. **Green Fees** £19 per day; £13 per round (£21/£15 weekends). **Facilities** ⊗ ⋙ by prior arrangement ⌶ ▪ ♀ ⚲ **Location** S side of town on A922

Hotel ★★ 67% The Glenfarg Hotel & Restaurant, Main St, GLENFARG ☎ 01577 830241 17 rms (16 en suite)

Muthill Peat Rd PH5 2DA
☎ 01764 681523 🗎 01764 681557
e-mail: muthillgolfclub@lineone.net
A 9 hole course which, although short, requires accurate shot making to match the SSS. The three par 3s are all challenging holes with the 9th, a 205 yard shot to a small well bunkered green making a fitting end to 9 holes characterised by great views and springy well maintained fairways.
9 holes, 4700yds, Par 66, SSS 63, Course record 61.
Club membership 420.
Visitors no restrictions telephone in advance. **Societies** book in advance. **Green Fees** £15 per day; £10 per 9 holes (£18 weekends). **Course Designer** Members **Facilities** ⊗ ⌶ ▪ ⚲ 🏴 ⚷ **Location** W side of village off A822   *continued*

Hotel ★★ 65% Locke's Acre Hotel, 7 Comrie Rd, CRIEFF ☎ 01764 652526 7 rms (4 en suite)

Craigie Hill Cherrybank PH2 0NE
☎ 01738 620829 & 622644 🗎 01738 620829
e-mail: chgc@fairieswell.freeserve.co.uk
Slightly hilly, heathland course. Panoramic views over Perth and surrounding hills.
18 holes, 5386yds, Par 66, SSS 67, Course record 60.
Club membership 600.
Visitors no access Sat. Telephone up to 3 days in advance. **Societies** must contact in writing. **Green Fees** £30 per day; £18 per round (£30/£25 Sun). **Prof** Ian Muir **Course Designer** Fernie/Anderson **Facilities** ⊗ ⋙ ⌶ ▪ ♀ ⚲ 🕿 🏴 ⚷ **Conf** Board 15 **Location** 1m SW of city centre off A952

Hotel ★★★ 65% Queens Hotel, Leonard St, PERTH ☎ 01738 442222 50 en suite

King James VI Moncreiffe Island PH2 8NR
☎ 01738 445132 (Secretary) 🗎 01738 445132
e-mail: info@kjvigc.fsnet.co.uk
Parkland course, situated on island in the middle of River Tay. Easy walking.
18 holes, 6038yds, Par 70, SSS 69, Course record 62.
Club membership 650.
Visitors visitors restricted on competition days. Must contact professional in advance for bookings. May not play Sat. **Societies** book by telephone. **Green Fees** £18 per round;£25 per day(£30 per day;£20 after 10am). **Prof** Andrew Crerar **Course Designer** Tom Morris **Facilities** ⊗ ⌶ ▪ ♀ ⚲ 🕿 🏴 🛺 ⚷ **Location** SE side of city centre

Hotel ★★★ 65% Queens Hotel, Leonard St, PERTH ☎ 01738 442222 50 en suite

> If the name of the club appears in *italics*, details have not been confirmed for this edition of the guide

Murrayshall Country House Hotel Murrayshall, Scone PH2 7PH ☎ 01738 552784 & 551171
🗎 01738 552595
e-mail: info@murrayshall.com
Set within 350 acres of undulating parkland, Murrayshall now offers 36 holes of outstanding golf. The original championship course is set out within the parkland estate and the Lyndoch is a woodland-style course, full of natural features. Many of the fairways are lined by majestic trees while white sand bunkers, and water hazards with natural stone bridges, protect the generous greens.
Murrayshall Course: 18 holes, 6441yds, Par 73, SSS 72.
Lyndoch Course: 18 holes, 5800yds, Par 69.
Club membership 350.
Visitors telephone in advance. **Societies** telephone in advance. **Green Fees** terms on application. **Cards** ▭ ▭ ▭ ▭ ▭ **Prof** Alan Reid **Course Designer** Hamilton Stutt **Facilities** ⊗ ⋙ ⌶ ▪ ♀ ⚲ 🕿 🏴 🏴 🛺 ⚷ (**Leisure** hard tennis courts, sauna, gymnasium.**Conf** Max 180 Thtr 180 Class 80 Board 40 Banquet 130 Del from £22 * **Location** E side of village off A94

continued

MURRAYSHALL HOUSE HOTEL AND GOLF COURSE
SCONE, BY PERTH

Set within 300 acres of parkland surrounded by 2 18 hole golf courses, this 4 star, STB highly commended country house hotel has 41 bedrooms. Leisure facilities include sauna, gymnasium, jacuzzi, tennis courts, driving range and indoor golf school.
Special golf packages available
Society welcome groups
Our clubhouse facilities are available to non members
Pro Shop 01738 552784

Hotel ★★★ 76% Murrayshall Country House Hotel & Golf Course, New Scone, PERTH ☎ 01738 551171 27 en suite 14 annexe en suite

North Inch North Inch, off Hay St PH1 5PH ☎ 01738 636481
An enjoyable short and often testing course incorporating mature trees, open parkland with fine views and attractive riverside. This ancient course has recently been transformed by a new layout. This has resulted in one or two more challenging holes. Situated beside the Tay, this course offers both links and parkland characteristics.
18 holes, 5401yds, Par 65.
Club membership 476.
Visitors advisable to telephone in advance. Due to a flood prevention wall to be built late 97/98 there may be disruption. Societies apply in writing. Green Fees not confirmed. Course Designer Tom Morris Facilities ⊗ ⊪ ⅃ 🍺 ♀ ⚲ ⚷ Leisure squash, gymnasium. Location N of City
continued

Hotel ★★★ 65% Queens Hotel, Leonard St, PERTH ☎ 01738 442222 50 en suite

PITLOCHRY Map 14 NN95

Pitlochry PH16 5QY
☎ 01796 472792 📄 01796 473599
A varied and interesting heathland course with fine views and posing many problems. Its SSS permits few errors in its achievement.
18 holes, 5811yds, Par 69, SSS 69, Course record 63.
Club membership 500.
Visitors Must book times in advance. Societies must contact in advance. Green Fees £29 per day, £20 per round (£35/£23 weekends). Cards ▭ ▨ 🔀 💳 Prof George Hampton Course Designer Willy Fernie Facilities ⊗ ⅃ 🍺 ♀ ⚲ 🏠 ⚷ ↘ ⚷ Location N side of town off A924

Hotel ★★★▟▟ 76% Pine Trees Hotel, Strathview Ter, PITLOCHRY ☎ 01796 472121 19 en suite

ST FILLANS Map 11 NN62

St Fillans South Loch Earn Rd PH6 2NJ
☎ 01764 685312 📄 01764 685312
Fairly flat, beautiful parkland course. Beside the river Earn and set amongst the Perthshire hills. Wonderfully rich in flora, animal and bird life. Easy to play but hard to score.
9 holes, 6054yds, Par 69, SSS 69, Course record 73.
Club membership 400.
Visitors advisable to contact in advance. Societies Apr-Oct, apply to starter. Green Fees terms on application. Course Designer W Auchterlonie Facilities ⊗ ⊪ ⅃ 🍺 ♀ ⚲ ⚷ ↘ ⚷ Location E side of village off A85

Hotel ★★★ 68% The Four Seasons Hotel, Loch Earn, ST FILLANS ☎ 01764 685333 12 en suite 6 annexe en suite

STRATHTAY Map 14 NN95

Strathtay Lyon Cottage PH9 0PG ☎ 01887 840211
A wooded mainly hilly course with pleasing panoramic views. 5th hole 'Spion Kop' is especially difficult. It is steep, with heavy rough on both sides of the hilly fairway and an unsighted green on the back of the hill which is affected by winds.
9 holes, 4082yds, Par 63, SSS 63, Course record 61.
Club membership 260.
Visitors may be restrictions May-Sep. Societies in writing/telephone Secretary. Green Fees £12 per day(£15 weekends and bank holidays). Facilities ⚲ Location Eastern end of minor rd to Weem, off A827

Hotel ★★▟▟ 72% Guinach House Hotel, By The Birks, Urlar Rd, ABERFELDY ☎ 01887 820251 7 en suite

RENFREWSHIRE

BISHOPTON Map 10 NS47

Erskine PA7 5PH ☎ 01505 862302
Parkland course.
18 holes, 6287yds, Par 71, SSS 70.
Club membership 700.
Visitors introduced by member or by prior arrangement. Societies apply in writing. Green Fees not confirmed. Prof Peter Thomson Facilities ⊗ ⊪ ⅃ 🍺 ♀ ⚲ 🏠 ⚲ ⚷ Location 0.75 NE off B815
continued

Hotel ★★★ 68% The Erskine Bridge Hotel, North Barr, ERSKINE ☎ 0141 812 0123 177 en suite

BRIDGE OF WEIR   Map 10 NS36

Ranfurly Castle The Clubhouse, Golf Rd PA11 3HN
☎ 01505 612609 ⏷ 01505 610406
e-mail: ranfurlycastle@lineone.net
A highly challenging, 240 acre, picturesque moorland course.
18 holes, 6284yds, Par 70, SSS 71, Course record 65.
Club membership 825.
Visitors golf club members on weekends only. **Societies** weekdays only, apply in writing. **Green Fees** £25 per round;£35 per day. **Cards** ▭ ▬ ▭ ▤ ▨ **Prof** Tom Eckford **Course Designer** A Kirkcaldy/W Auchterlomie **Facilities** ⊗ ⅷ ⮞ ⬛ ♀ ♨ 🖾 🏱 ♣ ℰ **Location** 5m NW of Johnstone

Hotel ★★★ 68% Bowfield Hotel & Country Club, HOWWOOD ☎ 01505 705225 23 en suite

JOHNSTONE   Map 10 NS46

Cochrane Castle Scott Av, Craigston PA5 0HF
☎ 01505 320146 ⏷ 01505 325338
Fairly hilly parkland course,wooded with two small streams running through it.
18 holes, 6194yds, Par 71, SSS 71, Course record 63.
Club membership 721.
Visitors contact professional for booking, may play at weekends if introduced by a member. **Societies** apply in writing. **Green Fees** £30 per day; £22per round. **Prof** Alan J Logan **Course Designer** J Hunter **Facilities** ⊗ ⅷ ⮞ ⬛ ♀ ♨ 🖾 ℰ **Location** 1m from Johnstone town centre, off Beith Rd

Hotel ★★★ 69% Lynnhurst Hotel, Park Rd, JOHNSTONE ☎ 01505 324331 & 324600 ⏷ 01505 324219 21 en suite

Elderslie 63 Main Rd, Elderslie PA5 9AZ
☎ 01505 323956 ⏷ 01505 340346
e-mail: anneanderson@eldersliegolfclub.freeserve.co.uk
Parkland course, undulating, with good views.
18 holes, 6175yds, Par 70, SSS 70, Course record 61.
Club membership 940.
Visitors may not play at weekends & bank holidays. Must contact club in advance and preferably have a handicap certificate. **Societies** must telephone in advance. **Green Fees** £40 per day incl meal;£24 per round;£32 per day. **Prof** Richard Bowman **Course Designer** J Braid **Facilities** ⊗ ⅷ ⮞ ⬛ ♀ ♨ 🖾 ℰ **Location** E side of town on A737

Hotel ★★★ 69% Lynnhurst Hotel, Park Rd, JOHNSTONE ☎ 01505 324331 & 324600 ⏷ 01505 324219 21 en suite

LANGBANK   Map 10 NS37

Gleddoch Golf and Country Club PA14 6YE
☎ 01475 540304 ⏷ 01475 540201
Parkland and heathland course with other sporting facilities available to temporary members. Good views over Firth of Clyde.
18 holes, 6330yds, Par 71, SSS 71, Course record 64.
Club membership 600.
Visitors must contact in advance. **Societies** must contact in advance. **Green Fees** terms on application. **Cards** ▭ ▬ ▤ ▨ **Prof** Keith Campbell **Course Designer** Hamilton Strutt **Facilities** ⊗ ⅷ ⮞ ⬛ ♀ ♨ 🖾 🏱 🖾 ♣ ℰ
continued

Leisure heated indoor swimming pool. **Conf** Max 110 Thtr 150 Class 70 Board 52 Banquet 110 Del £23 to £140 * **Location** B789-Old Greenock Road

Hotel ★★★★⚑ 67% Gleddoch House Hotel, LANGBANK ☎ 01475 540711 39 en suite

LOCHWINNOCH   Map 10 NS35

Lochwinnoch Burnfoot Rd PA12 4AN
☎ 01505 842153 & 01505 843029 ⏷ 01505 843668
18 holes, 6243yds, Par 71, SSS 71, Course record 63.
Location W side of town off A760, between Johnstone & Beith, off A737 on Largs road A760
Telephone for further details

Hotel ★★★ 68% Bowfield Hotel & Country Club, HOWWOOD ☎ 01505 705225 23 en suite

PAISLEY   Map 11 NS46

Barshaw Barshaw Park PA1 3TJ ☎ 0141 889 2908
Municipal parkland course.
18 holes, 5703yds, Par 68, SSS 67, Course record 63.
Club membership 100.
Visitors no restrictions. **Societies** by prior arrangement with Parks Manager, Renfrewshire Council, Enviorment House, Bridge Street, Paisley PA3 2AB. **Green Fees** not confirmed. **Course Designer** J R Stutt **Facilities** ♨ ℰ **Location** 1m E off A737

Hotel ★★★ 70% Glynhill Hotel & Leisure Club, Paisley Rd, RENFREW ☎ 0141 886 5555 & 885 1111 ⏷ 0141 885 2838 125 en suite

Paisley Braehead PA2 8TZ
☎ 0141 884 3903 884 4114 ⏷ 0141 884 3903
e-mail: paisleygc@onetel.net.uk
Moorland course with good views which suits all handicaps. The course has been designed in two loops of nine holes. Holes feature trees and gorse.
18 holes, 6215yds, Par 71, SSS 72.
Club membership 850.
Visitors must have handicap certificate. May not play weekends or public holidays, or after 4pm weekdays. **Societies** handicaps certificate essential. Groups over 12 must apply in writing, smaller groups may phone in advance. **Green Fees** not confirmed. **Prof** Gordon Stewart **Facilities** ⊗ ⅷ ⮞ ⬛ ♀ ♨ 🖾 ➴ ℰ **Location** S side of town off B774

Hotel ★★★ 70% Glynhill Hotel & Leisure Club, Paisley Rd, RENFREW ☎ 0141 886 5555 & 885 1111 ⏷ 0141 885 2838 125 en suite

Ralston Strathmore Av, Ralston PA1 3DT
☎ 0141 882 1349 ⏷ 0141 883 9837
Parkland course.
18 holes, 6071yds, Par 71, SSS 69, Course record 62.
Club membership 750.
Visitors Mon-Fri only and must be accompanied by member, contact in advance. **Societies** written notice required **Green Fees** £28 per day; £18 per round. **Cards** ▭ ▬ ▤ **Prof** Colin Munro **Course Designer** J Braid **Facilities** ⊗ ⅷ ⮞ ⬛ ♀ ♨ 🖾 ℰ **Location** 2m E off A737

Hotel ★★★ 68% Swallow Hotel, 517 Paisley Rd West, GLASGOW ☎ 0141 427 3146 117 en suite

Where to stay, where to eat?
Visit www.theAA.com

RENFREW   Map 11 NS46

Renfrew Blythswood Estate, Inchinnan Rd PA4 9EG
☎ 0141 886 6692 📄 0141 886 1808
e-mail: secretary@renfrew.scottishgolf.com
Tree-lined parkland course.
18 holes, 6818yds, Par 72, SSS 73, Course record 65.
Club membership 800.
Visitors restricted to Mon, Tue & Thu, apply in advance.
Societies apply in writing in advance. **Green Fees** terms on application. **Course Designer** Commander Harris **Facilities** ⊗ ⫪ ⬟ ♥ ⚲ ⚬ 🏠 ✐ **Location** 0.75m W off A8

Hotel ★★★ 70% Glynhill Hotel & Leisure Club, Paisley Rd, RENFREW ☎ 0141 886 5555 & 885 1111
📄 0141 885 2838 125 en suite

SCOTTISH BORDERS

COLDSTREAM   Map 12 NT83

Hirsel Kelso Rd TD12 4NJ
☎ 01890 882678 & 882233 📄 01890 882233
18 holes, 6092yds, Par 70, SSS 70, Course record 65.
Location At W end of Coldstream on A697
Telephone for further details

Hotel ★★★ 71% Ednam House Hotel, Bridge St, KELSO
☎ 01573 224168 30 en suite

DUNS   Map 12 NT75

Duns Hardens Rd TD11 3NR ☎ 01361 882194
Interesting upland course, with natural hazards of water and hilly slopes. Views south to the Cheviot Hills. A burn comes into play at 7 of the holes.
18 holes, 6209yds, Par 70, SSS 70.
Club membership 520.
Visitors welcome except competition days and Mon, Tue and Wed after 4pm. Advisable to contact in advance Apr-Oct. **Societies** write or telephone the secretary in advance for booking details. **Green Fees** £21 per day; £18 per round (£26/£21 weekends). **Course Designer** A H Scott **Facilities** ⊗ ⫪ ⬟ ♥ ⚲ ✐ **Location** 1m W off A6105

Hotel ★★★ 69% Marshall Meadows Country House Hotel,
BERWICK-UPON-TWEED ☎ 01289 331133 19 en suite

EYEMOUTH   Map 12 NT96

Eyemouth Gunsgreen Hill TD14 5SF
☎ 01890 750551 & 750004 (Starter)
e-mail: eyemouth@globalnet.co.uk
A superb course set on the East Berwickshire coast, containing interesting and challenging holes, in particular the intimidating 6th hole, a formidable par 3 across a vast gully with the waves crashing below and leaving little room for error. The clubhouse overlooks the picturesque fishing village of Eyemouth and provides panoramic views over the course and North Sea.
18 holes, 6520yds, Par 72, SSS 72, Course record 66.
Club membership 400.
Visitors May play at any time by arrangement.Some competition restrictions on saturday & sunday mornings.Telephone pro shop. **Societies** apply in writing or telephone. **Green Fees** not confirmed. **Cards** ▦ ▬ ▬ 🗐
Prof Paul Terras, Tony McLeman **Course Designer** J R Bain **Facilities** ⊗ ⬟ ♥ ⚲ 🏠 ⛳ ✐ **Location** E side of town, 8m N of Berwick and 2m off A1

continued

Hotel ★★★ 69% Marshall Meadows Country House Hotel,
BERWICK-UPON-TWEED ☎ 01289 331133 19 en suite

GALASHIELS   Map 12 NT43

Galashiels Ladhope Recreation Ground TD1 2NJ
☎ 01896 753724
Hillside course, superb views from the top; 10th hole very steep.
18 holes, 5185yds, Par 67, SSS 66, Course record 61.
Club membership 311.
Visitors must contact the secretary in advance especially for weekends. **Societies** arrangements with secretary especially for weekends. **Green Fees** terms on application. **Course Designer** James Braid **Facilities** ⊗ by prior arrangement ⫪ by prior arrangement ⬟ by prior arrangement ⚲ by prior arrangement ⚬ ✐ **Location** N side of town centre off A7

Hotel ★★★ 66% Kingsknowes Hotel, Selkirk Rd,
GALASHIELS ☎ 01896 758375 11 en suite

Torwoodlee Edinburgh Rd TD1 2NE
☎ 01896 752260 📄 01896 752260
Parkland course with natural hazards designed by Willie Park with a new extension by John Garner, provides a good test for all abilities of play.
18 holes, 6021yds, Par 69, SSS 70, Course record 68.
Club membership 550.
Visitors restricted Thu - ladies day and Sat - mens competitions. **Societies** letter to secretary. **Green Fees** £35 per day; £25 per round (£40/£30 weekends). **Cards** ▦ ▬
🗐 **Prof** R Elliot **Course Designer** Willie Park **Facilities** ⊗ ⫪ ⬟ ♥ ⚲ ⚬ 🖣 🛒 ✐ **Location** 1.75m NW off A7

Hotel ★★★ 66% Kingsknowes Hotel, Selkirk Rd,
GALASHIELS ☎ 01896 758375 11 en suite

HAWICK   Map 12 NT51

Hawick Vertish Hill TD9 0NY ☎ 01450 372293
e-mail: thesecretary@hawickgolfclub.fsnet.co.uk
Hill course with good views.
18 holes, 5929yds, Par 68, SSS 69, Course record 63.
Club membership 600.
Visitors must contact in advance. 1st tee off time for visitors on Sun 10.30pm. **Societies** write or telephone for booking arrangement. **Green Fees** £26 per day; £21 per round.
Facilities ⊗ ⫪ ⬟ ♥ ⚲ ⚬ 🖣 ✐ **Location** SW side of town

INNERLEITHEN   Map 11 NT33

Innerleithen Leithen Water, Leithen Rd EH44 6NL
☎ 01896 830951
Moorland course, with easy walking. Burns and rivers are natural hazards. Testing 5th hole (100 yds) par 3.
9 holes, 6066yds, Par 70, SSS 69, Course record 65.
Club membership 280.
Visitors advisable to check for availability for weekends.
Societies by prior booking. **Green Fees** terms on application.
Course Designer Willie Park **Facilities** ⬟ ♥ ⚲
Location 1.5m N on B709

Hotel ★★★ 73% Peebles Hydro Hotel, PEEBLES
☎ 01721 720602 133 en suite

Looking for a driving range?
See the index at the back of the guide

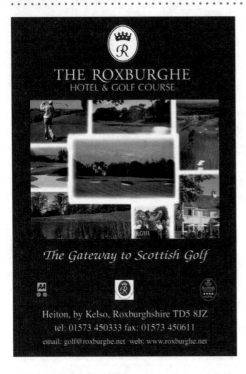

THE ROXBURGHE
HOTEL & GOLF COURSE

The Gateway to Scottish Golf

Heiton, by Kelso, Roxburghshire TD5 8JZ
tel: 01573 450333 fax: 01573 450611
email: golf@roxburghe.net web: www.roxburghe.net

Teviot, provide a good test for all golfing abilities.
18 holes, 6925yds, Par 72, SSS 74, Course record 66.
Club membership 310.

The Roxburghe Golf Course

Visitors dress code (smart casual, no jeans, no training shoes). **Societies** please telephone in advance, a number of packages available. **Green Fees** not confirmed. **Cards** ▨▨▨▨▨ **Prof** Gordon Niven **Course Designer** Dave Thomas **Facilities** ⊗ ⊤ ▯ ▯ ♀ ⌂ ⌂ ⊡ ↝ ↝ ♕ ⚐ **Leisure** hard tennis courts, fishing, Clay pigeon shooting,falconry,archery,health & beauty suite. **Location** 5m E of Jedburgh on A698, 2m W of Kelso on A698

Hotel ★★★♨ 76% The Roxburghe Hotel & Golf Course, Heiton, KELSO ☎ 01573 450331
16 en suite 6 annexe en suite

JEDBURGH   Map 12 NT62

Jedburgh Dunion Rd TD8 6TA
☎ 01835 863587 📠 01835 862360
Undulating parkland course, windy, with young trees.
9 holes, 5760yds, Par 68, SSS 67, Course record 62.
Club membership 320.
Visitors weekend restrictions.Weekdays prior to 6pm.
Societies must contact at least one month in advance by writing or telephone. **Green Fees** £16 per day. **Course Designer** William Park **Facilities** ⊗ ⊤ ▯ ▯ ♀ ⌂
Location 1m W on B6358

KELSO   Map 12 NT73

Kelso Racecourse Rd TD5 7SL
☎ 01573 223009 📠 01573 228490
Parkland course. Easy walking.
18 holes, 6046yds, Par 70, SSS 69, Course record 64.
Club membership 500.
Visitors advisable to telephone in advance. **Societies** apply in writing. **Green Fees** £18 per 18 holes(£22 weekends).
Course Designer James Braid **Facilities** ⊗ ⊤ ▯ ▯ ♀ ⌂
⌂ ⚐ ♕ ⚐ **Location** N side of town centre off B6461

Hotel ★★★ 63% Cross Keys Hotel, 36-37 The Square, KELSO ☎ 01573 223303 27 en suite

Roxburghe Heiton TD5 8JZ
☎ 01573 450333 📠 01573 450611
e-mail: golf@roxburghe.net
Opened in 1996 and designed by Dave Thomas, this undulating course is set in 200 acres of mature parkland. Deep challenging bunkers, rolling greens and dramatic water hazards, including the River

continued

LAUDER   Map 12 NT54

Lauder Galashiels Rd TD2 6RS ☎ 01578 722240
e-mail: laudergc@aol.com
Inland course and practice area on gently sloping hill with stunning views of the Lauderdale district. The 'signature' holes are "The Wood", a dog-leg par 4 played round the corner of a wood which is itself out of bounds, and "The Quarry", a 150 yard par 3 played over several old quarry holes into a bowl shaped green.
9 holes, 3001yds, Par 72, SSS 69, Course record 66.
Club membership 260.
Visitors restricted Tues & Wed 4.30-6pm and Sun before noon. **Societies** telephone in advance. **Green Fees** terms on application. **Course Designer** Willie Park Jnr **Facilities** ⌂
Location On Galashiels Rd, off A68, 0.5m from Lauder

Hotel ★★ 68% Lauderdale Hotel, 1 Edinburgh Rd, LAUDER ☎ 01578 722231 9 en suite

MELROSE   Map 12 NT53

Melrose Dingleton TD6 9HS ☎ 01896 822855
Undulating tree-lined fairways with spendid views. Many bunkers.
9 holes, 5579yds, Par 70, SSS 68, Course record 61.
Club membership 380.
Visitors competitions all Sats and many Suns Apr-Oct, ladies priority Tue, junior priority Wed am in holidays. **Societies** apply in writing. **Green Fees** £16 per round;£20 per day. **Course Designer** James Braid **Facilities** ⌂ **Location** Off A68, S side of town centre on B6359

Hotel ★★★ 66% Burt's Hotel, The Square, MELROSE ☎ 01896 822285 20 en suite

MINTO   Map 12 NT52

Minto TD9 8SH ☎ 01450 870220 📠 01450 870126
e-mail: pat@mintogolfclub.freeserve.co.uk
Pleasant, undulating parkland course featuring mature trees and panoramic views of Scottish Border country. Short but quite testing.
18 holes, 5542yds, Par 69, SSS 67, Course record 63.
Club membership 650.
Visitors advisable to telephone in advance, and essential for weekends. **Societies** contact in advance. **Green Fees** £27.50 per day; £22 per round (£35/£27.50 weekends & bank holidays). **Cards** 🔤 ▦ £35/£ 🔤 💳 **Facilities** ⊗ ⅷ ⅃ ⚑ ♥ ♀ ⚑ ⛳ **Location** 5m from Hawick, 1.25m off A698 at Denholm

NEWCASTLETON   Map 12 NY48

Newcastleton Holm Hill TD9 0QD ☎ 01387 375257
Hilly course with scenic views over the Liddesdale Valley and Newcastleton.
9 holes, 5503yds, Par 69, SSS 70, Course record 69.
Club membership 100.
Visitors contact the Secretary in advance. **Societies** contact by telephone or in writing in advance. **Green Fees** £10 per day/round. **Course Designer** J Shade **Facilities** ⚑ ⚑
Leisure fishing. **Location** W side of village

Hotel ★★★ 66% Garden House Hotel, Sarkfoot Rd, GRETNA ☎ 01461 337621 21 en suite

PEEBLES   Map 11 NT24

Peebles Kirkland St EH45 8EU
☎ 01721 720197 📠 01721 724441
e-mail: secretary@peeblesgolfclub.co.uk
Parkland course with fine views.
18 holes, 6160yds, Par 70, SSS 70, Course record 63.
Club membership 750.
Visitors advisable to ring for information on availability, no visitors on Sat. **Societies** apply by telephone or in writing in advance. **Green Fees** £30 per round. **Cards** 🔤 ▦ 💳 **Prof** Craig Imlah **Course Designer** H S Colt **Facilities** ⊗ ⅷ ⅃
♥ ♀ ⚑ ⚑ ⚑ ⛳ **Location** W side of town centre off A72

Hotel ★★★ 73% Peebles Hydro Hotel, PEEBLES ☎ 01721 720602 133 en suite

ST BOSWELLS   Map 12 NT53

St Boswells Braeheads TD6 0DE ☎ 01835 823527
Attractive parkland course by the banks of the River Tweed; easy walking.
9 holes, 5274yds, Par 68.
Club membership 320.
Visitors contact in advance. **Societies** booking by writing to secretary. **Green Fees** £15 per round/day. **Course Designer** W Park **Facilities** ⅷ by prior arrangement ♥ ♀ ⚑ **Leisure** fishing. **Location** 500yds off A68 east end of village

Hotel ★★★⚑ 76% Dryburgh Abbey Hotel, ST BOSWELLS ☎ 01835 822261 37 en suite 1 annexe en suite

SELKIRK   Map 12 NT42

Selkirk Selkirk Hill TD7 4NW ☎ 01750 20621
Pleasant moorland course set around Selkirk Hill. Unrivalled views.
9 holes, 5620yds, Par 68, SSS 68, Course record 61.
Club membership 349.
Visitors contact in advance, may not play Mon evening, competition/match days. **Societies** must telephone in

continued

advance. **Green Fees** terms on application. **Facilities** ⊗ by prior arrangement ⅃ by prior arrangement ⚑ by prior arrangement ♀ ⚑ ⚑ ⛳ **Location** 1m S on A7

Hotel ★★★ 66% Burt's Hotel, The Square, MELROSE ☎ 01896 822285 20 en suite

WEST LINTON   Map 11 NT15

Rutherford Castle Golf Club EH46 7AS
☎ 01968 661 233 📠 01968 661 233
e-mail: info@ruth-castlegc.co.uk
Undulating parkland set beneath the Pentland hills. With many challenging holes. A good test for the better player whilst offering great enjoyment to the average player.
18 holes, 6525yds, Par 72, SSS 71.
Club membership 360.
Visitors telephone booking anytime. **Societies** application form forwarded on request. **Green Fees** not confirmed. **Prof** Martin Brown **Course Designer** Bryan Moore **Facilities** ⅃
♥ ♀ ⚑ ⚑ ⚑ ⛳ **Leisure** fishing. **Location** S of Edinburgh city bypass (A720) on A702 towards Carlisle

Hotel ★★★ 73% Peebles Hydro Hotel, PEEBLES ☎ 01721 720602 133 en suite

West Linton EH46 7HN
☎ 01968 660256 & 660970 📠 01968 660970
e-mail: secretarywlgc@btinternet.com
Moorland course with beautiful views of Pentland Hills. The 14th hole is usually played into the prevailing west wind from an elevated tee and subsequently ranks as one of the toughest holes. The finish could not be more demanding, a 230 yard par 3 which is played uphill to a small elevated green.
18 holes, 6132yds, Par 69, SSS 70, Course record 63.
Club membership 800.
Visitors weekdays anytime, weekends not before 1pm. Contact Professional. **Societies** contact the secretary by telephone. **Green Fees** £35 per day; £23 per round (£35 per round weekends). **Prof** Ian Wright **Course Designer** Millar/Braid/Fraser **Facilities** ⊗ ⅷ ⅃ ♥ ♀ ⚑ ⚑ ⚑ ⚑ ⛳ **Location** NW side of village off A702

Hotel ★★★ 73% Peebles Hydro Hotel, PEEBLES ☎ 01721 720602 133 en suite

SOUTH AYRSHIRE

AYR   Map 10 NS32

Belleisle Belleisle Park KA7 4DU
☎ 01292 441258 📠 01292 442632
Parkland course with beautiful sea views. First-class conditions.
Belleisle Course: 18 holes, 6431yds, Par 71, SSS 72, Course record 63.
Seafield Course: 18 holes, 5498yds, Par 68, SSS 67.
Club membership 2400.
Visitors advised to contact in advance, telephone to book. **Societies** advised to contact in advance telephone 01292 441258. **Green Fees** Belleisle:£19 (£26 weekends) Seafield:£13(£16 weekends). **Cards** 🔤 ▦ 💳 🔤 💳 **Prof** David Gemmell **Course Designer** James Braid **Facilities** ⊗ ⅷ ⅃ ♥ ♀ ⚑ ⚑ ⚑ ⚑ ⛳ **Conf** Max 200 **Location** 2m S of Ayr on Coastal Road

Hotel ★★★ 72% Savoy Park Hotel, 16 Racecourse Rd, AYR ☎ 01292 266112 15 en suite

Dalmilling Westwood Av KA8 0QY
☎ 01292 263893 01292 610543
Meadowland course, with easy walking. Tributaries of the River Ayr add interest to early holes.
18 holes, 5724yds, Par 69, SSS 68, Course record 61.
Club membership 260.
Visitors must contact in advance. **Societies** must contact in advance. **Green Fees** not confirmed. **Cards** **Prof** Philip Cheyney **Facilities** **Location** 1.5m E of town centre off A77

Hotel ★★ 72% Grange Hotel, 37 Carrick Rd, AYR
☎ 01292 265679 8 en suite

BARASSIE Map 10 NS33

Kilmarnock (Barassie) 29 Hillhouse Rd KA10 6SY ☎ 01292 313920 01292 318300
e-mail: secretarykbgc@lineone.net
The club now has a 27 hole layout. Magnificent seaside links, relatively flat with much heather and small, undulating greens.
18 holes, 6817yds, Par 72, SSS 74, Course record 63.
9 hole course: 9 holes, 2888yds, Par 34.
Club membership 600.
Visitors limited availability Wed & weekends. May not play Fri am. Contact secretary in advance. **Societies** must telephone in advance and confirm in writing. **Green Fees** £50 per day(£60 per round weekends). **Cards** **Prof** Gregor Howie **Course Designer** Theodore Moone **Facilities** **Location** E side of village on B746, 2m N of Troon

Hotel ★★★★ 64% Marine Hotel, Crosbie Rd, TROON
☎ 01292 314444 74 en suite

Brunston Castle Golf Course

6700 yds SSS 72 par 72

Set within 250 acres of spectacular Ayrshire countryside, this parkland course is 20 minutes from Ayr and 7 miles from Turnberry. The superb clubhouse offers spectacular views over the course and has full dining and bar facilities. Visitors and societies are welcome at any time, including weekends. Our professional staff are available for lessons and clinics and can advise on a wide range of equipment. A covered driving range is available and two seater buggies can be hired.

For bookings call:
Tel: 01465 811471 Fax: 01465 811545
Golf Course Road, Daily, Ayrshire KA26 9GD

GIRVAN Map 10 NX19

Brunston Castle Golf Course Rd, Dailly KA26 9GD
☎ 01465 811471 01465 811545
e-mail: golf@brunstoncastle.co.uk
Sheltered inland parkland course. A championship design by Donald Steel, the course is bisected by the River Girvan and shaped to incorporate all the natural surroundings. Lined with mature trees and incorporating a number of water features in addition to the river.

Burns: 18 holes, 6662yds, Par 72, SSS 72, Course record 63.
Club membership 400.
Visitors reserved for members at weekends 8-10 & 12.30-1.30. Must contact in advance. **Societies** telephone 01465 811471 to book. **Green Fees** £28 per 18 holes;£45 per day (£32/£50 weekends). **Cards** **Prof** Alan Reid **Course Designer** Donald Steel **Facilities** **Location** 6m SE of Turnberry, 5m E of Girvan

Hotel ★★★ 77% Malin Court, TURNBERRY
☎ 01655 331457 18 en suite

Girvan Golf Course Rd KA26 9HW
☎ 01465 714346 01465 714272
First eight holes run along the shore with Ailsa Craig as a back drop. Last ten holes parkland played over and around the Water of Girvan.
18 holes, 5098yds, Par 64, SSS 65, Course record 61.
Club membership 175.
Visitors telephone to book. **Societies** book in advance **Green Fees** not confirmed. **Cards** **Course Designer** D Kinnell/J Braid **Facilities** **Location** N side of town off A77

Hotel ★★★ 77% Malin Court, TURNBERRY
☎ 01655 331457 18 en suite

MAYBOLE Map 10 NS20

Maybole Municipal Memorial Park KA19 7DX
☎ 01655 889770
Hilly parkland course with wonderful views over the Carrick Hills.
9 holes, 2635yds, Par 33, SSS 65, Course record 64.
Club membership 100.
Visitors no restrictions, telephone to check,pay as you play course. **Societies** must contact in advance. **Green Fees** terms on application. **Leisure** heated indoor swimming pool, bowling green. **Location** Off A77 S of town

Hotel ★★ Ladyburn, MAYBOLE
☎ 01655 740585 8 rms (7 en suite)

Royal Troon

Troon, *South Ayrshire*   ☎ 01292 311555   Fax 01292 318204 Map 10 NS33

e-mail: bookings@royaltroon.com

Troon was founded in 1878 with just 5 holes on linksland, in its first decade it grew from 5 holes to 6, then 12, and finally 18 holes. It became Royal Troon in 1978 on the occasion of its 100th anniversary.

Royal Troon has been one of the venues of the Open Championship in Western Scotland since 1923. Troon's reputation is based on its combination of rough and sandy hills, bunkers, and a severity of finish that has diminished the championship hopes of many. The most successful players have relied on an equal blend of finesse and power. The British Open Championship has been played at Royal Troon in 1923, 1950, 1962, 1973, 1982, 1989 and 1997. It is recommended that you apply to the course in advance for full visitor information.

Visitors Mon, Tue and Thu only. Must write in advance and have a letter of introduction from own club and a handicap certificate of under 20. Ladies and under 18s may only play on the Portland

Green Fees £150 per day, 1 round each Old Course and Portland Course plus lunch. ⊟ ⚍ ⚍ 🎏 🔲

Facilities ⊗ 🍺 ♟ ♀ ☂ 🏠 ⛴ 🏌 ⚔ 🍴

Professional (R. B. Anderson)

Location Craigend Rd, Troon KA10 6EP (S side of town on B749 5 miles from Prestwick airport)

Holes/Par/Course record 36 holes. Old Course: 18 holes, 6641 yds, Par 71, SSS 73, Course record 64
Portland: 18 holes, 6289 yds, Par 71, SSS 71, Course record 65

Championship Course

WHERE TO STAY NEARBY

Hotels
TROON

★★★★64% Marine, Crosbie Rd.
☎ 01292 314444. 74 en suite

★★★⑥⑥⑥ ♨ Lochgreen House, Monktonhill Rd, Southwood.
☎ 01292 313343. 7 en suite 8 annexe en suite

★★★⑥⑥ 75% Highgrove House, Old Loans Rd. ☎ 01292 312511.
9 en suite

★★★⑥⑥ 74% Piersland House, Craigend Rd.
☎ 01292 314747.
15 en suite 13 annexe en suite

PRESTWICK   Map 10 NS32

Prestwick 2 Links Rd KA9 1QG
☎ 01292 477404 📄 01292 477255
Seaside links with natural hazards, tight fairways and
difficult fast undulating greens.
18 holes, 6544yds, Par 71, SSS 73, Course record 67.
Club membership 575.
Visitors restricted Thu; may not play at weekends. Must
contact in advance and have a handicap certificate.
Societies must contact in writing. Green Fees not
confirmed. Cards ▭ ▭ 🖼 Prof F C Rennie Course
Designer Tom Morris Facilities ⊗ 🏌 🍴 🍺 ♀ ♨ 🏧 ⛳ ⚒
Location In town centre off A79

Hotel ★★★ 68% Parkstone Hotel, Esplanade,
PRESTWICK ☎ 01292 477286 22 en suite

Prestwick St Cuthbert East Rd KA9 2SX
☎ 01292 477101 📄 01292 671730
e-mail: prestwick.stcuthbert@virgin.net
Parkland course with easy walking, natural hazards and
sometimes windy.
18 holes, 6470yds, Par 71, SSS 71, Course record 64.
Club membership 880.
Visitors must contact in advance but may not play at
weekends & bank holidays. Societies Mon-Fri, apply in
writing. Green Fees £35 per day; £26 per round. Cards ▭
▭ 🖼 Course Designer Stutt & Co Facilities ⊗ 🏌 🍴 🍺 ♀
♨ ⚒ Location 0.5m E of town centre off A77

Hotel ★★★ 68% Parkstone Hotel, Esplanade,
PRESTWICK ☎ 01292 477286 22 en suite

Prestwick St Nicholas Grangemuir Rd KA9 1SN
☎ 01292 477608 📄 01292 473900
Seaside links course with whins, heather and tight
fairways. It provides easy walking and has an
unrestricted view of the Firth of Clyde.
18 holes, 5952yds, Par 69, SSS 69, Course record 63.
Club membership 750.
Visitors except Sat, Sun am. Must contact in advance.
Societies must contact in advance. Green Fees £56 per day;
£36 per round (£41 per round Sundays). Cards ▭ ▭ 🖼
🖼 Course Designer Charles Hunter Facilities ⊗ 🏌 🍴 🍺 ♀
♨ 🏧 ⛳ ⚒ Location S side of town off A79

Hotel ★★★ 68% Parkstone Hotel, Esplanade,
PRESTWICK ☎ 01292 477286 22 en suite

TROON See page 347

TROON   Map 10 NS33

Troon Municipal Harling Dr KA10 6NE
☎ 01292 312464 📄 01292 312578
Three links courses, two Championship.
Lochgreen Course: 18 holes, 6820yds, Par 74, SSS 73.
Darley Course: 18 holes, 6360yds, Par 71, SSS 63.
Fullarton Course: 18 holes, 4870yds, Par 72, SSS 72.
Club membership 3000.
Visitors no restrictions. Societies apply in writing. Green
Fees Lochgreen: £29 per day; £19 per round (£36/£26
weekends). Darley: £25 per day; £15 per round (£30/£20
weekends); Fullarton £21 per day; £13 per round (£29/£16.50
weekends). Cards ▭ ▭ 🖼 🖼 Prof Gordon McKinlay
Facilities ⊗ 🏌 🍴 🍺 ♀ ♨ 🏧 ⛳ Location 100yds from
railway station

Hotel ★★★★ 64% Marine Hotel, Crosbie Rd, TROON
☎ 01292 314444 74 en suite

TURNBERRY See page 349

SOUTH LANARKSHIRE

BIGGAR   Map 11 NT03

Biggar The Park, Broughton Rd ML12 6AH
☎ 01899 220618(club) & 220319(course)
Flat parkland course, easy walking and fine views.
18 holes, 5600yds, Par 68, SSS 67, Course record 61.
Club membership 240.
Visitors Must contact in advance. Smart casual wear
required. Societies must book in advance, observe dress
code. Green Fees not confirmed. Course Designer W Park
Jnr Facilities ⊗ 🏌 🍴 🍺 ♀ ♨ 🏧 ⚒ Leisure hard tennis
courts, boating. Location S side of town

Hotel ★★★♨♨ 73% Shieldhill Castle, Quothquan, BIGGAR
☎ 01899 220035 16 en suite

BOTHWELL   Map 11 NS75

Bothwell Castle Blantyre Rd G71 8PJ
☎ 01698 853177 📄 01698 854052
Flattish tree lined parkland course in residential area.
18 holes, 6200yds, Par 71, SSS 70, Course record 63.
Club membership 1000.
Visitors may only play Mon-Fri 9.30-10.30am & 2-3pm.
Societies (Tues only, apply in writing) Green Fees £32 per
day; £24 per round. Prof Alan McCloskey Facilities ⊗ 🏌 🍴
🍺 ♀ ♨ 🏧 ⛳ 🏧 ⚒ Location NW of village off B7071

Hotel ★★★ 67% Bothwell Bridge Hotel, 89 Main St,
BOTHWELL ☎ 01698 852246 90 en suite

BURNSIDE   Map 11 NS65

Blairbeth Fernbrae Av, Fernhill G73 4SF
☎ 0141 634 3355 & 634 3325 📄 0141 634 3325
Parkland course.
18 holes, 5518yds, Par 70, SSS 68, Course record 63.
Club membership 600.
Visitors must contact in advance & may not play weekends.
Societies apply in advance. Green Fees £21 per day; £18 per
round. Facilities ⊗ 🏌 🍴 🍺 ♀ ♨ Location 2m S of
Rutherglen off Burnside road

Hotel ★★★ 64% Kings Park Hotel, Mill St,
RUTHERGLEN ☎ 0141 647 5491 26 en suite

Cathkin Braes Cathkin Rd G73 4SE
☎ 0141 634 6605 📄 0141 630 9186
e-mail: golf@cathkinbraes.freeserve.co.uk
Moorland course, prevailing westerly wind, small loch
hazard at 5th hole. Very strong finishing holes.
18 holes, 6208yds, Par 71, SSS 71, Course record 64.
Club membership 920.
Visitors must contact in advance & have handicap certificate
but may not play at weekends. Societies apply in writing.
Green Fees £35 per day; £25 per round. Prof Stephen Bree
Course Designer James Braid Facilities ⊗ 🏌 🍴 🍺 ♀ ♨
🏧 ⛳ ♨ 🏧 ⚒ Location 1m S on B759

Hotel ★★★ 64% Kings Park Hotel, Mill St,
RUTHERGLEN ☎ 0141 647 5491 26 en suite

The Westin Turnberry Resort

Turnberry, *South Ayrshire*   ☎ 01655 331000   Fax 01655 331706   Map 10 NS20

e-mail: turnberry@westin.com

G olf at Turnberry began in 1906. The Ailsa course was developed by the Glasgow and South Western Railway Company and continued to prosper until the outbreak of war in 1914 and again in 1939. Golf course architect Mackenzie Ross was given the task of rebuilding the courses and by 1951 the transformation was complete.

The Ailsa course has staged three memorable Open Championships in 1977, 1986 and 1994. The Kintyre course was designed by Donald Steel with spectacular views and is, some say, more challenging than the Ailsa. The Colin Montgomerie Links Golf Academy opened in April 2000, featuring 12 driving bays, 4 short game bays, 2 dedicated teaching rooms and a group teaching room.

Visitors golf courses for residents of hotel only

Societies contact in advance as courses are for hotel residents only

Green Fees fees on application

Facilities ⊗ 🎪 👟 🖥 ♀ 🏻 ⛳ 🏠 ⛳ 🏌 (Professional (David Fleming) Golf Academy

Leisure tennis, private fishing, swimming, sauna, solarium, gymnasium Conf max 275 Thtr 275 Class 145 Board 54 Banquet 260

Location Turnberry KA26 9LT (15m SW of Ayr on A77)

Holes/Par/Course record 36 holes. Ailsa Course: 18 holes, 6440 yds, Par 69, SSS 72, Course record 63 Kintyre Course: 18 holes, 6481 yds, Par 72, SSS 72

WHERE TO STAY NEARBY

Hotel
TURNBERRY

★★★★★ 74% The Westin Turnberry Resort
☎ 01655 331000. 132 en suite 89 annexe en suite

Championship Course

CARLUKE　　　　　　　　Map 11 NS85

Carluke Mauldslie Rd, Hallcraig ML8 5HG
☎ 01555 770574 & 771070
e-mail: admin.carlukegolf@supanet.com
**Parkland course with views over the Clyde Valley.
Testing 11th hole, par 3.**
*18 holes, 5853yds, Par 70, SSS 68, Course record 63.
Club membership 750.*
Visitors must contact in advance & may not play weekends
and bank holidays. **Societies** prior arrangement required.
Green Fees not confirmed. **Prof** Richard Forrest **Facilities**
⊗ ⅷ ⅊ ♥ ♀ ⅄ 🖻 ⌀ **Location** 1m W off A73

Hotel ★★★ 70% Popinjay Hotel, Lanark Rd, ROSEBANK
☎ 01555 860441 38 en suite

CARNWATH　　　　　　　Map 11 NS94

Carnwath 1 Main St ML11 8JX
☎ 01555 840251 ▤ 01555 841070
**Picturesque parkland course slightly hilly, with small
greens calling for accuracy. Panoramic views.**
*18 holes, 5222yds, Par 66, SSS 66, Course record 63.
Club membership 576.*
Visitors restricted after 5pm, no visitors Sat. **Societies** apply
in writing or telephone. **Green Fees** £26 per day; £16 per
round (£32/£22 Sun). **Facilities** ⊗ ⅷ ⅊ ♥ ♀ ⅄ ⌀
Location W side of village on A70

Hotel ★★★ 67% Cartland Bridge Hotel, Glasgow Rd,
LANARK ☎ 01555 664426 20 rms (18 en suite)

EAST KILBRIDE　　　　　Map 11 NS65

East Kilbride Chapelside Rd, Nerston G74 4PF
☎ 01355 247728
**Parkland course of variable topography. Generous
fairways and greens but a challenging test of golf.**
*18 holes, 6419yds, Par 71, SSS 71, Course record 64.
Club membership 850.*
Visitors by appointment. **Societies** must telephone in
advance & submit formal application. **Green Fees** not
confirmed. **Prof** Willy Walker **Facilities** ⅄ 🖻 ⅌ ♥ ⌀
Location 0.5m N off A749

Hotel ★★★ 70% Bruce Hotel, Cornwall St, EAST
KILBRIDE ☎ 01355 229771 65 en suite

Torrance House Calderglen Country Park, Strathaven
Rd G75 0QZ ☎ 01355 248638 ▤ 01355 570916
A mature parkland course.
*18 holes, 6476yds, Par 72, SSS 69, Course record 71.
Club membership 1000.*
Visitors welcome, may book up to six days in advance.
Societies Mon-Fri. Apply in writing to John Dunlop, South
Lanarkshire Council, Hamilton Palace Sports Grounds
Hamilton **Green Fees** terms on application. **Course
Designer** Hawtree & Son **Facilities** ⊗ ⅷ ⅊ ♥ ♀ ⅄ 🖻 ⅌
⌀ **Location** 1.5m SE of Kilbride on A726

Hotel ★★★ 70% Bruce Hotel, Cornwall St, EAST
KILBRIDE ☎ 01355 229771 65 en suite

HAMILTON　　　　　　　Map 11 NS75

Hamilton Carlisle Rd, Ferniegair ML3 7UE
☎ 01698 459537
Beautiful parkland course.
18 holes, 6243yds, Par 70, SSS 70, Course record 62.
Visitors must contact in advance, may not play weekends.
Societies apply in writing. **Green Fees** terms on application.

continued

Prof Maurice Moir **Course Designer** James Braid **Facilities**
⊗ ⅷ ⅊ ♥ ♀ ⅄ 🖻 ⌀ **Location** 1.5m SE on A72

Hotel ⇧ Express by Holiday Inn, Hamilton Rd,
HAMILTON ☎ 01698 858585 120 en suite

Strathclyde Park Mote Hill ML3 6BY
☎ 01698 429350
**Municipal wooded parkland course with views into the
Strathclyde Park sailing loch.**
*9 holes, 3128yds, Par 36, SSS 70, Course record 64.
Club membership 180.*
Visitors telephone, same day booking system in operation.
May book up to 1 week in advance in summer months.
Societies must contact in advance on above telephone
number, for prior booking. **Green Fees** £3.20 per 9
holes(£3.60 weekends). **Prof** William Walker **Facilities** ⅄
🖻 ⅃ **Location** N side of town off B7071

Hotel ⇧ Express by Holiday Inn, Hamilton Rd,
HAMILTON ☎ 01698 858585 120 en suite

LANARK　　　　　　　　Map 11 NS84

Lanark The Moor, Whitelees Rd ML11 7RX
☎ 01555 663219 & 661456 ▤ 01555 663219
e-mail: lanarkgolfclub@talk21.com
**The address of the club, 'The Moor', gives some
indication as to the kind of golf to be found there. Golf
has been played at Lanark for well over a century and
the Club dates from 1851.**
*Old Course: 18 holes, Par 70, SSS 71,
Course record 62.
Wee Course: 9 holes, 1489yds, Par 28.
Club membership 880.*
Visitors booking advisable, no visitors weekends.
Societies apply in advance. **Green Fees** £40 per day; £26
per round.Wee Course;£6 per day. **Prof** Alan White
Course Designer Tom Morris **Facilities** ⊗ ⅷ ⅊ ♥ ♀
⅄ 🖻 ♘ ⚒ ⌀ **Location** E side of town centre off A73

Hotel ★★★ 67% Cartland Bridge Hotel, Glasgow Rd,
LANARK ☎ 01555 664426 20 rms (18 en suite)

LARKHALL　　　　　　　Map 11 NS75

Larkhall Burnhead Rd ML9 3AA ☎ 01698 889597
9 holes, 6234yds, Par 70, SSS 70, Course record 69.
Location E side of town on B7019
Telephone for further details

Hotel ★★★ 70% Popinjay Hotel, Lanark Rd, ROSEBANK
☎ 01555 860441 38 en suite

LEADHILLS　　　　　　　Map 11 NS81

Leadhills ML12 6XR ☎ 01659 74456
**A testing, hilly course with high winds. At 1500ft above
sea level it is the highest golf course in Scotland.**
*9 holes, 4354yds, Par 66, SSS 64.
Club membership 80.*
Visitors groups must contact in advance. **Societies** must
contact in advance. **Green Fees** not confirmed. **Location** E
side of village off B797

Hotel ★★ 65% Blackaddie House Hotel, Blackaddie Rd,
SANQUHAR ☎ 01659 50270 9 en suite

350

LESMAHAGOW
Map 11 NS83

Holland Bush Acretophead ML11 0JS
☎ 01555 893484 & 893646 📠 01555 893984
e-mail: mail@hollandbushgolfclub.co.uk
Fairly difficult, tree-lined municipal parkland and moorland course. 1st half is relatively flat, while 2nd half is hilly.
18 holes, 6246yds, Par 71, SSS 70, Course record 63.
Club membership 400.
Visitors contact shop on 01555 893646 for times etc.
Societies contact shop on 01555 893646 in advance. **Green Fees** terms on application. **Course Designer** J Lawson/K Pate **Facilities** ⊗ ⅷ ㉃ ☕ ♀ ⚲ 🏠 🖍 **Location** 2-3m S of Lesmahagow on the Lesmahagow-Coalburn Road

Hotel ★★★ 72% Strathaven Hotel, Hamilton Rd, STRATHAVEN ☎ 01357 521778 22 en suite

RIGSIDE
Map 11 NS83

Douglas Water Ayr Rd ML11 9NP ☎ 01555 880361
A 9-hole course with good variety and some hills and spectacular views. An interesting course with a challenging longest hole of 564 yards but, overall, not too testing for average golfers.
9 holes, 5890yds, Par 72, SSS 69, Course record 63.
Club membership 150.
Visitors no restrictions weekdays or Sun, competitions on Sat normal restrictions. **Societies** apply in writing/telephone in advance. **Green Fees** £8per day (£10 weekends).
Facilities ♀ ⚲ **Location** Ayr road A70

Hotel ★★★ 67% Cartland Bridge Hotel, Glasgow Rd, LANARK ☎ 01555 664426 20 rms (18 en suite)

STRATHAVEN
Map 11 NS64

Strathaven Glasgow Rd ML10 6NL
☎ 01357 520421 📠 01357 520539
e-mail: manager@strathavengolfclub.fsbusiness.co.uk
Gently undulating, tree-lined, Championship parkland course with panoramic views over town and Avon valley.
18 holes, 6250yds, Par 71, SSS 71, Course record 65.
Club membership 1050.
Visitors welcome weekdays up to 4pm only. May not play at weekends. Must contact in advance. **Societies** apply in writing to general manager. **Green Fees** terms on application. **Prof** Stuart Kerr **Course Designer** Willie Fernie/J Stutt **Facilities** ⊗ ⅷ ㉃ ☕ ♀ ⚲ 🏠 🚲 🖍 **Location** NE side of town on A726

Hotel ★★★ 72% Strathaven Hotel, Hamilton Rd, STRATHAVEN ☎ 01357 521778 22 en suite

UDDINGSTON
Map 11 NS66

Calderbraes 57 Roundknowe Rd G71 7TS
☎ 01698 813425
Parkland course with good view of Clyde Valley. Testing 4th hole (par 4), hard uphill.
9 holes, 5046yds, Par 66, SSS 67, Course record 65.
Club membership 230.
Visitors weekdays before 5pm. **Societies** welcome **Green Fees** £13 per day. **Facilities** ⊗ ⅷ ㉃ ☕ ♀ ⚲ **Location** 1.5m NW off A74

Hotel ★★★ 67% Bothwell Bridge Hotel, 89 Main St, BOTHWELL ☎ 01698 852246 90 en suite

STIRLING

ABERFOYLE
Map 11 NN50

Aberfoyle Braeval FK8 3UY ☎ 01877 382493
Scenic heathland course with mountain views.
18 holes, 5210yds, Par 66, SSS 66.
Club membership 665.
Visitors weekend restrictions. **Societies** must contact in advance. **Green Fees** £15 per round;£20 per day(£20/£28 weekends). **Facilities** ⊗ ⅷ ㉃ ☕ ♀ ⚲ 🖍 **Location** 1m E on A81

Hotel ★★★★ 64% Forest Hills Hotel, Kinlochard, ABERFOYLE ☎ 01877 387277 56 en suite

BANNOCKBURN
Map 11 NS89

Brucefields Family Golfing Centre Pirnhall Rd FK7 8EH ☎ 01786 818184 📠 01786 817770
Gently rolling parkland with fine views. Most holes can be played without too much difficulty with the exception of the 2nd which is a long and tricky par 4 and the 6th, a par 3 which requires exact club selection and a straight shot.
Main Course: 9 holes, 2513yds, Par 68, SSS 68.
Visitors no restrictions **Societies** apply in writing.
Green Fees £14 per 18 holes, £8 per 9 holes (£16/£9 weekends) Par 3;£3 per 9 holes (£4 weeekends). **Cards** 🟥 🟫 🟦 🟩 💳 **Course Designer** Souters Sportsturf **Facilities** ⊗ ⅷ ㉃ ☕ ♀ ⚲ 🏠 🍴 🖍 ⚲ Ⓣ **Leisure** golf academy, par 3 9 hole course. **Conf** Max 20 **Location** Exit at inerchange of M80/M9 (junct 9), from roundabout take A91, 1st left at sign for Brucefields

Hotel ★★ 65% Terraces Hotel, 4 Melville Ter, STIRLING ☎ 01786 472268 17 en suite

BRIDGE OF ALLAN
Map 11 NS79

Bridge of Allan Sunnylaw FK9 4LY ☎ 01786 832332
Parkland course, very hilly with good views of Stirling Castle and beyond to the Trossachs. Testing 1st hole, 221 yds (par 3) uphill 6 ft wall 25 yds before green.
9 holes, 4932yds, Par 66, SSS 66, Course record 59.
Club membership 400.
Visitors restricted Mon & Thur evenings, Sat, contact in advance. **Societies** must contact in advance. **Green Fees** £15 per round(£18 weekends). **Course Designer** Tom Morris **Facilities** ⊗ by prior arrangement ㉃ ☕ ♀ ⚲ 🖍 **Location** 0.5m N off A9

Hotel ★★★ 69% Royal Hotel, Henderson St, BRIDGE OF ALLAN ☎ 01786 832284 32 en suite

CALLANDER
Map 11 NN60

Callander Aveland Rd FK17 8EN
☎ 01877 330090 & 330975 📠 01877 330062
e-mail: callandergc@nextcall.net
Challenging parkland course with tight fairways and a number of interesting holes. Designed by Tom Morris Snr and overlooked by the Trossachs.
18 holes, 5151yds, Par 66, SSS 66, Course record 61.
Club membership 600.
Visitors prior booking 24-48 hrs is advised in the playing season. Handicap certificate Wed/Sun. **Societies** write or telephone for booking form. **Green Fees** terms on

continued

application. **Prof** Allan Martin **Course Designer**
Morris/Fernie **Facilities** ⊗ ⫣ ᛒ ⬛ ♀ ⚷ 🗂 ⚐ ⚑
Location E side of town off A84

Hotel ★★★⚘ 76% Roman Camp Country House Hotel,
CALLANDER ☎ 01877 330003 14 en suite

DRYMEN
Map 11 NS48

Buchanan Castle G63 0HY
☎ 01360 660307 📠 01360 870382
e-mail: buchanancastle@sol.co.uk
**Parkland course, with easy walking and good views.
Owned by the Duke of Montrose.**
*18 holes, 6059yds, Par 70, SSS 69.
Club membership 830.*
Visitors must contact professional on 01360 660330 in
advance. **Societies** must contact in advance. **Green Fees** not
confirmed. **Cards** ▦ **Prof** Keith Baxter **Course Designer**
James Braid **Facilities** ⚷ 🗂 ⚐ ⚑ **Location** 1m W

Hotel ★★★ 65% Winnock Hotel, The Square, DRYMEN
☎ 01360 660245 48 en suite

Strathendrick G83 8EL
☎ 01360 660695 📠 01389 600567
e-mail: marrisonpe@aol.com
**Hillside course with breathtaking views of the Campsie
and Luss Hills and Ben Lomond. Mainly natural hazards
with few bunkers. Greens are comparatively small but in
immaculate condition.**
*9 holes, 4982yards, Par 66, SSS 64, Course record 60.
Club membership 470.*
Visitors may not play weekends/evenings. **Societies** apply in
advance. **Green Fees** £15 per day; £12 per 18 holes; £8 per 9
holes. **Facilities** ⚷ ⚑ **Leisure** hard tennis courts, driving
net. **Location** 0.5m S of Drymen via access lane E of A811

Hotel ★★★★★ 64% Cameron House Hotel, BALLOCH
☎ 01389 755565 96 en suite

DUNBLANE
Map 11 NN70

Dunblane New Golf Club Perth Rd FK15 0LJ
☎ 01786 821521 📠 01786 821522
**Well maintained parkland course, with reasonably hard
walking. Testing 6th and 9th holes.**
*18 holes, 5536yds, Par 69, SSS 67.
Club membership 1000.*
Visitors may play 9.30am-noon & 2.30-4pm Mon-Fri. Must
contact in advance. **Societies** welcome Mon, Wed-Fri,
contact in advance. **Green Fees** not confirmed. **Prof** Bob
Jamieson **Facilities** ⊗ ⫣ ᛒ ⬛ ♀ ⚷ 🗂 ⚐ **Location** E
side of town on A9

Hotel ★★★⚘ Cromlix House Hotel, Kinbuck, Nr
DUNBLANE ☎ 01786 822125 14 en suite

KILLIN
Map 11 NN53

Killin FK21 8TX ☎ 01567 820312 📠 01567 820312
e-mail: info@killingolfclub.co.uk
Parkland course with good views. Glorious setting.
*9 holes, 2600yds, Par 66, SSS 65, Course record 61.
Club membership 250.*
Visitors may not play competition days, parties must book in
advance. **Societies** previous record of courses visited
required. Apply in writing or telephone in advance. **Green
Fees** £15 per round;£22.50 per day. **Cards** ▦ ▦ ▦ ▦ 🗂

continued

Killin Golf Club

Course Designer John Duncan/J Braid **Facilities** ⊗ ⫣ ᛒ
⬛ ♀ ⚷ 🗂 ⚐ ⚑ ⚷ **Location** 0.5m N of centre of
village on A827

Hotel ★★★ 68% Dall Lodge Country House Hotel, Main
St, KILLIN ☎ 01567 820217 10 en suite

STIRLING
Map 11 NS79

Stirling Queens Rd FK8 3AA
☎ 01786 464098 📠 01786 450748
e-mail: enquiries@stirlinggolfclub.tv
**Undulating parkland course with magnificent views of
Stirling Castle and the Grampian Mountains. Testing
15th, 'Cotton's Fancy', 384 yds (par 4).**
*18 holes, 6438yds, Par 72, SSS 71, Course record 64.
Club membership 1100.*
Visitors may reserve tee off times mid week 9-4.30pm. At
weekends tee off times may be reserved on day of play
subject to availability. **Societies** must apply in writing or
telephone. **Green Fees** £40 per day; £28 per round. **Cards**
▦ ▦ 🗂 **Prof** Ian Collins **Course Designer** James
Braid/Henry Cotton **Facilities** ⊗ ⫣ ᛒ ⬛ ♀ ⚷ 🗂 ⚐ ⚑ ⚷
Location W side of town on B8051

Hotel ★★ 65% Terraces Hotel, 4 Melville Ter, STIRLING
☎ 01786 472268 17 en suite

BONHILL
Map 10 NS37

Vale of Leven North Field Rd G83 9ET
☎ 01389 752351 📠 0870 749 8950
e-mail: clubadministrator@valeoflevengolfclub.org.uk
**Hilly moorland course, tricky with many natural hazards
- gorse, burns, trees. Overlooks Loch Lomond.**
*18 holes, 5162yds, Par 67, SSS 66, Course record 60.
Club membership 750.*

continued

Visitors may not play Sat. **Societies** apply to the secretary in writing or telephone call. **Green Fees** £24 per day; £16 per round (£30/£20 Sundays). **Prof** Bary Campbell **Facilities** ⊗ ⁕ ৳ ➡ ♀ ⚐ 🏠 ⚐ **Location** E side of town off A813

Hotel ★★★★★ 64% Cameron House Hotel, BALLOCH ☎ 01389 755565 96 en suite

CLYDEBANK   Map 11 NS56

Clydebank & District Glasgow Rd, Hardgate G81 5QY ☎ 01389 383831 & 383833 📠 01389 383831
An undulating parkland course established in 1905 overlooking Clydebank.
18 holes, 5823yds, Par 68, SSS 68, Course record 64.
Club membership 889.
Visitors round only, weekdays only and no bank holidays. Must tee off before 4.30pm. Apply to professional 01389 383835 **Societies** must apply in writing. **Green Fees** terms on application. **Prof** Paul Jamieson **Course Designer** Members **Facilities** ⊗ ⁕ ৳ ➡ ♀ ⚐ 🏠 ⚐ **Location** 2m E of Erskine Bridge

Hotel ★★★ 65% Patio Hotel, 1 South Av, Clydebank Business Park, CLYDEBANK ☎ 0141 951 1133 82 en suite

Dalmuir Municipal Overtoun Rd, Dalmuir G81 3RE ☎ 0141 952 6372
Hilly, compact parkland course with tough finishing holes.
18 holes, 5349yds, Par 67, SSS 66, Course record 63.
Visitors contact in advance. **Societies** contact in advance. **Green Fees** not confirmed. **Prof** Stewart Savage **Facilities** ➡ 🏠 ⚐ **Location** 2m NW of town centre

Hotel ★★★ 65% Patio Hotel, 1 South Av, Clydebank Business Park, CLYDEBANK ☎ 0141 951 1133 82 en suite

DUMBARTON   Map 10 NS37

Dumbarton Broadmeadow G82 2BQ ☎ 01389 732830 📠 01389 765995
Flat parkland course.
18 holes, 5992yds, Par 71, SSS 69, Course record 64.
Club membership 700.
Visitors may play Mon-Fri only. **Societies** must apply in writing to Secretary. **Green Fees** £25 per day. **Facilities** ⊗ ⁕ ৳ ➡ ♀ **Location** 0.25m N off A814

Guesthouse ♦♦♦♦♦ Kirkton House, Darleith Rd, CARDROSS ☎ 01389 841951 6 en suite

WEST LOTHIAN

BATHGATE   Map 11 NS96

Bathgate Edinburgh Rd EH48 1BA ☎ 01506 630553 & 652232 📠 01506 636775
e-mail: bathgate.golfclub@lineone.net
Moorland course. Easy walking. Testing 11th hole, par 3.
18 holes, 6328yds, Par 71, SSS 70, Course record 58.
Club membership 900.
Visitors casual visitors welcome other than on competition days. Handicap certificate advisable. **Societies** apply in writing. **Green Fees** £25 per day; £20 per round (£35 per day weekends). **Prof** Sandy Strachan **Course Designer** W Park **Facilities** ⊗ ⁕ ৳ ➡ ♀ 🏠 ⚐ ⚐ **Location** E side of town off A89

Hotel ★★★ 65% The Hilcroft Hotel, East Main St, WHITBURN ☎ 01501 740818 31 en suite

FAULDHOUSE   Map 11 NS96

Greenburn 6 Greenburn Rd EH47 9HJ ☎ 01501 770292
e-mail: secretary@greenburngolfclub.fsnet.co.uk
Exposed rolling course with sparse tree cover. Water hazards from a pond and a burn.
18 holes, 6045yds, Par 71, SSS 70, Course record 65.
Club membership 900.
Visitors contact in advance for details. **Societies** by prior arrangement. **Green Fees** £18 per round;£26 per day(£21/£31 weekends). **Prof** Malcolm Leighton **Facilities** ⊗ ⁕ ৳ ➡ ♀ 🏠 ⚐ **Location** 3m SW of Whitburn

Hotel ★★★ 65% The Hilcroft Hotel, East Main St, WHITBURN ☎ 01501 740818 31 en suite

LINLITHGOW   Map 11 NS97

Linlithgow Braehead EH49 6QF ☎ 01506 842585 (Secretary) & 844356 (Pro) 📠 01506 842764
e-mail: info@linlithgowgolf.co.uk
A short but testing undulating parkland course with panoramic views of the Forth valley.
18 holes, 5800yds, Par 70, SSS 68, Course record 64.
Club membership 450.
Visitors may not play Weds & Sat. **Societies** must contact in writing. **Green Fees** £25 per day; £20 per round (£30/£25 Sunday). **Cards** ▭ ▨ ▩ **Prof** Steven Rosie **Course Designer** R Simpson of Carnoustie **Facilities** ⊗ ⁕ ৳ ➡ ♀ 🏠 ⚐ ⚐ **Location** 1m S off Bathgate Road off A803

Hotel ★★★★ 70% Inchyra Grange Hotel, Grange Rd, POLMONT ☎ 01324 711911 109 en suite

West Lothian Airngath Hill EH49 7RH ☎ 01506 826030 📠 01506 826030
18 holes, 6228yds, Par 71, SSS 71.
Course Designer Fraser Middleton **Location** 1m S off A706
Telephone for further details

Hotel ★★★★ 70% Inchyra Grange Hotel, Grange Rd, POLMONT ☎ 01324 711911 109 en suite

LIVINGSTON   Map 11 NT06

Deer Park Golf & Country Club Golfcourse Rd EH54 9EG ☎ 01506 431037 📠 01506 435608
e-mail: deerpark@dial.pipek.com
Long testing course, fairly flat, championship standard.
18 holes, 6688yds, Par 72, SSS 72, Course record 65.
Club membership 650.
Visitors proper golfing attire to be worn, must book in advance, Sun after 10am. **Societies** telephone or write **Green Fees** terms on application. **Cards** ▭ ▨ ▩ ▨ ▩ ▨ **Prof** Brian Dunbar **Course Designer** Alliss/Thomas **Facilities** ⊗ ⁕ ৳ ➡ ♀ 🏠 ⚐ ➴ ⚐ **Leisure** heated indoor swimming pool, squash, sauna, solarium, gymnasium. **Location** N side of town off A809

Hotel ★★★ 67% Cairn Hotel, Blackburn Rd, BATHGATE ☎ 01506 633366 61 en suite

Pumpherston Drumshoreland Rd, Pumpherston EH53 0LH ☎ 01506 432869
Undulating parkland course with testing 6th hole (par 4), and view of Pentland Hills.
9 holes, 4950yds, Par 66, SSS 64, Course record 64.
Club membership 440.
Visitors must be accompanied by a member. **Societies** apply in writing to the secretary. **Green Fees** not confirmed.

continued

Facilities ⊗ ⓑ ⬛ ♀ ⏃ **Location** 1m E of Livingston between A71 & A89

Hotel ★★★ 67% Cairn Hotel, Blackburn Rd, BATHGATE
☎ 01506 633366 61 en suite

UPHALL   Map 11 NT07

Uphall EH52 6JT ☎ 01506 856404 ▤ 01506 855358
18 holes, 5588yds, Par 69, SSS 67, Course record 62.
Location W side of village on A899
Telephone for further details

Hotel ★★★★ 67% Houstoun House Hotel and
Country Club, UPHALL ☎ 01506 853831
25 en suite 47 annexe en suite

WEST CALDER   Map 11 NT06

Harburn EH55 8RS
☎ 01506 871131 & 871256 ▤ 01506 870286
E-mail: harburn@whsmithnet.co.uk
Moorland, reasonably flat.

18 holes, 5921yds, Par 69, SSS 69, Course record 62.
Club membership 870.
Visitors contact secretary. **Societies** contact by telephone.
Green Fees £25 per day; £18 per round (£29/£21 Fri,
£34/£23 weekends). **Prof** Stephen Mills **Facilities** ⊗ ⫟ ⓑ
⬛ ♀ ⏃ 🏠 ⏏ ✤ *Location* 2m S of West Calder
on B7008

Hotel ★★★ 65% The Hilcroft Hotel, East Main St,
WHITBURN ☎ 01501 740818 31 en suite

WHITBURN   Map 11 NS96

Polkemmet Country Park EH47 0AD
☎ 01501 743905 ▤ 01506 846256
e-mail: mail@beecraigs.com
**Public parkland course surrounded by mature woodland
and rhododendron bushes. 15-bay floodlit driving range.**
9 holes, 2969mtrs, Par 37.
Visitors no restrictions. **Green Fees** £4.95 per 9 holes;£8.55
per 18 holes(£5.75/£10.05 weekends & bank holidays).
Facilities ✤ ⏏ **Location** 2m W on B7066

Hotel ★★★ 65% The Hilcroft Hotel, East Main St,
WHITBURN ☎ 01501 740818 31 en suite

ARRAN, ISLE OF

BLACKWATERFOOT   Map 10 NR82

Shiskine Shore Rd KA27 8HA
☎ 01770 860226 ▤ 01770 860205
e-mail: info@shiskinegolf.com
**Unique 12-hole links course with gorgeous outlook to the
Mull of Kintyre. The course is crossed by two burns and**
continued

**includes the longest par 5 on the island at 509 yards.
There are several blind holes at which various signals
indicate when the green is clear and it is safe to play.**
12 holes, 2990yds, Par 42, SSS 42, Course record 38.
Club membership 670.
Visitors must contact in advance. **Societies** must contact in
writing in advance. Jul and Aug no parties. **Green Fees** £18
per day; £13 per round (£25/£17 weekends). **Course
Designer** Fernie of Troon **Facilities** ⊗ ⫟ ⓑ ⬛ ⏃ 🏠 ⏏ ✤
♂ **Leisure** hard tennis courts, bowling green. **Location** W
side of village off A841

Hotel ★★⚹ Kilmichael Country House Hotel, Glen Cloy,
BRODICK ☎ 01770 302219 4 en suite 3 annexe en suite

BRODICK   Map 10 NS03

Brodick KA27 8DL
☎ 01770 302349 & 302513 ▤ 01770 302349
**Short seaside course, very flat, incorporating both links
and parkland holes to offer a diverse and scenic round of
golf.**
18 holes, 4736yds, Par 65, SSS 64, Course record 60.
Club membership 621.
Visitors must contact in advance but may not play at
competition times. **Societies** must contact secretary in
writing/telephone. **Green Fees** £25 per day; £18 per round
(£30/£20 weekends). **Prof** Peter McCalla **Facilities** ⊗ ⫟ ⓑ
⬛ ♀ ⏃ 🏠 ✤ ♂ **Location** N side of village, 0.5m N of
Brodick Ferry Terminal

Hotel ★★★ 75% Auchrannie Country House Hotel,
BRODICK ☎ 01770 302234 28 en suite

LAMLASH   Map 10 NS03

Lamlash KA27 8JU
☎ 01770 600296 & 600196 (Starter) ▤ 01770 600296
**Undulating heathland course with magnificent views of
the mountains and sea.**
18 holes, 4640yds, Par 64, SSS 64, Course record 60.
Club membership 480.
Visitors book in advance by letter **Societies** must contact in
writing. **Green Fees** £16 per day; £12 per round from 4pm
(£20 weekends) **Cards** 🗎 **Course Designer** Auchterlonie
Facilities ⊗ ⫟ ⓑ ⬛ ♀ ⏃ 🏠 ⏏ ✤ 🚲 ♂ **Location** 0.75m
N of Lamlash on A841. 3m S of Brodick Ferry Terminal

Hotel ★★★ 75% Auchrannie Country House Hotel,
BRODICK ☎ 01770 302234 28 en suite

LOCHRANZA   Map 10 NR95

Lochranza KA27 8HL
☎ 01770 830273 ▤ 01770 830600
e-mail: office@lochgolf.demon.co.uk
**This course is mainly on the level, set amid spectacular
scenery where the fairways are grazed by wild red deer,
while overhead buzzards and golden eagles may be seen.
There are water hazards including the river which is
lined by mature trees. The final three holes, nicknamed
the Bermuda Triangle, provide an absorbing finish right
to the 18th hole - a 530 yard dogleg through trees and
over the river. The large greens, six single and six double,
are played off 18 tees.**
18 holes, 5033mtrs, Par 70, SSS 67, Course record 72.
Club membership 40.
Visitors no restrictions; course closed Nov-mid Apr.
Societies advance booking preferred. **Green Fees** not
confirmed. **Course Designer** re laid 1991 I Robertson
Facilities ⬛ ⏃ 🏠 ⏏ ♂ **Location** Main road, Lochranza
village.
continued

Hotel ★★≜≜ Kilmichael Country House Hotel, Glen Cloy, BRODICK ☎ 01770 302219 4 en suite 3 annexe en suite

MACHRIE   Map 10 NR83

Machrie Bay KA27 8DZ ☎ 01770 850232
Fairly flat seaside course. Designed at turn of century by William Fernie.
9 holes, 4400yds, Par 66, SSS 62, Course record 70.
Club membership 315.
Visitors no restrictions. **Societies** write in advance. **Green Fees** not confirmed. **Course Designer** W Fernie **Facilities** ⊗ ⬛ ⚘ ⛳ ✆ **Leisure** hard tennis courts. **Location** 9m W of Brodick via String Rd

Hotel ★★≜≜ Kilmichael Country House Hotel, Glen Cloy, BRODICK ☎ 01770 302219 4 en suite 3 annexe en suite

SANNOX   Map 10 NS04

Corrie KA27 8JD ☎ 01770 810223 & 600403
A heathland course on the coast with beautiful mountain scenery. An upward climb to 6th hole, then a descent from the 7th. All these holes are subject to strong winds in bad weather.
9 holes, 1948yds, Par 62, SSS 61, Course record 56.
Club membership 300.
Visitors welcome except Sat pm and first Thu afternoon of the month. **Societies** maximum size of party 12, apply in advance. **Green Fees** £10 per day. **Facilities** ⊗ �𝄪 ⬛ ⚘
Location 6m N of A841

Hotel ★★★ 75% Auchrannie Country House Hotel, BRODICK ☎ 01770 302234 28 en suite

WHITING BAY   Map 10 NS02

Whiting Bay KA27 8QT ☎ 01770 700487
Heathland course.
18 holes, 4405yds, Par 63, SSS 63, Course record 59.
Club membership 350.
Visitors tee reserved 8.45-9.30am, also Sun 11.45-1pm.
Societies apply by telephone and confirm in writing with deposit. **Green Fees** £20 per day; £15 per round. **Cards** ▣
Facilities ⊗ ⬛ ⚘ ⚘ 🏠 ⚘ ⛳ ⚘ **Location** NW side of village off A841

Hotel ★★≜≜ Kilmichael Country House Hotel, Glen Cloy, BRODICK ☎ 01770 302219 4 en suite 3 annexe en suite

BUTE, ISLE OF

KINGARTH   Map 10 NS05

Bute St Ninians, 32 Marine Place, Ardbeg, Rothesay PA20 0LF ☎ 01700 502158
Flat seaside course with good fenced greens and fine views.
9 holes, 2361mtrs, Par 68, SSS 64, Course record 65.
Club membership 206.
Visitors restricted Sat until after 11.30am. **Societies** apply in advance. **Green Fees** £8 per round/day. **Facilities** ⚘
Location From Rothesay pier 6m on A845

Hotel ★★ 74% Royal Hotel, Shore Rd, TIGHNABRUAICH ☎ 01700 811239 11 en suite

AA website: www.theAA.com

PORT BANNATYNE   Map 10 NS06

Port Bannatyne Bannatyne Mains Rd PA20 0PH
☎ 01700 502009 504544
e-mail: macleodbute@btopenworld.com
Seaside hill course with panoramic views. Almost unique in having 13 holes, with the first 5 holes being played again before a separate 18th. Difficult hole: 4th (par 3).
13 holes, 5085yds, Par 68, SSS 65, Course record 63.
Club membership 150.
Societies must telephone in advance. **Green Fees** £11 per round;£15 per day(£16/£20 weekends)reductions in winter.
Course Designer Peter Morrison **Facilities** ⊗ ⚘ ⬛ ⚘ ⚘
Location W side of village off A886

Hotel ★★ 74% Royal Hotel, Shore Rd, TIGHNABRUAICH ☎ 01700 811239 11 en suite

ROTHESAY   Map 10 NS06

Rothesay Canada Hill PA20 9HN
☎ 01700 503554 ▤ 01700 503554
A scenic island course designed by James Braid and Ben Sayers. The course is fairly hilly, with views of the Firth of Clyde, Rothesay Bay or the Kyles of Bute from every hole. Winds are a regular feature which makes the two par 5 holes extremely challenging.
18 holes, 5419yds, Par 69, SSS 66, Course record 62.
Club membership 400.
Visitors pre-booking essential for weekends, telephone professional 01700 503554. **Societies** contact in advance, booking essential at weekends. **Green Fees** terms on application. **Cards** ▦▦ ▦▦ ▦ ▦ ▦▦ ▦ **Prof** James M Dougal **Course Designer** James Braid & Ben Sayers
Facilities ⊗ �𝄪 ⚘ ⬛ ⚘ ⚘ 🏠 ⚘ ⚘ ✆ **Location** 2 min drive from main ferry terminal

Hotel ★★ 74% Royal Hotel, Shore Rd, TIGHNABRUAICH ☎ 01700 811239 11 en suite

COLONSAY, ISLE OF

SCALASAIG   Map 10 NR39

Colonsay Machrins Farm PA61 7YP
☎ 01951 200364 ▤ 01951 200312
e-mail: golf@machrin.free-online.co.uk
Traditional links course on natural machair (hard wearing short grass), challenging, primitive. Colonsay Hotel, 2 miles away, is the headquarters of the club, offering accommodation and facilities.
18 holes, 4775yds, Par 72, SSS 72.
Club membership 200.
Visitors no restrictions. **Societies** apply in writing. **Green Fees** not confirmed. **Facilities** ⚘ **Location** 2m W on A870

Hotel ★★ 70% Isle of Colonsay Hotel, SCALASAIG ☎ 01951 200316 11 rms (9 en suite)

ISLAY, ISLE OF

PORT ELLEN   Map 10 NR34

Machrie Hotel Machrie PA42 7AN
☎ 01496 302310 ▤ 01496 302404
e-mail: machrie@machrie.com
Championship links course opened in 1891, where golf's first £100 Open Championship was played in 1901. Fine turf and many blind holes. Par 4.
continued

18 holes, 6226yds, Par 71, SSS 71, Course record 65.
Club membership 340.
Visitors no restrictions. **Societies** apply in writing or telephone. **Green Fees** £50 per day;£35 per round. **Cards** ▨ ▨ ▨ ▨ ▨ Ⓢ **Course Designer** W Campbell **Facilities** ⊗ ⅢⅢ ⅃ ⚑ ♥ ♀ ♨ ♙ ♨ ✓ Ⓛ **Leisure** fishing, snooker, table tennis.**Conf** Max 120 Thtr 120 Class 60 Board 30 Del £5 to £25 * **Location** 4m N off A846

Hotel ★★ 60% Lochside Hotel, 19 Shore St, BOWMORE ☎ 01496 810244 8 en suite

LEWIS, ISLE OF

STORNOWAY   Map 13 NB43

Stornoway Lady Lever Park HS2 0XP ☎ 01851 702240
e-mail: admin@stornowaygolfclub.co.uk
A short but tricky undulating parkland course set in grounds of Lews Castle with fine views over the Minch to the mainland. The terrain is peat based and there has been substantial investment in drainage works.
18 holes, 5252yds, Par 68, SSS 67, Course record 62.
Club membership 450.
Visitors no golf on Sun. **Societies** apply in writing. **Green Fees** terms on application. **Facilities** ⅃ ♥ ♀ ♨ ▤ ♙ ✓ **Location** 0.5m from town centre off A857

MULL, ISLE OF

CRAIGNURE   Map 10 NM73

Craignure Scallastle PA65 6PB
☎ 01680 812487 & 812416 📠 01680 300402
A natural links course designed round the estuary of the Scallastle Burn that flows into the Sound of Mull. Continual improvements such as five new tees in 1998 have provided 18 teeing areas for the 9 hole layout.
9 holes, 5233yds, Par 69, SSS 66, Course record 72.
Club membership 100.
Visitors may not play on competition days, contact for fixture list. **Societies** write to the secretary 10 days in advance. **Green Fees** not confirmed. **Facilities** ♨ ♙ ✓ **Location** 1.5m N of Craignure A849

TOBERMORY   Map 13 NM55

Tobermory PA75 6PG
☎ 01688 302338 📠 01688 302140
e-mail: tobgolf@fsmail.net
A beautifully maintained hilltop course with superb views over the Sound of Mull. Testing 7th hole (par 3). Often described as the best 9 hole course in Scotland.
9 holes, 4890yds, Par 64, SSS 64, Course record 65.
Club membership 150.
Visitors no restrictions except competition days. **Societies** preferable to contact in advance. **Green Fees** not confirmed. **Course Designer** David Adams **Facilities** ⅃ ♥ ♀ ♨ ♙ ⊶ ✓ **Location** 0.5m N off A848

Hotel ★★♨ 78% Druimard Country House Hotel, DERVAIG ☎ 01688 400345 & 400291 📠 01688 400345 5 en suite 2 annexe en suite

ORKNEY

KIRKWALL   Map 16 HY41

Orkney Grainbank KW15 1RB ☎ 01856 872457
Open parkland course with few hazards and superb views over Kirkwall and Islands.
18 holes, 5411yds, Par 70, SSS 67, Course record 64.
Club membership 402.
Visitors may not play on competition days. **Societies** write or telephone if possible. **Green Fees** £15 per day. **Facilities** ⅃ ♥ ♀ ♨ ♙ ✓ **Location** 0.5m W off A965

STROMNESS   Map 16 HY20

Stromness Ness KW16 3DW ☎ 01856 850772
e-mail: sgc@stromnessgc.co.uk
Testing parkland/seaside course with easy walking. Beautiful holiday course with magnificent views of Scapa Flow. New clubhouse opened 1999.
18 holes, 4762yds, Par 65, SSS 63, Course record 61.
Club membership 350.
Visitors no restrictions except during major competitions. **Societies** no restrictions. **Green Fees** £15 per day. **Facilities** ⊗ ⅃ ♥ ♀ ♨ ♙ ✓ **Leisure** hard tennis courts, Bowling. **Conf** Banquet 110 **Location** S side of town centre off A965

WESTRAY   Map 16 HY44

Westray Rosevale KW17 2DH ☎ 01857 677373
Interesting, picturesque seaside course, easy walking.
9 holes, 2405yds, Par 33.
Club membership 60.
Green Fees not confirmed. **Facilities** ♙ **Location** 1m NW of Pierowall off B9066

SHETLAND

LERWICK   Map 16 HU44

Shetland PO Box 18, Dale ZE2 9SB
☎ 01595 840369 📠 840369
e-mail: clubhousemanager@shetlandgolfclub.co.uk
Challenging moorland course, hard walking. A burn runs the full length of the course and provides a natural hazard. Testing holes include the 3rd (par 4), 5th (par 4).
Dale Course: 18 holes, 5776yds, Par 68, SSS 68,
Course record 67.
Club membership 430.
Visitors advisable to contact in advance. **Societies** Apply in writing or telephone in advance. **Green Fees** not confirmed. **Course Designer** Fraser Middleton **Facilities** ⅃ ♥ ♀ ♨ ♙ ✓ **Location** 4m N on A970

Hotel ★★★ 68% Lerwick Hotel, 15 South Rd, LERWICK ☎ 01595 692166 35 en suite

WHALSAY, ISLAND OF   Map 16 HU56

Whalsay Skaw Taing ZE2 9AA
☎ 01806 566450 566705
The most northerly golf course in Britain, with a large part of it running round the coastline, offering spectacular holes in an exposed but highly scenic setting. There are no cut fairways as yet, these are defined by marker posts, with preferred lies in operation all year round.
18 holes, 6009yds, Par 70, SSS 68, Course record 65.
Club membership 205.

continued

Visitors contact in advance for weekend play. **Societies** telephone in advance. **Green Fees** £10 per round/day. **Facilities** ⊗ by prior arrangement ⫟ by prior arrangement ⫪ ⫩ ♀ ♨ **Location** Whalsay Island

Hotel ★★ 64% The Baltasound Hotel, UNST
☎ 01957 711334 8 rms (6 en suite) 17 annexe en suite

SKYE, ISLE OF

Isle of Skye IV48 8TD ☎ 01478 650414
e-mail: isleofskye.golfclub@btinternet.com
Seaside course with spectacular views. **9 holes with 18 tees. Suitable for golfers of all abilities.**
18 holes, 4677yds, Par 66, SSS 64, Course record 62.
Club membership 270.
Visitors no restrictions. **Societies** apply in advance. **Green Fees** £16 per day. **Facilities** ⊗ ⫪ ⫩ ♨ ☖ ⌇ ⌁ **Location** A87 between Broadford and Portree

Hotel ★★ 73% Rosedale Hotel, Beaumont Crescent, PORTREE ☎ 01478 613131 20 en suite 3 annexe en suite

> Prices may change during the
> currency of the Guide, please
> check when booking

Skeabost Skeabost House Hotel IV51 9NR
☎ 01470 532202
Short woodland and seaside course featuring some very tight fairways and greens.
9 holes, 3056yds, Par 62, SSS 60, Course record 58.
Club membership 80.
Societies contact in advance. **Green Fees** not confirmed.
Cards ▦ ▤ ▣ **Course Designer** John Stuart **Facilities** ⊗ ⫟ ⫪ ⫩ ♀ ♨ ☖ ⌇ ⌁ **Leisure** fishing.

Hotel ★★★ 74% Cuillin Hills Hotel, PORTREE
☎ 01478 612003 21 en suite 9 annexe en suite

SOUTH UIST

Askernish Lochboisdale PA81 5SY ☎ 01878 700298
e-mail: askernish.golf.club@cwcom.net
Golfers play on machair (hard-wearing short grass), close to the Atlantic shore. Excellent views from all tees with constantly changing conditions.
18 holes, 5042yds, Par 68, SSS 67, Course record 64.
Club membership 45.
Visitors no restrictions. **Societies** welcome. **Green Fees** not confirmed. **Course Designer** Tom Morris **Facilities** ⌇ **Location** 5m NW of Lochboisdale off A865

357

Wales

WALES

ANGLESEY, ISLE OF

AMLWCH   Map 06 SH49

Bull Bay LL68 9RY ☎ 01407 830960 📠 01407 832612
e-mail: secretary@bullbaygolf.freeserve.co.uk
Wales's northernmost course, Bull Bay is a pleasant coastal, heathland course with natural rock, gorse and wind hazards. Views from several tees across Irish Sea to Isle of Man, and across Anglesey to Snowdonia.
18 holes, 6217yds, Par 70, SSS 70, Course record 60.
Club membership 700.
Visitors advisable to contact in advance. **Societies** advance booking essential. **Green Fees** £20 per day(£25 weekends & bank holidays). **Cards** 🔲 🔳 🔲 🔲 🔲 🔲 **Prof** John Burns **Course Designer** W H Fowler **Facilities** ⊗ ⊪ ⓑ 🍺 ♀ ♣ 🏠 ❓ 🏌 🚃 ✓ **Location** 1m W of Amlwch on A5025

Hotel ★★ 67% Trecastell Hotel, Bull Bay, AMLWCH
☎ 01407 830651 13 rms (11 en suite)

BEAUMARIS   Map 06 SH67

Baron Hill LL58 8YW
☎ 01248 810231 📠 01248 810231
e-mail: baronhill@line1.net
Undulating course with natural hazards of rock and gorse. Testing 3rd and 4th holes (par 4s). Hole 5/14 plays into the prevailing wind with an elevated tee across two streams. The hole is between two gorse covered mounds.
9 holes, 5062mtrs, Par 68, SSS 69, Course record 62.
Club membership 400.
Visitors ladies have priority on Tue am & club competitions Sun, seniors Thurs only. **Societies** apply in writing to secretary. **Green Fees** £15 per day;£45 per week. **Facilities** ⊗ ⓑ 🍺 ♀ ♣ ✓ **Location** Take A545 from Menai Bridge to Beaumaris, course signed on approach to town

Hotel ★★ 75% Ye Olde Bulls Head Inn, Castle St, BEAUMARIS ☎ 01248 810329
12 en suite 1 annexe en suite

Princes Henllys Hall LL58 8HU
☎ 01248 811717 📠 01248 811511
e-mail: henllys@hpbsite.com
The Menai Straits and the Snowdonia mountains form a magnificent backdrop to the course. Full use has been made of the mature parkland trees and natural water hazards to provide a really testing and enjoyable game of golf.
18 holes, 6062yards.
Club membership 300.
Visitors contact 7 days in advance. **Societies** telephone in advance **Green Fees** £20 (£25 weekend and bank holidays). **Prof** Peter Maton **Course Designer** Roger Jones **Facilities** ⓑ 🍺 ♀ ♣ 🏠 ❓ 🚃 ✓ **Location** A545 to Beaumaris and through town. After " mile, Henllys Hall signed on left

Hotel ★★ 75% Ye Olde Bulls Head Inn, Castle St, BEAUMARIS ☎ 01248 810329
12 en suite 1 annexe en suite

Looking for a driving range?
See the index at the back of the guide

HOLYHEAD   Map 06 SH28

Holyhead Lon Garreg Fawr, Trearddur Bay LL65 2YL
☎ 01407 763279 📠 01407 763279
Treeless, undulating seaside course which provides a varied and testing game, particularly in a south wind. The fairways are bordered by gorse, heather and rugged outcrops of rock. Accuracy from most tees is paramount as there are 43 fairway and greenside bunkers and lakes. Designed by James Braid.
18 holes, 6058yds, Par 70, SSS 70, Course record 64.
Club membership 1350.
Visitors must contact in advance. **Societies** must contact in advance. **Green Fees** £25 per day; £19 per round (£29/£25 weekends & bank holidays). **Cards** 🔲 🔳 **Prof** Stephen Elliot **Course Designer** James Braid **Facilities** ⊗ ⊪ ⓑ 🍺 ♀ ♣ 🏠 ❓ 🏌 🚃 ✓ **Location** A55 to rdbt at Hollyhead, left on B4545 to Trearddur Bay 1 mile

Hotel ★★★ 71% Trearddur Bay Hotel, TREARDDUR BAY ☎ 01407 860301 37 en suite

LLANGEFNI   Map 06 SH47

Llangefni (Public) Clai Rd LL77 7LJ
☎ 01248 722193 📠 01248 750156
9 holes, 1342yds, Par 28, SSS 28.
Course Designer Hawtree & Sons **Location** 1.5m off A5
Telephone for further details

Hotel ★★ 66% Anglesey Arms, MENAI BRIDGE
☎ 01248 712305 16 en suite

RHOSNEIGR   Map 06 SH37

Anglesey Station Rd LL64 5QX
☎ 01407 811202 & 811127 📠 01407 811127
e-mail: info@theangleseygolfclub.com
Links course, low and fairly level with sand dunes and tidal river.
18 holes, 6300yds, Par 68, SSS 68.
Club membership 500.
Visitors phone in advance, some times are reserved for members. Dress restrictions. **Societies** telephone & confirm in writing. **Green Fees** terms on application. **Cards** 🔲 🔳 🔲 🔲 **Prof** Mr Steve Elliot **Course Designer** H Hilton **Facilities** ⊗ ⊪ ⓑ 🍺 ♀ ♣ 🏠 🚃 ✓ **Location** NE side of village on A4080

Hotel ★★★ 71% Trearddur Bay Hotel, TREARDDUR BAY ☎ 01407 860301 37 en suite

BLAENAU GWENT

NANTYGLO   Map 03 SO11

West Monmouthshire Golf Rd, Winchestown NP23 4QT ☎ 01495 310233 📠 01495 310361
Established in 1906, this mountain and heathland course was officially designated by the Guinness Book of Records in 1994 as being the highest above sea level, with the 14th tee at a height of 1513ft. The course has plenty of picturesque views, hard walking and natural hazards. Testing 3rd hole, par 5, and 7th hole, par 4.
18 holes, 6300yds, Par 71, SSS 69, Course record 65.
Club membership 350.
Visitors welcome. **Societies** apply in writing or contact golf shop 01495 310233 **Green Fees** £12 per day (£15 weekends). **Course Designer** Ben Sayers **Facilities** ⊗ ⊪ ⓑ

continued

359

♦♥♣♠ 🏌 ⚐ **Conf** Max 50 Del from £1-£6.50 *
Location 0.25m W off A467

Hotel ★★ 70% Pantrhiwgoch Hotel & Riverside
Restaurant, Brecon Rd, ABERGAVENNY
☎ 01873 810550 18 en suite

TREDEGAR
Map 03 SO10

Tredegar and Rhymney Cwmtysswg, Rhymney
NP2 3BQ ☎ 01685 840743 (club) & 843400 (office)
e-mail: golfclub@tredegarandrhymney.fsnet.co.uk
**Mountain course with lovely views. The course is being
developed into an 18 hole course.**
9 holes, 5504yds, Par 68, SSS 68, Course record 69.
Club membership 194.
Visitors cannot play Sun before 12. **Societies** must contact
in advance. **Green Fees** not confirmed. **Facilities** ⚐
Location 1.75m SW on B4256

Hotel ★★★ 69% Tregenna Hotel, Park Ter,
MERTHYR TYDFIL ☎ 01685 723627 & 382055
🗎 01685 721951 29 en suite

BRIDGEND

BRIDGEND
Map 03 SS97

Coed-Y-Mwstwr The Clubhouse, Coychurch
CF35 6AF ☎ 01656 862121 & 864 934 🗎 01656 864934
e-mail: coed-y-mwstwr@lineone.net
**Challenging holes on this 12-hole course include the par 3
11th(180yds) involving a drive across a lake and the par 4
5th (448yds) which is subject to strong prevailing winds.**
12 holes, 6144yds, Par 70, SSS 70, Course record 71.
Club membership 300.
Visitors must have handicap certificate, advisable to contact
in advance. May only play Sat if with member. **Societies** by
prior application. **Green Fees** £16 per 18 holes(£18
weekends). **Cards** ⊞ ▭ ▤ ▨ ⚐ **Course Designer**
Chapman/Warren **Facilities** ⊗ 〗 🍴 ⚑ ♀ ♠ 🏠 ⚐ **Leisure**
pool table. **Conf** Max 25 Class 25 Board 18 Banquet 25
Location 1m out of Coychurch, turn at village garage. 2m W
of junct 35 on M4

Hotel ★★★ 76% Coed-Y-Mwstwr Hotel, Coychurch,
BRIDGEND ☎ 01656 860621 23 en suite

Southerndown Ewenny CF32 0QP
☎ 01656 880476 🗎 01656 880317
e-mail: southerndowngolf@btconnect.com
**Downland-links championship course with rolling
fairways and fast greens. The par-3 5th is played
across a valley and the 18th, with its split level fairway,
is a demanding finishing hole. Superb views.**
18 holes, 6441yds, Par 70, SSS 72, Course record 64.
Club membership 710.
Visitors must contact in advance & have handicap
certificate. **Societies** by arrangement with secretary.
Green Fees £30(£40 weekends)£5 extra holes. **Prof** D G
McMonagle **Course Designer** W Fernie **Facilities** ⊗ 〗
🍴 ♀ ♠ 🏠 ♥ 🏌 ⚐ **Location** 3m SW of Bridgend
on B4524

Hotel ★★★ 69% Heronston Hotel, Ewenny Rd,
BRIDGEND ☎ 01656 668811
69 en suite 6 annexe en suite

MAESTEG
Map 03 SS89

Maesteg Mount Pleasant, Neath Rd CF34 9PR
☎ 01656 734106 & 732037 🗎 01656 734106
18 holes, 5929yds, Par 70, SSS 69, Course record 69.
Course Designer James Braid **Location** 0.5m W off B4282
Telephone for further details

Hotel ★★★ 68% Aberavon Beach Hotel, PORT TALBOT
☎ 01639 884949 52 en suite

PENCOED
Map 03 SS98

St Mary's Hotel Golf & Country Club St Mary
Hill CF35 5EA ☎ 01656 861100 🗎 01656 863400
**A parkland course with many American-style features.
The par 3 10th, called 'Alcatraz', has a well deserved
reputation.**

*St Mary's Course: 18 holes, 5291yds, Par 69, SSS 66,
Course record 68.*
Sevenoaks Course: 12 holes, 3125yds, Par 35.
Club membership 830.
Visitors St. Mary's Course: must contact in advance,
handicap certificate not required between 9-4 Mon-Fri, after
1pm weekends. Seven Oaks: no restrictions **Societies**
telephone in advance **Green Fees** terms on application.
Cards ⊞ ▭ ▤ ⚐ **Prof** John Peters **Facilities**
⊗ 〗 🍴 ⚑ ♀ ♠ 🏠 🍴 ▦ 🏌 ⚐ ♣ **Leisure** hard tennis
courts.**Conf** Max 120 Thtr 120 Class 30 Board 40 Banquet
110 Del £16.95 to £30.50 * **Location** 5m from junct 35 of M4

Hotel ★★★ 73% St Mary's Hotel & Country Club, St
Marys Golf Club, PENCOED ☎ 01656 861100 & 860280
🗎 01656 863400 24 en suite

PORTHCAWL
Map 03 SS87

Royal Porthcawl CF36 3UW
☎ 01656 782251 🗎 01656 771687
e-mail: royalporthcawl@cs.com
**This championship-standard heathland/downland
links course is always in sight of the sea. With holes
facing every point of the compass, the golfer is always
tested by the wind and the course has hosted many
major tournaments.**
18 holes, 6406yds, Par 72, SSS 74, Course record 65.
Club membership 800.
Visitors must contact in advanced & produce handicap
certificate limit men 20, ladies 30. Restricted at weekends
& bank holidays. **Societies** apply in writing. **Green Fees**
terms on application. **Cards** ⊞ ▭ ⚐ **Prof** Peter Evans
Course Designer Charles Gibson **Facilities** ⊗ 〗 🍴 ♀ ⚐
♠ 🏠 🍴 ▦ 🏌 ⚐ ♣ **Location** 1.5m NW of town centre

Hotel ★★★ 65% Seabank Hotel, The Promenade,
PORTHCAWL ☎ 01656 782261 67 en suite

★ ★ ★
St. Mary's Hotel, Golf & Country Club

A luxury country hotel converted from a 17th century farmhouse, we offer elegance and comfort with first class friendly service. Set in picturesque surroundings on a privately owned 150 acre 27 hole golf complex 2 mins from M4, making it the perfect location for business or pleasure.

- 18 hole St Mary's Course
- 9 hole Sevenoaks Course
- 15 bay floodlit driving range
- Tennis court and practice area
- Bars
- Restaurant

All rooms fitted with:
- Whirlpool baths
- Satellite TV
- Coffee & tea facilities
- Direct dial telephone

Golf, Equestrian and Weekend Breaks available.

Please call us for a brochure and sample for yourselves "The Magic of St. Mary's".

**St. Mary's Golf Club Ltd. St. Mary's Hill Pencoed, South Glamorgan CF35 5EA.
Hotel Reservation: Tel: (01656) 861100 Fax: (01656) 863400**

PYLE   Map 03 SS88

Pyle & Kenfig Waun-Y-Mer CF33 4PU
☎ 01656 783093 🖹 01656 772822
18 holes, 6688yds, Par 71, SSS 73, Course record 68.
Course Designer Colt **Location** S side of Pyle off A4229.
Access via junct 37 on M4
Telephone for further details

Hotel ★★★ 65% Seabank Hotel, The Promenade, PORTHCAWL ☎ 01656 782261 67 en suite

CAERPHILLY

BARGOED   Map 03 ST19

Bargoed Heolddu CF81 9GF
☎ 01443 830143 & 836411 (Prof)
e-mail: bargoedgc@barbox.net
Mountain parkland course, challenging par 70 course with panoramic views. Easy walking.
18 holes, 6049yds, Par 70, SSS 70, Course record 64.
Club membership 600.
Visitors must contact professional in advance, must play with member at weekends. **Societies** must contact in advance. **Green Fees** terms on application. **Prof** B Hunter
Facilities 🏌 🍺 ♀ ⛳ 🏪 ♂ **Location** NW side of town

Hotel ★★★ 67% Maes Manor Hotel, BLACKWOOD
☎ 01495 224551 & 220011 🖹 01495 228217
8 en suite 14 annexe en suite

BLACKWOOD   Map 03 ST19

Blackwood Cwmgelli NP12 1BR
☎ 01495 222121 (Office) & 223152 (Club)
Heathland course with sand bunkers. Undulating, with hard walking. Testing 2nd hole par 4. Good views.
9 holes, 5332yds, Par 67, Course record 62.
Club membership 310.
Visitors contact club or turn up and pay greens staff, may not play at weekends & bank holidays unless with member. Must be members of recognised golf club. **Societies** by prior arrangement for members of a recognised golf club. **Green Fees** £14(£18 weekends). **Facilities** ⊗ 🏌 🍺 ♀ ⛳ **Location** 0.25m N of Blackwood, off A4048

Hotel ★★★ 67% Maes Manor Hotel, BLACKWOOD
☎ 01495 224551 & 220011 🖹 01495 228217
8 en suite 14 annexe en suite

CAERPHILLY   Map 03 ST18

Caerphilly Pencapel, Mountain Rd CF83 1HJ
☎ 029 20883481 & 20863441 🖹 029 20863441
Undulating mountain course with woodland affording good views especially from 9th hole, 700 ft above sea level.
13 holes, 5944yds, Par 71, SSS 70.
Club membership 650.
Visitors telephone in advance, must produce a current handicap certificate or letter from club secretary, may not play at weekends except with member, no visitors bank holidays. **Societies** apply in writing in advance to the secretary. **Green Fees** terms on application. **Prof** Joel Hill
Facilities 🏌 🍺 ♀ ⛳ 🏪 ♂ **Location** 0.5m S on A469

continued

Hotel ★★★ 75% Manor Parc Country Hotel & Restaurant,
Thornhill Rd, Thornhill, CARDIFF
☎ 029 2069 3723 12 en suite

Mountain Lakes & Castell Heights

Blaengwynlais CF83 1NG
☎ 029 20861128 & 20886666 🖹 029 20863243
e-mail: sales@golfclub.co.uk
The 9-hole Castell Heights course within the Mountain
Lakes complex was established in 1982 on a 45-acre site.
In 1988 a further 18-hole course, Mountain Lakes was
designed by Bob Sandow to take advantage of 160-acres
of mountain heathland, combining both mountain top
golf and parkland. Most holes are tree lined and there are
20 'lakes' as hazards. Host of major PGA tournaments.
*Mountain Lakes Course: 18 holes, 6046mtrs, Par 74, SSS 73,
Course record 69.*
*Castell Heights Course: 9 holes, 2751mtrs, Par 35, SSS 32,
Course record 32.*
Club membership 500.
Societies written or telephone notice in advance. **Green Fees**
terms on application. **Cards** 〰 〰 〰 〰 🔟 **Prof** Sion
Bebb **Course Designer** Bob Sandow **Facilities** ⊗ ⅏ 🍴 ☷ ♨ ♀
⚶ 🏠 🍴 🏌 ♨ ♂ ⟨ **Conf** Max 100 Del £5 to £20 *
Location Near Black Cock Inn, Caerphilly Mountain,
junct 32 M4

Hotel ★★★ 75% Manor Parc Country Hotel & Restaurant,
Thornhill Rd, Thornhill, CARDIFF
☎ 029 2069 3723 12 en suite

Virginia Park Golf Club Virginia Park CF83 3SW
☎ 024 20863919 & 20585368
9 holes, 2566yds, Par 33.
Location Off Pontyewindy Rd
Telephone for further details

Hotel ★★★ 75% Manor Parc Country Hotel & Restaurant,
Thornhill Rd, Thornhill, CARDIFF
☎ 029 2069 3723 12 en suite

Bryn Meadows Golf & Country Hotel

Mr G Mayo CF82 7FN
☎ 01495 225590 or 224103 🖹 01495 228272
e-mail: information@brynmeadows.co.uk
A heavily wooded parkland course with panoramic views
of the Brecon Beacons.
18 holes, 6132yds, Par 72, SSS 69, Course record 68.
Club membership 540.
Visitors may not play Sun mornings. Must contact in
advance. **Societies** Mon-Fri **Green Fees** not confirmed.
Cards 〰 〰 〰 〰 🔟 **Prof** Bruce Hunter **Course**
Designer Mayo/Jeffries **Facilities** ⊗ ⅏ 🍴 ☷ ♀ ⚶ 🏠 🍴
🛏 ♨ ♂ ⟨ **Leisure** heated indoor swimming pool, sauna,
solarium, gymnasium. **Location** On the A4048 Blackwood to
Ystrad Mynach rd

Hotel ★★★ 67% Maes Manor Hotel, BLACKWOOD
☎ 01495 224551 & 220011 🖹 01495 228217
8 en suite 14 annexe en suite

Whitehall The Pavilion CF46 6ST ☎ 01443 740245
Hilltop course. Testing 4th hole (225 yds) par 3, and 6th
hole (402 yds) par 4. Pleasant views.
9 holes, 5666yds, Par 69, SSS 68, Course record 63.
Club membership 300.

Visitors must be a member of a recognised golf club & have
a handicap certificate. Must contact in advance to play at
weekends. **Societies** must contact in writing 4 weeks in
advance. **Green Fees** £15 per round. **Facilities** 🍴 ♀ ⚶
Leisure snooker. **Location** Turn off A470 to Nelson and
take A4054 S

Hotel ★★★ 70% Llechwen Hall Hotel, Llanfabon,
PONTYPRIDD ☎ 01443 742050 & 743020
🖹 01443 742189 12 en suite 8 annexe en suite

Oakdale Llwynon Ln NP12 0NF
☎ 01495 220044 220440
9 holes, 1344yds, Par 28, Course record 27.
Visitors no restrictions pay & play. **Societies** telephone in
advance **Green Fees** terms on application. **Course Designer**
Ian Goodenough **Facilities** 🍴 ♀ ⚶ 🏠 🍴 🏌 ♨ ♂ ⟨
Leisure fishing, Snooker tables. **Location** Situated off the
B4251 to Portllanfraith Road at Oakdale.

Hotel ★★★ 67% Maes Manor Hotel, BLACKWOOD
☎ 01495 224551 & 220011 🖹 01495 228217
8 en suite 14 annexe en suite

Cardiff Sherborne Av, Cyncoed CF23 6SJ
☎ 029 20753320 🖹 029 20680011
e-mail: cardiff.golfclub@virgin.net
Parkland course, where trees form natural hazards.
Interesting variety of holes, mostly bunkered. A stream
flows through course and comes into play on nine
separate holes.
18 holes, 6016yds, Par 70, SSS 70, Course record 66.
Club membership 900.
Visitors Must contact in advance, only with member at
weekends. **Societies** Thu only, pre-booking essential. **Green**
Fees £35 per day (£40 weekends). **Cards** 〰 〰 🔟 **Prof**
Terry Hanson **Facilities** ⊗ ⅏ 🍴 ☷ ♀ ⚶ 🏠 ♂ **Leisure**
snooker. **Conf** Max 100 Board 15 Banquet 150 **Location** 3m
N of city centre

Hotel ★★★ 71% Holiday Inn Cardiff North, Pentwyn Rd,
Pentwyn, CARDIFF ☎ 0870 400 8141 142 en suite

Cottrell Park Cottrell Park, St Nicholas CF5 6SJ
☎ 01446 781781 🖹 01446 781187
e-mail: admin@cottrell-park.co.uk
Two well designed courses, opened in 1996, set in
undulating parkland with mature trees and spectacular
views, especially from the par 35 9-hole course. An

continued

continued

enjoyable yet testing game of golf for players of all abilities.
Mackintosh: 18 holes, 6110yds, Par 72, SSS 71, Course record 65.
Button: 18 holes, 6007yds, Par 72.
Club membership 1050.
Visitors Should have a valid handicap certificate,or be a member of a golf club. **Societies** minimum of 12 players. **Green Fees** £25 Mon-Thur(£35 Fri-Sun). **Cards** 🔲 🔲 🔲 📱 **Prof** Steve Birch **Course Designer** MRM Sandow **Facilities** ⊗ ⅷ ᇈ 🍺 ♀ 占 🏠 ↑ 🚶 ⚲ ⅽ **Conf** Max 120 Thtr 120 Class 60 Board 40 Banquet 100 Del £19 to £35 * **Location** M4 junct 33 to Culverhouse Cross A48 to Cowbridge, through St Nicholas on right hand side

Hotel ★★★★ 70% Copthorne Hotel Cardiff-Caerdydd, Copthorne Way, Culverhouse Cross, CARDIFF ☎ 029 2059 9100 135 en suite

Llanishen Cwm Lisvane CF4 5UD
☎ 029 20755078 📠 029 20755078
Sloping course overlooking the Bristol Channel.
18 holes, 5327yds, Par 68, SSS 67, Course record 63.
Club membership 900.
Visitors must play with member at weekends & bank holidays, may not play Wed. Must contact in advance. **Societies** contact in advance. **Green Fees** £30 per 18 holes. **Prof** Adrian Jones **Facilities** ⊗ ⅷ ᇈ 🍺 ♀ 占 🏠 ⚲ **Conf** Max 150 Class 100 Banquet 140 **Location** 5m N of city centre off A469

Hotel ★★★ 71% Holiday Inn Cardiff North, Pentwyn Rd, Pentwyn, CARDIFF ☎ 0870 400 8141 142 en suite

Peterstone Peterstone, Wentloog CF3 2TN
☎ 01633 680009 📠 01633 680563
e-mail: peterstone_lakes@yahoo.com
Parkland course with abundant water features and several long drives (15th, 601yds).
18 holes, 6555yds, Par 72.
Club membership 600.
Visitors contact in advance for tee times. **Societies** telephone enquiries welcome. **Green Fees** £15(Mon&Tue);£18 (Wed-Fri);£25(weekends) per round. Reductions in winter. **Cards** 🔲 🔲 📱 **Prof** Paul Glyn **Course Designer** Bob Sandow **Facilities** ⊗ ⅷ ᇈ 🍺 ♀ 占 🏠 ↑ 🚶 ⚲ **Conf** Max 175 Thtr 175 Class 150 Board 150 Banquet 150 Del £5 to £30 * **Location** 2m from Castleton off A48

Hotel ★★★ 72% St Mellons Hotel & Country Club, Castleton, CARDIFF ☎ 01633 680355 21 en suite 20 annexe en suite

Radyr The Clubhouse, Drysgol Rd, Radyr CF15 8BS
☎ 029 20842408 📠 029 20843914
e-mail: manager@radyrgolf.co.uk
Parkland course which celebrated its centenary year in 2002. Good views. Venue for many county and national championships.
18 holes, 6031yds, Par 69, SSS 70, Course record 62.
Club membership 920.
Visitors must play with member at weekends,or by special arrangement with club office. **Societies** must contact in advance. **Green Fees** £38 per day. **Cards** 🔲 🔲 📱 🔲 **Prof** Robert Butterworth **Course Designer** Colt **Facilities** ⊗ ⅷ ᇈ 🍺 ♀ 占 🏠 ↑ 🚶 ⚲ **Leisure** Table tennis, snooker room. **Conf** Max 120 Thtr 120 Class 80 Board 80 Banquet 130 **Location** M4 junct32, 4.5m NW of city centre off A4119

Hotel ★★★ 75% Manor Parc Country Hotel & Restaurant, Thornhill Rd, Thornhill, CARDIFF ☎ 029 2069 3723 12 en suite

St Mellons St Mellons CF3 2XS
☎ 01633 680408 📠 01633 681219
This parkland course comprises five par 3 holes and provides some testing golf. It is indeed a challenge to the single handicap golfer.
18 holes, 6275yds, Par 70, SSS 70, Course record 63.
Club membership 700.
Visitors must contact in advance. With member only at weekends. **Societies** must contact in advance. **Green Fees** terms on application. **Prof** Barry Thomas **Facilities** ⊗ ⅷ ᇈ 🍺 ♀ 占 🏠 ↑ 🚶 ⚲ **Location** 5m NE off A48

Hotel ★★★ 72% St Mellons Hotel & Country Club, Castleton, CARDIFF ☎ 01633 680355 21 en suite 20 annexe en suite

Whitchurch Pantmawr Rd, Whitchurch CF14 7TD
☎ 029 20620985 (Sec) 📠 029 20529860
e-mail: whitchurch@golfclub14.fsnet.co.uk
Well manicured parkland course, slightly undulating, with fine views over the city centre and the Bristol Channel beyond.
18 holes, 6321yds, Par 71, SSS 70, Course record 62.
Club membership 750.
Visitors may not play on competition days, contact secretary/professional in advance. **Societies** Thu only. Must contact in advance. **Green Fees** £35 per day (£40 weekends). **Prof** Eddie Clark **Course Designer** F Johns **Facilities** ⊗ ⅷ ᇈ 🍺 ♀ 占 🏠 ↑ ⚲ **Location** 4m N of city centre on A470, 600 yds south of junct 32 off M4

Hotel ★★★ 75% Manor Parc Country Hotel & Restaurant, Thornhill Rd, Thornhill, CARDIFF ☎ 029 2069 3723 12 en suite

CREIGIAU (CREIYIAU)   Map 03 ST08
Creigiau Llantwit Rd CF15 9WN
☎ 029 20890263 📠 20890706
Downland course, with small greens and many interesting water hazards.
18 holes, 6063yds, Par 70.
Club membership 1300.
Visitors must contact in advance **Societies** Deposit required.Apply by telephone or writing. **Green Fees** not confirmed. **Cards** 🔲 🔲 🔲 📱 🔲 🔲 📱 **Prof** Iain Luntz **Facilities** ⊗ ⅷ ᇈ 🍺 ♀ 占 🏠 ↑ ⚲ **Location** 6m NW of Cardiff on A4119

Hotel ★★★★ 69% Miskin Manor Hotel & Health Club LTD, Groes Faen, Pontyclun, MISKIN ☎ 01443 224204 35 en suite 11 annexe en suite

CARMARTHENSHIRE

AMMANFORD   Map 03 SN61
Glynhir Glynhir Rd, Llandybie SA18 2TF
☎ 01269 850472 & 851365 📠 01269 851365
e-mail: glynhir.golfclub@virgin.net
Parkland course with good views, latter holes close to Upper Loughor River. The 14th is a 394yd dog-leg.
18 holes, Par 69, SSS 70, Course record 66.
Club membership 700.

continued

continued

Visitors no visitors Sun. Contact professional in advance (01269 851010). **Societies** welcome weekdays only. Contact in advance. **Green Fees** not confirmed. **Prof** Duncan Prior **Course Designer** F Hawtree **Facilities** ⊗ ⅷ ⅼ ♨ ♀ ⚘ 🏠 ⚑ 🛏 ⚒ **Location** 2m N of Ammanford

Hotel ★★ 67% Mill at Glynhir, Glynhir Rd, Llandybie, AMMANFORD ☎ 01269 850672
7 en suite 3 annexe en suite

BURRY PORT   Map 02 SN40

Ashburnham Cliffe Ter SA16 0HN
☎ 01554 832269 & 833846
18 holes, 6916yds, Par 72, SSS 74, Course record 70.
Course Designer J H Taylor **Location** 5m W of Llanelli, A484 road
Telephone for further details

Hotel ★★ 69% Ashburnham Hotel, Ashburnham Rd, Pembrey, LLANELLI ☎ 01554 834343 & 834455
🖥 01554 834483 12 en suite

CARMARTHEN   Map 02 SN42

Carmarthen Blaenycoed Rd SA33 6EH
☎ 01267 281588 🖥 01267 281493
e-mail: jonseccgc@aol.com
Hilltop course with good views.
18 holes, 6245yds, Par 71, SSS 71, Course record 66.
Club membership 700.
Visitors must have a handicap certificate, telephone for times at weekends. **Societies** apply in writing minimum of ten days in advance. **Green Fees** £20(£25 weekends). **Prof** Pat Gillis **Course Designer** J H Taylor **Facilities** ⊗ ⅷ ⅼ ♨ ♀ ⚘ 🏠 ⚑ ⚒ **Location** 4m N of town

Hotel ★★ 63% Falcon Hotel, Lammas St, CARMARTHEN ☎ 01267 234959 & 237152 🖥 01267 221277 14 en suite

Derllys Court Llysonnen Rd SA33 5DT
☎ 01267 211575 🖥 01267 211575
e-mail: derllys@hotmail.com
Gently undulating parkland course with challenging par 3s (5th and 8th) and a testing par 5 involving a shot across a lake.
18 holes, 5915yds, Par 70, SSS 68.
Club membership 60.
Visitors welcome at all times. **Societies** telephone in advance. **Green Fees** terms on application. **Cards** 🖃 ▦ 📇 🔳 ▨ **Course Designer** Peter Johnson/Stuart Finney **Facilities** ⊗ ⅷ ⅼ ♨ ♀ ⚘ 🏠 ⚑ 🛏 ⚒ **Location** Just off A40 between Carmarthen/St Clears

Hotel ★★ 63% Falcon Hotel, Lammas St, CARMARTHEN ☎ 01267 234959 & 237152 🖥 01267 221277 14 en suite

KIDWELLY   Map 02 SN40

Glyn Abbey Trimsaran SA17 4LB
☎ 01554 810278 🖥 01554 810889
e-mail: course-enquiries@glynabbey.co.uk
Beautiful parkland course on the slopes of the Gwendraeth valley, set in 200 acres with mature wooded backdrops.
18 holes, 6173yds, Par 70, SSS 70, Course record 68.
Club membership 200.
Visitors telephone booking advisable. **Societies** must contact in advance. **Green Fees** £14 per round (£17 weekends).

continued

Course Designer Hawtree **Facilities** ⊗ ⅷ ⅼ ♨ ♀ ⚘ 🏠 ⚑ 🛏 ⚒ **Leisure** gymnasium.**Conf** Max 88 Banquet 88 **Location** 4.5m W of Llanelli, on B4317 between Trimsaran and Carway

Hotel ★★ 69% Ashburnham Hotel, Ashburnham Rd, Pembrey, LLANELLI ☎ 01554 834343 & 834455
🖥 01554 834483 12 en suite

CEREDIGION

ABERYSTWYTH   Map 06 SN58

Aberystwyth Brynymor Rd SY23 2HY
☎ 01970 615104 🖥 01970 626622
e-mail: aberystwythgolf@talk21.com
Undulating meadowland course. Testing holes: 16th (The Loop) par 3; 17th, par 4; 18th, par 3. Good views over Cardigan Bay.
18 holes, 6109yds, Par 70, SSS 70, Course record 67.
Club membership 400.
Visitors must contact in advance. **Societies** write or telephone in advance. **Green Fees** not confirmed. **Cards** 🖃 ▦ 📇 🔳 ▨ **Course Designer** Harry Vardon **Facilities** ⊗ ⅷ ⅼ ♨ ♀ ⚘ 🏠 ⚒ **Location** N side of town

Hotel ★★★ 70% Belle Vue Royal Hotel, Marine Ter, ABERYSTWYTH ☎ 01970 617558 34 en suite

BORTH   Map 06 SN69

Borth & Ynyslas SY24 5JS
☎ 01970 871202 🖥 01970 871202
e-mail: secretary@borthgolf.co.uk
Seaside links, over 100 years old, with strong winds at times although part of the course is sheltered amongst the dunes. Some narrow fairways and plenty of natural hazards.
18 holes, 6116yds, Par 70, SSS 70, Course record 65.
Club membership 550.
Visitors must contact in advance, may play weekends ring to check no competitions in progress. **Societies** telephone in advance. **Green Fees** terms on application. **Prof** J G Lewis **Facilities** ⊗ ⅼ ♨ ♀ ⚘ 🏠 ⚑ ⚒ **Location** 0.5m N on B4353

Hotel ★★★✦♣ Ynyshir Hall, EGLWYSFACH ☎ 01654 781209 8 en suite 2 annexe en suite

CARDIGAN   Map 02 SN14

Cardigan Gwbert-on-Sea SA43 1PR
☎ 01239 621775 & 612035 🖥 01239 621775
e-mail: golf@cardigan.fsnet.co.uk
A links course, very dry in winter, with wide fairways, light rough and gorse. Every hole overlooks the sea.
18 holes, 6687yds, Par 72, SSS 73, Course record 68.
Club membership 600.
Visitors may not play between 1-2pm. Handicap certificate preferred. Contact in advance **Societies** must telephone in advance. **Green Fees** £20 per day (£25 weekends & bank holidays). **Cards** 🖃 ▦ 📇 🔳 ▨ **Prof** Colin Parsons **Course Designer** Hawtree **Facilities** ⊗ ⅷ ⅼ ♨ ♀ ⚘ 🏠 ⚑ 🛏 ⚒ **Leisure** squash. **Location** 3m N off A487

Hotel ★★★ 67% Cliff Hotel, GWBERT-ON-SEA ☎ 01239 613241 61 en suite

GWBERT-ON-SEA   Map 02 SN15

Cliff Hotel   SA43 1PP

☎ 01239 613241   🖹 01239 615391

e-mail: cliffhotel@btopenworld.com

This is a short course with two par 4s and the remainder are challenging par 3s. Particularly interesting holes are played across the sea on to a small island.

9 holes, 1545yds, Par 29.

Visitors telephone to book in advance. **Societies** telephone in advance. **Green Fees** from £6. **Cards** 🌐 📧 💳 💷 🔣 💷 **Facilities** ⊗ ⅷ ᴌ 💺 ♀ ⚒ ⛾ 🥂 🍴 *⛿* **Leisure** heated outdoor swimming pool, squash, fishing, sauna, solarium, gymnasium. **Conf** Thtr 200 Class 60 Board 60 Banquet 200 Del £5 to £30 * **Location** 3 miles from Cardigan

Hotel ★★★ 67% Cliff Hotel, GWBERT-ON-SEA
☎ 01239 613241 61 en suite

LLANDYSSUL   Map 02 SN44

Saron   Saron SA44 5EL   ☎ 01559 370705

Set in 50 acres of mature parkland with large trees and magnificent Teifi Valley views. Numerous water hazards and bunkers.

9 holes, 2400yds, Par 32, Course record 34.

Visitors may play at all times no arrangements required. **Societies** telephone for details. **Green Fees** £8 per 18 holes, £6 per 9 holes. **Course Designer** Adas **Facilities** 💺 ⛾ 🥂 *⛿* **Leisure** fishing. **Location** Off A484 at Saron

Hotel ★★ 73% The Penbontbren Farm Hotel, Glynarthen, Llandysul, CARDIGAN ☎ 01239 810248
10 annexe en suite

LLANGYBI   Map 02 SN65

Cilgwyn   SA48 8NN   ☎ 01570 493286

Picturesque parkland course in secluded valley, with natural features of ponds, stream and woodland.

9 holes, 5309yds, Par 68, SSS 66, Course record 66.

Club membership 300.

Visitors no restrictions, apart from Sun when advisable to telephone. **Societies** apply in advance by letter or telephone. **Green Fees** not confirmed. **Course Designer** Sandor **Facilities** ⊗ by prior arrangement ⅷ by prior arrangement ᴌ by prior arrangement 💺 ♀ 🥂 *⛿* **Location** 5m N of Lampeter on A485

Hotel ★★★ 66% Falcondale Mansion, LAMPETER
☎ 01570 422910 19 en suite

LLANRHYSTUD   Map 06 SN56

Penrhos Golf & Country Club   SY23 5AY

☎ 01974 202999   🖹 01974 202100

e-mail: info@penrhosgolf.co.uk

Beautifully scenic course incorporating lakes and

spectacular coastal and inland views. Many leisure facilities.

Penrhos: 18 holes, 6641yds, Par 72, SSS 73, Course record 71.

Academy: 9 holes, 1827yds, Par 31.

Club membership 300.

Visitors must telephone, no jeans allowed on main course. **Societies** must telephone in advance. **Green Fees** terms on application. **Cards** 🌐 📧 💳 🔣 💷 **Prof** Paul Diamond **Course Designer** Jim Walters **Facilities** ⊗ ⅷ ᴌ 💺 ♀ 🥂 🍴 ⛾ 🚩 🏌 🛒 *⛿* (**Leisure** hard tennis courts, heated indoor swimming pool, sauna, solarium, gymnasium, bowling green. **Conf** Max 100 Thtr 100 Class 20 Board 20 **Location** Turn off A487 onto B4337 in Llanrhystud. Course 0.25m on left

Hotel ★★★⚜ 75% Conrah Hotel, Ffosrhydygaled, Chancery, ABERYSTWYTH ☎ 01970 617941
11 en suite 6 annexe en suite

CONWY

ABERGELE   Map 06 SH97

Abergele   Tan-y-Gopa Rd LL22 8DS

☎ 01745 824034   🖹 01745 824034

A beautiful parkland course with views of the Irish Sea and Gwyrch Castle. There are splendid finishing holes, a testing par 5, 16th; a 185 yd, 17th to an elevated green, and a superb par 5 18th with out of bounds just behind the green.

18 holes, 6520yds, Par 72, SSS 71, Course record 66.

Club membership 1250.

Visitors must contact in advance. Limited play weekends. **Societies** must contact in advance. **Green Fees** £28 per day (£32 weekends). **Prof** Iain R Runcie **Course Designer** Hawtree **Facilities** ⊗ ⅷ ᴌ 💺 ♀ 🥂 🍴 🛒 *⛿* **Location** 0.5m W off A547/A55

Hotel ★★★ 65% Kinmel Manor Hotel, St George's Rd, ABERGELE ☎ 01745 832014 51 en suite

BETWS-Y-COED   Map 06 SH75

Betws-y-Coed   LL24 0AL   ☎ 01690 710556

e-mail: betwsycoed.golfclub@tesco.net

Attractive flat meadowland course set between two rivers in Snowdonia National Park.

9 holes, 4996yds, Par 64, SSS 63, Course record 63.

Club membership 350.

Visitors advisable to contact in advance. **Societies** must telephone in advance. **Green Fees** £16 per 18 holes(£21 weekends)reductions in winter. **Facilities** ⊗ ⅷ ᴌ 💺 ♀ 🥂 *⛿* **Location** NE side of village off A5

Hotel ★★★ 70% The Royal Oak Hotel, Holyhead Rd, BETWS-Y-COED ☎ 01690 710219 26 en suite

COLWYN BAY   Map 06 SH87

Old Colwyn   Woodland Av, Old Colwyn LL29 9NL

☎ 01492 515581

Hilly, meadowland course with sheep and cattle grazing on it in parts.

9 holes, 5243yds, Par 68, SSS 66, Course record 63.

Club membership 267.

Visitors welcome ex Sat. Contact in advance. **Societies** must contact in advance. **Green Fees** £10 per day (£15 weekends & bank holidays). **Course Designer** James Braid **Facilities** ᴌ ♀ 🥂 **Location** E side of town centre on B5383

continued

continued

Hotel ★★★ 65% Hopeside Hotel, 63-67 Prince's Dr, West End, COLWYN BAY ☎ 01492 533244 18 en suite

CONWY　　　　　　　　　　Map 06 SH77

Conwy (Caernarvonshire) Beacons Way,
Morfa LL32 8ER ☎ 01492 592423 ▤ 01492 593363
Founded in 1890, Conwy has hosted national and international championships since 1898. Set among sandhills, possessing true links greens and a profusion of gorse on the latter holes, especially the 16th, 17th and 18th. This course provides the visitor with real golfing enjoyment against a background of stunning beauty.
18 holes, 6647yds, Par 72, SSS 72, Course record 69.
Club membership 1050.
Visitors advisable to contact secretary in advance. Limited play weekends. **Societies** must contact in advance. **Green Fees** £35 per day; £28 per round (£40/£35 weekends & bank holidays). **Prof** Peter Lees **Facilities** ⊗ ⅏ ⊾ ☛ ♀ ♧ ➡ ᛏ ♒ ⚒ ♂ **Location** 1m W of town centre on A55

Hotel ★★★ 73% The Groes Inn, Tyn-y-Groes, CONWY ☎ 01492 650545 14 en suite

LLANDUDNO　　　　　　　　Map 06 SH78

Llandudno (Maesdu) Hospital Rd LL30 1HU
☎ 01492 876450 ▤ 01492 871570
Part links, part parkland, this championship course starts and finishes on one side of the main road, the remaining holes, more seaside in nature, being played on the other side. The holes are pleasantly undulating and present a pretty picture when the gorse is in bloom. Often windy, this varied and testing course is not for beginners.
18 holes, 6545yds, Par 72, SSS 72, Course record 65.
Club membership 1045.
Visitors must book in advance. **Societies** must apply in advance to secretary. **Green Fees** terms on application. **Prof** Simon Boulden **Facilities** ⊗ ⅏ ⊾ ☛ ♀ ♧ ➡ ᛏ ♒ ⚒ ♂ **Leisure** snooker. **Location** S side of town centre on A546

Hotel ★★★ 72% Imperial Hotel, The Promenade, LLANDUDNO ☎ 01492 877466 100 en suite

North Wales 72 Bryniau Rd, West Shore LL30 2DZ
☎ 01492 875325 ▤ 01492 873355
e-mail: golf@nwgc.freeserve.co.uk
Challenging seaside links with superb views of Anglesey and Snowdonia. It possesses humpy, hillocky fairways, awkward stances and the occasional blind shot. Heather and gorse lurk beyond the fairways and several of the greens are defended by deep bunkers. The first outstanding hole is the 5th, a par 5 that dog-legs into the wind along a rollercoasting, bottle-neck shaped fairway. Best par 4s include the 8th, played through a narrow valley manaced by a railway line and the beach and the 11th, which runs uphill into the wind and where the beach again threatens. The finest par 3 is the 16th with a bunker to the left of a partially hidden, bowl shaped green.
18 holes, 6287yds, Par 71, SSS 71, Course record 66.
Club membership 670.

continued

Visitors must contact in advance. **Societies** must contact in advance. **Green Fees** £19 per round;£26 per day(£24/£36 weekends), reductions in winter. **Cards** ▤ ▤ ▤ **Prof** Richard Bradbury **Course Designer** Tancred Cummins **Facilities** ⊗ ⅏ ⊾ ☛ ♀ ♧ ➡ ᛏ ♒ ⚒ ♂ **Leisure** snooker. **Location** W side of town on A546

Hotel ★★ St Tudno Hotel and Restaurant, The Promenade, LLANDUDNO ☎ 01492 874411 19 en suite

Rhos-on-Sea Penrhyn Bay LL30 3PU
☎ 01492 548115 (Prof) ▤ 01492 549100
Seaside course, with easy walking and panoramic views.
18 holes, 6064yds, Par 69, SSS 69, Course record 68.
Club membership 400.
Visitors advised to telephone beforehand to guarantee tee times. **Societies** booking essential, telephone in advance. **Green Fees** £22(£30 weekends). **Prof** Mike Macara **Course Designer** J J Simpson **Facilities** ⊗ ⅏ ⊾ ☛ ♀ ♧ ➡ ⚒ ♂ **Location** 0.5m W of LLandudno, off the A55

Hotel ★★★ 65% Hopeside Hotel, 63-67 Prince's Dr, West End, COLWYN BAY ☎ 01492 533244 18 en suite

LLANFAIRFECHAN　　　　　Map 06 SH67

Llanfairfechan Llannerch Rd LL33 0ES
☎ 01248 680144 & 680524
Hillside course with panoramic views of coast.
9 holes, 3119yds, Par 54, SSS 57, Course record 53.
Club membership 176.
Visitors contact in advance, booking necessary at weekends. **Societies** apply in writing. **Green Fees** terms on application. **Facilities** ♀ ♧ **Location** W side of town on A55

Hotel ★★ 67% Castle Bank Hotel, Mount Pleasant, CONWY ☎ 01492 593888 9 en suite

PENMAENMAWR　　　　　　Map 06 SH77

Penmaenmawr Conway Old Rd LL34 6RD
☎ 01492 623330 ▤ 01492 622105
Hilly course with magnificent views across the bay to Llandudno and Anglesey. Dry-stone wall natural hazards.
9 holes, 5350yds, Par 67, SSS 66, Course record 62.
Club membership 600.
Visitors advisable to contact in advance. May not play Sat. **Societies** must contact in advance. **Green Fees** £12 per day(£18 Sundays and bank holidays). **Facilities** ⊗ ⅏ ⊾ ☛ ♀ ♧ ♂ **Location** 1.5m NE off A55

Hotel ★★★ 66% Castle Hotel Conwy, High St, CONWY ☎ 01492 582800 29 en suite

DENBIGHSHIRE

BODELWYDDAN　　　　　　Map 06 SJ07

Kimnel Park LL18 5SR
☎ 01745 833548 ▤ 01745 833544
Flat parkland pay and play course that is suitable for beginners.
9 holes, 3100, Par 58, SSS 58.
Visitors no restrictions. **Societies** telephone for details. **Green Fees** not confirmed. **Prof** Peter Stebbings **Course Designer** Peter Stebbings **Facilities** ⊾ ☛ ♧ ᛏ ♂ ℓ **Leisure** golf academy.

continued

Hotel ★★★ 67% Oriel House Hotel, Upper Denbigh Rd,
ST ASAPH ☎ 01745 582716 19 en suite

DENBIGH
Map 06 SJ06

Bryn Morfydd Hotel Llanrhaedr LL16 4NP
☎ 01745 890280 ▤ 01745 890488
In a beautiful setting in the Vale of Clwyd, the original 9-
hole Duchess course was designed by Peter Alliss in 1982.
In 1992, the 18-hole Dukes course was completed: a
parkland course designed to encourage use of finesse in
play.
*Dukes Course: 18 holes, 5650yds, Par 70, SSS 67,
Course record 74.*
Duchess Course: 9 holes, 2098yds, Par 27.
Club membership 200.
Visitors must book in advance, good standards of dress
apply. Societies apply in writing. Green Fees not confirmed.
Cards ▦ ▦ ▦ ▦ ▨ Prof Ivor Jones Course Designer
Peter Allis/Duncan Muirhead Facilities ⅷ ⅃ ❤ ♀ ⚑ ⬖ ⊤
❦ ➣ ⚓ ⌀ Location On A525 between Denbigh and
Ruthin

Hotel ★★★ 68% Ruthin Castle, RUTHIN
☎ 01824 702664 58 en suite

Denbigh Henllan Rd LL16 5AA
☎ 01745 814159 ▤ 814888
e-mail: secretary@denbighgolfclub.fsbusiness.co.uk
Parkland course, giving a testing and varied game. Good
views.
18 holes, 5712yds, Par 69, SSS 68, Course record 64.
Club membership 725.
Visitors must contact in advance. Societies apply in
writing/telephone. Green Fees £24.50 per day;£18.50 per
round (£30.50/£24.50 weekends & bank holidays). Prof
Mike Jones Course Designer John Stockton Facilities ⊗ ⅷ
⅃ ❤ ♀ ⚑ ⬖ ⊤ ⌀ Location 1.5m NW on B5382

Hotel ★★★ 67% Oriel House Hotel, Upper Denbigh Rd,
ST ASAPH ☎ 01745 582716 19 en suite

LLANGOLLEN
Map 07 SJ24

Vale of Llangollen Holyhead Rd LL20 7PR
☎ 01978 860906 ▤ 01978 860906
Parkland course, set in superb scenery by the River Dee.
18 holes, 6656yds, Par 72, SSS 73, Course record 66.
Club membership 800.
Visitors must contact in advance. Restricted club
competition days. Handicap certificate required. Societies
apply in writing to the secretary. Green Fees £25 per round
(£35 weekends). Cards ▦ ▦ ▦ ▦ ▨ Prof David
Vaughan Facilities ⊗ ⅷ ⅃ ❤ ♀ ⚑ ⬖ ⚓ ⌀ Location
1.5m E on A5

Hotel ★★★⚑ 69% Bryn Howel Hotel & Restaurant,
LLANGOLLEN ☎ 01978 860331 36 en suite

PRESTATYN
Map 06 SJ08

Prestatyn Marine Rd East LL19 7HS
☎ 01745 854320 ▤ 01745 888327
e-mail: prestatyngcmanager@freenet.co.uk
Very flat seaside links exposed to stiff breeze. The course
has a reputation for fine greens. Testing holes: par 5 3rd
with out of bounds on the left dog leg followed by The
Ridge, a par 4 of 468 yards; the par 4 10th; the par 3 13th
with elevated green and pot bunkers.
18 holes, 6564yds, Par 72, SSS 72, Course record 66.
Club membership 695.
continued

Visitors welcome except Sat & Tue mornings. Must contact
in advance. Societies prior booking required. Green Fees
£25 per day(£30 Sundays and bank holidays). Prof Malcolm
Staton Course Designer S Collins Facilities ⊗ ⅷ ⅃ ❤ ♀
⬖ ⚑ ⊤ ⚓ ⌀ Leisure snooker. Location 0.5m N off A548

Hotel ★★ 60% Hotel Marina, Marine Dr, RHYL
☎ 01745 342371 29 en suite

St Melyd The Paddock, Meliden Rd LL19 8NB
☎ 01745 854405 ▤ 01745 856908
e-mail: info@stmelydgolf.co.uk
Parkland course with good views of mountains and Irish
Sea. Testing 1st hole (423 yds) par 4. 18 tees.
9 holes, 5829yds, Par 68, SSS 68, Course record 65.
Club membership 400.
Visitors must contact in advance. Societies must telephone
in advance. Green Fees £18(£22 weekends & bank
holidays). Prof Andrew Carr Facilities ⊗ ⅷ ⅃ ❤ ♀ ⬖ ⚑
Leisure snooker. Location 0.5m S on A547

Hotel ★★ 60% Hotel Marina, Marine Dr, RHYL
☎ 01745 342371 29 en suite

RHUDDLAN
Map 06 SJ07

Rhuddlan Meliden Rd LL18 6LB
☎ 01745 590217 (Sec) & 590898(Pro) ▤ 01745 590472
e-mail: golf@rhuddlangolfclub.fsnet.co.uk
Attractive, gently undulating parkland course with good
views. Well bunkered with trees and water hazards. The
476 yard 8th and 431 yard 11th require both length and
accuracy. The clubhouse has been refurbished.
18 holes, 6471yds, Par 71, SSS 71, Course record 66.
Club membership 1060.
Visitors must contact in advance. Sun with member only.
Societies telephone to book reservation. Green Fees not
confirmed. Cards ▦ ▦ ▦ ▨ Prof Andrew Carr Course
Designer Hawtree & Son Facilities ⊗ ⅷ ⅃ ❤ ♀ ⬖ ⚑ ⊤
➣ ⚓ ⌀ Location E side of town on A547

Hotel ★★★ 65% Kinmel Manor Hotel, St George's Rd,
ABERGELE ☎ 01745 832014 51 en suite

RHYL
Map 06 SJ08

Rhyl Coast Rd LL18 3RE
☎ 01745 353171 ▤ 01745 360007
e-mail: rhylgolfclub@hotmail.com
Seaside course.

9 holes, 6220yds, Par 70, SSS 70, Course record 65.
Club membership 600.
Visitors must contact in advance. Limited availability at
weekends due to club competitions. Societies must contact in
advance/see web site Green Fees £20 per 18 holes(£25
weekends). Prof Tim Leah Course Designer James Braid
Facilities ⊗ ⅷ ⅃ ❤ ♀ ⬖ ⚑ ⊤ ➣ ⚓ ⌀ Location 1m E
on A548
continued

Hotel ★★ 60% Hotel Marina, Marine Dr, RHYL
☎ 01745 342371 29 en suite

RUTHIN — Map 06 SJ15

Ruthin-Pwllglas Pwllglas LL15 2PE
☎ 01978 790692 ⓘ 01978 790692
Hilly parkland course in elevated position with panoramic views. Stiff climb to 3rd and 9th holes. At 600 feet above sea level, the 355 yard 5th hole is the highest point at Pwllglas. When the seventh is played the second time - as the 16th - the tee is from a spectacular sheer rock face.
10 holes, 5362yds, Par 66, SSS 66.
Club membership 380.
Visitors welcome except for competition days. **Societies** apply in writing or telephone. **Green Fees** £14(£20 weekends and bank holidays). **Prof** M Jones **Facilities** ⊗ by prior arrangement ♀△ **Location** 2.5m S off A494

Hotel ★★★ 68% Ruthin Castle, RUTHIN
☎ 01824 702664 58 en suite

ST ASAPH — Map 06 SJ07

Llannerch Park North Wales Golf Range,
Llannerch Park LL17 0BD ☎ 01745 730805
Mainly flat parkland course with one dog-leg hole.
9 holes, 1587yds, Par 30.
Visitors pay & play. **Societies** telephone in advance. **Green Fees** £3 per round. **Course Designer** B Williams **Facilities** �ⓘ **Location** 200yds S off A525

Hotel ★★ 67% Plas Elwy Hotel & Restaurant, The Roe, ST ASAPH ☎ 01745 582263 & 582089 ⓘ 01745 583864
7 en suite 6 annexe en suite

FLINTSHIRE

BRYNFORD — Map 07 SJ17

Holywell Brynford CH8 8LQ
☎ 01352 713937 & 710040 ⓘ 01352 713937
e-mail: holywell_golf_club@lineone.net
Links type course on well drained mountain turf, with bracken and gorse flanking undulating fairways. 720 ft above sea level.
18 holes, 6100yds, Par 70, SSS 70, Course record 67.
Club membership 505.
Visitors advisable to book in advance particularly for weekends. **Societies** by prior arrangement with the secretary. **Green Fees** not confirmed. **Prof** Matt Parsleyr **Facilities** ⊗ ⊓ⓘ ♀△ 🏌 **Location** 1.25m SW off B5121

Hotel ★★ 68% Stamford Gate Hotel, Halkyn Rd, HOLYWELL ☎ 01352 712942 12 en suite

CAERWYS — Map 06 SJ17

Caerwys Nine Of Clubs CH7 5AQ
☎ 07703 558840 ⓘ 01691 777793
e-mail: tevans@nineofclubs.fsnet.co.uk
Following the natural contours of the land and with a south-west aspect, this course could be considered a litle gem. Each approach to every green is different and there are many interesting and challenging holes.
9 holes, 3080yds, Par 60, Course record 61.
Club membership 150.
Visitors no restrictions. **Societies** telephone then confirm in writing. **Green Fees** £9 per 18 holes;£7 per 9 holes. **Course**

continued

Designer Eleanor Barlow **Facilities** ⊗ ⓘ ▱ △ ⌂ ⊓ ◖
Location 1.5m SW of A55, midway between St Asaph and Holywell

Hotel ★★ 66% Bryn Awel Hotel, Denbigh Rd, MOLD
☎ 01352 758622 8 en suite 10 annexe en suite

FLINT — Map 07 SJ27

Flint Cornist Park CH6 5HJ
☎ 01352 735645
e-mail: owens.trave@ukonline.co.uk
Parkland course incorporating woods and streams. Excellent views of Dee estuary and the Welsh hills.
9 holes, 6984yds, Par 69, SSS 69, Course record 65.
Club membership 300.
Visitors must contact in advance, not weekends. **Societies** apply in writing or telephone,not weekends. **Green Fees** £12 per day. **Course Designer** H G Griffith **Facilities** ⊗ ⓘ ▱ ♀ △ **Location** 1m W, follow signs from A55 for Flint, on entering Flint look for signs for Cornish Hall & Flint Golf Club

Hotel ★★★ 64% Mountain Park Hotel, Northop Rd, Flint Mountain, FLINT ☎ 01352 736000 & 730972 ⓘ 01352 736010 21 annexe en suite

HAWARDEN — Map 07 SJ36

Hawarden Groomsdale Ln CH5 3EH
☎ 01244 531447 & 520809 ⓘ 01244 536901
Parkland course with comfortable walking and good views.
18 holes, 5842yds, Par 69, SSS 69.
Club membership 750.
Visitors arrange visit with the professional. **Societies** by prior arrangement. **Green Fees** £20(£25 Sundays). **Prof** Alex Rowland **Facilities** ⊗ ⫙ ⓘ ▱ ♀ △ ⌂ **Location** W side of town off B5125

Hotel ★★★ 66% The Gateway To Wales Hotel, Welsh Rd, Sealand, Deeside, CHESTER ☎ 01244 830332 39 en suite

MOLD — Map 07 SJ26

Old Padeswood Station Ln, Padeswood CH7 4JL
☎ 01244 547401 & 547701 ⓘ 01244 545082
Situated in the beautiful Alyn Valley, half on flat parkland and half undulating. Striking mountain views.
18 holes, 6685yds, Par 72, SSS 72, Course record 66.
Club membership 600.
Visitors welcome, subject to tee availability. **Societies** telephone in advance. **Green Fees** £20 per round (£25 weekends & bank holidays). **Prof** Tony Davies **Course Designer** Jeffries **Facilities** ⊗ ⫙ ⓘ ▱ ♀ △ ⌂ ⊓ ⏆ ◖ **Conf** 50 **Location** 3m SE off A5118

Hotel ★★ 66% Bryn Awel Hotel, Denbigh Rd, MOLD
☎ 01352 758622 8 en suite 10 annexe en suite

Padeswood & Buckley The Caia, Station Ln,
Padeswood CH7 4JD ☎ 01244 550537 ⓘ 01244 541600
e-mail: padeswoodgc@compuserve.com
Gently undulating parkland course, with natural hazards and good views of the Welsh Hills.
18 holes, 5982yds, Par 70, SSS 69.
Club membership 700.
Visitors weekdays only, contact secretary in advance. **Societies** apply in writing/telephone. **Green Fees** £20 per round;£25 per day. **Prof** David Ashton **Course Designer** Williams Partnership **Facilities** ⊗ ⫙ ⓘ ▱ ♀ △ ⌂ ⊓ ◖ ⏆ ◖ **Leisure** snooker. **Location** 3m SE off A5118

continued

Hotel ★★ 66% Bryn Awel Hotel, Denbigh Rd, MOLD
☎ 01352 758622 8 en suite 10 annexe en suite

NORTHOP
Map 07 SJ26

Northop Country Park CH7 6WA
☎ 01352 840440 ▤ 01352 840445
e-mail: northop@stdavidshotel.co.uk
Designed by former British Ryder Cup captain, John
Jacobs, the parkland course gives the impression of
having been established for many years. No two holes are
the same and designed to allow all year play.
18 holes, 6750yds, Par 72, SSS 73, Course record 64.
Club membership 500.
Visitors must contact in advance and have own equipment.
Societies apply in writing or by telephone in advance. Green
Fees terms on application. Cards ▨ ▨ ▨ ▨ ▨ ▨
Prof Matthew Pritchard Course Designer John Jacobs
Facilities ⊗ ⋔ ♠ ♥ ♀ ♣ ☎ ⚑ ♦ ♨ ♂ ⛾ Leisure hard
tennis courts, sauna, gymnasium.Conf Max 90 Thtr 60 Class
30 Board 30 Banquet 80 Del from £44 * Location 150 yds
from Connahs Quay turnoff on A55

Hotel ★★★★ 70% De Vere St Davids Park, St Davids
Park, EWLOE ☎ 01244 520800 145 en suite

PANTYMWYN
Map 07 SJ16

Mold Cilcain Rd CH7 5EH
☎ 01352 740318 & 741513 ▤ 01352 741517
e-mail: info@moldgolfclub.co.uk
Meadowland course with some hard walking and natural
hazards. Fine views.
18 holes, 5512yds, Par 67, SSS 67, Course record 63.
Club membership 700.
Visitors contact in advance. Restricted play at weekends
Societies provisional booking by telephone. Green Fees £18
per day (£25 per day, £20 per round weekends). Reductions
in winter. Prof Mark Jordan Course Designer Hawtree
Facilities ⊗ ⋔ ♠ ♥ ♀ ♣ ☎ ⚑ ♦ ♨ ♂ Location E side
of village

Hotel ★★ 66% Bryn Awel Hotel, Denbigh Rd, MOLD
☎ 01352 758622 8 en suite 10 annexe en suite

GWYNEDD

ABERDYFI
Map 06 SN69

ABERDYFI See page 371

ABERSOCH
Map 06 SH32

Abersoch LL53 7EY
☎ 01758 712622(shop) 712636(office) ▤ 01758 712777
e-mail: admin@abersochgolf.co.uk
Seaside links, with five parkland holes.
18 holes, 5819yds, Par 69, SSS 68, Course record 66.
Club membership 650.
Visitors must contact in advance. Competition days Sun &
Thu. Societies must apply in advance. Green Fees not
confirmed. Prof A D Jones Course Designer Harry Vardon
Facilities ⊗ ⋔ ♠ ♥ ♀ ♣ ☎ ⚑ ♦ ♨ ♂ ⛾ Location S
side of village

Hotel ★★ 77% Neigwl Hotel, Lon Sarn Bach, ABERSOCH
☎ 01758 712363 7 en suite 2 annexe en suite

AA ★ ★ ★   **73%**

TREFEDDIAN HOTEL

En-suite bedrooms, some balcony. Lift, indoor
swimming pool, tennis, snooker. Children's
playroom. Ideal base for touring North/Mid Wales.
½ mile north of Aberdyfi village.
Family owned/managed three-star country hotel.
Close to sea in Snowdonia National Park. Views of
sand dunes, beaches, Cardigan Bay and Aberdovey
Championship Golf Links.
Telephone for full colour brochure
Aberdyfi (Aberdovey) LL35 0SB Wales
Telephone: (01654) 767213
Fax: (01654) 767777
www.trefwales.com

BALA
Map 06 SH93

Bala Penlan LL23 7YD
☎ 01678 520359 & 521361 ▤ 01678 521361
Upland course with natural hazards. All holes except first
and last affected by wind. First hole is a most challenging
par3. Irrigated greens and good views of surrounding
countryside.
10 holes, 4962yds, Par 66, SSS 64, Course record 64.
Club membership 229.
Visitors book in advance at weekends. Parties of more than 4
people contact the secretary in advance. Societies must
contact in advance. Green Fees £12 per day (£15 weekends
& bank holidays). Prof A R Davies Facilities ♣ by prior
arrangement ♀ ♣ ☎ ⚑ ♂ Location 0.5m SW off A494

Hotel ★★ 65% Plas Coch Hotel, High St, BALA
☎ 01678 520309 10 en suite

BANGOR
Map 06 SH57

St Deiniol Penybryn LL57 1PX
☎ 01248 353098 & 370792
e-mail: secretary@stdeiniol.fsbusiness.co.uk
Elevated parkland course with panoramic views of
Snowdonia, Menai Straits, and Anglesey.
18 holes, 5654yds, Par 68, SSS 67, Course record 61.
Club membership 300.
Visitors must contact in advance. Societies must contact in
advance. Green Fees £14 (£18 weekends). Cards ▨ ▨
▨ ▨ ▨ Course Designer James Braid Facilities ⊗ ⋔ ♠
♥ ♀ ♣ ☎ ⚑ ♂ Location E side of town centre off A5122

Hotel ★★ 66% Anglesey Arms, MENAI BRIDGE
☎ 01248 712305 16 en suite

CAERNARFON   Map 06 SH46

Caernarfon Llanfaglan LL54 5RP
☎ 01286 673783 & 678359 📠 01286 672535
e-mail: caerngc@talk21.com
Parkland course with gentle gradients.

18 holes, 5891yds, Par 69, SSS 68, Course record 63.
Club membership 660.
Visitors must contact in advance. **Societies** must apply in
advance, in writing or by telephone. **Green Fees** £22 per
day; £19 per round (£25/£22 weekends). **Cards** ▦ ▦ ▦
▦ ▣ **Prof** Aled Owen **Facilities** ⊗ ⽊ ⽓ ♨ ♀ ♨ ☕ ☜
◌ **Location** 1.75m SW

Hotel ★★★ 68% Celtic Royal Hotel, Bangor St,
CAERNARFON ☎ 01286 674477 110 en suite

CRICCIETH   Map 06 SH43

Criccieth Ednyfed Hill LL52 0PH
☎ 01766 522154
18 holes, 5787yds, Par 69, SSS 68.
Location 1m NE
Telephone for further details

Hotel ★★★🏌 74% Bron Eifion Country House Hotel,
CRICCIETH ☎ 01766 522385 19 en suite

DOLGELLAU   Map 06 SH71

Dolgellau Hengwrt Estate, Pencefn Rd LL40 2ES
☎ 01341 422603 📠 01341 422603
e-mail: dolgellaugolfclub@hengwrt.fsnet.co.uk
**Undulating parkland course. Good views of mountains
and Mawddach estuary.**
9 holes, 4671yds, Par 66, SSS 63, Course record 62.
Club membership 150.
Visitors no restrictions **Societies** must contact in advance.
Green Fees £15(£18 weekends). **Cards** ▦ ▦ ▣ ▦
▦ ▣ **Course Designer** Jack Jones **Facilities** ⊗ ⽊ ⽓ ☕ ♨
⊤◌ **Location** 0.5m N, near to Town Bridge

Hotel ★★★🏌 72% Plas Dolmelynllyn, Ganllwyd,
DOLGELLAU ☎ 01341 440273 10 en suite

HARLECH   Map 06 SH53

Royal St Davids LL46 2UB
☎ 01766 780361 📠 01766 781110
e-mail: secretary@royalstdavids.co.uk
**Championship links, with easy walking and natural
hazards.**
18 holes, 6427yds, Par 69, SSS 72. Course record 62.
Club membership 800.
Visitors pre booking essential, must hold current
handicap certificate. **Societies** contact secretary in
advance. Handicap certificates required. **Green Fees** £36
continued

per round;£46 per day(£50/£40 weekends). reductions in
winter. **Cards** ▦ ▦ ▦ ▣ **Prof** John Barnett **Facilities**
⊗ ⽊ ⽓ ♨ ♀ ♨ ☕ ☜ ◌ **Location** W side of town
on A496

Hotel ★★ 64% Ty Mawr Hotel, LLANBEDR
☎ 01341 241440 10 en suite

MORFA NEFYN   Map 06 SH24

Nefyn & District LL53 6DA
☎ 01758 720966 📠 01758 720476
e-mail: nefyngolf@tesco.net
A 27-hole course played as two separate 18s, Nefyn is a
cliff top links where you never lose sight of the sea. A
well-maintained course which will be a very tough test
for the serious golfer, is still user friendly for the
casual visitor. Every hole has a different challenge and
the old 13th fairway is approximately 30 yards arcross
from sea-to-sea. The course has an added bonus of a
pub on the beach roughly halfway round for those
whose golf may need some bolstering!
Old Course: 18 holes, 6201yds, Par 71, SSS 71,
Course record 67.
New Course: 18 holes, 6317yds, Par 71, SSS 71,
Course record 66.
Club membership 800.
Visitors must contact in advance. **Societies** apply by
telephone. **Green Fees** £33 per day, £26 per round
(£38/£31 weekends & bank holiday). **Cards** ▦ ▦ ▦
▣ ▣ **Prof** John Froom **Course Designer** James Braid
Facilities ⊗ ⽊ ⽓ ♨ ♀ ♨ ☕ ⊤ ☜ ◌ **Conf** Max
24 **Location** 0.75m NW

Hotel ★★★🏌 74% Porth Tocyn Hotel, Bwlch Tocyn,
ABERSOCH ☎ 01758 713303 17 en suite

PORTHMADOG   Map 06 SH53

Porthmadog Morfa Bychan LL49 9UU
☎ 01766 514124 📠 01766 514638
e-mail: secretary@porthmadog-golf-club.co.uk
**Seaside links, very interesting but with easy walking and
good views.**
18 holes, 6363yds, Par 71, SSS 71.
Club membership 900.
Visitors must contact in advance. Handicap certificate
required. **Societies** apply by telephone initially. **Green Fees**
£25 per round;£32 per day (£30/£37 weekends). **Prof** Peter L
Bright **Course Designer** James Braid **Facilities** ⊗ ⽊ ⽓ ♨
♀ ♨ ☜ ◌ **Leisure** snooker. **Location** 1.5m SW

Hotel ★★★🏌 74% Bron Eifion Country House Hotel,
CRICCIETH ☎ 01766 522385 19 en suite

PWLLHELI   Map 06 SH33

Pwllheli Golf Rd LL53 5PS ☎ 01758 701644
**Easy walking on flat seaside course with outstanding
views of Snowdon, Cader Idris and Cardigan Bay.**
18 holes, 6091yds, Par 69, SSS 69, Course record 66.
Club membership 880.
Visitors restricted Tue,Thu & weekends. **Societies** must
telephone in advance. **Green Fees** £22 (£27
weekends)reductions in winter. **Cards** ▦ ▦ ▦ ▦ ▦ ▣
Prof John Pilkington **Course Designer** Tom Morris
Facilities ⊗ ⽊ ⽓ ♨ ♀ ♨ ☕ ◌ **Location** 0.5m SW
off A497

continued

Aberdovey

Aberdyfi, *Gwynedd* ☎ 01654 767493 Fax 01654 767027 Map 06 SN69

Golf was first played at Aberdovey in 1886, with the club founded in 1892. The links has since developed to become one of the finest championship courses in Wales. The club has hosted many prestigious events over the years and is popular with golfing societies and clubs who regularly return here.

Golfers can enjoy spectacular view from the course, which has all the characteristics of a true seaside links. Fine holes include the 3rd, the 11th and a good short hole at the 12th.

The late Bernard Darwin, former President and Captain of the club, was also golf correspondent for The Times. Many of his writings feature the course which he referred to as 'the course that my soul loves best of all the courses in the world.' and he was a major contributor to its success. Darwin would easily recognise the course if he were to play it today.

In 1995 the old clubhouse was destroyed by fire, however with the help of a lottery grant it was rebuilt. The fine new clubhouse which now graces the course was opened by HRH the Duke of York in 1998.

Visitors visitors welcome, handicap certificate required, must contact in advance, restrictions at weekends

Societies prior arrangement essential.

Green Fees 1pm Sun - 1pm Fri full day £45 one round £32.50 (after 2.30pm £24) winter £26

1pm Fri - 1pm Sun full day £50 one round £37.50 (after 2.30pm £26) winter £28

Facilities ⊗ ⏳ 🍴 🍺 ♀ ⛳ 🏌 🛄 ✎ Professional (John Davies) Conf max 20 (Boardroom only)

Location Aberdyfi LL35 ORT (0.5m W on A493).

Holes/Par/Course record 18 holes, 6445 yds Par 71m SSS 71, Course record 66

WHERE TO STAY AND EAT NEARBY

Hotels and Restaurants
ABERDYFI

★★★ 73% Trefeddian Hotel LL35 0NA.
☎ 01654 767213. 59 en suite

★★ 74% ⓦ Penhelig Arms Hotel & Restaurant, LL35 OLT
☎ 01654 767215. 10 en suite

Championship Course

Hotel ★★★♨ 74% Porth Tocyn Hotel, Bwlch Tocyn, ABERSOCH ☎ 01758 713303 17 en suite

MERTHYR TYDFIL

MERTHYR TYDFIL   Map 03 SO00

Merthyr Tydfil Cilsanws Mountain, Cefn Coed CF48 2NU ☎ 01685 723308
Mountain-top course in the Brecon Beacons National Park with beautiful views of the surrounding area. The course plays longer than its card length and requires accuracy off the tee.
18 holes, 5625yds, Par 69, SSS 68, Course record 65.
Club membership 210.
Visitors may not play on Sun. **Societies** by prior arrangement. **Green Fees** £10 per day(£15 weekends). **Course Designer** V Price/R Mathias **Facilities** ⊗ by prior arrangement ⫿ by prior arrangement ♭ by prior arrangement ♥ by prior arrangement ♀ ♨ **Location** Off A470 at Cefn Coed

Hotel ★★★ 74% Nant Ddu Lodge Hotel, Cwm Taf, Nant Ddu, MERTHYR TYDFIL ☎ 01685 379111 12 en suite 10 annexe en suite

Morlais Castle Pant, Dowlais CF48 2UY
☎ 01685 722822 ▤ 01685 388700
Beautiful moorland course overlooking National Park with excellent views of Brecon Beacons and surrounding countryside. The interesting layout of the course makes for a testing game.
18 holes, 6320yds, Par 71, SSS 71, Course record 64.
Club membership 600.
Visitors must contact in advance for weekends. **Societies** apply in writing. **Green Fees** £16 per day(£20 weekends & bank holidays). **Prof** H Jarrett **Course Designer** James Braid **Facilities** ⊗ ⫿ ♭ ☕ ♀ ♨ 🏠 ♥ ♣ ✓ **Location** 2.5m N off A465. Follow signs for Mountain Railway. Course entrance opposite railway car park

Hotel ★★★ 74% Nant Ddu Lodge Hotel, Cwm Taf, Nant Ddu, MERTHYR TYDFIL ☎ 01685 379111 12 en suite 10 annexe en suite

MONMOUTHSHIRE

ABERGAVENNY   Map 03 SO21

Monmouthshire Gypsy Ln, Llanfoist NP7 9HE
☎ 01873 852606 ▤ 01873 852606
e-mail: secretary@mgcabergavenny.fsnet.co.uk
This parkland course is very picturesque, with the beautifully wooded River Usk running alongside. There are a number of par 3 holes and a testing par 4 at the 16th.
18 holes, 5806yds, Par 70, SSS 69, Course record 65.
Club membership 700.
Visitors must play with member at weekends. Must contact in advance & have handicap certificate. **Societies** must confirm in writing. **Green Fees** £30 per day (£35 weekends & bank holidays). **Prof** B Edwards **Course Designer** James Braid **Facilities** ⊗ ⫿ by prior arrangement ♭ ☕ ♀ ♨ 🏠 ♥ ✓ **Location** 2m S off B4269

Hotel ★★ 70% Pantrhiwgoch Hotel & Riverside Restaurant, Brecon Rd, ABERGAVENNY ☎ 01873 810550 18 en suite

Wernddu Golf Centre Old Ross Rd NP7 8NG
☎ 01873 856223 ▤ 01873 852177
e-mail: wernddugolfclub.co.uk
A parkland course with magnificent views, wind hazards on several holes in certain conditions and water hazards on four holes. There is a 26 bay floodlit driving range.
18 holes, 5403yds, Par 68, SSS 67, Course record 64.
Club membership 550.
Visitors advisable to book in advance. **Societies** telephone in advance. **Green Fees** terms on application. **Cards** ▭▭ ▭▭ 🌐 **Prof** Alan Ashmead **Course Designer** G Watkins **Facilities** ⊗ ♭ ☕ ♀ ♨ ⫿ ♥ ✓ ♣ **Location** 1.5m NE on B4521

Hotel ★★★ 65% Llansantffraed Court Hotel, Llanvihangel Gobion, ABERGAVENNY ☎ 01873 840678 21 en suite

BETTWS NEWYDD   Map 03 SO30

Alice Springs NP15 1JY
☎ 01873 880708 ▤ 01873 880838
Two 18-hole undulating parkland courses set back to back with magnificent views of the Usk Valley. The Monow course has testing 7th and 15th holes.
Monow Course: 18 holes, 5544yds, Par 69, SSS 69.
Usk Course: 18 holes, 5934, Par 70, SSS 70.
Club membership 350.
Visitors should contact the club in advance for weekend play. **Societies** must telephone in advance. **Green Fees** £16 per round (£20 weekends & bank holidays). **Cards** ▭▭ ▭▭ ▭▭ 🌐 **Prof** Mike Davies **Course Designer** Keith R Morgan **Facilities** ⊗ ⫿ by prior arrangement ♭ ☕ ♀ ♨ 🏠 ♥ ✓ ♥ ♣ ✓ **Conf** Max 180 Thtr 180 Class 90 Banquet 120 Del £2 to £22 * **Location** N of Usk on B4598 towards Abergavenny

Hotel ★★★ 72% Three Salmons Hotel, Porthycarne St, USK ☎ 01291 672133 10 en suite 14 annexe en suite

CAERWENT   Map 03 ST49

Dewstow NP26 5AH ☎ 01291 430444 ▤ 01291 425816
Two picturesque parkland courses with easy walking and spectacular views over the Severn estuary towards Bristol. Testing holes include the par three 7th, Valley Course, which is approached over water, some 50 feet lower than the tee, and the par four 15th, Park Course, which has a 50ft totem pole in the middle of the fairway, a unique feature. There is also a 26-bay floodlit driving range.
Valley Course: 18 holes, 6141yds, Par 72, SSS 70, Course record 68.
Park Course: 18 holes, 6200yds, Par 69, SSS 69, Course record 67.
Club membership 950.
Visitors may book 4 days in advance (six days in advance in winter). **Societies** apply in writing or telephone for details. **Green Fees** terms on application. **Cards** ▭▭ ▭▭ ▭▭ ▭▭ 🌐 **Prof** Jonathan Skuse **Facilities** ⊗ ⫿ ♭ ☕ ♀ ♨ 🏠 ♥ ✓ ♣ ✓ ♣ **Location** 0.5m S of A48 at Caerwent

Hotel ★★★ 63% George Hotel, Moor St, CHEPSTOW ☎ 01291 625363 14 en suite

CHEPSTOW See page 373

Looking for a driving range?
See the index at the back of the guide

Marriott St Pierre

Chepstow, *Monmouthshire* ☎ 01291 625261 Fax 01291 629975 Map 03 ST59

Set in 400 acres of beautiful parkland, Marriott St Pierre offers two 18 hole golf courses. the Old Course is one of the finest in the country and has played host to many major championships. The par 3 18th is famous for its tee shot over the lake to an elevated green.

The Mathern course presents its own challenges and is highly enjoyable for golfers of all abilities.

The hotel has teaching professionals as well as hire of clubs and equipment. A 13 bay driving range was added in 1998.

Visitors Must book at least ten days in advance if not resident at hotel

Societies must make advance reservation

Green Fees Mathern from £30, old from £45 ▦ ▦ ▦ ▦ ▦ ▦ ▦

Facilities ⊗ ⑂ ▙ ☕ ♀ ⊨ ⛬ ⑂ ▟ ✍ ⟨
Professional (Craig Dun)

Leisure tennis, swimming, sauna, solarium, gymnasium, steam room, health and beauty suite, private fishing

Location St Pierre Park, Chepstow NP16 6YA (3m SW off A48)

Holes/Par/Course record 36 holes. Old Course: 18 holes, 6700 yds, par 71, SSS 73, course record 64 Mathern Course: 18 holes, 5732 yds, Par 68, SSS 68

WHERE TO STAY AND EAT NEARBY

Hotels
CHEPSTOW

★★★★ 71% St Marriott Pierre Hotel & Country Club ☎ 01291 625261, 148 en suite

★★★ 65% The Old Course, Newport Road ☎ 01291 626261 31 en suite

★★ 70% Castle View, 16 Bridge St. ☎ 01291 620340 9 en suite 4 annexe en suite

★★ 63% The George Hotel, Moor St ☎ 01291 625363 14 en suite

TINTERN

★★ ⑯ 73% Parva Farmhouse Hotel ☎ 01291 689411 9 en suite

★★★ ⑯ 66% Royal George Hotel ☎ 01291 689205 2 en suite 14 annexe en suite

WHITEBROOK

★★ ⑯⑯ 72% The Crown at Whitebrook ☎01600 860254 10 en suite

Restaurant
CHEPSTOW

⑯⑯ Wye Knot, The Bank ☎ 01291 622929

Championship Course

CHEPSTOW Map 03 ST59

Shirenewton Shirenewton NP16 6RL
☎ 01291 641642 📠 01291 641472
Parkland course with magnificent views over the Severn estuary and extending to the Devon coastline.
18 holes, 6605yds, Par 72, SSS 72.
Club membership 350.
Visitors welcome, advisable to reserve tee times, must book at weekends Societies apply in writing/telephone. Green Fees not confirmed. Cards ⊟ 💳 Prof Lee Pagett
Facilities ⊗ ⽈ 🏌 🍴 🏌 👤 🛒 🏠 ⛳ Location Junct 2 of M48 off A48 at Crick

Hotel ★★ 66% Beaufort Hotel, Beaufort Square, CHEPSTOW ☎ 01291 622497 18 en suite

MONMOUTH Map 03 SO51

Monmouth Leasebrook Ln NP25 3SN ☎ 01600 712212 (clubhouse) & 772399 (sec) 📠 01600 772399
e-mail: sec.mongc@barbox.net
Parkland course in scenic setting. High, undulating land with good views.
18 holes, 5698yds, Par 69, SSS 69, Course record 68.
Club membership 600.
Visitors advisable to contact in advance, bank holidays only with member. Societies advance notice advisable, write or telephone secretary. Green Fees £22 per day; £17.50 per round (£25/£20 weekends and bank holidays). Cards ⊟ 💳 Prof Brian Girling Course Designer George Walden Facilities ⊗ ⽈ 🏌 🍴 👤 🏠 ⛳ Location 1.5m NE off A40

Hotel ★★ 66% Riverside Hotel, Cinderhill St, MONMOUTH ☎ 01600 715577 & 713236 📠 01600 712668 17 en suite

Rolls of Monmouth The Hendre NP25 5HG
☎ 01600 715353 📠 01600 713115
A hilly and challenging parkland course encompassing several lakes and ponds and surrounded by woodland. Set within a beautiful private estate complete with listed mansion and panoramic views towards the Black Mountains. The short 4th has a lake beyond the green and both the 17th and 18th holes are magnificent holes with which to end your round.
18 holes, 6733yds, Par 72, SSS 73, Course record 69.
Club membership 147.
Visitors must telephone in advance. Societies must contact in advance. Green Fees £36 per day (£40 weekends). Cards ⊟ 💳 Facilities ⊗ ⽈ 🏌 🍴 👤 🏠 ⛳ Location 4m W on B4233

Hotel ★★ 66% Riverside Hotel, Cinderhill St, MONMOUTH ☎ 01600 715577 & 713236 📠 01600 712668 17 en suite

RAGLAN Map 03 SO40

Raglan Parc Parc Lodge, Station Rd NP5 2ER
☎ 01291 690077
18 holes, 6604yds, Par 72, SSS 73, Course record 67.
Location Off junct of A449/A40
Telephone for further details

Hotel ★★★ 65% Llansantffraed Court Hotel, Llanvihangel Gobion, ABERGAVENNY ☎ 01873 840678 21 en suite

NEATH PORT TALBOT

GLYNNEATH Map 03 SN80

Glynneath Pen-y-graig, Pontneathvaughan SA11 5UH
☎ 01639 720452 & 720872 📠 01639 720452
Attractive hillside golf overlooking the Vale of Neath in the foothills of the Brecon Beacons National Park. Reasonably level parkland/wooded course.
18 holes, 5656yds, Par 69, SSS 68, Course record 63.
Club membership 603.
Visitors restricted starting times at weekend. Societies must contact in advance. Green Fees £17 per day (£22 weekends and bank holidays). Prof Neil Evans Course Designer Cotton/Pennick/Lawrie Facilities ⊗ ⽈ 🏌 🍴 👤 🏠 ⛳ Location 2m NE of Glynneath on B4242

Hotel ★★ 65% Castle Hotel, The Parade, NEATH ☎ 01639 641119 & 643581 📠 01639 641624 29 en suite

MARGAM Map 03 SS78

Lakeside Water St SA13 2PA ☎ 01639 899959
A parkland course with bunkers and natural hazards. Eight par 4s and ten par 3s.
18 holes, 4550yds, Par 63, SSS 63, Course record 65.
Club membership 250.
Visitors no restrictions. Societies apply in advance by letter or telephone. Green Fees not confirmed. Cards ⊟ 💳 Prof Mathew Wootton Course Designer Matthew Wootton Facilities ⊗ ⽈ 🏌 🍴 👤 🏠 ⛳ ♿ Location Off junct 38 of M4

Hotel ★★★ 68% Aberavon Beach Hotel, PORT TALBOT ☎ 01639 884949 52 en suite

NEATH Map 03 SS79

Earlswood Jersey Marine SA10 6JP ☎ 01792 321578
Earlswood is a hillside course offering spectacular scenic views over Swansea Bay. The terrain is gently undulating downs with natural hazards and is designed to appeal to both the new and the experienced golfer.
18 holes, 5084yds, Par 68, SSS 68.
Visitors no restrictions. Societies advisable to contact in advance. Green Fees not confirmed. Prof Mike Day Course Designer Gorvett Estates Facilities 🏌 🍴 👤 🏠 ⛳ Location Approx 4m E of Swansea, off A483

Hotel ★★ 65% Castle Hotel, The Parade, NEATH ☎ 01639 641119 & 643581 📠 01639 641624 29 en suite

Neath Cadoxton SA10 8AH ☎ 01639 643615 (clubhouse) & 632759 (secretary)
Mountain course, with spectacular views. Testing holes: 10th par 4; 12th par 5; 15th par 4.

continued

18 holes, 6492yds, Par 72, SSS 72, Course record 66.
Club membership 700.
Visitors with member only at weekends & bank holidays.
Societies should either telephone or write in advance. **Green Fees** Apr-Sep: £21; Oct-Mar: £11. **Prof** M Bennett **Course Designer** James Braid **Facilities** ⊗ ⟩Ⅲ ⬧ 💺 ♀ 🛆 🏠 ⛳ ✐
Leisure snooker. **Location** 2m NE off A4230

Hotel ★★ 65% Castle Hotel, The Parade, NEATH
☎ 01639 641119 & 643581 📋 01639 641624 29 en suite

Swansea Bay Jersey Marine SA10 6JP
☎ 01792 812198 & 814153
Fairly level seaside links with part-sand dunes.

18 holes, 6605yds, Par 72, SSS 72, Course record 69.
Club membership 500.
Visitors welcome. **Societies** telephone enquiry or letter stating requirements. **Green Fees** £17 per round (£24 weekends & bank holidays). **Prof** Mike Day **Facilities** ⊗ ⟩Ⅲ ⬧ 💺 ♀ 🛆 🏠 ⛳ ✐ **Location** 4m E of Swansea off A483

Hotel ★★ 65% Castle Hotel, The Parade, NEATH
☎ 01639 641119 & 643581 📋 01639 641624 29 en suite

PONTARDAWE   Map 03 SN70

Pontardawe Cefn Llan SA8 4SH
☎ 01792 863118 📋 01792 830041
e-mail: pontardawe@btopenworld.com
Meadowland course situated on plateau 600 ft above sea-level with good views over Bristol Channel and Brecon Beacons.
18 holes, 6038yds, Par 70, SSS 70, Course record 64.
Club membership 500.
Visitors must contact in advance, but may not play on weekends. **Societies** apply in writing. **Green Fees** £18 per round. **Cards** 🔲 🔲 🔲 🔲 **Prof** Gary Hopkins **Facilities** ⊗ ⟩Ⅲ ⬧ 💺 ♀ 🛆 🏠 ✐ **Conf** Max 50 Class 50 Board 50 **Location** N side of town centre M4 junc 45 off A4067

Hotel ★★ 65% Castle Hotel, The Parade, NEATH
☎ 01639 641119 & 643581 📋 01639 641624 29 en suite

PORT TALBOT   Map 03 SS78

British Steel Port Talbot Sports & Social Club,
Margam SA13 2NF ☎ 01639 791938
e-mail: tony.edwards@ntlworld.com
A 9 hole course with two lakes. All the holes are affected by crosswinds and the 7th, Par 3, is alongside a deep stream, so is very tight.
9 holes, 4726yds, Par 62, SSS 63, Course record 60.
Club membership 250.
Visitors contact in advance, may not play at weekends.
Societies by prior arrangement. **Green Fees** £10(£12 weekends). **Facilities** ⊗ ⟩Ⅲ ⬧ 💺 ♀ 🛆 **Leisure** hard tennis courts, fishing. **Location** M4 junct 40 near Corus Steelworks.
continued

Hotel ★★★ 68% Aberavon Beach Hotel, PORT TALBOT
☎ 01639 884949 52 en suite

NEWPORT

CAERLEON   Map 03 ST39

Caerleon NP6 1AY ☎ 01633 420342 📋 01633 420342
Parkland course.
9 holes, 2900yds, Par 34, SSS 34, Course record 29.
Club membership 148.
Visitors play is allowed on all days, contact for details.
Societies telephone 01633 420342. **Green Fees** £6.20 per 18 holes; £4.15 per 9 holes (£7.70/£5.20 weekends). **Prof** M Phillips **Course Designer** Steel **Facilities** ⊗ ⟩Ⅲ ⬧ 💺 ♀ 🛆 🏠 ⛳ ✐ (**Location** 3m from M4 turn off for Caerleon, 1st left after Priory hotel, follow road to bottom

Hotel ★★★★★ 74% The Celtic Manor Resort, Coldra Woods, NEWPORT ☎ 01633 413000 400 en suite

LLANWERN   Map 03 ST38

Llanwern Tennyson Av NP18 2DY
☎ 01633 412029 📋 01633 412029
e-mail: llanwerngc@hotmail.com
Parkland Course.
18 holes, 6177yds, Par 70, SSS 69, Course record 66.
Club membership 650.
Visitors welcome, but with member only at weekends.
Societies telephone and confirm in writing. **Green Fees** not confirmed. **Prof** Stephen Price **Facilities** ⊗ ⟩Ⅲ ⬧ 💺 ♀ 🛆 🏠 **Location** 0.5m S off A455

Hotel ★★★★★ 74% The Celtic Manor Resort, Coldra Woods, NEWPORT ☎ 01633 413000 400 en suite

NEWPORT   Map 03 ST38

Celtic Manor Resort Coldra Woods NP18 1HQ
☎ 01633 410255 & 413000 📋 01633 410269
e-mail: rholland@celtic-manor.com
Three different courses - Wentwood Hills combines hilly landscapes and links-like features. Roman Road has a long and wide front nine, the back nine weaves its way through ravines, lakes and streams beside the Usk valley. Coldra Woods is a scenic short course and is a challenging test of accuracy.
Roman Road: 18 holes, 6495yds, Par 69, SSS 72, Course record 68.
Coldra Woods: 18 holes, 3807yds, Par 59, SSS 61.
Wentwood Hills: 18 holes, 7097yds, Par 72, SSS 75.
Club membership 400.
Visitors may play subject to availability, must book in advance **Societies** telephone with details in advance. **Green Fees** terms on application. **Cards** 🔲 🔲 🔲 🔲 **Prof** Scott Patience **Course Designer** Robert Trent Jones **Facilities** ⊗ ⟩Ⅲ ⬧ 💺 ♀ 🛆 🏠 ⛳ 🎾 ⛴ 🏊 ✐ (**Leisure** hard tennis courts, heated indoor swimming pool, sauna, solarium, gymnasium.**Conf** Max 1500 **Location** Off junct 24 on M4, midway between Bristol & Cardiff, take A48 to Newport,turn R after 300 metres

Hotel ★★★★★ 74% The Celtic Manor Resort, Coldra Woods, NEWPORT ☎ 01633 413000 400 en suite

Where to stay, where to eat?
Visit www.theAA.com

Newport Great Oak, Rogerstone NP10 9FX
☎ 01633 892643 🖹 01633 896676
e-mail: newportgolfclub.gwent@euphony.net
An undulating parkland course, in an ideal situation on an inland plateau 300ft above sea level with fine views over the surrounding wooded countryside. There are no blind holes, but plenty of natural hazards and bunkers.
18 holes, 6460yds, Par 72, SSS 71, Course record 63.
Club membership 800.
Visitors must contact in advance, handicap certificate required. Not on Sat, limited time Sun. **Societies** must contact in writing or telephone **Green Fees** £35 per day;£30 per round. **Prof** Paul Mayo **Course Designer** W Fernie **Facilities** ⊗ ⅷ 🖢 🖳 ♀ ♨ 🏠 ✸ ♣ ✓ **Location** 1m NW of junct 27 on M4 on B4591 just beyond 'Promotive' Garage

Hotel ★★★★★ 74% The Celtic Manor Resort, Coldra Woods, NEWPORT ☎ 01633 413000 400 en suite

Parc Church Ln, Coedkernew NP10 8TU
☎ 01633 680933 🖹 01633 681011
A challenging but enjoyable 18-hole course with water hazards and accompanying wildlife. The 38-bay driving range is floodlit until 10pm.
18 holes, 5619yds, Par 70, SSS 68, Course record 71.
Club membership 400.
Visitors must contact in advance 01633 680933. **Societies** telephone in advance. **Green Fees** not confirmed. **Prof** B Thomas/D Griffiths **Course Designer** B Thomas/T F Hicks **Facilities** ⊗ ⅷ 🖢 🖳 ♀ ♨ 🏠 ✸ ♣ ✓ ♟ **Location** 3m SW of Newport, off A48

Hotel ★★★ 65% The Kings Hotel, High St, NEWPORT ☎ 01633 842020 61 en suite

Tredegar Park Parc-y-Brain Rd, Rogerstone
NP10 9TG ☎ 01633 894433 🖹 01633 897152
e-mail: tpgc@btinternet.com
A new course completed in 1999 with two balanced halves, mostly in view from the clubhouse. A rolling, open course with fine scenic views.
18 holes, 6150yds, Par 72, SSS 72.
Club membership 822.
Visitors must be a member of a golf club affiliated to a national golf union, please contact in advance. **Societies** apply to secretary. **Green Fees** £15 per 18 holes. **Cards** ▧▧ ▦▦ **Prof** M L Morgan **Course Designer** R Sandow **Facilities** ⊗ ⅷ 🖢 🖳 ♀ ♨ 🏠 ✸ ✓ **Location** N of M4, Junct 27, B4591, club signposted from here

Hotel ★★★ 65% The Kings Hotel, High St, NEWPORT ☎ 01633 842020 61 en suite

PEMBROKESHIRE

HAVERFORDWEST   Map 02 SM91
Haverfordwest Arnolds Down SA61 2XQ
☎ 01437 764523 & 768409 🖹 01437 764143
e-mail: haverwestgolf@lineone.net
Fairly flat parkland course, a good challenge for golfers of all handicaps. Set in attractive surroundings with fine views over the Preseli Hills.
18 holes, 5966yds, Par 70, SSS 69, Course record 58.
Club membership 770.

Visitors restricted at weekends. **Societies** apply in writing or telephone for booking form. **Green Fees** £19 per day(£21 weekends). **Cards** ▧▧ ▦▦ ▤▤ 🖳 📲 **Prof** Alex Pile **Facilities** ⊗ ⅷ 🖢 🖳 ♀ ♨ 🏠 ✸ ♣ ✓ **Location** 1m E on A40

Hotel ★★ 67% Hotel Mariners, Mariners Square, HAVERFORDWEST ☎ 01437 763353 28 en suite

LETTERSTON   Map 02 SM92
Priskilly Forest Castlemorris SA62 5EH
☎ 01348 840276 🖹 01348 840276
e-mail: jevans@priskilly-forest.co.uk
Testing parkland course surrounded by rhododendrons. Beautiful panoramic views. Challenging dog-leg 4th with hazards both sides.
9 holes, 5874yds, Par 70, SSS 68, Course record 73.
Club membership 70.
Visitors advance booking advisable at weekends during summer. **Societies** telephone in advance. **Green Fees** £10 per 9 holes;£14 per 18 holes;£16 per day. **Cards** ▧▧ ▦▦ 📲 **Prof** S Parsons **Course Designer** J Walters **Facilities** ⊗ 🖢 🖳 ♀ ♨ 🏠 ✸ ♣ ✓ **Leisure** fishing. **Location** Off B4331 between Letterston and Mathry

Hotel ★★ 62% Abergwaun Hotel, The Market Square, FISHGUARD ☎ 01348 872077 10 en suite

MILFORD HAVEN   Map 02 SM90
Milford Haven Woodbine House, Hubberston
SA73 3RX ☎ 01646 697762 🖹 01646 697870
e-mail: enquiries@mhgc.co.uk
Parkland course with excellent greens and views of the Milford Haven waterway.
18 holes, 6030yds, Par 71, SSS 70, Course record 64.
Club membership 650.
Visitors no restrictions, advisable to contact in advance. **Societies** telephone to book. **Green Fees** £17.50 per 18 holes;£25 per day(£22.50/£30 weekends and bank holidays). **Cards** ▧▧ ▦▦ ▤▤ 📲 **Prof** Dylan Williams **Facilities** ⊗ ⅷ 🖢 🖳 ♀ ♨ 🏠 ✸ ✓ **Location** 1.5m W of M.Haven

Hotel ★★★ 69% Cleddau Bridge Hotel, Essex Rd, PEMBROKE DOCK ☎ 01646 685961 & 0800 279 4055 🖹 01646 685746 24 en suite

NEWPORT (PEMBROKESHIRE)   Map 02 SN03
Newport (Pemb) The Golf Club SA42 0NR
☎ 01239 820244 🖹 01239 820085
e-mail: newportgc@lineone.net
Seaside links course, with easy walking and good view of the Preselli Hills and Newport Bay.
9 holes, 5815yds, Par 70, SSS 68, Course record 64.
Club membership 350.
Visitors telephone in advance. **Societies** must telephone in advance. **Green Fees** £20 per 18 holes(£24 weekends). **Cards** ▧▧ ▦▦ ▤▤ 📲 **Prof** Julian Noott **Course Designer** James Baird **Facilities** ⊗ ⅷ 🖢 🖳 ♀ ♨ 🏠 ✸ ♣ ✓ **Location** 1.25m N

Hotel ★★ 68% Trewern Arms, NEVERN ☎ 01239 820395 10 en suite

PEMBROKE DOCK   Map 02 SM90
South Pembrokeshire Military Rd SA72 6SE
☎ 01646 621453 🖹 01646 621453
Parkland course overlooking the Cleddau River.

continued

continued

18 holes, 6100yds, Par 71, SSS 70, Course record 65.
Club membership 350.
Visitors must contact in advance, especially during season.
Societies apply in advance. **Green Fees** terms on application.
Course Designer Committee **Facilities** ⊗ ⅷ ⅃ 🏌 🍴 ⅄ ⚲ ❧
Location SW side of town centre off B4322

Hotel ★★ 64% Old Kings Arms, Main St, PEMBROKE
☎ 01646 683611 21 en suite

ST DAVID'S   Map 02 SM72

St David's City Whitesands Bay SA62 6HR
☎ 01437 720572 & 721751
Links course with alternative tees for 18 holes. Panoramic
views of St David's Head, Ramsey Island and Whitesands
Bay. The course is playable all year.
9 holes, 6117yds, Par 70, SSS 70, Course record 68.
Club membership 200.
Visitors prior booking with secretary is encouraged but no
always necessary, please check for weekends, Ladies Day Fri
pm. **Societies** book with the secretary in advance. **Green
Fees** not confirmed. **Facilities** 🏌 ⅄ ⚲ **Location** 2m W
overlooking Whitesands Bay

Hotel ★★★ 77% Warpool Court Hotel, ST DAVID'S
☎ 01437 720300 25 en suite

TENBY   Map 02 SN10

Tenby The Burrows SA70 7NP
☎ 01834 844447 📠 01834 844447
e-mail: tenbygolfclub@netscapeonline.co.uk
The oldest club in Wales, this fine old seaside links,
with sea views and natural hazards provides good golf
all the year round. Hosts for the Welsh Amateur
Championship in 1999.
18 holes, 6224yds, Par 69, SSS 71, Course record 65.
Club membership 800.
Visitors subject to competition & tee reservation. Must
produce handicap certificate. **Societies** must apply in
advance. **Green Fees** £26.50 (£32.50 weekends). **Prof**
Mark Hawkey **Course Designer** James Braid **Facilities**
⊗ ⅷ ⅃ 🏌 🍴 ⅄ ⚲ ❧ ⚹ ⚲ **Location** Close to railway
station in the town

Hotel ★★★ 74% Atlantic Hotel, The Esplanade,
TENBY ☎ 01834 842881 & 844176
📠 01834 842881 ex 256 42 en suite

Trefloyne Trefloyne Park, Penally SA70 7RG
☎ 01834 842165 📠 01834 842165
Idyllic parkland course with backdrop of mature mixed
woodlands and distant views of Tenby, Carmarthen bay
and Caldey Island. Opened in 1996, natural features and
hazards such as the Old Quarry make for exciting and
challenging golf.
18 holes, 6635yds, Par 71, SSS 73.
Club membership 263.
Visitors must contact in advance, must play a reasonable
standard of golf and adhere to golf etiquette and dress code
of club. **Societies** must book in advance by telephone or in
writing. **Green Fees** not confirmed. **Cards** 🃏 🃏 🃏 🃏 🃏
Prof Steven Laidler **Course Designer** F H Gillman
Facilities ⊗ 🏌 ⅄ ⚲ 🍴 ⚹ ❧ ⚲ **Leisure** lessons by
PGA Professional. **Location** Within Trefloyne Park, just
west of Tenby

Hotel ★★★ 69% Fourcroft Hotel, North Beach, TENBY
☎ 01834 842886 43 en suite

POWYS

BRECON   Map 03 SO02

Brecon Newton Park LD3 8PA ☎ 01874 622004
Parkland course, with easy walking. Natural hazards
include two rivers on its boundary. Good river and
mountain scenery.
9 holes, 5476yds, Par 68, SSS 68, Course record 61.
Club membership 360.
Visitors advisable to contact in advance, limited availability
at weekends. **Societies** apply in writing. **Green Fees** £12 per
day. **Course Designer** James Braid **Facilities** ⊗ 🏌 🍴 ⅄ ⚲
Location 0.75m W of town centre on A40

Hotel ★★ 68% Best Western Castle of Brecon Hotel,
Castle Square, BRECON ☎ 01874 624611
31 en suite 12 annexe en suite

Cradoc Penoyre Park, Cradoc LD3 9LP
☎ 01874 623658 📠 01874 611711
e-mail: secretary@cradoc.co.uk
Parkland with wooded areas, ponds and spectacular
views over the Brecon Beacons. Challenging golf.

18 holes, 6331yds, Par 72, SSS 72, Course record 65.
Club membership 700.
Visitors must contact secretary in advance. Limited
availability on Sundays **Societies** apply in writing or
telephone in advance to secretary. **Green Fees** £20 per day
(£25 weekends & bank holidays). **Cards** 🃏 🃏 🃏 **Prof**
Richard Davies **Course Designer** C K Cotton **Facilities** ⊗
ⅷ ⅃ 🏌 🍴 ⅄ ⚲ ❧ ⚹ 🥏 ⚲ ⚲ **Location** 2m N on B4520

Hotel ★★ 68% Best Western Castle of Brecon Hotel,
Castle Square, BRECON ☎ 01874 624611
31 en suite 12 annexe en suite

BUILTH WELLS   Map 03 SO05

Builth Wells Golf Links Rd LD2 3NF
☎ 01982 553296 📠 01982 551064
e-mail: builthwellsgolfclub@btinternet.com
Well guarded greens and a stream running thorough the
centre of the course add interest to this 18-hole
undulating parkland course. The clubhouse is a
converted 16th-century Welsh long house.
18 holes, 5386yds, Par 66, SSS 67, Course record 63.
Club membership 380.
Visitors contact secretary. Handicap certificate perferred.
Societies by prior arrangement. **Green Fees** £22 per day; £17
per round (£28/£23 weekends & bank holidays). **Prof** Simon
Edwards **Facilities** ⊗ ⅷ ⅃ 🏌 🍴 ⅄ ⚲ ❧ ⚹ ⚲ **Location** N
of A483

Hotel ★★★🏌 71% Caer Beris Manor Hotel, BUILTH
WELLS ☎ 01982 552601 23 en suite

CAERSWS — Map 06 SO09

Mid-Wales Golf Centre SY17 5SB
☎ 01686 688303 📠 01686 688303
A 9-hole, par 3 course with sand bunkers and three ponds.
9 holes, 2554yds, Par 54, SSS 54.
Club membership 95.
Visitors welcome, restricted during competitions on Sun am. Societies telephone in advance. Green Fees £5 per 9 holes (£6 weekends & bank holidays). Course Designer Jim Walters Facilities ⓑ ⚑ ⚐ ⚒ ⓕ ⚐ ⓕ 《 Location 0.75m off A470 out of Caersws

KNIGHTON — Map 07 SO27

Knighton Ffrydd Wood LD7 1DB ☎ 01547 528646
Upland course with some hard walking. Fine views over the Welsh/English border.
9 holes, 5362yds, Par 68, SSS 66, Course record 65.
Club membership 150.
Visitors may not play on Sun until after 4.30pm. Societies telephone in advance Green Fees £10 per day (£12 weekends & bank holidays). Course Designer Harry Vardon Facilities ⓧ ⓑ ⚑ ⚐ ⚒ Location 0.5m S off B4355

Hotel ★★★ 63% The Knighton Hotel, Broad St, KNIGHTON ☎ 01547 520530 15 en suite

LLANDRINDOD WELLS — Map 03 SO06

Llandrindod Wells The Clubhouse LD1 5NY
☎ 01597 823873 (sec) & 822247 (shop) 📠 01597 823873
e-mail: secretary@lwgc.co.uk
An upland links course, designed by Harry Vardon, with easy walking and panoramic views. One of the highest courses in Wales. (1,100 ft above sea level).
18 holes, 5759yds, Par 69, SSS 69, Course record 65.
Club membership 430.
Visitors no restrictions. Societies must telephone in advance. Green Fees terms on application. Course Designer H Vardon Facilities ⓧ ⚒ ⓑ ⚑ ⚐ ⚒ ⓕ ⚐ ⓕ ⚒ ⓕ
Location 1m SE off A483

Hotel ★★★ 68% Hotel Metropole, Temple St, LLANDRINDOD WELLS ☎ 01597 823700 121 en suite

LLANGATTOCK — Map 03 SO21

Old Rectory NP8 1PH
☎ 01873 810373 📠 018373 810373
Sheltered course with easy walking.
9 holes, 2200yds, Par 54, SSS 59, Course record 53.
Club membership 80.
Visitors no play Sun mornings, telephone for information. Societies telephone for booking. Green Fees £5 per day.
Cards ▭▭ ▬▬ ▦▦ ⚐⚐ Facilities ⓧ ⚒ ⓑ ⚑ ⚐ ⚒ ⓕ
Leisure fishing. Conf Board 80 Del £10-£16.50 Location SW of village

Hotel ★★★ 71% Gliffaes Country House Hotel, CRICKHOWELL ☎ 01874 730371 & 0800 146719 (Freephone) 📠 01874 730463 19 en suite 3 annexe en suite

LLANIDLOES — Map 06 SN98

St Idloes Penrallt SY18 6LG ☎ 01686 412559
Hill-course, slightly undulating but walking is easy. Good views, partly lined with trees. Sand and grass bunkers.
9 holes, 5540yds, Par 66, SSS 66, Course record 61.
Club membership 339.
Visitors may not play on Sun mornings or Wed evenings.
continued

Societies apply in writing to the secretary at least one month in advance. Green Fees £12.50 (£15.50 weekends and bank holidays). Facilities ⓧ by prior arrangement ⚒ by prior arrangement ⓑ ⚑ ⚐ ⚒ ⓕ Conf Max 30 Location 1m N off B4569

Guesthouse ♦♦♦♦ Old Vicarage, LLANGURIG
☎ 01686 440280 4 en suite

MACHYNLLETH — Map 06 SH70

Machynlleth Ffordd Drenewydd SY20 8UH
☎ 01654 702000
Lowland course with mostly natural hazards.
9 holes, 5726yds, Par 68, SSS 68, Course record 65.
Club membership 250.
Visitors Thur ladies day, Sun morning mens competition. Societies telephone in advance. Green Fees £12(£15 weekends & bank holidays). Course Designer James Braid Facilities ⓧ ⓑ ⚑ ⚐ ⚒ ⓕ Location 0.5m E off A489

Hotel ★★ 63% Wynnstay Hotel, Maengwyn St, MACHYNLLETH ☎ 01654 702941 23 en suite

NEWTOWN — Map 06 SO19

St Giles Pool Rd SY16 3AJ
☎ 01686 625844 📠 01686 625844
e-mail: st.giles.newtown@euphony.net
Inland country course with easy walking. Testing 2nd hole, par 3, and 4th hole, par 4. River Severn skirts four holes.
9 holes, 6012yds, Par 70, SSS 70, Course record 67.
Club membership 350.
Visitors advisable to contact in advance. Societies must contact in advance. Green Fees £13.50 per day (£16 weekends & bank holidays). Prof D P Owen Facilities ⓧ ⚒ ⓑ ⚑ ⚐ ⚒ ⓕ ⚐ ⓕ Leisure fishing. Location 0.5m NE on A483

Hotel ★★ 63% Wynnstay Hotel, Maengwyn St, MACHYNLLETH ☎ 01654 702941 23 en suite

WELSHPOOL — Map 07 SJ20

Welshpool Golfa Hill SY21 9AQ ☎ 01938 850249
e-mail: welshpool.golfclub@virgin.net
Undulating, hilly, heathland course with bracing air. Testing holes are 2nd (par 5), 14th (par 3), 17th (par 3) and a memorable 18th.
18 holes, 5708yds, Par 70, SSS 68, Course record 68.
Club membership 400.
Visitors must book in advance, restricted some weekends. Societies must book in advance. Green Fees £12.50 per day (£20.50 weekend & bank holiday, £15.50 winter). Prof Bob Barlow Course Designer James Braid Facilities ⓧ ⚒ ⓑ ⚑ ⚐ ⚒ ⓕ Location 3m W off A458

Hotel ★★★ 68% Royal Oak Hotel, The Cross, WELSHPOOL ☎ 01938 552217 24 en suite

RHONDDA CYNON TAFF

ABERDARE — Map 03 SO00

Aberdare Abernant CF44 0RY
☎ 01685 872797 📠 01685 872797
Mountain course with parkland features overlooking Brecon Beacons. Tree-lined with many mature oak trees.
18 holes, 5875yds, Par 69, SSS 69, Course record 64.
Club membership 550.
continued

Visitors must have handicap certificate. May play weekends by prior arrangment with Professional. **Societies** apply in writing in advance to the secretary. **Green Fees** £16 (£20 weekends). **Prof** A Palmer **Facilities** ⊗ ⅲ 🖪 ♥ ⚑ ♀ ♨ 🗃 ♂ **Conf** Max 50 **Location** A470 to Abercynon, take A4059 to Aberdare. Follow sign to hospital, 400 yds on right

Hotel ★★★ 69% Tregenna Hotel, Park Ter, MERTHYR TYDFIL ☎ 01685 723627 & 382055 ▤ 01685 721951 29 en suite

MOUNTAIN ASH   Map 03 ST09

Mountain Ash Cefnpennar CF45 4DT
☎ 01443 479459 ▤ 01443 479459
Mountain course on heathland with panoramic views of the Brecon Beacons.
18 holes, 5553yds, Par 69, SSS 67, Course record 60.
Club membership 600.
Visitors contact in advance for details. **Societies** must contact in writing. **Green Fees** £20(£30 weekends). **Cards** ▦ ▦ ▣ ▦ ▦ ▨ **Prof** Darren Clark **Facilities** ⊗ ⅲ 🖪 ♥ ♀ ♨ 🗃 ♂ **Conf** Max 130 Thtr 100 Class 130 Banquet 100 **Location** 1m NW off A4059

Hotel ★★★ 69% Tregenna Hotel, Park Ter, MERTHYR TYDFIL ☎ 01685 723627 & 382055 ▤ 01685 721951 29 en suite

PENRHYS   Map 03 ST09

Rhondda Golf Club House CF43 3PW
☎ 01443 441384 ▤ 01443 441384
e-mail: rhondda@btinternet.com
Mountain course with good views.
18 holes, 6205yds, Par 70, SSS 71, Course record 67.
Club membership 600.
Visitors contact secretary for weekend play. **Societies** contact for details. **Green Fees** not confirmed. **Cards** ▦ ▦ ▦ ▨ **Prof** G A Bebb **Facilities** ⊗ ⅲ 🖪 ♥ ♀ ♨ 🗃 ♥ 🚜 ♂ 🏌 **Location** 0.5m W off B4512

Hotel ★★★ 66% Heritage Park Hotel, Coed Cae Rd, Trehafod, PONTYPRIDD ☎ 01443 687057 44 en suite

PONTYCLUN   Map 03 ST08

Vale of Glamorgan Hotel Golf & Country Club Hensol Park CF72 8JY
☎ 01443 222221 ▤ 01443 222220
Lake: *18 holes, 6507yds, Par 72, SSS 71.*
Hensol: *9 holes, 3115yds, Par 72, SSS 71.*
Course Designer Peter Johnson **Location** 2 mins from junct 34 of M4
Telephone for further details

Hotel ★★★★ 71% Vale Hotel Golf & Country Club, Hensol Park, HENSOL
☎ 01443 667800 30 en suite 113 annexe en suite

PONTYPRIDD   Map 03 ST09

Pontypridd Ty Gwyn Rd CF37 4DJ
☎ 01443 409904 ▤ 01443 491622
Well-wooded mountain course with springy turf. Good views of the Rhondda Valleys and coast.
18 holes, 5721yds, Par 69, SSS 68, Course record 65.
Club membership 850.
Visitors must contact in advance. Must play with member on weekends & bank holidays. Must have a handicap certificate. **Societies** weekdays only. Must contact in advance. **Green Fees** terms on application. **Prof** Wade Walters **Facilities** ⊗
continued

ⅲ 🖪 ♨ 🗃 ♥ 🚜 ♂ **Conf** Max 100 **Location** E side of town centre off A470

Hotel ★★★ 66% Heritage Park Hotel, Coed Cae Rd, Trehafod, PONTYPRIDD ☎ 01443 687057 44 en suite

TALBOT GREEN   Map 03 ST08

Llantrisant & Pontyclun Off Ely Valley Rd
CF72 8AL ☎ 01443 228169 ▤ 01443 224601
Parkland course.
18 holes, 5328yds, Par 68, SSS 66.
Club membership 600.
Visitors must have handicap certificate, must contact in advance, not at weekends **Societies** telephone in advance **Green Fees** terms on application. **Prof** Mark Phillips **Facilities** ⊗ ⅲ 🖪 ♥ ♀ ♨ 🗃 🏌 ♂

Hotel ★★★★ 69% Miskin Manor Hotel & Health Club LTD, Groes Faen, Pontyclun, MISKIN
☎ 01443 224204 35 en suite 11 annexe en suite

SWANSEA

CLYDACH   Map 03 SN60

Inco SA6 5PQ ☎ 01792 843336
Flat meadowland course recently extended to 18 holes.
18 holes, 6064yds, Par 70, SSS 69.
Club membership 450.
Visitors no restrictions. **Societies** must contact in advance. **Green Fees** not confirmed. **Facilities** ⊗ 🖪 ♥ ♀ ♨ **Location** 0.75m SE on B4291

Hotel ⇧ Travel Inn, Upper Fforest Way, Morriston, SWANSEA ☎ 01792 311920 40 en suite

PONTLLIW   Map 02 SS69

Allt-y-Graban Allt-y-Grabam Rd SA4 1DT
☎ 01792 885757
A challenging parkland course with fine panoramic views, opened in 1993.It is a 9-hole course but with plans for 12 holes. There are 6 par 4 holes and 3 par 3 holes. The 6th is a challenging hole with a blind tee shot into the valley and a dogleg to the left onto an elevated green.
9 holes, 2210yds, Par 66, SSS 66, Course record 63.
Club membership 158.
Visitors no restrictions. **Societies** telephone in advance. **Green Fees** terms on application. **Course Designer** F G Thomas **Facilities** 🖪 ♥ ♀ ♨ 🏌 ♂ **Location** From junct 47 on M4 take A48 towards Pontardulais. Turn left after Glamorgan Arms

Hotel ★★★ 65% Holiday Inn Swansea, The Kingsway Circle, SWANSEA ☎ 0870 400 9078 106 en suite

SOUTHGATE   Map 02 SS58

Pennard 2 Southgate Rd SA3 2BT
☎ 01792 233131 & 233451 ▤ 01792 234797
Undulating, cliff-top seaside links with good coastal views.
18 holes, 6265yds, Par 71, SSS 72, Course record 69.
Club membership 1020.
Visitors advisable to contact Professional in advance. **Societies** by prior arrangement, telephone in advance. **Green Fees** £27 per 18 holes(£35 weekends & bank holidays). **Prof** M V Bennett **Course Designer** James Braid **Facilities** ⊗ ⅲ 🖪 ♥ ♀ ♨ 🗃 🏌 ♂ **Conf** Max 100 Banquet 100 **Location** 8m W of Swansea by A4067 and B4436
continued

Hotel ★★♨️ Fairyhill, REYNOLDSTON
☎ 01792 390139 8 en suite

SWANSEA — Map 03 SS69

Clyne 120 Owls Lodge Ln, The Mayals, Blackpyl
SA3 5DP ☎ 01792 401989 🗎 01792 401078
e-mail: clynegolfclub@supanet.com
Challenging moorland course with excellent greens and scenic views of Swansea Bay and The Gower.
18 holes, 6334yds, Par 70, SSS 71, Course record 64.
Club membership 900.
Visitors must be member of a club with handicap certificate. Groups over 8 advised to book in advance. **Societies** must contact in advance. **Green Fees** £25 per round (£30 weekends). Winter £20 up to 27 holes Tue-Fri (inc. meal). **Prof** Jonathan Clewett **Course Designer** H S Colt & Harries **Facilities** ⊗ ⫴ ⮞ 🍽️ ♀ ⛳ 🍴 ♂ ♟ **Leisure** chipping green,driving nets,indoor practice net. **Location** 3.5m SW on B4436 off A4067

Hotel ★★★ 67% Langland Court, Langland Court Rd, LANGLAND ☎ 01792 361545 14 en suite 5 annexe en suite

Langland Bay Langland Bay SA3 4QR
☎ 01792 361721 🗎 01792 361082
e-mail: golf@langlandbay.sagehost.co.uk
Parkland course overlooking Gower coast. The par 4, 6th is an uphill dog-leg open to the wind, and the par 3, 16th (151 yds) is aptly named 'Death or Glory'.

18 holes, 5857yds, Par 70, SSS 69.
Club membership 850.
Visitors no restrictions. Tue is Ladies Day. No societies at weekends **Societies** must telephone in advance. **Green Fees** not confirmed. **Prof** Mark Evans **Course Designer** Henry Cotton **Facilities** ⊗ ⫴ ⮞ 🍽️ ♀ ⛳ 🍴 ♂ ♟ **Location** 6m W on A4067

Hotel ★★★ 67% Langland Court, Langland Court Rd, LANGLAND ☎ 01792 361545 14 en suite 5 annexe en suite

Morriston 160 Clasemont Rd SA6 6AJ
☎ 01792 796528 🗎 01792 796528
Pleasant parkland course with a very difficult par 3 15th hole, one of the most challenging short holes in Wales. The 17th is aptly nicknamed "Temple of Doom".
18 holes, 5891yds, Par 68, SSS 68, Course record 61.
Club membership 700.
Visitors may not play Sat. Must contact in advance. **Societies** apply in writing. **Green Fees** £18 per round (£30 weekends). **Prof** D A Rees **Facilities** ⊗ ⫴ ⮞ 🍽️ ♀ ⛳ 🍴 ♟ **Conf** Max 120 Del £75 * **Location** 5m N of Swansea on A48. 1m E of junct 46 of M4

continued

Hotel ⌂ Travel Inn, Upper Fforest Way, Morriston, SWANSEA ☎ 01792 311920 40 en suite

THREE CROSSES — Map 02 SS59

Gower Cefn Goleu SA4 3HS
☎ 01792 872480 (Off) 879905 (Pro) 🗎 01792 872480
e-mail: adrian.richards@gower-golf-club.demon.co.uk
Set in attractive rolling countryside, this Donald Steel designed course provides good strategic hazards, including trees, water and bunkers, outstanding views and a challenging game of golf.
18 holes, 6441yds, Par 71, SSS 72, Course record 70.
Club membership 500.
Visitors tee booking upto 7 days in advance, reservations recommended, some weekend vacancies, dress code and course etiquette must be observed. **Societies** by prior notice for established golfers. **Green Fees** £15 per 18 holes Mon-Thurs(£20 Fri-Sun). **Cards** 💳 💳 💳 💳 💳 **Prof** Alan Williamson **Course Designer** Donald Steel **Facilities** ⊗ ⫴ ⮞ 🍽️ ♀ ⛳ 🍴 🏌️ ♂ ♟ **Conf** Max 120 **Location** Sign posted from the village of Three Crosses

Hotel ★★ 72% Beaumont Hotel, 72-73 Walter Rd, SWANSEA ☎ 01792 643956 16 en suite

UPPER KILLAY — Map 02 SS59

Fairwood Park Blackhills Ln SA2 7JN
☎ 01792 203648 🗎 01792 297849
Parkland championship course on the beautiful Gower Peninsula.
18 holes, 6754yds, Par 72, SSS 72, Course record 68.
Club membership 720.
Visitors welcome except when championship or club matches are being held. Must contact in advance. **Societies** must contact in advance. **Green Fees** £25 per day (£30 weekends & bank holidays). **Cards** 💳 **Prof** Gary Hughes **Course Designer** Hawtree **Facilities** ⊗ ⫴ ⮞ 🍽️ ♀ ⛳ 🍴 🏌️ ♟ **Location** 1.5m S off A4118

Hotel ★★ 71% Windsor Lodge Hotel, Mount Pleasant, SWANSEA ☎ 01792 642158 & 652744 🗎 01792 648996 18 en suite

TORFAEN

CWMBRAN — Map 03 ST29

Green Meadow Golf & Country Club Treherbert Rd, Croesyceiliog NP44 2BZ ☎ 01633 869321 & 862626 🗎 01633 868430
Undulating parkland course with panoramic views. Tree lined undulating fairways, water hazards and pot bunkers. The greens are excellent and are playable all year round.
18 holes, 6029yds, Par 70, SSS 70, Course record 66.
Club membership 400.
Visitors by prior arrangement advised especially at weekends, tel 01633 862626. Correct standard of dress compulsory. **Societies** telephone for brochure, Golf Shop 01633 862626. **Green Fees** not confirmed. **Cards** 💳 💳 💳 **Prof** Peter Stebbings **Course Designer** Peter Richardson **Facilities** ⊗ ⫴ ⮞ 🍽️ ♀ ⛳ 🍴 🏌️ ♂ ♟ **Leisure** hard tennis courts. **Location** 5m N of junct 26 M4, off A4042 from Cardiff

Hotel ★★★★ 65% Parkway Hotel, Cwmbran Dr, CWMBRAN ☎ 01633 871199 70 en suite

Pontnewydd Maesgwyn Farm, West Pontnewydd
NP44 1AB ☎ 01633 482170 ▤ 01633 484447
e-mail: ctphillips@ukgateway.net
**Mountainside course, with hard walking. Good views
across the Severn Estuary.**
18 holes, 5278yds, Par 68, SSS 67, Course record 63.
Club membership 250.
Visitors must be accompanied by a member weekends &
bank holidays. **Green Fees** £15 per round. **Facilities** ⊗ 〗ℍ ⓛ
♨ ♀ ♔ **Location** N side of town centre

Hotel ★★★★ 65% Parkway Hotel, Cwmbran Dr,
CWMBRAN ☎ 01633 871199 70 en suite

PONTYPOOL   Map 03 SO20

Pontypool Lasgarn Ln, Trevethin NP4 8TR
☎ 01495 763655
Undulating, mountain course with magnificent views.
18 holes, 6046yds, Par 69, SSS 69, Course record 64.
Club membership 638.
Visitors must have a handicap certificate, restricted
availability at weekends, advisable to call in advance.
Societies apply in writing or by phone, deposit required.
Green Fees not confirmed. **Prof** James Howard **Facilities** ⊗
〗ℍ ⓛ ♨ ♀ ♔ ⓐ ⫟ ➘ ⛳ ⟁ **Location** 1.5m N off A4043

Hotel ★★ 67% Mill at Glynhir, Glynhir Rd, Llandybie,
AMMANFORD ☎ 01269 850672
7 en suite 3 annexe en suite

Woodlake Park Golf & Country Club

Glascoed NP4 0TE ☎ 01291 673933 ▤ 01291 673811
e-mail: golf@woodlake.co.uk
**Undulating parkland course with magnificent views over
Llandegfedd Reservoir. Superb green constructed to
USGA specification. Holes 4, 7 & 16 are par 3s which are
particularly challenging. Holes 6 & 17 are long par 4s
which can be wind affected.**
18 holes, 6278yds, Par 71, SSS 72, Course record 67.
Club membership 500.
Visitors book in advance. **Societies** telephone or write for
society package. **Green Fees** £20 per 18 holes(£25 weekends
and bank holidays). **Cards** ▭ ▬ **Prof** Adrian Pritchard
Facilities ⊗ 〗ℍ ⓛ ♨ ♀ ♔ ⓐ ⫟ ➘ ⟁ **Leisure** fishing.
Location Overlooking Llandegfedd Reservoir

Hotel ★★ 67% Mill at Glynhir, Glynhir Rd, Llandybie,
AMMANFORD ☎ 01269 850672
7 en suite 3 annexe en suite

VALE OF GLAMORGAN

BARRY   Map 03 ST16

Brynhill Port Rd CF62 8PN
☎ 01446 720277 ▤ 01446 740422
e-mail: gershenson@lineone.net
**Meadowland course with some hard walking. Prevailing
west wind.**
18 holes, 6336yds, Par 72, SSS 71.
Club membership 500.
Visitors must contact in advance. May not play on Sun.
Societies phone secretary for details. **Green Fees** terms on
application. **Cards** ▬ **Prof** Mike Herbert **Facilities** ⊗ 〗ℍ ⓛ
♨ ♀ ♔ ⓐ ⫟ ⟁ **Location** 1.25m N on B4050

Hotel ★★★ 66% Mount Sorrel Hotel, Porthkerry Rd,
BARRY ☎ 01446 740069 42 en suite

RAF St Athan St Athan CF62 4WA
☎ 01446 797186 & 751043 ▤ 01446 751862
**This is a very windy course with wind straight off the sea
to make all holes interesting. Further interest is added by
this being a very tight course with lots of trees. Beware of
low flying RAF jets.**
9 holes, 6480yds, Par 72, SSS 72.
Club membership 450.
Visitors contact in advance, Sun mornings club competitions
only. **Societies** apply in advance. **Green Fees** not confirmed.
Facilities ⊗ ⓛ ♨ ♀ ♔ ⓐ **Location** Between Barry &
Llantwit Major

Hotel ★★★♨♨ 77% Egerton Grey Country House Hotel,
Porthkerry, BARRY ☎ 01446 711666 10 en suite

St Andrews Major Argae Ln, Coldbrook Rd East,
Cadoxton CF63 1BL ☎ 01446 722227
**A new 9-hole, Pay and Play course with 6 par 4s, 1 par 5
and 2 par 3s. Further extensions planned.**
9 holes, 3000yds, Par 70, SSS 68.
Club membership 520.
Visitors must contact in advance. **Societies** telephone in
advance. **Green Fees** not confirmed. **Course Designer**
Richard Hurd **Facilities** ⓛ ♨ ♀ ♔ ⓐ ⫟ ⟁ **Location** Off
Barry new link road, Coldbrook Road East

Hotel ★★★♨♨ 77% Egerton Grey Country House Hotel,
Porthkerry, BARRY ☎ 01446 711666 10 en suite

DINAS POWYS   Map 03 ST17

Dinas Powis High Walls Av CF64 4AJ
☎ 029 2051 2727 ▤ 029 2051 2727
**Parkland/downland course with views over the Bristol
Channel and the seaside resort of Barry.**
18 holes, 5486yds, Par 67, SSS 67, Course record 60.
Club membership 550.
Visitors must contact in advance (call G Bennett 02920
513682) **Societies** telephone in advance. **Green Fees** not
confirmed. **Prof** Gareth Bennett **Facilities** ⊗ 〗ℍ ⓛ ♨ ♀ ♔
ⓐ ➘ ⫟ ⟁ **Location** NW side of village

Hotel ★★★ 66% Mount Sorrel Hotel, Porthkerry Rd,
BARRY ☎ 01446 740069 42 en suite

PENARTH   Map 03 ST17

Glamorganshire Lavernock Rd CF64 5UP
☎ 029 20701185 ▤ 029 20701185
e-mail: glamgolf@btconnect.com
Parkland course, overlooking the Bristol Channel.
18 holes, 6039yds, Par 70, SSS 70, Course record 64.
Club membership 1000.
Visitors contact professional in advance. **Societies** must
contact in advance. **Green Fees** £35 per day(£40 weekends).
Cards ▭ ▬ ▦ ▩ **Prof** Andrew Kerr-Smith **Course
Designer** James Braid **Facilities** ⊗ 〗ℍ ⓛ ♨ ♀ ♔ ⓐ ⫟ ➘
⫟ ⟁ **Location** S side of town centre on B4267

Hotel ★★★ 66% Mount Sorrel Hotel, Porthkerry Rd,
BARRY ☎ 01446 740069 42 en suite

WENVOE   Map 03 ST17

Wenvoe Castle CF5 6BE ☎ 029 20594371
18 holes, 6422yds, Par 72, SSS 71, Course record 64.
Location 1m S off A4050
Telephone for further details

Hotel ★★★♨♨ 77% Egerton Grey Country House Hotel,
Porthkerry, BARRY ☎ 01446 711666 10 en suite

WREXHAM

CHIRK Map 07 SJ23

Chirk Golf Club LL14 5AD
☎ 01691 774407 & 0800 7318598 Fax 01691 773878
e-mail: fiona.barnes@lineone.net
Overlooked by the National Trust's Chirk Castle, is a championship-standard 18-hole course with a 664 yard, par 5 at the 9th - one of the longest in Europe. Also a 9-hole course, driving range and golf academy.

Manor Course: 18 holes, 7045yds, Par 72, SSS 73, Course record 72.
Club membership 750.
Visitors advisable to contact in advance. May not play in members' preferred tee times 7-10am daily. **Societies** must telephone for provisonal booking. **Green Fees** not confirmed. **Cards** **Prof** Mark Maddison **Facilities** **Leisure** squash, fishing. **Location** 5m N of Oswestry

Hotel ★★★ 66% Moreton Park Lodge, Moreton Park, Gledrid, CHIRK ☎ 01691 776666 46 en suite

EYTON Map 07 SJ34

Plassey LL13 0SP ☎ 01978 780028 Fax 01978 781397
Pleasant 9-hole course set in naturally contoured parkland with water hazards. It is within Plassey Leisure Park and Craft Centre and all park facilities are available to golfers.
9 holes, 2434yds, Par 32, SSS 32, Course record 64.
Club membership 180.
Visitors must contact in advance. **Societies** telephone then confirm in writing. **Green Fees** £16 per day; £12 per 18 holes; £8 per 9 holes (£18/£13.50/£9 weekends & bank holidays). **Cards** **Prof** Simon Ward **Course Designer** Welsh Golf Union **Facilities** **Location** 2.5m off A483 Chester/Oswestry

Hotel ★★★ 67% Cross Lanes Hotel & Restaurant, Cross Lanes, Bangor Rd, Marchwiel, WREXHAM ☎ 01978 780555 16 en suite

RUABON Map 07 SJ34

Penycae Ruabon Rd, Penycae LL14 1TP
☎ 01978 810108
An architecturally designed and built 9 hole parkland course offering a challenge for players of all standards. After a lazy par 4 start the 2nd par 3 is wooded to one side and guarded by water on the other. The 6th, a 317yds par 4 makes a very difficult approach to the green. The 7th is another par 3 , elevated and wooded to one side. The 8th crosses water twice as the river meanders down the fairway.
9 holes, 2140yds, Par 64, SSS 62, Course record 62.
Club membership 200.
Visitors advisable to book in advance. **Societies** telephone or write in advance. **Green Fees** not confirmed. **Course Designer** John Day **Facilities** **Location** 1m off A5

Hotel ★★★ 66% Moreton Park Lodge, Moreton Park, Gledrid, CHIRK ☎ 01691 776666 46 en suite

WREXHAM Map 07 SJ35

Clays Farm Golf Centre Bryn Estyn Rd, Llan-y-Pwll LL13 9UB ☎ 01978 661406 Fax 01978 661417
e-mail: claysgolf@tinyworld.co.uk
Gently undulating parkland course in a rural setting with views of the Welsh mountains and noted for the difficulty of its par 3s.
Clays Farm Golf Centre: 18 holes, 5908yds, Par 69, SSS 69, Course record 63.
Club membership 420.
Visitors must contact in advance. **Societies** prior arrangement in writing. **Green Fees** £14 per round (£19 weekends). **Cards** **Prof** David Larvin **Course Designer** R D Jones **Facilities** **Location** Off A534

Hotel ★★★ 66% Llwyn Onn Hall Hotel, Cefn Rd, WREXHAM ☎ 01978 261225 13 en suite

Wrexham Holt Rd LL13 9SB
☎ 01978 351476 Fax 01978 364268
Inland, sandy course with easy walking. Testing dog-legged 7th hole (par 4), and short 14th hole (par 3) with full carry to green.
18 holes, 6233yds, Par 70, SSS 70, Course record 64.
Club membership 600.
Visitors may not play competition days, and are advised to contact in advance. A handicap certificate is required. **Societies** welcome Mon & Wed-Fri. Apply in writing **Green Fees** £22 (£25 weekends and bank holidays). **Prof** Paul Williams **Course Designer** James Braid **Facilities** **Location** 2m NE on A534

Hotel ★★★ 66% Llwyn Onn Hall Hotel, Cefn Rd, WREXHAM ☎ 01978 261225 13 en suite

Ireland

NORTHERN IRELAND

CO ANTRIM

ANTRIM
Map 01 D5

Massereene 51 Lough Rd BT41 4DQ
☎ 028 94428096 📠 028 94487661
The first nine holes are parkland, while the second, adjacent to the shore of Lough Neagh, have more of a links character with sandy ground.
18 holes, 6602yds, Par 72, SSS 72, Course record 63. Club membership 969.
Visitors must contact in advance. **Societies** book in advance. **Green Fees** not confirmed. **Cards** 🖅 🖅 🖅 🖭 **Prof** Jim Smyth **Course Designer** F Hawtree **Facilities** ⊗ ⊪ ⅃ ♥ ♀ ♣ 🛈 ✔ **Location** 1m SW of town

Hotel ★★★★ 69% Galgorm Manor, BALLYMENA
☎ 028 2588 1001 24 en suite

BALLYCASTLE
Map 01 D6

Ballycastle Cushendall Rd BT54 6QP
☎ 028 20762536 📠 028 20769909
An unusual mixture of terrain beside the sea, with magnificent views from all parts. The first five holes are inland type; the middle holes on the Warren are links type and the rest, on high ground, are heath type.
18 holes, 5927mtrs, Par 71, SSS 70, Course record 64. Club membership 920.
Visitors are welcome during the week. **Societies** apply in writing. **Green Fees** £20 per round (£30 weekends). **Prof** Ian McLaughlin **Facilities** ⊗ ⊪ ⅃ ♥ ♀ ♣ 🛈 ✔ **Location** Between Portrush & Cushendall (A2)

Hotel ★★★ 71% The Royal Court Hotel, 233 Ballybogey Rd, PORTRUSH ☎ 028 7082 2236 18 en suite

BALLYCLARE
Map 01 D5

Ballyclare 23 Springdale Rd BT39 9JW
☎ 028 93322696 & 93344541 📠 028 93322696
Parkland course with lots of trees and shrubs and water hazards provided by the river, streams and lakes.
18 holes, 5745mtrs, Par 71, SSS 71, Course record 66. Club membership 580.
Visitors must contact in advance. **Societies** must contact in advance. **Green Fees** terms on application. **Prof** Alan Johnston **Course Designer** T McCauley **Facilities** ⊗ ⊪ ⅃ ♥ ♀ ♣ 🛈 ✔ **Location** 1.5m N of Ballyclare

Hotel ★★★ 66% Adair Arms Hotel, 1 Ballymoney Rd, BALLYMENA ☎ 028 2565 3674 44 en suite

Greenacres 153 Ballyrobert Rd BT39 9RT
☎ 028 93354111 📠 028 93354166
Designed and built into the rolling countryside, and with the addition of lakes at five of the holes, provides a challenge for both the seasoned golfer and the higher-handicapped player.
18 holes, 5819yds, Par 71, SSS 69. Club membership 440.
Visitors may not play Sat mornings. **Societies** apply in writing. **Green Fees** £12 Mon-Thur;£16 Fri (£18 weekends). **Cards** 🖅 🖅 🖭 **Prof** Roy Skillen **Facilities** ⊗ ⊪ ⅃ ♥ ♀ ♣ 🛈 ✔ **Conf** Max 100 Del £2.50 to £12 * **Location** 12miles from Belfast city centre

continued

Hotel ★★★ 66% Adair Arms Hotel, 1 Ballymoney Rd, BALLYMENA ☎ 028 2565 3674 44 en suite

BALLYGALLY
Map 01 D5

Cairndhu 192 Coast Rd BT40 2QG
☎ 028 28583324 📠 028 28583324
e-mail: cairndhu@globalgolf.com
Built on a hilly headland, this course is both testing and scenic, with wonderful coastal views. The par 3 second hole can require anything from a 9 to 3 iron depending on the wind while the 3rd has a carry of 180 yds over a headland to the fairway. The 10th, 11th and 12th holes constitute Cairndhu's 'Amen Corner', feared and respected by any standard of golfer.
18 holes, 5611mtrs, Par 70, SSS 69, Course record 64. Club membership 905.
Visitors may not play on Sat. **Societies** must apply in writing. **Green Fees** £20 Mon-Fri (£25 Sun). **Cards** 🖅 🖅 🖭 **Prof** Robert Walker **Course Designer** Mr Morrison **Facilities** ⊗ ⊪ ⅃ ♥ ♀ ♣ 🛈 ✔ **Location** 4m N of Larne on coast road

Hotel ★★★ 69% Londonderry Arms Hotel, 20 Harbour Rd, CARNLOUGH ☎ 028 2888 5255 35 en suite

BALLYMENA
Map 01 D5

Ballymena 128 Raceview Rd BT42 4HY
☎ 028 25861487
18 holes, 5299mtrs, Par 68, SSS 67, Course record 64.
Location 2m E on A42
Telephone for further details

Hotel ★★★★ 69% Galgorm Manor, BALLYMENA
☎ 028 2588 1001 24 en suite

Galgorm Castle Golf & Country Club
Galgorm Rd BT42 1HL ☎ 028 25646161 📠 028 25651151
e-mail: golf@galgormcastle.co.uk
18 hole championship course set in 220 acres of mature parkland in the grounds of a historic castle. The course is bordered by two rivers which come into play and includes five lakes. A course of outstanding beauty offering a challenge to both the novice and low handicapped golfer.
18 holes, 6736yds, Par 72, SSS 72, Course record 68. Club membership 450.
Visitors ring to book times. **Societies** telephone in advance to book tee time. **Green Fees** £35 per day; £23 per round (£44/£35 weekends). **Cards** 🖅 🖅 🖭 **Prof** Phil Collins **Course Designer** Simon Gidman **Facilities** ⊗ ⊪ ⅃ ♥ ♀ ♣ 🛈 ✔ **Leisure** fishing, PGA staffed Academy. **Conf** Max 40 Del £10 to £20 * **Location** 1m S of Ballymena on A42

Hotel ★★★★ 69% Galgorm Manor, BALLYMENA
☎ 028 2588 1001 24 en suite

CARRICKFERGUS
Map 01 D5

Carrickfergus 25 North Rd BT38 8LP
☎ 028 93363713 📠 028 93363023
Parkland course, fairly level but nevertheless demanding, with a notorious water hazard at the 1st. Well-maintained, with an interesting in-course riverway and fine views across Belfast Lough.
18 holes, 5768yds, Par 68, SSS 68. Club membership 850.
Visitors restrictions at weekends. **Societies** must contact in advance. **Green Fees** not confirmed. **Cards** 🖅 🖅 🖅 🖭

continued on page 386

Royal Portrush

Portrush, *Co Antrim*   ☎ 028 70822311   Fax 028 70823139   Map 01 D4

e-mail: rpgc@dnet.co.uk

This course, designed by Harry S Colt, is considered among the six best in the UK. Founded in 1888, it was the venue of the first professional golf event held in Ireland, in 1895, where Sandy Herd beat Harry Vardon in the final.

It is spectacular, breathtaking, but one of the tightest driving tests known to man. On a clear day, you have a fine view of Islay and the Paps of Jura from the 3rd tee and the Giant's Causeway from the 5th. While the greens have to be 'read' from the start, there are fairways up and down valleys, and holes called Calamity Corner and Purgatory for good reason! The second hole - Giant's Grave, is 509 yards, there is an even longer hole at the 17th.

Visitors must contact in advance, have a letter of introduction from their own club and a handicap certificate. Restricted Wed & Fri pm, Sat & Sun am on Dunluce Links.

Societies must apply in writing

Green Fees Dunluce £85-£95, Valley £30-£35.

Facilities ⊗ ⅏ ᛒ ♊ ♀ ⚲ 🖼 ⚲ ⚳ ⚳
Professional (Gary McNeill)

Location Dunluce Rd, Portrush BT56 8JQ (0.5m from Portrush, on main Bushmills Road)

Holes/Par/Course record
Dunluce: 18 holes, 6641 yds, Par 72, SSS 73
Valley: 18 holes, 6054 yds, Par 70, SSS 69

Championship Course

WHERE TO STAY AND EAT NEARBY

Hotel
PORTRUSH
★★★71% The Royal Court,
233 Ballybogey Rd. BT56 8NF
☎ 028 70822236
18 en suite

Restaurant
PORTRUSH
Ramore, The Harbour.
☎ 028 70824313

Prof Mark Johnstonnson **Facilities** ⊗ ⅢⅢ ⚑ ⬛ ♀ ⚑ ✎
Location 9m NE of Belfast on A2

Hotel ★★ 67% Dobbins Inn Hotel, 6-8 High St,
CARRICKFERGUS ☎ 028 9335 1905 15 en suite

Greenisland 156 Upper Rd, Greenisland BT38 8RW
☎ 028 90862236
A parkland course nestling at the foot of Knockagh Hill
with scenic views over Belfast Lough.
9 holes, 6045mtrs, Par 71, SSS 69.
Club membership 660.
Visitors contact club in advance. Play restricted Sat and Thu.
Societies by prior arrangement. **Green Fees** £12 per round
(£18 weekends & bank holidays). **Facilities** ⊗ ⅢⅢ ⚑ ⬛ ♀
⚑ **Location** N of Belfast, close to Carrickfergus

Hotel ★★ 67% Dobbins Inn Hotel, 6-8 High St,
CARRICKFERGUS ☎ 028 9335 1905 15 en suite

CUSHENDALL   Map 01 D6

Cushendall 21 Shore Rd BT44 0NG ☎ 028 21771318
e-mail: cdda@antrim-glens.demon.co.uk
Scenic course with spectacular views over the Sea of
Moyle and Red Bay to the Mull of Kintyre. The River
Dall winds through the course, coming into play in seven
of the nine holes.
9 holes, 4386mtrs, Par 66, SSS 63, Course record 62.
Club membership 834.
Visitors Ladies day Thursday, time sheet at weekends.
Societies must contact in writing. **Green Fees** £13 per day
(£18 weekends and bank holidays). **Course Designer** D
Delargy **Facilities** ⚑ ⬛ ♀ ⚑

Hotel ★★★ 69% Londonderry Arms Hotel, 20 Harbour Rd,
CARNLOUGH ☎ 028 2888 5255 35 en suite

LARNE   Map 01 D5

Larne 54 Ferris Bay Rd, Islandmagee BT40 3RT
☎ 028 93382228 ▤ 028 93382088
e-mail: info@larnegolfclub.co.uk
An exposed part links, part heathland course offering a
good test, particularly on the last three holes along the sea
shore.
9 holes, 6686yds, Par 70, SSS 70, Course record 64.
Club membership 430.
Visitors may not play on Sat, advisable to avoid Fridays.
Societies apply in writing or telephone in advance. **Green
Fees** £10 per day (£18 weekends and bank holidays). **Course
Designer** G L Bailie **Facilities** ⊗ ⅢⅢ ⚑ ⬛ ♀ ⚑ **Location**
6m N of Whitehead on Browns Bay rd

Hotel ★★★ 69% Londonderry Arms Hotel, 20 Harbour Rd,
CARNLOUGH ☎ 028 2888 5255 35 en suite

LISBURN   Map 01 D5

Aberdelghy Bell's Ln, Lambeg BT27 4QH
☎ 028 92662738 ▤ 028 92603432
This parkland course, extended to 18 holes in 1997, has
no bunkers. The hardest hole on the course is the 340m
3rd, a dog-leg through trees to a green guarded by water.
The par 3 12th high on the hill and the 14th hole over the
dam provide a challenge. The par 4 15th hole is a long
dog-leg.
18 holes, 4139mtrs, Par 66, SSS 62, Course record 64.
Club membership 200.
Visitors restricted Sat 7.15am-1pm. Ring in advance for Sun.
Societies telephone in advance. **Green Fees** not confirmed.
Cards ▭ ▭ ▨ ▧ ▨ **Prof** Ian Murdoch **Course**
continued

Designer Alec Blair **Facilities** ⬛ ⚑ ⚑ ⚑ ✎ **Location**
1.5m N of Lisburn off A1

Hotel ★★★ 66% White Gables Hotel, 14 Dromore Rd,
HILLSBOROUGH ☎ 028 9268 2755 31 en suite

Lisburn 68 Eglantine Rd BT27 5RQ
☎ 028 92677216 ▤ 92603608
e-mail: lisburngolfclub@aol.com
Meadowland course, fairly level, with plenty of trees and
shrubs. Challenging last three holes, the par 3 finishing
hole is a spectacular downhill hole and reaching par is a
bonus.
18 holes, 6647yds, Par 72, SSS 72, Course record 67.
Club membership 1200.
Visitors must play with member on Sun. Must tee off before
3pm weekdays unless with a member. **Societies** must apply
in writing. **Green Fees** £30 per day (£35 bank holidays).
Prof Stephen Hamill **Course Designer** Hawtree
Facilities ⊗ ⅢⅢ ⚑ ⬛ ♀ ⚑ ⚑ ✎
Location 2m from town on A1

Hotel ★★★ 66% White Gables Hotel, 14 Dromore Rd,
HILLSBOROUGH ☎ 028 9268 2755 31 en suite

MAZE   Map 01 D5

Down Royal Park Dunygarton Rd BT27 5RT
☎ 028 92621339 ▤ 028 92621339
The 9 hole Valley course and the 18 hole Down Royal
Park are easy walking, undulating heath land courses.
Down Royal's 2nd hole is 628yds and thought to be
among the best par 5 holes in Ireland.
*Down Royal Park Course: 18 holes, 6824yds, Par 72, SSS
72, Course record 69.*
Valley Course: 9 holes, 2019, Par 33.
Club membership 80.
Visitors no restrictions, except dress code. **Societies**
reservations in advance. **Green Fees** Down Royal Park; £17
(£20 weekends),Valley Course; £5 (£6 weekends). **Cards**
▭ ▭ ▨ ▨ **Prof** C J Calder **Facilities** ⊗ by prior
arrangement ⅢⅢ ⚑ ⬛ ♀ ⚑ ⚑ ✎ ⚑ ⚑ ✎ ☏ **Conf** Max
150 Banquet 180 **Location** Inside Down Royal Race Course

Hotel ★★★ 66% White Gables Hotel, 14 Dromore Rd,
HILLSBOROUGH ☎ 028 9268 2755 31 en suite

NEWTOWNABBEY   Map 01 D5

Ballyearl Golf & Leisure Centre 585 Doagh Rd,
Mossley BT36 5RZ ☎ 028 90848287 ▤ 028 90844896
9 holes, 2520yds, Par 27.
Visitors no restrictions. **Societies** telephone in advance.
Green Fees not confirmed. **Cards** ▭ ▭ ▨ **Prof** Richard
Johnston **Course Designer** V Lathery **Facilities** ⬛ ⚑ ⚑
⚑ ☏ **Leisure** squash, solarium, gymnasium, Theatre and
arts centre.

Mallusk Antrim Rd BT36 ☎ 028 90843799
9 holes, 4444yds, Par 62, SSS 62, Course record 62.
Course Designer David Fitzgerald
Telephone for further details

PORTBALLINTRAE   Map 01 C6

Bushfoot 50 Bushfoot Rd, Portballintrae BT57 8RR
☎ 028 20731317 ▤ 028 20731852
A seaside links course with superb views in an area of
outstanding beauty. A challenging par 3 7th is ringed by
bunkers with out-of-bounds beyond, while the 3rd has a
blind approach. Also a putting green and pitch & putt
course.
continued

9 holes, 5914yds, Par 70, SSS 67, Course record 68.
Club membership 850.
Visitors must contact in advance. **Societies** must contact in advance. **Green Fees** terms on application. **Facilities** ⊗ ⋙
𝄐 ■ ♀ ♨ ⚘ ✓ **Location** Off Ballaghmore rd

Hotel ★★★ 71% The Royal Court Hotel, 233 Ballybogey Rd, PORTRUSH ☎ 028 7082 2236 18 en suite

PORTRUSH See page 385	Map 01 C6

WHITEHEAD	Map 01 D5

Bentra Municipal Slaughterford Rd BT38 9TG
☎ 028 93378996
A well matured course designed with the experienced golfer and novice in mind with wide fairways and some particularly long holes.
9 holes, 2885mtrs, Par 37, SSS 35.
Visitors no restrictions. **Societies** contact in advance. **Green Fees** not confirmed. **Facilities** ■ 🍴 ⚘ ✓ ⚑

Hotel ★★ 67% Dobbins Inn Hotel, 6-8 High St, CARRICKFERGUS
☎ 028 9335 1905 15 en suite

Whitehead McCrae's Brae BT38 9NZ
☎ 028 93370820 & 93370822 ⬛ 028 93370825
e-mail: robin@whiteheadgc.fsnet.co.uk
Undulating parkland course with magnificent sea views.
18 holes, 6050yds, Par 69, SSS 69, Course record 67.
Club membership 962.
Visitors may not play on Sat. Must play with member on Sun. **Societies** must contact in advance. **Green Fees** not confirmed. **Prof** Colin Farr **Course Designer** A B Armstrong **Facilities** 𝄐 ■ ♀ ♨ 🍴 **Location** 1m from town

Hotel ★★ 67% Dobbins Inn Hotel, 6-8 High St, CARRICKFERGUS ☎ 028 9335 1905 15 en suite

CO ARMAGH

ARMAGH	Map 01 C5

County Armagh The Demesne, Newry Rd BT60 1EN
☎ 028 37525861 ⬛ 028 37525861
Mature parkland course with excellent views of Armagh city and its surroundings.
18 holes, 6212yds, Par 70, SSS 69, Course record 63.
Club membership 1300.
Visitors time sheet operates at weekends. Must contact in advance. **Societies** must contact in advance. **Green Fees** £15 per round(£20 weekends). **Prof** Alan Rankin **Facilities** ⊗ ⋙ 𝄐 ■ ♀ ♨ 🍴 ⚘ ✓ ⚑ **Location** On the Newry road

Hotel ⬧ The Cohannon Inn, 212 Ballynakilly Rd, DUNGANNON ☎ 028 8772 4488 50 en suite

LURGAN	Map 01 D5

Craigavon Golf & Ski Centre Turmoyra Ln,
Silverwood BT66 6NG ☎ 028 38326606 ⬛ 028 38347272
e-mail: geoffcoupland@craigavon.gov.uk
Parkland course with a lake and stream providing water hazards.
18 holes, 6496yds, Par 72, SSS 72.
Club membership 400.
Visitors restricted Sat am. **Societies** telephone in advance. **Green Fees** £13 per round (£16.50 weekends & bank

continued

holidays). **Cards** ▭ ▨ ▨ **Prof** Des Paul **Facilities** ⊗ ■
♨ 🍴 ✓ ⚑ **Leisure** gymnasium, Ski slope. **Location** 2m N at Silverwood off the M1

Hotel ★★★ 66% White Gables Hotel, 14 Dromore Rd, HILLSBOROUGH ☎ 028 9268 2755 31 en suite

Lurgan The Demesne BT67 9BN
☎ 028 38322087 ⬛ 028 38316166
e-mail: lurgan@btclick.com
Testing parkland course bordering Lurgan Park Lake with a need for accurate shots. Drains well in wet weather and suits a long straight hitter.
18 holes, 6257yds, Par 70, SSS 70, Course record 66.
Club membership 903.
Visitors may not play Sat, contact in advance. **Societies** must contact in advance, not Sat. **Green Fees** £15 per round (£20 weekends). **Prof** Des Paul **Course Designer** A Pennink **Facilities** ⊗ ⋙ 𝄐 ■ ♀ ♨ 🍴 ✓ **Location** 0.5m from town centre near Lurgan Park

Hotel ★★★ 66% White Gables Hotel, 14 Dromore Rd, HILLSBOROUGH ☎ 028 9268 2755 31 en suite

PORTADOWN	Map 01 D5

Portadown 192 Gilford Rd BT63 5LF
☎ 028 38355356 ⬛ 028 38355356
Well wooded parkland course on the banks of the River Bann, which features among the water hazards.
18 holes, 5649mtrs, Par 70, SSS 70, Course record 65.
Club membership 981.
Visitors may not play on Tue & Sat. **Societies** apply in writing. **Green Fees** not confirmed. **Prof** Paul Stevenson **Facilities** ⊗ ⋙ 𝄐 ■ ♀ ♨ 🍴 ⚘ ✓ **Leisure** squash. **Location** SE via A59

Hotel ⬧ The Cohannon Inn, 212 Ballynakilly Rd, DUNGANNON ☎ 028 8772 4488 50 en suite

TANDRAGEE	Map 01 D5

Tandragee Markethill Rd BT62 2ER
☎ 028 38841272 ⬛ 028 38840664
e-mail: office@tandragee.co.uk
Pleasant parkland course, the signature hole is the demanding par 4 11th known as 'The Wall Hole', the real strength of Tandragee is in the short holes.
18 holes, 5747mtrs, Par 71, SSS 70, Course record 65.
Club membership 1340.
Visitors contact in advance. Ladies day Thur, after 3.30pm Sat & Sun. **Societies** must contact in advance. **Green Fees** terms on application. **Prof** Paul Stevenson **Course Designer** John Stone **Facilities** ⊗ ⋙ 𝄐 ■ ♀ ♨ 🍴 ⚘ ✓ **Leisure** sauna, gymnasium, snooker tables,indoor bowls. **Location** On B3 out of Tandragee towards Markethill

CO BELFAST

BELFAST	Map 01 D5

See also The Royal Belfast, Holywood, Co Down.

Balmoral 518 Lisburn Rd BT9 6GX
☎ 028 90381514 ⬛ 028 90666759
Parkland course, mainly level, with tree-lined fairways and a stream providing a water hazard.
18 holes, 6276yds, Par 69, SSS 70, Course record 64.
Club membership 912.

continued

Visitors may not play Sat or Sun before 2.30pm. **Societies** Mon & Thu. Must contact in advance. **Green Fees** £20(£30 weekends). **Prof** Geoff Bleakley **Facilities** ⛳ 🏌 ⚐ *✓* **Location** 2m S next to Kings Hall

Hotel ★★★ 71% Malone Lodge Hotel, 60 Eglantine Av, BELFAST ☎ 028 9038 8000 51 en suite

Cliftonville 44 Westland Rd BT14 6NH
☎ 028 90744158 & 90746595
e-mail: martinhenders43@hotmail.com
Parkland course with rivers bisecting two fairways.
9 holes, 6242yds, Par 70, SSS 70, Course record 65.
Club membership 430.
Visitors may not play: after 5pm unless with member, on Sat or on Sun mornings. **Societies** must contact in writing.
Green Fees terms on application. **Prof** Robert Hutton
Facilities ⛳ 🏌 *✓* **Location** Between Cavehill Rd & Cliftonville Circus

Hotel ⬦ Holiday Inn Express Belfast, 106a University St, BELFAST ☎ 028 9031 1909 114 en suite

Dunmurry 91 Dunmurry Ln, Dunmurry BT17 9JS
☎ 028 90610834 🖹 028 90602540
Maturing very nicely, this tricky parkland course has several memorable holes which call for skilful shots.
18 holes, 6080yds, Par 69, SSS 69, Course record 64.
Club membership 900.
Visitors telephone in advance. May not play Sat . **Societies** must contact in writing. **Green Fees** terms on application.
Prof John Dolan **Facilities** ⊗ ⫿ 🏌 ♥ ♀ ⛳ 🏌 ⚐ *✓*

Hotel ★★★ 71% Malone Lodge Hotel, 60 Eglantine Av, BELFAST ☎ 028 9038 8000 51 en suite

Fortwilliam Downview Ave BT15 4EZ
☎ 028 90370770 (Office) & 90770980 (Pro)
🖹 028 90781891
Parkland course in most attractive surroundings. The course is bisected by a lane.
18 holes, 5993yds, Par 70, SSS 68, Course record 65.
Club membership 1000.
Visitors contact professional in advance. **Societies** must contact in advance. **Green Fees** £22 (£29 weekends). **Cards** 🖿 ▬▬ ▦ 🔄 **Prof** Peter Hanna **Facilities** ⊗ ⫿ 🏌 ♥ ♀ ⛳ 🏌 ⚐ *✓* **Conf** Max 80 Del from £30 * **Location** Off Antrim road

Hotel ⬦ Holiday Inn Express Belfast, 106a University St, BELFAST ☎ 028 9031 1909 114 en suite

---

Malone 240 Upper Malone Rd, Dunmurry BT17 9LB
☎ 028 90612758 (Office) & 90614917 (Pro)
🖹 028 90431394
e-mail: manager@malonegolfclub.co.uk
Two parkland courses, extremely attractive with a large lake, mature trees and flowering shrubs and bordered by the River Lagan. Very well maintained and offering a challenging round.
Main Course: 18 holes, 6599yds, Par 71, SSS 71.
Edenderry: 9 holes, 6320yds, Par 72, SSS 70.
Club membership 1300.
Visitors advisable to contact pro-shop in advance. Main Course: Unable to play Sat, before 3pm, Sun morning, Wed or Tues after 12 noon. **Societies** apply in writing or fax to club manager. Large group normally Mon & Thu only. **Green Fees** Main Course: £40 per day (£45 weekends); Edenberry: £18 per day (£20 weekends)
continued

Malone Golf Club

reduction for ladies. **Cards** 🖿 ▬▬ ▦ 🔄 **Prof** Michael McGee **Course Designer** C K Cotton **Facilities** ⊗ ⫿ 🏌 ♥ ♀ ⛳ 🏌 ⚐ *✓* **Leisure** squash, fishing, Outdoor bowling green. **Location** 4.5m S opposite Lady Dixon Park

Hotel ★★★ 71% Malone Lodge Hotel, 60 Eglantine Av, BELFAST ☎ 028 9038 8000 51 en suite

Mount Ober Golf & Country Club
24 Ballymaconaghy Rd BT8 6SB
☎ 028 90401811 & 90795666 🖹 028 90705862
Inland parkland course which is a great test of golf for all handicaps.
18 holes, 5419yds, Par 67, SSS 66, Course record 67.
Club membership 400.
Visitors must contact in advance at weekends & bank holidays, may play Sat after 3.30pm and Sun after 10.30am.
Societies book by telephone or fax. **Green Fees** £14 (£16 weekends). **Cards** 🖿 ▬▬ **Prof** Geoff Loughrey/Steve Rourke **Facilities** ⊗ ⫿ 🏌 ♥ ♀ ⛳ 🏌 ⚐ *✓ ✓ ⫼* **Leisure** ski slopes, American billiards hall. **Location** Off Saintfield Road

Hotel ★★★ 70% The Crescent Townhouse, 13 Lower Crescent, BELFAST ☎ 028 9032 3349 11 en suite

Ormeau 50 Park Rd BT7 2FX
☎ 028 90640700 🖹 028 90646250
e-mail: ormeau.golfclub@virgin.net
Nine hole parkland course which provides a challenge for low and high handicap golfers, good shots being rewarded and those that stray offline receiving due punishment. The long par 4 5th hole has an intimidating out of bounds on the right and a narrow sloping green, well protected by trees and bunkers. Two long par 3 holes each demand an accurate drive and when playing the 3rd and 12th holes, visitors are advised to look for the Fairy Tree which graces the middle of the fairway. Club folklore states that if a golfer hits this tree he should apologise to the fairies or his game will suffer!
9 holes, 2688yds, Par 68, SSS 66.
Club membership 520.
Visitors welcome weekdays except Tue after 2pm. May play Sat after 5.30pm & Sun by arrangement. **Societies** contact in advance. **Green Fees** not confirmed. **Prof** Mr B Wilson
Facilities ⊗ ⫿ 🏌 ♥ ♀ ⛳ 🏌 ⚐ *✓* **Location** S of city centre between Ravenhill & Ormeau roads

Hotel ★★★ 70% The Crescent Townhouse, 13 Lower Crescent, BELFAST ☎ 028 9032 3349 11 en suite

Shandon Park 73 Shandon Park BT5 6NY
☎ 028 90401856
18 holes, 6261yds, Par 70, SSS 70.
Location Off Knock road
Telephone for further details

Hotel ★★★ 70% The Crescent Townhouse, 13 Lower Crescent, BELFAST ☎ 028 9032 3349 11 en suite

DUNDONALD   Map 01 D5

Knock Summerfield BT16 2QX
☎ 028 90483251 & 90482249 🖳 028 90483251
Parkland course with huge trees, deep bunkers and a river cutting across several fairways. This is a hard but fair course and will test the best of golfers.
18 holes, 6435yds, Par 70, SSS 71, Course record 66.
Club membership 920.
Visitors with member only on Sat, Mon & Thu are Society Days, Tue is Ladies Day, advisable to contact in advance. **Societies** must contact in advance. **Green Fees** not confirmed. **Prof** Gordon Fairweather **Course Designer** Colt, Allison & McKenzie **Facilities** ⊗ ⊪ ⓑ 🍷 ♀ ⌂ 🏌 🏐 ⚒ ♂ **Location** 5miles E of Belfast

Hotel ★★★ 76% Old Inn, 15 Main St, CRAWFORDSBURN ☎ 028 9185 3255 32 en suite

NEWTOWNBREDA   Map 01 D5

The Belvoir Park 73 Church Rd BT8 7AN
☎ 028 90491693 🖳 028 90646113
This undulating parkland course is not strenuous to walk, but is certainly a test of your golf, with tree-lined fairways and a particularly challenging finish at the final four holes.
18 holes, 6516yds, Par 71, SSS 71, Course record 65.
Club membership 1000.
Visitors must contact in advance, may not play Sat. **Societies** must contact in writing. **Green Fees** £35 (£40 weekends & bank holidays). **Cards** 〰 ▰ 💷 **Prof** Maurice Kelly **Course Designer** H Holt **Facilities** ⊗ ⊪ ⓑ 🍷 ♀ ⌂ 🏌 🏐 ♂ **Location** 2m from city centre off Saintfield/Newcastle rd

Hotel ★★★ 75% Clandeboye Lodge Hotel, 10 Estate Rd, Clandeboye, BANGOR ☎ 028 9185 2500 43 en suite

CO DOWN

ARDGLASS   Map 01 D5

Ardglass Castle Place BT30 7TP
☎ 028 44841219 🖳 028 44841841
e-mail: golfclub@ardglass.force9.co.uk
A scenic cliff-top seaside course with championship standard greens. The first five holes, with the Irish Sea and cliffs tight to the left, should be treated with respect as anything resembling a hook will meet with disaster. The 2nd hole is a daunting par 3. The tee-shot must carry a cliff and canyon - meanwhile the superb views of the Mountains of Mourne should not be missed.
18 holes, 5498mtrs, Par 70, SSS 69, Course record 65.
Club membership 800.
Visitors must contact in advance. **Societies** must contact in advance, welcome weekdays & restricted times Sun. **Green Fees** not confirmed. **Cards** 〰 ▰ 💷 📗 🔳 💷 **Prof** Philip Farrell **Course Designer** David Jones **Facilities** ⊗ ⊪ ⓑ 🍷 ♀ ⌂ 🏌 🏐 ⚒ ♂ **Location** 7m from Downpatrick on the B1

continued

Hotel ★★ 65% Enniskeen House Hotel, 98 Bryansford Rd, NEWCASTLE ☎ 028 4372 2392 12 en suite

ARDMILLAN   Map 01 D5

Mahee Island 14 Mahee Island, Comber BT23 6EP
☎ 028 97541234
e-mail: mahee_gents@hotmail.com
An undulating parkland course, almost surrounded by water, with magnificent views of Strangford Lough and its islands, with Scrabo Tower in the background. The greens are small and tricky to play. The first professional here was Fred Daly (1933-4) who became British Open Champion in 1947.
9 holes, 5590yds, Par 68, SSS 68, Course record 63.
Club membership 600.
Visitors may not play Sat before 5pm. **Societies** contact in advance. **Green Fees** £10 per 18 holes (£15 weekends). **Prof** Archie McCracken **Course Designer** Mr Robinson **Facilities** ⊗ by prior arrangement ⊪ by prior arrangement ⓑ by prior arrangement 🍷 by prior arrangement ⌂ 🏌 ♂ **Location** Off Comber/Killyleagh road to the left 0.5m from Comber

Hotel ★★★ 75% Clandeboye Lodge Hotel, 10 Estate Rd, Clandeboye, BANGOR ☎ 028 9185 2500 43 en suite

BALLYNAHINCH   Map 01 D5

Spa 20 Grove Rd BT24 8PN
☎ 028 97562365 🖳 028 97564158
e-mail: spagolfclub@btconnect.com
Parkland course with tree-lined fairways and scenic views of the Mourne Mountains. A long and demanding course and feature holes include the par 3 2nd and 405 yard par 4 11th.

18 holes, 6003mtrs, Par 72, SSS 72, Course record 66.
Club membership 907.
Visitors must contact in advance. No play on Sat. **Societies** must contact in advance. **Green Fees** £15 per round (£20 Suns & bank holidays). **Course Designer** F Ainsworth **Facilities** ⊗ ⊪ ⓑ 🍷 ♀ ⌂ 🏌 🏐 ♂ **Leisure** gymnasium. **Location** 1m S on the Grove Rd

Hotel ★★ 65% Enniskeen House Hotel, 98 Bryansford Rd, NEWCASTLE ☎ 028 4372 2392 12 en suite

BANBRIDGE   Map 01 D5

Banbridge 116 Huntly Rd BT32 3UR
☎ 028 40662211 🖳 028 40669400
e-mail: info@banbridge-golf.freeserve.co.uk
A mature parkland course with excellent views of the Mourne mountains. The holes are not long, but are tricky. Signature holes are the 6th with its menacing pond and the par 3 10th where playing for a safe 4 is usually the best option.

continued

18 holes, 5003mtrs, Par 69, SSS 67, Course record 61.
Club membership 800.
Visitors may not play Sat or before 11am on Sun. Ladies
Day Tue. **Societies** must contact in writing. **Green Fees**
£15(£20 weekends). **Course Designer** F Ainsworth
Facilities ⊗ 爪 ᛒ ♨ ♀ ♨ 🏠 𝄇 ᛏ **Location** 0.5m along
Huntly road

Hotel ★★★ 66% White Gables Hotel, 14 Dromore Rd,
HILLSBOROUGH ☎ 028 9268 2755 31 en suite

BANGOR   Map 01 D5

Bangor Broadway BT20 4RH
☎ 028 91270922 🗐 028 91453394
Undulating parkland course in the town. It is well
maintained and pleasant and offers a challenging round,
particularly at the 5th.
18 holes, 6410yds, Par 71, SSS 71, Course record 62.
Club membership 1147.
Visitors may not play Sat & weekdays 1-2. **Societies** must
contact in advance, Mon/Wed by telephone, Fri by letter.
Green Fees not confirmed. **Prof** Michael Bannon **Course
Designer** James Braid **Facilities** ⊗ 爪 ᛒ ♨ ♀ ♨ 🏠 ᛏ 🚜
𝄇 **Location** 1m from town on Donaghadee Road

Hotel ★★★ 62% Royal Hotel, Seafront, BANGOR
☎ 028 9127 1866 50 en suite

Blackwood Golf Centre 150 Crawfordsburn Rd,
Clandeboye BT19 1GB ☎ 028 91852706 🗐 028 91853785
The golf centre is a pay and play development with a
computerised booking system for the 18-hole
championship-standard Hamilton course. The course is
built on mature woodland with man-made lakes that
come into play on 5 holes. The Temple course is an 18-
hole par 3 course with holes ranging from the 75yd 1st to
the 185yd 10th, which has a lake on the right of the green.
Banked by gorse with streams crossing throughout, this
par 3 course is no pushover.
Hamilton Course: 18 holes, 6392yds, Par 71, SSS 70,
Course record 62.
Temple Course: 18 holes, 2492yds, Par 54.
Visitors pay as you play, computerised booking system for
the Hamilton Course, bookable 7 days in advance. **Societies**
telephone in advance. **Green Fees** Hamilton: £19 per round;
£11 per 9 holes (£25 weekends). Temple: £9 per round; £6
per 9 holes (£11weekends). **Cards** 🔳 ▆▆ ▆▆ **Prof** Debbie
Hanna **Course Designer** Simon Gidman **Facilities** ⊗ ᛒ ♨
♀ ♨ ᛏ 𝄇 ᛏ **Location** 2m from Bangor, off A2 to Belfast

Hotel ★★★ 75% Clandeboye Lodge Hotel, 10 Estate Rd,
Clandeboye, BANGOR ☎ 028 9185 2500 43 en suite

Carnalea Station Rd BT19 1EZ
☎ 028 91270368 🗐 028 91273989
A scenic course on the shores of Belfast Lough.
18 holes, 5647yds, Par 69, SSS 67, Course record 63.
Club membership 1354.
Visitors restricted Sat. **Societies** must contact in advance.
Green Fees terms on application. **Prof** Tom Loughran
Facilities ⊗ 爪 ᛒ ♀ ♨ 🏠 ᛏ 𝄇 **Location** 2m W adjacent
to railway station

Hotel ★★★ 76% Old Inn, 15 Main St,
CRAWFORDSBURN ☎ 028 9185 3255 32 en suite

Looking for a driving range?
See the index at the back of the guide

Clandeboye Tower Rd, Conlig, Newtownards BT23 3PN
☎ 028 91271767 🗐 028 91473711
e-mail: contact@cgc-ni.com
Parkland/heathland courses. The Dufferin is the
championship course and offers a tough challenge
demanding extreme accuracy, with its mass of gorse,
bracken and strategically placed trees that flank every
hole. The slightest error will be punished. The Ava
compliments the Dufferin perfectly. Accuracy is also the
key with a notable 2nd hole.
Dufferin Course: 18 holes, 6469yds, Par 71, SSS 71.
Ava Course: 18 holes, 5465yds, Par 70, SSS 68.
Club membership 1450.
Visitors must contact in advance,weekends after 2.30pm.
Societies Mon-Wed, Fri & after 3pm Sat & Sun. Must
contact in advance. **Green Fees** terms on application. **Cards**
🔳 **Prof** Peter Gregory **Course Designer** William Robinson
Facilities ⊗ 爪 ᛒ ♨ ♀ ♨ 🏠 ᛏ 🍴 🚜 𝄇 **Location** 2m S
on A1 between Bangor & Newtownards

Hotel ★★★ 62% Royal Hotel, Seafront, BANGOR
☎ 028 9127 1866 50 en suite

Helen's Bay Golf Rd, Helen's Bay BT19 1TL
☎ 028 91852815 & 91852601 🗐 028 91852815
e-mail: mail@helensbaygc.com
A parkland course on the shores of Belfast Lough with
panoramic views along the Antrim coast. The 4th hole
par 3 is particularly challenging as the green is screened
by high trees.
9 holes, 5161mtrs, Par 68, SSS 67, Course record 67.
Club membership 750.
Visitors welcome Sun, Mon, Wed, Thu (before 1.30pm), Fri
(after 11.30am during Jul & Aug) & Sat after 6pm. Book in
advance with secretary. **Societies** welcome Sun, Mon, Wed,
Thu (before 1.30pm), Fri & Sat after 6pm. Telephone
secretary in advance. **Green Fees** £17 per 18 holes (Mon-
Thu) £20 (Fri-Sun & bank holidays). **Facilities** ⊗ 爪 ᛒ ♨ ♀
♨ 🚜 𝄇 **Location** A2 from Belfast

Hotel ★★★ 76% Old Inn, 15 Main St,
CRAWFORDSBURN ☎ 028 9185 3255 32 en suite

CARRYDUFF   Map 01 D5

Rockmount 28 Drumalig Rd, Carryduff BT8 8EQ
☎ 028 90812279 🗐 020 90815851
e-mail: rockmountgc@btconnect.com
A demanding 18-hole course set in open parkland with
mature trees, several streams, and a tricky lake at the
11th hole. Panoramic views.
18 holes, 6373yds, Par 71, SSS 71, Course record 68.
Club membership 750.
Visitors welcome except for Sat or Wed afternoon. **Societies**
welcome except for Wed & Sat, book by telephone. **Green
Fees** terms on application. **Cards** 🔳 ▆▆ ▆▆ 🔳 **Course
Designer** Robert Patterson **Facilities** ⊗ 爪 ᛒ ♨ ♀ ♨ 🏠 ᛏ
🚜 𝄇 **Conf** Max 40 Thtr 40 Class 20 Board 15 Banquet 30
Del £30 to £100 * **Location** 10m S of Belfast

Hotel ★★★ 66% White Gables Hotel, 14 Dromore Rd,
HILLSBOROUGH ☎ 028 9268 2755 31 en suite

CLOUGHEY   Map 01 D5

Kirkistown Castle 142 Main Rd, Cloughey BT22 1JA
☎ 028 42711233 🗐 028 42771699
e-mail: kirkistown@aol.com
A seaside semi-links, designed by James Braid, popular
with visiting golfers because of its quiet location. The
course is exceptionally dry and remains open when others
continued

Royal County Down

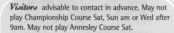

Newcastle, *Co Down*   ☎ 028 43723314   Fax 028 43726281   Map 01 D5

e-mail: golf@royalcountydown.org

The Championship Course is consistently rated among the world's top ten courses. Laid out beneath the imperious gaze of the Mountains of Mourne, the course enjoys a magnificent stage-like setting as it stretches out along the shores of Dundrum Bay. As well as being one of the world's most beautiful courses, it is also one of the most challenging, with great swathes of heather and gorse lining fairways that tumble beneath vast sand hills, and wild tussocky faced bunkers defending small subtly contoured greens.

The Annesley Links offers a less formidable, yet extremely characterful game played against the same incomparable backcloth. Recently substantially revised under the direction of Donald Steel, the course begins quite benignly before charging headlong into the dunes. Several charming, and one or two teasing holes have been carved out amid the gorse, heather and bracken.

Visitors advisable to contact in advance. May not play Championship Course Sat, Sun am or Wed after 9am. May not play Annesley Course Sat.

Societies telephone for availability and confirm in writing

Green Fees Championship €90 per round; Annesley €18 per round ═ ▬ ▬ ═ ▬ ▣

Facilities ⊗ ⅃ 🍺 ♀ 🧍 🏠 🍴 ♂
Professional (Kevan Whitson)

Location 36 Golf Links Road. Newcastle BT33 0AN (30m S of Belfast via A24)

Holes/Par/Course record 36 holes.
Championship Course: 18 holes, 7037 yds, Par 71, SSS 74, Course record 66
Annesley Course: 18 holes, 4681 yds, Par 66, SSS 63

Situated thirty miles south of Belfast and fringed by the impressive sweep of Dundrum Bay, Newcastle is where, in the immortal words of Percy French, 'the Mountains of Mourne sweep down to the sea'.

Championship Course

WHERE TO STAY NEARBY

Hotel
NEWCASTLE

★★ 65% Enniskeen Hotel,
98 Bryansford Rd.
☎ 028 43722392.
12 en suite

in the area have to close. The short but treacherous par 4 15th hole was known as 'Braid's Hole'. The 2nd and 10th holes are long par 4s with elevated greens, which are a feature of the course. The 10th is particularly distinctive with a long drive and a slight dogleg to a raised green with a gorse covered motte waiting for the wayward approach shot. It has the reputation of being one of the hardest par 4s in Ireland.
18 holes, 6167yds, Par 69, SSS 70, Course record 65.
Club membership 1050.
Visitors must contact in advance, restricted weekends. **Societies** contact in writing or by phone. **Green Fees** £18.75 (£25.75 weekends). **Prof** Jonathan Peden **Course Designer** James Braid **Facilities** ⊗ ⅏ ⅃ ⅃ ♀ ⚒ 🛍 ⚐ ♂ **Location** 16m from Newtownards on the A2

Hotel ★★★ 76% Old Inn, 15 Main St, CRAWFORDSBURN ☎ 028 9185 3255 32 en suite

Donaghadee Warren Rd BT21 0PQ
☎ 028 91883624 📱 028 91888891
e-mail: deegolf@freenetname.co.uk
Undulating seaside course, part links, part parkland, requiring a certain amount of concentration. Splendid views.
18 holes, 5570mtrs, Par 71, SSS 69, Course record 64.
Club membership 1200.
Visitors contact in advance. **Societies** write in advance.
Green Fees £22 (£25 Sun). **Cards** 💳 **Prof** Gordon Drew **Facilities** ⊗ ⅏ ⅃ ⅃ ♀ ⚒ 🛍 ♂ **Location** 5 miles S Bangor on Coast Rd

Hotel ★★★ 76% Old Inn, 15 Main St, CRAWFORDSBURN ☎ 028 9185 3255 32 en suite

Bright Castle 14 Coniamstown Rd, Bright BT30 8LU
☎ 028 44841319
Parkland course in elevated position with views of the Mountains of Mourne. A good challenge for the energetic golfer.
18 holes, 7300yds, Par 74, SSS 74, Course record 69.
Club membership 60.
Visitors no restrictions, only societies may book tee times in advance. **Societies** must contact in advance. **Green Fees** terms on application. **Course Designer** Mr Ennis Snr **Facilities** ⊗ ⅃ ⅃ ♀ ⚒ ♂ **Conf** Max 100 **Location** 5m S

Hotel ★★ 65% Enniskeen House Hotel, 98 Bryansford Rd, NEWCASTLE ☎ 028 4372 2392 12 en suite

Downpatrick 43 Saul Rd BT30 6PA
☎ 028 44615947 📱 028 44617502
e-mail: info@downpatrickgolfclub.com
A classic parkland course with most holes boasting spectacular views of Co Down, Strangford Lough and even the Isle of Man, on a clear day. Undulating fairways, strategically placed sand traps and quick but true greens make the course a testing yet pleasurable challenge to golfers of all abilities.
18 holes, 6100yds, Par 70, SSS 69, Course record 66.
Club membership 960.
Visitors must contact in advance. **Societies** must telephone in advance. **Green Fees** not confirmed. **Cards** 💳 💳 **Course Designer** Hawtree & Son **Facilities** ⊗ ⅏ ⅃ ⅃ ♀ ⚒ 🛍 ⚐ ♂ **Leisure** snooker. **Location** 1.5m from town centre   *continued*

Hotel ★★ 65% Enniskeen House Hotel, 98 Bryansford Rd, NEWCASTLE ☎ 028 4372 2392 12 en suite

Holywood Nuns Walk, Demesne Rd BT18 9LE
☎ 028 90423135 📱 028 90425040
e-mail: mail@holywoodgolfclub.co.uk
Hilly parkland course, providing some fine views and an interesting game. Several feature holes, including the short 6th 'Nuns Walk', fondly remembered by the many who have 'holed out in one'. In contrast, the treacherous 12th 'White House' is a most difficult par 4. The tee shot must be placed precisely on the fairway to allow the long approach to a green which is protected out of bounds to the right and a perilous drop to the left.
18 holes, 5480mtrs, Par 69, SSS 68, Course record 64.
Club membership 1100.
Visitors must contact in advance.Tee closed 1.30-2.15 for members, member only Saturdays. **Societies** must contact in writing. **Green Fees** terms on application. **Cards** 💳 **Prof** Paul Gray **Facilities** ⊗ ⅏ ⅃ ⅃ ♀ ⚒ 🛍 ⚐ 🚗 ♂ ⛳

Hotel ★★★ 76% Old Inn, 15 Main St, CRAWFORDSBURN ☎ 028 9185 3255 32 en suite

The Royal Belfast Station Rd, Craigavad BT18 0BP
☎ 028 90428165 📱 028 90421404
e-mail: royalbelfastgc@btclick.com
On the shores of Belfast Lough, this attractive course consists of wooded parkland on undulating terrain which provides a pleasant, challenging game.
18 holes, 6185yds, Par 70, SSS 69.
Club membership 1200.
Visitors may not play on Wed or Sat before 4.30pm; must be accompanied by a member or present a letter of introduction from their own golf club. Must contact in advance. **Societies** must contact in writing. **Green Fees** not confirmed. **Cards** 💳 💳 💳 **Prof** Chris Spence **Course Designer** H C Colt **Facilities** ⊗ ⅏ ⅃ ⅃ ♀ ⚒ 🛍 ⚐ 🚗 ♂ **Leisure** hard tennis courts, squash. **Location** 2m E on A2

Hotel ★★★ 76% Old Inn, 15 Main St, CRAWFORDSBURN ☎ 028 9185 3255 32 en suite

Kilkeel Mourne Park BT34 4LB
☎ 028 41765095 & 41762296 📱 028 41765579
e-mail: kilkeelgolfclub@tinyonline.co.uk
Picturesquely situated at the foot of the Mourne Mountains. Eleven holes have tree-lined fairways with the remainder in open parkland. The 13th hole is testing and a well positioned tee shot is essential.
18 holes, 6579yds, Par 72, SSS 72, Course record 69.
Club membership 750.
Visitors contact in advance for weekend play. **Societies** must contact in advance. **Green Fees** £18 per round (£22 weekends). **Course Designer** Babington/Hackett **Facilities** ⊗ ⅏ ⅃ ⅃ ♀ ⚒ 🛍 ⚐ 🚗 ♂ **Location** 3m from Kilkeel on Newry road

Hotel ★★ 65% Enniskeen House Hotel, 98 Bryansford Rd, NEWCASTLE ☎ 028 4372 2392 12 en suite

AA website: www.theAA.com

KILLYLEAGH   Map 01 D5

Ringdufferin Golf Course 31 Ringdufferin Rd,
Toye BT30 9PH ☎ 028 44828812 📋 028 44828812
The course overlooks Strangford Lough.
18 holes, 4652mtrs, Par 68, SSS 66.
Club membership 300.
Visitors contact in advance on Saturdays. **Societies** apply in
writing/telephone in advance. **Green Fees** terms on
application. **Prof** Mark Lavery **Course Designer** Frank
Ainsworth **Facilities** ⊗ 🍴 💺 ♀ 🛋 🏡 ⛳ 🏌 ✂ 🏌 **Leisure**
fishing. **Location** 2m N of Killyleagh

Hotel ★★★ 67% Portaferry Hotel, 10 The Strand,
PORTAFERRY ☎ 028 4272 8231 14 en suite

MAGHERALIN   Map 01 D5

Edenmore Edenmore House, 70 Drumnabreeze Rd
BT67 0RH ☎ 028 92611310 📋 92613310
e-mail: edenmoregc@aol.com
Set in mature parkland with gently rolling slopes. The
front nine holes provide an interesting contrast to the
back nine with more open play involved. Many new paths
and features have been added. The 13th hole, Edenmore,
is the most memorable hole with a small lake protecting a
contoured green.
18 holes, 6244yds, Par 71, SSS 70, Course record 70.
Club membership 520.
Visitors telephone in advance, may not play until after 3pm
Sat. **Societies** telephone in advance. **Green Fees** £13 per
round(£16 weekends). **Cards** 🔳 🔳 🔳 **Course**
Designer F Ainsworth **Facilities** ⊗ 💺 ⛳ 🛋 🏡 ⛳ 🏌 ✂ 🏌 ✂
Leisure sauna, gymnasium. **Conf** Max 80 Board 16

Hotel ★★★ 76% Old Inn, 15 Main St,
CRAWFORDSBURN ☎ 028 9185 3255 32 en suite

NEWCASTLE See page 391   Map 01 D5

NEWRY   Map 01 D5

Newry 11 Forkhill Rd BT35 8LZ
☎ 028 30263871 📋 028 30263871
18 holes, 3000mtrs, Par 53, SSS 52, Course record 51.
Course Designer Michael Heaney **Location** 1m from Newry
off the main Dublin road
Telephone for further details

Hotel ★★ 65% Enniskeen House Hotel, 98 Bryansford Rd,
NEWCASTLE ☎ 028 4372 2392 12 en suite

NEWTOWNARDS   Map 01 D5

Scrabo 233 Scrabo Rd BT23 4SL
☎ 028 91812355 📋 028 91822919
e-mail: scrabogc@compuserve.com
Hilly and picturesque, this course offers a good test of
golf for golfers of all abilities. It benefits from good
drainage and remains dry and playable most of the year.
18 holes, 5722mtrs, Par 71, SSS 71, Course record 65.
Club membership 1002.
Visitors may not play on Saturdays. Contact in advance.
Societies must contact in advance. **Green Fees** £15 per
round(£20 Sundays). **Prof** Paul McCrystal **Facilities** ⊗ 🏌 💺
💺 ♀ 🛋 🏡 ✂ **Location** Borders of Newtownards on the
Ards Peninsula, follow signs for Scrabo Country Park

Hotel ★★★ 75% Clandeboye Lodge Hotel, 10 Estate Rd,
Clandeboye, BANGOR ☎ 028 9185 2500 43 en suite

WARRENPOINT   Map 01 D5

Warrenpoint Lower Dromore Rd BT34 3LN
☎ 028 41753695 📋 028 41752918
e-mail: warrenpointgolfclub@talk21.com
Parkland course with marvellous views and a need for
accurate shots.
18 holes, 6108yds, Par 71, SSS 70, Course record 61.
Club membership 1385.
Visitors must contact in advance. **Societies** must contact in
advance. **Green Fees** £20 per round (£27 weekends & bank
holidays). **Cards** 🔳 🔳 **Prof** Nigel Shaw **Course Designer**
Tom Craddock/Pat Ruddy **Facilities** ⊗ 🏌 💺 💺 ♀ 🛋 🏡 🏌
✂ **Leisure** squash. **Location** 1m W

Hotel ★★ 65% Enniskeen House Hotel, 98 Bryansford Rd,
NEWCASTLE ☎ 028 4372 2392 12 en suite

CO FERMANAGH

ENNISKILLEN   Map 01 C5

Ashwoods Golf Centre Sligo Rd BT74 7JY
☎ 028 66325321 & 66322908 📋 028 66329411
Only one mile from Enniskillen, this course is open
meadowland. It has been well planted with many
young trees.
14 holes, 1930yds, Par 42.
Visitors no restrictions. **Societies** must book in advance.
Green Fees terms on application. **Cards** 🔳 🔳 🔳 🔳
Prof L McCool **Course Designer** P Loughran **Facilities** ⊗
🏌 by prior arrangement 💺 💺 ♀ 🛋 🏡 🏌 ✂ 🏌 **Location**
1.5m W of Enniskillen on main Sligo road

Hotel ★★★★ 67% Killyhevlin Hotel, ENNISKILLEN
☎ 028 6632 3481 43 en suite

Castle Hume Castle Hume, Belleek Rd BT93 7ED
☎ 028 66327077 📋 028 66327076
Castle Hume is a particularly scenic and challenging
course. Set in undulating parkland with large rolling
greens, rivers, lakes and water hazards all in play on a
championship standard course.
18 holes, 5770mtrs, Par 72, SSS 70, Course record 69.
Club membership 350.
Visitors may play any time subject to advance arrangement.
Societies telephone in advance. **Green Fees** not confirmed.
Cards 🔳 🔳 🔳 **Course Designer** B Browne **Facilities** ⊗ 🏌
💺 ♀ 🛋 🏡 🏌 ✂ 🏌 🏌 ✂ **Leisure** fishing. **Location**
4m from Enniskillen on the Belleek/Donegal Road

Hotel ★★★★ 67% Killyhevlin Hotel, ENNISKILLEN
☎ 028 6632 3481 43 en suite

Enniskillen Castlecoole BT74 6HZ
☎ 028 66325250 📋 028 66326510
e-mail: enniskillen.golf@btclick.com
Tree lined parkland course offering panoramic views of
Enniskillen town and the surrounding lakeland area.
Situated beside the National Trust's Castlecoole Estate.
18 holes, 6189yds, Par 71, SSS 69, Course record 67.
Club membership 460.
Visitors restricted Tue and weekends. Contact Hon Secretary
or bar steward. **Societies** must contact club steward in
advance by telephone or writing. **Green Fees** £15 per day
(£18 weekends & bank holidays). **Facilities** ⊗ by prior
arrangement 🏌 by prior arrangement 💺 💺 ♀ 🛋 🏡 🏌 🏌 ✂
✂ **Location** 1m E

continued

Hotel ★★★★ 67% Killyhevlin Hotel, ENNISKILLEN
☎ 028 6632 3481 43 en suite

CO LONDONDERRY

AGHADOWEY   Map 01 C6

Brown Trout Golf & Country Inn 209 Agivey
Rd BT51 4AD ☎ 028 70868209 ▤ 028 70868878
e-mail: bill@browntroutinn.com
A challenging course with two par 5s. During the course
of the 9 holes, players have to negotiate water 7 times and
all the fairways are lined with densely packed fir trees.
9 holes, 5510yds, Par 70, SSS 68, Course record 64.
Club membership 100.
Visitors no restrictions. **Societies** must contact by telephone,
restricted tee-off times Sun. **Green Fees** £10 per day (£15
weekends & bank holidays). **Cards** ▦ ▤ ▨ ▨ ▨ ▨
Prof Ken Revie **Course Designer** Bill O'Hara Snr **Facilities**
⊗ ⫟ ᖯ ⬛ ♀ ♨ ⫟ ♿ ⬛ ✔ **Leisure** fishing, gymnasium.
Location Junc of A54 & B66, 7m S of Coleraine

Hotel ★★ 71% Brown Trout Golf & Country Inn, 209
Agivey Rd, AGHADOWEY ☎ 028 7086 8209 15 en suite

CASTLEDAWSON   Map 01 C5

Moyola Park 15 Curran Rd BT45 8DG
☎ 028 79468468 & 79468830 (Prof) ▤ 028 79468626
e-mail: golf@moyola-park-n-ireland.freeserve.co.uk
Parkland championship course with some difficult shots,
calling for length and accuracy. The Moyola River
provides a water hazard at the 8th. Newly designed par 3
17th demands good shot placement to a green on an
island in the Moyola river, players capabilities will be
tested by the undulating green.
18 holes, 6522yds, Par 71, SSS 70, Course record 67.
Club membership 1000.
Visitors contact professional in advance, G.U.I. dress code
applies, Ladies day Wednesday, Sat & Sun after 1.30pm,
book in advance to avoid disappointment. **Societies** must
contact in advance, preferably in writing **Green Fees** not
confirmed. **Cards** ▨ **Prof** Vivian Teague **Course Designer**
Don Patterson **Facilities** ⊗ ⫟ ᖯ ⬛ ♀ ⬛ ⫟ ♿ ⬛ ✔
Location Take sign for Castledawson. Golf Club signposted

Hotel ★★★★ 69% Galgorm Manor, BALLYMENA
☎ 028 2588 1001 24 en suite

CASTLEROCK   Map 01 C6

Castlerock 65 Circular Rd BT51 4TJ
☎ 028 70848314 ▤ 028 70849440
e-mail: castlerock18@hotmail.com
A most exhilarating course with three superb par 4s,
four testing short holes and five par 5s. After an uphill
start, the hazards are many, including the river and a
railway, and both judgement and accuracy are called
for. A challenge in calm weather, any trouble from the
elements will test your golf to the limits.
Mussenden Course: 18 holes, 6499yds, Par 73, SSS 71,
Course record 64.
Bann Course: 9 holes, 2938yds, Par 34, SSS 33.
Club membership 1430.
Visitors contact in advance, limited number of places at
weekends. Must be members of a recognised club.
Societies must contact in advance. **Green Fees** £35 per
continued

round;£50 per day(£60 weekends and bank holidays).
Cards ▦ ▨ ▨ **Prof** Robert Kelly **Course Designer**
Ben Sayers **Facilities** ⊗ ⫟ ᖯ ⬛ ♀ ♨ ⬛ ⫟ ✔
Location 6m from Coleraine on A2

Hotel ★★★ 71% The Royal Court Hotel,
233 Ballybogey Rd, PORTRUSH
☎ 028 7082 2236 18 en suite

KILREA   Map 01 C5

Kilrea Drumagarner Rd BT51 5TB ☎ 028 25821048
A relatively short undulating inland course with tight
fairways and small greens. The opening hole is a long
par 3, particularly into the wind.
9 holes, 4514yds, Par 62, SSS 62, Course record 61.
Club membership 300.
Visitors welcome but restricted Tue pm, Wed pm during
summer and Sat all year. **Societies** contact D P Clarke (Sec),
37 Townhill Rd, Portglenone, Co Antrim BT44 8AD. **Green
Fees** not confirmed. **Facilities** ᖭ **Location** 0.5m outside
village of Kilrea on Drumagarner Road

Hotel ★★ 71% Brown Trout Golf & Country Inn, 209
Agivey Rd, AGHADOWEY ☎ 028 7086 8209 15 en suite

LIMAVADY   Map 01 C6

Benone 53 Benone Ave BT49 0LQ
☎ 028 77750555 ▤ 77750919
9 holes, 1334mtrs, Par 27.
Club membership 100.
Visitors no restrictions. **Societies** contact in advance during
July & August **Green Fees** £5.25 per day (£6 weekends).
continued

Benone Golf Course, beside golden Benone Beach,
overlooks the spectacular scenery of the Causeway Coast
at the foot of majestic Binevenagh mountain. Enjoy
picturesque views and stimulating sea air as you tackle the
9 hole par 3 course, indulge in complementary facilities,
including splash pools, bowling green and tennis courts,
and explore the beautiful coastline, immersed in history
and romantic legends.
For further information and booking, contact:
The Warden, Benone Tourist Complex,
53 Benone Avenue, Limavady BT49 0LQ
Tel: 028 7775 0555   Fax: 028 7775 0919

Benone Golf Course

Prof Ken Revie **Facilities** ⊗ ⅲ ⅃ ♥ ♨ ⚑ (**Leisure** hard tennis courts, heated outdoor swimming pool. **Location** Between Coleraine/Limavady on A2

Radisson Roe Park Hotel & Golf Resort Roe
Park BT49 9LB ☎ 028 77722222 ▤ 028 77722313
e-mail: sales@radissonroepark.com
A parkland course opened in 1992 on an historic
Georgian estate. The course surrounds the original
buildings and a driving range has been created in the old
walled garden. Final holes 15-18 are particularly
memorable with water, trees, out-of-bounds, etc. to
provide a testing finish.
18 holes, 6318yds, Par 70, SSS 35.
Club membership 500.
Visitors advance booking recommended. Handicap
certificate required. May not play before 10.30am at
weekends. **Societies** contact in advance. **Green Fees** £20
(£25 weekends). **Cards** ▦ ▬ ▭ ▣ ▤ ▦ ▨ **Prof**
Seamus Duffy **Course Designer** Frank Ainsworth **Facilities**
⊗ ⅲ ⅃ ♥ ♨ ⚑ ⚑ 🏊 ╲ 🏌 ((**Leisure** heated
indoor swimming pool, fishing, sauna, solarium, gymnasium,
indoor golf academy. **Conf** Max 450 Thtr 450 Class 190
Board 75 Banquet 300 Del from £20 * **Location** Just outside
Limavady on A2 Ballykelly/Londonderry road

Hotel ★★★★ 69% Radisson Roe Park Hotel & Golf
Resort, LIMAVADY ☎ 028 7772 2222 64 en suite

City of Derry 49 Victoria Rd BT47 2PU
☎ 028 71346369 ▤ 028 71310008
e-mail: cityofderry@aol.com
Two parkland courses on undulating parkland with good
views and lots of trees. The 9-hole course will particularly
suit novices.
Prehen Course: 18 holes, 6406yds, Par 71, SSS 71,
Course record 68.
Dunhugh Course: 9 holes, 2354yds, Par 66, SSS 66.
Club membership 823.
Visitors must make a booking to play on Prehen Course at
weekends or before 4.30pm on weekdays. **Societies** must
contact in advance. **Green Fees** not confirmed. **Cards** ▭
Prof Michael Doherty **Facilities** ⊗ ⅲ ⅃ ♥ ♨ 🏊 ⚑ (
Location 2m S

Hotel ★★★ 72% Beech Hill Country House Hotel, 32
Ardmore Rd, LONDONDERRY ☎ 028 7134 9279
17 en suite 10 annexe en suite

Where to stay, where to eat?
Visit www.theAA.com

Foyle International Golf Centre 12 Alder Rd
BT48 8DB ☎ 028 71352222 ▤ 028 71353967
e-mail: mail@foylegolf.club24.co.uk
Foyle International boasts a championship course, a 9 hole
par 3 course and a driving range. It is a fine test of golf
with water coming into play on the 3rd, 10th and 11th
holes. The 6th green overlooks the Amelia Earhart centre.
18 holes, 6678yds, Par 72, SSS 71, Course record 70.
Club membership 320.
Visitors welcome any time, no retrictions. **Societies** booking
up to 12 months in advance with deposit. **Green Fees** £12
per round (£15 weekends & bank holidays). **Cards** ▦ ▬
▨ ▣ **Prof** Kieran McLaughlin **Course Designer** Frank
Ainsworth **Facilities** ⊗ ⅲ ⅃ ♥ ♨ 🏊 ⚑ ⚑ (**Leisure**
9 hole par 3 course .**Conf** Max 30 Thtr 30 Class 20 Board 16
Banquet 20 **Location** 1.5m from Foyle Bridge driving
torwards Moville

Hotel ★★★ 61% White Horse Hotel, 68 Clooney Rd,
Campsie, LONDONDERRY ☎ 028 7186 0606 57 en suite

Portstewart 117 Strand Rd BT55 7PG
☎ 028 70832015 & 70833839 ▤ 028 70834097
e-mail: bill@portstewartgc.co.uk
Three links courses with spectacular views, offering a
testing round on the Strand course in particular.
Strand Course: 18 holes, 6784yds, Par 72, SSS 72,
Course record 67.
Old Course: 18 holes, 4733yds, Par 64, SSS 62.
Riverside: 9 holes, 2622yds, Par 32.
Club membership 1630.
Visitors preferred on weekdays Sat after 3pm, Sun 9.15-
10.15 and after 2.30pm. **Societies** must contact in advance.
Green Fees Strand: £60 per round; £80 per day (£80 per
round weekends); Old Course: £10 (£14 weekends);
Riverside: £12 (£17 weekends). **Cards** ▦ ▭ ▨ **Prof**
Alan Hunter **Course Designer** Des Giffin **Facilities** ⊗ ⅲ
⅃ ♥ ♨ 🏊 ⚑ ⚑ ╲ 🏌 **Conf** Max 200

Hotel ★★★ 71% The Royal Court Hotel, 233
Ballybogey Rd, PORTRUSH
☎ 028 7082 2236 18 en suite

Killymoon 200 Killymoon Rd BT80 8TW
☎ 028 86763762 & 86762254 ▤ 028 867 63762
Parkland course on elevated, well drained land.
18 holes, 5481mtrs, Par 70, SSS 69, Course record 64.
Club membership 950.
Visitors booking essential through proshop on 016487
63460.Must contact in advance,have a golf handicap and
play after 3.30pm saturdays. **Societies** must contact in
advance. **Green Fees** not confirmed. **Prof** Gary Chambers
Facilities ⊗ ⅲ ⅃ ♥ ♨ 🏊 ⚑ (**Leisure** snooker & pool.

Guesthouse ♦♦♦♦ Grange Lodge, 7 Grange Rd,
DUNGANNON ☎ 028 8778 4212 5 en suite

Dungannon 34 Springfield Ln BT70 1QX
☎ 028 87722098 or 87727338 ▤ 028 87727338
Parkland course with five par 3s and tree-lined fairways.
18 holes, 6046yds, Par 72, SSS 69, Course record 62.
Club membership 600.

continued

Visitors contact in advance, may not play before 3.30pm Sat and Sun.Handicap certificate required. **Societies** apply in writing to secretary. **Green Fees** £18(£22 weekends & bank holidays). **Course Designer** Sam Bacon **Facilities** ⊗ ⅍ 🍺 🖵 🏌 🏖 🛍 ⚘ ⚑ **Location** 0.5m outside town on Donaghmore road

Hotel ⇧ The Cohannon Inn, 212 Ballynakilly Rd, DUNGANNON ☎ 028 8772 4488 50 en suite

FINTONA Map 01 C5

Fintona Ecclesville Demesne, 1 Kiln St BT78 2BJ
☎ 028 82841480 & 82840777 (office) ▤ 028 82841480
Attractive 9-hole parkland course with a notable water hazard - a trout stream that meanders through the course causing many problems for badly executed shots.
9 holes, 5765mtrs, Par 72, SSS 70.
Club membership 400.
Visitors advised to contact in advance at weekends. **Societies** apply in writing well in advance, weekends not advisable as competitions played. **Green Fees** £15 per 18 holes. **Prof** Paul Leonard **Facilities** ⊗ by prior arrangement ⅍ by prior arrangement 🍺 by prior arrangement 🖵 🏌 🏖 **Location** 8m S of Omagh

Hotel ★★ 63% Mahons Hotel, Mill St, IRVINESTOWN
☎ 028 6862 1656 18 en suite

NEWTOWNSTEWART Map 01 C5

Newtownstewart 38 Golf Course Rd BT78 4HU
☎ 028 81661466 & 81662242 (pro shop) ▤ 028 81662506
e-mail: newtown.stewart@lineone.net
Parkland course bisected by a stream. Deer and pheasant are present on the course.
18 holes, 5468mtrs, Par 70, SSS 69, Course record 65.
Club membership 700.
Visitors contact club secretary in advance, to obtain tee times. **Societies** must contact secretary in advance. **Green Fees** £12 per day (£17 weekends & bank holidays). **Course Designer** Frank Pennick **Facilities** ⊗ 🖵 🏌 🏖 🛍 ⚘ 🏇 🛵 ⚑ **Location** 2m SW on B84

Guesthouse ◆◆◆◆ Hawthorn House, 72 Old Mountfield Rd, OMAGH ☎ 028 8225 2005 5 en suite

OMAGH Map 01 C5

Omagh 83a Dublin Rd BT78 1HQ
☎ 028 82243160 ▤ 028 82243160
Undulating parkland course beside the River Drumnagh, with the river coming into play on 4 of the holes.
18 holes, 5683mtrs, Par 71, SSS 70.
Club membership 850.
Visitors play restricted Sat, no need to contact unless large numbers. **Societies** must contact in advance. **Green Fees** not confirmed. **Course Designer** Dun Patterson **Facilities** ⊗ by prior arrangement ⅍ by prior arrangement 🍺 by prior arrangement 🖵 🏌 🏖 **Location** On S outskirts of town

Guesthouse ◆◆◆◆ Hawthorn House, 72 Old Mountfield Rd, OMAGH ☎ 028 8225 2005 5 en suite

STRABANE Map 01 C5

Strabane Ballycolman Rd ☎ 028 71382271 & 71382007
18 holes, 5537mtrs, Par 69, SSS 69, Course record 62.
Course Designer Eddie Hackett/P Jones
Telephone for further details

Guesthouse ◆◆◆◆ Hawthorn House, 72 Old Mountfield Rd, OMAGH ☎ 028 8225 2005 5 en suite

REPUBLIC OF IRELAND

CO CARLOW

BORRIS Map 01 C3

Borris Deerpark ☎ 0503 73310 ▤ 0503 73750
Testing parkland course with tree-lined fairways situated within the McMorrough Kavanagh Estate at the foot of Mount Leinster. Modern sand based greens.
9 holes, 6120mtrs, Par 70, SSS 69, Course record 66.
Club membership 600.
Visitors advisable to contact in advance, weekends very restricted. **Societies** applications in writing. **Green Fees** not confirmed. **Facilities** ⊗ ⅍ 🍺 🖵 🏌 🏖 ⚘

Hotel ★★★★🏖 Mount Juliet Hotel, THOMASTOWN
☎ 056 73000 32 en suite 27 annexe en suite

CARLOW Map 01 C3

Carlow Deerpark ☎ 0503 31695 ▤ 0503 40065
e-mail: carlowgolfclub@tinet.ie
Created in 1922 to a design by Tom Simpson, this testing and enjoyable course is set in a wild deer park, with beautiful dry terrain and a varied character. With sandy sub-soil, the course is playable all year round. There are water hazards at the 2nd, 10th and 11th and only two par 5s, both offering genuine birdie opportunities.
18 holes, 5974mtrs, Par 70, SSS 71, Course record 65.
Club membership 1200.
Visitors are welcome, although play is limited on Tue and difficult on Sat & Sun. Must contact in advance. **Societies** must book in advance. **Green Fees** €44 (€57 weekends). **Cards** 🖃 🖃 **Prof** Andrew Gilbert **Course Designer** Tom Simpson **Facilities** ⊗ ⅍ 🍺 🖵 🏌 🏖 🛍 ⚘ **Location** 2m N of Carlow on N9

Hotel ★★★ 70% Dolmen Hotel, Kilkenny Rd, CARLOW ☎ 0503 42002 40 en suite 12 annexe en suite

TULLOW Map 01 C3

Mount Wolseley Hotel, Golf & Country Club ☎ 0503 51674 ▤ 0503 52123
e-mail: sanderson@mountwolseley.ie
A magnificent setting, a few hundred yards from the banks of the river Slaney with its mature trees and lakes set against the backdrop of the East Carlow and Wicklow mountains. There are no easy holes, with wide landing areas the only concession to demanding approach shots to almost every green. There is water in play on eleven holes, with the eleventh, an all water carry off the tee of 207 yards.
18 holes, 6300yds, Par 72, SSS 70, Course record 68.
Club membership 350.
Visitors must contact in advance. **Societies** must contact in advance. **Green Fees** €45 per 18 holes Mon-Thur(€55 Fri-Sun). **Cards** 🖃 🖃 **Course Designer** Christy O'Connor **Facilities** ⊗ ⅍ 🍺 🖵 🏌 🏖 🛍 ⚘ 🏇 🛵 ⚑ **Leisure** hard tennis courts, heated indoor swimming pool, sauna, solarium, gymnasium. **Conf** Thtr 230 Class 106 Board 45 Del €82.55 to €92.07 * **Location** 1 mile from centre of Tullow

Hotel ★★★ 70% Dolmen Hotel, Kilkenny Rd, CARLOW ☎ 0503 42002 40 en suite 12 annexe en suite

CO CAVAN

BALLYCONNELL   Map 01 C4

Slieve Russell Hotel Golf & Country Club
☎ 049 9526444 & 9526458 🖷 049 9526640
e-mail: slieve-russell@quinn-hotels.com
**An 18-hole course opened in 1992 and rapidly
establishing itself as one of the finest parkland courses
in the country. A 9-hole course was recently opened to
complement it. On the main course, the 2nd plays
across water while the 16th has water surrounding the
green. The course finishes with a 519 yard, par 5 18th.**
18 holes, 6650yds, Par 72, SSS 72, Course record 65.
Club membership 900.
Visitors must book in advance for Saturdays. **Societies**
write or telephone in advance, not allowed Sat. **Green
Fees** on application. **Cards** 💳 💳 💳 💳 💳
Prof Liam McCool **Course Designer** Paddy Merrigan
Facilities ⊗ ⊪ ⓑ 🍺 ♀ 👤 🏠 ⚓ 🏌 ᠅ ᠅ **Leisure**
hard tennis courts, heated indoor swimming pool, squash,
sauna, solarium, gymnasium.**Conf** Max 900 **Location**
1.5m E of Ballyconnell

Hotel ★★★★ 67% Slieve Russell Hotel Golf and
Country Club, BALLYCONNELL
☎ 049 9526 444 159 en suite

BELTURBET   Map 01 C4

Belturbet Erne Hill ☎ 049 9522287 & 9524044
**Beautifully maintained parkland course with
predominantly family membership and popular with
summer visitors.**
9 holes, 5480yds, Par 68, SSS 65, Course record 64.
Club membership 200.
Visitors must contact in advance. **Societies** must contact
secretary in advance. **Green Fees** not confirmed. **Course
Designer** Eddie Hackett **Facilities** ⓑ 🍺 ♀ 👤 🏌 ᠅ ᠅

Hotel ★★★★ 67% Slieve Russell Hotel Golf and Country
Club, BALLYCONNELL ☎ 049 9526 444 159 en suite

BLACKLION   Map 01 C5

Blacklion Toam ☎ 072 53024 & 53418 🖷 072 53418
**Parkland course established in 1962, with coppices of
woodland and mature trees. The lake comes into play on
two holes and there are some magnificent views of the
lake, islands and surrounding hills. It has been described
as one of the best maintained scenic inland courses in
Ireland.**
9 holes, 5614mtrs, Par 72, SSS 69.
Club membership 350.
Visitors groups of 8 or more must contact in advance on Thu
or Sat. No societies Sun. **Societies** must contact in advance.
Green Fees €15(€20 weekends). **Cards** 💳 💳 💳 **Course
Designer** Eddie Hackett **Facilities** ⊗ ⊪ ⓑ 🍺 ♀ 👤 ᠅
Leisure fishing, snooker.**Hotel** ★★★ 71% Sligo Park Hotel,
Pearse Rd, SLIGO ☎ 071 60291 110 en suite

CAVAN   Map 01 C4

County Cavan Drumelis
☎ 049 4331541 & 049 4371313 🖷 049 31541
e-mail: info@cavangolf.ie
**Parkland course with number of mature trees, some over
100 years old. The closing six holes are an exacting
challenge for both the handicap and professional golfer
alike.**

continued

18 holes, 5519mtrs, Par 70, SSS 69, Course record 64.
Club membership 830.
Visitors welcome but restricted at weekends. **Societies**
contact for details. **Green Fees** not confirmed. **Cards** 💳
💳 **Prof** Ciaran Carroll **Course Designer** Eddie Hackett
Facilities ⊗ ⊪ ⓑ 🍺 ♀ 👤 🏠 🏌 ᠅ **Location** On
Killeshandra rd,out of Cavan town

Hotel ★★★ 65% Kilmore Hotel, Dublin Rd, CAVAN
☎ 049 4332288 39 en suite

VIRGINIA   Map 01 C4

Virginia ☎ 049 47235 & 48066
9 holes, 4139mtrs, Par 64, SSS 62, Course record 57.
Location By Lough Ramor
Telephone for further details

Hotel ★★★ 61% Conyngham Arms Hotel, SLANE
☎ 041 9884444 16 en suite

CO CLARE

BODYKE   Map 01 B3

East Clare ☎ 061 921322 🖷 061 921717
e-mail: eastclaregolfclub@eircon.net
**An 18-hole championship course designed by Arthur
Spring beside Lough Derg, in 148 acre site with natural
trees and water on well-drained land.**
18 holes, 5922yds, Par 70, SSS 70.
Club membership 500.
Visitors no restrictions unless there is a club competition or a
society playing. **Societies** apply in writing, deposit required.
Green Fees not confirmed. **Cards** 💳 💳 💳 💳 **Course
Designer** Dr Arthur Spring **Facilities** ⓑ 🍺 👤 🏌 ᠅ ᠅ ᠅

Hotel ★★★ 65% Temple Gate Hotel, The Square, ENNIS
☎ 065 6823300 70 en suite

CLONLARA   Map 01 B3

Clonlara Golf & Leisure
☎ 061 354141 🖷 061 354143
12 holes, 5187mtrs, Par 71, SSS 69.
Course Designer Noel Cassidy **Location** 7m NE of
Limerick
Telephone for further details

Hotel ★★★★ 67% Castletroy Park Hotel, Dublin Rd,
LIMERICK ☎ 061 335566 107 en suite

ENNIS   Map 01 B3

Ennis Drumbiggle ☎ 065 6824074 🖷 065 6841848
e-mail: egc@eircom.net
**On rolling hills, this immaculately manicured course
presents an excellent challenge to both casual visitors and
aspiring scratch golfers, with tree-lined fairways and well
protected greens.**
18 holes, 5338mtrs, Par 70, SSS 69, Course record 65.
Club membership 1000.
Visitors advisable to contact in advance, course available
Mon-Sat at most times. **Societies** apply in writing/telephone
Green Fees not confirmed. **Prof** Martin Ward **Facilities** ⊗
⊪ ⓑ 🍺 ♀ 👤 🏠 🏌 ᠅ **Location** Close to town, well
signposted

Hotel ★★★ 65% Temple Gate Hotel, The Square, ENNIS
☎ 065 6823300 70 en suite

Woodstock Golf and Country Club Shanaway Rd
☎ 065 6829463 & 6842406 🖹 065 6820304
This parkland course stands on 155 acres of land and
includes 4 holes where water is a major hazard. The
course is playable all year and the sand based greens
offer a consistent surface for putting
*Woodstock Golf & Country Club: 18 holes, 5864mtrs,
Par 71, SSS 71.*
Club membership 250.
Visitors booking advisable at weekends. Societies advisable
to telephone in advance. Green Fees not confirmed. Cards
🖃 ■ Course Designer Arthur Spring Facilities ⊗ ⅢⅠ 🖳
🍷 ♀ 👤 🏌 ⚐ ⅃ 🛢 🏌 ⚐ Leisure heated indoor swimming
pool, sauna, gymnasium. Location Off N85

Hotel ★★★★ 68% Woodstock Hotel, Shanaway Rd,
ENNIS ☎ 065 684 6600 67 en suite

KILKEE   Map 01 B3
Kilkee East End
☎ 065 9056048 & 9056977 🖹 065 9656977
e-mail: kilkeegolfclub@eircom.net
Well established course on the cliffs of Kilkee Bay.
Mature championship course with a great variety of
challenges - seaside holes, cliff-top holes and holes that
feature well-positioned water hazards.
18 holes, 6500yds, Par 72, SSS 71, Course record 68.
Club membership 390.
Visitors must book in advance. Societies apply in
writing/telephone/fax/e-mail Green Fees not confirmed.
Cards 🖃 ■ ▄ Course Designer Eddie Hackett
Facilities ⊗ ⅢⅠ 🖳 🍷 ♀ 👤 🏌 ⚐ ⅃ Leisure squash,
sauna. Location On Cilff-Edge, East End, Kilkee

Hotel ★★ 64% Halpin's Hotel, Erin St, KILKEE
☎ 065 9056032 12 en suite

Ocean Cove Golf & Leisure Hotel Kilkee Bay
☎ 065 9083111 🖹 065 9083123
e-mail: oceancove1@eircom.net
A typical coastal course surrounded on two sides by
the Atlantic Ocean and the sea can be seen from nearly
every hole. A number of greens are situated in a
spectacular position along the edge of the Clare Cliffs.
18 holes, 5265metres, Par 69, SSS 69.
Club membership 500.
Visitors must contact in advance, may not play
competition days, Societies apply in writing Green Fees
terms on application. Cards 🖃 ■ ▄ Prof Y Facilities
⊗ ⅢⅠ 🖳 🍷 ♀ 👤 🏌 ⚐ ⅃ Leisure squash, gymnasium.
Conf Max 60 Thtr 60 Class 20 Board 30 Banquet 120
Del €30 to €50 *

Hotel ★★ 64% Halpin's Hotel, Erin St, KILKEE
☎ 065 9056032 12 en suite

KILRUSH   Map 01 B3
Kilrush Parknamoney ☎ 065 51138 🖹 065 52633
e-mail: kelgolf@iol.ie
Parkland course that was extended to 18 holes in the
summer of 1994.
18 holes, 5986yds, Par 70, SSS 70, Course record 68.
Club membership 425.
Visitors welcome, contact in advance. Societies by prior
arrangement. Green Fees not confirmed. Course Designer
Arthur Spring Facilities ⊗ ⅢⅠ 🖳 🍷 ♀ 👤 🏌 ⚐ ⅃

continued

Hotel ★★ 64% Halpin's Hotel, Erin St, KILKEE
☎ 065 9056032 12 en suite

LAHINCH   Map 01 B3
Lahinch ☎ 065 7081592 🖹 065 81592
e-mail: info@lahinchgolf.com
Originally designed by Tom Morris and later modified
by Dr Alister MacKenzie, Lahinch has hosted every
important Irish amateur fixture and the Home
Internationals. The par five 5th - The Klondike - is
played along a deep valley and over a huge dune; the
par three 6th may be short, but calls for a blind shot
over the ridge of a hill to a green hemmed in by hills
on three sides.
Old Course: 18 holes, 6696yds, Par 72, SSS 73.
Castle Course: 18 holes, 5594yds, Par 70, SSS 70.
Club membership 1840.
Visitors must contact in advance. Societies apply in
writing Green Fees Old Course €110 ; Castle Course
€50. Cards 🖃 ■ ▄ Prof R McCavery Course
Designer Alister MacKenzie Facilities ⊗ ⅢⅠ 🖳 🍷 ♀ 👤
🏌 ⚐ ⅃ Location 2m W of Ennistymon on N67

Hotel ★★★ 63% Sheedys Country House Hotel,
LISDOONVARNA ☎ 065 7074026 11 en suite

MILLTOWN MALBAY   Map 01 B3
Spanish Point ☎ 065 7084198 & 7084219
e-mail: dkfitzgerald@tinet.ie
A 9-hole links course with 3 elevated greens and 4
elevated tees. Overlooking Spanish Point beach.
Improvements to the course are planned, the existing
course being redesigned and lengthened.
9 holes, 4600mtrs, Par 64, SSS 63, Course record 59.
Club membership 410.
Visitors contact in advance. Not before 1pm Sun. Societies
apply in writing to the secretary. Green Fees €20 (€25
weekends & bank holidays). Facilities 🖳 🍷 ♀ 👤 🏌 ⚐
Location 2m SW of Miltown Malbay, on N67

Hotel ★★ 64% Halpin's Hotel, Erin St, KILKEE
☎ 065 9056032 12 en suite

NEWMARKET-ON-FERGUS   Map 01 B3
Dromoland Castle Golf & Country Club
☎ 061 368444 & 368144 🖹 061 363355/368498
e-mail: dromolandgc@tinet.ie
Set in 200 acres of parkland, the course is enhanced by
numerous trees and a lake. Three holes are played
around the lake which is in front of the castle.
18 holes, 6098yds, Par 71, SSS 72, Course record 65.
Club membership 500.
Visitors must contact in advance. Societies contact in
writing. Green Fees terms on application. Cards 🖃 ■ ▄
▟ Course Designer Wigginton Facilities ⊗ ⅢⅠ 🖳 🍷 ♀ 👤
🏌 ⚐ 🍴 🏌 ⚐ Leisure hard tennis courts, heated indoor
swimming pool, fishing, sauna, solarium, gymnasium.
Conf Max 300 Thtr 300 Class 250 Board 300 Banquet
300 Location 2m N, on main Limerick/Galway rd

Hotel ★★★★ 68% Woodstock Hotel, Shanaway Rd,
ENNIS ☎ 065 684 6600 67 en suite

Looking for a driving range?
See the index at the back of the guide

SHANNON AIRPORT
Map 01 B3

Shannon ☎ 061 471849 ☒ 061 471507
e-mail: shannongolfclub@eircom.net
Superb parkland course with tree-lined fairways, strategically placed bunkers, water hazards and excellent greens, offering a challenge to all levels of players - including the many famous golfers who have played here.
18 holes, 6874yds, Par 72, SSS 74, Course record 65. Club membership 1000.
Visitors must contact in advance & have handicap certificate. Restricted play at certain times. **Societies** must contact in writing. **Green Fees** not confirmed. **Cards** ☒ ☒ **Prof** Artie Pyke **Course Designer** John Harris **Facilities** ⊗ 𝄞 🏧 💷 ♀ ♿ 🏠 🍴 🐾 ⛟ ♂ **Location** 2m from Shannon Airport

Hotel ★★★ 69% Fitzpatrick Bunratty Hotel, BUNRATTY ☎ 061 361177 115 en suite 4 annexe en suite

CO CORK

BANDON
Map 01 B2

Bandon Castlebernard ☎ 023 41111 ☒ 023 44690
e-mail: bandongolfclub@eircom.net
Lovely parkland course in pleasant rural surroundings.
18 holes, 5663mtrs, Par 70, SSS 69, Course record 66. Club membership 900.
Visitors welcome but may not play during club competitions. Must contact in advance, no green fees on Sundays. **Societies** must apply in writing or telephone well in advance. **Green Fees** €30 (€35 Saturdays). **Cards** ☒ **Prof** Paddy O'Boyle **Facilities** ⊗ 𝄞 🏧 💷 ♀ ♿ 🏠 🍴 🐾 ⛟ ♂ **Leisure** hard tennis courts, caddies available. **Location** 2.5km W

Hotel ★★★ 66% Innishannon House Hotel, INNISHANNON ☎ 021 4775121
12 en suite 1 annexe en suite

BANTRY
Map 01 B2

Bantry Bay Donemark ☎ 027 50579 ☒ 027 53790
e-mail: info@bantrygolf.com
Designed by Christy O'Connor Jnr and extended in 1997 to 18 holes, this challenging and rewarding course is idyllically set at the head of Bantry Bay. Testing holes include the par 5 of 487mtrs and the little par 3 of 127mtrs where accuracy is all-important.
18 holes, 5910mtrs, Par 71, SSS 72, Course record 71. Club membership 600.
Visitors advance booking recommended. At weekends and bank holidays visitors between 11.30-1.30pm and 3-4.30pm. Catering Mar-Oct only. **Societies** must apply in writing. **Green Fees** €40 per 18 holes,reductions in winter. **Cards** ☒ ☒ **Course Designer** Christy O'Connor/Eddie Hackett **Facilities** ⊗ 𝄞 🏧 💷 ♀ ♿ 🍴 🐾 ⛟ ♂ **Location** 3km N of Bantry town on the N71 Glengarrif road

Hotel ★★★ 64% Westlodge Hotel, BANTRY ☎ 027 50360 90 en suite

BLACKROCK
Map 01 B2

Mahon Clover Hill ☎ 021 4294280
Parkland course along the Mahon estuary. Includes 3 holes where water makes a major contribution to the difficulty of play.
18 holes, 4862metres, Par 70, SSS 67, Course record 64. Club membership 550.

continued

Visitors contact Tim O'Connor by phone **Societies** telephone for availability **Green Fees** terms on application. **Course Designer** Eddie Hackett **Facilities** ⊗ 𝄞 🏧 💷 ♀ ♿ 🏠 🍴 ♂

Hotel ★★★★ 70% Rochestown Park Hotel, Rochestown Rd, Douglas, CORK ☎ 021 4892233 160 en suite

BLARNEY
Map 01 B2

Muskerry Carrigrohane
☎ 021 4385297 ☒ 021 4516860
An adventurous game is guaranteed at this course, with its wooded hillsides and the meandering Shournagh River coming into play at a number of holes. The 15th is a notable hole - not long, but very deep - and after that all you need to do to get back to the clubhouse is stay out of the water.
18 holes, 5520mtrs, Par 71, SSS 70. Club membership 801.
Visitors may not play Wed afternoon & Thu morning. Some limited play at weekends after 3.30pm & members hour 12.30-1.30pm daily. Must contact in advance. **Societies** must telephone in advance and then confirm in writing. **Green Fees** €35 per round(€40 weekends). **Cards** ☒ ☒ **Prof** W M Lehane **Course Designer** Dr A McKenzie **Facilities** ⊗ 𝄞 🏧 💷 ♀ ♿ 🏠 🍴 ♂ **Location** 2.5m W of Blarney

Hotel ★★★ 68% Christy's Hotel, BLARNEY ☎ 021 4385011 49 en suite

CARRIGALINE
Map 01 B2

Fernhill Hotel & Golf Club ☎ 021 4372226 ☒ 021 4371011
e-mail: fernhill@iol.ie
Parkland course featuring large undulating greens and tree lined fairways. Generally flat course with challenging holes.
18 holes, 5000mtrs, Par 69, SSS 68. Club membership 150.
Visitors available any time. **Societies** telephone in advance. **Green Fees** not confirmed. **Cards** ☒ ☒ ☒ **Prof** Wayne O'Callaghaw **Course Designer** M L Bowes **Facilities** ⊗ 𝄞 🏧 💷 ♀ ♿ 🏠 🍴 🐟 🐾 ⛟ ♂ **Leisure** hard tennis courts, heated indoor swimming pool, fishing, sauna, 3 hole academy. **Location** 2m from Ringaskiddy

Hotel ★★ 65% Whispering Pines Hotel, CROSSHAVEN ☎ 021 4831843 & 4831448 ☒ 021 4831679 15 en suite

CASTLETOWNBERE
Map 01 A2

Berehaven Millcove ☎ 027 70700 ☒ 027 71957
Seaside links founded in 1902. Moderately difficult with four holes over water.
9 holes, 2398mtrs, Par 68, SSS 66, Course record 63. Club membership 150.
Visitors welcome. Please check for major events. **Societies** telephone or write in advance. **Green Fees** €20 per round/day. **Cards** ☒ **Course Designer** Royal Navy **Facilities** ⊗ 𝄞 🏧 💷 ♀ ♿ 🍴 ♂ ⛷ **Leisure** hard tennis courts, sauna. **Location** 2m from Castletownbere on Glen Garriff Rd

Hotel ★★★♨ 76% Sea View Hotel, BALLYLICKEY ☎ 027 50073 & 50462 ☒ 027 51555 17 en suite

AA website: www.theAA.com

CHARLEVILLE   Map 01 B2

Charleville ☎ 063 81257 & 81515 📄 063 81274
e-mail: charlevillegolf@eircom.net
Wooded parkland course.

West Course: 18 holes, 6212yds, Par 71, SSS 69,
Course record 65.
East Course: 9 holes, 6702yds, Par 72, SSS 72.
Club membership 1000.
Visitors only prebooked at weekends. **Societies** contact in advance. **Green Fees** terms on application. **Cards** 🔲 🔳 🔳 **Prof** David Keating **Course Designer** Eddie Connaughton **Facilities** ⊗ 🍴 🛒 🍺 ♀ ♨ 🏠 🏌 ➴ 🚬 ♿ ✂ (**Location** 2m W from town centre

Hotel ★★★★♨ Longueville House Hotel, MALLOW
☎ 022 47156 & 47306 📄 022 47459 20 en suite

CLONAKILTY   Map 01 B2

Dunmore Dunmore, Muckross ☎ 023 33352
A hilly, rocky 9-hole course overlooking the Atlantic.
9 holes, 4464yds, Par 64, SSS 61, Course record 57.
Club membership 380.
Visitors must contact in advance, may not play weekends. **Societies** apply in writing. **Green Fees** terms on application. **Course Designer** E Hackett **Facilities** ⊗ 🍴 🛒 🍺 ♀ ♨ 🏠 ♿ ✂ **Location** 3.5m S of Clonakilty

Hotel ★ 60% Courtmacsherry, COURTMACSHERRY
☎ 023 46198 12 rms (10 en suite)

CORK   Map 01 B2

Cork Little Island ☎ 021 4353451 📄 021 4353410
e-mail: corkgolfclub@eircom.net
This championship-standard course is kept in superb condition and is playable all year round. Memorable and distinctive features include holes at the water's edge and in a disused quarry. The 4th hole is considered to be among the most attractive and testing holes in Irish golf.
18 holes, 5910mtrs, Par 72, SSS 72, Course record 67.
Club membership 750.
Visitors may not play 12.30-2pm or on Thu (Ladies Day), and only after 2pm Sat & Sun. **Societies** must contact in advance. **Green Fees** €70(€80 weekends). **Cards** 🔳 🔳 📖 **Prof** Peter Hickey **Course Designer** Alister Mackenzie **Facilities** ⊗ 🍴 🛒 🍺 ♀ ♨ 🏠 🏌 ✂ **Location** 5m E, on N25 of Cork City

Hotel ★★★★ 69% Jurys Cork Hotel, Western Rd, CORK ☎ 021 4276622 185 en suite

Fitzpatrick Silver Springs Tivoli
☎ 021 507533 & 505128
Five par 4s and 4 par 3s make up this short 9-hole course.
9 holes, 1786mtrs, Par 32, Course record 26.
Club membership 84.
Visitors no restrictions. **Societies** apply by telephone. **Green Fees** not confirmed. **Cards** 🔳 🔳 🔳 **Prof** Freddy Twomey **Course Designer** Eddie Hackett **Facilities** ⊗ 🍴 🛒 🍺 ♀ ♨ 🏠 🏌 ✂ **Leisure** hard tennis courts, heated indoor swimming pool, squash, sauna, solarium, gymnasium. **Location** 1m E of city centre off Tivoli bypass

Hotel ★★★★ 65% Silver Springs Moran Hotel, Tivoli, CORK ☎ 021 4507533 109 en suite

Fota Island Carrigtwohill
☎ 021 4883700 📄 021 4883713
e-mail: reservations@fotaisland.ie
Set in the heart of a 780 acre island in Cork Harbour. The course is routed among mature woodlands with occasional views of the harbour. The traditional design features pot bunkers and undulating putting surfaces. Fota has hosted the Irish Club Professional Championship and the Irish PGA Championship.
18 holes, 6500yds, Par 71, SSS 71, Course record 63.
Club membership 400.
Visitors advisable to contact in advance. Metal spikes and blue jeans not permitted. **Societies** contact in advance. **Green Fees** €65(Mon), €77(Tues-Thur); €90(Fri-Sun). **Cards** 🔳 🔳 🔳 **Prof** Kevin Morris **Course Designer** Jeff Hoves **Facilities** ⊗ 🍴 🛒 🍺 ♀ ♨ 🏠 🏌 ➴ 🚬 ✂ (**Conf** Thtr 40 Class 35 Board 15 Banquet 25 Del €5 to €10 * **Location** Off N25 E of Cork City. Take exit for Cobh, course 500m on right

Hotel ★★★ 66% Midleton Park, MIDLETON
☎ 021 4631767 40 en suite

The Ted McCarthy Municipal Golf Course
Blackrock ☎ 021 294280
Municipal course which stretches alongside the river estuary, with some holes across water.

18 holes, 4862mtrs, Par 70, SSS 66, Course record 63.
Club membership 380.
Visitors please telephone in advance, may not play mornings at weekends. **Societies** please telephone in advance. **Green Fees** €18 per day(€19 weekends & bank holidays). **Course Designer** E Hackett **Facilities** ⊗ ⍤ 🏌 🛒 ♀ ⛳ 🏠 ⛳ ♂ **Location** 2m from city centre

Hotel ★★★ 65% Silver Springs Moran Hotel, Tivoli, CORK ☎ 021 4507533 109 en suite

DONERAILE
Map 01 B2

Doneraile ☎ 022 24137 & 24379
Parkland.
9 holes, 5528yds, Par 68, SSS 67, Course record 61.
Club membership 750.
Visitors may play weekdays, weekends restricted **Societies** welcome. **Green Fees** €20 per day. **Facilities** ⊗ by prior arrangement ⍤ by prior arrangement 🏌 🛒 ♀ ⛳ ♂ **Leisure** Doneraile National Heritage Park. **Location** Off T11

Hotel ★★★ 63% Springfort Hall Hotel, MALLOW ☎ 022 21278 50 en suite

DOUGLAS
Map 01 B2

Douglas ☎ 021 4895297 📱 021 4895297
e-mail: admin@douglasgolfclub.ie
Level inland course overlooking the city of Cork. Suitable for golfers of all ages and abilities. The course is under re-development.
18 holes, 5607mtrs, Par 72, SSS 69.
Club membership 900.
Visitors Contact in advance. May not play Sat or Sun am or Tues(ladies day).Reserved for members 12.30-2 pm. **Societies** must contact in writing, by end of Jan. **Green Fees** €45. **Cards** 💳 💳 **Prof** Gary Nicholson **Course Designer** Peter McEvoy **Facilities** ⊗ ⍤ 🏌 🛒 ♀ ⛳ 🏠 ⛳ ♂ ♣ **Location** 6km east of Cork City.

Hotel ★★★★ 69% Jurys Cork Hotel, Western Rd, CORK ☎ 021 4276622 185 en suite

FERMOY
Map 01 B2

Fermoy Corrin Cross
☎ 025 32694 (office) & 31472 (shop) 📱 025 33072
e-mail: fermoygolfclub@eircom.net
Rather exposed heathland course, bisected by a road.
18 holes, 5596mtrs, Par 70, SSS 69.
Club membership 950.
Visitors contact in advance, must telephone in advance for weekends bookings **Societies** advisable to write or telephone in advance. **Green Fees** €25(€35 weekends and bank holidays). **Cards** 💳 💳 **Prof** Brian Moriarty **Course Designer** John Harris **Facilities** ⊗ ⍤ 🏌 🛒 ♀ ⛳ 🏠 ⛳ ♂ **Location** 2m SW

Hotel ★★★🍴 Longueville House Hotel, MALLOW ☎ 022 47156 & 47306 📱 022 47459 20 en suite

GLENGARRIFF
Map 01 B2

Glengarriff ☎ 027 63150 📱 027 63575
Founded 1935.
9 holes, 2042mtrs, Par 66, SSS 62.
Club membership 300.
Visitors welcome, details not supplied **Societies** apply to club. **Green Fees** not confirmed. **Facilities** 🏌 🛒 ♀ ⛳ ♂ ♣ **Location** On N71

Hotel ★★★ 64% Westlodge Hotel, BANTRY ☎ 027 50360 90 en suite

KANTURK
Map 01 B2

Kanturk Fairyhill ☎ 029 50534
Scenic parkland course set in the heart of the Duhallow region with superb mountain views. It provides a good test of skill for golfers of all standards, with tight fairways requiring accurate driving and precise approach shots to small and tricky greens.
18 holes, 5721mtrs, Par 72, SSS 70, Course record 73.
Club membership 550.
Visitors Ladies day Wed. Please ring in advance. **Societies** apply in writing or telephone the Secretary. **Green Fees** not confirmed. **Course Designer** Richard Barry **Facilities** ⛳ ♂ **Location** 1m from Kanturk on Fairyhill road, 2m off main Mallow/Killarney road from Ballymacquirke Cross

Guesthouse ◆◆◆◆◆ Assolas Country House, KANTURK ☎ 029 50015 6 en suite 3 annexe en suite

KINSALE
Map 01 B2

Kinsale Farrangalway ☎ 021 4774722 📱 021 4773114
e-mail: kinsaleg@indigo.ie
In addition to the existing 9-hole (Ringenane) course, a new 18-hole (Farrangalway) course was opened in 1994. Set in unspoilt farmland and surrounded by peacefull rolling countryside, it offers a stiff yet fair challenge to be enjoyed by all standards of golfers. New putting green.
Farrangalway: 18 holes, 6609yds, Par 71, SSS 71, Course record 70.
Ringenane: 9 holes, 5332yds, Par 70, SSS 68.
Club membership 800.
Visitors welcome but may not be able to play at weekends. Contact in advance. **Societies** by reservation **Green Fees** €30 Mon-Thur(€40 Fri-Sun and bank holidays)€20 before 10am Mon-Thur. **Cards** 💳 💳 **Prof** Ger Broderick **Course Designer** Jack Kenneally **Facilities** ⊗ ⍤ 🏌 🛒 ♀ ⛳ 🏠 ⛳ 🏌 ♂ **Location** On main Cork/Kinsale rd

Hotel ★★★ 69% Trident Hotel, Worlds End, KINSALE ☎ 021 4772301 58 en suite

Old Head ☎ 021 4778444 📠 021 4778022

e-mail: info@oldheadgolf.ie

Opened for play in 1997 and designed by Paddy Merrigan, Ron Kirby and Joe Carr, the Old Head course is spectacularly situated on a promontory jutting out into the Atlantic. As well as bringing the sea and cliffs into play, you have to contend with strong prevailing winds - a fine test for all serious golfers.

18 holes, 7200yds, Par 72, SSS 73.
Club membership 250.
Visitors tee time must be booked in advance. **Societies** pre booking necessary, rates for groups over 24. **Green Fees** not confirmed. **Cards** 🔲 🔲 🔲 🔲 **Prof** David Murray **Course Designer** R Kirby/J Carr/P Merrigan/E Hackett **Facilities** ⊗ ⌇ ⌂ ⌇ ⌇ ⌇ ⌇ ⌇ ⌇ ⌇ **Location** From Cork city/airport, follow R600 to Kinsale, then signed to golf course

Hotel ★★★ 73% Actons Hotel, Pier Rd, KINSALE
☎ 021 4772135 76 en suite

LITTLE ISLAND   Map 01 B2

Harbour Point Clash Rd

☎ 021 4353094 📠 021 4354408
e-mail: hpoint@iol.ie

A championship-standard course in rolling countryside on the banks of the River Lee at Cork's scenic harbour. A distinctive and testing course for every standard of golfer, providing for a full range of shots in its design. The large undulating greens and difficult par 3s are a feature of this course.

18 holes, 5883metres, Par 72, SSS 71, Course record 71.
Visitors must contact in advance. **Societies** telephone for bookings. **Green Fees** terms on application. **Cards** 🔲 🔲 **Prof** Morgan O'Donovan **Course Designer** Patrick Merrigan **Facilities** ⊗ ⌇ ⌂ ⌇ ⌇ ⌇ ⌇ ⌇ ⌇ ⌇ ⌇ **Location** 5m E of Cork, take Rosslare road E from Cork city & exit at Little Island

Hotel ★★★★ 65% Silver Springs Moran Hotel, Tivoli,
CORK ☎ 021 4507533 109 en suite

MACROOM   Map 01 B2

Macroom Lackaduve ☎ 026 41072 📠 026 41391

e-mail: mcroomgc@iol.ie

A particularly scenic parkland course located on undulating ground along the banks of the River Sullane. Bunkers and mature trees make a variable and testing course and the 12th has a 50 yards carry over the river to the green.

18 holes, 5574mtrs, Par 72, SSS 70, Course record 68.
Club membership 650.

continued

Visitors Booking essential for at all times **Societies** Telephone in advance. **Green Fees** €25 per day(€30 weekends and bank holidays). **Cards** 🔲 🔲 **Course Designer** Jack Kenneally/Eddie Hackett **Facilities** ⊗ ⌇ ⌇ ⌇ ⌇ ⌇ ⌇ ⌇ ⌇ **Location** Through castle entrance in town square

Hotel ★★ 72% Castle Hotel, Main St, MACROOM
☎ 026 41074 42 en suite

MALLOW   Map 01 B2

Mallow Ballyellis ☎ 022 21145 📠 022 42501

e-mail: golfmall@gofree.indigo.ie

Mallow Golf Club was first established in the late 1800s. A well wooded parkland course overlooking the Blackwater Valley, Mallow is straightforward, but no less of a challenge for it. The front nine is by far the longer, but the back nine is demanding in its call for accuracy and the par 3 18th provides a tough finish.

18 holes, 5769metres, Par 72, SSS 71, Course record 67.
Club membership 1250.
Visitors must contact in advance. **Societies** apply in advance. **Green Fees** €32 per round (€38 weekends & bank holidays). **Cards** 🔲 🔲 🔲 **Prof** Sean Conway **Course Designer** D W Wishart **Facilities** ⊗ ⌇ ⌇ ⌇ ⌇ ⌇ ⌇ ⌇ ⌇ **Leisure** hard tennis courts, squash, sauna. **Location** 1m E of Mallow town

Hotel ★★★★♨ Longueville House Hotel, MALLOW
☎ 022 47156 & 47306 📠 022 47459 20 en suite

MIDLETON   Map 01 C2

East Cork Gortacrue

☎ 021 4631687 & 4631273 📠 021 4613695
A well wooded course calling for accuracy of shots.
18 holes, 5491yds, Par 69, SSS 67, Course record 64.
Club membership 640.
Visitors may not play Sun mornings. **Societies** must telephone. **Green Fees** €25. **Cards** 🔲 🔲 **Prof** Don MacFarlane **Course Designer** E Hackett **Facilities** ⊗ ⌇ ⌂ ⌇ ⌇ ⌇ ⌇ ⌇ **Location** On the A626

Hotel ★★★ 66% Midleton Park, MIDLETON
☎ 021 4631767 40 en suite

MITCHELSTOWN   Map 01 B2

Mitchelstown Limerick Rd

☎ 025 24072 & 087 2650110
Attractive, gently undulating parkland course set in the Golden Vale, noted for the quality of the greens, the magnificent views of the Galtee Mountains and its

continued

friendly atmosphere. Ideal for golfers seeking tranquility and a golfing challenge.
18 holes, 5160mtrs, Par 67, SSS 68, Course record 65. Club membership 400.
Visitors advisable to check in advance (information line 025 24231) **Societies** apply in writing or telephone. **Green Fees** not confirmed. **Course Designer** David Jones **Facilities** ⊗ ⓑ ♥ ♀ ♨ ♂ **Location** 0.75m on Limerick rd from Mitchelstown

Hotel ★★★⚑ Longueville House Hotel, MALLOW ☎ 022 47156 & 47306 🖺 022 47459 20 en suite

MONKSTOWN   Map 01 B2

Monkstown Parkgariffe, Monkstown
☎ 021 4841376 🖺 021 4841376
Undulating parkland course with five tough finishing holes.
18 holes, 5441mtrs, Par 70, SSS 68, Course record 66. Club membership 960.
Visitors restricted weekends, must contact in advance. **Societies** apply in writing or telephone. Large groups (24+) should book before Xmas. **Green Fees** not confirmed. **Prof** Batt Murphy **Facilities** ⊗ ⌦ ⓑ ♥ ♀ ♨ 🖻 ⚐ ♦ ♂ ⚑ **Location** 0.5m SE of Monkstown village

Hotel ★★★★ 69% Jurys Cork Hotel, Western Rd, CORK ☎ 021 4276622 185 en suite

OVENS   Map 01 B2

Lee Valley Golf & Country Club Clashanure
☎ 021 7331721 🖺 021 7331695
e-mail: leevalleygolfclub@eircom.net
An undulating test of all golfing abilities designed by Ryder Cup star Christy O'Connor Junior. Seven of the 18 holes have water and the unusual feature of two fairy forts which are over 300 years old - can they be blamed for errors on the testing par 5 8th and 12th holes?! The 508yard, par 5 8th is already regarded as one of the best holes in Ireland with its spectacular lake a feature from tee to green.
18 holes, 6434yds, Par 72, SSS 70, Course record 62. Club membership 400.
Visitors telephone in advance. Avoid Sat/Sun before 11.15am. **Societies** telephone in advance. **Green Fees** not confirmed. **Prof** John Savage **Course Designer** Christy O'Connor **Facilities** ⊗ ⌦ ⓑ ♥ ♀ ♨ 🖻 ⚐ ♦ ♂ ⚑ **Location** 8m from Cork on Cork/Killarney road N22

Hotel ★★ 72% Castle Hotel, Main St, MACROOM ☎ 026 41074 42 en suite

SKIBBEREEN   Map 01 B2

Skibbereen & West Carbery Licknavar
☎ 028 21227 🖺 028 22994
Slightly hilly course in scenic location.
18 holes, 6004yds, Par 71, SSS 69, Course record 66. Club membership 700.
Visitors advisable to contact club secretary for dates in writing. **Societies** apply in writing or telephone. **Green Fees** not confirmed. **Cards** ⚏ ▆▆ ▆▆ ▢ ▆▆ ▆▆ 🖸 **Course Designer** Jack Kenneally **Facilities** ⊗ ⌦ ⓑ ♥ ♀ ♨ 🖻 ⚐ ♦ ♂ **Location** 1m W on Baltimore road

Hotel ★★★ 64% Baltimore Harbour Hotel & Leisure Cntr, BALTIMORE ☎ 028 20361 64 en suite

YOUGHAL   Map 01 C2

Youghal Knockaverry
☎ 024 92787 & 92861 🖺 024 92641
e-mail: youghalgolfclub@eircom.ie
For many years the host of various Golfing Union championships, Youghal offers a good test of golf and is well maintained for year-round play. There are panoramic views of Youghal Bay and the Blackwater estuary.
18 holes, 5646mtrs, Par 70, SSS 69, Course record 61. Club membership 994.
Visitors may not play Wed (Ladies Day) and should contact in advance for weekends. **Societies** must apply in writing a few months in advance. **Green Fees** €25 per round(€32 weekends). **Cards** ⚏ ▆▆ **Prof** Liam Burns **Course Designer** Cd. Harris **Facilities** ⊗ ⌦ ⓑ ♥ ♀ ♨ 🖻 ⚐ ♦ ♂ **Location** Located on the N25 main road from Rosslare, between Waterford and Cork City

Hotel ★★ 66% Devonshire Arms Hotel and Restaurant, Pearse Square, YOUGHAL ☎ 024 92827 10 en suite

CO DONEGAL

BALLINTRA   Map 01 B5

Donegal Murvagh, Laghy ☎ 073 34054 🖺 073 34377
e-mail: info@donegalgolfclub.ie
This massive links course was opened in 1973 and provides a world-class facility in peaceful surroundings. It is a very long course with some memorable holes, including five par 5s, calling for some big hitting.
18 holes, 6243mtrs, Par 73, SSS 73, Course record 68. Club membership 750.
Visitors must contact in advance, limited availability at weekends. **Societies** must contact in advance. **Green Fees** not confirmed. **Cards** ⚏ ▆▆ **Prof** Leslie Robinson **Course Designer** Eddie Hackett **Facilities** ⊗ ⌦ ⓑ ♥ ♀ ♨ 🖻 ⚐ ♦ ♂ **Location** 6m S of Donegal on Ballyshannon road

Hotel ★★★ 77% Sand House Hotel, ROSSNOWLAGH ☎ 072 51777 55 en suite

BALLYBOFEY   Map 01 C5

Ballybofey & Stranorlar Stranorlar ☎ 074 31093
A most scenic course incorporating pleasant valleys backed by mountains with three of its holes bordered by a lake. There are three par 3s on the first nine and two on the second. The most difficult hole is the long uphill par 4 16th. The only par 5 is the 7th.
18 holes, 5366mtrs, Par 68, SSS 68, Course record 64. Club membership 520.
Visitors may play on weekdays. Advisable to book in advance **Societies** contact golf shop **Green Fees** €20 (€25 weekends). **Facilities** ⊗ ⌦ ⓑ ♥ ♀ ♨ 🖻 ♂ **Location** 0.25m from Stranorlar

Hotel ★★★ 70% Kee's Hotel, Stranorlar, BALLYBOFEY ☎ 074 31018 53 en suite

Where to stay, where to eat?
Visit www.theAA.com

BALLYLIFFIN   Map 01 C6

Ballyliffin Clonmany ☎ 077 76119 📄 077 76672
e-mail: ballyliffingolfclub@eircom.net
The Old course is a links course with rolling fairways, surrounded by rolling hills and bounded on one side by the ocean. Nick Faldo said 'This is the most natural golf links I have ever played.' It has an old-fashioned charm with its uniquely contoured fairways. The 18 hole Glashedy course (opened summer 1995), offers a modern (and arguably 'fairer') championship test.
Old Links: 18 holes, 6604yds, Par 72, SSS 72, Course record 66.
Glashedy Links: 18 holes, 7135yds, Par 72, SSS 74, Course record 68.
Club membership 1200.
Visitors telephone in advance. **Societies** telephone in advance. **Green Fees** Old Links: €38 (€42 weekends); Glashedy:€57 (€64 weekends). **Cards** 🎫 💳 **Prof** Francis Howley **Course Designer** Tom Craddock/Pat Ruddy **Facilities** ⊗ ⅢⅠ 🖍 🏌 ♀ ❀ 🍴 🚪 ➤ 🚡 ♂ 🏌 **Conf** Max 50 Board 30 Banquet 30 Del from €20 *

Guesthouse ♦♦♦♦ Mount Royd Country Home, CARRIGANS ☎ 074 40163 4 en suite

BUNCRANA   Map 01 C6

Buncrana Municipal Railway Rd, Ballmacarry ☎ 077 62279 & 20749
e-mail: buncranagc@eircom.net
A 9-hole course with a very challenging Par-3 3rd with all carry out of bounds on either side.
9 holes, 2125yds, Par 62, SSS 60, Course record 59.
Club membership 200.
Visitors during open competitions only visitors with club handicaps.Telephone in advance to make arrangements for weekends. **Societies** write in advance/telephone. **Green Fees** terms on application. **Facilities** ⚑ 🍴

Guesthouse ♦♦♦♦ Mount Royd Country Home, CARRIGANS ☎ 074 40163 4 en suite

North West Lisfannon, Fahan
☎ 077 61027 & 61715 📄 077 63284
e-mail: nwgc@tinet.ie
A traditional-style links course on gently rolling sandy terrain with some long par 4s. Good judgement is required on the approaches and the course offers a satisfying test coupled with undemanding walking.
18 holes, 5968yds, Par 70, SSS 70, Course record 64.
Club membership 580.
Visitors contact in advance for weekends. Wed - Ladies Day **Societies** telephone in advance. **Green Fees** €21 (€28 weekends). **Prof** Seamus McBriarty **Course Designer** Thompson Davy **Facilities** ⊗ ⅢⅠ 🖍 🏌 ♀ 🍴 **Location** 1m S of Buncanna

Guesthouse ♦♦♦♦ Mount Royd Country Home, CARRIGANS ☎ 074 40163 4 en suite

> If the name of the club appears in *italics*, details have not been confirmed for this edition of the guide

BUNDORAN   Map 01 B5

Bundoran ☎ 072 41302 📄 072 42014
This popular course, acknowledged as one of the best in the country, runs along the high cliffs above Bundoran beach and has a difficult par of 70. Designed by Harry Vardon, it offers a challenging game of golf in beautiful surroundings and has been the venue for a number of Irish golf championships.
18 holes, 5688mtrs, Par 70, SSS 70, Course record 67.
Club membership 700.
Visitors must contact in advance for prior booking. **Societies** must contact in advance. **Green Fees** €30 per round (€40 weekends & bank holidays). **Prof** David T Robinson **Course Designer** Harry Vardon **Facilities** 🖍 💳 ♀ 🍴 🚪 🏌 ➤ 🚡 ♂ **Location** Just off Main St, Bundoran on the Sligo/Derry road, 22m N of Sligo

Hotel ★★★ 77% Sand House Hotel, ROSSNOWLAGH ☎ 072 51777 55 en suite

CRUIT ISLAND   Map 01 B5

Cruit Island Kincasslagh ☎ 075 43296 📄 075 48028
A links course on a small island. It is perched along the cliffs overlooking the Atlantic. The course is short but always challenging as the wind blows 90% of the time. It is crowned by a magnificent 6th hole which is played across a cove to an island green. With the prevailing wind in your face and the Atlantic waves crashing in front, it is not for the fainthearted.
9 holes, 4833mtrs, Par 68, SSS 66, Course record 62.
Club membership 350.
Visitors restricted Sun & Thu mornings for Club competitions. **Societies** apply in writing to secretary. **Green Fees** €20. **Cards** 🎫 💳 **Course Designer** Michael Doherty **Facilities** 🖍 💳 ♀ ♂ **Location** 8km N of Dungloe

Hotel ★★★ 65% Arnold's Hotel, DUNFANAGHY ☎ 074 36208 30 en suite

DUNFANAGHY   Map 01 C6

Dunfanaghy Kill ☎ 074 36335 📄 074 36335
e-mail: dunfanaghygolf@eircom.net
Overlooking Sheephaven Bay, the course has a flat central area with three difficult streams to negotiate. At the Port-na-Blagh end there are five marvellous holes, including one across the beach, while at the Horn Head end, the last five holes are a test for any golfer.
18 holes, 5066mtrs, Par 68, SSS 66, Course record 63.
Club membership 335.
Visitors must book in advance, time sheet in operation all year. **Societies** must telephone in advance. **Green Fees** €22 (€27 weekends). **Course Designer** Harry Vardon **Facilities** 🖍 💳 ♀ 🍴 🚪 🏌 ➤ 🚡 ♂ **Location** On N56

Hotel ★★★ 65% Arnold's Hotel, DUNFANAGHY ☎ 074 36208 30 en suite

GREENCASTLE   Map 01 C6

Greencastle Moville ☎ 077 81013
18 holes, 5118mtrs, Par 69, SSS 67.
Telephone for further details

Hotel ★★★ 69% Quality Hotel Davincis, 15 Culmore Rd, LONDONDERRY ☎ 028 7127 9111 70 en suite

GWEEDORE — Map 01 B6

Gweedore Derrybeg ☎ 075 31140
This 9-hole links course provides plenty of challenge with
two subtle par 3s and the par 5 5th/14th at 556yds into
the prevailing west wind is a monster.
9 holes, 6201yds, Par 71, SSS 69.
Club membership 175.
Visitors golf club must be notified if large numbers wish to
play.Telephone club for tee off weekend times. **Societies**
apply in writing. **Green Fees** €13 (€15 weekends and bank
holidays). **Facilities** ⓑ ☗ ♀ ⚒ ⚷

LETTERKENNY — Map 01 C5

Letterkenny Barnhill ☎ 074 21150 ▤ 074 21175
The fairways are wide and generous, but the rough, when
you find it, is short, tough and mean. The flat and
untiring terrain on the shores of Lough Swilly provides
good holiday golf. Many interesting holes include the
intimidating 1st with its high tee through trees and the
tricky dog-leg of the 2nd hole. The last 7 holes are on
undulating ground, steep climb from 11th green to
12th tee.
18 holes, 6239yds, Par 70, SSS 71, Course record 65.
Club membership 700.
Visitors preferred Mon-Fri, except Wed evenings after 5pm.
Advisable to contact in advance for weekends and bank
holidays. **Societies** apply by writing or telephone. **Green
Fees** not confirmed. **Course Designer** Eddie Hacket
Facilities ⊗ ⊪ ⓑ ☗ ♀ ⚒ 🏠 ⚑ ⚷ **Location** 2m from
town on Rathmelton road

Hotel ★★★ 70% Kee's Hotel, Stranorlar, BALLYBOFEY
☎ 074 31018 53 en suite

MOVILLE — Map 01 C6

Redcastle Redcastle ☎ 077 82073 ▤ 077 82214
e-mail: redcastle.hotel@oceanfree.net
A testing course enjoying a picturesque setting on the
shores of Loch Foyle. The two challenging par 3 holes
should be approached with the necessary respect.
9 holes, 3076yds, Par 36.
Club membership 200.
Visitors welcome except club times advisable to telephone.
Societies enquiries welcome by telephone or in writing.
Green Fees not confirmed. **Cards** ⊟ ▦ ▭ ▥ **Facilities**
⊗ ⊪ ⓑ ☗ ♀ 🏠 ⚑ 🏇 ⚷ **Leisure** hard tennis courts, heated
indoor swimming pool, fishing, sauna, gymnasium. **Location**
Main Londonderry/Moville road

NARIN — Map 01 B5

Narin & Portnoo ☎ 075 45107 ▤ 075 45107
Seaside links with every hole presenting its own special
feature. The par 4 5th, for instance, demands a perfectly
placed drive to get a narrow sight of the narrow entrance
to the elevated green. Cross winds from the sea can make
some of the par 4s difficult to reach with two woods.
18 holes, 5322mtrs, Par 69, SSS 68, Course record 63.
Club membership 700.
Visitors contact in advance for weekend tee times. **Societies**
telephone in advance. **Green Fees** €20 (€25 weekends &
bank holidays). **Facilities** ⓑ ☗ ♀ ⚒ 🏠 🏇 ⚷ **Location**
6m from Ardara

Hotel ★★★ 63% Abbey Hotel, The Diamond, DONEGAL
☎ 073 21014 95 en suite

PORTSALON — Map 01 C6

Portsalon ☎ 074 59459 ▤ 074 59919
Another course blessed by nature. The golden beaches of
Ballymastocker Bay lie at one end, while the beauty of
Lough Swilly and the Inishowen Peninsula beyond is a
distracting but pleasant feature to the west. Situated on
the Fanad Peninsula, this lovely links course provides
untiring holiday golf at its best. A redevelopment and
extension of the course is currently in progress.
18 holes, 5696yds, Par 68, SSS 66.
Club membership 450.
Visitors telephone in advance. **Societies** telephone in
advance. **Green Fees** €23(€28 weekends & bank holidays).
Course Designer Pat Ruddy **Facilities** ⊗ ⊪ ⓑ ☗ ♀
⚒ 🏇 ⚷

Hotel ★★★♨ 73% Fort Royal Hotel, Fort Royal,
RATHMULLAN ☎ 074 58100 11 en suite 4 annexe en suite

RATHMULLAN — Map 01 C6

Otway Saltpans ☎ 074 58319
9 holes, 4234yds, Par 64, SSS 60, Course record 60.
Location W shore of Loch Swilly
Telephone for further details

Hotel ★ 58% Pier Hotel, RATHMULLAN
☎ 074 58178 & 58115 ▤ 074 58115 10 en suite

ROSAPENNA — Map 01 C6

Rosapenna Downings ☎ 074 55301 ▤ 074 55128
e-mail: rosapenna@tinet.ie
Dramatic links course offering a challenging round.
Originally designed by Tom Morris and later modified by
James Braid and Harry Vardon, it includes such features
as bunkers in mid fairway. The best part of the links runs
in the low valley along the ocean.
18 holes, 6271yds, Par 70, SSS 71.
Club membership 200.
Visitors no restrictions. **Societies** must contact in advance.
Green Fees terms on application. **Cards** ⊟ ▦ ▭ ▥
Course Designer Old Tom Morris **Facilities** ⊪ ☗ ♀ ⚒ 🏠
⚑ 🏇 ⚷ ⚔ **Leisure** hard tennis courts, heated indoor
swimming pool. **Conf** Max 70 Thtr 70 Class 50

Hotel ★★★ 65% Arnold's Hotel, DUNFANAGHY
☎ 074 36208 30 en suite

CO DUBLIN

BALBRIGGAN — Map 01 D4

Balbriggan Blackhall ☎ 01 8412229 ▤ 01 8413927
e-mail: balbriggangolfclub@eircom.net
A parkland course with great variations and good views
of the Mourne and Cooley mountains.
18 holes, 5922mtrs, Par 71, SSS 71.
Club membership 650.
Visitors must contact in advance. With member only at
weekends. Tuesdays ladies day. **Societies** must apply in
writing. **Green Fees** €32 per round. **Course Designer**
Paramoir **Facilities** ⊗ ⊪ ⓑ ☗ ♀ ⚒ 🏇 🏠 ⚷ **Location**
1km S off Balbriggan on N1

Hotel ★★★ 61% Boyne Valley Hotel & Country Club,
Stameen, Dublin Rd, DROGHEDA
☎ 041 9837737 35 en suite

BALLYBOUGHAL   Map 01 D4
Hollywood Lakes
☎ 01 8433406 & 8433407 📖 01 8433002
e-mail: austinbrogan@hotmail
A parkland course opened in 1992 with large USGA-type, sand-based greens and tees. There are water features on seven holes. The front nine requires accuracy while the second nine includes a 636yd par 5.

18 holes, 6246mtrs, Par 72, SSS 72, Course record 67.
Club membership 630.
Visitors welcome Mon-Fri but may only play weekends from 1pm. **Societies** telephone then write in advance. **Green Fees** €30 per round (€35 weekends). **Cards** 💳 **Course Designer** Mel Flanagan **Facilities** ⊗ Ⅲ 🏌 💺 ♀ ⚐ 🍴 ➘ ⚒ ⚹ ❢ **Location** 3m off main Dublin/Belfast road

Hotel ★★★ 70% Marine Hotel, Sutton Cross, DUBLIN 13 ☎ 01 8390000 48 en suite

BRITTAS   Map 01 D4
Slade Valley Lynch Park
☎ 01 4582183 & 4582739 📖 01 4582784
This is a course for a relaxing game, being fairly easy and in pleasant surroundings.
18 holes, 5388mtrs, Par 69, SSS 68, Course record 65.
Club membership 800.
Visitors must contact in advance. **Societies** telephone in advance. **Green Fees** not confirmed. **Cards** 💳 💳 **Prof** John Dignam **Course Designer** W Sullivan & D O Brien **Facilities** ⊗ Ⅲ 🏌 💺 ♀ ⚐ 🍴 ⚹ **Location** 9m SW of Dublin on N81

Hotel ★★★ 66% Downshire House Hotel, BLESSINGTON ☎ 045 865199 14 en suite 11 annexe en suite

CASTLEKNOCK   Map 01 D4
Elm Green ☎ 01 8200797 📖 01 8226662
Located a short distance from Dublin, beside Phoenix Park, with a fine layout, tricky greens and year round playability.
18 holes, 5796yds, Par 71, SSS 66, Course record 65.
Club membership 400.
Visitors must book in advance. **Societies** telephone in advance. **Green Fees** not confirmed. **Cards** 💳 💳 💳 **Prof** Arnold O'Connor/Paul McGavan **Course Designer** Eddie Hackett **Facilities** ⊗ 🏌 💺 ♀ ⚐ 🍴 ❢ ⚹ **Leisure** pitch and putt course. **Location** Off Navan Rd, 15 mins from city centre

Hotel ★★★ 70% Finnstown Country House Hotel, Newcastle Rd, LUCAN ☎ 01 6010700 25 en suite 28 annexe en suite

Luttrellstown Castle Dublin15
☎ 01 8089988 📖 01 8089989
e-mail: golf@luttrellstown.ie
Set in the grounds of the magnificent 560-acre Luttrellstown Castle estate, this championship course has retained the integrity of a mature and ancient parkland. It is renowned for the quality of its greens and the log-built Clubhouse which provides excellent facilities.
18 holes, 6032mtrs, Par 72, SSS 73, Course record 66.
Club membership 400.
Visitors bookings made in advance only, no denims. **Societies** must phone in advance. **Green Fees** terms on application. **Cards** 💳 💳 💳 **Prof** Edward Doyle **Course Designer** N Bielenberg **Facilities** ⊗ Ⅲ 🏌 💺 ♀ ⚐ 🍴 ➘ ⚒ ⚹ ❢ **Leisure** hard tennis courts, heated outdoor swimming pool, fishing, clay shooting. **Conf** Thtr 100 Class 70 Board 40 Banquet 70 **Location** Porterstown rd

Hotel ★★★ 70% Finnstown Country House Hotel, Newcastle Rd, LUCAN ☎ 01 6010700 25 en suite 28 annexe en suite

CLOGHRAN   Map 01 D4
Forrest Little ☎ 01 8401183
18 holes, 5865mtrs, Par 70, SSS 70.
Location 6m N of Dublin on N1
Telephone for further details

Hotel ★★★ 70% Marine Hotel, Sutton Cross, DUBLIN 13 ☎ 01 8390000 48 en suite

DONABATE   Map 01 D4
Balcarrick Corballis
☎ 01 8436228 & 8436957 📖 01 8436957
Splendid 18-hole parkland course located close to the sea. A strong prevailing wind often plays a big part on every hole. Many challenging holes, notably the 7th - nicknamed 'Amen Corner'.
18 holes, 6273mtrs, Par 73, SSS 71.
Club membership 750.
Visitors must contact in advance. **Societies** telephone in advance. **Green Fees** not confirmed. **Prof** Stephen Rayfus **Course Designer** Barry Langan **Facilities** ⊗ Ⅲ 🏌 💺 ♀ ⚐ 🍴

Hotel ★★★ 69% Holiday Inn Dublin Airport, Dublin Airport, DUBLIN ☎ 01 8080500 249 en suite

Corballis Public Corballis ☎ 01 8436583
18 holes, 4971yds, Par 65, SSS 64.
Telephone for further details

Hotel ★★★ 69% Holiday Inn Dublin Airport, Dublin Airport, DUBLIN ☎ 01 8080500 249 en suite

Donabate Balcarrick ☎ 01 8436346 & 8436001
18 holes, 5704yds, Par 70, SSS 69, Course record 67.
Telephone for further details

Hotel ★★★ 69% Holiday Inn Dublin Airport, Dublin Airport, DUBLIN ☎ 01 8080500 249 en suite

The Island Corballis
☎ 01 8436104 & 8436205 📖 01 8436860
e-mail: islandgc@iol.ie
Links course on a promontory, with sea inlets separating some of the fairways. Accuracy as well as length of shots are required on some holes and sand hills provide an additional challenge.   *continued*

18 holes, 6078mtrs, Par 71, SSS 72, Course record 67.
Club membership 800.

The Island Golf Club

Visitors must contact in advance. Preferred on Mon, Tue & Fri limited availability on all other days. Telephone for appointment. **Societies** must apply in advance. **Green Fees** not confirmed. **Cards** 🔲 🔲 **Prof** Kevin Kelliher **Course Designer** Hackett/Hawtree **Facilities** ⊗ ⅏ ⅃ 🍺 ♀ ⅄ 🏠 ⚑ ❄ ⚓ ♂ **Location** Take main Dublin/Belfast road N1, pass airport, take turn for Donabate/Portrane, follow signs

Hotel ★★★ 69% Holiday Inn Dublin Airport, Dublin Airport, DUBLIN ☎ 01 8080500 249 en suite

DUBLIN   Map 01 D4

Carrickmines
Carrickmines ☎ 01 2955972
Meadowland course.
9 holes, 6100yds, Par 71, SSS 69.
Club membership 500.
Visitors may not play Wed,Sat or bank holidays. **Societies** contact for details. **Green Fees** €33 per 18 holes;€19 per 9 holes(€38/€ 22 Sunday). **Facilities** ⅃ 🍺 ♀ ⅄ ♂ **Location** 7m S of Dublin

Hotel ★★★ 68% The Gresham Royal Marine Hotel, Marine Rd, DUN LAOGHAIRE ☎ 01 2801911 103 en suite

Castle
Woodside Dr, Rathfarnham
☎ 01 4904207 ◨ 01 4920264
e-mail: leslie@castlegolfclub.dublin.com
A tight, tree-lined parkland course which is very highly regarded by all who play there.
18 holes, 5732mtrs, Par 70, SSS 70, Course record 63.
Club membership 1350.
Visitors welcome but may not play at weekends & bank holidays. **Societies** must apply in writing 6 months in advance. **Green Fees** €56. **Prof** David Kinsella **Course Designer** Barcroft-Pickman & Hood **Facilities** ⊗ ⅏ ⅃ 🍺 ♀ ⅄ 🏠 ♂ **Location** Off Dodder Park Road

Hotel ★★★★ 73% Jurys Ballsbridge Hotel, Pembroke Rd, Ballsbridge, DUBLIN 4 ☎ 01 6605000 294 en suite

Clontarf
Donnycarney House, Malahide Rd
☎ 01 8331892 & 8331520 ◨ 01 8331933
e-mail: info.cgc@indigo.ie
The nearest golf course to Dublin city, with a historic building as a clubhouse, Clontarf is a parkland type course bordered on one side by a railway line. There are several testing and challenging holes including the 12th, which involves playing over a pond and a quarry.
continued

18 holes, 5317mtrs, Par 69, SSS 68, Course record 64.
Club membership 1150.
Visitors welcome daily but must contact in advance. **Societies** Tue & Fri. Must contact in advance. **Green Fees** €38(€50 weekends). **Prof** Mark Callan **Course Designer** Harry Colt **Facilities** ⊗ ⅏ ⅃ 🍺 ♀ ⅄ 🏠 ⚑ ♂ **Leisure** bowling green, snooker room, golf teaching by pro. **Location** 2.5m N via Fairview

Hotel ★★★ 67% Jurys Skylon Hotel, Drumcondra Rd, DUBLIN 9 ☎ 01 8379121 88 en suite

Corrstown
Corrstown, Kilsallaghan
☎ 01 8640533 & 8640534 ◨ 01 8640537
e-mail: info@corrstown.com
The 18 hole course has a small river meandering through, coming into play at several holes culminating in a challenging Island green finish. Orchard course has mature trees and rolling pastureland offering golfers a relaxing enjoyable game.
River Course: 18 holes, 6077mtrs, Par 72, SSS 71, Course record 69.
Orchard Course: 9 holes, 2792mtre, Par 35, SSS 69.
Club membership 1050.
Visitors advisable to contact in advance. May play weekends after 3pm on River Course. Visitors welcome anytime on Orchard Course. **Societies** telephone or write in advance. **Green Fees** terms on application. **Cards** 🔲 🔲 🔲 **Prof** Pat Gittens **Course Designer** Eddie Connaughton **Facilities** ⊗ ⅏ ⅃ 🍺 ♀ ⅄ 🏠 ⚓ ♂ **Conf** Max 20 Del €125 to €225 * **Location** 10 minutes W of Dublin Airport via St Margarets

Hotel ★★★ 67% Jurys Skylon Hotel, Drumcondra Rd, DUBLIN 9 ☎ 01 8379121 88 en suite

Deer Park Hotel & Golf Course
Howth D13
☎ 01 8322624 ◨ 01 8392405
e-mail: sales@deerpark.iol.ie
Claiming to be Ireland's largest golf/hotel complex, be warned that its popularity makes it quite busy at times and only hotel residents can book tee-off times.
St Fintans: 9 holes, 3373yds, Par 37.
Deer Park: 18 holes, 6830yds, Par 72.
Grace O'Malley: 9 holes, 3130yds, Par 35.
Short Course: 12 holes, 1810yds, Par 36.
Club membership 350.
Visitors no restrictions. There may be delays especially Sun mornings. **Societies** must contact by telephone. **Green Fees** €14.50-€22 per 18 holes;€7.50-€11.50 per 9 holes. **Cards** 🔲 🔲 🔲 **Course Designer** Fred Hawtree **Facilities** ⊗ ⅏ ⅃ 🍺 ♀ ⅄ ⚑ ⚓ ♂ **Leisure** hard tennis courts, heated indoor swimming pool, sauna. **Conf** Max 120 Thtr 120 Class 65 Board 45 Banquet 90 **Location** On right 0.5m before Howth Harbour

Hotel ★★★ 70% Marine Hotel, Sutton Cross, DUBLIN 13 ☎ 01 8390000 48 en suite

Edmonstown
Edmondstown Rd, Edmondstown
☎ 01 4931082 & 4932461 ◨ 01 4933152
e-mail: info@edmondstowngolfclub.ie
A popular and testing parkland course situated at the foot of the Dublin Mountains in the suburbs of the city. An attractive stream flows in front of the 4th and 6th greens calling for an accurate approach shot. Currently undergoing upgrading to championship standard.
18 holes, 6113mtrs, Par 71, SSS 72.
Club membership 750.
continued

407

Edmondstown Golf Club

Visitors must contact in advance as there are daily times reserved for members. Limited times after 3.30pm weekends. **Societies** must contact in advance. **Green Fees** €55(€65 weekends). **Cards** ▨ ▰▰ ▨ **Prof** Andrew Crofton **Course Designer** McEvoy/Cooke **Facilities** ⊗ ⅲ ⅱ ⅱ ♀ ⚲ ⚑ ⚑ ⚐ ⚷ **Conf** Max 50

Hotel ★★★ 68% Jurys Montrose Hotel, Stillorgan Rd, DUBLIN
☎ 01 2693311 178 en suite

Elm Park Golf & Sports Club Nutley House,
Nutley Ln, Dennybrook ☎ 01 2693438 ▤ 01 2694505
e-mail: office@elmparkgolfclub.ie
Interesting parkland course requiring a degree of accuracy, particularly as half of the holes involve crossing the stream.
18 holes, 5355mtrs, Par 69, SSS 68, Course record 64.
Club membership 1850.
Visitors must contact in advance. **Societies** apply in advance. **Green Fees** €65 (€75 weekends). **Cards** ▨ ▰▰ ▨ **Prof** Seamus Green **Facilities** ⊗ ⅲ ⅱ ⅱ ♀ ⚲ ⚑ ⚷ **Leisure** hard and grass tennis courts. **Location** 3m from city centre

Hotel ★★★★ 73% Jurys Ballsbridge Hotel, Pembroke Rd, Ballsbridge, DUBLIN 4 ☎ 01 6605000 294 en suite

Foxrock Torquay Rd, Foxrock
☎ 01 2895668 & 2893992
9 holes, 5667mtrs, Par 70, SSS 69.
Telephone for further details

Hotel ★★★ 68% The Gresham Royal Marine Hotel, Marine Rd, DUN LAOGHAIRE ☎ 01 2801911 103 en suite

Grange Rathfarnham ☎ 01 4932889
18 holes, 5517mtrs, Par 68, SSS 69.
Location 6m from city centre
Telephone for further details

Hotel ★★★ 68% Jurys Montrose Hotel, Stillorgan Rd, DUBLIN ☎ 01 2693311 178 en suite

Howth St Fintan's, Carrickbrack Rd, Sutton
☎ 01 8323055 ▤ 01 8321793
e-mail: secretary@howthgolfclub.ie
A heathland course with scenic views of Dublin Bay. It is very hilly and presents a good challenge to the novice or expert golfer.
18 holes, 5618mtrs, Par 72, SSS 69.
Club membership 1200.

continued

Visitors contact in advance. May not play Wed and weekends. **Societies** must contact in advance. **Green Fees** terms on application. **Prof** John McGuirk **Course Designer** James Braid **Facilities** ⅱ ⅱ ♀ ⚲ ⚑ ⚷ **Location** 9m NE of City Centre, 2m from Sutton Cross, on Sutton side of Hill of Howth

Hotel ★★★ 70% Marine Hotel, Sutton Cross, DUBLIN 13 ☎ 01 8390000 48 en suite

Milltown Lower Churchtown Rd
☎ 01 4976090 ▤ 01 4976008
e-mail: millgolf@iol.ie
Level parkland course on the outskirts of the city.
18 holes, 5638mtrs, Par 71, SSS 69, Course record 64.
Club membership 1400.
Visitors must contact in advance but may not play weekends. **Societies** apply in writing. **Green Fees** not confirmed. **Cards** ▰▰ ▨ **Prof** John Harnett **Course Designer** Freddie Davis **Facilities** ⊗ ⅲ ⅱ ⅱ ♀ ⚲ ⚑ ⚑ ⚷ **Location** Lower Churchtown Road, Dublin 14

Hotel ★★★★ 73% Jurys Ballsbridge Hotel, Pembroke Rd, Ballsbridge, DUBLIN 4 ☎ 01 6605000 294 en suite

Newlands Clondalkin 22
☎ 01 4593157 & 4593498 ▤ 01 4593498
Mature parkland course offering a testing game.
18 holes, 5714mtrs, Par 71, SSS 70.
Club membership 1000.
Visitors must contact in advance and may play Mon, Thu, Fri and Wed mornings only. **Societies** must contact in writing. **Green Fees** not confirmed. **Prof** Karl O'Donnell **Course Designer** James Braid **Facilities** ⊗ ⅲ ⅱ ⅱ ♀ ⚲ ⚑ ⚷

Hotel ★★★ 68% Jurys Green Isle Hotel, Naas Rd, DUBLIN 22 ☎ 01 4593406 90 en suite

The Open Golf Centre Newton House, St Margaret's
☎ 01 8640324 ▤ 01 8341400
e-mail: rwwright@iol.ie
Yellow & Red Course: 18 holes, 5973yds, Par 71, SSS 69, Course record 66.
Blue Course: 9 holes, 2479yds, Par 31.
Course Designer M Hawtree **Location** Adjacent to Dublin airport
Telephone for further details

Hotel ★★★ 70% Marine Hotel, Sutton Cross, DUBLIN 13 ☎ 01 8390000 48 en suite

Rathfarnham Newtown
☎ 01 4931201 & 4931561 ▤ 01 4931561
e-mail: rgc@oceanfree.net
Parkland course designed by John Jacobs in 1962.
14 holes, 5815mtrs, Par 71, SSS 70, Course record 69.
Club membership 685.
Visitors must contact in advance, by arrangement only. **Societies** restricted to Mon, Wed & Fri. **Green Fees** €30 per round (€38 weekends and bank holidays). **Prof** Brian O'Hara **Course Designer** John Jacobs **Facilities** ⅱ ⅱ ♀ ⚲ ⚑ ⚷

Hotel ★★★★ 73% Jurys Ballsbridge Hotel, Pembroke Rd, Ballsbridge, DUBLIN 4 ☎ 01 6605000 294 en suite

Royal Dublin North Bull Island, Dollymount
☎ 01 8336346 📠 01 8336504
e-mail: jlambe@theroyaldublingolfclub.com
A popular course with visitors, for its design subtleties, for the condition of the links and the friendly atmosphere. Founded in 1885, the club moved to its present site in 1889 and received its Royal designation in 1891. A notable former club professional was Christy O'Connor, who was appointed in 1959 and immediately made his name. Along with its many notable holes, Royal Dublin has a fine and testing finish. The 18th is a sharply dog-legged par 4, with out of bounds along the right-hand side. The decision to try the long carry over the 'garden' is one many visitors have regretted.

18 holes, 6002mtrs, Par 72, SSS 71, Course record 63.
Club membership 800.
Visitors must contact in advance & have handicap certificate. May not play Wed, Sat until 3.30 summer. **Societies** must book one year in advance. **Green Fees** €100 Mon-Thur(€115 Fri-Sun). **Cards** ▭ ▭ ▭ **Prof** Leonard Owens **Course Designer** H S Colt **Facilities** ⊗ ⵊ ⅃ ⅃ ♀ ⚎ ⌂ ⛳ ⎘ ⚐ **Conf** Del from €175 *
Location 3.5m NE of city centre

Hotel ★★★ 64% Longfield's Hotel, Fitzwilliam St, DUBLIN 2 ☎ 01 6761367 24 en suite

St Anne's North Bull Island, Dollymount ☎ 01 8336471
18 holes, 5652mtrs, Par 70, SSS 69.
Telephone for further details

Hotel ★★★ 64% Longfield's Hotel, Fitzwilliam St, DUBLIN 2 ☎ 01 6761367 24 en suite

St Margaret's Golf & Country Club
St Margaret's ☎ 01 8640400 📠 01 8640289
e-mail: sales@stmargarets.net
A championship standard course which measures nearly 7,000 yards off the back tees, but flexible teeing offers a fairer challenge to the middle and high handicap golfer. The modern design makes wide use of water hazards and mounding. The par 5 8th hole is set to become notorious - featuring lakes to the left and right of the tee and a third lake in front of the green. Ryder Cup player, Sam Torrance, has described the 18th as 'possibly the strongest and most exciting in the world'.
18 holes, 6917yds, Par 73, SSS 73, Course record 69.
Club membership 200.
Visitors telephone in advance. **Societies** apply in writing or telephone **Green Fees** not confirmed. **Cards** ▭ ▭ ▭ 🏧 **Course Designer** Craddock/Ruddy **Facilities** ⊗
continued

ⵊ ⅃ ⅃ ♀ ⚎ ⌂ ⛳ ⎘ ⚐ ⚐ ⚐ **Location** 9m NW of city centre

Hotel ★★★ 70% Marine Hotel, Sutton Cross, DUBLIN 13 ☎ 01 8390000 48 en suite

Stackstown Kellystown Rd, Rathfarnham
☎ 01 4942338 & 4941993 📠 01 4933934
e-mail: stackstowngc@eircom.net
Pleasant course in scenic surroundings.
18 holes, 6152yds, Par 72, SSS 72, Course record 68.
Club membership 1092.
Visitors preferred Mon-Fri. **Societies** telephone in advance and confirm in writing. **Green Fees** €30 (€38 Sundays).
Prof Michael Kavanagh **Course Designer** Shaftrey
Facilities ⊗ ⵊ ⅃ ⅃ ♀ ⚎ ⌂ ⛳ ⎘ ⚐ **Leisure** snooker.
Conf Max 150 Thtr 100 Class 40 Board 16 Banquet 150
Location South on M50 junct 13, follow signs for Rathfarnham. At 3rd lights left for Leopardstown and Ticknock. At next lights, follow road under M50, club 300 metres

Hotel ★★★ 68% Jurys Montrose Hotel, Stillorgan Rd, DUBLIN ☎ 01 2693311 178 en suite

DUN LAOGHAIRE   Map 01 D4

Dun Laoghaire Eglinton Park, Tivoli Rd
☎ 01 2803916 📠 01 2804868
e-mail: dlgc@iol.ie
This is a well wooded parkland course, not long, but requiring accurate club selection and placing of shots. The course was designed by Harry Colt in 1918.

18 holes, 5298mtrs, Par 69, SSS 68, Course record 63.
Club membership 1118.
Visitors may play Mon,Tue & Fri.Restricted on all other days. **Societies** must apply in writing. **Green Fees** €50 per 18 holes. **Cards** ▭ ▭ ▭ ▭ 🏧 **Prof** Vincent Carey **Course Designer** Harry Colt **Facilities** ⊗ ⵊ ⅃ ⅃ ♀ ⚎ ⌂ ⛳ ⚐ **Conf** Max 250 Thtr 250 Class 35 Board 20 Banquet 150 **Location** 0.75m from town centre and ferry port

Hotel ★★★ 68% The Gresham Royal Marine Hotel, Marine Rd, DUN LAOGHAIRE ☎ 01 2801911 103 en suite

KILLINEY   Map 01 D4

Killiney Ballinclea Rd ☎ 01 2852823 📠 01 2852823
The course is on the side of Killiney Hill with picturesque views over south Dublin and the Wicklow Mountains.
9 holes, 5655mtrs, Par 70, SSS 70.
Club membership 450.
Visitors welcome Mon, Wed, Fri & Sun afternoons.
Societies Apply in writing. **Green Fees** not confirmed. **Prof** P O'Boyle **Facilities** ⵊ ⅃ ⅃ ♀ ⚎ ⌂ ⛳ ⎘ ⚐
continued

Hotel ★★★★ 65% Fitzpatrick Castle Hotel, KILLINEY
☎ 01 2305400 113 en suite

KILTERNAN   Map 01 D4

Kilternan Golf & Country Club Hotel
☎ 01 2955550 📠 01 2955670
e-mail: kgc@kilternan-hotel.ie
Interesting and testing course overlooking Dublin Bay.

18 holes, 5223yds, Par 68, SSS 66, Course record 66.
Club membership 940.
Visitors may not play before 1.30pm at weekends. Contact in advance. **Societies** apply in writing/telephone in advance. **Green Fees** not confirmed. **Cards** 〰 ▥ ▥ 🖳 **Course Designer** Eddie Hackett **Facilities** ⊗ ⑂ 🎒 💺 ⛳ ♀ ⚓ 🛒 ⛾ **Leisure** hard tennis courts, heated indoor swimming pool, sauna, gymnasium.

Hotel ★★★★ 65% Fitzpatrick Castle Hotel, KILLINEY
☎ 01 2305400 113 en suite

LUCAN   Map 01 D4

Hermitage Ballydowd
☎ 01 6265049 & 6268491 📠 01 6268491
Part level, part undulating course bordered by the River Liffey and offering some surprises.
18 holes, 6034mtrs, Par 71, SSS 70.
Club membership 1100.
Visitors Must contact in advance. **Societies** must telephone well in advance. **Green Fees** not confirmed. **Cards** ▥ **Prof** Simon Byrne **Course Designer** J McKenna **Facilities** ⊗ ⑂ 🎒 💺 ♀ ⚓ 🛒 ⛾

Hotel ★★★ 70% Finnstown Country House Hotel,
Newcastle Rd, LUCAN ☎ 01 6010700
25 en suite 28 annexe en suite

Lucan Celbridge Rd ☎ 01 6282106 📠 01 6282929
e-mail: luncangolf@eircom.net
Founded in 1897 as a nine hole course and extended to 18 holes in 1988, Lucan involves playing over a lane which bisects the 1st and 7th holes. The first nine is undulating while the back nine is flatter and features water hazards and a 538mtr 5 par 18th hole.
18 holes, 5958mtrs, Par 71, SSS 71, Course record 67.
Club membership 780.
Visitors may play Mon, Tue & Fri. **Societies** must apply in writing. **Green Fees** €40 per 18 holes. **Course Designer** Eddie Hackett **Facilities** ⊗ ⑂ 🎒 💺 ♀ ⚓ 🛒 ⛾ **Location** N4 W to Celbridge

Hotel ★★★ 64% Lucan Spa Hotel, LUCAN ☎ 01 6280495
& 6280497 📠 01 6280841 71 rms (61 en suite)

MALAHIDE   Map 01 D4

Malahide Beechwood, The Grange
☎ 01 8461611 📠 01 8461270
e-mail: malgc@clubi.ie
Splendid parkland course with an 18 hole championship course and also a further 9 holes known as the Beechwood 9. A scenically beautiful course with a combination of trees, water and bunker hazards to test the most skilful of golfers.

Main Course: 18 holes, 6066mtrs, Par 71.
Club membership 1100.
Visitors must contact in advance. **Societies** must contact in advance. **Green Fees** €50(€85 weekends and bank holidays). **Cards** 〰 ▥ 🖳 **Prof** John Murray **Course Designer** E Hackett **Facilities** ⊗ ⑂ 🎒 💺 ♀ ⚓ 🛒 ⛾ **Location** 1m from coast road at Portmarnock

Hotel ★★★★ 78% Portmarnock Hotel & Golf Links,
Strand Rd, PORTMARNOCK
☎ 01 8460611 103 en suite

PORTMARNOCK   See page 411   Map 01 D4

RATHCOOLE   Map 01 D4

Beech Park Johnstown ☎ 01 4580522 📠 01 4588365
e-mail: info@beechpark.ie
Relatively flat parkland with heavily wooded fairways. Famous for its 'Amen Corner' (holes 10-13).
18 holes, 5730mtrs, Par 72, SSS 70, Course record 67.
Club membership 955.
Visitors may not play weekends, telephone in advance. **Societies** apply in writing. **Green Fees** €38 per 18 holes. **Cards** 〰 ▥ **Course Designer** Eddie Hackett **Facilities** ⑂ 🎒 💺 ♀ ⛾

Hotel ★★★ 70% Finnstown Country House Hotel,
Newcastle Rd, LUCAN ☎ 01 6010700
25 en suite 28 annexe en suite

RUSH   Map 01 D4

Rush ☎ 01 8438177 (Office) 8437548 (Clubhouse)
📠 01 8438177
Seaside borders three fairways on this links course. There are 28 bunkers and undulating fairways to add to the challenge of the variable and strong winds that blow at all times and change with the tides. There are no easy holes!
9 holes, 5598mtrs, Par 70, SSS 69.
Club membership 350.

continued on page 412

Portmarnock

Portmarnock, *Co Dublin*   ☎ 01 8462968   Fax 01 8462601   Map 01 D4

e-mail: liz@portmarnockgolfclub.ie

Universally acknowledged as one of the truly great links courses, Portmarnock has hosted many great events from the British Amateur Championship of 1949 and the Canada Cup in 1960, to 12 stagings of the revived Irish Open. Founded in 1894, the championship course offers a classic challenge. Surrounded by water on three sides and laid out in a serpentine fashion, no two successive holes play in the same direction. Unlike many courses which play nine out and nine home, Portmarnock demands a continual discernment of wind direction.

The course has some extraordinary holes including the 14th, which Henry Cotton regarded as the best hole in golf; the 15th which Arnold Palmer regards as the best par-3 in the world, and the 5th regarded as the best on the course by the late Harry Bradshaw, 40 years Portmarnock's golf professional and runner-up to AD Locke in the 1949 British Open after playing his ball from an empty bottle of stout.

Visitors must contact in advance and confirm in writing. Restricted Saturday, Sunday and public holidays. Handicap certificate required

Societies must contact in advance in writing.

Green Fees Unconfirmed.

Facilities
Professional (Joey Purcell)

Location 12m from Dublin, 1m from village down Golf Rd.

Holes/Par/Course record 27 holes
Old Course: 18 holes, 7182yds, Par 72, SSS73
New Course: 9 holes, 3370yds, Par 37

WHERE TO STAY AND EAT NEARBY

Hotel
PORTMARNOCK
★★★★ 78% Portmarnock Hotel & Golf Links.
☎ 01 8460611. 103 en suite

Championship Course

Visitors restricted Wed, Thu, weekends & bank holidays. **Societies** apply in writing. **Green Fees** not confirmed. **Facilities** ⊗ ⍟ ⅃ ♨ ⤙ ⩛ ♌ ♂

Hotel ★★★ 69% Holiday Inn Dublin Airport, Dublin Airport, DUBLIN ☎ 01 8080500 249 en suite

SAGGART
Map 01 D4

City West Hotel & Golf Resort
☎ 01 4010500 & 4010900 (shop) 🗎 01 4588565
e-mail: info@citywest-hotel.iol.ie
18 holes, 6314yds, Par 70, SSS 70, Course record 65.
Visitors time sheet in operation, telephone in advance. **Societies** apply in writing/telephone in advance. **Green Fees** not confirmed. **Cards** ▭ ▬ ▭ 🖳 **Prof** Mac Gregor **Course Designer** Christy O'Connor Jnr **Facilities** ⊗ ⍟ ⅃ ♨ ⅃ ♨ ⤙ ♌ ♂ ♌ ♂ ₵ **Leisure** heated indoor swimming pool, fishing, sauna, solarium, gymnasium. **Location** Naas road, southbound N7

Hotel ★★★ 65% Bewley's Hotel Newlands Cross, Newlands Cross, Naas Rd, DUBLIN 22 ☎ 01 464 0140 260 en suite

SKERRIES
Map 01 D4

Skerries Hacketstown ☎ 01 8491567 🗎 01 8491591
e-mail: skerriesgolfclub@eircom.net
Tree-lined parkland course on gently rolling countryside, with sea views from some holes. The 1st and 18th are particularly challenging. The club can be busy on some days, but is always friendly.
18 holes, 6081mtrs, Par 73, SSS 72.
Club membership 800.
Visitors must contact in advance but may not play at weekends. **Societies** must contact well in advance in writing. **Green Fees** not confirmed. **Cards** ▭ ▬ **Prof** Jimmy Kinsella **Facilities** ⊗ ⍟ ⅃ ♨ ⅃ ♨ ⤙ 🖳 ♌ ♂ ♂ **Location** E of Dublin-Belfast road

Hotel ★★★ 61% Boyne Valley Hotel & Country Club, Stameen, Dublin Rd, DROGHEDA ☎ 041 9837737 35 en suite

SWORDS
Map 01 D4

Swords Open Golf Course Balheary Av, Swords
☎ 01 8409819 & 8901030 🗎 01 8409819
e-mail: swordsgc@indigo.ie
Parkland course situated beside the River Broadmeadow in unspoilt countryside, 10 miles from Dublin.

18 holes, 5612mtrs, Par 70, SSS 70, Course record 73.
Club membership 475.
Visitors timesheet bookings available all year, telephone to book, may play at any time **Societies** telephone well in advance. **Green Fees** €13 per 18 holes (€20 weekends).
continued

Course Designer T Halpin **Facilities** ⅃ ♨ ⤙ ♌ ♂ **Location** 5 mins from Swords

Hotel ★★★ 67% Jurys Skylon Hotel, Drumcondra Rd, DUBLIN 9 ☎ 01 8379121 88 en suite

TALLAGHT
Map 01 D4

Dublin City Ballinascorney
☎ 01 4516430 🗎 01 4598445
e-mail: info@dublincitygolf.com
Set in the valley of Glenasmole, this very scenic course offers a variety of terrain, where every hole is different, many would be considered feature holes.
18 holes, 5535yds, Par 69, SSS 67, Course record 63.
Visitors please contact in advance, welcome weekdays and weekends after 4pm. **Societies** contact for details. **Green Fees** €25 (€35 weekends). **Cards** ▭ ▭ **Course Designer** Eddie Hackett **Facilities** ⅃ ♨ ⅃ ♨ ⤙ ♌ ♂ ♌ ♂ **Conf** Class 50 Board 50 **Location** 8m SW of Dublin city centre, M50 junct 11(Firhouse) club 5 mins on R114

Hotel ★★★ 68% Jurys Green Isle Hotel, Naas Rd, DUBLIN 22 ☎ 01 4593406 90 en suite

CO GALWAY

BALLINASLOE
Map 01 B4

Ballinasloe Rosglos ☎ 0905 42126 🗎 0905 42538
e-mail: ballinasloegolfclub@eircom.net
Well maintained parkland course, recently extended from a par 68 to a par 72.
18 holes, 5865mtrs, Par 72, SSS 70, Course record 69.
Club membership 884.
Visitors preferably Mon-Sat, contact in advance. **Societies** contact in advance. **Green Fees** €20 per round;€25 weekends. **Prof** n **Course Designer** E Hackett/E Connaughton **Facilities** ⊗ ⍟ ⅃ ♨ ⤙ 🖳 ♌ ♂ ♂ ₵ **Location** 2 miles from Ballinasloe Town

Hotel ★★★ 64% Haydens Gateway Business & Leisure Hotel, BALLINASLOE ☎ 065 68 23000 48 en suite

BALLYCONNEELY
Map 01 A4

Connemara ☎ 095 23502 & 23602 🗎 095 23662
e-mail: links@iol.ie
This championship links course is situated on the verge of the Atlantic Ocean in a most spectacular setting, with the Twelve Bens Mountains in the background. Established as recently as 1973, it is a tough challenge, due in no small part to its exposed location, with the back 9 the equal of any in the world. The last six holes are exceptionally long and offer a great challenge to golfers of all abilities. When the wind blows, club selection is crucial. Notable holes are the 13th (200 yd par 3), the long par 5 14th, the 15th with a green nestling in the hills, the 16th guarded by water and the 17th and 18th, both par 5s over 500 yds long.
18 holes, 6611mtrs, Par 72, SSS 75, Course record 67.
Club membership 970.
Visitors advisable to book in advance. **Societies** telephone in advance. **Green Fees** not confirmed. **Cards** ▭ ▬ **Prof** Hugh O'Neill **Course Designer** Eddie Hackett **Facilities** ⊗ ⍟ ⅃ ♨ ⅃ ♨ ⤙ 🖳 ♌ ♂ ♂ ₵ ₵ **Location** 9m SW of Clifden

Hotel ★★★ 76% Abbeyglen Castle Hotel, Sky Rd, CLIFDEN ☎ 095 21201 38 en suite

BEARNA
Map 01 B3

Bearna Golf and Country Club Corboley
☎ 091 592677 📠 091 592674
e-mail: bearnagc@eircom.net
Set amid the beautiful landscape of the west of Ireland and enjoying commanding views of Galway Bay, the golf course covers more than 100 hectares of unique countrside. This has resulted in generously proportioned fairways, many elevated tees and some splendid carries. Water comes into play at thirteen holes and the final four holes provide a memorable finish.
18 holes, 5746mtrs, Par 72, SSS 72, Course record 68.
Club membership 500.
Visitors must telephone in advance. Societies contact in advance. Green Fees terms on application. Cards ⊟ ▦ ▦ Course Designer Robert J Brown Facilities ⊗ ♿ ▼ ♀ ♨ 🏠 🍴 ⛳ ⚑ Location 5miles W Galway City on Spiddal Rd.
....
Hotel ★★★ 65% Galway Ryan Hotel, Dublin Rd, GALWAY ☎ 091 753181 96 en suite

GALWAY
Map 01 B4

Galway Blackrock, Salthill
☎ 091 522033 📠 091 529783
Designed by Dr Alister McKenzie, this course is inland by nature, although some of the fairways run close to the ocean. The terrain is of gently sloping hillocks with plenty of trees and furze bushes to catch out the unwary. Although not a long course, it provided a worthy challenge as the venue of the Celtic International Tournament in 1984 and continues to delight the visiting golfer.
18 holes, 6376yds, Par 70, SSS 71, Course record 67.
Club membership 1050.
Visitors preferred on weekdays, except Tue. Societies must apply in writing. Green Fees not confirmed. Prof Don Wallace Course Designer McKenzie Facilities ⊗ ⽊ ♿ ▼ ♀ ♨ 🏠 🍴 ⛳ Location 2m W in Salthill
....
Hotel ★★★ 60% Lochlurgain Hotel, 22 Monksfield, Upper Salthill, GALWAY ☎ 091 529595 13 en suite

Glenlo Abbey Bushypark ☎ 091 526666 📠 091 527800
e-mail: glenlo@iol.ie
A parkland course overlooking the magnificent Lough Corrib but only 10 minutes from the centre of Galway city. Nine fairways but large double green with two flags and four tee postions allows 18 different holes. The par 3, 4th hole is on an island-like green extending into the lough.
9 holes, 6009mtrs, Par 71, SSS 71.
Club membership 100.
Societies telephone in advance. Green Fees not confirmed. Cards ⊟ ▦ ▦ 🔢 Prof Philip Murray & Bill Daly Course Designer Jeff Howes Facilities ⊗ ⽊ ♿ ▼ ♀ ♨ 🏠 🍴 🏹 ⛳ ⚑ Leisure fishing, clay pigeon shooting. Location On N59 Galway/Clifden road 4km from Galway City Centre
....
Hotel ★★★★♨ Glenlo Abbey Hotel, Bushypark, GALWAY ☎ 091 526666 46 en suite

GORT
Map 01 B3

Gort Kilmacduagh Rd, Castlequarter
☎ 091 632244 📠 091 632387
e-mail: gortgolf@tinet.ie
Replacing the original 9-hole course, this new 18-hole course, opened in June 1996, offers golfers a real challenge. The 564yd 9th and the 516yd 17th are played into a prevailing wind and the par 4 dog-leg 7th will test the best.
18 holes, 5705mtrs, Par 71, SSS 69.
Club membership 1060.
Visitors advisable to telephone in advance. Sun am reserved for members. Societies apply in writing or telephone. Green Fees not confirmed. Cards ⊟ ▦ Course Designer Christy O'Connor Jnr Facilities ⊗ by prior arrangement ⽊ by prior arrangement ♿ ▼ ♀ ♨ 🏠 🍴 🏹 ⛳ ⚑
....
Hotel ★★★ 65% Galway Ryan Hotel, Dublin Rd, GALWAY ☎ 091 753181 96 en suite

LOUGHREA
Map 01 B3

Loughrea Bullaun Rd, Graigue
☎ 091 841049 📠 091 847472
18 holes, 5261metres, Par 69, SSS 67, Course record 68.
Course Designer Eddie Hackett
Telephone for further details
....
Hotel ★★★ 64% Haydens Gateway Business & Leisure Hotel, BALLINASLOE ☎ 065 68 23000 48 en suite

MOUNTBELLEW
Map 01 B4

Mountbellew Ballinasloe
☎ 0905 79259 📠 0905 79274
A 9-hole wooded parkland course with two quarries and penalty drains to provide hazards.
9 holes, 5143mtrs, Par 69, SSS 66.
Club membership 400.
Visitors welcome. Contact club if you wish to play at weekends. Societies by prior arrangement. Green Fees terms on application. Facilities ♿ ▼ ♀ ♨ ⛳ ⚑ Location Of N63 midway between Roscommon/Galway
....
Hotel ★★★ 64% Haydens Gateway Business & Leisure Hotel, BALLINASLOE ☎ 065 68 23000 48 en suite

ORANMORE
Map 01 B3

Athenry Palmerstown ☎ 091 794466 📠 091 794971
e-mail: athenrygc@eircom.net
A mixture of parkland and heathland built on a limestone base against the backdrop of a large pine forest. The par 3 holes are notable with a feature hole at the 12th - from an elevated tee played between beech and pine trees.
18 holes, 5687metres, Par 70, SSS 70, Course record 67.
Club membership 1000.
Visitors advisable to telephone in advance, may not play Sun or Sat am. Societies must apply in writing,telephone,e-mail. Green Fees €26(€32 weekends).reductions in winter. Cards ⊟ ▦ Prof Raymond Ryan Course Designer Eddie Hackett Facilities ⊗ ⽊ ♿ ▼ ♀ ♨ 🏠 🍴 🏹 ⛳ ⚑ Location On R348 to Athenry 10km E of Galway City
....
Hotel ★★★ 65% Galway Ryan Hotel, Dublin Rd, GALWAY ☎ 091 753181 96 en suite

AA website: www.theAA.com

Where to stay, where to eat?
Visit www.theAA.com

Galway Bay Golf & Country Club Renville
☎ 091 790503 📠 091 792510
e-mail: gbaygolf@iol.ie
A championship golf course surrounded on three sides by the Atlantic Ocean and featuring water hazards on a number of holes. Each hole has its own characteristics made more obvious by the everchanging seaside winds. The design of the course highlights and preserves the ancient historic features of the Renville Peninsula. A spectacular setting distractingly beautiful and cleverly designed mix of holes presents a real golfing challenge, demanding total concentration.
18 holes, 6091mtrs, Par 72, SSS 73, Course record 68.
Club membership 260.
Visitors Contact in advance. Societies Telephone in advance. Green Fees €65. Cards ⚏ ■■ ⚏ ⚏ Prof Eugene O'Connor Course Designer Christy O'Connor Jnr Facilities ⊗ ⋔ ⅃ ⅃ ♀ ⌂ 🏐 🤾 ♘ ⚑
Leisure sauna. Location N18 S towards Limerick/ Shannon, turn right for Oranmore at rdbt, through village, follow signs
· ·
Hotel ★★★ 58% Victoria Hotel, Victoria Place, Eyre Square, GALWAY ☎ 091 567433 57 en suite

Oughterard ☎ 091 552131 📠 091 552377
e-mail: golfough@iol.ie
Redesigned in 1998 to USPGA standard, incorporating natural woodland and water features.
18 holes, 6660yds, Par 70, SSS 69, Course record 67.
Club membership 1000.
Visitors contact secretary or professional in advance. Societies must apply in writing. Green Fees not confirmed. Cards ⚏ ■■ ⚏ Prof Michael Ryan Course Designer P Merrigan Facilities ⊗ ⋔ ⅃ ♀ ⌂ 🏐 🤾 ♘ ⚑
Location 1m from Oughterard on N59 from Galway
· ·
Hotel ★★★ 69% Ross Lake House Hotel, Rosscahill, OUGHTERARD ☎ 091 550109 & 550154
📠 091 550184 13 en suite

Portumna ☎ 0509 41059 📠 0509 41798
Parkland course with mature trees.
18 holes, 6225mtrs, Par 72, SSS 71.
Club membership 800.
Visitors restricted Sat, no green fees Sunday . Societies must contact in writing. Green Fees €25 per day. Prof Richard Clarke Course Designer E Connaughton Facilities ⊗ ⋔ ⅃ ♀ ⌂ 🏐 🤾 ♘ ⚑ Location 2.5m from town on Woodford/Ennis road
· ·
Hotel ★★★ 61% County Arms Hotel, BIRR
☎ 0509 20791 24 en suite

Renvyle House Hotel
☎ 095 43511 📠 43515
e-mail: renvyle@iol.ie
Pebble Beach course at Renvyle House is an exceptionally demanding 9 hole course. Exposed to Atlantic winds, crosswinds are a regular feature. A lake comes into play on 3 holes on one of which is a drive over water. On 4 holes pebble beach and the sea demand precision.
continued

Pebble Beach: 9 holes, 3500yds, Par 36, Course record 34.
Club membership 250.
Visitors Must contact in advance. Societies Telephone in advance. Green Fees not confirmed. Cards ⚏ ■■ ⚏ ⚏
Facilities ⊗ ⋔ ⅃ ♀ ⌂ 🏐 🤾 ⚑ Leisure hard tennis courts, heated outdoor swimming pool, fishing. Location From N59 West, right into Recess, left at Kylemore, right at Letterfrack, proceed for 5m
· ·
Hotel ★★★ 68% Renvyle House Hotel, RENVYLE
☎ 095 43511 65 en suite

Tuam Barnacurragh ☎ 093 28993 📠 093 26003
Parkland course with plenty of trees and bunkers.
18 holes, 5513mtrs, Par 72, SSS 69.
Club membership 800.
Visitors preferred Mon-Fri, must contact in advance. No visitors weekends. Societies telephone/write in advance. Green Fees terms on application. Prof Larry Smyth Course Designer Eddie Hackett Facilities ⊗ ⋔ ⅃ ♀ ⌂ 🏐 🤾 ♘ ⚑ Location 0.5m from town on Athenry road
· ·
Hotel ★★★ 65% Galway Ryan Hotel, Dublin Rd, GALWAY ☎ 091 753181 96 en suite

CO KERRY

Ceann Sibeal ☎ 066 9156255 📠 066 9156409
e-mail: dinglegc@iol.ie
This most westerly golf course in Europe has a magnificent scenic location. It is a traditional links course with beautiful turf, many bunkers, a stream that comes into play on 14 holes and, usually, a prevailing wind.
18 holes, 6700yds, Par 72, SSS 71, Course record 72.
Club membership 432.
Visitors telephone in advance. Societies must contact in advance. Green Fees from €40 per round;from €60 per day(€45/€60 weekends)reductions in winter. Cards ⚏ ■■ Prof Dermot O'Connor Course Designer Hackett/O'Connor Jnr Facilities ⊗ ⋔ ⅃ ♀ ⌂ 🏐 🤾 ⚑ Leisure buggies for hire May-Oct. Location 1.5m from Ballyferriter
· ·
Hotel ★★★ 72% Dingle Skellig Hotel, DINGLE
☎ 066 9150200 112 en suite

Castlegregory Stradbally ☎ 066 7139444
A links course sandwiched between the sea and a freshwater lake and mountains on two sides. The 3rd hole is visually superb with a 365yard drive into the wind.
9 holes, 2569mtrs, Par 68, SSS 68, Course record 67.
Club membership 350.
Visitors advisable to contact in advance. Societies apply in advance. Green Fees €25 per 18 holes. Course Designer Dr Arthur Spring Facilities ⅃ ⅃ ♀ ⌂ 🤾 ⚑ Leisure fishing. Location On Main Tralee/Castlegregory/Conor-pass road
· ·
Hotel ★★★ 64% Abbey Gate Hotel, Maine St, TRALEE
☎ 066 7129888 100 en suite

Looking for a driving range?
See the index at the back of the guide

Ballybunion

Ballybunion, *Co Kerry* ☎ 068 27146 Fax 068 27387 Map 01 A3

e-mail: bbgolfgc@ioe.ie

Hailed for its excellent links courses, Ballybunion is recognised for its fine development of the natural terrain. Mr Murphy built the Old Course in 1906. With large sand dunes and an Atlantic backdrop, Ballybunion offers the golfer an exciting round of golf in a scenic location but be warned, the Old Course is difficult to play in the wind. President Clinton played Ballybunion on his historic visit to Ireland in 1998.

Although overshadowed by the Old Course, the Cashen Course designed by Robert Trent Jones is also world class. Narrow fairways, small greens and large dunes characterise the course.

Visitors must contact in advance for reservations and details, subject to availability.

Societies apply in advance

Green Fees Old Course €110 per round, Cashen Course €75 per round Both courses same day €135

Facilities ⊗ ⅂ ⌸ ⌸ ⌸ ⌸ ⌸ ⌸ ⌸ ⌸
Professional (Brian O'Callaghan)

Location Sandhill Rd, Ballybunion (20 miles N of Tralee).

Holes/Par/Course record 36 holes.
Old Course: 18 holes, 6603 yds, Par 71, SSS 72, Course record 67
Cashen Course: 18 holes, 6216 yds, Par 72, SSS 71, Course record 69

Championship Course

WHERE TO STAY NEARBY

Hotels
BALLYHEIGE

★★★◉ 65% The White Sands
☎ 066 7133102. 81 en suite

TRALEE

★★★ 69% Meadowlands Hotel
☎ 066 7180444. 27 en suite

★★★ 64% Abbey Gate, Maine St.
☎ 066 7129888. 100 en suite

GLENBEIGH   Map 01 A2

Dooks ☎ 066 9768205 🖷 066 9768476
e-mail: office@dooks.com
**Old-established course on the sea shore between the
Kerry mountains and Dingle Bay. Sand dunes are a
feature (the name Dooks is a derivation of the Gaelic
word for sand bank) and the course offers a fine
challenge in a superb Ring of Kerry location.**
18 holes, 6071yds, Par 70, SSS 68.
Club membership 800.
Visitors must contact in advance. Members time reserved.
Societies contact in advance. **Green Fees** €40 per
round; €55 per day. **Cards** 🖃 ▦ ▦ 🖳 **Course
Designer** Members/D Steel **Facilities** ⊗ ⪫ ⬚ ♚ ♨ ♀ ♨
🖾 ♕ ✐ **Location** On N70, between Killorglin and
Glenbeigh

Hotel ★★★ 69% Gleneagle Hotel, KILLARNEY
☎ 064 36000 250 en suite

KENMARE   Map 01 B2

Kenmare Kilgarvan Rd ☎ 064 41291 🖷 064 42061
18 holes, 5615yds, Par 71.
Course Designer Eddie Hackett
Telephone for further details

Hotel ★★★★⚏ Park Hotel Kenmare, KENMARE
☎ 064 41200 49 en suite

KILLARNEY   Map 01 B2

Beaufort Churchtown, Beaufort
☎ 064 44440 🖷 064 44752
e-mail: beaufortgc@eircom.net
**A championship standard par 71 parkland course
designed by Dr Arthur Spring. This relatively new course
is in the centre of south-west Ireland's golfing mecca. Old
ruins of an 11th century castle dominate the back nine
and the whole course is overlooked by the MacGillycuddy
Reeks. The par 3 8th and par 4 11th are two of the most
memorable holes.**

18 holes, 6587yds, Par 71, SSS 72, Course record 70.
Club membership 350.
Visitors booking advisable for weekends. **Societies** advance
booking essential. **Green Fees** €45(€55 weekends). **Cards**
🖃 ▦ ▦ **Prof** Hugh Duggan **Course Designer** Arthur
Spring **Facilities** ⊗ ⪫ ⬚ ♚ ♨ ♀ ♨ 🖾 ♕ ♠ ♨ ✐ **Location**
7m W of Killarney, off N72 w

Hotel ★★★ 68% Castlerosse Hotel, KILLARNEY
☎ 064 31144 121 en suite

AA website: www.theAA.com

Killarney Golf & Fishing Club Mahony's Point
☎ 064 31034 🖷 064 33065
e-mail: kgc@iol.ie or reservations@killarney-golf.com
**The three courses are parkland with tree-lined fairways,
many bunkers and small lakes which provide no mean
challenge. Mahoney's Point Course has a particularly
testing par 5, 4, 3 finish and the courses call for great skill
from the tee. Killarney has been the venue for many
important events, including the 1996 Curtis Cup, and is a
favourite of many famous golfers.**
*Mahony's Point: 18 holes, 5826mtrs, Par 72, SSS 72,
Course record 64.*
*Killeen: 18 holes, 6001mtrs, Par 72, SSS 72,
Course record 68.*
Lackabane: 18 holes, 6011mtrs, Par 72, SSS 72.
Club membership 1300.
Visitors must contact in advance & have a handicap
certificate. **Societies** must telephone in advance/apply in
writing. **Green Fees** terms on application. **Cards** 🖃 ▦ ▦
🖳 **Prof** Tony Coveney **Course Designer** H Longhurst/Sir
Guy Campbell **Facilities** ⊗ ⪫ ⬚ ♚ ♨ ♀ ♨ 🖾 ♕ ✐
Leisure sauna, gymnasium. **Location** On N 72, Ring of
Kerry road

Hotel ★★★★ 79% Aghadoe Heights Hotel, KILLARNEY
☎ 064 31766 69 en suite

KILLORGLIN   Map 01 A2

Killorglin Stealroe ☎ 066 9761979 🖷 066 9761437
e-mail: kilgolf@iol.ie
**A parkland course designed by Eddie Hackett as a
challenging but fair test of golf, surrounded by
magnificent views.**
18 holes, 6497yds, Par 72, SSS 71, Course record 68.
Club membership 510.
Visitors pre booking of tee time advisable, must be
confirmed in writing. Deposit required for groups. **Societies**
book by telephone, confirm in writing. **Green Fees** €23 per
18 holes (€26 weekends). **Cards** 🖃 ▦ ▦ 🖳 **Course
Designer** Eddie Hackett **Facilities** ⊗ ⪫ ⬚ ♚ ♨ ♀ ♨ 🖾 ♕
♨ ✐ **Leisure** fishing. **Location** 3km from Killorglin, on
N70 to Tralee

Guesthouse ♦♦♦♦ The Grove Lodge, Killarney Rd,
KILLORGLIN ☎ 066 9761157 10 en suite

PARKNASILLA   Map 01 A2

Parknasilla ☎ 064 45122 🖷 064 45323
9 holes, 5400mtrs, Par 70, SSS 69.
Course Designer Arthur Spring **Location** 2m E of Sneem
village on Ring of Kerry road

Telephone for further details

Hotel ★★★★ 79% Great Southern Hotel, PARKNASILLA
☎ 064 45122 24 en suite 59 annexe en suite

TRALEE
Map 01 A2

Tralee West Barrow ☎ 066 7136379 🖺 066 7136008
e-mail: info@traleegolfclub.com
The first Arnold Palmer designed course in Europe, the magnificent 18-hole links are set in spectacular scenery on the Barrow peninsula surrounded on three sides by the sea. Perhaps the most memorable hole is the par four 17th which plays from a high tee, across a deep gorge to a green perched high against a backdrop of mountains. The back 9 are very difficult and challenging. Not suitable for beginners.
18 holes, 5939mtrs, Par 71, SSS 71, Course record 66.
Club membership 1190.
Visitors may play before 4.20pm on weekdays but only between 7.30-10.30am on Wed & 11am-1.30pm on Sat & 11.30-1pm bank holidays. Must have a handicap certificate and contact in advance. May not play Sun. **Societies** weekdays only; must contact in writing. **Green Fees** €110 per round. **Cards** 🖃 💳 💳 **Prof** David Power **Course Designer** Arnold Palmer **Facilities** ⊗ ⅶ 🖪 💄 ♀ ♨ 🖆 ☈ ⁄ **Location** 8m NW of Tralee off Spa-Fenit Road

Hotel ★★★ 69% Meadowlands Hotel, Oakpark, TRALEE ☎ 066 7180444 27 en suite

WATERVILLE
Map 01 A2

Waterville House & Golf Links
☎ 066 9474102 🖺 066 9474482
e-mail: wvgolf@iol.ie
On the western tip of the Ring of Kerry, this course is highly regarded by many top golfers. The feature holes are the par five 11th, which runs along a rugged valley between towering dunes, and the par three 17th, which features an exceptionally elevated tee. Needless to say, the surroundings are beautiful.
18 holes, 6549yds, Par 72, SSS 72, Course record 65.
Visitors must contact in advance. **Societies** must contact secretary/manager in advance. **Green Fees** not confirmed. **Cards** 🖃 💳 💳 **Prof** Liam Higgins **Course Designer** Eddie Hackett **Facilities** ⊗ ⅶ 🖪 💄 ♀ ♨ 🖆 ☈ 🖅 ⁄ **Leisure** heated outdoor swimming pool, fishing, sauna.

Hotel ★★★ 75% Butler Arms Hotel, WATERVILLE ☎ 066 9474144 40 en suite

CO KILDARE

ATHY
Map 01 C3

Athy Geraldine ☎ 0507 31729 🖺 0507 34710
e-mail: info@athygolfclub.com
A meadowland course approaching its centenary year having been founded in 1906.
18 holes, 6159yds, Par 71, SSS 69, Course record 69.
Club membership 700.
Visitors advisable to call in advance, no green fees on Sundays **Societies** contact for infromation. **Green Fees** €20 per 18 holes (€30 weekends and bank holidays). **Facilities** ⊗ ⅶ by prior arrangement 🖪 💄 ♀ ♨ ⁄ **Location** 1m N of Athy on Kildare road

Guesthouse ◆◆◆◆◆ Courestown Country House, Stradbally Rd, ATHY ☎ 0507 31101 5 en suite

CARBURY
Map 01 C4

Highfield Highfield House
☎ 0405 31021 🖺 0405 31021
e-mail: hgc@indigo.ie
A relatively flat parkland course but with interesting undulations, especially by the fast flowing stream which runs through many holes. The 7th doglegs over the lake, the 10th is a great par 5 with a challenging green, the 14th par 3 is over rushes onto a plateau green (out of bounds on left) and the 18th par 3 green is tucked between bunkers and a huge chestnut tree.
18 holes, 5707mtrs, Par 72, SSS 69.
Club membership 500.
Visitors welcome, must contact in advance for weekend play. **Societies** telephone or apply in writing. **Green Fees** €20 (€30 weekends). **Cards** 🖃 💳 💳 **Prof** Peter O'Hagan **Course Designer** Alan Duggan **Facilities** 🖪 💄 ♀ ♨ 🖆 ☈ ⁄ ☈ **Location** take M4 from Dublin, situated 9m S of Enfield

Hotel ★★★ 74% Keadeen Hotel, NEWBRIDGE ☎ 045 431666 55 en suite

CASTLEDERMOT
Map 01 C3

Kilkea Castle ☎ 0503 45555 🖺 0503 45505
e-mail: kilkeagolfclub@eircom.net
A beautiful course in the grounds of a 12th-century castle - visible from all over the course. The River Griese and two lakes create numerous water hazards. The 16th and 17th are considered to be two of the best parkland holes in the country.

18 holes, 6200mtrs, Par 71, SSS 71.
Club membership 230.
Visitors must contact in advance for details. **Societies** welcome, contact for details. **Green Fees** not confirmed. **Cards** 🖃 💳 💳 💳 **Facilities** 💄 🖆 ☈ ⁄ **Leisure** hard tennis courts, heated indoor swimming pool, fishing, sauna, solarium, gymnasium.

Hotel ★★★ 68% Seven Oaks Hotel, Athy Rd, CARLOW ☎ 0503 31308 60 en suite

DONADEA
Map 01 C4

Knockanally Golf & Country Club
☎ 045 869322 🖺 045 869322
e-mail: golf@knockanally.com
Home of the Irish International Professional Matchplay championship, this parkland course is set in a former estate, with a Palladian-style clubhouse.
18 holes, 6485yds, Par 72, SSS 72, Course record 66.
Club membership 500.
Visitors may not play on Sun 8.30am-noon. **Societies** must contact in writing or telephone. **Green Fees** terms on *continued*

application. **Prof** Martin Darcy **Course Designer** Noel Lyons **Facilities** ⊗ ⊪ ⅃ ▮ ♀ ⚐ ⌂ ⚑ ⚑ ✓ **Leisure** fishing. **Location** 3m off main Dublin-Galway road between Kilcock & Enfield

Hotel ★★★ 64% Lucan Spa Hotel, LUCAN ☎ 01 6280495 & 6280497 ◨ 01 6280841 71 rms (61 en suite)

KILDARE   Map 01 C3

Cill Dara Cill Dara, Little Curragh
☎ 045 521295 & 521433
e-mail: cilldaragolfclub@ireland.com
Only 1 mile from the famous Curragh racecourse, this 9-hole parkland course is unusual in having links type soil as well as plenty of trees.
9 holes, 5852mtrs, Par 71, SSS 70, Course record 64.
Club membership 500.
Visitors welcome, Wed is Ladies Day and may only play after 1.30pm Sun (winter) and 4pm Sun (Summer). **Societies** apply in writing to Mr M O'Boyle, Professional. **Green Fees** €20(€25 weekends). **Prof** Mark O'Boyle **Facilities** ⊗ ⊪ ▯ ▮ ♀ ⚐ ⌂ ⚑ ✓ **Leisure** snooker room, darts and pool room. **Location** 1m E of Kildare

Hotel ★★★ 74% Keadeen Hotel, NEWBRIDGE ☎ 045 431666 55 en suite

The Curragh Curragh
☎ 045 441238 & 441714 ◨ 045 441714
A particularly challenging course, well wooded and with lovely scenery all around.
18 holes, 6035mtrs, Par 72, SSS 71, Course record 63.
Club membership 1040.
Visitors must contact in advance, preferred on Mon, Wed, Thu & Fri. **Societies** apply in writing. **Green Fees** not confirmed. **Prof** Gerry Burke **Facilities** ⊗ ⊪ ▯ ▮ ♀ ⚐ ⌂ ⚑ ✓ **Location** Off N7 between Newbridge & Kildare

Hotel ★★★ 74% Keadeen Hotel, NEWBRIDGE ☎ 045 431666 55 en suite

KILL   Map 01 D4

Killeen ☎ 045 866003 ◨ 045 875881
e-mail: admin@killeengc.ie
Set in pleasant countryside, the attractive course is characterised by its many lakes. It provides a challenge to test the skills of the moderate enthusiast and the more experienced golfer.
18 holes, 5561mtrs, Par 71, SSS 71, Course record 70.
Club membership 170.
Visitors please ring for tee-times **Societies** must contact in advance. **Green Fees** €26Mon-Thur;€28 Fri;€32 weekends(€13 per 9 holes). **Cards** ▤ ▢ **Course Designer** Pat Ruddy/M Kelly **Facilities** ⊗ ⊪ ▯ ▮ ♀ ⚐ ⌂ ⚑ ✓ **Location** Off N7 at Kill signposted

Hotel ★★★ 76% Barberstown Castle, STRAFFAN ☎ 01 6288157 22 en suite

NAAS   Map 01 D4

Bodenstown Sallins ☎ 045 897096
Bodenstown: 18 holes, 6132mtrs, Par 71, SSS 71.
Ladyhill: 18 holes, 5428mtrs, Par 71, SSS 68.
Course Designer Richard Mather **Location** 4m from town near Bodenstown graveyard
Telephone for further details

Hotel ★★★ 66% Downshire House Hotel, BLESSINGTON ☎ 045 865199 14 en suite 11 annexe en suite

Craddockstown Blessington Rd
☎ 045 897610 ◨ 045 896968
A gradually maturing parkland course featuring four testing par 3 holes, all over 140 metres in length, sand-based greens, and many trees. Easy walking.
18 holes, 5726mtrs, Par 71, SSS 69, Course record 66.
Club membership 800.
Visitors should ring in advance to verify tee times available, limited at weekends. **Societies** apply in writing. **Green Fees** terms on application. **Cards** ▤ **Course Designer** A Spring **Facilities** ⊗ ⊪ ▯ ▮ ♀ ⚐ ✓ **Location** Off the main dual carriageway (N7/N97), head towards Naas, turn left on to Blessington Road

Hotel ★★★ 63% Ambassador Hotel, KILL ☎ 045 886700 & 877064 ◨ 045 877515 36 en suite

Naas Kerdiffstown
☎ 045 897509 & 874644 ◨ 045 896109
Scenic parkland course well bunkered, with a substantial number of trees, greens are both sand based and natural.
18 holes, 5663mtrs, Par 71, SSS 69, Course record 65.
Club membership 1000.
Visitors may not play on Sun, Tue or Thu. **Societies** must contact in advance by telephone. **Green Fees** €27 (€35 weekends). **Cards** ▤ ▤ **Course Designer** E Hackett/A Spring **Facilities** ⊗ ⊪ ▯ ▮ ♀ ⚐ ✓ **Location** 1m from town on Sallins-Johnstown road

Hotel ★★★ 66% Downshire House Hotel, BLESSINGTON ☎ 045 865199 14 en suite 11 annexe en suite

Woodlands Cooleragh, Coill Dubh
☎ 045 860777 ◨ 045 860988
9 holes, 6408yds, Par 72, SSS 71.
Course Designer Tommy Halpin **Location** Off the Clane/Edenderry road
Telephone for further details

Hotel ★★★ 74% Keadeen Hotel, NEWBRIDGE ☎ 045 431666 55 en suite

STRAFFAN   Map 01 D4

Castlewarden
☎ 01 4589254 & 4589838 ◨ 01 458897
e-mail: castlewarden@clubi.ie
Founded in 1990, Castlewarden is maturing into a delightful parkland course with water features and excellent greens.
18 holes, 6496yds, Par 72, SSS 70.
Club membership 765.
Visitors welcome contact for details. Tues Ladies Day. **Societies** by prior application. **Green Fees** terms on application. **Prof** Gerry Egan **Course Designer** Tommy Halpin **Facilities** ⊗ ⊪ ▯ ▮ ♀ ⚐ ⌂ ⚑ ✓ **Location** Between Naas/Rathcoole

Hotel ★★★ 63% Ambassador Hotel, KILL ☎ 045 886700 & 877064 ◨ 045 877515 36 en suite

The K Club ☎ 01 6017300 ◨ 01 6017399
e-mail: golf@kclub.ie
Designed by Arnold Palmer, its 6,456 metre length is a challenge to even the best golfers. Covering 177 acres of prime Kildare woodland there are 14 man-made lakes as well as the River Liffey to create water hazards. There is the promise of a watery

continued on page 420

Mount Juliet

Mount Juliet, *Co Kilkenny*   ☎ 056 73000   Fax 056 73019   Map 01 C3

e-mail: info@mountjuliet.ie

Venue for the American Express World Golf Championships in September 2002, Mount Juliet's superb 18-hole golf course was designed by Jack Nicklaus, and has also been the chosen venue for many prestigious golfing events including the Irish Open on three occasions. The course boasts a cleverly concealed drainage and irrigation system, perfect even when inclement weather would otherwise preclude play, and takes advantage of the estate's mature landscape to provide a world-class 72-par challenge for professionals and high-handicap golfers alike. A unique three-hole golf academy has been added to offer both novice and experienced players ample opportunity to improve their games, while a new 18-hole putting course provides an extra dimension of golfing pleasure, and is the venue for the National Putting Championships.

Visitors welcome, no restrictions but preferable to contact in advance

Societies book in advance by telephone or in writing

Green Fees €70 - €150 depending on season. Discounts for groups and hotel residents.

Facilities
Conf Thtr 75; Class 40; Board 30; Banquet 70. Del max €65. Professional (Ted Higgins)

Leisure tennis, indoor swimming pool, private fishing, sauna, solarium, gym, horse riding, clay target shooting, archery

Location Thomastown (N9, Dublin/Waterford Rd).

Holes/Par/Course record 18 holes, 6641 yds, Par 72, SSS 72, Course record 65

Championship Course

WHERE TO STAY NEARBY

Hotels
THOMASTOWN
★★★★◎◎ ♨ Mount Juliet Hotel
☎ 056 73000. 32 en suite 27 annexe en suite

KILKENNY
★★★64% Langton House
☎ 056 65133. 10 en suite 16 annexe en suite

★★★71% New Park Hotel
☎ 056 22122. 111 en suite

grave at the monster 7th (par 5, 520 metres) and at the 17th the tee shot is to the green on the water's edge. There is also a practise area and driving range.
18 holes, 6163mtrs, Par 72, SSS 72, Course record 60. Club membership 540.

The K Club

Visitors contact in advance to book prefered tee times, restricted at members times. **Societies** telephone & write in advance, societies not allowed on weekends & Wed afternoon. **Green Fees** terms on application. **Cards** 📶 💷 🖼 **Prof** Ernie Jones **Course Designer** Arnold Palmer **Facilities** ⊗ 🍴 🛍 💺 🎱 🏊 🍽 🏌 🛥 🚪 ⛳ 🏇 **Leisure** hard tennis courts, heated indoor swimming pool, squash, fishing, sauna, solarium, gymnasium. **Conf** Max 160 Banquet 160 **Location** From Dublin take N4 and exit R406, entrance to hotel on right in Straffan

Hotel ★★★★★⭐⭐ The Kildare Hotel & Golf Club, STRAFFAN ☎ 01 6017200
69 en suite 10 annexe en suite

CO KILKENNY

CALLAN
Map 01 C3

Callan Geraldine ☎ 056 25136 & 25949 🖨 056 55155
e-mail: info@callangolfclub.com
Meadowland course with well positioned spinneys and water hazards. Not difficult walking and a good test for golfers of all standards.
18 holes, 6422yds, Par 72, SSS 70, Course record 66. Club membership 800.
Visitors contact in advance. **Societies** must apply in writing. **Green Fees** €25. **Cards** 📶 💷 🖼 **Prof** John O'Dwyer **Course Designer** B Moore/J Power **Facilities** ⊗ 🍴 🛍 💺 🎱 🍽 🏌 🛥 🚪 ⛳ **Leisure** fishing. **Location** 1m from Callan on the Knocktopher Road

Hotel ★★★ 71% Newpark Hotel, KILKENNY
☎ 056 60500 111 en suite

KILKENNY
Map 01 C3

Kilkenny Glendine ☎ 056 65400 🖨 056 23593
e-mail: kilkennygc@eircom.net
One of Ireland's most pleasant inland courses, noted for its tricky finishing holes and its par threes. Features of the course are its long 11th and 13th holes and the challenge increases year by year as thousands of trees planted over the last 30 years or so are maturing. As host of the Kilkenny Scratch Cup annually, the course is permanently maintained in championship condition. The Irish Dunlop

continued

Tournament and the Irish Professional Matchplay Championship have also been held here.
18 holes, 5925mtrs, Par 71, SSS 70, Course record 68. Club membership 1200.
Visitors must contact in advance. **Societies** must contact in advance. **Green Fees** €35 per 18 holes(€40 weekends & bank holidays). **Cards** 📶 💷 **Prof** Jimmy Bolger **Facilities** ⊗ 🍴 🛍 💺 🎱 🏊 🍽 🏌 🛥 🚪 ⛳ 🏇 **Location** 1m from centre on Castlecomer road

Hotel ★★★ 64% Langton House, 69 John St, KILKENNY ☎ 056 65133 10 en suite 16 annexe en suite

THOMASTOWN See page 419
Map 01 C3

CO LAOIS

ABBEYLEIX
Map 01 C3

Abbeyleix Rathmoyle ☎ 0502 31450 🖨 0502 30108
A pleasant, parkland 9 hole course.
18 holes, 5557mtrs, Par 72, SSS 70. Club membership 470.
Visitors welcome weekdays. **Societies** apply in writing. **Green Fees** €17 per round(€22 weekends). **Course Designer** Mel Flanagan **Facilities** ⊗ 🛍 💺 🎱 ⛳ **Location** 0.4m outside town of Abbeyleix on Ballyroaw road

Hotel ★★★ 71% Newpark Hotel, KILKENNY
☎ 056 60500 111 en suite

MOUNTRATH
Map 01 C3

Mountrath Knockanina ☎ 0502 32558 & 32643 (office) 🖨 0502 32643
A picturesque course at the foot of the Slieve Bloom Mountains in central Ireland. The 18 hole course has fine fairways and well bunkered greens, the River Nore flows through the course.
18 holes, 5493mtrs, Par 71, SSS 69, Course record 68. Club membership 800.
Visitors check for availability at weekends, other days no problem but safer to check. **Societies** must contact in advance. **Green Fees** terms on application. **Facilities** ⊗ by prior arrangement 🛍 💺 🎱 🚪 ⛳ **Location** 1.5m from town on Dublin-Limerick road

Hotel ★★★ 74% Keadeen Hotel, NEWBRIDGE
☎ 045 431666 55 en suite

PORTARLINGTON
Map 01 C3

Portarlington Garryhinch
☎ 0502 23115 🖨 0502 23044
e-mail: portalingtongc@eircom.net
Lovely parkland course designed around a pine forest. It is bounded on the 16th and 17th by the River Barrow which makes the back 9 very challenging.
18 holes, 5723mtrs, Par 71, SSS 70, Course record 66. Club membership 562.
Visitors welcome but restricted Tue-Ladies Day, Sat & Sun societies and club competitions. Must contact in advance **Societies** must apply in writing. **Green Fees** €20 per round(€25 weekends). **Cards** 📶 💷 **Course Designer** Eddie Hackett **Facilities** ⊗ 🍴 🛍 💺 🎱 🚪 ⛳ **Location** 4m from town on Mountmellick road

Hotel ★★★ 74% Keadeen Hotel, NEWBRIDGE
☎ 045 431666 55 en suite

PORTLAOISE   Map 01 C3

The Heath
☎ 0502 46533 & 46622 (Pro shop) 🖹 0502 46866
One of the oldest clubs in Ireland. The course is set in pretty countryside and offers a good challenge.
18 holes, 5736mtrs, Par 71, SSS 69, Course record 69.
Club membership 800.
Visitors contact in advance, preferred on weekdays. **Societies** apply in writing to Pat Malone **Green Fees** €13 weekdays (€26 weekends and bank holidays). **Prof** Eddie Doyle **Facilities** ⊗ ⊮ ⊾ ♥ ♀ ♨ ⬚ ↘ ♂ ⌇ **Location** 3m N on N7

Hotel ★★★ 74% Keadeen Hotel, NEWBRIDGE
☎ 045 431666 55 en suite

RATHDOWNEY   Map 01 C3

Rathdowney ☎ 0505 46170 🖹 0505 46065
An 18 hole course, recently opened. Undulating terrain, 17th hole is a tricky par 3, 12th and 15th are particularly tough par 4s, 6th is a challenging par 5 (550yds) into the prevailing wind. A good test for golfers of all abilities.
18 holes, 5894mtrs, Par 71, SSS 70, Course record 67.
Club membership 400.
Visitors welcome. Ladies have priority on Wed, Sat & Sun mornings are reserved for member & societies. **Societies** must apply in writing and pay deposit to confirm booking. **Green Fees** €20(€25 weekends). **Course Designer** Eddie Hackett **Facilities** ⊗ by prior arrangement ⊾ ♥ ♀ ♨ ⬚ ♂ **Location** 0.5m SE. Follow signs from town square

Hotel ★★★ 71% Newpark Hotel, KILKENNY
☎ 056 60500 111 en suite

CO LEITRIM

BALLINAMORE   Map 01 C4

Ballinamore ☎ 087 7673471
A very dry and very testing 9-hole parkland course along the Ballinamore/Ballyconnell Canal.
9 holes, 5680yds, Par 68, SSS 66, Course record 66.
Club membership 300.
Visitors welcome 6 days per week, competition on most Sundays. Visitors welcome to play in open competitions. **Societies** must contact in writing or telephone secretary. **Green Fees** €15 per day. **Course Designer** A Spring **Facilities** ♥ ♀ ♨ **Leisure** fishing. **Location** 2m from Ballinamore, along Shannon-Erne water-way canal

Hotel ★★★★ 67% Slieve Russell Hotel Golf and Country Club, BALLYCONNELL ☎ 049 9526 444 159 en suite

CARRICK-ON-SHANNON   Map 01 C4

Carrick-on-Shannon Woodbrook ☎ 079 67015
A pleasant 9-hole course overlooking the River Shannon. A fine test of golf for both those with low and high handicaps.
9 holes, 5545mtrs, Par 70, SSS 68.
Club membership 400.
Visitors welcome, contact in advance to avoid competitions. **Societies** must contact in advance. **Green Fees** terms on application. **Course Designer** Eddie Hackett **Facilities** ⊗ ⊮ ⊾ ♥ ♀ ♨ ⬚ ♂ **Location** 4m W beside N4

Hotel ★★★★ 67% Slieve Russell Hotel Golf and Country Club, BALLYCONNELL ☎ 049 9526 444 159 en suite

CO LIMERICK

ADARE   Map 01 B3

Adare Manor ☎ 061 396204 🖹 061 396800
e-mail: brayfab@hotmail.com
An 18-hole parkland course, par 69, in an unusual setting. The course surrounds the ruins of a castle, a friary and an abbey.
18 holes, 5800yds, Par 69, SSS 69.
Club membership 600.
Visitors welcome weekdays, weekends only by arrangement and subject to availability. **Societies** by prior arrangement, preferably in writing. **Green Fees** not confirmed. **Course Designer** Ben Sayers/Eddie Hacket **Facilities** ⊗ ⊮ ⊾ ♥ ♀ ♨ ⬚ ⚑ **Location** 10m from Limerick City

Hotel ★★★ 77% Dunraven Arms Hotel, ADARE
☎ 061 396633 75 en suite

LIMERICK   Map 01 B3

Castletroy Castletroy
☎ 061 335753 & 335261 🖹 061 335373
e-mail: cgc@iol.ie
Parkland course with out of bounds on the left of the first two holes. The long par five 10th features a narrow entrance to a green guarded by a stream. The par three 13th has a panoramic view of the course and surrounding countryside from the tee and the 18th is a daunting finish, with the drive played towards a valley with the ground rising towards the green which is protected on both sides by bunkers. In recent years the club has hosted the finals of the Irish Mixed Foursomes and the Senior Championships.
18 holes, 5802mtrs, Par 71, SSS 71.
Club membership 1062.
Visitors must contact in advance & have handicap certificate but may not play Sun or 1-2.30pm weekdays. **Societies** apply in writing. **Green Fees** not confirmed. **Cards** ▦ **Facilities** ⊗ ⊮ ⊾ ♥ ♀ ♨ ⬚ ⚑ ↘ ♂ ⌇ **Location** 3m from city on Dublin road

Hotel ★★★★ 67% Castletroy Park Hotel, Dublin Rd, LIMERICK ☎ 061 335566 107 en suite

Limerick Ballyclough ☎ 061 415146 🖹 061 319219
e-mail: lgc@eircom.net
Tree-lined parkland course which hosted the 1991 Ladies Senior Interprovincial matches. The club are the only Irish winners of the European Cup Winners Team Championship.
18 holes, 5938mtrs, Par 72, SSS 71, Course record 63.
Club membership 1300.
Visitors may not play after 4pm or on Tue & weekends. **Societies** must contact in writing. **Green Fees** €50. **Cards** ▦ ▦ **Prof** Lee Harrington **Course Designer** A McKenzie **Facilities** ⊗ ⊮ ⊾ ♥ ♀ ♨ ⬚ ⚑ ♂ **Location** 3m S on Fedamore Road

Hotel ★★★ 73% Jurys Hotel, Ennis Rd, LIMERICK
☎ 061 327777 95 en suite

Limerick County Golf & Country Club
Ballyneety ☎ 61 351881 🖹 61 351384
e-mail: lcgolf@ioi.ie
Limerick County was designed by Des Smyth and presents beautifully because of the strategic location of the main features. It stretches over undulating terrain

continued

with one elevated section providing views of the surrounding countryside. It features over 70 bunkers with six lakes and several unique design features.
18 holes, 6712yds, Par 72, SSS 74, Course record 70.
Club membership 400.
Visitors welcome but prebooking essential. **Societies** book by telephone or in writing. **Green Fees** not confirmed. **Cards** 🌐 🔲 💳 💷 **Prof** Donal McSweeney **Course Designer** Des Smyth **Facilities** ⊗ ⅷ ⅃ ☕ 🍽 ♀ ⚐ 🍴 ⚲ 🛄 ⚸ ⚷ **Location** 5m SE of Limerick on R512

....

Hotel ★★★ 64% Greenhills Hotel, Caherdavin, LIMERICK
☎ 061 453033 58 en suite

NEWCASTLE WEST   Map 01 B3

Killeline Cork Rd ☎ 069 61600 🖹 069 77428
e-mail: killeline@eircom.net
Set in 160 acres of gently contoured parkland in the heart of the Golden Vale with views to the Galtee Mountains. Because of its design and many mature trees, accuracy in playing is the key to good scoring.
18 holes, 6671yds, Par 72, SSS 68.
Club membership 200.
Visitors welcome weekdays, by arrangement weekends, must contact in advance **Societies** telephone in advance.
Green Fees not confirmed. **Cards** 🌐 🔲 💳 💷 **Prof** Kevin Dorrian **Facilities** ⊗ ⅷ ⅃ ☕ 🍽 ♀ ⚐ 🍴 ⚸ **Leisure** heated indoor swimming pool, sauna, solarium, gymnasium.
Location 0.25m off main Limerick/Killarney route

....

Hotel ★★★ 77% Dunraven Arms Hotel, ADARE
☎ 061 396633 75 en suite

Newcastle West Ardagh ☎ 069 76500 🖹 069 76511
A new course set in 150 acres of unspoilt countryside, built to the highest standards on sandy free draining soil. A practice ground and driving range are included. Hazards on the course include lakes, bunkers, streams and trees. A signature hole is likely to be the par 3 6th playing 185 yards over a lake.

18 holes, 6317yds, Par 71, SSS 72, Course record 67.
Club membership 730.
Visitors advisable to contact in advance, but available most days. **Societies** contact in advance. **Green Fees** not confirmed. **Cards** 🌐 💳 **Prof** Ger Jones **Course Designer** Dr Arthur Spring **Facilities** ⊗ ⅷ ⅃ ☕ 🍽 ♀ ⚐ 🍴 ⚸ ⚷ **Location** 2m off N21 between Limerick & Killarney

....

Hotel ★★★ 77% Dunraven Arms Hotel, ADARE
☎ 061 396633 75 en suite

Where to stay, where to eat?
Visit www.theAA.com

CO LONGFORD

LONGFORD   Map 01 C4

County Longford Glack, Dublin Rd
☎ 043 46310 🖹 043 47082
e-mail: colonggolf@eircom.net
A lovely 18-hole parkland course with lots of trees.
18 holes, 6044yds, Par 70, SSS 69, Course record 69.
Club membership 819.
Visitors very welcome, but advisable to telephone in advance for Tue and Sun play. **Societies** by prior arrangement. **Green Fees** not confirmed. **Facilities** ⅃ ☕ 💷 ♀ ⚐ 🍴 🛄 ⚷ **Location** E of town

....

Hotel ★★★ 65% Abbey Hotel, Galway Rd,
ROSCOMMON ☎ 0903 26240 & 26505
🖹 0903 26021 25 en suite

CO LOUTH

ARDEE   Map 01 D4

Ardee Townparks ☎ 041 6853227 🖹 041 6856137
Pleasant parkland course with mature trees and a stream. Five new holes laid out in 1996. The 13th hole is a par 3 over water and is the main feature of the course.
18 holes, 6100yds, Par 70, SSS 71, Course record 64.
Club membership 680.
Visitors may normally play on weekdays (except Wed).
Societies apply in writing to Secretary/Manager **Green Fees** €35 per 18 holes(€50 weekends). **Cards** 🌐 🔲 💳 **Prof** Scott Kirkpatrick **Course Designer** Eddie Hackett **Facilities** ⊗ ⅃ ☕ 💷 ♀ ⚐ 🍴 🛄 ⚷ **Location** 400 yards from Northern end of Ardee Main Street

....

Hotel ★★★ 71% Ballymascanlon House Hotel,
DUNDALK ☎ 042 9371124 90 en suite

BALTRAY   Map 01 D4

County Louth ☎ 041 9881530 🖹 041 9881531
e-mail: baltray@indego.ie
Generally held to have the best greens in Ireland, this links course was designed by Tom Simpson to have well guarded and attractive greens without being overly dependant on bunkers. It provides a good test for the modern champion, notably as the annual venue for the East of Ireland Amateur Open.
18 holes, 6613yds, Par 73, SSS 71.
Club membership 1100.
Visitors must contact in advance. **Societies** by prior arrangement. **Green Fees** €80 per round (€100 weekends). **Cards** 🌐 🔲 💳 **Prof** Paddy McGuirk **Course Designer** Tom Simpson **Facilities** ⊗ ⅷ ⅃ ☕ 💷 ♀ ⚐ 🍴 🍽 ⚸ **Leisure** hard tennis courts.
Location 5m NE of Drogheda

....

Hotel ★★★ 61% Conyngham Arms Hotel, SLANE
☎ 041 9884444 16 en suite

DUNDALK   Map 01 D4

Ballymascanlon House Hotel
☎ 042 9371124 🖹 042 9371598
e-mail: info@ballymascanlon.com
Now a testing 18-hole parkland course with numerous water hazards and two difficult holes through woodland, this very scenic course is set at the edge of the Cooley Mountains.

continued

Ballymascanlon House Hotel Golf Course

18 holes, 5548yds, Par 68, SSS 66.
Visitors must telephone in advance to check availability. **Societies** booking by telephone or letter. **Green Fees** €22/€26 per 18 holes. **Cards** ⊞ ▦ ▦ 💳 **Course Designer** Craddock/Ruddy **Facilities** ⊗ 🍴 🛌 💺 ♀ 🏔 🛍 ⛳ 🚶 🏌 **Leisure** grass tennis courts, heated indoor swimming pool, sauna, gymnasium. **Conf** Max 200 Thtr 300 Class 150 Board 75 Banquet 250 Del from €25 * **Location** 3m N of Dundalk on the Carlingford road

Hotel ★★★ 71% Ballymascanlon House Hotel, DUNDALK ☎ 042 9371124 90 en suite

Dundalk Blackrock ☎ 042 9321731 📠 042 22022
e-mail: dwgc@iol.ie
Championship course with fine views of mountain and sea.
18 holes, 6028mtrs, Par 72, SSS 71.
Club membership 1500.
Visitors must contact in advance and may not play Tue or Sun. **Societies** must apply in writing in advance. **Green Fees** €45 per day. **Cards** ⊞ ▦ **Prof** Leslie Walker **Facilities** ⊗ 🍴 🛌 💺 ♀ 🏔 🛍 ⛳ 🚶 🏌 **Leisure** sauna.
Location 2.5m S on coast road from Dundalk

Hotel ★★★ 71% Ballymascanlon House Hotel, DUNDALK ☎ 042 9371124 90 en suite

Killinbeg Killin Park ☎ 042 39303
Opened in 1991 and designed by Eddie Hackett, this undulating 18-hole parkland course has mature woodland and river features.
18 holes, 5293yds, Par 69, SSS 65, Course record 67.
Club membership 100.
Visitors no restrictions. **Societies** apply by telephone or in writing in advance. **Green Fees** terms on application.
Course Designer Eddie Hackett **Facilities** 🛌 💺 ♀ 🏔 ⛳ 🏌
Location Bridge-a-Crinn

Hotel ★★★ 71% Ballymascanlon House Hotel, DUNDALK ☎ 042 9371124 90 en suite

Greenore ☎ 042 9373212 & 9373678 📠 042 9383898
e-mail: greenoregolfclub@eircom.net
Situated amidst beautiful scenery on the shores of Carlingford Lough, with views of the Mourne Mountains. The pine trees here are an unusual feature on a semi-links course. There are quite a number of water facilities, tight fairways and very good greens.
18 holes, 6647yds, Par 71, SSS 73, Course record 69.
Club membership 1028.
Visitors must contact in advance at weekends. **Societies** must contact in advance. **Green Fees** €32 per round (€45
continued

weekends & bank holidays). **Cards** ⊞ ▦ **Course Designer** Eddie Hackett **Facilities** ⊗ 🍴 🛌 💺 ♀ 🏔 🛍 🚶 🏌
Leisure Golf lessons available on request but must be pre booked.

Hotel ★★★ 71% Ballymascanlon House Hotel, DUNDALK ☎ 042 9371124 90 en suite

Seapoint ☎ 041 9822333 📠 041 9822331
e-mail: golflinks@seapoint.ie
A very long championship links course of 7,000 yards with a particularly interesting 17th hole.
18 holes, 6420mtrs, Par 72, SSS 74.
Club membership 470.
Visitors phone in advance for restrictions. **Societies** telephone in advance. **Green Fees** €35 Mon-Thur; €40 Fri; €50 weekends. **Cards** ⊞ ▦ **Prof** David Carroll **Course Designer** Des Smyth **Facilities** ⊗ 🍴 🛌 💺 ♀ 🏔 🛍 🏌 ❧ 🚶 🏌 **Location** 4m NE of Drogheda

Hotel ★★★ 61% Conyngham Arms Hotel, SLANE ☎ 041 9884444 16 en suite

CO MAYO

Ballina Mossgrove, Shanaghy
☎ 096 21050 📠 096 21718
e-mail: ballinagc@eircom.net
Undulating but mostly flat inland course.
18 holes, 6103yds, Par 71, SSS 69, Course record 69.
Club membership 478.
Visitors welcome but may not play Sun before 3.30pm. Restrictions apply depending on competitions/society visits. **Societies** apply in writing or telephone in advance. **Green Fees** €20 per 18 holes(€25 weekends and bank holidays). **Cards** ⊞ ▦ ▦ **Course Designer** E Hackett **Facilities** 🛌 💺 ♀ 🏔 🏌 🚶 🏌 **Location** 1m outside town on Bonnocolon Rd

Ballinrobe Cloonagashel ☎ 092 41118 📠 092 41889
e-mail: bgcgolf@iol.ie
18 holes, 6043mtrs, Par 73, SSS 72, Course record 69.
Course Designer Eddie Hackett **Location** Off N84 onto R331 to Claremorris
Telephone for further details

Hotel ★★★ 68% Breaffy House Hotel, CASTLEBAR ☎ 094 22033 59 en suite

Ballyhaunis Coolnaha ☎ 0907 30014 📠 094 81829
e-mail: tmack@tinet.ie
Undulating parkland course with 9 holes, 10 greens and 18 tees.
9 holes, 5413mtrs, Par 70, SSS 68, Course record 68.
Club membership 340.
Visitors welcome all times but must avoid members competitions on Sun & Thu. **Societies** must apply in writing or telephone. **Green Fees** not confirmed. **Facilities** 🛌 💺 ♀ 🏔 🏌 ❧ **Location** 3m N on N83

Hotel ★★★ 68% Breaffy House Hotel, CASTLEBAR ☎ 094 22033 59 en suite

BELMULLET
Map 01 A5

Carne Carne ☎ 097 82292 ▤ 097 81477
e-mail: carngolf@iol.ic
18 holes, 6119mtrs, Par 72, SSS 72, Course record 72.
Club membership 460.
Visitors welcome, booking essential to guarantee tee-time.
Societies booking advisable. **Green Fees** €40 per day(€40
per round weekends). **Cards** ▤▤ Course Designer
Eddie Hackett **Facilities** ⊗ ⫴ ఓ ⚑ ♀ ᐃ 🛅 ⛳ ◥ ⮾ ∅
Location 2m from Belmullet

CASTLEBAR
Map 01 B4

Castlebar Hawthorn Av, Rocklands
☎ 094 21649 ▤ 094 26088
e-mail: castlebargolf@eircom.ie
**New course opened September 2000. Fast greens with
severe borrows. Accuracy is essential from the tee on
most holes. Long difficult course from blue
(championship) tees.**
18 holes, 5698mtrs, Par 71, SSS 70.
Club membership 950.
Visitors very welcome weekdays, must contact in advance
for weekend play. No vistors on Sun. **Societies** must contact
in advance. **Green Fees** not confirmed. **Course Designer**
Peter McEvoy **Facilities** ఓ ⚑ ♀ ᐃ ◥ ⮾ ∅ **Location** 1m
from town on Belcarra road

Hotel ★★★ 68% Breaffy House Hotel, CASTLEBAR
☎ 094 22033 59 en suite

CLAREMORRIS
Map 01 B4

Claremorris Castlemagarrett ☎ 094 71527
e-mail: claremorris@ebookireland.com
**A 18 hole parkland course designed by Tom Craddock,
designer of Druids Glen. It consists of many eye-catching
water features, bunkers, trees and wooded backgrounds.
Noted by golfers for its layout, variation on each hole and
the quality of the sand based greens.**
*Claremorris Golf Course: 18 holes, 6600mtrs,
Par 73, SSS 70, Course record 68.*
Club membership 550.
Visitors contact club for availability. **Societies** contact 094
71527 for details. **Green Fees** terms on application. **Course
Designer** Tom Craddock **Facilities** ⊗ by prior arrangement
⫴ by prior arrangement ఓ ⚑ ♀ ᐃ ⛳ ⮾ ∅ **Location**
1.5m from town, on N17 S of Claremorris

Hotel ★★★ 61% Belmont Hotel, KNOCK
☎ 094 88122 63 en suite

KEEL
Map 01 A4

Achill Achill Island, Westport ☎ 098 43456
**Seaside links in a scenic location on the edge of the
Atlantic Ocean.**
9 holes, 2723yds, Par 70, SSS 66, Course record 69.
Club membership 200.
Visitors welcome but cannot play on some Sundays
Societies must write or telephone in advance. **Green Fees**
not confirmed. **Facilities** ⚑ ᐃ ⛳ ∅ **Location** 15 Km
towards Keel Village

Hotel ★★★ 73% Hotel Westport Conference & Leisure
Centre, Newport Rd, WESTPORT ☎ 098 25122
129 en suite

SWINFORD
Map 01 B4

Swinford Brabazon Park ☎ 094 51378 ▤ 094 51378
**A pleasant parkland course with good views of the
beautiful surrounding countryside.**
9 holes, 5542mtrs, Par 70, SSS 68.
Club membership 420.
Visitors must contact in advance in peak season. **Societies**
must apply in writing or telephone in advance. **Green Fees**
not confirmed. **Facilities** ᐃ ∅

Hotel ★★★ 68% Breaffy House Hotel, CASTLEBAR
☎ 094 22033 59 en suite

WESTPORT
Map 01 B4

Westport Carrowholly
☎ 098 28262 & 27070 ▤ 098 27217
e-mail: wpgolf@iol.ie
**This is a beautiful course with wonderful views of
Clew Bay, with its 365 islands, and the holy mountain
called Croagh Patrick, famous for the annual
pilgrimage to its summit. Golfers indulge in a different
kind of penance on this challenging course with many
memorable holes. Perhaps the most exciting is the par
five 15th, 580 yards long and featuring a long carry
from the tee over an inlet of Clew Bay.**
18 holes, 6667yds, Par 73, SSS 71, Course record 65.
Club membership 820.
Visitors must contact in advance. No visitors during
members times. **Societies** apply in writing or telephone
well in advance. **Green Fees** €35–€38 Mon-Thur: €41–
€47 weekends. **Cards** ▤▤ **Prof** Alex Mealia **Course
Designer** Fred Hawtree **Facilities** ⊗ ⫴ ఓ ⚑ ♀ ᐃ 🛅 ⛳
◥ ⮾ ∅ **Location** 2.5m from town

Hotel ★★★ 73% Hotel Westport Conference & Leisure
Centre, Newport Rd, WESTPORT
☎ 098 25122 129 en suite

BETTYSTOWN
Map 01 D4

Laytown & Bettystown ☎ 041 27170 ▤ 041 28506
**A very competitive and trying links course, home of
famous golfer, Des Smyth.**
18 holes, 5652mtrs, Par 71, SSS 70.
Club membership 950.
Visitors may not play 1-2pm. Advisable to contact in
advance. **Societies** must contact in writing. **Green Fees** €45
(€55 weekends and bank holidays). **Cards** ▤▤ **Prof**
Robert J Browne **Facilities** ⊗ ⫴ ఓ ⚑ ♀ ᐃ 🛅 ⛳ ∅
Leisure hard tennis courts.

Hotel ★★★ 61% Conyngham Arms Hotel, SLANE
☎ 041 9884444 16 en suite

DUNSHAUGHLIN
Map 01 D4

Black Bush Thomastown ☎ 01 8250021 ▤ 01 8250400
e-mail: golf@blackbush.iol.ie
Black Bush: 18 holes, 6930yds, Par 73, SSS 72.
Agore: 18 holes, 6598yds, Par 71, SSS 69.
Thomastown: 18 holes, 6433yds, Par 70, SSS 68.
Course Designer Bobby Browne **Location** 1.5m from
village on Dunshaughlin-Ratoath road

continued

Black Bush Golf Club

Telephone for further details
· ·
Hotel ★★★ 70% Finnstown Country House Hotel, Newcastle Rd, LUCAN ☎ 01 6010700 25 en suite 28 annexe en suite

KELLS
Map 01 C4

Headfort ☎ 046 40857 40146 ▤ 046 49282
A delightful parkland course which is regarded as one of the best of its kind in Ireland. There are ample opportunities for birdies, but even if these are not achieved, Headfort provides for a most pleasant game. A further 18 hole course has recently opened is proving very popular especially with low handicapped players.
Headfort Golf Club-Old Course: 36 holes, 5973mtrs, Par 72, SSS 71.
Headfort Golf Club-New Course: 18 holes, 6164, Par 72, SSS 75.
Club membership 1162.
Visitors restricted Tues Ladies Day. Must contact in advance. **Societies** must apply in writing. **Green Fees** Old Course:€35 per round(€40 Sat).New Course;€50 per round. **Cards** 🌐 ▆ ▆ **Prof** Brendan McGovern **Facilities** ⊗ ⅷ ⅃ ▆ ♀ ⚲ 🏠 ⚑ ↘ ⚐
· ·
Hotel ★★ 62% Ardboyne Hotel, Dublin Rd, NAVAN ☎ 046 23119 29 en suite

KILCOCK
Map 01 C4

Kilcock Gallow ☎ 01 6287592 ▤ 01 6287283
e-mail: kilcockgolfclub@eircom.net
A parkland course with wide, gently undulating fairways, flat greens and light rough only.
18 holes, 5775mtrs, Par 72, SSS 70, Course record 69.
Club membership 450.
Visitors must contact in advance for weekends, no problem weekdays. **Societies** telephone for dates available. **Green Fees** €20 per 18 holes(€25 weekends & bank holidays). **Course Designer** Eddie Hackett **Facilities** ⊗ ⅷ ⅃ ▆ ♀ ⚲ 🏠 ⚐ **Location** 2m from end of M4
· ·
Hotel ★★★ 64% Lucan Spa Hotel, LUCAN ☎ 01 6280495 & 6280497 ▤ 01 6280841
71 rms (61 en suite)

NAVAN
Map 01 C4

Royal Tara Bellinter
☎ 046 25508 & 25244 ▤ 046 25508
e-mail: info@royaltaragolfclub.com
Pleasant parkland course offering plenty of variety. Situated close to the Hill of Tara, the ancient seat of the Kings of Ireland.
continued

New Course: *18 holes, 5757mtrs, Par 71, SSS 70.*
Bellinter Nine: *9 holes, 3184yds, Par 35, SSS 35.*
Club membership 1000.
Visitors prior arrangement is advisable. Tue is ladies day. **Societies** apply in writing or telephone. **Green Fees** not confirmed. **Prof** Adam Whiston **Course Designer** Des Smyth **Facilities** ⊗ ⅷ ⅃ ▆ ♀ ⚲ 🏠 ⚑ ↘ ⚐ 🚲 ⚐
Location 6m from town on N3
· ·
Hotel ★★★ 62% Ardboyne Hotel, Dublin Rd, NAVAN ☎ 046 23119 29 en suite

TRIM
Map 01 C4

County Meath Newtownmoynagh
☎ 046 31463 ▤ 046 37554
Originally a 9-hole course opened in 1971, it was extended to 18-holes in 1990. It is maturing into a very challenging and formidable parkland course with four testing par 5s. Luxurious clubhouse with panoramic views across the course.
18 holes, 6720mtrs, Par 73, SSS 72, Course record 68.
Club membership 900.
Visitors welcome; some restrictions telephone for details. **Societies** not Sun, enquiries welcome. **Green Fees** terms on application. **Cards** 🌐 ▆ ▆ 📱 **Prof** Robin Machin **Course Designer** Eddie Hackett/Tom Craddock **Facilities** ⊗ ⅷ ⅃ ▆ ♀ ⚲ 🏠 ⚐ **Leisure** snooker. **Location** 3m outside Trim on Trim/Longwood rd
· ·
Hotel ★★★ 61% Conyngham Arms Hotel, SLANE ☎ 041 9884444 16 en suite

CO MONAGHAN

CARRICKMACROSS
Map 01 C4

Mannan Castle Donaghmoyne
☎ 042 9663308 ▤ 042 9663195
Parkland and picturesque, the course features the par 3 2nd to an island green. The short par 4 12th through the woods and the 14th to 18th, all crossing water at least once. A test of golf for both amateur and professional.
18 holes, 6500yds, Par 70, SSS 69.
Club membership 700.
Visitors may play anytime except competition times Sat, Sun & Wed from 2-2.30pm. **Societies** apply in writing to the secretary. **Green Fees** terms on application. **Course Designer** F Ainsworth **Facilities** ⊗ ⅷ ⅃ ▆ ♀ ⚲ ↘ ⚐ **Location** 4m N
· ·
Hotel ★★★ 71% Ballymascanlon House Hotel, DUNDALK ☎ 042 9371124 90 en suite

Nuremore ☎ 042 9661438 & 9664016 ▤ 042 9661853
e-mail: nuremore@eircom.net
Picturesque parkland course of championship length incorporating the drumlins and lakes which are a natural feature of the Monaghan countryside. Precision is required on the 10th to drive over a large lake and between a narrow avenue of trees. Signature hole 18th.
18 holes, 6400yds, Par 71, SSS 69, Course record 64.
Club membership 250.
Visitors welcome all times but must contact Maurice Cassidy in advance. **Societies** must contact in advance. **Green Fees** €30(€37 weeekends and bank holidays). **Cards** 🌐 ▆ ▆ 📱 **Prof** Maurice Cassidy **Course Designer** Eddie Hackett **Facilities** ⊗ ⅷ ⅃ ▆ ♀ ⚲ 🏠 ⚑ 🚲 ↘ 🚲 ⚐ **Leisure** hard tennis courts, heated indoor swimming pool,
continued

squash, fishing, sauna, gymnasium. **Conf** Max 500 Thtr 300 Class 180 Banquet 180 **Location** 1m S of Carrickmacross, on main N2

Hotel ★★★★ 72% Nuremore Hotel, CARRICKMACROSS ☎ 042 9661438 72 en suite

CASTLEBLAYNEY   Map 01 C4

Castleblayney Onomy ☎ 042 40451 ▧ 042 40451
e-mail: rayker@eircom.com
Scenic course on Muckno Park estate, adjacent to Muckno Lake and Hope Castle.
9 holes, 5378yds, Par 68, SSS 66, Course record 66.
Club membership 275.
Visitors no visitors allowed during major weekend competitions. **Societies** must contact in advance. **Green Fees** €10 (€12 weekends). **Course Designer** Bobby Browne **Facilities** ⬛ ♥ ♀ ⬭ **Leisure** fishing. **Location** Situated on the Hope Castle Estate, in the town of Castleblayney

Hotel ★★★ 71% Ballymascanlon House Hotel, DUNDALK ☎ 042 9371124 90 en suite

CLONES   Map 01 C5

Clones Hilton Park ☎ 047 56017 & 56913 ▧ 047 56913
Parkland course set in Drumlin country. Due to limestone belt, the course is very dry and playable all year round. There is a timesheet in operation on Saturday and Sunday.
18 holes, 5549mtrs, Par 69, SSS 67, Course record 62.
Club membership 330.
Visitors must contact in advance.Timesheets in operation at weekends. **Societies** apply in writing. **Green Fees** €20.
Cards ▦ ▨ **Course Designer** Cromwell **Facilities** ⊗ 〕⏡ ⬛ ♥ ♀ ⬭ ⬭ **Location** 3m from Clones on Scotshouse rd

Hotel ★★★★ 63% Hillgrove Hotel, Old Armagh Rd, MONAGHAN ☎ 047 81288 44 en suite

MONAGHAN   Map 01 C5

Rossmore Rossmore Park, Cootehill Rd ☎ 047 71222
An undulating 18-hole parkland course amidst beautiful countryside.
18 holes, 5590mtrs, Par 70, SSS 69, Course record 62.
Club membership 800.
Visitors must contact in advance, telephone Pro Shop on 047 71222. **Societies** must apply in writing. **Green Fees** not confirmed. **Prof** Mark Nicholson **Course Designer** Des Smyth **Facilities** ⬛ ♥ ♀ ⬭ ⬔ ⬭ ⬭ **Leisure** snooker & pool. **Location** 2m S on Cootehill Road

Hotel ★★★★ 63% Hillgrove Hotel, Old Armagh Rd, MONAGHAN ☎ 047 81288 44 en suite

CO OFFALY

BIRR   Map 01 C3

Birr The Glenns ☎ 0509 20082 ▧ 0509 22155
The course has been laid out over undulating parkland utilising the natural contours of the land, which were created during the ice age. The sandy subsoil means that the course is playable all year round.
18 holes, 5700mtrs, Par 70, SSS 70, Course record 62.
Club membership 750.
Visitors contact in advance. **Societies** advance contact to secretary. **Green Fees** €23 (€32 weekends and bank holidays). **Course Designer** Eddie Connaughton **Facilities** ⊗ 〕⏡ ⬛ ♥ ♀ ⬭ ⬔ ⬭ ⬭ ⬭ **Location** 2 miles W of Birr town en route to Banagher)

Hotel ★★★ 61% County Arms Hotel, BIRR ☎ 0509 20791 24 en suite

DAINGEAN   Map 01 C4

Castle Barna ☎ 0506 53384 ▧ 0506 53077
e-mail: info@castlebarna.ie
Parkland course on the bank of the Grand Canal. Many mature trees, natural streams and the naturally undulating landscape provide a great challenge for golfers of all abilities.
Castle Barna Golf Course: 18 holes, 5600mtrs, Par 72, SSS 69, Course record 67.
Club membership 600.
Visitors may not play Sun am from 8-noon. **Societies** telephone to check availability. **Green Fees** €15 per round (€20 weekends and bank holidays). **Cards** ▦ **Course Designer** Alan Duggan **Facilities** ⊗ by prior arrangement 〕⏡ by prior arrangement ⬛ ♥ ♀ ⬭ ⬭ ⬭ ⬭ ⬭ **Location** 7m S of N6 at Tyrellspass

EDENDERRY   Map 01 C4

Edenderry ☎ 0405 31072 ▧ 0405 33911
e-mail: enquiries@edenderrygolfclub.com
A most friendly club which offers a relaxing game in pleasant surroundings. In 1992 the course was extended to 18 holes.
18 holes, 6029mtrs, Par 72, SSS 72, Course record 66.
Club membership 700.
Visitors restricted Thu & weekends, ring for times. **Societies** may not play on Thu & Sun; must contact the secretary in writing. **Green Fees** €30(€35 weekends). **Course Designer** Havers/Hackett **Facilities** ⊗ 〕⏡ ⬛ ♥ ♀ ⬭ ⬭ **Conf** Board 30

Guesthouse ◆◆◆◆◆ Crookedwood House, Crookedwood, MULLINGAR ☎ 044 72165 8 en suite

TULLAMORE   Map 01 C4

Tullamore Brookfield ☎ 0506 21439 ▧ 0506 41806
e-mail: tullamoregolfclub@eircom.net
Parkland course set amongst mature hardwood trees on the edge of the town. The visitor is guaranteed delightful scenery, splendid fairways, well manicured rough and superb greens. The course is level and suitable for all ages and abilities.
18 holes, 6500yds, Par 70, SSS 71, Course record 68.
Club membership 975.
Visitors must contact in advance, restricted on Tue & at weekends. **Societies** must contact in writing. **Green Fees** €32 per 18 holes(€40 weekends). **Cards** ▦ ▨ ▦ **Prof** Donagh McArdle **Course Designer** James Braid/Paddy

continued

Merrigam **Facilities** ⊗ ⋙ ﹄ ♨ ♀ ⚥ 🏠 ⛴ ✐
Location 2.5m SW on Kinnity road

Hotel ★★★ 70% Hodson Bay Hotel, Hodson Bay,
ATHLONE ☎ 0902 80500 133 en suite

CO ROSCOMMON

ATHLONE   Map 01 C4

Athlone Hodson Bay ☎ 0902 92073 🖩 0902 94080
A picturesque course with a panoramic view of Lough
Ree. Overall, it is a tight, difficult course with some
outstanding holes and is noted for its magnificent greens.
Many championships have taken place here including the
1998 All Ireland Cups and Shields finals.
18 holes, 5854mtrs, Par 71, SSS 71, Course record 66.
Club membership 1250.
Visitors must contact in advance. **Societies** apply in writing.
Green Fees €27 per round (€30 weekends and bank
holidays). **Cards** ▦ ▦ **Prof** Martin Quinn **Course**
Designer J McAllister **Facilities** ⊗ ⋙ ﹄ ♨ ♀ ⚥ 🏠 ⛴ 🏌
🛒 ✐ **Location** 4m from town beside Lough Ree

Hotel ★★★ 70% Hodson Bay Hotel, Hodson Bay,
ATHLONE ☎ 0902 80500 133 en suite

BALLAGHADERREEN   Map 01 B4

Ballaghaderreen ☎ 0907 60295
Mature 9-hole course with an abundance of trees.
Accuracy off the tee is vital for a good score. Small
protected greens require a good short-iron plan. The par
3, 5th hole at 178 yards has ruined many a good score.
9 holes, 5727yds, Par 70, SSS 67, Course record 68.
Club membership 250.
Visitors no restrictions. **Societies** apply in writing or
telephone during office hours. **Green Fees** not confirmed.
Course Designer Paddy Skerritt **Facilities** ﹄ ♨ ♀ ⚥ ✐
Location 2m S of town

Hotel ★★★ 56% Markree Castle, COLLOONEY
☎ 071 67800 30 en suite

BOYLE   Map 01 B4

Boyle Roscommon Rd ☎ 079 62594
Situated on a low hill and surrounded by beautiful
scenery, this is an undemanding course where, due to the
generous fairways and semi-rough, the leisure golfer is
likely to finish the round with the same golf ball.
9 holes, 5324yds, Par 67, SSS 66, Course record 65.
Club membership 288.
Visitors no restrictions. **Societies** must contact in writing.
Green Fees €15 per day. **Course Designer** E Hackett
Facilities ⊗ by prior arrangement ⋙ by prior arrangement ﹄
♨ ♀ ⚥ 🏌 **Location** 2m from Boyle on the Roscommon
road

Hotel ★★★ 56% Markree Castle, COLLOONEY
☎ 071 67800 30 en suite

CASTLEREA   Map 01 B4

Castlerea Clonalis ☎ 0907 20068 & 20705
9 holes, 4974mtrs, Par 68, SSS 66, Course record 62.
Location On Dublin/Castlebar road
Telephone for further details

Hotel ★★★ 65% Abbey Hotel, Galway Rd,
ROSCOMMON ☎ 0903 26240 & 26505
🖩 0903 26021 25 en suite

ROSCOMMON   Map 01 B4

Roscommon Mote Park
☎ 0903 26382, 26931 🖩 0903 26043
e-mail: rosegolfclub@eircom.net
Located on the rolling pastures of the old Mote Park
estate, this recently extended 18-hole course successfully
blends the old established nine holes with an exciting and
equally demanding new 9-hole lay-out. Numerous water
hazards, notably on the tricky 13th, multi-tiered greens
and an excellent irrigation to give an all-weather surface.
18 holes, 6290mtrs, Par 72, SSS 70.
Club membership 700.
Visitors contact in advance,especially Sundays. **Societies**
apply in writing or telephone. **Green Fees** €25. **Course**
Designer E Connaughton **Facilities** ⊗ ⋙ ﹄ ♨ ♀ ⚥ 🛒 ✐
Location 0.5m S of Roscommon town

Hotel ★★★ 65% Abbey Hotel, Galway Rd,
ROSCOMMON ☎ 0903 26240 & 26505
🖩 0903 26021 25 en suite

STROKESTOWN   Map 01 C4

Strokestown Bumlin ☎ 078 33528
Picturesque 9-hole course set in parkland with fine views.
A new 9 hole course completed in summer 2001.
9 holes, 2615mtrs, Par 68.
Club membership 250.
Visitors may play any times except during competitions.
Societies apply in writing or telephone at least 2 weeks in
advance. **Green Fees** €15 per 18 holes. **Facilities** ⚥
Location 1.5m from Strokestown

Hotel ★★★ 65% Abbey Hotel, Galway Rd,
ROSCOMMON ☎ 0903 26240 & 26505
🖩 0903 26021 25 en suite

CO SLIGO

BALLYMOTE   Map 01 B4

Ballymote Ballinascarrow ☎ 071 83158 & 83089
e-mail: jocon@iol.ie
Although Ballymote was founded in 1940, the course
dates from 1993 and has matured well into a parkland
course with ample fairways and large greens. It has
recently been improved with new tees, 20 bunkers and 2
new greens. The feature par 4 7th hole has been
redesigned with the green surrounded by water and
Ballinascarrow Lake in the background.
9 holes, 5302mtrs, Par 68, SSS 67.
Club membership 250.
Visitors must contact in advance. **Societies** telephone in
advance. **Green Fees** not confirmed. **Prof** Leslie Robinson
Course Designer Eddie Hacket **Facilities** ♨ ⚥ 🏌 ✐
Leisure fishing. **Location** 1m N

Hotel ★★★ 56% Markree Castle, COLLOONEY
☎ 071 67800 30 en suite

ENNISCRONE   Map 01 B5

Enniscrone ☎ 096 36297 🖩 096 36657
e-mail: enniscronegolf@eircom.net
In a magnificent situation with breathtaking views of
mountain, sea and rolling countryside, this course
offers some unforgettable golf. It was host to the West
of Ireland championship and the Ladies Irish Close in
1997. It offers an exciting challenge among its splendid
continued

sandhills and a particularly favourite hole is the tenth, with a marvellous view from the elevated tee and the chance of a birdie with an accurate drive.
18 holes, 6671yds, Par 73, SSS 72.
Club membership 620.
Visitors must contact in advance, may not play before 11am or between 1.00 & 4pm on Sun. **Societies** must book in advance. **Green Fees** €45 (€60 weekend & bank holidays)per round. **Cards** 🖮 💳 💳 **Prof** Charlie McGoldrick **Course Designer** E Hackett/Donald Steel **Facilities** ⊗ ⅷ ⅃ 🏌 💷 ♀ ⚐ 🏠 ⛳ 🛒 ♨ ⛳ 🏌 **Location** 0.5m S on Ballina road

SLIGO   Map 01 B5

County Sligo Rosses Point
☎ 071 77134 or 77186 🖃 071 77460
e-mail: cosligo@iol.ie
Now considered to be one of the top links courses in Ireland, County Sligo is host to a number of competitions, including the West of Ireland Championships and Internationals. Set in an elevated position on cliffs above three large beaches, the prevailing winds provide an additional challenge. Tom Watson described it as 'a magnificent links, particularly the stretch of holes from the 14th to the 17th.'
18 holes, 6043mtrs, Par 71, SSS 72, Course record 67.
Bowmore: 9 holes, 2785mtrs, Par 35, SSS 35.
Club membership 1050.
Visitors advisable to contact in advance, available most days except Captains or Presidents days. Deposit required to secure. **Societies** must contact in writing & pay a deposit. **Green Fees** Championship Course:€55 per 18 holes Mon-Thur(€70 Fri-Sun and bank holidays) Bowmore:€35 per 18 holes;€20 per 9 holes. **Cards** 🖮 💳 💳 **Prof** Jim Robinson **Course Designer** Harry Colt **Facilities** ⊗ ⅷ ⅃ 🏌 💷 ♀ ⚐ 🏠 ⛳ 🛒 ♨ ⛳ **Location** Off N15 to Donegal

Hotel ★★★ 65% Tower Hotel, Quay St, SLIGO
☎ 071 44000 58 en suite

Strandhill Strandhill ☎ 071 68188 🖃 071 68811
This scenic course is situated between Knocknarea Mountain and the Atlantic, offering golf in its most natural form amid the sand dunes of the West of Ireland. The 1st, 16th and 18th are par 4 holes over 364 metres in length; the 2nd and 17th are testing par 3s which vary according to the prevailing wind; the par 4 13th is a testing dogleg right. This is a course where accuracy will be rewarded.
18 holes, 5516mtrs, Par 69, SSS 68.
Club membership 450.
Visitors must contact in advance. **Societies** apply in advance. **Green Fees** €35 per round Mon-Thur; €45 Fri-Sat. **Facilities** ⊗ ⅷ ⅃ 🏌 ♀ 🏠 ⛳ 🛒 ♨ ⛳ **Location** 5m from town

Hotel ★★★ 71% Sligo Park Hotel, Pearse Rd, SLIGO
☎ 071 60291 110 en suite

TOBERCURRY   Map 01 B4

Tobercurry ☎ 071 85849
A 9-hole parkland course designed by Edward Hackett. The 8th hole, a par 3, is regarded as being one of the most testing in the west of Ireland.

continued

9 holes, 5490mtrs, Par 70, SSS 69.
Club membership 300.
Visitors may not play on Sundays. **Societies** telephone in advance on 071 85770. **Green Fees** not confirmed. **Course Designer** Eddie Hackett **Facilities** ⊗ ⅷ ⅃ 🏌 💷 ♀ ⛳ ⛳ **Location** 0.25m from Tobercurry

CO TIPPERARY

CAHIR   Map 01 C3

Cahir Park Kilcommon ☎ 052 41474 🖃 052 42717
Parkland course dissected by the River Suir which adds a challenge to the par 4 8th and par 3 16th. Water in play on 7 holes.
18 holes, 6350yds, Par 71, SSS 71, Course record 67.
Club membership 600.
Visitors may play any time except during competitions. **Societies** by prior arrangement, apply in writing. **Green Fees** €20 (€25 weekends). **Prof** Markus Joseph **Course Designer** Eddie Hackett **Facilities** ⅃ 🏌 💷 ♀ 🏠 ⛳ ⛳ **Location** 1m from Cahir on the Clogheen road

Hotel ★★★ 67% Cahir House Hotel, The Square, CAHIR
☎ 052 42727 41 en suite

CARRICK-ON-SUIR   Map 01 C2

Carrick-on-Suir Garvonne
☎ 051 640047 🖃 051 640558
e-mail: cosgc@eircom.net
18 hole parkland course with the backdrop of the Comeragh Mountains on one side and views of the Suir Valley on the other.
18 holes, 6061mtrs, Par 72, SSS 71, Course record 69.
Club membership 600.
Visitors may not play on Sun morning.contact in advance. **Societies** contact for details. **Green Fees** not confirmed. **Cards** 🖮 💳 **Course Designer** Eddie Hackett **Facilities** ⊗ ⅷ ⅃ 🏌 💷 ♀ 🛒 ♨ ⛳ **Location** 2m SW

Hotel ★★★ 74% Minella Hotel, CLONMEL
☎ 052 22388 70 en suite

CLONMEL   Map 01 C2

Clonmel Lyreanearla, Mountain Rd
☎ 052 24050 & 21138 🖃 052 24050
e-mail: cgc@indigo.ie
Set in the scenic, wooded slopes of the Comeragh Mountains, this is a testing course with lots of open space and plenty of interesting features. It provides an enjoyable round in exceptionally tranquil surroundings.
18 holes, 6347yards, Par 72, SSS 71.
Club membership 950.
Visitors must contact in advance. **Societies** apply in advance by writing or phone. **Green Fees** €30 per round (€35 weekends). **Cards** 💳 **Prof** Robert Hayes **Course Designer** Eddie Hackett **Facilities** ⊗ ⅷ by prior arrangement ⅃ 🏌 💷 ♀ 🏠 ⛳ 🛒 ♨ ⛳ **Location** 3m from Clonmel off N24

Hotel ★★★ 74% Minella Hotel, CLONMEL
☎ 052 22388 70 en suite

Looking for a driving range?
See the index at the back of the guide

MONARD   Map 01 B3

Ballykisteen Ballykisteen, Limerick Junction
☎ 062 33333 ▤ 062 52457
Ballykisteen is set in emerald green countryside just two miles from Tipperary. The course, with landscaped surroundings against a backdrop of mountains, lakes and streams, offers an excellent challenge for the champion golfer. The use of forward tees provide a course that is playable and enjoyable for the average golfer.
18 holes, 6765yds, Par 72, SSS 72.
Club membership 220.
Visitors no restrictions. **Societies** must contact in advance. **Green Fees** €28 (€30 weekends). **Prof** David Reddan **Course Designer** Des Smith **Facilities** ⊗ ⅷ ▱ ⬛ ♀ ⌲ 🏠 🍴 ⛳ 🏌 ♂ ℓ ↑ **Location** On N24 2m from Tipperary towards Limerick

Guesthouse ♦♦♦ Ach-na-Sheen Guesthouse, Clonmel Rd, TIPPERARY ☎ 062 51298 10 rms (7 en suite)

NENAGH   Map 01 B3

Nenagh Beechwood ☎ 067 31476 ▤ 067 34808
Interesting gradients call for some careful approach shots. Some magnificent views. A major re-development including 13 new holes completed in 2001.
18 holes, 6009mtrs, Par 72, SSS 72, Course record 71.
Club membership 950.
Visitors must contact in advance.May not play Sundays. **Societies** must apply in writing. **Green Fees** €30 per 18 holes. **Cards** ▦ **Prof** Robert Kelly **Course Designer** Patrick Merrigan **Facilities** ⊗ ⅷ ▱ ⬛ ♀ ⌲ 🏠 🍴 ♂ ↘ 🛒 ℓ **Location** 3m from town on old Birr rd

Hotel ★★★ 68% Abbey Court Hotel & Trinity Leisure Club, Dublin Rd, NENAGH ☎ 067 41111 82 en suite

ROSCREA   Map 01 C3

Roscrea Golf Club Derryvale
☎ 0505 21130 ▤ 0505 23410
An 18-hole parkland course.
18 holes, 5750mtrs, Par 71, SSS 70, Course record 66.
Club membership 600.
Visitors telephone in advance, on Sun by arrangement. **Societies** apply in writing to Hon Secretary. **Green Fees** €15(€20 weekends). **Course Designer** A Spring **Facilities** ⊗ ⅷ ▱ ⬛ ♀ ⌲ ℓ **Location** N7, Dublin side of Roscrea

Hotel ★★★ 61% County Arms Hotel, BIRR
☎ 0509 20791 24 en suite

TEMPLEMORE   Map 01 C3

Templemore Manna South
☎ 0504 31400 & 32923 ▤ 0504 35450
e-mail: johnkm@tinet.ie
Parkland course with many mature and some newly planted trees which offers a pleasant test to visitors without being too difficult. Ideal for holiday makers.
9 holes, 5443mtrs, Par 70, SSS 69, Course record 68.
Club membership 330.
Visitors may not play during Special Events. **Societies** must contact in advance. **Green Fees** €15 per 18 holes(€20 weekends). **Cards** ▦ **Facilities** ⊗ ⅷ ▱ ⬛ ♀ ⌲ ℓ **Leisure** hard tennis courts. **Location** 0.5m S, beside N62

Hotel ★★★ 61% County Arms Hotel, BIRR
☎ 0509 20791 24 en suite

THURLES   Map 01 C3

Thurles Turtulla ☎ 0504 21983 & 22466 ▤ 0504 24647
Superb parkland course with a difficult finish at the 18th.
18 holes, 5904mtrs, Par 72, SSS 71, Course record 65.
Club membership 920.
Visitors welcome, limited availability at weekends, Tuesday is Ladies day. **Societies** apply in writing to Hon Secretary. **Green Fees** terms on application. **Prof** Sean Hunt **Facilities** ⊗ ⅷ ▱ ⬛ ♀ ⌲ 🏠 🍴 ♂ ℓ ↑ **Leisure** squash, sauna, gymnasium. **Location** 1m from town on Cork road

Guesthouse ♦♦♦ Ach-na-Sheen Guesthouse, Clonmel Rd, TIPPERARY ☎ 062 51298 10 rms (7 en suite)

TIPPERARY   Map 01 C3

County Tipperary Dundrum House Hotel, Dundrum
☎ 062 71116
18 holes, 6709yds, Par 72, SSS 72, Course record 70.
Course Designer Philip Walton **Location** 7m W of Cashel off N8
Telephone for further details

Guesthouse ♦♦♦ Ach-na-Sheen Guesthouse, Clonmel Rd, TIPPERARY ☎ 062 51298 10 rms (7 en suite)

Tipperary Rathanny ☎ 062 51119
18 holes, 5761mtrs, Par 71, SSS 71, Course record 66.
Location 1m S
Telephone for further details

Guesthouse ♦♦♦ Ach-na-Sheen Guesthouse, Clonmel Rd, TIPPERARY ☎ 062 51298 10 rms (7 en suite)

CO WATERFORD

DUNGARVAN   Map 01 C2

Dungarvan Knocknagranagh
☎ 058 41605 & 43310 ▤ 058 44113
e-mail: dungarvangolf@cablesurf.com
A championship-standard course beside Dungarvan Bay, with seven lakes and hazards placed to challenge all levels of golfer. The greens are considered to be among the best in Ireland.
18 holes, 6560yds, Par 72, SSS 71, Course record 66.
Club membership 900.
Visitors welcome weekdays, booking advisable weekends. **Societies** telephone then write to confim booking. **Green Fees** not confirmed. **Prof** David Hayes **Course Designer** Moss Fives **Facilities** ⊗ ⅷ ▱ ⬛ ♀ ⌲ 🏠 🍴 ♂ ℓ **Leisure** snooker. **Location** Off N25 between Waterford & Youghal

Hotel ★★★ 61% Lawlors Hotel, DUNGARVAN
☎ 058 41122 & 41056 ▤ 058 41000 89 en suite

Gold Coast Golf & Leisure Ballinacourty
☎ 058 42249 & 44055 ▤ 058 43378
e-mail: info@cionea.com
A parkland course bordered by the Atlantic Ocean with unrivalled panoramic views of Dungarvan Bay. The mature tree-lined fairways of the old course are tastefully integrated with the long and challenging newer holes to create a superb course.
18 holes, 6171mtrs, Par 72, SSS 72, Course record 70.
Club membership 450.

continued

Visitors book in advance, times available throughout the week. **Societies** apply by telephone in advance. **Green Fees** €30 (€40 weekends). **Cards** ▨ ▨ ▨ ▨ **Course Designer** Maurice Fives **Facilities** ⊗ ⅏ ⅊ ♨ ♀ ⅄ ☎ ⚐ ⛴ ➤ ⚒ ⚓ ⛳ **Leisure** hard tennis courts, heated indoor swimming pool, sauna, gymnasium. **Location** Left of N25, 2m bfore Dungarvan

Hotel ★★★ 61% Lawlors Hotel, DUNGARVAN
☎ 058 41122 & 41056 ▨ 058 41000 89 en suite

West Waterford ☎ 058 43216 & 41475 ▨ 058 44343
e-mail: info@westwaterfordgolf.com
Designed by Eddie Hackett, the course is on 150 acres of rolling parkland by the Brickey River with a backdrop of the Comeragh Mountains, Knockmealdowns and Drum Hills. The first nine holes are laid out on a large plateau featuring a stream which comes into play at the 3rd and 4th holes. The river at the southern boundary affects several later holes.
18 holes, 6732yds, Par 72, SSS 72, Course record 70.
Club membership 300.
Visitors pre book for tee times. **Societies** telephone or write in advance. **Green Fees** €26 per 18 holes; €15 per 9 holes (€32/€20 weekends and bank holidays). **Cards** ▨ ▨ **Course Designer** Eddie Hackett **Facilities** ⊗ ⅏ ⅊ ♨ ♀ ⅄ ☎ ⚐ ⛴ ⚒ ⚓ ⛳ **Leisure** hard tennis courts. **Location** Approx 3m W of Dungarvan, off N25

Hotel ★★★ 61% Lawlors Hotel, DUNGARVAN
☎ 058 41122 & 41056 ▨ 058 41000 89 en suite

DUNMORE EAST

Map 01 C2

Dunmore East ☎ 051 383151 ▨ 051 383151
Overlooking the village of Dunmore East, with panoramic views of the village, bay and Hook peninsula. This course promises to offer idyllic surroundings and challenging golf for the high or low handicap golfer.
18 holes, 6655yds, Par 72, SSS 70, Course record 69.
Club membership 300.
Visitors welcome, no restrictions. **Societies** telephone in advance. **Green Fees** €21 per 18 holes (€26 weekends and bank holidays). **Cards** ▨ ▨ **Prof** Derry Kiely **Course Designer** W H Jones **Facilities** ⊗ ⅏ ⅊ ♨ ♀ ⅄ ☎ ⚐ ⛴ ⚒ ⚓ ⛳ **Location** Follow signs to Dunmore East. After Petrol Stn take left fork. Left at The Strand Inn & 1st right

Hotel ★★★ 63% Majestic Hotel, TRAMORE
☎ 051 381761 60 en suite

LISMORE

Map 01 C2

Lismore Ballyin ☎ 058 54026 ▨ 058 53338
e-mail: dooleybernard@eircom.net
Picturesque tree-dotted sloping course on the banks of the Blackwater River. Rothwell's is a difficult hole with a sloping green and trees to either side.
9 holes, 2748mtrs, Par 69, SSS 68.
Club membership 350.
Visitors telephone in advance, especially weekends. **Societies** must apply in writing or phone. **Green Fees** €20. **Facilities** ⅊ ♨ ♀ ⅄ ⚒ ⛳ **Location** 1 m from Lismore on Ballyduff Road

Hotel ★★★ 61% Lawlors Hotel, DUNGARVAN
☎ 058 41122 & 41056 ▨ 058 41000 89 en suite

AA website: www.theAA.com

TRAMORE

Map 01 C2

Tramore Newtown Hill ☎ 051 386170 ▨ 051 390961
e-mail: tragolf@iol.ie
This course has matured nicely over the years to become a true championship test and has been chosen as the venue for the Irish Professional Matchplay Championship and the Irish Amateur Championship. Most of the fairways are lined by evergreen trees, calling for accurate placing of shots, and the course is continuing to develop.
18 holes, 5918mtrs, Par 72, SSS 72, Course record 65.
Club membership 1200.
Visitors pre-booking required. **Societies** contact in advance. **Green Fees** €40 per 18 holes (€ 45 weekends). **Cards** ▨ ▨ **Prof** Derry Kiely **Course Designer** Capt H C Tippet **Facilities** ⊗ ⅏ ⅊ ♨ ♀ ⅄ ☎ ⚐ ⛴ ⚒ ⚓ ⛳ **Leisure** squash. **Location** 0.5m from Tramore on Dungaruan coast road

Hotel ★★★ 63% Majestic Hotel, TRAMORE
☎ 051 381761 60 en suite

WATERFORD

Map 01 C2

Faithlegg Faithlegg ☎ 051 382241 ▨ 051 382664
e-mail: golf@faithlegg.com
Some wicked slopes and borrows on the immaculate greens, a huge 432yd 17th that has a host of problems and a dog-leg approach to the two-tier 18th green are just some of the novel features on this course. Set on the banks of the River Suir, the course has been integrated into a landscape textured with mature trees, flowing parkland and five lakes.
18 holes, 6057mtrs, Par 72, SSS 72, Course record 69.
Club membership 200.
Visitors no restrictions. **Societies** apply in writing or telephone at least a month in advance. **Green Fees** €35 per 18 holes (€50 weekends). **Cards** ▨ ▨ ▨ ▨ **Prof** Ted Higgins **Course Designer** Patrick Merrigan **Facilities** ⊗ ⅏ ⅊ ♨ ♀ ⅄ ☎ ⚐ ⛴ ⚒ ⚓ ⛳ **Leisure** hard tennis courts, heated indoor swimming pool, sauna, solarium, gymnasium.

Hotel ★★★ 61% Jurys Hotel, Ferrybank, WATERFORD
☎ 051 832111 98 en suite

Waterford Newrath ☎ 051 876748 ▨ 051 853405
Undulating parkland course in pleasant surroundings.
18 holes, 5722mtrs, Par 71, SSS 70, Course record 64.
Club membership 983.
Visitors must contact in advance. **Societies** must apply in writing. **Green Fees** terms on application. **Prof** Brendan McDermott **Course Designer** W Park/J Braid **Facilities** ⊗ ⅏ ⅊ ♨ ♀ ⅄ ☎ ⚐ ⛴ ⚒ ⚓ ⛳ **Location** 1m N

Hotel ★★★ 61% Jurys Hotel, Ferrybank, WATERFORD
☎ 051 832111 98 en suite

Waterford Castle The Island, Ballinakill
☎ 051 871633 ▨ 051 871634
e-mail: golf@waterfordcastle.com
Parkland course situated on a 310 acre private island which is serviced by a privately owned ferry and features many mature trees, 4 inland lakes and 79 testing bunkers.
18 holes, 5827mtrs, Par 72, SSS 71, Course record 70.
Club membership 650.
Visitors must contact in advance, pre booking required. **Societies** apply in advance. **Green Fees** €41 per 18 holes (€49 Fri-Sun and bank holidays) reductions in

continued

winter. **Cards** 🔲 🔳 **Course Designer** Den Smyth **Facilities** ⊗ 〣 ⓛ 🖳 ⛴ ♀ ♎ ⛳ 🏠 🚶 ⛰ ✓ ⌇ **Leisure** hard tennis courts.**Conf** Thtr 80 Class 40 Board 40 Banquet 120 **Location** 2m E of Waterford City, on Island approached by private ferry

....

Hotel ★★★★ 77% Waterford Castle Hotel, The Island, WATERFORD ☎ 051 878203 19 en suite

CO WESTMEATH

ATHLONE   Map 01 C4

Glasson Golf & Country Club Glasson
☎ 0902 85120 📠 0902 85444
e-mail: info@glassongolf.ie
Opened for play in 1993 the course has earned a reputation for being one of the most challenging and scenic courses in Ireland. Designed by Christy O'Connor Jnr it is reputedly his best yet! Surrounded on three sides by Lough Ree the views from everywhere on the course are breathtaking.
21 holes, 6664yds, Par 72, SSS 72, Course record 65.
Club membership 220.
Visitors must book in advance. **Societies** book in advance.
Green Fees €45 (Mon-Thur);€50 (Fri-Sun);€60(Sat)per round. **Cards** 🔲 ▬ 🔳 🔳 **Course Designer** Christy O'Connor Jnr **Facilities** ⊗ 〣 ⓛ 🖳 ⛴ ♀ ♎ 🏠 ⛳ 🚶 ⛰ ✓ **Conf** Max 100 Thtr 100 Class 30 Board 30 Del from €30 * **Location** 6m N of Athlone on N55

DELVIN   Map 01 C4

Delvin Castle Clonyn
☎ 044 64315 & 64671 📠 044 64315
Situated in the mature parkland of Clonyn Castle, the course is well known for its unique historic setting with a 16th century ruin in the back nine holes and an imposing Victorian castle in the front nine.
18 holes, 5800mtrs, Par 70, SSS 68.
Club membership 400.
Visitors no restrictions. Advance booking recommemded.
Societies apply in writing in advance. **Green Fees** €24 per 18 holes;€14 per 9 holes (€26/€16 weekends & bank holidays). **Prof** David Keenaghan **Course Designer** John Day **Facilities** ⊗ 〣 ⓛ 🖳 ⛴ ♀ ♎ 🏠 ⛳ ✓ **Location** On N52, Dundalk to Mullingar road

....

Hotel ★★★ 62% Ardboyne Hotel, Dublin Rd, NAVAN ☎ 046 23119 29 en suite

MOATE   Map 01 C4

Moate ☎ 0902 81271 📠 0902 81267
Extended in 1994 to 18 holes, the course is parkland with

continued

---

trees. Although the original 9-holes did not have water hazards the new section has lakes and many bunkers.
18 holes, 5742mtrs, Par 72, SSS 70, Course record 67.
Club membership 650.
Visitors welcome, advisable to telephone in advance.
Societies must contact in advance. **Green Fees** not confirmed. **Prof** Paul Power **Course Designer** B Browne **Facilities** ⊗ 〣 ⓛ 🖳 ⛴ ♀ ♎ 🏠 🚶 ✓ **Location** 1m N

....

Hotel ★★ 68% Royal Hoey Hotel, Mardyke St, ATHLONE ☎ 0902 72924 & 75395 📠 0902 75194 38 en suite

Mount Temple Mount Temple Village
☎ 0902 81841 & 81545 📠 0902 81957
e-mail: mttemple@iol.ie
A traditionally built, highly-rated, all year round course with parkland and unique links-type greens and natural undulating fairways. A challenge for all levels of golfers as the wind plays a major part in the scoring on this course.
18 holes, 6020mtrs, Par 72, SSS 72, Course record 71.
Club membership 200.
Visitors welcome but must book for weekends. **Societies** telephone in advance. **Green Fees** €25 per round(€32 weekends & bank holidays). **Cards** 🔲 ▬ **Prof** David Keenan **Course Designer** Michael Dolan **Facilities** ⊗ 〣 ⓛ ♎ 🏠 ⛳ 🚶 ✓ **Location** 4m off N6 to Mount Temple village, 5m from Athlone

....

Hotel ★★ 68% Royal Hoey Hotel, Mardyke St, ATHLONE ☎ 0902 72924 & 75395 📠 0902 75194 38 en suite

MULLINGAR   Map 01 C4

Mullingar ☎ 044 48366 📠 044 41499
18 holes, 6406yds, Par 72, SSS 71, Course record 63.
Course Designer James Braid **Location** 3m S
Telephone for further details

Hotel ★★ 68% Royal Hoey Hotel, Mardyke St, ATHLONE ☎ 0902 72924 & 75395 📠 0902 75194 38 en suite

CO WEXFORD

ENNISCORTHY   Map 01 D3

Enniscorthy Knockmarshall
☎ 054 33191 📠 054 37367
A pleasant course suitable for all levels of ability.
18 holes, 6115mtrs, Par 72, SSS 72.
Club membership 900.
Visitors must telephone for booking. **Societies** must book in advance. **Green Fees** €24 Mon-Thur(€33 Fri-Sun and bank holidays). **Prof** Martin Sludds **Course Designer** Eddie Hackett **Facilities** ⊗ 〣 ⓛ 🖳 ⛴ ♀ ♎ 🏠 ⛳ 🚶 ✓ ⌇ **Location** 1m from town on New Ross road

....

Hotel ★ 60% Murphy-Flood's Hotel, Market Square, ENNISCORTHY ☎ 054 33413 19 rms (17 en suite)

GOREY   Map 01 D3

Courtown Kiltennel ☎ 055 25166 📠 055 25553
e-mail: courtown@iol.ie
A pleasant parkland course which is well wooded and enjoys views across the Irish Sea near Courtown Harbour.
18 holes, 5898mtrs, Par 71, SSS 71, Course record 65.
Club membership 1637.

continued

Courtown Golf Club

Visitors must contact in advance. **Societies** advisable to contact in advance. **Green Fees** €36 per 18 holes(€42 weekends). Reductions in winter. **Cards** 💳 💳 **Prof** John Coone **Course Designer** Harris & Associates **Facilities** ⊗ 🏯 🛍 💄 ♀ 🛆 🏠 🍴 🏐 🚣 ♿ **Location** 3m from town, off Courtown Road

Hotel ★★★🏨 Marlfield House Hotel, GOREY
☎ 055 21124 20 en suite

NEW ROSS   Map 01 C3

New Ross Tinneranny ☎ 051 421433 🖨 051 420098
Recently extended to 18-holes, this well kept parkland course has an attractive backdrop of hills and mountains. Straight hitting and careful placing of shots is very important, especially on the 2nd, 6th, 10th and 15th, all of which are challenging holes.
18 holes, 5751yds, Par 71, SSS 70.
Club membership 700.
Visitors welcome, booking required for weekend play. **Societies** apply to secretary/manager. **Green Fees** €20 per round(€30 weekends & bank holidays). **Course Designer** Des Smith **Facilities** ⊗ 🛍 💄 ♀ 🛆 🏠 ♿ **Location** 3m from town centre

Hotel ★★★ 64% Clarion Brandon House Hotel Health Club & Spa, Wexford Rd, NEW ROSS ☎ 051 421703 61 en suite

ROSSLARE   Map 01 D2

Rosslare Rosslare Strand ☎ 053 32203 🖨 053 32263
e-mail: office@rosslaregolf.com
This traditional links course is within minutes of the ferry terminal at Rosslare, but its popularity is not confined to visitors from Fishguard or Le Havre. It is a great favourite with the Irish too. Many of the greens are sunken and are always in beautiful condition, but the semi-blind approaches are among features of this course which provide a healthy challenge.
Old Course: 18 holes, 6608yds, Par 72, SSS 72,
Course record 66.
New Course: 12 holes, 3956yds, Par 46.
Club membership 1000.
Visitors telephone 053 32203 ext3 in advance. **Societies** apply in writing/telephone. **Green Fees** Old Course: €35(€50 weekends) New Course: €17. **Cards** 💳 💳 **Prof** Johnny Young **Course Designer** Hawtree/Taylor **Facilities** ⊗ 🏯 🛍 💄 ♀ 🛆 🏠 🍴 🏐 🚣 ♿ **Leisure** sauna. **Location** 6m N of Rosslare Ferry Terminal

Hotel ★★★★ 78% Kelly's Resort Hotel, ROSSLARE
☎ 053 32114 99 annexe en suite

St Helen's Bay Golf & Country Club

St Helens, Kilrane ☎ 053 33234 🖨 053 33803
e-mail: sthelens@iol.ie
A championship-standard golf course designed by Philip Walton. Link and parkland with water hazards, bunkers and trees incorporated generously. Overlooking the beach with accommodation on site.
18 holes, 5813mtrs, Par 72, SSS 72, Course record 69.
Club membership 500.
Visitors contact in advance. **Societies** telephone in advance. **Green Fees** €25-€40 per 18 holes. **Cards** 💳 💳 **Course Designer** Philip Walton **Facilities** ⊗ 🏯 🛍 💄 ♀ 🛆 🏠 🍴 🏐 🚣 ♿ **Leisure** hard tennis courts, golf academy and tuition area.

Hotel ★★★★ 68% Ferrycarrig Hotel, Ferrycarrig Bridge, WEXFORD ☎ 053 20999 103 en suite

WEXFORD   Map 01 D3

Wexford Mulgannon ☎ 053 42238 🖨 053 42243
Parkland course with panoramic view of the Wexford coastline and mountains.
18 holes, 6100yds, Par 72, SSS 70.
Club membership 800.
Visitors must contact in advance but may not play Thu & Sundays. **Societies** must contact in writing. **Green Fees** not confirmed. **Prof** Damien McGrane **Facilities** ⊗ 🏯 🛍 💄 ♀ 🛆 🏠 🍴 🏐 ♿

Hotel ★★★ 73% Talbot Hotel Conference & Leisure Centre, Trinity St, WEXFORD
☎ 053 22566 100 en suite

CO WICKLOW

ARKLOW   Map 01 D3

Arklow Abbeylands ☎ 0402 32492 🖨 0402 91604
e-mail: arklowgolflinks@eircom.net
Scenic links course.
18 holes, 5802mtrs, Par 69, SSS 68, Course record 64.
Club membership 780.
Visitors may play Mon-Fri and 4hrs Sat 9am-1 oclock, must book in advance. **Societies** must apply in writing or telephone in advance. **Green Fees** €40. **Cards** 💳 💳 💳 **Course Designer** Hawtree & Taylor **Facilities** ⊗ 🏯 🛍 💄 ♀ 🛆 🏠 🍴 🏐 ♿ **Location** 0.5m from town centre

Hotel ★★★🏨 Marlfield House Hotel, GOREY
☎ 055 21124 20 en suite

BALTINGLASS   Map 01 D3

Baltinglass Dublin Rd ☎ 0508 81350 🖨 0508 81842
On the banks of the River Slaney, the 9-hole course has 4 par 4s over 400 yards which have to be played twice. Reputed to be one of the hardest 9-hole courses in the Republic. A further 9 holes are being developed with tree lined fairways to make a 18 hole course with many mature hardwood trees.
9 holes, 5554mtrs, Par 68, SSS 69, Course record 68.
Club membership 500.
Visitors advisable to check availability for weekends. **Societies** apply in writing or by telephone. **Green Fees** €16(€20 weekends and bank holidays). **Course Designer** Lionel Hewston **Facilities** ⊗ 🛍 💄 ♀ 🛆 ♿ **Location** 500 metres N of Baltinglass

continued

Hotel ★★★ 68% Seven Oaks Hotel, Athy Rd, CARLOW
☎ 0503 31308 60 en suite

Rathsallagh ☎ 045 403316 045 403295
e-mail: info@rathsallagh.com
Designed by Peter McEvoy and Christy O'Connor Jnr, this is a spectacular course which will test the pro's without intimidating the club golfer. Set in 252 acres of lush parkland with thousands of mature trees, natural water hazards and gently rolling landscape. The greens are of high quality, in design, construction and condition.
18 holes, 6916yds, Par 72, SSS 74.
Club membership 270.
Visitors prior booking and neat dress is essential.Metal spikes are prohibited. **Societies** apply in writing **Green Fees** €55(€70 Fri-Sat & bank holidays). **Cards** **Prof** Brendan McDaid **Course Designer** McEvoy/O'Connor **Facilities** **Leisure** hard tennis courts, heated indoor swimming pool, sauna. **Conf** Max 150 Thtr 40 Class 75 Board 40 Banquet 150 Del €40 to €50 * **Location** 15m SE of Naas off main Dublin/Carlow road

Hotel ★★★ 66% Downshire House Hotel, BLESSINGTON
☎ 045 865199 14 en suite 11 annexe en suite

BLAINROE Map 01 D3

Blainroe ☎ 0404 68168 0404 69369
e-mail: blainroegolfclub@eircom.net
Parkland course overlooking the sea on the east coast, offering a challenging round to golfers of all abilities. Some holes are situated right on the coast and two holes worth noting are the 14th and the par 3 15th over the lake
18 holes, 6070mtrs, Par 72, SSS 72, Course record 71.
Club membership 1060.
Visitors must contact in advance. **Societies** must telephone in advance. **Green Fees** €41(€53 weekends). **Cards** **Prof** John McDonald **Course Designer** Fred Hawtree **Facilities** **Location** 3 miles S of Wicklow, on coast road

Hotel ★★★ Tinakilly Country House & Restaurant, RATHNEW ☎ 0404 69274 51 en suite

BLESSINGTON Map 01 D3

Tulfarris House Hotel & Country Club
☎ 045 867644 045 867000
Designed by Paddy Merrigan, this course is on the Blessington lakeshore with the Wicklow Mountains as a backdrop. The use of the natural landscape is evident throughout the whole course, the variety of trees guarding fairways and green approaches.
18 holes, 7116yds, Par 72, SSS 74, Course record 68.
Club membership 150.
Visitors tee booking advisable; may not play Sun 8-11.30pm. **Societies** must contact in writing or telephone in advance. **Green Fees** €65 per round (€80 weekends & bank holidays). **Cards** **Prof** A Williams **Course Designer** Patrick Merrigan **Facilities** **Leisure** hard tennis courts, heated indoor swimming pool, fishing, sauna, solarium, gymnasium.**Conf** Max 250 **Location** Via N81, 2m from Blessington village

Hotel ★★★ 66% Downshire House Hotel, BLESSINGTON
☎ 045 865199 14 en suite 11 annexe en suite

BRAY Map 01 D4

Bray Ravenswell Rd ☎ 01 2862484 01 2862484
A 9-hole parkland course with plenty of trees and bunkers.
9 holes, 5761mtrs, Par 70, SSS 70, Course record 65.
Club membership 500.
Visitors restricted Mon, Sat & Sun. **Societies** contact in advance. **Green Fees** not confirmed. **Prof** Michael Walby **Facilities**

Hotel ★★★★ 65% Fitzpatrick Castle Hotel, KILLINEY
☎ 01 2305400 113 en suite

Old Conna Ferndale Rd
☎ 01 2826055 & 2826766 01 2825611
e-mail: info@oldconna.com
Parkland course set in wooded terrain with panoramic views of Irish Sea and Wicklow mountains.
18 holes, 6550yds, Par 72, SSS 72, Course record 70.
Club membership 900.
Visitors advisable to contact in advance but may not play weekends. Smart dress essential on course & in clubhouse. **Societies** must telephone well in advance. **Green Fees** €45 per round (€25 early bird special). **Cards** **Course Designer** Eddie Hackett **Facilities** **Location** 2m from Bray

Hotel ★★★ 59% Royal Hotel & Leisure Centre, Main St, BRAY ☎ 01 2862935 91 en suite

Woodbrook Dublin Rd ☎ 01 2824799 01 2821950
e-mail: woodbrook@internet-ireland.ie
Pleasant parkland with magnificent views and bracing sea breezes which has hosted a number of events, including the Irish Close and the Irish Open Championships. A testing finish is provided by an 18th hole with out of bounds on both sides.
18 holes, 6017mtrs, Par 72, SSS 71, Course record 65.
Club membership 1100.
Visitors must contact in advance and have a handicap certificate. **Societies** must contact in advance. **Green Fees** not confirmed. **Cards** **Prof** Billy Kinsella **Course Designer** Peter McEvoy **Facilities** **Location** 11m S of Dublin on N11

Hotel ★★★ 59% Royal Hotel & Leisure Centre, Main St, BRAY ☎ 01 2862935 91 en suite

BRITTAS BAY Map 01 D3

The European Club
☎ 0404 47415 0404 47449
e-mail: info@europeanclub.com
A links course that runs through a large dunes system. Since it was opened in 1992 it is rapidly gaining recognition as one of Irelands Best Courses. Notable holes include the 7th, 13th and 14th.
18 holes, 7105yds, Par 71, SSS 73, Course record 69.
Club membership 100.
Visitors pre-booking advised especially for weekends, no denim. **Societies** must book in advance. **Green Fees** €75 Nov-Mar;€100 Apr-Oct. **Cards** **Course Designer** Pat Ruddy **Facilities** **Location** 1m from Brittas Bay Beach

Hotel ★★★ Tinakilly Country House & Restaurant, RATHNEW ☎ 0404 69274 51 en suite

DELGANY Map 01 D3

Delgany ☎ 01 2874536 🖥 01 2873977
e-mail: delganygolf@eircom.net
An undulating parkland course amidst beautiful scenery.
18 holes, 5480mtrs, Par 69, SSS 68, Course record 61.
Club membership 1070.
Visitors may play Mon, Wed (until 9am), Thu & Fri. Contact in advance. **Societies** contact in advance. **Green Fees** €20 per 9 holes;€38 per 18 holes. **Cards** 🖃 ▦ **Prof** Gavin Kavanagh **Course Designer** H Vardon **Facilities** ⊗ ∭ ⓑ ⛳ ♀ ⚒ 🏠 ⛳ ↘ ⚒ ✇ **Conf** Max 35 **Location** 0.75m from village

Hotel ★★★ 59% Royal Hotel & Leisure Centre, Main St, BRAY ☎ 01 2862935 91 en suite

ENNISKERRY Map 01 D4

Powerscourt Powerscourt Estate
☎ 01 2046033 🖥 01 2761303
e-mail: golfclub@powerscourt.ie
A free draining course with links characteristics. This championship course with top quality tees and exceptional tiered greens, is set in some of Ireland's most beautiful parkland. The course has an abundance of mature trees and natural features, with stunning views of the sea and the Sugarloaf mountain.
East Course: 18 holes, 5930mtrs, Par 72, SSS 72.
Club membership 715.
Visitors necessary to book in advance. **Societies** necessary to book in advance. **Green Fees** € 100 per round. **Prof** Paul Thompson **Course Designer** Peter McEvoy **Facilities** ⊗ ∭ ⓑ ✇ ♀ ⚒ 🏠 ⛳ 🏳 ↘ ⚒ ⛳ ⚒ **Location** 12m S of Dublin just off N11 in Enniskerry

Hotel ★★★ 59% Royal Hotel & Leisure Centre, Main St, BRAY ☎ 01 2862935 91 en suite

GREYSTONES Map 01 D3

Charlesland Golf & Country Club Hotel
☎ 01 2874350 & 2878200 🖥 01 2874360
e-mail: teetimes@charlesland.com
Championship length, Par 72 course with a double dog-leg at the 9th and 18th. Water hazards at the 3rd and 11th.
18 holes, 5963mtrs, Par 72, SSS 72.
Visitors must contact in advance. **Societies** must apply in advance. **Green Fees** €32 Mon-Thur(€45 Fri-Sun). **Cards** 🖃 ▦ **Prof** Peter Duignan **Course Designer** Eddie Hackett **Facilities** ⊗ ∭ ⓑ ✇ ♀ ⚒ 🏠 ⛳ 🏳 ↘ ⚒ ⛳ ⚒ **Leisure** sauna. **Conf** Max 200 Thtr 200 Class 160 Board 80 Banquet 100 Del €5 to €20 * **Location** 1m S of Greystones on the road to Delgany village

Hotel ★★★★≜ Tinakilly Country House & Restaurant, RATHNEW ☎ 0404 69274 51 en suite

Greystones ☎ 01 2874136 🖥 01 2873749
e-mail: secretary@greystonesgc.com
A part level and part hilly parkland course.
18 holes, 5322mtrs, Par 69, SSS 68.
Club membership 995.
Visitors may only play Mon, Tue & Fri morning. Must contact in advance. **Societies** must contact in writing/telephone. **Green Fees** €40 per round. **Cards** 🖃 ▦ **Prof** Karl Holmes **Course Designer** P Merrigan **Facilities** ⊗ ∭ ⓑ ✇ ♀ ⚒ 🏠 ⛳ ⚒

continued

Hotel ★★★★≜ Tinakilly Country House & Restaurant, RATHNEW ☎ 0404 69274 51 en suite

KILCOOLE See page 435

KILCOOLE Map 01 D3

Kilcoole ☎ 01 2872066 2872070 🖥 01 2010497
e-mail: admin.kg@eircom.net
9 holes, 5506mtrs, Par 70, SSS 69.
Club membership 250.
Visitors restricted Sat & Sun 8-10am. **Societies** apply in writing **Green Fees** €26 per 18 holes;€17 per 9 holes (€32 per 18 holes weekends). **Cards** 🖃 ▦ **Facilities** ⊗ ⓑ ✇ ♀ ⚒ ⛳ **Location** N11 Kilcoole/Newcastle

Hotel ★★★★≜ Tinakilly Country House & Restaurant, RATHNEW ☎ 0404 69274 51 en suite

RATHDRUM Map 01 D3

Glenmalure Greenane ☎ 0404 46679 🖥 0404 46783
e-mail: golf@glenmalure-golf.ie
18 holes, 5300yds, Par 71, SSS 67, Course record 71.
Course Designer P Suttle **Location** 2m W
Telephone for further details

Hotel ★★★ 64% Woodenbridge Hotel, WOODEN BRIDGE ☎ 0402 35146 23 en suite

ROUNDWOOD Map 01 D3

Roundwood Newtown, Mountkennedy
☎ 01 2818488 & 2802555 🖥 01 2843642
e-mail: rwood@indigo.ie
Heathland and parkland course with forest and lakes set in beautiful countryside with views of the coast and the Wicklow Mountains.
18 holes, 6685yds, Par 72, SSS 72.
Club membership 160.
Visitors no restrictions **Societies** pre booking necessary. **Green Fees** €35(€45 weekends). **Facilities** ⊗ ∭ ⓑ ✇ ⚒ ⛳ ↘ ⚒ ⛳ **Location** 2.5m off N11 at Newtown Mountkennedy on N765

Hotel ★★★ 61% The Glendalough Hotel, GLENDALOUGH ☎ 0404 45135 44 en suite

SHILLELAGH Map 01 D3

Coollattin Coollattin ☎ 055 29125 🖥 055 29125
Plenty of trees provide features on this 18-hole parkland course.
18 holes, 6148yds, Par 70, SSS 68, Course record 70.
Club membership 976.
Visitors Must contact in advance. **Societies** contact for details. **Green Fees** I€30 (€40 weekends & bank holidays).

continued on page 436

Druid's Glen

Kilcoole, *Co Wicklow*   ☎ 01 2873600   Fax 01 2873699   Map 01 D3

e-mail: info@druidsglen.ie

ruid's Glen, from the first tee to the eighteenth green creates an exceptional golfing experience that is totally unique, with its distinguished surroundings and spectacular views. A masterpiece of inspired planning and golfing architecture, designed by Tom Craddock and Pat Ruddy, it is the culmination of years of preparation, creating a unique inland golf course that challenges and satisfies in equal parts. Special features include an island green on the 17th hole and a Celtic Cross on the 12th.

Druids Glen hosted the Murphy's Irish Open in 1996, 1997, 1998 and an unprecedented fourth time in 1999. In 2000 Druid's Glen won the title of European Golf Course of the Year and in 2002 it hosted the Seve Trophy. The world's top professionals and club golfers alike continue to enjoy the challenge offered here. A variety of teeing positions are available and there is a practice area, including three full-length 'academy holes'. Individual and corporate members enjoy generous reserved tee times, visitors are very welcome but it is recommended that you book well in advance.

Visitors advance booking essential

Societies advance booking essential

Green Fees €125 per round Groups (16 or more) €105 per round

Facilities ⊗ 🍴 🧺 🍺 ♀ 🏌 🏠 🍽 🐾 🥄 🛒 ⚙ 🏌 Touring Professional (Eamonn Darcy)

Leisure swimming, sauna, gym

Location 20m S of Dublin, 3m off N11 motorway, immediately S of Glen of the Downs

Holes/Par/Course record 18 holes, 6547 yds, Par 71, SSS 73, Course record 62

Championship Course

WHERE TO STAY NEARBY

Hotels
RATHNEW
★★★ ◎◎ ♨ Tinakilly Country House & Restaurant.
☎ 0404 69274. 51 en suite

★★★◎ 67% Hunters Hotel.
☎ 0404 40106. 16 en suite

Cards ⬛ **Prof** Peter Jones **Course Designer** Peter McEvoy
Facilities ⊗ �𝍢 🝢 ☕ ♀ ⚲ 🏠 ❦ ⛳ ⚐

Hotel ★★★♨ Marlfield House Hotel, GOREY
☎ 055 21124 20 en suite

WICKLOW   Map 01 D3

Wicklow Dunbur Rd ☎ 0404 67379
**Situated on the cliffs overlooking Wicklow Bay this
parkland course does not have many trees. It was
extended to 18 holes in 1994, it provides a challenging test
of golf with each hole having its own individual features.**
18 holes, 5126mtrs, Par 71, SSS 70.
Club membership 500.
Visitors welcome, restrictions on Wed/Thu evening and Sun.
Recommended to call in advance for times **Societies** contact
for details. **Green Fees** not confirmed. **Cards** ⬛ ⬛ **Prof**
Darren McLoughlin **Course Designer** Craddock & Ruddy
Facilities ⊗ �𝍢 🝢 ☕ ♀ ⚲ 🏠 ⚐

Hotel ★★★♨ Tinakilly Country House & Restaurant,
RATHNEW ☎ 0404 69274 51 en suite

WOODENBRIDGE   Map 01 D3

Woodenbridge Woodenbridge, Arklow
☎ 0402 35202 ▤ 0402 35754
e-mail: wgc@eircom.net
**A level parkland course with undulating fairways and
greens, traversed by two lovely meandering rivers.**
18 holes, 6400yds, Par 71, SSS 70, Course record 71.
Club membership 650.
Visitors may not play Thu and Sat, prior booking strongly
recommended. **Societies** Mon, Tue & Fri only, book well in
advance. **Green Fees** €51 per 18 holes(€63 Sun and bank
holidays). **Cards** ⬛ ⬛ **Course Designer** Patrick Merrigan
Facilities ⊗ �𝍢 🝢 ☕ ♀ ⚲ ⛳ ⚐ **Location** 4m NW of
Arklow

Hotel ★★★ 64% Woodenbridge Hotel, WOODEN
BRIDGE ☎ 0402 35146 23 en suite

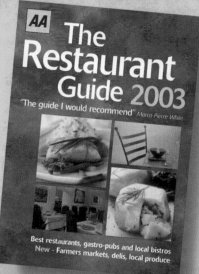
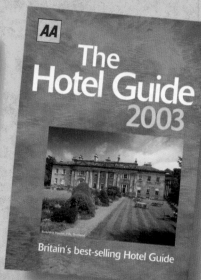
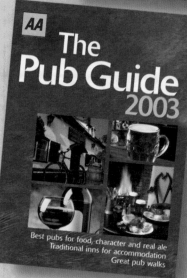
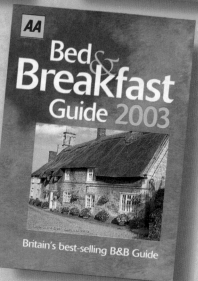

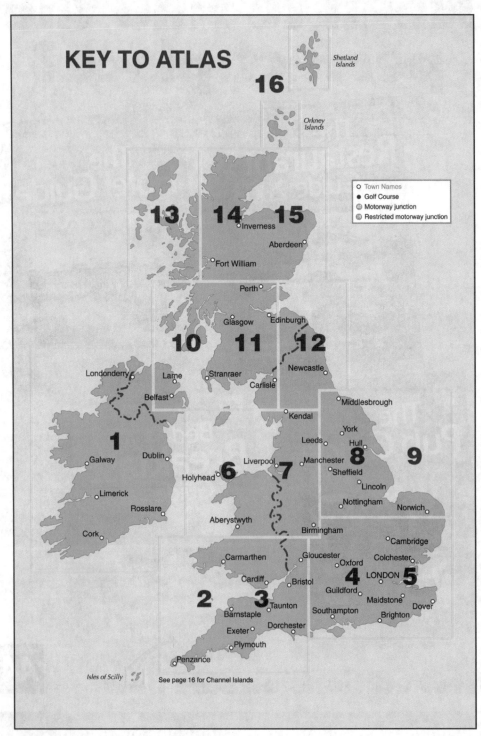

KEY TO ATLAS

Shetland Islands

16

Orkney Islands

○	Town Names
●	Golf Course
Ⓐ	Motorway junction
Ⓡ	Restricted motorway junction

13   **14**   **15**

Inverness

Aberdeen

Fort William

Perth

Glasgow   Edinburgh

10   **11**   **12**

Londonderry   Larne   Stranraer   Newcastle

Belfast   Carlisle

Middlesbrough

Kendal

York

Leeds   Hull

Galway   Dublin   Liverpool   Manchester   **8**   **9**

1   Holyhead   **6**   **7**   Sheffield

Limerick   Lincoln

Rosslare   Aberystwyth   Nottingham   Norwich

Cork   Birmingham

Cambridge

Carmarthen   Gloucester   Colchester

2   Cardiff   Bristol   Oxford   **4**   LONDON   **5**

3   Taunton   Guildford

Barnstaple   Southampton   Maidstone   Dover

Exeter   Dorchester   Brighton

Plymouth

Penzance

Isles of Scilly   See page 16 for Channel Islands

© Automobile Association Developments Limited 2002

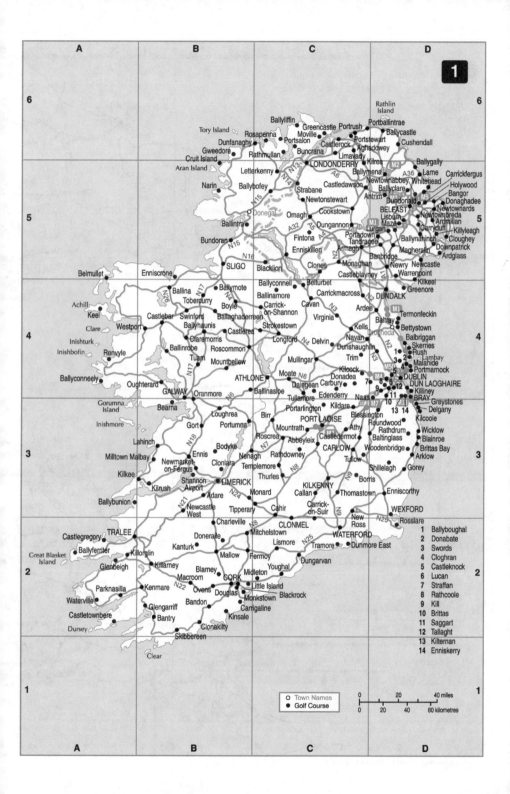

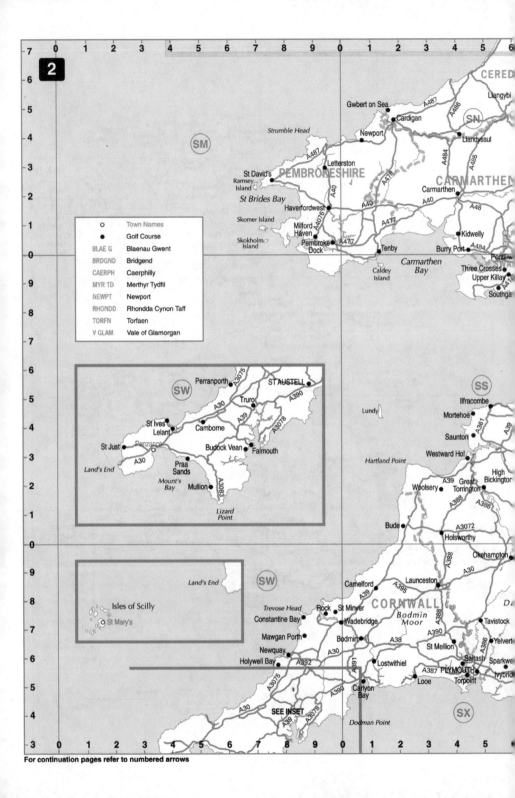

2

CERED

Llangybi

SN

Gwbert on Sea

Cardigan

A487 A486

Strumble Head

Newport

Llandyssul

SM

A487

PEMBROKESHIRE

A484 A485

Letterston

CARMARTHEN

St David's

A40

Ramsey
Island

Carmarthen

St Brides Bay

A40 A40

A478

Haverfordwest

A48

Skomer Island

A4076

A477

Milford
Haven

Kidwelly

Skokholm
Island

Pembroke
Dock

A477

Burry Port

A484

Pontlliw

Tenby

Three Crosses

Carmarthen
Bay

Upper Killay

Caldey
Island

Southga

○	Town Names
●	Golf Course
BLAE G	Blaenau Gwent
BRDGND	Bridgend
CAERPH	Caerphilly
MYR TD	Merthyr Tydfil
NEWPT	Newport
RHONDD	Rhondda Cynon Taff
TORFN	Torfaen
V GLAM	Vale of Glamorgan

Perranporth

A3075

ST AUSTELL

SS

Ilfracombe

SW

Truro

A390

Mortehoe

Lundy

Saunton

A361

A39

St Ives
Lelant

Camborne

A39

A3078

Westward Ho!

St Just

Penzance

A30

Budock Vean

Falmouth

Hartland Point

High
Bickington

Land's End

A30

Praa
Sands

Woolsery

A39

Great
Torrington

Mount's
Bay

A3083

Mullion

A388

A386

Lizard
Point

Bude

A3072

Holsworthy

A388

Okehampton

Land's End

SW

Camelford

A30

Launceston

A395

A30

Isles of Scilly

Trevose Head

Rock

St Minver

CORNWALL

Da

St Mary's

Constantine Bay

Wadebridge

Bodmin
Moor

Tavistock

Mawgan Porth

Bodmin

A390

A386

Yelvert

Newquay

A30

A38

St Mellion

Saltash

Sparkwe

Holywell Bay

A392

A391

Lostwithiel

A387

PLYMOUTH

Ivybrid

A3075

Looe

Torpoint

Carlyon
Bay

A390

SX

SEE INSET

A39

A3078

Dodman Point

For continuation pages refer to numbered arrows

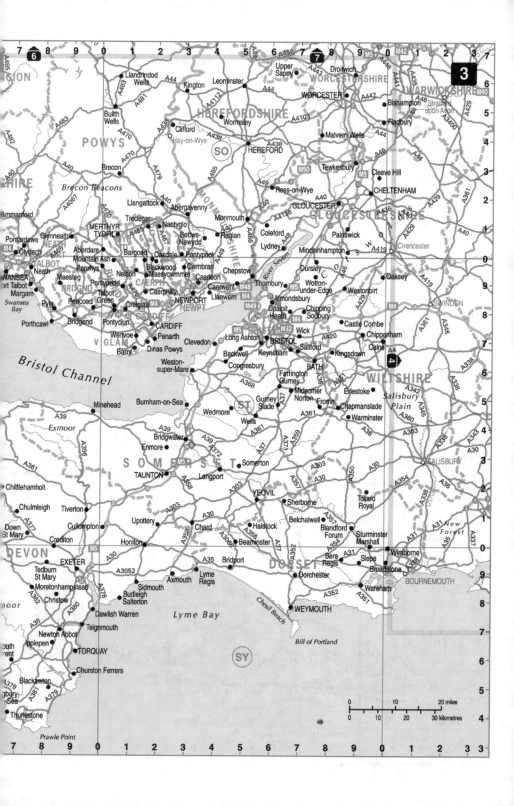

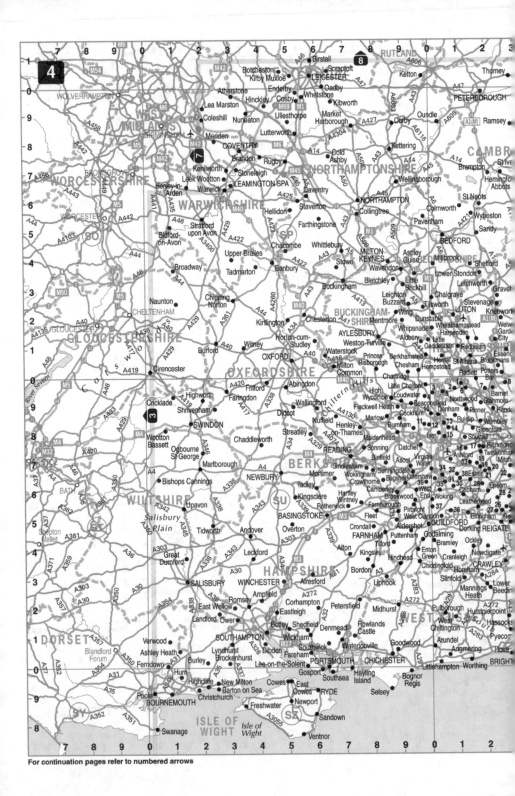

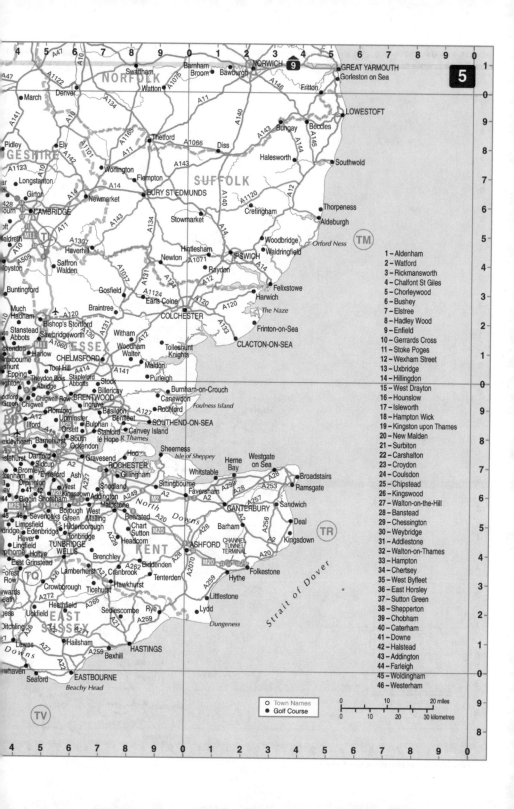

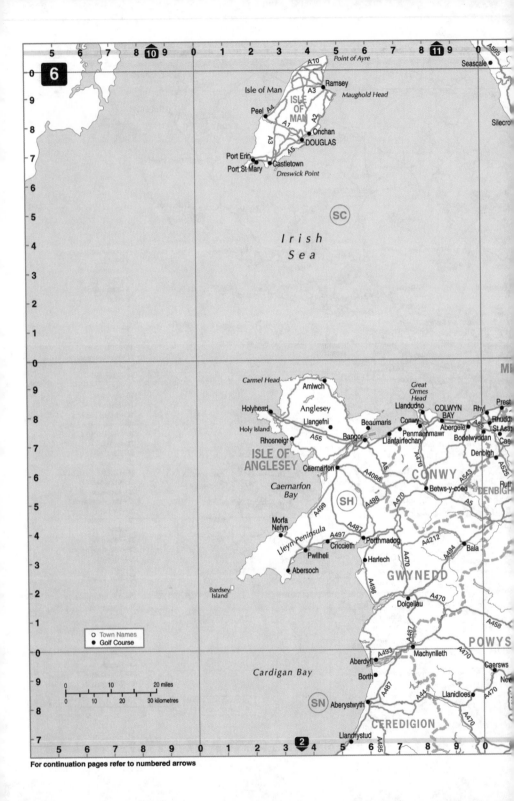

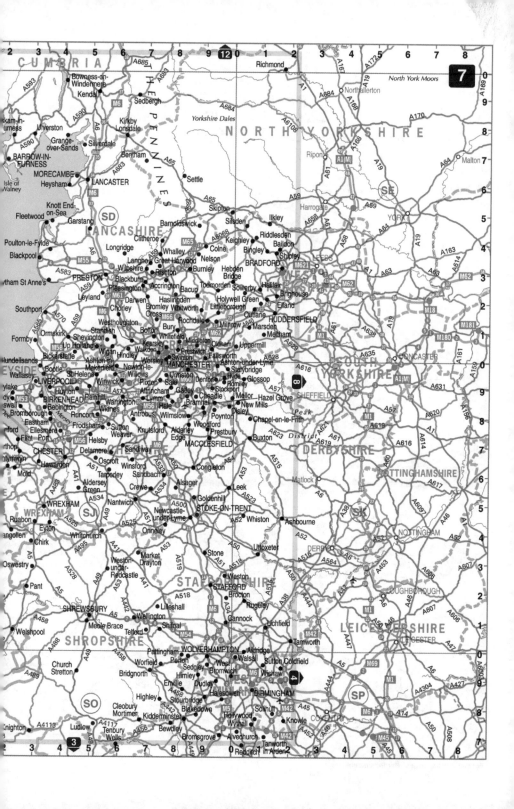

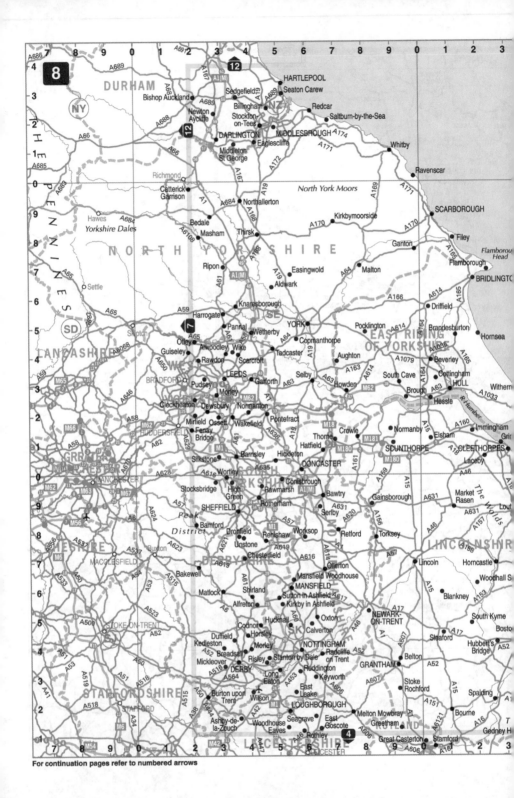

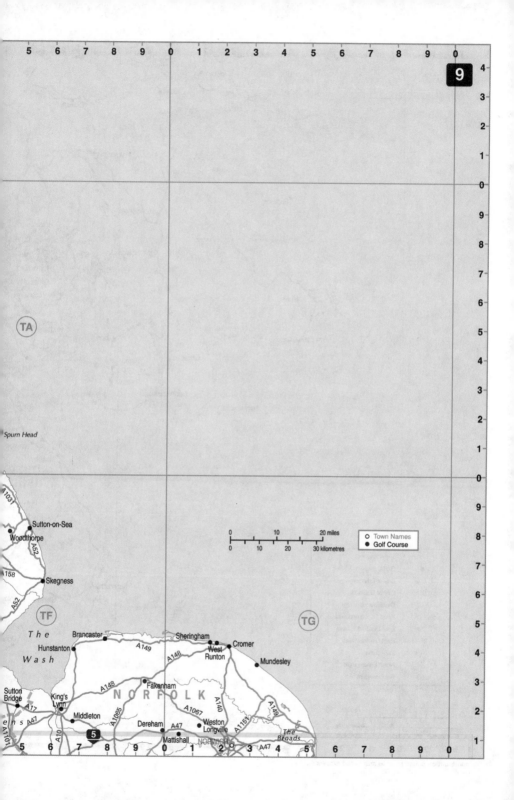

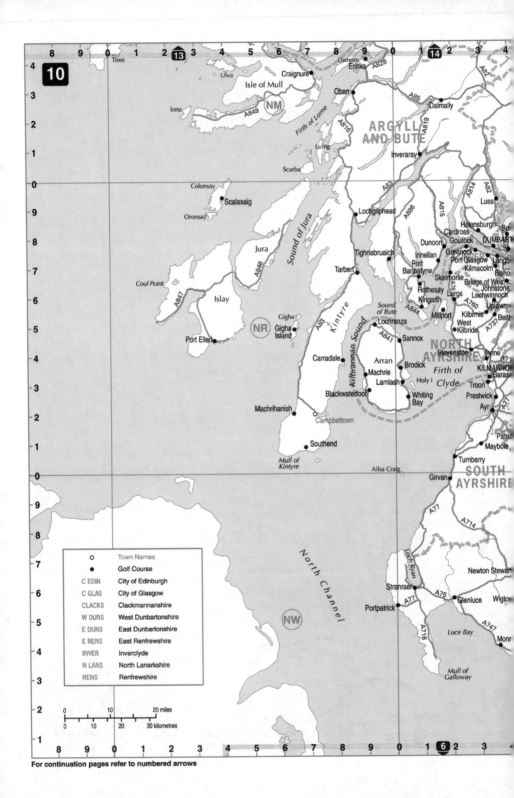

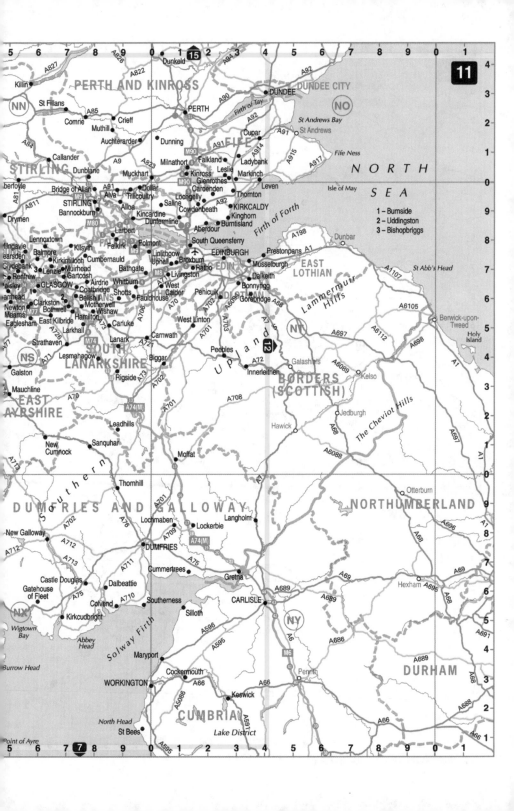

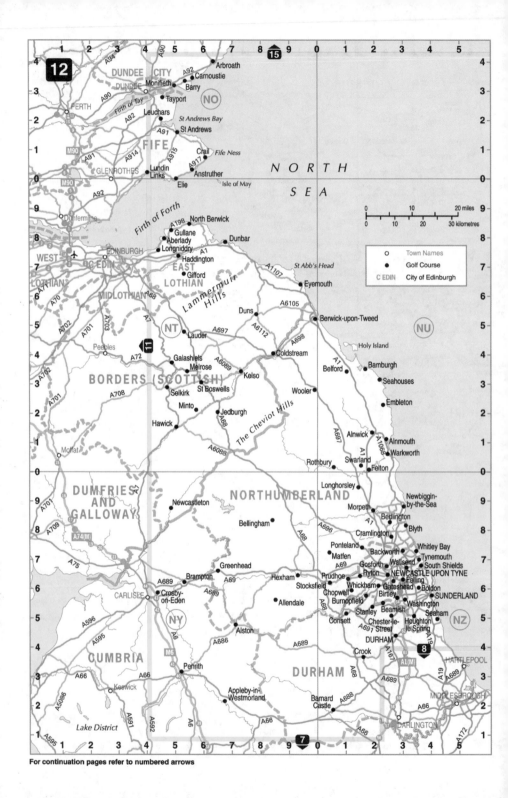

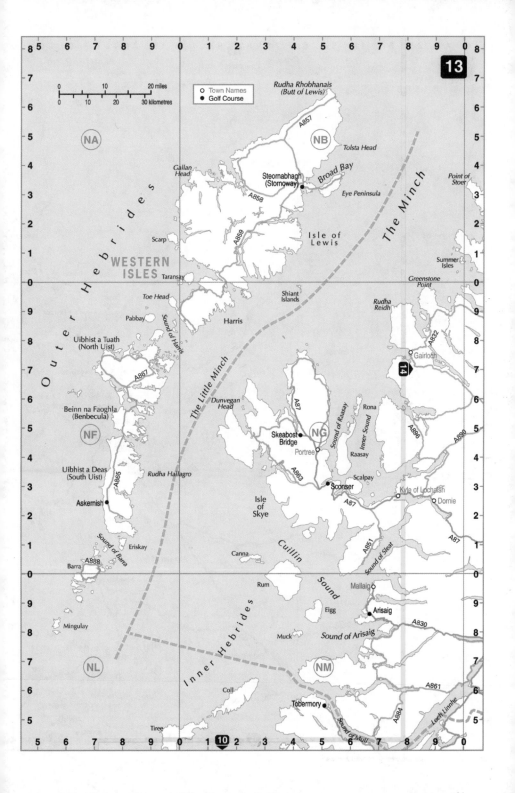

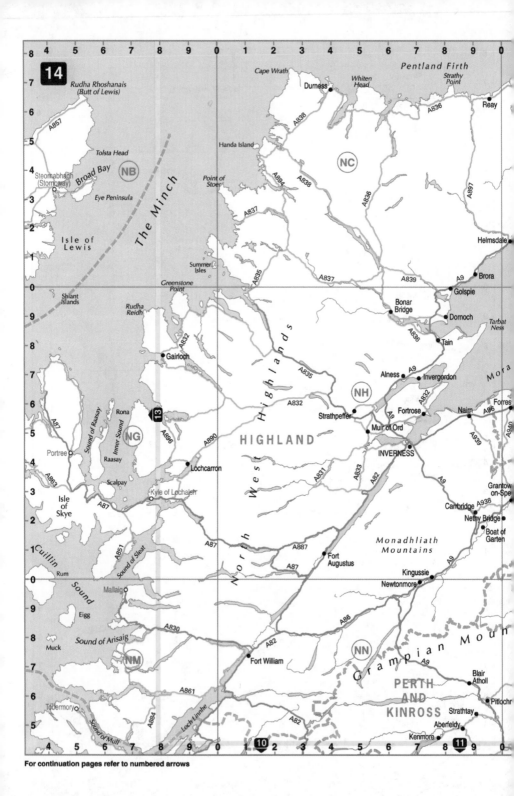

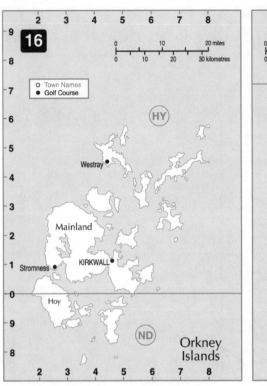
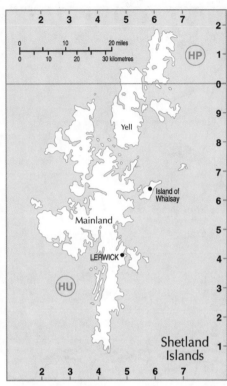
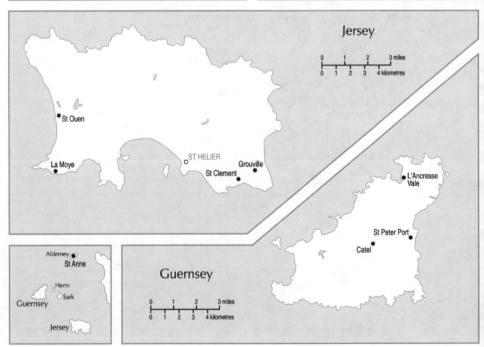

16

Town Names ○
Golf Course ●

0 ___ 10 ___ 20 miles
0 ___ 10 ___ 20 ___ 30 kilometres

HY

Westray ●

Mainland

Stromness ●   KIRKWALL ●

Hoy

ND

Orkney Islands

0 ___ 10 ___ 20 miles
0 ___ 10 ___ 20 ___ 30 kilometres

HP

Yell

Mainland

Island of Whalsay ●

LERWICK ●

HU

Shetland Islands

Jersey

0 ___ 1 ___ 2 ___ 3 miles
0 ___ 1 ___ 2 ___ 3 ___ 4 kilometres

St Ouen ●

ST HELIER ○

La Moye ●

St Clement ●   Grouville ●

L'Ancresse Vale ●

St Peter Port ●

Catel ●

Alderney ●
St Anne

Herm

Guernsey   Sark

Jersey

Guernsey

0 ___ 1 ___ 2 ___ 3 miles
0 ___ 1 ___ 2 ___ 3 ___ 4 kilometres

AA Hotels
with special arrangements for golf

The following index lists hotels, inspected and rated by the AA, that have a special arrangement with a golf course or courses. These hotels may have their own golf course attached to the hotel or nearby, or they may offer discounted green fees, reserved tee times or other golfing packages to residents. This list was believed correct at our press date, please contact the hotels directly for information on golfing packages or arrangements. Further details of these and other hotels can be found in the AA Hotel Guide, published annually. For the most up-to-date information visit the AA web site: www.theAA.com

ENGLAND

ABBOT'S SALFORD
Salford Hall Hotel   01386 871300

ALBRIGHTON
Lea Manor Hotel   01902 373266

ALDEBURGH
The Brudenell   01728 452071

ALDEBURGH
Wentworth Hotel   01728 452312

ALDEBURGH
White Lion Hotel   01728 452720

ALDERMINSTER
Ettington Park Hotel   01789 450123

ALMONDSBURY
Aztec Hotel   01454 201090

ALNWICK
White Swan Hotel   01665 602109

ALTRINCHAM
Cresta Court Hotel   016192 77272

ALTRINCHAM
Quality Hotel Altrincham
          016192 87121

AMBLESIDE
Nanny Brow Country House Hotel
          01539 432036

AMBLESIDE
Regent Hotel   01539 432254

AMESBURY
Antrobus Arms Hotel   01980 623163

ANDOVER
Quality Hotel Andover   01264 369111

ANSTY
Ansty Hall   02476 612222

ASCOT
The Berystede   0870 400 8111

ASCOT
The Royal Berkshire Hotel
          01344 623322

ASHBOURNE
The Dog & Partridge   01335 343183

ASHBURTON
Holne Chase Hotel   01364 631471

ASHBURTON
The Lavender House Hotel
          01364 652697

ASHFORD
Eastwell Manor   01233 213000

AXMINSTER
Fairwater Head Hotel   01297 678349

AYLESBURY
Hartwell House   01296 747444

BALSALL COMMON
Nailcote Hall   024 7646 6174

BAMBURGH
The Mizen Head Hotel 01668 214254

BAMBURGH
Victoria Hotel   01668 214431

BAMBURGH
Waren House Hotel   01668 214581

BANBURY
Banbury House   01295 259361

BANBURY
Wroxton House Hotel   01295 730777

BARLBOROUGH
Hotel Ibis   01246 813222

BARTON
Barton Grange Hotel   01772 862551

BASINGSTOKE
Apollo Hotel   01256 796700

BASSENTHWAITE
Castle Inn Hotel   017687 76401

BATH
The Bath Spa Hotel   0870 400 8222

BATH
The Francis   0870 400 8223

BATH
The Lansdown Grove   01225 483888

BATH
Wentworth House Hotel
          01225 339193

BEACONSFIELD
The Bellhouse   01753 887211

BEAMINSTER
Bridge House Hotel   01308 862200

BELFORD
Blue Bell Hotel   01668 213543

BELLINGHAM
Riverdale Hall Hotel   01434 220254

BERWICK-UPON-TWEED
Marshall Meadows
Country House Hotel   01289 331133

BERWICK-UPON-TWEED
Queens Head   01289 307852

BIDEFORD
Yeoldon Country House Hotel
          01237 474400

BIGBURY-ON-SEA
Henley Hotel   01548 810240

BIRKENHEAD
Bowler Hat Hotel   0151 652 4931

BIRMINGHAM
Express by Holiday Inn
Castle Bromwich   0121 747 6633

BIRMINGHAM
Holiday Inn Birmingham
          0870 400 9009

BIRMINGHAM
Oxford Hotel   0121 449 3298

BIRMINGHAM
The Westley Hotel   0121 706 4312

BIRMINGHAM AIRPORT
Novotel Birmingham Airport
          0121 782 7000

BISHOP'S STORTFORD
Down Hall Country House Hotel
          01279 731441

BOLTON ABBEY
The Devonshire Arms
Country House Hotel   01756 710441

BORROWDALE
Borrowdale Hotel   017687 77224

BOSCASTLE
The Wellington Hotel   01840 250202

BOURNEMOUTH
Belvedere Hotel   01202 297556

BOURNEMOUTH
Bourne Hall Hotel   01202 299715

BOURNEMOUTH
Cumberland Hotel   01202 290722

BOURNEMOUTH
Elstead Hotel   01202 293071

BOURNEMOUTH
Queens Hotel   01202 554415

BOURNEMOUTH
The Connaught Hotel 01202 298020

BOURNEMOUTH
The Montague Hotel 01202 551074

BOURTON-ON-THE-WATER
Chester House Hotel & Motel
01451 820286

BOURTON-ON-THE-WATER
Dial House Hotel 01451 822244

BOVEY TRACEY
Coombe Cross Hotel 01626 832476

BRACKNELL
Coppid Beech 01344 303333

BRACKNELL
Grange Bracknell 01344 474000

BRADFORD
Apperley Manor 0113 250 5626

BRADFORD
Courtyard by Marriott Leeds/Bradford
0113 285 4646

BRADFORD
Hanover International Hotel & Club
01274 406606

BRADFORD-ON-AVON
Leigh Park Hotel 01225 864885

BRADFORD-ON-AVON
Woolley Grange 01225 864705

BRAMHALL
County Hotel Bramhall
0161 455 9988

BRAMPTON
Farlam Hall Hotel 016977 46234

BRAMPTON
The Tarn End House Hotel
016977 2340

BRANDESBURTON
Burton Lodge Hotel 01964 542847

BRANDS HATCH
Brandshatch Place 01474 875000

BRANSTON
Branston Hall Hotel 01522 793305

BRAY
Chauntry House Hotel & Restaurant
01628 673991

BRENT KNOLL
Battleborough Grange Hotel
01278 760208

BRIDGNORTH
Falcon Hotel 01746 763134

BRIDGWATER
Walnut Tree Hotel 01278 662255

BRIDLINGTON
Expanse Hotel 01262 675347

BRIDPORT
Haddon House Hotel 01308 423626

BRIDPORT
Roundham House Hotel
01308 422753

BRIGHOUSE
Holiday Inn Leeds/Brighouse
0870 400 9013

BRIGHTON
Brighton Hotel 01273 820555

BRIGHTON
Old Ship Hotel 01273 329001

BRISTOL
Bristol Marriott City Centre
0117 929 4281

BRISTOL
Bristol Marriott Royal Hotel
0117 925 5100

BRISTOL
Henbury Lodge Hotel 0117 950 2615

BRIXHAM
Berryhead Hotel 01803 853225

BRIXHAM
Maypool Park 01803 842442

BRIXHAM
Quayside Hotel 01803 855751

BROADWAY
The Broadway Hotel 01386 852401

BROCKENHURST
Balmer Lawn Hotel 01590 623116

BROCKENHURST
Rhinefield House 01590 622922

BROME
The Cornwallis Country
Hotel & Restaurant 01379 870326

BROMLEY
Bromley Court Hotel 020 8461 8600

BROMSGROVE
Hanover International Hotel & Club
01527 576600

BROXTON
Broxton Hall Country House Hotel
01829 782321

BROXTON
De Vere Carden Park Hotel
01829 731000

BUCKINGHAM
Villiers Hotel 01280 822444

BUDE
Atlantic House Hotel 01288 352451

BUDE
Camelot Hotel 01288 352361

BUDE
Falcon Hotel 01288 352005

BUDE
Hotel Penarvor 01288 352036

BUDE
Maer Lodge Hotel 01288 353306

BURFORD
The Inn For All Seasons
01451 844324

BURNHAM
Burnham Beeches 01628 429955

BURNHAM
Grovefield Hotel 01628 603131

BURNLEY
Oaks Hotel 01282 414141

BURRINGTON
Northcote Manor 01769 560501

BURY ST EDMUNDS
Ravenwood Hall Hotel 01359 270345

BUXTON
Buckingham Hotel 01298 70481

BUXTON
Palace Hotel 01298 22001

BUXTON
Portland Hotel & Park Restaurant
01298 71493

CALNE
Lansdowne Strand Hotel
01249 812488

CAMBRIDGE
Crowne Plaza Cambridge
01223 464466

CAMBRIDGE
Royal Cambridge Hotel 01223 351631

CANTERBURY
County Hotel 01227 766266

CANTERBURY
The Chaucer 0870 400 8106

CARLISLE
Crown Hotel 01228 561888

CARLISLE
The Crown & Mitre 01228 525491

CHADDESLEY CORBETT
Brockencote Hall
Country House Hotel 01562 777876

CHALE
Clarendon Hotel & Wight Mouse Inn
01983 730431

CHARD
Lordleaze Hotel 01460 61066

CHELTENHAM
Cheltenham Park Hotel
01242 222021

CHELTENHAM
The Greenway 01242 862352

CHELTENHAM
The Prestbury House
Hotel & Restaurant 01242 529533

CHESTER
Grosvenor Pulford Hotel
01244 570560

CHESTER
Innkeeper's Lodge Chester
01244 332200

CHESTER
The Chester Crabwell Manor Hotel
01244 851666

CHICHESTER
The Ship Hotel 01243 778000

CHIDEOCK
Chideock House Hotel
01297 489242

CHIPPING CAMPDEN
Cotswold House   01386 840330

CHOLLERFORD
Swallow George Hotel   01434 681611

CHORLEY
Park Hall Hotel   01257 452090

CHRISTCHURCH
The Avonmouth   0870 400 8120

CHURT
Frensham Pond Hotel   01252 795161

CHURT
Pride of the Valley Hotel
                        01428 605799

CLACTON-ON-SEA
Esplanade Hotel   01255 220450

CLEARWELL
Tudor Farmhouse Hotel & Restaurant
                        01594 833046

CLEATOR
Ennerdale Country House Hotel
                        01946 813907

CLEOBURY MORTIMER
The Redfern Hotel   01299 270395

CLEVEDON
Walton Park Hotel   01275 874253

CLITHEROE
Shireburn Arms Hotel   01254 826518

COLCHESTER
Holiday Inn Colchester
                        0870 400 9020

COLERNE
Lucknam Park   01225 742777

CONSTANTINE BAY
Treglos Hotel   01841 520727

COPTHORNE
Copthorne Hotel London Gatwick
                        01342 348800

CORFE CASTLE
Mortons House Hotel   01929 480988

CORNHILL-ON-TWEED
Tillmouth Park Country House Hotel
                        01890 882255

CRANBROOK
The George Hotel   01580 713348

CRATHORNE
Crathorne Hall Hotel   01642 700398

DARLINGTON
Blackwell Grange   01325 509955

DARLINGTON
Devonport Hotel   01325 332255

DARTFORD
Rowhill Grange Hotel & Spa
                        01322 615136

DARTMOUTH
Endsleigh Hotel   01803 770381

DARTMOUTH
Royal Castle Hotel   01803 833033

DARTMOUTH
Stoke Lodge Hotel   01803 770523

DARTMOUTH
The Dart Marina Hotel
                        01803 832 580

DAVENTRY
Hanover International Hotel & Club
                        01327 307000

DAWLISH
Langstone Cliff Hotel   01626 868000

DEDDINGTON
Deddington Arms   0800 3287031

DERBY
Hotel Ristorante La Gondola
                        01332 332895

DERBY
Menzies Mickleover Court
                        0870 6003013

DORKING
The White Horse   0870 400 8282

DOVER
The Churchill   01304 203633

DROITWICH
The Hadley Bowling Green Inn
                        01905 620294

DURHAM
Bowburn Hall Hotel   0191 377 0311

DURHAM
Durham Marriott Hotel,
Royal County   0191 386 6821

EASINGWOLD
George Hotel   01347 821698

EAST GRINSTEAD
Woodbury House Hotel
                        01342 313657

EASTBOURNE
Chatsworth Hotel   01323 411016

EASTBOURNE
Grand Hotel   01323 412345

EASTBOURNE
Hydro Hotel   01323 720643

EASTBOURNE
Lansdowne Hotel   01323 725174

EASTBOURNE
New Wilmington Hotel   01323 721219

EASTBOURNE
Quality Hotel Langham
                        01323 731451

EASTBOURNE
Wish Tower Hotel   01323 722676

EGHAM
Runnymede Hotel & Spa
                        01784 436171

ELSTREE
Edgwarebury Hotel   020 8953 8227

EMBLETON
Dunstanburgh Castle Hotel
                        01665 576111

EMPINGHAM
The White Horse Inn   01780 460221

EPWORTH
Red Lion Hotel   01427 872208

EVESHAM
Northwick Hotel   01386 40322

EVESHAM
The Mill At Harvington
                        01386 870688

EVESHAM
Wood Norton Hall   01386 420007

EWEN
Wild Duck Inn   01285 770310

EXETER
Gipsy Hill Hotel   01392 465252

EXETER
Lord Haldon Country House Hotel
                        01392 832483

EXETER
Royal Clarence   01392 319955

EXETER
The Southgate   0870 400 8333

EXMOUTH
Royal Beacon Hotel   01395 264886

FAILAND
Redwood Lodge Hotel   01275 393901

FAIRFORD
Bull Hotel   01285 712535

FALMOUTH
Falmouth Beach Resort Hotel
                        01326 312999

FALMOUTH
Falmouth Hotel   01326 312671

FALMOUTH
Green Lawns Hotel   01326 312734

FALMOUTH
Park Grove Hotel   01326 313276

FALMOUTH
Penmere Manor   01326 211411

FALMOUTH
Penmorvah Manor   01326 250277

FALMOUTH
Rosslyn Hotel   01326 312699

FALMOUTH
Royal Duchy Hotel   01326 313042

FAREHAM
Holiday Inn Fareham   0870 400 9028

FAREHAM
Lysses House Hotel   01329 822622

FAREHAM
Solent Hotel   01489 880000

FARINGDON
Sudbury House Hotel
& Conference Centre   01367 241272

FARNHAM
Bishop's Table Hotel   01252 710222

FELIXSTOWE
Orwell Hotel   01394 285511

FERNDOWN
The Dormy   01202 872121

FOREST ROW
Ashdown Park Hotel
and Country Club   01342 824988

FOWNHOPE
Green Man Inn   01432 860243

FRINTON-ON-SEA
Maplin Hotel   01255 673832

GILLAN
Tregildry Hotel   01326 231378

GISBURN
Stirk House Hotel   01200 445581

GLENRIDDING
The Inn on the Lake   017684 82444

GLOSSOP
Wind in the Willows Hotel
   01457 868001

GLOUCESTER
Hatton Court   01452 617412

GOODRICH
Ye Hostelrie Hotel   01600 890241

GRANTHAM
Grantham Marriott Hotel
   01476 593000

GRANTHAM
Kings Hotel   01476 590800

GRASMERE
Rothay Garden Hotel   015394 35334

GRASMERE
The Swan   0870 400 8132

GRASMERE
Wordsworth Hotel   015394 35592

GREAT YARMOUTH
Burlington Palm Court Hotel
   01493 844568

GREAT YARMOUTH
Imperial Hotel   01493 842000

GRIMSBY
Humber Royal   01472 240024

GUILDFORD
The Manor   01483 222624

HADLEY WOOD
West Lodge Park Hotel
   020 8216 3900

HALIFAX
The Rock Inn Hotel   01422 379721

HARLESTON
J D Young Hotel   01379 852822

HARROW WEALD
Grim's Dyke Hotel   020 8385 3100

HASTINGS & ST LEONARDS
Royal Victoria Hotel   01424 445544

HATFIELD
Quality Hotel Hatfield   01707 275701

HAYWARDS HEATH
The Birch Hotel   01444 451565

HEBDEN BRIDGE
Carlton Hotel   01422 844400

HELLAND BRIDGE
Tredethy House   01208 841262

HELMSLEY
Feversham Arms Hotel   01439 770766

HELMSLEY
Pheasant Hotel   01439 771241

HELMSLEY
The Crown Hotel   01439 770297

HELSTON
The Gwealdues Hotel   01326 572808

HEMEL HEMPSTEAD
The Bobsleigh Inn   01442 833276

HEREFORD
Ancient Camp Inn   01981 250449

HEREFORD
Graftonbury Garden Hotel
   01432 268826

HETHERSETT
Park Farm Hotel   01603 810264

HEXHAM
Beaumont Hotel   01434 602331

HIGH WYCOMBE
The Kings Arms   01494 609090

HINCKLEY
Hanover International Hotel & Club
   01455 631122

HINCKLEY
Sketchley Grange Hotel
   01455 251133

HINTON CHARTERHOUSE
Homewood Park Hotel   01225 723731

HOLMFIRTH
Old Bridge Hotel   01484 681212

HOLSWORTHY
Court Barn Country House Hotel
   01409 271219

HONITON
Combe House Hotel at Gittisham
   01404 540400

HOPE COVE
Cottage Hotel   01548 561555

HORLEY
Stanhill Court Hotel   01293 862166

HORNCASTLE
Admiral Rodney Hotel   01507 523131

HOUNSLOW
The Renaissance London Heathrow
   020 8897 6363

HUDDERSFIELD
Old Golf House Hotel   01422 379311

HUDDERSFIELD
The Lodge Hotel   01484 431001

HULL
Holiday Inn Hull Marina
   0870 400 9043

HUNMANBY
Wrangham House Hotel
   01723 891333

HUNSTRETE
Hunstrete House   01761 490490

HURSTBOURNE TARRANT
Esseborne Manor   01264 736444

HYTHE
Stade Court   01303 268263

HYTHE
The Hythe Imperial Hotel
   01303 267441

ILFRACOMBE
Westwell Hall Hotel   01271 862792

ILKLEY
Innkeeper's Lodge   01943 607335

ILKLEY
The Craiglands Hotel   01943 430001

ILMINSTER
Shrubbery Hotel   01460 52108

IPSWICH
County Hotel Ipswich   01473 209988

IPSWICH
Novotel Ipswich   01473 232400

IVYBRIDGE
Glazebrook House
Hotel & Restaurant   01364 73322

KENDAL
Riverside Hotel   01539 734861

KENILWORTH
Le Meridien Warwick   01926 859331

KESWICK
Keswick Country House Hotel
   017687 72020

KESWICK
Skiddaw Hotel   017687 72071

KETTERING
Kettering Park Hotel   01536 416666

KING'S LYNN
Stuart House Hotel   01553 772169

KINGSBRIDGE
Buckland-Tout-Saints   01548 853055

KINGTON
Burton Hotel   01544 230323

KIRKBY LONSDALE
Hipping Hall   015242 71187

KIRKBY LONSDALE
Plough Hotel   015395 67227

KIRKBYMOORSIDE
George & Dragon Hotel
   01751 433334

KNUTSFORD
Cottons Hotel   01565 650333

KNUTSFORD
Mere Court Hotel &
Conference Centre   01565 831000

LANDFORD
New Forest Lodge Hotel
   01794 390999

LANGAR
Langar Hall   01949 860559

LANGHO
Northcote Manor   01254 240555

LAVENHAM
The Swan   0870 400 8116

LEATHERHEAD
Bookham Grange Hotel
   01372 452742

LEEDS
42 The Calls Townhouse
0113 244 0099

LEEDS
Crowne Plaza Leeds   0113 244 2200

LEEDS
Haley's Hotel & Restaurant
0113 278 4446

LEICESTER
Hermitage Hotel   0116 256 9955

LEICESTER
Leicester Stage Hotel   0116 288 6161

LENHAM
Chilston Park Hotel   01622 859803

LEOMINSTER
Royal Oak Hotel   01568 612610

LEOMINSTER
Talbot Hotel   01568 616347

LEWES
White Hart Hotel   01273 476694

LICHFIELD
Little Barrow Hotel   01543 414500

LIFTON
Arundell Arms   01566 784666

LIFTON
Lifton Hall Hotel   01566 784863

LONDON W1
Claridge's   020 7629 8860

LONDON W1
The Westbury Hotel   020 7629 7755

LONDON WC2
The Savoy   020 7836 4343

LONG MELFORD
The Black Lion   01787 312356

LONG MELFORD
The Bull   01787 378494

LOOE
Fieldhead Hotel   01503 262689

LOOE
Hannafore Point Hotel 01503 263273

LOOE
Rivercroft Hotel & Apartments
01503 262251

LOSTWITHIEL
Lostwithiel Hotel Golf &
Country Club   01208 873550

LOSTWITHIEL
Restormel Lodge Hotel
01208 872223

LOUGHBOROUGH
Quality Hotel   01509 211800

LOWER BEEDING
South Lodge Hotel   01403 891711

LOWER SLAUGHTER
Lower Slaughter Manor
01451 820456

LOWER SLAUGHTER
Washbourne Court Hotel
01451 822143

LOWESTOFT
Ivy House Farm Hotel   01502 501353

LUDLOW
Dinham Hall Hotel   01584 876464

LYDFORD
Lydford House   01822 820347

LYMPSHAM
Batch Country Hotel   01934 750371

LYNDHURST
Crown Hotel   023 8028 2922

LYNTON
Lynton Cottage Hotel 01598 752342

LYTHAM ST ANNES
Clifton Arms   01253 739898

LYTHAM ST ANNES
Glendower Hotel   01253 723241

MAIDENHEAD
Elva Lodge Hotel   01628 622948

MALTON
Burythorpe House Hotel
01653 658200

MALVERN
Foley Arms Hotel   01684 573397

MALVERN
The Cottage in the Wood Hotel
01684 575859

MANCHESTER
Le Meridien Victoria & Albert
0870 400 8585

MANCHESTER
The Lowry Hotel   0161 827 4000

MANCHESTER
The Waterside Hotel   0161 445 0225

MARCH
Olde Griffin Hotel   01354 652517

MARKET HARBOROUGH
Three Swans Hotel   01858 466644

MASHAM
Swinton Park   01765 680900

MAWGAN PORTH
Tredragon Hotel   01637 860213

MAWNAN SMITH
Budock Vean-The Hotel on the River
01326 252100

MAWNAN SMITH
Meudon Hotel   01326 250541

MAWNAN SMITH
Trelawne Hotel   01326 250226

MERIDEN
Manor Hotel   01676 522735

MIDSOMER NORTON
Centurion Hotel   01761 417711

MILFORD ON SEA
Westover Hall Hotel   01590 643044

MILTON COMMON
The Oxford Belfry   01844 279381

MILTON KEYNES
Holiday Inn Milton Keynes
0870 400 9057

MILTON KEYNES
Quality Hotel & Suites Milton Keynes
01908 561666

MINEHEAD
Channel House Hotel   01643 703229

MINEHEAD
Periton Park Hotel   01643 706885

MORECAMBE
Strathmore Hotel   01524 421234

MORETON
Leasowe Castle Hotel 0151 606 9191

MORETON-IN-MARSH
Manor House Hotel   01608 650501

MORTEHOE
Lundy House Hotel   01271 870372

MOUSEHOLE
Old Coastguard Hotel 01736 731222

MULLION
Mullion Cove Hotel   01326 240328

MULLION
Polurrian Hotel   01326 240421

MUNDFORD
Lynford Hall Hotel   01842 878351

NAILSWORTH
Egypt Mill Hotel   01453 833449

NANTWICH
Crown Hotel & Restaurant
01270 625283

NANTWICH
Rookery Hall   01270 610016

NEWBURY
Newbury Manor Hotel 01635 528838

NEWBURY
The Vineyard at Stockcross
01635 528770

NEWCASTLE UPON TYNE
Vermont Hotel   0191 233 1010

NEWCASTLE UPON TYNE
Whites Hotel   0191 281 5126

NEWICK
Newick Park Hotel & Country Estate
01825 723633

NEWQUAY
Barrowfield Hotel   01637 878878

NEWQUAY
Cedars Hotel   01637 874225

NEWQUAY
Esplanade Hotel   01637 873333

NEWQUAY
Headland Hotel   01637 872211

NEWQUAY
Hotel Bristol   01637 875181

NEWQUAY
Hotel Riviera   01637 874251

NEWQUAY
Philema Hotel   01637 872571

NEWQUAY
Porth Veor Manor Hotel
01637 873274

NEWQUAY
Trebarwith Hotel 01637 872288

NORTH WALTHAM
Premier Lodge (Basingstoke)
0870 700 1312

NORTHAMPTON
Courtyard by Marriott Northampton
01604 622777

NORTHAMPTON
Lime Trees Hotel 01604 632188

NORTHAMPTON
Northampton Marriott Hotel
01604 768700

NORTHWICH
Quality Hotel Northwich
01606 44443

NORWICH
Quality Hotel 01603 741161

NORWICH
Stower Grange 01603 860210

NOTTINGHAM
Bestwood Lodge 0115 920 3011

NOTTINGHAM
Hotel des Clos 0115 986 6566

NOTTINGHAM
Nottingham Gateway 0115 979 4949

NUNNEY
The George at Nunney
01373 836458

OAKHAM
Hambleton Hall 01572 756991

OAKHAM
Whipper-in Hotel 01572 756971

OKEHAMPTON
Ashbury Hotel 01837 55453

OKEHAMPTON
Manor House Hotel 01837 53053

OKEHAMPTON
White Hart Hotel 01837 52730

ORMSKIRK
Beaufort Hotel 01704 892655

OSWESTRY
Pen-y-Dyffryn Country Hotel
01691 653700

OSWESTRY
Wynnstay Hotel 01691 655261

OTTERBURN
The Otterburn Tower Hotel
01830 520620

OXFORD
Hawkwell House 01865 749988

OXFORD
Linton Lodge Hotel 01865 553461

PAIGNTON
Dainton Hotel 01803 550067

PAIGNTON
Torbay Holiday Motel 01803 558226

PAINSWICK
Painswick Hotel 01452 812160

PEASLAKE
Hurtwood Inn Hotel 01306 730851

PENKRIDGE
Quality Hotel Stafford 01785 712459

PENRITH
North Lakes Hotel 01768 868111

PENRITH
The George Hotel 01768 862696

PICKERING
Cottage Leas Country Hotel
01751 472129

PICKERING
White Swan 01751 472288

PICKHILL
Nags Head Country Inn
01845 567391

PLYMOUTH
Grand Hotel 01752 661195

PLYMOUTH
Grosvenor Park Hotel 01752 229312

PLYMOUTH
Kitley House Hotel 01752 881555

PLYMOUTH
New Continental Hotel
01752 220782

POCKLINGTON
Yorkway Motel Ltd 01759 303071

POOLE
Haven Hotel 01202 707333

POOLE
Mansion House Hotel 01202 685666

POOLE
Salterns Hotel 01202 707321

POOLE
Sandbanks Hotel 01202 707377

PORLOCK
Anchor Hotel & Ship Inn
01643 862753

PORTSMOUTH
Portsmouth Marriott Hotel
023 9238 3151

PORTSMOUTH
Westfield Hall Hotel 023 9282 6971

PRESTON
Preston Marriott Hotel
01772 864087

PULBOROUGH
Chequers Hotel 01798 872486

READING
Millennium Madejski Hotel Reading
0118 925 3500

READING
Royal County Hotel 0118 958 3455

REDDITCH
Montville Hotel and Restaurant
01527 544411

REDDITCH
The Abbey Hotel Golf &
Country Club 01527 406600

REDHILL
Nutfield Priory 01737 824400

REDWORTH
Redworth Hall Hotel 01388 770600

RENISHAW
Sitwell Arms Hotel 01246 435226

RICHMOND
King's Head Hotel 01748 850220

RINGWOOD
Tyrrells Ford Country House Hotel
01425 672646

RIPON
Ripon Spa Hotel 01765 602172

ROMSEY
Potters Heron Hotel 023 8026 6611

ROSEDALE ABBEY
White Horse Farm Hotel
01751 417239

ROSS-ON-WYE
Chase Hotel 01989 763161

ROSS-ON-WYE
Chasedale Hotel 01989 562423

ROSS-ON-WYE
Orles Barn Hotel and Restaurant
01989 562155

ROSS-ON-WYE
Pencraig Court Hotel 01989 770306

ROSS-ON-WYE
Pengethley Manor 01989 730211

ROSS-ON-WYE
The Royal 01989 565105

ROSS-ON-WYE
Wilton Court Hotel 01989 562569

ROWSLEY
East Lodge Country House Hotel
01629 734474

ROYAL TUNBRIDGE WELLS
The Spa Hotel 01892 520331

SALCOMBE
Bolt Head Hotel 01548 843751

SALCOMBE
Soar Mill Cove Hotel 01548 561566

SALCOMBE
South Sands Hotel 01548 843741

SALCOMBE
Tides Reach Hotel 01548 843466

SALISBURY
Milford Hall Hotel 01722 417411

SALISBURY
Rose & Crown Hotel 01722 399955

SANDIWAY
Nunsmere Hall Country House Hotel
01606 889100

SANDWICH
The Blazing Donkey
Country Hotel & Inn 01304 617362

SAUNTON
Preston House Hotel 01271 890472

SAUNTON
Saunton Sands Hotel 01271 890212

SCARBOROUGH
Crown Hotel 01723 357400

SCOTCH CORNER
Quality Hotel Scotch Corner
01748 850900

SEAHOUSES
Bamburgh Castle Hotel
01665 720283

SEATON
Seaton Heights Hotel
& Leisure Centre 01297 20932

SEAVIEW
Springvale Hotel & Restaurant
01983 612533

SEDGEFIELD
Hardwick Hall Hotel 01740 620253

SEDLESCOMBE
Brickwall Hotel 01424 870253

SEVENOAKS
Royal Oak Hotel 01732 451109

SHEFFIELD
Beauchief Hotel 0114 262 0500

SHERINGHAM
Dales Country House Hotel
01263 824555

SHIPLEY
Marriott Hollins Hall
Hotel & Country Club 01274 530053

SHREWSBURY
Albrighton Hall Hotel 01939 291000

SIDMOUTH
Belmont Hotel 01395 512555

SIDMOUTH
Devoran Hotel 01395 513151

SIDMOUTH
Fortfield Hotel 01395 512403

SIDMOUTH
Hunters Moon Hotel 01395 513380

SIDMOUTH
Kingswood Hotel 01395 516367

SIDMOUTH
Mount Pleasant Hotel 01395 514694

SIDMOUTH
Riviera Hotel 01395 515201

SIDMOUTH
Royal Glen Hotel 01395 513221

SIDMOUTH
Salcombe Hill House Hotel
01395 514697

SIDMOUTH
The Royal York & Faulkner Hotel
01395 513043 & 0800 220714

SIDMOUTH
Victoria Hotel 01395 512651

SIDMOUTH
Westbourne Hotel 01395 513774

SIDMOUTH
Westcliff Hotel 01395 513252

SKIPTON
Coniston Hall Hotel 01756 748080

SKIPTON
Hanover International Hotel & Club
01756 700100

SOUTH NORMANTON
Renaissance Derby/Nottingham Hotel
01773 812000

SOUTHAMPTON
De Vere Grand Harbour
023 8063 3033

SOUTHPORT
Balmoral Lodge Hotel 01704 544298

SPENNYMOOR
Whitworth Hall &
Country Park Hotel 01388 811772

ST AGNES
Rose in Vale Country House Hotel
01872 552202

ST ALBANS
Sopwell House Hotel,
Country Club & Spa 01727 864477

ST ALBANS
St Michael's Manor 01727 864444

ST AUSTELL
Boscundle Manor Hotel
01726 813557

ST AUSTELL
Cliff Head Hotel 01726 812345

ST IVES
Carbis Bay Hotel 01736 795311

ST IVES
Garrack Hotel & Restaurant
01736 796199

ST IVES
Olivers Lodge Hotel 01480 463252

ST IVES
Pedn-Olva Hotel 01736 796222

ST IVES
Porthminster Hotel 01736 795221

ST IVES
Tregenna Castle Hotel 01736 795254

ST LAWRENCE
Rocklands Hotel 01983 852964

ST MARY'S
Star Castle Hotel 01720 422317

STAFFORD
The Moat House 01785 712217

STAFFORD
Tillington Hall Hotel 01785 253531

STEEPLE ASTON
The Holt Hotel 01869 340259

STEVENAGE
Novotel Stevenage 01438 346100

STEYNING
The Old Tollgate Restaurant & Hotel
01903 879494

STOCKPORT
Bredbury Hall Hotel & Country Club
0161 430 7421

STOKE D'ABERNON
Woodlands Park Hotel 01372 843933

STOKE GABRIEL
Gabriel Court Hotel 01803 782206

STON EASTON
Ston Easton Park 01761 241631

STONE
Stone House Hotel 01785 815531

STONEHOUSE
Stonehouse Court 01453 825155

STOW-ON-THE-WOLD
Fosse Manor 01451 830354

STOW-ON-THE-WOLD
Grapevine Hotel 01451 830344

STOW-ON-THE-WOLD
Old Stocks Hotel 01451 830666

STOW-ON-THE-WOLD
The Royalist at Stow-on-the-Wold
01451 830670

STOW-ON-THE-WOLD
The Unicorn 01451 830257

STOW-ON-THE-WOLD
Wyck Hill House Hotel 01451 831936

STRATFORD-UPON-AVON
Billesley Manor Hotel 01789 279955

STRATFORD-UPON-AVON
Charlecote Pheasant 01789 279954

STRATFORD-UPON-AVON
Stratford Manor 01789 731173

STRATFORD-UPON-AVON
The Alveston Manor 0870 400 8181

STRATFORD-UPON-AVON
The Falcon Hotel 01789 279953

STRATFORD-UPON-AVON
The Swan's Nest 0870 400 8183

STREATLEY
The Swan at Streatley 01491 878800

STROUD
The Bell Hotel & Restaurant
01453 763556

SUNDERLAND
Quality Hotel 0191 519 1999

SUTTON COLDFIELD
Quality Hotel Sutton Court
0121 354 4991

SWINDON
Holiday Inn Swindon 0870 400 9079

SWINDON
Stanton House Hotel 01793 861777

SWINDON
Villiers Inn 01793 814744

TALLAND BAY
Talland Bay Hotel 01503 272667

TAPLOW
Cliveden 01628 668561

TARPORLEY
Willington Hall 01829 752321

TAUNTON
Farthings Hotel and Restaurant
01823 480664

TAUNTON
The Mount Somerset Hotel
01823 442500

TELFORD
Buckatree Hall Hotel   01952 641821

TELFORD
Clarion Hotel Madeley Court
01952 680068

TELFORD
Valley Hotel   01952 432247

TELFORD
White House Hotel   01952 604276

TENTERDEN
London Beach Hotel & Golf Club
01580 766279

TETBURY
Calcot Manor   01666 890391

TETBURY
Hare & Hounds Hotel 01666 880233

THORNE
Belmont Hotel   01405 812320

THORNTON WATLASS
Buck Inn   01677 422461

THORPE
The Peveril of the Peak
0870 400 8109

THURLESTONE
Thurlestone Hotel   01548 560382

TIVERTON
The Tiverton Hotel   01884 256120

TORPOINT
Whitsand Bay Hotel,
Golf & Country Club   01503 230276

TORQUAY
Anchorage Hotel   01803 326175

TORQUAY
Corbyn Head Hotel
& Orchid Restaurant   01803 213611

TORQUAY
Grand Hotel   01803 296677

TORQUAY
Kistor Hotel   01803 212632

TORQUAY
Meadfoot Bay Hotel   01803 294722

TORQUAY
Norcliffe Hotel   01803 328456

TORQUAY
The Imperial   01803 294301

TORQUAY
The Osborne Hotel   01803 213311

TORQUAY
Toorak Hotel   01803 291444

TORQUAY
Torcroft Hotel   01803 298292

TOTLAND BAY
Sentry Mead Hotel   01983 753212

TRING
Pendley Manor   01442 891891

TROUTBECK [NEAR WINDERMERE]
Mortal Man Hotel   015394 33193

TRURO
Alverton Manor   01872 276633

TRURO
Brookdale Hotel   01872 273513

TUTBURY
Ye Olde Dog & Partridge Hotel
01283 813030

TWO BRIDGES
Prince Hall Hotel   01822 890403

UCKFIELD
Buxted Park Country House Hotel
01825 732711

UCKFIELD
Horsted Place   01825 750581

ULLESTHORPE
Ullesthorpe Court Country
Hotel & Golf Club   01455 209023

UMBERLEIGH
Rising Sun Inn   01769 560447

UPHOLLAND
Quality Hotel Skelmersdale
01695 720401

VENTNOR
Eversley Hotel   01983 852244

VENTNOR
Hillside Hotel   01983 852271

VENTNOR
The Royal Hotel   01983 852186

VENTNOR
Ventnor Towers Hotel 01983 852277

VERYAN
The Nare Hotel   01872 501111

VIRGINIA WATER
The Wheatsheaf   01344 842057

WADEBRIDGE
The Molesworth Arms Hotel
01208 812055

WALSALL
Beverley Hotel   01922 614967

WALSALL
The Fairlawns at Aldridge
01922 455122

WALTERSTONE
Allt-yr-Ynys Country House Hotel
01873 890307

WALTHAM ABBEY
Waltham Abbey Marriott Hotel
01992 717170

WAREHAM
Kemps Country House Hotel
01929 462563

WAREHAM
Worgret Manor Hotel 01929 552957

WARMINSTER
Bishopstrow House   01985 212312

WARRINGTON
Daresbury Park Hotel 01925 267331

WATERGATE BAY
Tregurrian Hotel   01637 860280

WATTON
Broom Hall Country Hotel
01953 882125

WELLS
Swan Hotel   01749 836300

WELWYN
Quality Hotel Welwyn 01438 716911

WENTBRIDGE
Wentbridge House Hotel
01977 620444

WEST BEXINGTON
Manor Hotel   01308 897616

WESTON-SUPER-MARE
Beachlands Hotel   01934 621401

WETHERBY
Wood Hall Hotel   01937 587271

WEYMOUTH
Crown Hotel   01305 760800

WEYMOUTH
Hotel Prince Regent   01305 771313

WEYMOUTH
Moonfleet Manor   01305 786948

WHICKHAM
Gibside Hotel   0191 488 9292

WHITBY
Dunsley Hall   01947 893437

WHITBY
Saxonville Hotel   01947 602631

WILLITON
The Masons Arms Hotel
01984 639200

WILMSLOW
Stanneylands Hotel   01625 525225

WIMBORNE MINSTER
Beechleas Hotel & Restaurant
01202 841684

WINCHESTER
Lainston House Hotel 01962 863588

WINCHESTER
Marwell Hotel & Conference Centre
01962 777681

WINCHESTER
The Winchester Royal 01962 840840

WINDERMERE
Beech Hill Hotel   015394 42137

WINDERMERE
Cedar Manor Hotel & Restaurant
015394 43192

WINDERMERE
Gilpin Lodge Country House
Hotel & Restaurant   015394 88818

WINDERMERE
Langdale Chase Hotel 015394 32201

WINDERMERE
Lindeth Fell Country House Hotel
015394 43286

WINDERMERE
Lindeth Howe Country House Hotel
& Restaurant   015394 45759

WINDERMERE Wild Boar Hotel	015394 45225	

WINDERMERE
Wild Boar Hotel — 015394 45225

WINDSOR
Christopher Hotel — 01753 852359

WINDSOR
The Castle Hotel — 0870 400 8300

WISBECH
White Lion Hotel — 01945 463060

WOLVERHAMPTON
Quality Hotel Wolverhampton
— 01902 429216

WOOLACOMBE
Little Beach Hotel — 01271 870398

WOOLACOMBE
Woolacombe Bay Hotel
— 01271 870388

WOOTTON BASSETT
Marsh Farm Hotel — 01793 848044

WORKSOP
Clumber Park Hotel — 01623 835333

YARMOUTH
George Hotel — 01983 760331

YORK
Dean Court Hotel — 01904 625082

YORK
Heworth Court Hotel — 01904 425156

YORK
Jacobean Lodge Hotel — 01904 762749

YORK
York Marriott Hotel — 01904 701000

CHANNEL ISLANDS

PERELLE
L'Atlantique Hotel — 01481 264056

ST BRELADE
Hotel La Place — 01534 744261

HELIER
Pomme D'Or Hotel — 01534 880110

ST LAWRENCE
Hotel Cristina — 01534 758024

ST MARTIN
Green Acres Hotel — 01481 235711

ST PETER PORT
Old Government House Hotel
— 01481 724921

ISLE OF MAN

DOUGLAS
The Empress Hotel — 01624 661155

DOUGLAS
Welbeck Hotel — 01624 675663

PEEL
Ballacallin House Hotel
— 01624 841100

PORT ERIN
Ocean Castle Hotel — 01624 836399

SCOTLAND

ABERDEEN
Aberdeen Marriott Hotel
— 01224 770011

ABERDEEN
Copthorne Hotel Aberdeen
— 01224 630404

ABERDEEN
Mariner Hotel — 01224 588901

ABERDEEN
Maryculter House Hotel
— 01224 732124

ABERDEEN
The Marcliffe at Pitfodels
— 01224 861000

ABERDEEN
Westhill Hotel — 01224 740388

AUCHENCAIRN
Balcary Bay Hotel — 01556 640217

AUCHTERARDER
Cairn Lodge — 01764 662634

AVIEMORE
Aviemore Highlands Hotel
— 01479 810771

AYR
Grange Hotel — 01292 265679

BALLANTRAE
Glenapp Castle — 01465 831212

BALLOCH
Cameron House Hotel — 01389 755565

BANCHORY
Burnett Arms Hotel — 01330 824944

BANFF
Banff Springs Hotel — 01261 812881

BEAULY
Priory Hotel — 01463 782309

BLAIRGOWRIE
Angus Hotel — 01250 872455

BLAIRGOWRIE
Kinloch House Hotel — 01250 884237

BRIDGE OF ALLAN
Royal Hotel — 01786 832284

BRORA
Royal Marine Hotel — 01408 621252

CAIRNDOW
Cairndow Stagecoach Inn
— 01499 600286

CALLANDER
Dalgair House Hotel — 01877 330283

CALLANDER
Roman Camp Country House Hotel
— 01877 330003

CARRUTHERSTOWN
Hetland Hall Hotel — 01387 840201

CASTLE DOUGLAS
Douglas Arms — 01556 502231

CASTLE DOUGLAS
Imperial Hotel — 01556 502086

CASTLE DOUGLAS
King's Arms Hotel — 01556 502626

CASTLE DOUGLAS
Urr Valley Hotel — 01556 502188

CLACHAN-SEIL
Willowburn Hotel — 01852 300276

CLEISH
Nivingston House Hotel
— 01577 850216

COMRIE
Royal Hotel — 01764 679200

CONTIN
Coul House Hotel — 01997 421487

CRAIGELLACHIE
Craigellachie Hotel — 01340 881204

CRIEFF
Crieff Hydro — 01764 655555

CRUDEN BAY
Red House Hotel — 01779 812215

CUPAR
Eden House Hotel — 01334 652510

DORNOCH
Burghfield House Hotel
— 01862 810212

DORNOCH
Royal Golf Hotel — 01862 810283

DRYMEN
Buchanan Arms Hotel
and Leisure Club — 01360 660588

DRYMEN
Winnock Hotel — 01360 660245

DUMFRIES
Station Hotel — 01387 254316

DUNDEE
Sandford Country House Hotel
— 01382 541802

DUNFERMLINE
King Malcolm — 01383 722611

DUNFERMLINE
Pitbauchlie House Hotel
— 01383 722282

DUNFERMLINE
The Hideaway Lodge & Restaurant
— 01383 725474

DUNOON
Enmore Hotel — 01369 702230

DUNOON
Esplanade Hotel — 01369 704070

DUNOON
Lyall Cliff Hotel — 01369 702041

DUNOON
Royal Marine Hotel — 01369 705810

EAST KILBRIDE
Crutherland Country House Hotel
— 01355 577000

EDINBURGH
Braid Hills Hotel — 0131 447 8888

EDINBURGH
Carlton Hotel — 0131 472 3000

EDINBURGH Dalhousie Castle And Spa	**KELSO** The Roxburghe Hotel & Golf Course	**PEEBLES** Kingsmuir Hotel 01721 720151
01875 820153	01573 450331	**PEEBLES** Park Hotel 01721 720451
EDINBURGH Edinburgh Marriott Hotel	**KILLIN** Dall Lodge Country House Hotel	**PEEBLES** Peebles Hydro Hotel 01721 720602
0131 334 9191	01567 820217	**PERTH** Kinfauns Castle 01738 620777
EDINBURGH Greens Hotel 0131 337 1565	**KILMARNOCK** Fenwick Hotel 01560 600478	**PERTH** The New County Hotel
EDINBURGH Orwell Lodge Hotel 0131 229 1044	**KINROSS** Green Hotel 01577 863467	01738 623355
EDZELL Glenesk Hotel 01356 648319	**KIRKCUDBRIGHT** Royal Hotel 01557 331213	**PETERHEAD** Palace Hotel 01779 474821
ELGIN Mansion House Hotel 01343 548811	**KIRKCUDBRIGHT** Selkirk Arms Hotel 01557 330402	**PITLOCHRY** Dundarach Hotel 01796 472862
ERISKA Isle of Eriska 01631 720371	**LADYBANK** Fernie Castle 01337 810381	**PORT ASKAIG** Port Askaig Hotel 01496 840245
ERSKINE The Erskine Bridge Hotel	**LARGS** Willowbank Hotel 01475 672311	**PORTMAHOMACK** Caledonian Hotel 01862 871345
0141 812 0123	**LOCHCARRON** Lochcarron Hotel 01520 722226	**PORTPATRICK** Fernhill Hotel 01776 810220
FORFAR Idvies House Hotel 01307 818787	**LOCHEARNHEAD** Lochearnhead Hotel 01567 830229	**PORTREE** Cuillin Hills Hotel 01478 612003
FORRES Ramnee Hotel 01309 672410	**LOCHINVER** Inver Lodge Hotel 01571 844496	**PORTREE** Royal Hotel 01478 612525
FREUCHIE Lomond Hills Hotel 01337 857329	**LOCKERBIE** Kings Arms Hotel 01576 202410	**PRESTWICK** Parkstone Hotel 01292 477286
GALASHIELS Abbotsford Arms Hotel 01896 752517	**LOCKERBIE** The Dryfesdale Country House Hotel	**RENFREW** Glynhill Hotel & Leisure Club
GALASHIELS Kingsknowes Hotel 01896 758375	01576 202427	0141 886 5555
GALASHIELS Woodlands House	**LUNDIN LINKS** Old Manor Hotel 01333 320368	**ROSEBANK** Popinjay Hotel 01555 860441
Hotel & Restaurants 01896 754722	**MELROSE** George & Abbotsford Hotel	**ST BOSWELLS** Dryburgh Abbey Hotel 01835 822261
GATEHOUSE OF FLEET Murray Arms Hotel 01557 814207	01896 822308	**ST FILLANS** Achray House Hotel 01764 685231
GLAMIS Castleton House Hotel 01307 840340	**MONTROSE** Links Hotel 01674 671000	**STRACHUR** Creggans Inn 01369 860279
GLASGOW The Ewington 0141 423 1152	**MONTROSE** Montrose Park Hotel 01674 663400	**STRANRAER** Corsewall Lighthouse Hotel
GLENFARG The Glenfarg Hotel & Restaurant	**MUIR OF ORD** Ord House Hotel 01463 870492	01776 853220
01577 830241	**MUIR OF ORD** The Dower House 01463 870090	**STRANRAER** North West Castle Hotel
GLENLUCE Kelvin House Hotel 01581 300303	**NAIRN** Alton Burn Hotel 01667 452051	01776 704413
GLENROTHES Balgeddie House Hotel 01592 742511	**NAIRN** Boath House 01667 454896	**STRATHBLANE** Strathblane Country House Hotel
GLENROTHES Rescobie House Hotel & Restaurant	**NEWTON STEWART** Bruce Hotel 01671 402294	01360 770491
01592 749555	**NEWTON STEWART** Creebridge House Hotel	**TAIN** Mansfield House Hotel 01862 892052
HALKIRK Ulbster Arms Hotel 01847 831206	01671 402121	**TAIN** Morangie House Hotel 01862 892281
HOWWOOD Bowfield Hotel & Country Club	**NEWTON STEWART** Kirroughtree House 01671 402141	**TANGASDALE** Isle of Barra Hotel 01871 810383
01505 705225	**NORTH BERWICK** Nether Abbey Hotel 01620 892802	**THORNHILL** Trigony House Hotel 01848 331211
INVERARAY Loch Fyne Hotel 01499 302148	**NORTH BERWICK** The Marine 0870 400 8129	**THURSO** Royal Hotel 01847 893191
INVERARAY The Argyll Hotel 01499 302466	**PEEBLES** Castle Venlaw Hotel 01721 720384	**TOBERMORY** Highland Cottage 01688 302030
JOHNSTONE Lynnhurst Hotel 01505 324331		

TONGUE
Ben Loyal Hotel   01847 611216

TROON
Marine Hotel   01292 314444

TURNBERRY
Malin Court   01655 331457

UPHALL
Houstoun House Hotel
and Country Club   01506 853831

UPLAWMOOR
Uplawmoor Hotel   01505 850565

WICK
Mackay's Hotel   01955 602323

WALES

ABERDYFI
Dovey Inn   01654 767332

ABERDYFI
Penhelig Arms Hotel Restaurant
01654 767215

ABERDYFI
Trefeddian Hotel   01654 767213

ABERGAVENNY
Llansantffraed Court Hotel
01873 840678

ABERGELE
Kinmel Manor Hotel   01745 832014

ABERPORTH
Hotel Penrallt   01239 810227

ABERSOCH
Deucoch Hotel   01758 712680

ABERSOCH
Neigwl Hotel   01758 712363

ABERYSTWYTH
Belle Vue Royal Hotel   01970 617558

ABERYSTWYTH
Four Seasons Hotel   01970 612120

ABERYSTWYTH
Marine Hotel   01970 612444

ABERYSTWYTH
Richmond Hotel   01970 612201

AMLWCH
Lastra Farm Hotel   01407 830906

AMLWCH
Trecastell Hotel   01407 830651

AMMANFORD
Mill at Glynhir   01269 850672

BALA
Plas Coch Hotel   01678 520309

BETWS-Y-COED
Best Western Waterloo Hotel
01690 710411

BETWS-Y-COED
Craig-y-Dderwen Riverside Hotel
01690 710293

BETWS-Y-COED
Tan-y-Foel Country House
01690 710507

BETWS-Y-COED
The Royal Oak Hotel   01690 710219

BRIDGEND
Coed-Y-Mwstwr Hotel 01656 860621

BRIDGEND
Heronston Hotel   01656 668811

CAERNARFON
Seiont Manor Hotel   01286 673366

CAERNARFON
Stables Hotel   01286 830711

CARDIFF
Cardiff Marriott Hotel
029 2039 9944

CARDIFF
New House Country Hotel
029 2052 0280

CARDIFF
St Mellons Hotel & Country Club
01633 680355

CARMARTHEN
Falcon Hotel   01267 234959

CHEPSTOW
Beaufort Hotel   01291 622497

CHEPSTOW
The Old Course Hotel   01291 626261

CHIRK
Moreton Park Lodge   01691 776666

CONWY
Castle Hotel Conwy   01492 582800

CRICCIETH
Caerwylan Hotel   01766 522547

CRICCIETH
Lion Hotel   01766 522460

CRICKHOWELL
Bear Hotel   01873 810408

CRICKHOWELL
Gliffaes Country House Hotel
01874 730371 & 0800

DOLGELLAU
Penmaenuchaf Hall Hotel
01341 422129

DOLGELLAU
Plas Dolmelynllyn   01341 440273

EGLWYSFACH
Ynyshir Hall   01654 781209

EWLOE
De Vere St Davids Park
01244 520800

GWBERT-ON-SEA
Cliff Hotel   01239 613241

HAVERFORDWEST
Hotel Mariners   01437 763353

HAVERFORDWEST
Wolfscastle Country Hotel
01437 741688

HAY-ON-WYE
The Swan-at-Hay Hotel
01497 821188

HOLYHEAD
Bull Hotel   01407 740351

KNIGHTON
The Knighton Hotel   01547 520530

LAMPETER
Falcondale Mansion   01570 422910

LANGLAND BAY
Wittemberg Hotel   01792 369696

LLANARMON DYFFRYN CEIRIOG
West Arms Hotel   01691 600665

LLANBEDR
Ty Mawr Hotel   01341 241440

LLANBERIS
Royal Victoria Hotel   01286 870253

LLANDEILO
Cawdor Arms Hotel   01558 823500

LLANDEILO
White Hart Inn   01558 823419

LLANDRILLO
Tyddyn Llan Country
Hotel & Restaurant   01490 440264

LLANDRINDOD WELLS
Hotel Metropole   01597 823700

LLANDUDNO
Ambassador Hotel   01492 876886

LLANDUDNO
Bodysgallen Hall Hotel
01492 584466

LLANDUDNO
Epperstone Hotel   01492 878746

LLANDUDNO
Esplanade Hotel
0800 318688 (freephone)

LLANDUDNO
Headlands Hotel   01492 877485

LLANDUDNO
Risboro Hotel   01492 876343

LLANDUDNO
St George's Hotel   01492 877544

LLANDUDNO
St Tudno Hotel and Restaurant
01492 874411

LLANDUDNO
Tanlan Hotel   01492 860221

LLANGAMMARCH WELLS
Lake Country House Hotel
01591 620202

LLANGOLLEN
Bryn Howel Hotel & Restaurant
01978 860331

LLANGOLLEN
The Wild Pheasant Hotel &
Restaurant   01978 860629

LLANGYBI
Cwrt Bleddyn Hotel & Country Club
01633 450521

LLYSWEN
Llangoed Hall   01874 754525

MACHYNLLETH
Wynnstay Hotel   01654 702941

MERTHYR TYDFIL
Tregenna Hotel   01685 723627

MISKIN
Miskin Manor Hotel
& Health Club LTD   01443 224204

MOLD
Beaufort Park Hotel   01352 758646

MONMOUTH
Riverside Hotel   01600 715577

NEWPORT
Newport Lodge Hotel   01633 821818

NORTHOP
Soughton Hall Hotel   01352 840811

PEMBROKE
Lamphey Court Hotel   01646 672273

PONTERWYD
The George Borrow Hotel
01970 890230

PONTYPRIDD
Heritage Park Hotel   01443 687057

PONTYPRIDD
Llechwen Hall Hotel   01443 742050

RHYL
Hotel Marina   01745 342371

SAUNDERSFOOT
Jalna Hotel   01834 812282

SAUNDERSFOOT
Rhodewood House Hotel
01834 812200

SAUNDERSFOOT
St Brides Hotel   01834 812304

ST DAVID'S
Grove Hotel   01437 720341

ST DAVID'S
Old Cross Hotel   01437 720387

ST DAVID'S
Warpool Court Hotel   01437 720300

TALSARNAU
Estuary Motel   01766 771155

TALSARNAU
Tregwylan Hotel   01766 770424

TAL-Y-BONT
Lodge Hotel   01492 660766

TENBY
Atlantic Hotel   01834 842881

TENBY
Fourcroft Hotel   01834 842886

TENBY
Heywood Mount Hotel
01834 842087

TENBY
Panorama Hotel & Restaurant
01834 844976

TENBY
Penally Abbey Country House
01834 843033

TENBY
Tenby House Hotel   01834 842000

TINTERN
Parva Farmhouse Hotel & Restaurant
01291 689411

TREARDDUR BAY
Trearddur Bay Hotel   01407 860301

TREFRIW
Hafod Country Hotel   01492 640029

TREFRIW
Princes Arms Hotel   01492 640592

WELSHPOOL
Golfa Hall Hotel   01938 553399

WHITEBROOK
The Crown at Whitebrook
01600 860254

WREXHAM
Cross Lanes Hotel & Restaurant
01978 780555

NORTHERN IRELAND

AGHADOWEY
Brown Trout Golf & Country Inn
028 7086 8209

BALLYMENA
Adair Arms Hotel   028 2565 3674

BALLYMENA
Galgorm Manor   028 2588 1001

BANGOR
Clandeboye Lodge Hotel
028 9185 2500

BANGOR
Marine Court Hotel   028 9145 1100

BANGOR
Old Inn   028 9185 3255

BANGOR
Royal Hotel   028 9127 1866

CARNLOUGH
Londonderry Arms Hotel
028 2888 5255

DUNGANNON
The Cohannon Inn   028 8772 4488

ENNISKILLEN
Killyhevlin Hotel   028 6632 3481

IRVINESTOWN
Mahons Hotel   028 6862 1656

PORTAFERRY
Portaferry Hotel   028 4272 8231

REPUBLIC OF IRELAND

ABBEYLEIX
Abbeyleix Manor Hotel   0502 30111

ADARE
Dunraven Arms Hotel   061 396633

ADARE
Fitzgeralds Woodlands House Hotel
061 605100

AHERLOW
Aherlow House   062 56153

ARDARA
Nesbitt Arms   075 41103

ARDMORE
Round Tower Hotel   024 94494

ARTHURSTOWN
Dunbrody Country
House & Restaurant   051 389600

ATHLONE
Hodson Bay Hotel   0902 80500

ATHLONE
Royal Hoey Hotel   0902 72924

BALLINASLOE
Haydens Gateway Business
& Leisure Hotel   065 68 23000

BALLINLOUGH
Whitehouse Hotel   0907 40112

BALLYBOFEY
Kee's Hotel   074 31018

BALLYCOTTON
Bay View Hotel   021 4646746

BALLYHEIGE
The White Sands Hotel   066 7133102

BALLYLICKEY
Sea View Hotel   027 50073

BALTIMORE
Baltimore Harbour Hotel
& Leisure Center   028 20361

BALTIMORE
Casey's of Baltimore Hotel
028 20197

BARNA
The Twelve Pins Hotel   091 592368

BETTYSTOWN
Neptune Beach Hotel
& Leisure Club   041 9827107

BIRR
County Arms Hotel   0509 20791

BLARNEY
Christy's Hotel   021 4385011

BRAY
Royal Hotel & Leisure Centre
01 2862935

BUNBEG
Ostan Gweedore   075 31177

BUNRATTY
Fitzpatrick Bunratty Hotel
061 361177

CAHIR
Cahir House Hotel   052 42727

CAHIRCIVEEN
Cahirciveen Park Hotel   066 9472543

CARLOW
Dolmen Hotel   0503 42002

CARLOW
Seven Oaks Hotel   0503 31308

CARRICK-ON-SHANNON
The Landmark Hotel   078 22222

CASTLEBAR
Breaffy House Hotel   094 22033

CASTLEBAR
Welcome Inn Hotel   094 22288

CASTLECONNELL
Castle Oaks House Hotel   061 377666

CAVAN		
Kilmore Hotel	049 4332288	
CLONAKILTY		
The Lodge & Spa		
at Inchydoney Island	023 33143	
CLONMEL		
Minella Hotel	052 22388	
CORK		
Arbutus Lodge Hotel	021 4501237	
CORK		
Gresham Metropole		
Hotel & Leisure Centre	021 4508122	
CORK		
Hayfield Manor	021 4845900	
CORK		
Imperial Hotel	021 4274040	
CORK		
Jurys Cork Hotel	021 4276622	
CORK		
The Kingsley Hotel	021 4800500	
COURTMACSHERRY		
Courtmacsherry	023 46198	
COURTOWN HARBOUR		
Bay View Hotel	055 25307	
COURTOWN HARBOUR		
Courtown Hotel	055 25210	
DELGANY		
Glenview Hotel	01 2873399	
DINGLE		
Dingle Skellig Hotel	066 9150200	
DONEGAL		
Abbey Hotel	073 21014	
DUBLIN		
Abberley Court Hotel	01 4596000	
DUBLIN		
Herbert Park Hotel	01 6672200	
DUBLIN		
Jurys Skylon Hotel	01 8379121	
DUBLIN		
Red Cow Moran Hotel	01 4593650	
DUBLIN		
Stillorgan Park Hotel	01 2881621	
DUBLIN		
The Clarence	01 4070800	
DUBLIN		
The Fitzwilliam Hotel	01 4787000	
DUNDALK		
Fairways Hotel	042 9321500	
DUNFANAGHY		
Arnold's Hotel	074 36208	
DUNGARVAN		
Lawlors Hotel	058 41122	
ENNIS		
Magowna House Hotel	065 6839009	
ENNISCORTHY		
Murphy-Flood's Hotel	054 33413	
ENNISCORTHY		
Riverside Park Hotel	054 37800	

FERMOY		
Castlehyde Hotel	025 31865	
GALWAY		
Ardilaun House Hotel Conference		
Centre and LC	091 521433	
GALWAY		
Galway Bay Hotel Conference &		
Leisure Centre	091 520520	
GALWAY		
Menlo Park Hotel	091 761122	
GALWAY		
Westwood House Hotel	091 521442	
GOREY		
Marlfield House Hotel	055 21124	
KENMARE		
Riversdale House Hotel	064 41299	
KENMARE		
Sheen Falls Lodge	064 41600	
KILKEE		
Halpin's Hotel	065 9056032	
KILL		
Ambassador Hotel	045 886700	
KILLARNEY		
Aghadoe Heights Hotel	064 31766	
KILLARNEY		
Cahernane Hotel	064 31895	
KILLARNEY		
Castlerosse Hotel	064 31144	
KILLARNEY		
Gleneagle Hotel	064 36000	
KILLARNEY		
International Hotel	064 31816	
KILLARNEY		
Killarney Court Hotel	064 37070	
KILLARNEY		
Lake Hotel	064 31035	
KILLINEY		
Court Hotel	01 2851622	
KILLINEY		
Fitzpatrick Castle Hotel	01 2305400	
KILTIMAGH		
Cill Aodain Hotel	094 81761	
KINGSCOURT		
Cabra Castle	042 9667030	
KINSALE		
Actons Hotel	021 4772135	
KINSALE		
Trident Hotel	021 4772301	
KNOCK		
Belmont Hotel	094 88122	
LAHINCH		
Quality Aberdeen Arms Hotel		
	065 81100	
LEIGHLINBRIDGE		
Lord Bagenal Inn	0503 21668	
LEIXLIP		
Leixlip House Hotel	01 6242268	
LIMERICK		
Castletroy Park Hotel	061 335566	

LIMERICK		
The Gresham Ardhu	061 453922	
LISMORE		
Ballyrafter House Hotel	058 54002	
LUCAN		
Finnstown Country House Hotel		
	01 6010700	
LUCAN		
Lucan Spa Hotel	01 6280495	
MACREDDIN		
Brooklodge at MacCreddin		
	0402 36444	
MACROOM		
Castle Hotel	026 41074	
MALLOW		
Longueville House Hotel	022 47156	
MALLOW		
Springfort Hall Hotel	022 21278	
MAYNOOTH		
Moyglare Manor	01 6286351	
MIDLETON		
Midleton Park	021 4631767	
NAAS		
Killashee House Hotel	045 879277	
NEW ROSS		
Clarion Brandon House		
Hotel Health Club & Spa	051 421703	
NEWBRIDGE		
Keadeen Hotel	045 431666	
PORTMARNOCK		
Portmarnock Hotel & Golf Links		
	01 8460611	
PORTUMNA		
Shannon Oaks Hotel & Country Club		
	0509 41777	
RATHMULLAN		
Fort Royal Hotel	074 58100	
RATHNEW		
Tinakilly Country House & Restaurant		
	0404 69274	
RENVYLE		
Renvyle House Hotel	095 43511	
ROSCOMMON		
Abbey Hotel	0903 26240	
ROSSCARBERY		
Celtic Ross Hotel	023 48722	
ROSSLARE		
Crosbie Cedars Hotel	053 32124	
ROSSLARE		
Kelly's Resort Hotel	053 32114	
ROSSNOWLAGH		
Sand House Hotel	072 51777	
SHANNON		
Quality Shannon Hotel	061 364588	
SKIBBEREEN		
Eldon Hotel	028 22000	
SLANE		
Conyngham Arms Hotel	041 9884444	
SLIGO		
Sligo Park Hotel	071 60291	

AA HOTELS WITH SPECIAL ARRANGEMENTS FOR GOLF

SLIGO			WATERFORD			WESTPORT		
Tower Hotel	071 44000		Ivory's Hotel	051 358888		The Central Hotel	098 25027	
STRAFFAN			WATERFORD			WESTPORT		
Barberstown Castle	01 6288157		Jurys Hotel	051 832111		The Olde Railway Hotel	098 25166	
TRALEE			WATERFORD			WEXFORD		
Meadowlands Hotel	066 7180444		Tower Hotel	051 875801		Ferrycarrig Hotel	053 20999	
TRAMORE			WATERVILLE			WEXFORD		
Majestic Hotel	051 381761		Butler Arms Hotel	066 9474144		Talbot Hotel Conference & Leisure Centre	053 22566	
WATERFORD			WESTPORT			WEXFORD		
Bridge Hotel	051 877222		Clew Bay Hotel	098 28088		Whitford House Hotel	053 43444	
WATERFORD			WESTPORT			WOODENBRIDGE		
Dooley's Hotel	051 873531		Hotel Westport Conference & Leisure Centre	098 25122		Woodenbridge Hotel	0402 35146	
WATERFORD								
Granville Hotel	051 305555							

Golf
driving ranges

Kilworth Springs Golf Course
LUTTERWORTH 154
Lutterworth Golf Club LUTTERWORTH 155
Lydd Golf Club LYDD 138
Royal Lytham & St Annes Golf Club
LYTHAM ST ANNES 149
Bird Hills Golf Centre MAIDENHEAD 21
Forrester Park Golf Club MALDON 84
Blackley Golf Club MANCHESTER 106
Mannings Heath Golf Club
MANNINGS HEATH 238
Harleyford Golf Club MARLOW 29
Matfen Hall Country House Hotel & Golf Club
MATFEN 187
Merlin Golf Course MAWGAN PORTH 47-8
Malton Golf Course MELDRETH 34
Melton Mowbray Golf Club
MELTON MOWBRAY 155
Mentmore Golf & Country Club
MENTMORE 29-30
Marriott Forest of Arden Golf & Country Club
MERIDEN 251
Stonebridge Golf Centre MERIDEN 250
Middlesbrough Municipal Golf Centre
MIDDLESBROUGH 269
Manchester Golf Club MIDDLETON 108
Middleton Hall Golf Club MIDDLETON 178
The Oxfordshire Golf Club
MILTON COMMON 195
Abbey Hill Golf Club MILTON KEYNES 30
Minchinhampton Golf Club
MINCHINHAMPTON 90
Morley Hayes Golf Course MORLEY 60
Wokefield Park Golf Club MORTIMER 22
Mundesley Golf Club Ltd MUNDESLEY 178
New Mills Golf Club NEW MILLS 61
Chewton Glen Hotel NEW MILTON 118
Jack Barkers Keele Golf Centre
NEWCASTLE-UNDER-LYME 208
Rusper Golf Course NEWDIGATE 223
Dainton Park Golf Club
NEWTON ABBOT 65
Oakleaf Golf Complex
NEWTON AYCLIFFE 77-8
Romanby Golf & Country Club
NORTHALLERTON 269
Brampton Heath Golf Centre
NORTHAMPTON 182
Delapre Golf Complex NORTHAMPTON 182
Northamptonshire County Golf Club
NORTHAMPTON 183
Sandy Lodge Golf Club NORTHWOOD 99
De Vere Dunston Hall Hotel NORWICH 178
Marriott Sprowston Manor Hotel & Country
Club NORWICH 178-9
Wensum Valley Hotel, Golf & Country Club
NORWICH 179
Purley Chase Golf Club NUNEATON 245
Oaksey Park Golf & Leisure OAKSEY 258
Gatton Manor Hotel Golf & Country Club
OCKLEY 223
Ashbury Golf Course OKEHAMPTON 65
Rufford Park Golf & Country Club
OLLERTON 191

Hurlston Hall Golf Club ORMSKIRK 150
Chelsfield Lakes Golf Centre
ORPINGTON 99
Cray Valley Golf Club ORPINGTON 99
Lullingstone Park Golf Course
ORPINGTON 99
Ruxley Park Golf Centre ORPINGTON 99-100
Mile End Golf Course OSWESTRY 199
Foxhills Club and Resort OTTERSHAW 223
Paultons Golf Centre OWER 119
Hinksey Heights Golf Course OXFORD 195-6
Oakmere Park OXTON 191
Pannal Golf Club PANNAL 269
Penrith Golf Club PENRITH 55-6
Perton Park Golf Club PERTON 209
Elton Furze Golf Club PETERBOROUGH 34
Lakeside Lodge Golf Club PIDLEY 35
Elfordleigh Hotel Golf & Country Club
PLYMOUTH 65
Mid Yorkshire Golf Course
PONTEFRACT 284
Parkstone Golf Club POOLE 72-3
Great Salterns Public Course
PORTSMOUTH 119
Southsea Golf Club PORTSMOUTH 119
Poulton Le Fylde Golf Club
POULTON-LE-FYLDE 150-1
Prestbury Golf Club PRESTBURY 41
Preston Golf Club PRESTON 152
Heaton Park Golf Centre PRESTWICH 108
West Sussex Golf Club PULBOROUGH 238
Cotgrave Place Golf Club
RADCLIFFE ON TRENT 191
Porters Park Golf Club RADLETT 128
Blundells Hill Golf Club RAINHILL 172
Old Nene Golf & Country Club RAMSEY 35
Brett Vale Golf Club RAYDON 214-5
Hennerton Golf Club READING 22
Redbourn Golf Club REDBOURN 128
Abbey Hotel Golf & Country Club
REDDITCH 262
Reigate Hill Golf Club REIGATE 224
The Richmond Golf Club
RICHMOND UPON THAMES 100
Batchworth Park Golf Club
RICKMANSWORTH 128
Moor Park Golf Club RICKMANSWORTH 128
Castle Hawk Golf Club ROCHDALE 109
Rochester & Cobham Park Golf Club
ROCHESTER 139
St Enodoc Golf Club ROCK 49
Risebridge Golf Centre ROMFORD 101
South Herefordshire Golf Club
ROSS-ON-WYE 123
The Ross-on-Wye Golf Club
ROSS-ON-WYE 123
Grange Park Golf Club ROTHERHAM 274
Phoenix Golf Club ROTHERHAM 274
Heydon Grange Golf & Country Club
ROYSTON 128-9
Kingsway Golf Centre ROYSTON 129
Whitefields Hotel Golf & Country Club
RUGBY 245
Ruislip Golf Club RUISLIP 101

Saffron Walden Golf Club
SAFFRON WALDEN 85
China Fleet Country Club SALTASH 50
Hunley Hall Golf Club & Hotel
SALTBURN-BY-THE-SEA 270
Prince's Golf Club SANDWICH 139-40
Royal St George's Golf Club SANDWICH 141
Saunton Golf Club SAUNTON 67
Forest Pines Golf Club SCUNTHORPE 161
Seaford Golf Club SEAFORD 234
Park Hill Golf Club SEAGRAVE 155-6
Seascale Golf Club SEASCALE 56
Knotty Hill Golf Centre SEDGEFIELD 78
Sedgley Golf Centre SEDGLEY 252
Sedlescombe Golf Course
SEDLESCOMBE 234
Marriott Meon Valley Hotel & Country Club
SHEDFIELD 120
Concord Park Golf Club SHEFFIELD 275
Hillsborough Golf Club SHEFFIELD 275
Rother Valley Golf Centre SHEFFIELD 275
Beadlow Manor Hotel & Golf & Country Club
SHEFFORD 19
American Golf at Sunbury
SHEPPERTON 224
Marriott Hollins Hall Hotel & Country Club
SHIPLEY 285
Shrewsbury Golf Club SHREWSBURY 199
Bearwood Golf Club SINDLESHAM 23
The Oast Golf Centre SITTINGBOURNE 140
Upchurch River Valley Golf Centre
SITTINGBOURNE 140
Slinfold Park Golf & Country Club
SLINFOLD 238-9
Oastpark Golf Course SNODLAND 142
Widney Manor Golf Club SOLIHULL 252
Belhus Park Golf Course
SOUTH OCKENDON 85
Top Meadow Golf Course
SOUTH OCKENDON 85
Chilworth Golf Club SOUTHAMPTON 120
Hillside Golf Club SOUTHPORT 174
Porthpean Golf Club ST AUSTELL 49
St Austell Golf Club ST AUSTELL 49
St Mellion Hotel, Golf & Country Club ST
MELLION 51
Roserrow Golf & Country Club
ST MINVER 49-50
Abbotsley Golf Hotel & Country Club
ST NEOTS 35
Standish Court Golf Club STANDISH 110
St Clere's Hall Golf Club
STANFORD-LE-HOPE 85
Erewash Valley STANTON BY DALE 61
Staverton Park Golf Club STAVERTON 183
Stevenage Golf Centre STEVENAGE 130
Crondon Park Golf Club STOCK 86
Stoke Poges Golf Club STOKE POGES 30
Trentham Golf Club STOKE-ON-TRENT 210
Barlaston Golf Club STONE 210
Izaak Walton Golf Club STONE 210
Silverstone Golf Course STOWE 30, 32
Stowmarket Golf Club STOWMARKET 215

CHANNEL ISLANDS

ISLE OF MAN

NORTHERN IRELAND

REPUBLIC OF IRELAND

Index *of Golf Courses*

Index *of Golf Courses*

Index *of Golf Courses*

Index of Golf Courses

Index *of Golf Courses*

Index *of Golf Courses*

Index *of Golf Courses*

Index *of Golf Courses*

Index *of Golf Courses*

Index *of Golf Courses*

Index of Golf Courses

Index of Golf Courses

Index of Golf Courses